CLIMATOLOGY AND THE WORLD'S CLIMATES

GEORGE R. RUMNEY

Department of Geology and Geography
University of Connecticut

CLIMATOLOGY AND THE WORLD'S CLIMATES

THE MACMILLAN COMPANY
COLLIER-MACMILLAN LIMITED, LONDON

The Macmillan Company
Collier-Macmillan Canada, Ltd., Toronto, Ontario

Printed in the United States of America

To the memory of Stanley D. Dodge

preface

To introduce the reader to the nature and distribution of the world's climates is the primary purpose of this book. Its contents are thus preponderantly devoted to regional climatology (Chapters 7–24), beginning with the polar ice cap and ending with oceanic climates. The method of regional identification and distinction, though consistent with tradition, lays more than usual emphasis on the relation between the tangible qualities of the earth's surface and the more ephemeral qualities of the atmosphere. This arises principally from a desire to stress that the study of climatology and the world's climates is necessarily a geographical one. The perception and identification of visible landscape properties is taken as the vital key to understanding the geographical distribution of discrete climates, an approach deemed especially suitable for inviting the interest of the novice. A further thematic undercurrent is the thesis that change is an inherent quality of climate. The subject of climatic change is not given specific treatment in this book, but the changing balance of dynamic atmospheric forces is implicit throughout the regional chapters. In consequence, the concept of a climatic context is developed from region to region, and the transition from one context to another is brought out.

A grasp of the principles and processes governing atmospheric activity is essential for the successful study of the world's climates. Hence, a brief presentation of physical climatology (Chapters 2–6) precedes the regional chapters. This, it is hoped, will acquaint the reader with the dynamic integration of air, sea, and land in the complex exchange of energies initially derived from the sun.

The author owes a very considerable debt of gratitude to the late Stanley D. Dodge, to whose memory this volume is dedicated, for the original inspiration to undertake the work and for continued encouragement throughout its preparation. He is also greatly indebted to Dr. M. Ernest Sabbagh, whose critical analysis of the manuscript has been of utmost value. Deepest appreciation is also owed to the American Academy of Arts and Sciences for grants in support of regional field studies, to the National Science Foundation for support of marine climatic studies, and to the University of Connecticut Research Foundation for continuing aid in coastal climatological investigations.

Thanks are due to my students for the opportunity to test the efficacy of the book's approach to climatology through its many stages of development. I am very grateful to Lillian P. Piccin for typing assistance, and to Jane G. Seeber for typing the bulk of the manuscript. I also wish to thank Trudy Hayden and Barbara Davis, of The Macmillan Company, for their valuable aid in preparing the mansucript for publication.

G. R. R.

Storrs, Connecticut

contents

CLIMATOLOGY AND THE WORLD'S CLIMATES

chapter 1

INTRODUCTION

Climatology, like meteorology, is a science of the atmosphere. Meteorology is primarily concerned with atmospheric processes; climatology deals chiefly with the results of those processes.

From its origins in the science of ancient Greece, climatology has developed along two main lines of investigation, physical climatology and regional climatology. The first is the study of climate, a physical analysis of the fundamental relationships among atmospheric elements, primarily temperature, moisture, pressure, and movement of air. The second is the study of climates, the discrete and characteristic qualities of the atmosphere of a particular place or places, and ultimately of particular regions on the earth. In broadest terms, climatology may be thought of as a bilateral study whose beginnings are traceable to the science, philosophy, and scholarship of Ionian Greece, and its modern development to the methodical work of German scientists since 1800.

The earliest recorded references to man's interest in the climatic variety of the world are found in the writings of Greek scholars of the sixth century B.C. By that time the Greeks, who lived on the shores of the Aegean Sea, had begun to colonize (Fig. 1.1). To the north, on the shores of the Euxine, they had discovered Scythia, a cold, wet land. Southward they had reached the hot, dry land of Libya. Greece

itself was neither too hot nor too cold, neither too wet nor too dry, and was called temperate, a land thought to be ideal for the habitations of men. Ionian scholars of this time, whose capital was Miletus in Asia Minor, undertook to find an explanation for these differences, employing their own advanced knowledge of geography and the well-developed disciplines of astronomy and mathematics brought from Babylonia.

Anaximander of Miletus (611?–546? B.C.), who has been credited with making the first map of the known world, measured the angle made by the sun's rays with the surface of the earth, introducing for the purpose a Babylonian instrument called a *gnomon* (Fig. 1.2). At Miletus the angle of the sun's rays was discovered to be more acute than that in Libya, and the angle in Scythia was more acute than that at Miletus. It was concluded from these observations that the earth's surface must be curved, at least in a north-south direction, for the sun was believed to be at an infinite distance from the earth (Fig. 1.3).

During the latter half of the sixth century the followers of Pythagoras are known to have taught the theoretical assumption that the earth was round, and about 500 B.C. the philosopher Parmenides proposed for the first time that the earth could be divided into five zones: a torrid zone far to the south of Greece where

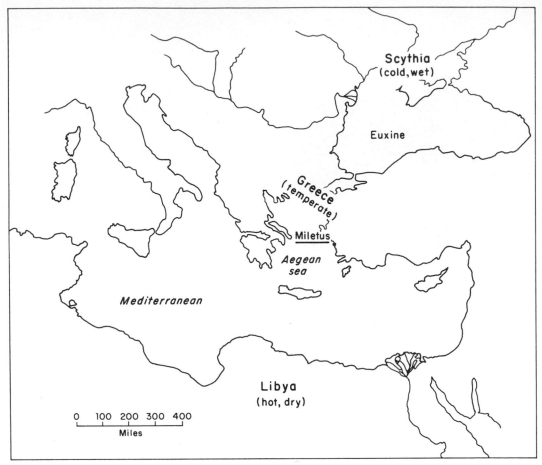

Figure 1.1. Part of the ancient world of Anaximander (ca. 600 B.C.).

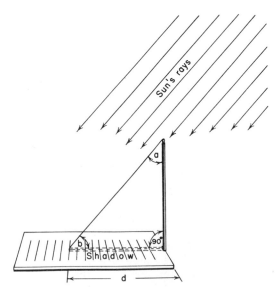

Figure 1.2. The gnomon. The length of the shadow is a measure of angle *b*.

the sun was always high in the sky, on either side of this a temperate zone, and beyond each of these a frigid zone. This simplified notion (Fig. 1.4) persisted well into modern times, although we now know that it is far too general to fit the actual arrangement of climates on the earth. In this the Greeks were more speculative scientists than practical ones, for they actually knew about only a small part of the world, and their information was too incomplete and too inaccurate for them to test their hypotheses adequately.

The idea of a spherical earth was upheld by a small number of philosophers and scholars during the fifth and fourth centuries B.C. Aristotle became the chief exponent of the idea and formulated six arguments to prove it (*De Caelus*, Book II, Part 14). Around the same time the inclination of the earth's axis was determined to be 23½ degrees from a perpendicular to the plane of its orbit around the sun,

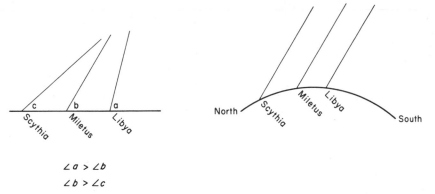

$$\angle a > \angle b$$
$$\angle b > \angle c$$

Figure 1.3. Curvature of the earth's surface suggested by the comparative angles made by the sun's rays between Libya and Scythia.

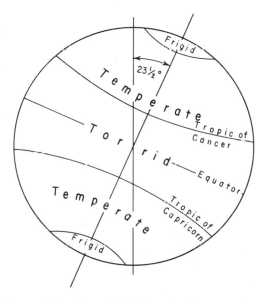

Figure 1.4. Parmenides' five climatic zones (ca. 500 B.C.).

and there also evolved the concept of the earth's rotation on its axis, the poles, the tropics, and the equator.

It had been known for some time that on the longest day of the year, around June 21, the sun shone longer at Miletus and other places in Greece than in Libya, and even longer on the shores of the Euxine. This was the time of the summer solstice (Fig. 1.5), when the sun "stood still" (*sol*—sun, *sistere*—to stand) at its northernmost limit above the Tropic of Cancer (*trope*—a turning), before turning southward toward the equator. Around 140 B.C. Hipparchus,

considered the leading astronomer of ancient Greece, devised a system of lines parallel to the equator by which to divide the earth's curved surface into zones according to the difference in the amount of sunlight received in each zone at the time of the summer solstice. These zones (Fig. 1.6), each representing a half-hour difference in the duration of sunlight, were called *klimata* (sing. *klima*), the origin of our term *climate*. The klimata were later identified according to the temperatures believed to typify them, and thus the word *climate* in its original sense was applied to a region, although in context designating only the length of the solar day as a basis of regional distinction. The present meaning of *a climate* is somewhat the same, that is, a region or zone on the earth throughout which the characteristics of observed weather are fairly distinct and typical of it. But there the resemblance ends, for the distribution of climates in the modern sense is only partly the result of mathematically determined astronomic relationships. We shall see in a later chapter that the arrangement of climates arises from a complex relationship among many contributing circumstances.

We are thus indebted to the ancient Greeks for the earliest recorded investigations of the world's climates, for originating the term *climate*, and for picturing the earth to be divided into a torrid zone, two temperate zones, and two frigid zones. We are also indebted to them for the term *meteorology* (*meteor*—any phenomenon in the atmosphere), which first appeared as the title of Aristotle's treatise on the atmosphere called *Meteorologica*. This and

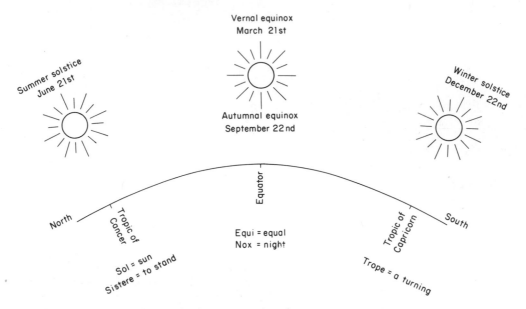

Figure 1.5. Periodic relationships between earth and sun.

the writings of his pupil Theophrastus are the earliest known systematic studies in meteorology. But for nearly 1800 years the study of the atmosphere advanced very little beyond the stage to which the learned men of Greece had brought it. This resulted chiefly from an ignorance of the real nature of most of the earth and the lack of suitable means of accurately measuring temperature, moisture, pressure, and movement of air.

After 1500 A.D., however, steps were taken toward the gradual elimination of these disadvantages. At first the greatest progress came in an expanding knowledge of geography,

slowly bringing to light the actual distribution of land and water on the earth, the existence of relatively steady trade winds, the more variable westerlies, major ocean currents, and varieties of weather experience unknown in the Mediterranean and western Europe. The first expression of man's widening acquaintance with the world appeared in general geographical treatises such as that of Bernhardus Varenius, who published in 1650 *A General and Comparative Geography*, introducing and organizing material that was used by many generations of scholars to follow. From the geographies and a growing accumulation of published charts and atlases the size and

Figure 1.6. Hipparchus' klimata (ca. 150 B.C.).

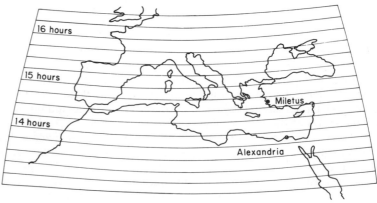

shape of land and water surfaces, the great variety of terrestrial landscapes, and an infinitude of weather phenomena were gradually made available to scientists of the seventeenth and eighteenth centuries. At the same time certain basic instruments essential for atmospheric measurement were developed, and the elementary physical laws of gases, liquids, and solids were formulated. Galileo Galilei introduced the thermometer in 1607, Evangelista Torricelli invented the barometer in 1643, and in 1659 Boyle's Law[1] was published. In 1735 George Hadley provided an explanation of the trade winds and for the first time dealt with the effect of the earth's rotation on the trajectories of winds. In 1783 Antoine Lavoisier analyzed the actual composition of air in nature, and in 1800 John Dalton explained for the first time the variations in atmospheric condensation and the expansion of air.

By 1800, then, the foundations of atmospheric study had been laid. At the same time philosophers and scientists alike began to pay increasing attention to the particular problem of climatic diversity within the frigid, torrid, and temperate zones of the ancients. Both Hobbes and Kant contributed important lines of reasoning to this and related problems.

Modern climatology is considered to have begun with the efforts of the great German naturalist Alexander von Humboldt, who drew heavily upon the philosophy of the seventeenth and eighteenth centuries and upon the studies of earlier naturalists like Varenius and Johann and George Forster, who were also of German extraction. Von Humboldt, in a series of discerning studies published around the beginning of the nineteenth century, took notice for the first time of the effects of altitude upon the temperature and pressure of air, and of differences in temperature and moisture conditions in coastal and interior locations on the world's land masses. He also introduced the use of the isotherm, a line joining points having equal temperatures, to indicate more realistically the pattern of variations of temperature on the earth. He published the first isotherm map of the world in 1817. In these and many other ways he led the way toward a more factual consideration of the climates of the world.

The modern approach to climatology remained chiefly a geographical one until nearly the end of the nineteenth century. Von Humboldt and his successors were mainly interested in unscrambling the vague and inaccurate thoughts that had prevailed for so long about what are now regarded to be rather elementary patterns of temperature and rainfall distribution, wind movement, and weather varieties. H. W. Dove produced the first world map of mean monthly temperatures in 1848. In 1866 A. H. R. Grisebach published the first world map of vegetation regions, and with it the earliest suggestion of climatic distribution as it has since become known. Indeed, a very large share of the progress made during the nineteenth century was the work of German phytogeographers. Carl Linsser in 1867 made the most important investigation of his time into the relation between plant life and climate, particularly with respect to the connection between plant development and temperature. His work marked the culmination of nearly a century of plant and environmental study by German and other European scholars.

The next significant step was taken when Wladimir Köppen presented a world map of temperature belts in 1884, on which each belt, ranging from polar to tropical latitudes, was distinguished by the number of months having temperatures above or below certain mean values. In 1890 Oscar Drude adopted Köppen's temperature belts as a basis for a map of the world's floral kingdoms, and at the same time introduced a new classification of plant forms: forest, bush and shrub, grass and scrub, steppe, desert, moss and lichen, alpine, and polar. In 1898 A. F. W. Schimper produced a major work in plant geography in which he mapped thirteen types of vegetation formations categorized according to the density and luxuriance of plant cover, ranging from tropical rain forest to desert. It was the first world map of the actual distribution of vegetation on an ecological basis.

Up to the end of the nineteenth century the guiding interest among the leading contributors to the budding science of climatology was a geographical one, and both their efforts and their accomplishments laid emphasis on the primary need for a sound and complete knowledge of the world. A climax in geographical

[1] "The volume of a given mass of gas is inversely proportional to its pressure."

climatology was attained with the introduction of Köppen's mathematical system of climatic classification in 1900,[2] in which the importance of plant distribution for identifying climatic regions and their boundaries was paramount. Since 1900 most of the acceptable systems of regional climatic classification have been based in some way upon Köppen's ideas, and he in turn founded his approach upon the earlier work of the phytogeographers.

Meanwhile, work in the field of physical climatology had been going forward since before the turn of the century. Most climatological progress since then has been made along this avenue of investigation, the primary concern of which is to describe, classify, and explain the highly complex and eternally variable relationships among the many qualities of the atmosphere.

Physical climatology, primarily an analysis of the recorded observations of such elements as temperature, humidity, precipitation, pressure, wind, cloud cover, and sunshine, requires the use of an enormous number of widely assorted weather data from all over the world, both in summary and in detail. The necessary mass of such data, assembled from observations made by instruments, has become available only during the past one hundred years.

The creation of government weather bureaus in many countries of western Europe and North America soon after 1850 led to the eventual publication of records from thousands of weather stations in many widely separated parts of the world. Physical climatology, depending upon the use of data for as long a period of record as possible, has thus become a practicable study only during recent decades and is valid only for certain well-populated areas where observations have been abundantly and reliably made. While there are many shortcomings both in regard to the distribution of observation points and the methods of weather observation, we are slowly coming into possession of a sizable quantity of data from which analyses can be made and systems of generalization devised.

For many years actual measurements of

rainfall, dry and wet bulb temperatures, and wind direction and velocity, could only be made very close to the ground. Thus, until a very short time ago, we had only a two-dimensional picture of the atmosphere's properties. In other words, the values we had to work with applied mainly to the lowest levels of the atmosphere. After 1900, however, the development and manufacture of a wide variety of devices permitted exploration of the atmosphere at increasingly higher elevations, to obtain values, to collect data, and to make possible for the first time a more elaborate consideration of the qualities of the atmosphere in three dimensions. The improvement in methods of vertical temperature measurement is a good illustration.

At first, high points on the earth's surface were used to sample the temperature of the upper air. Between 1870 and 1890 a small number of mountain weather stations were established in Europe and the United States. U.S. stations were set up at Pike's Peak, Colo. (el. 14,134), Mt. Washington, N.H. (el. 6280), and Blue Hill, Mass. (el. 640). Of these only Blue Hill and Mt. Washington are now in operation, and both have become important research centers. Eiffel Tower in Paris (el. 985) was built in 1889 and has since become a standard source of atmospheric data around Paris for levels under 1000 feet. But the conditions on low mountain tops are very much different from those in the free air high above. Balloons were introduced in 1803 for sounding the upper air and as early as 1893 were in common use. Filled with helium or hydrogen, and bearing light instruments aloft, they expanded as they rose and finally burst, the instruments being lowered to the ground by means of a small parachute. A trifling reward was offered to the finder of such an instrument for returning it to its point of origin.

Beginning in 1898 box kites were used by the U.S. Weather Bureau for regular observations. Between 1925 and 1937 they were replaced by the airplane, and since 1937 the airplane in turn has been replaced by the radiosonde, a tiny radio transmitter carried aloft by a gas-filled balloon and returned to earth by parachute. It transmits signals indicating temperature, pressure, and relative humidity. The signals are continuously and automatically received on the ground. They can be

[2] W. Köppen, "Versuch einer Klassifikation der Klimate, vorzugsweise nach ihren Beziehungen zur Pflantzentwelt," *Geographischen Zeitschrift*, **6**:593–611, 657–79, 1900.

transmitted to a continuous recording device and are available for interpretation while the instrument is in the air.

Since 1938 special weather reconnaissance aircraft, radar, high-altitude rockets, and, most recently, weather satellites equipped with television cameras have been introduced to probe the atmosphere's higher reaches.

The number of publications containing the results of investigations in both regional and physical climatology is now impressively large and increases annually. Many of them are referred to in this book and are listed in the bibliography. The reader's attention is here drawn to a few of the more important works. The first major textbook on climatology was Julius Hann's *Handbuch der Klimatologie* (2nd ed., 3 vols., 1897), the first volume of which was translated and published by R. DeCourcy Ward in 1903. In many respects it is unsur-

passed, although much of it is, of course, out of date.

In 1899 Bartholomew's *Atlas of Meteorology* was prepared at the Edinburgh Geographical Institute. The U.S. Navy's five-volume *Marine Climatic Atlas of the World*, published from 1955 to 1965, presents a variety of material on all the major ocean areas of the earth. Outstanding also are the Köppen–Geiger *Handbuch der Klimatologie*, Berlin, 1930–39, H. H. Clayton's *World Weather Records*, published by the Smithsonian Institution in 1927, 1934, and 1947, the U.S. Weather Bureau's *World Weather Records, 1941–50*, published in 1959, and *World Weather Records, 1951–60, Vol. I, North America*, Washington, 1965, and the Environmental Science Services Administration's *World Weather Records, Vol. 2, Europe*, and *Vol. 3, South America, Central America, West Indies, The Caribbean and Bermuda*, Washington, 1966.

References

AMERICAN METEOROLOGICAL SOCIETY: *Compendium of Meteorology*, Boston, 1951.

AMERICAN METEOROLOGICAL SOCIETY: *Glossary of Meteorology*, Boston, 1959.

COURT, ARNOLD: "Climatology: Complex, Dynamic, and Synoptic," *Annals of the Association of American Geographers*, 47(2): 125–36, 1957.

GREAT BRITAIN, METEOROLOGICAL OFFICE: *Tables of Temperature, Relative Humidity and Precipitation for the World*, London, Vols. 1–6, 1962–64.

HANN, JULIUS: *Handbook of Climatology*, The Macmillan Company, New York, 1903.

KÖPPEN, W., and GEIGER, R.: *Handbuch der Klimatologie*, Berlin, Vols. 1–5, 1930–38.

LEIGHLY, JOHN: "Climatology Since the Year 1800," *Transactions of the American Geophysical Union*, 30(5): 658–72, 1949.

"SMITHSONIAN METEOROLOGICAL TABLES," *Smithsonian Miscellaneous Collections*, Washington, D.C., Vol. 114, 1951.

U.S. ENVIRONMENTAL SCIENCE SERVICES ADMINISTRATION, *World Weather Records, 1951–60*, Vol. 2, Europe, Washington, D.C., 1966; Vol. 3, South America, Central America, West Indies, The Caribbean and Bermuda, Washington, D.C., 1966.

U.S. NAVAL OCEANOGRAPHIC OFFICE: *Sailing Directions* (H.O. 10–98), Washington, D.C., 1950–64.

U.S. WEATHER BUREAU: *World Weather Records, 1941–50*, Washington, D.C., 1959.

U.S. WEATHER BUREAU: *World Weather Records, 1951–60*, Vol. 1, North America, Washington, D.C., 1965.

"WORLD WEATHER RECORDS," *Smithsonian Miscellaneous Collections*, Washington, D.C., Vol. 79, 1927; Vol. 90, 1934; Vol. 105, 1947.

chapter 2

THE ATMOSPHERE

Clinging to the land and water surfaces of the spinning globe is a formless and invisible mantle of air. This enveloping mixture of gases, water vapor, and minute particles of solid material, called the atmosphere, is a highly unstable mass, sensitive alike to the motions of the earth and to the rays of the sun. Acted upon by the combined effects of the earth's motions and solar radiation, the variable qualities of the atmosphere unite to create an infinitude of weather varieties, which in turn create the fundamental pattern of the world's climates. This chapter will describe what is known of the main chemical and physical properties of the atmosphere.

Chemical Properties of the Atmosphere

Two gases alone make up about 99 per cent of the atmosphere's volume: nitrogen (78 per cent) and oxygen (21 per cent). To these are added traces of other gases: argon, neon, krypton, xenon, hydrogen, helium, and carbon dioxide (see Table 2–1). Argon, neon, krypton, xenon, and helium are chemically inert. Free hydrogen is considered to be present as an accidental and variable impurity given off in the effusions of volcanoes.

Nitrogen, oxygen, and carbon dioxide, along with water vapor, are the main atmospheric chemical supports of all forms of terrestrial life. Nitrogen, called "foul air" by K. Scheele, who discovered its existence in 1772, *azote* (a Greek term meaning *lifeless*) by Antoine Lavoisier, the great eighteenth century chemist, will not by itself support life but is present in all forms of life. It was named by J. A. C. Chaptal in 1790 to indicate that it is a constituent of nitre or saltpetre (potassium nitrate), a common compound. It is an important component of protein in meat, milk, and eggs and in the tissues of plants, especially grains and members of the pea family. Without it there could be no growth or reproduction among plants or animals. It cannot be ingested directly by organisms but is made available to plants, and hence ultimately to animals, in the form of nitrogen compounds in the soil. Some of these compounds are introduced into the soil by the action of lightning upon moist air, uniting nitrogen with oxygen to form small quantities of nitrous and nitric acid, which are carried to earth by falling rain or snow. But by far the greatest amount of atmospheric nitrogen gets into the soil through the action of nitrogen-fixing bacteria, micro-organisms whose life cycles require a fairly constant conversion of free nitrogen into compounds that are absorbed in solution through the rootlets of plants.

Oxygen is, like nitrogen, a colorless, odorless, and tasteless gas. But unlike nitrogen it is exceedingly active, combining readily with nearly all substances to form oxides at various rates of activity. With iron the rate is slow, producing rust; with combustible materials such as wood or coal oxygen unites at high temperatures with relative rapidity, producing flame. About 2.7 tons of oxygen are required to burn 1 ton of anthracite coal. Oxygen is supplied to the atmosphere mainly by the photosynthesis of plants in sunlight, although it is taken in by plants at night, and it is taken in at all times by animals. It is thus, like nitrogen, indispensable in the life functions of all plants and animals. Both nitrogen and oxygen are at present thought to occur in nearly the same proportion throughout the lower levels of the atmosphere.

The great importance of carbon dioxide in the life processes of plants and animals is surprising in view of the fact that it accounts for only a few hundredths of 1 per cent of the atmosphere's volume. It is the chief raw material out of which, by photosynthesis, plants manufacture their food. Carbon dioxide and water, in the presence of sunlight, are converted by the green chlorophyll of plants into compounds of carbon, hydrogen, and oxygen that resemble starches and sugars. It is in this process that oxygen is released into the air. Although photosynthesis is the most important way in which carbon dioxide is removed from the air, it is also removed through the formation of carbonates by organisms such as shellfish, by the ceaseless chemistry of bacterial action, and through the weathering of calcareous rocks. Carbon dioxide is added to the air by emanations from volcanoes, gas wells, and springs, by the combustion of wood, coal, petroleum, and gas, by the respiratory exhalations of plants and animals, by the decay of organic matter, and by certain industrial processes such as smelting, lime-burning, and fermentation.

The percentage by volume of nitrogen, oxygen, carbon dioxide, and other gases in dry air is shown in Table 2–1. In the absence of sufficiently accurate data to the contrary, it is assumed that a balance exists between the addition and the removal of the atmosphere's gases. The proportions shown in the table are thought to remain constant throughout the atmosphere, at least up to a height of 15 miles. This does not hold true, however, for the air around large cities, particularly industrial centers, where an increase in carbon dioxide and a decrease in oxygen generally result from the concentration of human beings and countless oxygen-using, carbon dioxide-producing agents of combustion.

TABLE 2–1

Volume of Gases in the Atmosphere (Dry Air) to Heights of About 15 Miles

Element	Percentage
Nitrogen	78.09
Oxygen	20.93
Argon	0.93
Carbon dioxide	0.03
Neon	0.0018
Helium	0.00524
Krypton	0.0001
Hydrogen	0.00005
Xenon	0.000008
Ozone	0.000001
Radon	6×10^{-18}

Water vapor is also essential to life. Unlike nitrogen, oxygen, and carbon dioxide, however, its volume in the atmosphere is primarily a function of temperature and is exceedingly variable. An increase in the temperature of air raises its moisture-retaining capacity; a decrease lowers it. Table 2–2 outlines the maximum moisture content of air at different temperatures in terms of vapor pressure.

TABLE 2–2

Maximum Vapor Pressure (Saturation) of Air at Various Temperatures

Temperature °F	°C	Vapor Pressure mbar	in.
	Over Ice		
−40	−40	0.13	0.0038
−20	−28.9	0.43	0.0127
0	−17.8	1.28	0.0378
20	− 6.7	3.48	0.1028
	Over Water		
32	0	6.11	0.180
50	10	12.27	0.362
70	21.1	25.03	0.739
90	32.2	48.15	1.422
110	43.3	87.94	2.597

Vapor pressure is simply the pressure exerted by the gaseous, usually invisible humidity of the atmosphere (independent of total atmospheric pressure excluding moisture content) as measured on the barometer. When the vapor pressure is less than the value indicated in the table for a given temperature—that is, the saturation vapor pressure—it can be expressed as a percentage of the maximum possible moisture content. In other words, it is an amount relative to the maximum possible moisture content and is known as relative humidity. If, for example, the vapor pressure at 70°F (saturation value 0.739 inches, 25.03 millibars) is found to be 0.366 inches (12.51 millibars), the relative humidity for that temperature is 50 per cent. Expressed in another way, 1 cubic meter of otherwise dry air at the same pressure will contain increasing amounts of moisture, measured in grams per cubic meter, as the temperature is increased. Table 2–3 illustrates the rate at which these values change. Invisible atmospheric humidity and

TABLE 2–3
Moisture Content of 1 Cubic Meter of Otherwise Dry Air at Various Temperatures

Temp. °F	Moisture Content in Grams
−40	$\frac{1}{12}$
−20	$\frac{1}{3}$
0	1
32	4.87
60	12.91
80	25.0
100	50.0

visible forms of moisture are dealt with at greater length in Chapter 3. For the present we will note only its broader climatic significance.

Water vapor is of utmost importance as the source of all forms of condensation and precipitation: rain, snow, sleet, hail, fog, clouds, dew, and frost. It is, besides, the chief means (along with carbon dioxide)[1] by which the atmos-

[1] Water vapor and carbon dioxide are the main atmospheric components in the exchange of terrestrial radiation in the troposphere; carbon dioxide and ozone are the chief agents in the stratosphere.

phere absorbs heat, both directly from the sun's rays and indirectly in the reradiation of solar energy from the earth's surface. (See Chapter 3.) It tends to remain close to the earth; about half the atmosphere's moisture lies within slightly more than 1 mile (about 6000 feet) of the earth's surface, and it is scarcely detectable at levels beyond 6 or 7 miles above the earth. Table 2–4 shows the approximate vertical distribution of water vapor in middle latitudes.

TABLE 2–4
Vertical Distribution of Water Vapor in Middle Latitudes

Height in Miles	Per cent of Volume
0	1.30
$\frac{1}{2}$	1.06
1	0.80
$1\frac{1}{2}$	0.63
2	0.46
$2\frac{1}{2}$	0.37
3	0.29
$3\frac{1}{2}$	0.19
4	0.13
$4\frac{1}{2}$	0.08
5	0.05

The invisible moisture of air is supplied through the endless process of evaporation from moist surfaces and water bodies in general, but particularly from the vast expanse of the world's oceans, which make up over 70 per cent of the earth's surface. Tropical oceans, parts of which are constantly being warmed by the direct rays of the sun, are the principal source of water evaporated into the air. To some extent atmospheric water vapor is also provided through the sublimation of ice and snow. Sublimation is the process by which a solid is converted to a gaseous state without apparent liquefaction; evaporation is the conversion of liquid to gas.

In addition to the relatively uniform mixture of gases and the variable quantities of water vapor in the air, there is an even more variable percentage of minute solid particles that, when visible, are called dust. By far the greater number are invisible, however, many beyond the range of powerful microscopes. Most dust particles have a terrestrial origin, although it is generally believed that a considerable volume of cosmic dust is present, resulting from the disintegration of meteors as they enter the upper layers of atmosphere from outer space. Of the many thousands of meteors that enter the earth's atmosphere each year, nearly all are consumed in the heat of friction generated by their passage through the air.

The chief terrestrial sources of atmospheric dust are familiar to everyone. Smoke and ash from volcanoes, forest and grass fires, smoke from industrial chimneys and domestic furnaces, the exhaust from engines of transportation, clouds of finely powdered rock material blown from the bare earth of arid regions, minute salt crystals borne into the air by ocean spray, and countless varieties of pollen, fungi spores, and bacteria.

The continuous outpouring of smoke from many of the world's thousands of active volcanoes is occasionally punctuated by the more dramatic explosion of a single cone. Krakatoa, a tiny islet between Sumatra and Java, erupted in 1883 with such force that one half of the islet was blown away. Although Krakatoa is about 6 degrees south of the equator, the fine dust from its explosion, carried high into the air, gradually drifted poleward to cause a deepening of sunset and sunrise coloration in midlatitudes for many months afterward and remained suspended at high altitudes for more than three years. When Mt. Katmai in the Aleutian Range of southern Alaska erupted explosively in 1912, the colors of sunrise and sunset in the northern hemisphere were affected for many months.

Forest, brush, and grass fires in Pennsylvania, New York, and New England during the unusually long, dry period in the autumn of 1953 produced a pall of smoky haze, gave the sun a coppery glow for several weeks, and was observed by mariners off the coast of New England, as it drifted out to sea in the path of the prevailing winds from the west.

Industrial centers, chiefly in eastern North America and western Europe, are the source of large volumes of smoke from heating plants, factories, smelters, and foundries. The smoke and even the dust of traffic in large cities, often associated with lingering fog, are now known to be detrimental to the health of the inhabitants. The public health authorities of London

estimated that around 2800 deaths from respiratory ailments were caused by a persistent damp, choking "smog" that hung over the city for an entire week in early winter of 1952. By reducing the intensity of solar radiation, particularly in the bacteria-destroying ultraviolet band of the spectrum, city haze is also known to be laden with a much larger number of germs than the clearer air of the countryside. The broad environmental variations in the number of suspended particles in the atmosphere are shown in Table 2–5.

TABLE 2–5
Quantity of Suspended Particles in Various Localities

Locality	Average No. Particles per Cubic In.
City	2,600,000
Town	610,000
Countryside	174,000
Mountain less than 3000 ft	105,000
Mountain 3000–6000 ft	36,000
Mountain greater than 6000 ft	17,400
Open ocean	17,400

After H. Landsberg, *Physical Climatology*, Gray Printing Co., Inc., Du Bois, Pa., 1958, p. 115.

It is common knowledge, of course, that wind raises dust from dry land everywhere. Much of it soon settles back to earth, but some is carried aloft over great distances. The chief sources of this form of atmospheric dust are the desert regions of the world, especially north Africa, southwest and central Asia, and interior Australia. The harmattan of west Africa is a dry, dust-laden wind of the winter season that blows southwestward out of the Sahara into the hot, wet, forested lowlands of the Guinea coast, bringing some relief from the normally warm, humid air of the region, bringing also so much dust that the reduced visibility impedes navigation on the rivers and for many miles offshore. The basin of Lake Chad, at the desert's edge, is said to be slowly filling wth dust laid down for centuries by the harmattan of the Sahara.

The oceans constantly provide the atmosphere with microscopic particles of salt, evaporated from the wind-blown spray of the waves.

Indeed, tiny salt crystals in air can often be felt at great distances inland from the sea when borne by a strong, steady onshore wind. An instance of this was reported in England during the great storm of 1839, when a westerly gale carried sufficient salt to encrust the trees and bridges at Alford in Lincolnshire, 120 miles inland from Liverpool, reaching almost entirely across the island to within a few miles of the North Sea coast.

During the growing season the air is supplied from various forms of plant life with large quantities of minute pollen grains and spores of fungi which, with a wide variety of air-borne bacteria, add organic minutiae to the composition of the atmosphere. Micro-organisms, like other solid particles in air, have been detected at relatively high altitudes. When the exploratory balloon *Explorer II* descended from a height of 13 miles in 1932, a sample of air was taken between heights of about 13 miles and 7 miles that was later discovered to contain five different kinds of bacteria and five different kinds of mold fungi, all of which are well known and widely distributed around the world.

Dust in the atmosphere along with molecules of water vapor is responsible for several visible effects: the warm reddish tones of sunrise and sunset; the yellowish glow of the moon; the coppery gleam of the sun as seen through the dusky haze of large cities or through the diffused cloudiness of a dust storm. Invisible particles of molecular size, especially the hygroscopic salts from ocean spray and products of combustion, are thought to provide the essential nuclei around which most condensation of moisture in air takes place to produce the tiny droplets of which fog and clouds are composed, and from them, the larger drops of rain, flakes of snow, or crystals of ice that fall on the earth. Particles of mineral origin are thought to be much less important in this process than salt and smoke particles. Dust particles supplied to the atmosphere tend to return to earth through the gradual settling of the heavier particles and in falling rain and snow, which often carry with them a quantity of dust sufficient to produce a light smudge on buildings, vehicles, and the foliage of plants and give rise to the term *mud rain*. The "red rains" off Cape Verde in west Africa are famous among mariners for the bloodlike color they impart to

decks, sails, and rigging, when the fine red dust of the desert, blown many miles out to sea, is carried down over the ocean by falling rain.

Emanations of radium, called radon, are another important component of the atmosphere (Table 2–1). So far as present observations indicate, they are produced by the minute quantities of radium present in soil. The proportion in which they have been detected in air varies considerably from place to place: a rapid decrease in volume with increasing altitude has been observed, a mantle of snow will completely prevent radium diffusion, and there is much less evidence of it over oceans than over land areas. It is climatologically significant because even very small amounts are believed to affect the health of human beings.

Theories of Atmospheric Layers

To ascribe to the formless mass of air those dimensions of length, breadth, and height or depth that may be applied to bodies of land or water is a practical impossibility. The constantly moving atmosphere is really a spherical shell, enveloping and concentric with the more substantial lithosphere and hydrosphere of the earth (Fig. 2.1). Being spherical,[2] it has neither

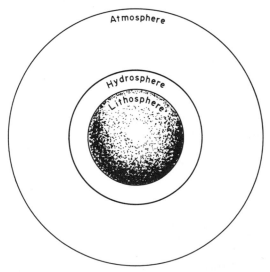

Figure 2.1. The earth's three main concentric spheres.

[2] The fact that the earth, having the figure of an oblate spheroid, is about 27 miles smaller in polar diameter than in equatorial diameter (7899.99 miles and 7926.68 miles respectively) does not materially alter the highly valuable concept of its sphericity.

length nor breadth. Nor is its height above sea level exactly measurable. Traces of its gases—especially oxygen, helium, and hydrogen—have been detected by spectrographic analysis at altitudes of several hundred miles. Its outermost extent is at present estimated to reach between 600 and 700 miles above the earth. Beyond this apparent limit of the earth's identifiable atmosphere are enveloping realms of very much more rarefied character that are believed to extend the earth's unique environment in space outward more than 50,000 miles. The theoretical arrangement of those ephemeral frontiers beyond the atmosphere is discussed briefly below, based upon information newly revealed by American satellites, especially the Vanguards and Explorers. The Tiros satellites have sent back information (from much lower altitudes) on solar and terrestrial radiation and the earth's cloud cover from heights averaging only about 475 miles above sea level.

Since January 31, 1958, when the first American satellite, Explorer I, went into orbit, a new concept has been evolved of the physical and chemical composition of those upper distances far above the clouds (Fig. 2.2). Beyond the atmosphere's estimated 600- to 700-mile upper limit is a far-reaching realm newly named the magnetosphere. It is conceived to be a region in which ionized particles are trapped in the earth's magnetic field. Layers of contrasting particles, some positively charged protons, some negatively charged electrons, having different energy values in terms of electron volts, are the main features. They are believed to play a major role both in the transfer of solar energy to the earth and in the occurrence of the Aurorae—the Aurora Borealis (Northern Lights) and the south polar counterpart, the Aurora Australis—those colorful and sometimes dazzling displays that form below the magnetosphere at levels roughly between 50 and 700 miles. Beyond the magnetosphere, which appears to end at around 40,000 miles above the earth, is a turbulent region of 12,000 miles of fluctuating magnetic fields, and beyond that is interplanetary space.

Chemically, the magnetosphere appears to be stratified. Outward from the atmosphere's

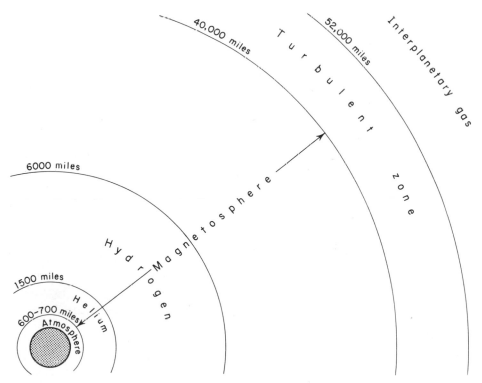

Figure 2.2. Theoretical profile of the atmosphere.

ceiling there is apparently a 900-mile layer in which helium is the dominant element. Above this is a layer, whose outermost limit is an estimated 6000 miles, in which hydrogen is the principal element, decreasing in density with increasing distance and finally merging indistinctly with interplanetary gas. The relationships between these outer strata and terrestrial weather and climate are by no means understood at present, although in time, with a great many more observations and the development of suitable theory, their significance will undoubtedly be revealed.

For many years it has been common practice to visualize the atmosphere's vertical structure in terms of three distinct layers: troposphere, stratosphere, and ionosphere (Fig. 2.3). In this concept the troposphere is the lowest layer, reaching from the earth's surface to an altitude of about 7 miles in the middle latitudes, the

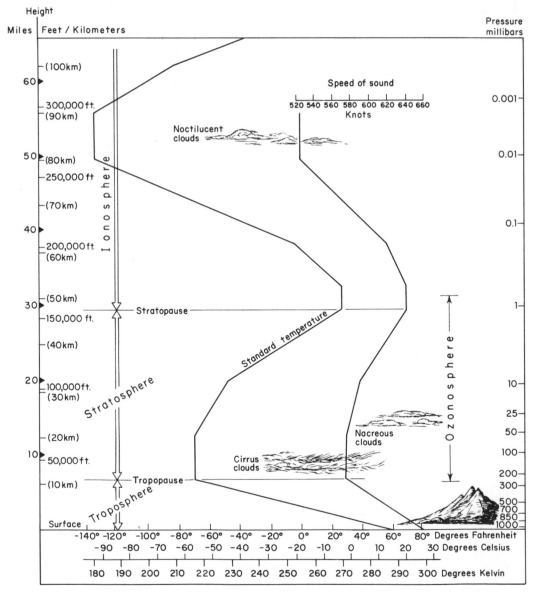

Figure 2.3. Vertical distribution of atmospheric qualities.

upper limit of which is the tropopause. Beginning at the tropopause is the stratosphere, considered by some to reach upward to about 20 miles, by others to 50 miles, above the earth. The ionosphere extends for several hundred miles above the stratosphere.

In recent years enough additional information has been gleaned from instruments sent higher and higher into the heavens to suggest the existence of various levels of both the stratosphere and ionosphere. Among these are the ozonosphere, a layer roughly 6 to 31 miles in height, where there is an appreciable concentra-

tion of ozone (O_3); the neutrosphere, a relatively un-ionized layer below the ionosphere; and the chemosphere, a high-level layer having no definite upward limitation, where photochemical reactions take place. At the same time, theoretical analysis of the new information has also led to some feeling that the "layer" idea is open to question. However, the proof of any one of many alternate ideas about the atmosphere's higher levels must await the accumulation of more data.

Meanwhile, efforts are continually being made to improve the practical usefulness both

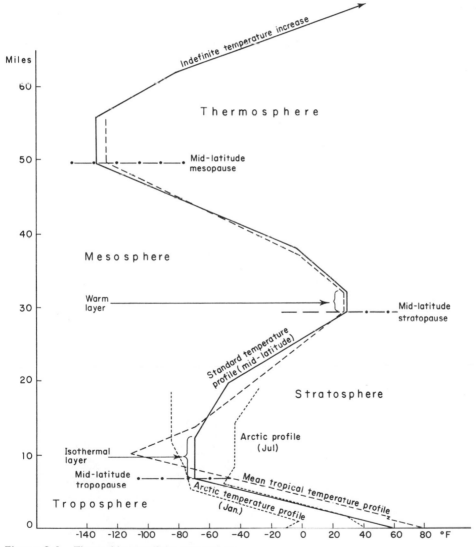

Figure 2.4. Thermal layers of the atmosphere.

of the newer information on conditions at very high altitudes and of the growing body of confirming evidence of conditions within just a few miles of the earth. Among the more recent of these is a theory that pictures the 600- to 700-mile over-all shell of the atmosphere as a set of four concentric layers identified by temperature alone. An acceptance of the "layer" idea is implied. This very reasonable suggestion was made at a meeting in Rome during August, 1961, of the Working Group on the High Atmosphere, Commission for Aerology, of the World Meteorological Organization, an agency of the United Nations, established at Geneva in 1950. Figure 2.4 is a generalized cross-sectional diagram portraying the suggested atmospheric stratification according to estimated heights for the mid-latitudes of the northern hemisphere. From the earth's surface upward, the four concentric shells are troposphere, stratosphere, mesosphere, and thermosphere. Temperature characteristics are the key to the identity of each shell. The upper limits of the three lower layers are marked by "pauses" (from the Greek *pauein*, to cause to change): tropopause, stratopause and mesopause. At each pause the identifying temperature trend for one layer comes to an end, and a new trend appears with increasing height.

The Troposphere

In the troposphere temperatures decrease fairly evenly with increasing altitude at a rate (3.6°F per 1000 feet) called the normal lapse rate of temperature change. The usefulness of this value will be seen in a later discussion of stability and instability in the atmosphere. Actual observed lapse rates vary with the time of day, with the seasons, and from place to place at any given time. Figures 2.5 and 2.6, in which a number of temperature soundings from the surface upward are plotted, indicate that the normal lapse rate varies considerably. Also apparent is the fact that on numerous occasions the lapse rate is interrupted somewhere in the lower 2000 or 3000 feet above the earth's surface by a reversal in the trend of temperature change. This is an inversion, about which more will be said in a later chapter. At about 7 miles above the earth in the middle latitudes air temperature abruptly ends its decrease and either remains the same—isothermal—in the lower stratosphere, or rises imperceptibly. At points where the normal lapse rate ceases, the troposphere ends and the stratosphere begins. The transition takes place at the tropopause, which may be thought of as the ceiling of the troposphere and the base of the stratosphere.

Figure 2.5. Mean temperature soundings above Fairbanks, Flint, Fort Worth, and Canton Island in January 1964.

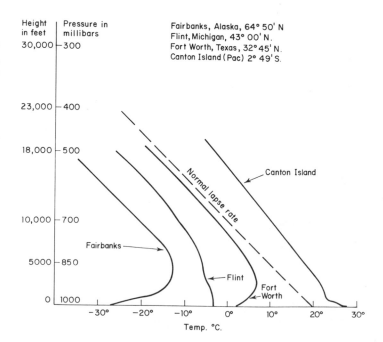

Figure 2.6. Mean temperature soundings above Fairbanks, Flint, Fort Worth, and Canton Island in July 1965.

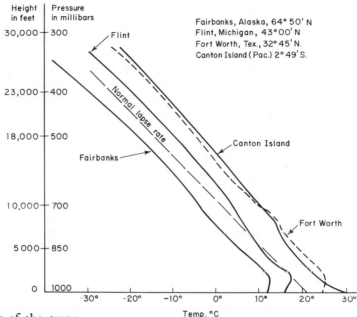

Fairbanks, Alaska, 64° 50' N
Flint, Michigan, 43°00' N
Fort Worth, Tex., 32° 45' N.
Canton Island (Pac.) 2° 49' S.

Within the variable thickness of the troposphere occur nearly all of those endless daily and seasonal changes in temperature, pressure, movement, and moisture conditions that make up the world's weather and climate. Most of the discussion in this book pertains to this lowest layer of the atmosphere, in fact, to the few thousand feet just above the earth's surface.

About 50 per cent of the mass of the entire atmosphere is thought to lie within 17,500 feet (the lower half of the troposphere), and about 75 per cent of its mass within 35,000 feet of the earth's surface, while 99 per cent is generally believed to reach outward no more than about 25 miles (Fig. 2.7). This results from the fact, true of all fluid mixtures, that the heavier components tend to sink to the bottom. Water vapor and solid particles of dust are concentrated near the earth's surface and diminish in density with increasing altitude. Below 6000 feet is nearly one half of the atmosphere's moisture, and much more than half of all its dust particles. Since both water vapor and dust are most important in absorbing the heat of the sun's rays, the capacity of the lower mile or so of the troposphere to heat and cool is one of its major qualities.

We have seen that temperature decreases with increasing altitude in the troposphere. Atmospheric pressure also decreases with

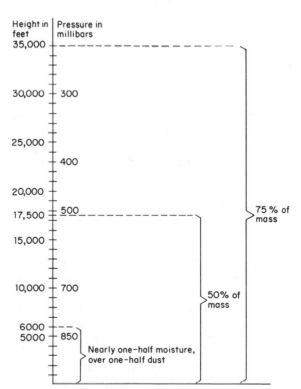

Figure 2.7. Proportional changes of mass, moisture, and dust in the atmosphere with height.

altitude. It is determined by the pressure exerted upon a barometer and is usually expressed in millibars or inches. The standard sea level pressure of the atmosphere is 29.92 inches (1013.2 millibars). At the top of Mt. Everest 29,002 feet above sea level air pressure is less than 10 inches (about 325 millibars), at 30 miles above sea level it is 1 millibar, or about one-thousandth of the sea level value, and at 60 miles it is only about one one-millionth of the pressure at sea level.

The mercurial barometer is the official standardization instrument of the United States Weather Bureau. It is essentially a refinement of the device invented by Torricelli in 1643, which consisted of a slender glass tube, about 3 feet long, filled with mercury and inverted with its open end in a cup of mercury. The mercury flows out of the tube into the cup until the weight of the atmosphere, pressing upon the open surface of the fluid metal, balances the column remaining in the tube. The length of the column of mercury is then a measure of atmospheric pressure or weight at a particular place. The standard sea level pressure of 29.92 inches (1013.2 mb, 760 mm) is based upon a temperature of 59°F (15°C). Allowances must be made when pressure readings are made at other temperatures.

For a great many years atmospheric pressure was expressed in inches in the United States, but in countries where the metric system is commonly used it was given in millimeters. For the past few decades air pressure has been measured in terms of millibars, a millibar being the weight of 1000 dynes upon a square centimeter at 59°F. A single dyne is a unit of force approximately equal to the weight of 1 milligram. Thus 1 millibar is approximately equal to the weight of 1 gram. Although the employment of the millibar as a uniform standard of measurement has certain advantages in universal science, most weather information given out to the public is still expressed in terms of inches or millimeters.

A second instrument widely used to measure air pressure is the aneroid barometer. This is the instrument by which official United States Weather Bureau pressure readings are made. *Aneroid* is derived from the Greek *an*, without, and *aer*, air. A small cylindrical chamber, with upper and lower surfaces of thin metal, is nearly emptied of air and is hermetically sealed and fitted inside with a strong spring to prevent its collapsing. The sensitive cylinder changes in height with changes in the pressure of the air around it and communicates these changes through a pivoted index arm to a scale calibrated in inches, millibars, or millimeters. It was invented by Vidi in 1848, and although less accurate and less durable than the mercurial barometer, has the advantage of being much smaller, more compact, and much more portable. It is in fact now widely used for measuring altitude as well as air pressure, and when so used is called an altimeter.

The decrease in atmospheric pressure with altitude closely parallels the change in atmospheric density. One way of visualizing contrasting densities is to consider the distance between air molecules. At sea level this distance is about one three-millionths of an inch, at 20 miles about one two-hundredths of an inch, at 60 miles slightly more than 1 inch, but at 200 miles the distance between molecules of air is about 80 feet.

The troposphere is still further distinguished from the loftier layers of the atmosphere as the region in which most clouds form, in which vertical wind movement and frequent turbulence take place, and in which may be observed the bright blue of the sky, the warm red colors of sunrise and sunset, halos around the sun and moon, rainbows, and the sparkle of stars.

Most of the clouds in the sky form within a few miles of the earth's surface, seldom more than 7 or 8 miles above the earth. They are formed by the condensation of invisible water vapor. It has been estimated that about 90 per cent of the atmosphere's water vapor lies within about $3\frac{1}{2}$ miles of the earth. Condensation occurs when the temperature of moisture-laden air is lowered sufficiently to form tiny droplets of water or ice crystals ranging in size from 0.0001 to 0.0004 inch. This takes place when the air temperature is lowered to the dew point, the temperature at which air is fully saturated. The various kinds of precipitation and the manner in which they form are discussed at length in Chapter 3; at this point we shall simply consider the principal types of clouds that appear as visual features of the troposphere.

Despite the endlessly changing variety of cloud shapes and sizes, all may be identified according to an international classification now in general use, sponsored by the International

Meteorological Committee, which represents the official meteorological agencies of many nations. Four "families" of clouds are recognized: high clouds, middle clouds, low clouds, and clouds with accentuated vertical development. Within each family are variants, some of which are illustrated in Fig. 2.8. Each variant may be recognized as one of three basic types: cirrus, cumulus, and stratus. These names, which have a meaningful Latin derivation,[3] have been in use since 1803, when they were introduced by the British scientist Luke Howard.

Stratus clouds may appear at elevations ranging from ground level to 20,000 feet or more. They often produce an unbroken overcast, which at lower elevations is dark and opaque and at higher altitudes is often light and translucent enough to reveal the dimly glowing forms of the sun or moon through a pale haze. Cumulus is the pillowy white form that most generally appears as a group of broken, discontinuous clouds slowly drifting across a serene blue sky at heights of 2000 to 10,000 feet. A particular distinction of cumulus clouds is their tendency to achieve great vertical growth under certain conditions, often to become the familiar thunderhead, a cumulonimbus cloud that produces heavy thundershowers, lightning, occasionally even a fall of hail. These clouds generally develop a vertical measurement of from 2000 to 20,000 feet, although many have been seen to tower above 50,000 feet, and some in central North America are known to have reached as high as 68,000 feet. Nimbus clouds, whether cumulonimbus or stratonimbus, are those releasing rain or snow upon the earth.

Cirrus clouds are high-altitude clouds entirely, and unlike either stratus or cumulus are formed of tiny ice crystals. They usually appear at altitudes of 20,000 to 40,000 feet or more and are commonly quite transparent.

In the visible motion of clouds at all levels is an indication of the invisible motions of the air within the troposphere, and the great complexities of air movement, especially in the vertical, provide another distinguishing quality of that variable space between the earth's surface and the base of the stratosphere. The ceaseless movement of air in both the horizontal and the vertical proceeds in highly complicated patterns and is initially born of contrasting

[3] *Cirrus:* a lock or tuft of hair; *cumulus:* a heap or pile; *stratus:* a cover or blanket.

qualities of the earth's surface. It, in turn, affects the earth's surface and its inhabitants.

Because the atmosphere in many respects resembles a fluid, it has a constant tendency to establish equilibrium between its lighter and heavier parts. Wind is a consequence of this tendency. Air that is warmed becomes lighter and less dense. It expands, rises, and is replaced by an inflow of cooler, denser, heavier air. Thus, in a very broad way, the cold air of polar latitudes may be thought to move in repeated surges equatorward to take the place of air nearer the tropics that is warm, has expanded, and tends to rise from the earth. The same relationship is seen between any two adjoining masses of air having different temperatures, and thus having different densities and different weights, giving rise to a barometric gradient, or barocline, that results in the movement of air.

Wind velocity as a rule increases with increasing altitude. It is sometimes said, for example, that wind 2000 feet up may have about three times the velocity of a surface wind. A common assumption is that wind speeds increase toward a maximum near the top of the troposphere, and indeed repeated measurements made since the end of World War II indicate that maximum velocities are attained somewhere between 35,000 and 40,000 feet, at least in the mid-latitudes.

Winds that blow along the earth's surface are slowed by the friction of their contact with land or water, the effect being more pronounced over the uneven surfaces of land than over the relatively smooth expanses of water bodies. Oceanic winds in general blow at higher velocities than inland winds and are very much steadier.

The blue of the daylight sky and the red and golden tones of sunrise and sunset are other phenomena distinguishing the troposphere from the stratosphere and ionosphere. The blue of the sky is caused by the scattering[4] of white

[4] Actual scattering of light from the solar beam is selective, occurring only when the diameters of interrupting particles are less than the wavelengths of the light oscillations, and thus being most effective at the short-wavelength, blue end of the spectrum. The denser the mass of obscuring particles through which the sun's rays must travel, the more complete is the process of scattering. Hence, when air is heavily laden with dust or moisture, even the longer light rays near the red end of the spectrum are scattered, producing a red glow in the sky.

A. Cirrus fibratus floccus.

B. Stratus opacus.

Figure 2.8. Three basic cloud types: cirrus, stratus, and cumulus. [U.S. Weather Bureau photos.]

light from the sun as it passes through the relatively dense dust- and moisture-laden medium of the lower troposphere. The short blue rays of the spectrum bend more readily than the longer red rays, are thus more sharply diverted, and are sent out in all directions from the main path of the sun's white light. Scattered blue rays are then reflected by the microscopic particles in the atmosphere, especially by water vapor, and produce the over-all blue of the sky.

With increasing altitude the sky becomes more brilliantly blue, especially above 3000 feet, beyond the haze caused by suspended dust particles. At very high altitudes the color gradually deepens, until within the stratosphere it appears nearly black, with just a suggestion of very dark blue, and the sun's light appears here as the white and undiffused gleam of a large star.

When the sun is near the horizon and acquires an orange or reddish glow, its light is seen through a much greater thickness of the atmosphere (Fig. 2.9). More of its shorter rays at the blue end of the spectrum are bent,

C. Stratus translucidus.

D. Cumulus humilis.

diffused, and reflected by atmospheric particles, and only the longer red rays reach the observer's eye. The sun often appears red or coppery overhead when the atmosphere is clouded with dust or a heavy pall of smoke, again diverting most of the rays at the blue or ultraviolet end of the spectrum. In various ways the composition and density of the lower troposphere act upon the light from celestial bodies to produce such familiar sights as rainbows, star sparkle, and halos about the sun and moon.

The tropopause itself is only imperfectly understood. It is commonly considered to be the fluctuating level at which the normal lapse rate of the troposphere abruptly ceases. Its average height is ordinarily assumed to be about 7 miles in the middle latitudes, about 5 miles near the poles, and about 10 miles near the equator. It was discovered, and its identity as the top of the troposphere and the base of the stratosphere established, by the French meteorologist Léon Teisserenc de Bort in 1902.

For some time during the latter part of the nineteenth century it had been recognized that air temperatures decreased about 3.6°F with every 1000 feet of increasing altitude. Temperature was thought to continue to decrease

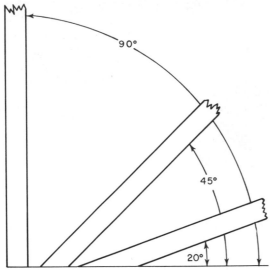

Figure 2.9. The sun's rays travel a shorter distance through the atmosphere and are concentrated on an increasingly smaller area of the earth's surface as the sun's angular elevation increases.

level, at values of around −67°F, usually warming slightly for some distance farther upward. Subsequent observations have revealed that temperatures normally rise very gradually from the tropopause up to heights (in the middle latitudes) of about 15 miles, creating a virtually isothermal layer whose thickness varies but is something on the order of 10 miles. The transition upward is from less stability in the troposphere to greater stability in the lower stratosphere. Stability depends largely on the vertical distribution of both temperature and moisture, and is treated more fully in a later chapter. The tropopause also marks the level at which the pronounced vertical motions of the troposphere give way to the zone of greatly reduced vertical motion in the stratosphere. In short, a major distinction of the troposphere is the presence there of constant vigorous, vertical motion, normally of a complex character called convective turbulence, or turbulent convection, in which the process of overturning is an integral feature. The stratosphere on the other hand is a zone in which the main fields of motion are believed to be laminar, that is to occur in some kind of broad, sweeping, horizontal flow, incorporating very little vertical displacement, very little overturning.

From observations made in recent years it has become apparent that the tropopause is by no means a single, unbroken boundary layer separating troposphere from stratosphere

indefinitely toward absolute zero with increasing distance from the earth. The information upon which this theory was based had been gathered by self-registering instruments sent aloft attached to gas-filled balloons. In 1902 de Bort, after a series of sounding balloon (*ballon-sonde*) observations begun in 1898, pointed out that temperature always leveled off near heights of about 7 miles above sea

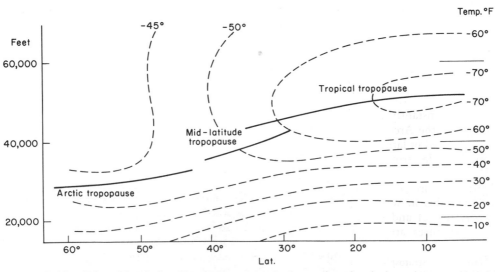

Figure 2.10.   Schematic relationship of tropopauses in the northern hemisphere.

and enveloping the entire earth in complete continuity. Instead, it appears to consist of several discontinuous and sometimes overlapping levels that increase in altitude from the polar regions toward the equator (Fig. 2.10), a multiple tropopause. It is becoming the practice[5] to speak of an Arctic tropopause, a mid-latitude tropopause, and a tropical tropopause. And although information about the upper air south of the equator is scarcer and less certain, a similar condition is believed to hold true there.

The height of each tropopause fluctuates widely. It might be thought of as an undulating ceiling, here bulging upward, there subsiding in basin-like or trough-like depressions, buoyed up to varying degrees by the thrust of convective turbulence. It is generally higher locally whenever the air near the surface is warmer, and also whenever atmospheric pressure is higher. Outside the tropics it is higher in summer than in winter.

The Arctic tropopause in winter averages a height of about 6.2 miles, although it often lowers to 3.7 miles, especially over areas of cyclonic activity. Identified as the level of minimum temperatures, which average around −67°F in winter, it is usually fairly distinct, although it becomes somewhat less so when the troposphere is very cold. In summertime its average height ranges between 6.2 and 7.5 miles, and its temperatures are higher, around −58°F.

In the northern hemisphere the Arctic tropopause extends from the pole to a position from 100 to 300 miles north of the point of maximum velocity of high-speed, high-altitude winds that flow in a roughly eastward direction. This is the polar jet stream. South of the jet stream is the mid-latitude tropopause. The position of the jet stream follows a decidedly sinuous course, constantly changing. Thus the southern edge of the Arctic tropopause is also constantly displaced in latitude.

The mid-latitude tropopause appears to extend for about 1000 miles equatorward of its northern limits in summertime and somewhat less than this in winter. In summer it averages between 8.1 and 8.7 miles in height, and its temperatures are around −85°F. In

winter it ranges in height between 5 and 7.5 miles, usually maintaining an upward slope toward the tropics, and its temperatures are about −67°F.

The tropical tropopause extends farther northward in summertime, often overlapping the mid-latitude tropopause by several hundred miles, and maintains an altitude at that season of between 10 and 11 miles, rising slightly in a poleward direction. Its temperatures range between about −94°F on its poleward side to about −112°F near the equator. In winter it does not usually overlap the mid-latitude tropopause, normally remaining south of 30°N. Lat. In winter it is higher than in summer, between 11 and 12 miles, and its temperatures are around −112°F.

The fact that the tropopause is nearly twice as high over the equator as it is near the poles indicates the much higher temperature of the earth's surface within the tropics, which in turn gives rise to much more vigorous convective activity and a much higher upthrust of warmed air that raises the tropopause. The troposphere is thus nearly twice as thick in low latitudes as it is near the poles.

The Stratosphere

Beyond the upper limits of the troposphere is the stratosphere, about which, until recently, very little was known. Although its exact relationship with terrestrial climate is not clear even now, certain of its characteristics have been identified, permitting a tentative portrayal of its structure (Fig. 2.11). Most of the information about the stratosphere has been acquired during recent years through the wider application of radio, rocket, aircraft, high-altitude balloon, weather satellite, and other improvements in observational tools and techniques.

Since 1937 most atmospheric observations from ground level upward into the lower stratosphere have been made by radiosonde, previously described in Chapter 1. The observations are called, in weatherman's jargon, RAOB's. By employing a radio direction-finding instrument to track the path of the radiosonde through the sky, the direction and speed of winds in the various layers through which it travels can be determined. Such observations are termed rawinsondes.

Observations are taken either twice or four times daily at about 135 stations in the western

[5] F. K. Hare, "The Stratosphere," *The Geographical Review*, **50**(4): 525–47, 1962.

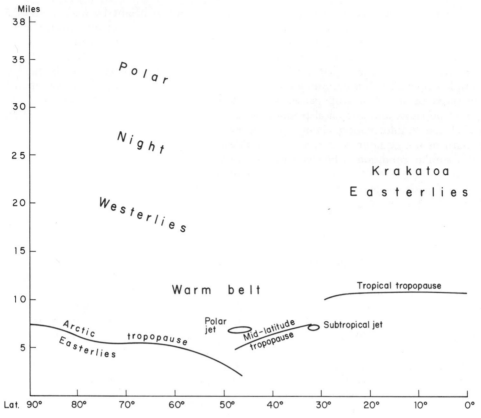

Figure 2.11.   Features of the upper atmosphere in the northern hemisphere.

hemisphere, and at about four hundred additional stations in other areas of the world. The observation network is considered adequate for only small segments of the earth's surface, however, for in remote, uninhabited regions like the Arctic and Antarctica there are few stations, and on the high seas only a small number of government-owned vessels regularly make upper air soundings. The U.S. Weather Bureau, for example, operates only four weather ships in the Atlantic and two in the Pacific. The average altitude reached by radiosonde is approximately 75,000 feet (about 14 miles), although a number have ascended to 125,000 feet, or nearly 24 miles.

Quite plainly, the upper air data normally supplied by radiosonde pertain only to the lower levels of the stratosphere. In the United States the upper usual limit of ascent is about 14 miles, but the international radiosonde network as a whole attains somewhat lower heights, averaging about 12.4 miles, with occasional ascents to 18.6 miles. To extend our

knowledge of the upper stratosphere, rockets have been used with increasing success, and since 1959 a network of meteorological rocket stations has been taking shape in the United States and Canada. Although scarcely more than a dozen stations are as yet engaged in the rocket-sounding program, the data on atmospheric levels up to nearly 38 miles (about 200,000 feet) are revealing the character of the stratosphere over North America more clearly than it was ever before known. The infrequent firing of larger rockets, usually from military establishments, provides valuable information on the very high layers of the atmosphere, up to heights of nearly 70 miles, well into the thermosphere.

Man's interest in the stratosphere has greatly increased in recent years, not only in response to his quest for scientific knowledge, but for practical reasons as well. Civil aircraft now fly at altitudes of 36,000 to 40,000 feet, while experimental and military aircraft operate up to more than 260,000 feet; the need for more and better information on these high levels of flight is obvious. Furthermore, the stratosphere is the main atmospheric reservoir in which debris from nuclear explosions can be held in suspension for long periods of time, up to two years in the reaches above the tropopause in the tropics. Nuclear explosions have been detonated from time to time ever since 1945, and it is largely from stratospheric levels that fallout occurs.

The temperature rise by which the stratosphere is primarily identified extends from a minimum at the tropopause to a maximum at the stratopause, which lies from 29 to 33 miles above the earth. This is believed to hold true between the poles and equator in both hemispheres, although very little is actually known about most of the stratosphere south of the equator. A discussion of the stratosphere in the northern hemisphere will serve to illustrate its general qualities.

Temperatures of the tropical tropopause average around −112°F near 20°N. Lat. at elevations ranging from about 9.3 miles in summer to about 11.2 miles in winter. At about 30°N. Lat. tropopause temperatures are about −94°F, rising northward to about −75°F over the variable latitude of the jet stream. The Arctic tropopause temperatures are about −58°F in summer but may be nearly twice as low in winter.

South of 30°N. Lat. temperatures from the tropopause to the stratopause rise steadily at about 6 degrees per mile, reaching a maximum at about 30 miles. In the mid-latitudes a nearly isothermal layer extends from the tropopause up to about 12 miles, and then temperatures rise fairly steadily to the stratopause. The Arctic stratosphere, however, experiences pronounced seasonal changes in temperature stratification.

In summertime, when from pole to equator the stratosphere's temperatures rise steadily above about 8.2 miles in height, temperatures in the lower Arctic stratosphere rise rapidly for a few miles from about −46°F at the tropopause to about −33°F at about 9.3 miles, but increase more slowly above that to the stratopause. In winter the situation is quite different. For six or seven months, from October to March or April, the stratosphere from the tropopause to about 14 miles has cold temperatures in both Arctic and tropical areas, while in the higher mid-latitudes (between 50° and 60°N. Lat.) temperatures are higher. This warm belt, according to Hare,[6] is one of the fundamental features of the atmosphere. It usually lies about 10°N. Lat. of the main jet stream. The cold temperatures of the Arctic stratosphere in winter are normally reached at levels between 12 and 22 miles above the earth. In short, there is a lowering of temperature from the tropopause to those heights, and then a rise to a maximum at the stratopause, a maximum that for this season is about 0°F.

Motion in the stratosphere consists in general of very broad, sweeping wind systems that are far from constant in strength and position. They are, however, relatively conservative and are thus more stable than those in the troposphere. In the Arctic stratosphere the great annual range of temperature change, from about −112°F in January to −40°F in July (a range of 72 degrees), causes a pronounced reversal of winds between winter and summer. In winter a strong westerly circulation, in the form of a sinuous circumpolar vortex called the polar-night westerlies, develops far above the frozen surfaces of the northern hemisphere. Wind speeds up to 160 miles per hour are attained at around 22 miles in altitude. Rocket observations have shown speeds of over 400 miles per hour at 37 miles in altitude, near the upper limit of the stratopause (Fig. 2.11). In summer at heights above about 10 miles winds from the opposite direction prevail, in the form of light easterlies attaining speeds of under 30 miles per hour at heights of around 20 miles. At this season these stratospheric easterlies are found as far south as the main summertime jet stream flow, which may attain speeds up to 170 miles per hour. It is considered probable that they are continuous all the way to the equator, where high altitude easterlies are much stronger.

According to recent soundings of the tropical stratosphere, a vast easterly jet stream system prevails. Below 12.4 miles the circulation is light and variable, increasing rapidly with height. At about 15.5 miles winds are reported as steady from day to day, averaging about 80 miles per hour between 15° and 20°N. Lat. Between 19 and 25 miles in height they may exceed 115 miles per hour, and these have been

[6] Hare, *op. cit.*, p. 533.

named the Krakatoa easterlies because they carried the dust of the Krakatoa eruption. This west-flowing current has recently been shown to experience a remarkable twenty-six-month oscillation, distinguished by a broad, strong flow at the start, becoming much narrower and weaker thirteen months later. After another thirteen-month period it regains its former breadth and strength, and the cycle begins again. No satisfactory explanation of this phenomenon has yet appeared.

Viewing the stratosphere as a part of the entire atmosphere, it may be said that the governing forces—gravity, friction, pressure gradient, and Coriolis (see Chapter 4)—are the same, and the same physical laws apply. Thermal properties in the stratosphere are distinctly different from those in the troposphere, however, and constitute one of its distinctive features. The stratosphere differs also in composition.

Ozone (O_3), water vapor, and sulfur compounds occur in strikingly different proportions in the stratosphere than they do in the troposphere. Ozone is a photochemical product of the reaction of ultraviolet radiation from the sun upon ordinary oxygen (O_2). In the upper stratosphere and in the mesosphere above it ozone production proceeds at a rapid rate, most abundantly at levels between 10 and 25 miles. The concentration of ozone at these levels is nearly constant and is believed to be in photochemical equilibrium. In the lower stratosphere, within a few miles of the tropopause, ozone, although in much smaller percentages, is nearly stable and is distributed by the wind systems. A primary function of ozone is the strong absorption of ultraviolet radiation from the sun; thus it acts as a filter of the sun's rays, reducing the percentage of ultraviolet light to just the right amount for the maintenance of life on the earth. Without it, in the opinion of some, the excess of ultraviolet radiation would be lethal to most forms of plant and animal life. Ozone is produced in the troposphere by the action of lightning and other electrical charges on ordinary oxygen, and it may sometimes be detected in the vicinity of electric motors in operation, and sometimes during a heavy thunderstorm, by its distinctive odor.

Because ozone absorbs some incoming sunlight, it is able to heat the atmosphere. Thus, where it is most abundant, a warm layer has been identified that marks the ceiling of the stratosphere and that bears the name *stratopause*.

The stratosphere is further distinguished by being exceedingly dry. One way of indicating the water vapor content of the atmosphere is by the mass mixing ratio, grams of water mixed with a kilogram of dry air. Mixing ratios are high near the earth's surface, and in the middle latitudes, between 40° and 50°N., range from 2 gm/kg in January to 10 gm/kg in July. They may exceed 15 gm/kg over the surface of the sea. In the lower stratosphere, however, mixing ratios that have been observed are below 0.1 gm/kg. Clouds are rarely seen, although they have been reported occasionally at heights around 15 miles, and clouds at that level have been named nacreous clouds—mother-of-pearl clouds—from the fact that they are very thin, transparent, iridescent pearly filaments composed of tiny ice crystals. Thin cirrus clouds sometimes form at or just above the tropopause and are also composed of minute ice crystals.

Small suspended particles in the atmosphere are called aerosols. There are many kinds, and some of them that are especially hygroscopic, like very minute salt particles, are believed to form condensation nuclei around which drops of water accumulate. Recent observations at high level indicate that the quantity of certain condensation nuclei, those having a radius of less than 0.1 micron (a micron is one one-thousandth of a millimeter), diminishes rapidly above the tropopause. Larger microscopic particles, those with radii of 0.1 to 1.0 micron, become more plentiful, and there may be a world-wide layer high in aerosol content at altitudes between roughly 10 and 15 miles. These particles are rich in sulfur and may originate from the upward diffusion of hydrogen sulfide and sulfur dioxide from the troposphere.

The stratosphere is a region of very low density. At the tropical tropopause atmospheric pressure ranges between 80 and 100 millibars; at the mid-latitude and Arctic tropopause it is nearer 240 millibars. At heights of around 120,000 feet (22.7 miles), well within the upper stratosphere, barometric pressure is about 5 millibars, or about 1/180 of sea level pressure. Still higher, about 29 miles above the earth at the stratopause, atmospheric pressure is near 1 millibar, or only about one one-thousandth of sea level pressure.

With increasing height temperatures in the stratosphere rise toward a maximum at the stratopause, a layer of variable thickness averaging between 29 and 33 miles in elevation. At the stratopause temperatures appear to be similar to those at the earth's surface, that is, averaging near the freezing point but rising occasionally to 50 or 60 degrees above freezing. These tentative figures are based upon what has been observed directly by rocket-propelled instruments in recent years, and indirectly through observing the behavior of meteors and sound impulses, and through studies of ozone in the upper air. The number of observations is small, and the figures obtained vary widely. Thus, at present, all that can be said for certain is that there exists a warm layer between roughly 29 and 33 miles above the earth where temperatures are frequently within the range of those generally recorded in the middle latitudes near sea level.

Beyond a height of about 33 miles, where temperatures again diminish with increasing altitude, is the mesosphere. The upper limit of the mesosphere is taken to be the level at which temperatures reach a new minimum of about −137°F and no longer lessen with altitude. This upper limit, the mesopause, ranges in height from about 50 to 56 miles. It is at the mesopause that filmy wisps of visible condensation, noctilucent clouds, are sometimes observed after sunset.

From the mesopause upward, temperatures have been observed, by rocket-borne instruments, by weather satellites, and by remote methods of spectrographic analysis, to rise indefinitely upward. This region has been termed the thermosphere and is considered to be extensively ionized.

The relationship between the atmosphere's upper levels and terrestrial climate is not understood at present. For the purpose of the present study it is sufficient to repeat that almost all of the normal occurrences in the world's weather and climates take place within the lowest layer, the troposphere.

References

BRANCAZIO, PETER J., and CAMERON, A. G. W., eds., *The Origin and Evolution of Atmospheres and Oceans*, John Wiley & Sons, Inc., New York, 1964.

GOODY, R. M., *The Physics of the Stratosphere*, Cambridge Monographs on Physics, Cambridge University Press, Cambridge, 1954.

HUMPHREYS, W. J., *Physics of the Air*, Dover Publications, Inc., New York, 1964.

INTERNATIONAL SYMPOSIUM ON ROCKET AND SATELLITE METEOROLOGY: *Proceedings of the First International Symposium on Rocket and Satellite Meteorology*, Interscience Publications, John Wiley & Sons, Inc., New York, 1963.

LANDSBERG, H.: "The Origin of the Atmosphere," *Scientific American*, **189**(2): 82–86, 1953.

LETTAU, H. H.: *Exploring the Atmosphere's First Mile*, The Pergamon Press, New York, 1957.

U.S. AIR FORCE, AIR RESEARCH AND DEVELOPMENT COMMAND: *Handbook of Geophysics*, The Macmillan Company, New York, 1961.

chapter 3

ATMOSPHERIC RELATIONSHIPS AND PROCESSES

Climate, as we have observed, is the synthesis of weather conditions over a long period of time, and includes all the varieties and extremes of weather from which the average, or normal weather experience is derived. It is now our purpose to examine some of the fundamental relationships and processes of the atmosphere that make it a single, dynamic, integrated system. The material in this chapter is largely within the field of physical meteorology and physical climatology, and must be understood to permit an eventual grasp of such matters as the general atmospheric circulation, air masses, fronts, storms, and the character, distribution, and causes of the world's climates.

It is sometimes useful, before undertaking a discussion of the technical details of complex interrelationships in nature, to provide a highly simplified explanatory generalization. In this way sufficient interest may be awakened in the subject to overcome the difficulties presented by matters of formidable complexity. For this reason the following general statement is presented.

Climate is a consequence of the motions of the earth. The broad pattern of weather experiences occurring anywhere is ultimately traceable to the planetary relationships of the spherical earth in the solar system. Moisture, temperature, wind, and pressures are separately observed elements in the atmosphere,

yet all are closely integrated in the production of the over-all state of the weather in any one place at any moment.

Water vapor, abundantly present everywhere about the earth in the lower levels of the atmosphere, becomes visible when it is condensed to form mist, fog, frost, dew, clouds, rain, hail, sleet, or snow. Except for the terrestrial condensation of dew and frost upon solid surfaces, these forms of condensation take place within the atmosphere as the result of the cooling of air when it moves into contact with cooler air masses, or cooler land or water surfaces, or simply is cooled adiabatically by rising to higher altitudes. The movements of the atmosphere thus give rise directly to the causes of moisture condensation. Air movements in turn result from differences in density, weight, or barometric pressure in the atmosphere. They represent a response to a tendency the air has in common with fluids to seek a state of equilibrium, a condition that is never reached. The differential densities giving rise to air movements are chiefly the consequences of temperature differences in the atmosphere. Air that is warmed expands, rises, and is replaced by an inflow of cooler, denser, heavier air which seeks a lower level. Because the atmosphere is primarily heated by the transmission of the sun's warmth from the surface of the earth, differences in air temperature arise from differences in the temperature of the earth's surface. A difference in surface temperature results primarily from a difference in the amount of solar radiation received on the earth, and the amount of radiation received from the sun depends initially upon latitude. Latitude, which is distance north or south of the equator expressed in degrees, minutes, and seconds of arc, is derived in part from the axial inclination of the earth $66\frac{1}{2}$ degrees to the plane of its orbit, and in part from the motions of the earth, the revolution of the earth's spinning sphere around the sun. The poleward limits of the sun's changing position with respect to the earth during the period of a single year are marked by the Tropics of Cancer and Capricorn. The equator, from which latitude is measured, is simply a theoretical line midway between the Tropics. Because the high-latitude polar regions of persistent ice and snow receive insufficient warmth from the sun to raise air temperatures above the freezing point for any great length of time, and are almost entirely without sunlight for about one half of the year, they remain firmly bound in continuous frost. Low-latitude equatorial lands, where ice and snow do not form except at very high elevations, are heated each day by the rays of the sun and remain constantly warm. Thus, climate and the distribution of the world's climatic regions are, in a general way, attributable to the motions of the

earth. Temperature differences in the atmosphere are the initial stage in the ceaseless process of atmospheric change. It is therefore of primary importance to know the ways in which the atmosphere is heated and how differences in its temperature arise.

Temperature

The sun is the source of virtually all the heat affecting the atmosphere. Its surface temperature is computed at nearly 10,000°F, yet only about 1 part in 2 million of the enormous energy emitted from the sun is intercepted by the earth. A measure of this quantity is provided in the term *solar constant*, which has the value of 1.94 calories per square centimeter per minute for a surface perpendicular to the solar beam just outside the atmosphere. (A calorie is the amount of heat required to raise 1 gram of water at sea level 1 degree Celsius—at a pressure of 1 atmosphere—from 15° to 16°C.) While the solar constant is by no means a fixed value—it varies as much as 5 per cent—it is useful as a means of computing general figures for solar energy input on the earth. The amount of solar heat reaching the earth at a mid-latitude of 40° in a year's time has been calculated at an average of more than 5,000,000 kilowatt hours per acre. The solar radiation which actually reaches the earth's surface is called insolation. Figure 3.1 is a diagram of the

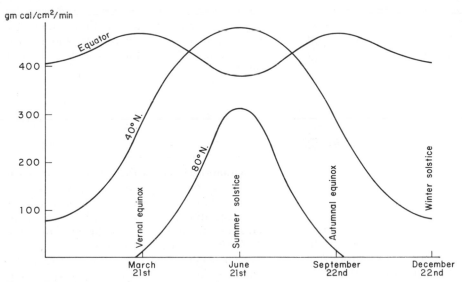

Figure 3.1. Annual variation of insolation (in gm cal/cm²/min) at the equator and at 40° and 80°N. Lat.

annual variation of insolation in gram calories per square centimeter per minute (gm cal/cm²/min) for 0°, 40°, and 80° of latitude.

Variations in solar energy output are generally thought to be related to sunspot activity in the sun's photosphere (outer, gaseous layer), gigantic disturbances extending over thousands of square miles of the sun's surface. Sunspot activity has been under observation for more than two centuries. During the last century these solar disturbances have been occurring with increased intensity about every eleven years.

Although the average distance between the earth and sun is around 93 million miles, the elliptical orbit of the earth brings us about 3 million miles closer to the sun during January, when the earth is 91.5 million miles away, than in July, when it is 94.5 million miles away. As heat intensity varies with the square of the distance from the source, about 7 per cent more solar radiation is received in January than in July. However, it is not an important difference climatically, and we shall see in Chapter 6 that other circumstances account for the principal climatic differences between the northern and southern hemispheres.

Because the earth is spheroid in shape, one half of its atmosphere is bathed in the rays of the sun at all times (Fig. 3.2). And, because the

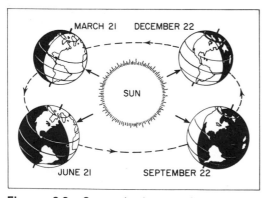

Figure 3.2. Seasonal change of the earth's illuminated half through the year.

earth's axis of rotation is tilted 66½ degrees to the plane of its orbit around the sun, the portions of the earth between the tropics and the poles receive, during the course of a single year, a regular increase and decrease of insolation, giving rise to the rhythm of the seasons. The

solar relationship to seasonal change may be expressed in the changing length of day and night. Poleward from the equator, where day and night are always approximately twelve hours long, the duration of daylight or darkness gradually increases (see Fig. 6.1) until at either pole the length of each is almost exactly six months. At the vernal and autumnal equinoxes (about March 21 and September 22, respectively), when the sun is directly over the equator, days and nights are equal everywhere.

The sun's height in the sky determines the angle, called the angle of incidence, at which its rays strike the surface of the earth. The sun's rays are at right angles to the surface, or the sun is directly overhead, at some time of the year only between the Tropics of Cancer and Capricorn. Toward the poles the angle of incidence becomes increasingly more acute because of the earth's sphericity, and at the Arctic and Antarctic circles it is never more than 47 degrees. As a result the heating effect of the sun's rays is diminished in two important ways. By striking the earth at a more oblique angle, the sun's beam is spread over a larger area than when it plays directly upon the earth (Fig. 2.9). It must also pass through a greater thickness of the atmosphere; thus more of its heat is intercepted in passage and less is available for warming the earth. An illustration of this effect may be seen during early morning and evening hours when the sun is just above the horizon. So much of the sun's brightness, and hence its heat radiation, is reduced at these times that its warmth can scarcely be felt, and it may easily and safely be observed with the naked eye (Fig. 3.3).

The amounts of dust and moisture in the air also determine the degree of heat depletion by the atmosphere, for they are the main heat-absorbing components (moisture is much the more important one) of the atmosphere. When the air is clear and dry, much more solar radiation reaches the earth's surface than when it is dusty or when water vapor is present in large quantities. Furthermore, the heat of direct solar radiation is increasingly effective with increasing altitude, arising chiefly from the increasing transparency of the atmosphere at greater heights. The amount of solar radiation reaching the earth's surface is greatly diminished when the sky is overcast, for not only is more insolation absorbed and diffused by

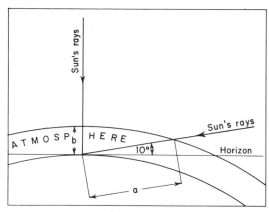

a = Length of path of son's rays through the atmosphere
    when sun is 10° above the horizon
b = Length of path when sun is overhead

Figure 3.3. Loss of less radiant energy on its way through the atmosphere when the sun is overhead.

saturated masses of cloud, but the upper cloud surfaces reflect and scatter a large amount of sunlight, sometimes as much as 75 or 80 per cent. Even in the absence of clouds the lower, denser layers of the transparent atmosphere normally reflect a certain amount of incoming light and heat from the sun. Atmospheric reflection of sunlight is roughly similar to the

reflection of solar light from the moon's surface and is called the earth's albedo. Thus the earth would appear from outer space to gleam with a brightness somewhat akin to that of Venus as viewed from the earth.

The chief way in which the atmosphere is heated by the sun (Fig. 3.4) is through the transmission of heat from the surface of the earth. It has been calculated that only 14 per cent of the sun's radiation is absorbed directly on its passage through the atmosphere, 2 per cent is reflected from the earth's surface, 6 per cent is reflected from the atmosphere, and 27 per cent is scattered and reflected back into space by the upper surfaces of clouds, assuming a worldwide mean cloudiness of about 50 per cent. The remaining 51 per cent of solar energy reaches the earth's surface as direct solar radiation. This and the scattered radiation from the sky are the main portions of solar radiation available for the earth's heat budget.

It is well known that a ray of light passed through a prism of transparent glass will spread out into a broad band of colors ranging from red to violet (Fig. 3.5). The sun's rays, examined prismatically, reveal these visible color components upon a white screen. Beyond

Figure 3.4. General disposition of solar radiation approaching the earth's surface.

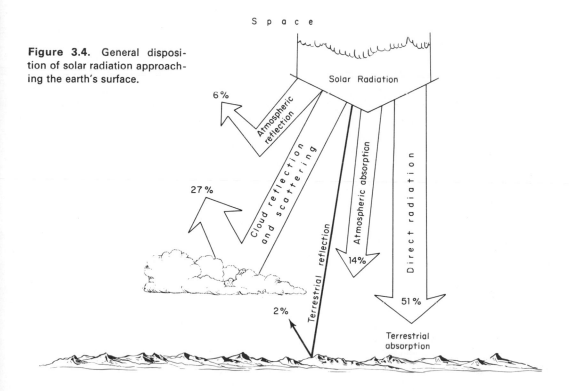

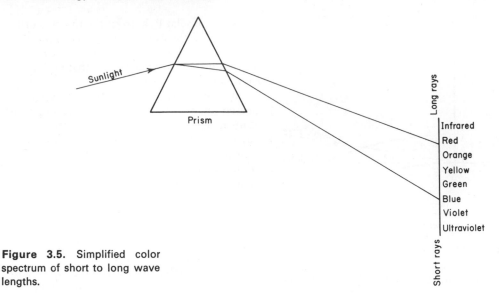

Figure 3.5. Simplified color spectrum of short to long wave lengths.

the short-ray, blue-violet end of the solar spectrum are invisible ultraviolet rays that exert a chemical influence upon organisms, destroying certain bacteria and darkening the skin of human beings. The 14 per cent of solar radiation absorbed directly by the atmosphere is derived from the blue end of the spectrum in a selective process in which molecules of water vapor play the leading part, although carbon dioxide, ozone, and minute dust and water particles are also important. Beyond the longer red rays of the spectrum are infrared rays which, although invisible, are felt as solar heat. Only a small percentage of the heat-producing rays near the red end of the spectrum are absorbed directly by the atmosphere on their way through it.

It is the intermediate rays—blue, green, yellow (from 0.39 to 0.76 micron, averaging 0.5 micron)—that, by absorption, warm the earth's surface, which in turn imparts heat to the air above. But solar heat must first be changed from short wave radiation to long wave, lower temperature radiation, a change that takes place at the earth's surface, making the earth a radiating body. The atmosphere permits approximately 51 per cent of solar short wave radiation to reach the earth's surface without interruption, but after the earth has converted these rays into longer wavelengths (about 12.5 microns, at a ratio of about 25 to 1), the atmosphere readily absorbs them, preventing their escape into outer space.

This is sometimes spoken of as the greenhouse effect, from its resemblance to the way in which a glass-enclosed greenhouse allows the sun's rays to enter as light, and yet confines within the structure the heat into which they are converted.

Heat from the earth's surface is transmitted to the atmosphere by three primary processes: radiation, conduction, and convection. All masses of solid, liquid, or gas tend to give off energy by radiation, which is evident in a loss of heat to cooler solids, liquids, or gases. Radiant energy travels in waves, with the speed of light, and it travels most easily through empty space. To illustrate, the warmth one feels on a cool autumn evening from the flames of a blazing bonfire is transmitted to one's body without appreciably changing the temperature of the intervening air. This is its heat of radiation, which can be felt even in the presence of an icy wind when the surrounding air temperature may be well below freezing. This is the way solar heat is radiated to the cooler earth, and it is one way in which the earth's surface imparts heat to the cooler air above.

Returning to the example of the bonfire, if one thrusts the end of an iron rod into the glowing coals it will, in time, become red hot, and if one then grasps the opposite end that has remained outside the fire, it too will prove hot, having become so through the transfer of heat from molecule to molecule of the iron's solid

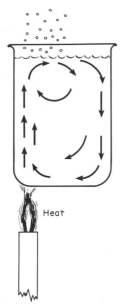

Figure 3.6. Convective circulation induced in a beaker of water by applying heat from below.

substance, and ultimately to one's hand, by the process of conduction. Only the lowest molecular layer of the troposphere in contact with the land and calmer water surfaces of the earth is heated by means of conduction, by the molecular heat of conduction.

Convection takes place within such unstable media as water or gases when one part is heated, becomes lighter, rises, and is replaced by cooler, heavier portions seeking a lower level (Fig. 3.6). Climatologists usually apply the term *convection* to the vertical movement of air that has been warmed. The horizontal movement of air due to temperature differences is called advection. The upward movement of warmed air and the related downward movement of cooler air are of primary importance in atmospheric heat exchange. Taken together, the conductive heating of the atmosphere's lowest layers and the upward transport of heat by the convection to which it gives rise are usually considered more important in changing the temperature of the lower troposphere than radiation and absorption. A special type of convection, called dynamical convection, atmospheric turbulence, turbulent diffusion, or, preferably, eddy diffusion, is considered the chief means of conveying heat from the earth's surface into the mass of the atmosphere. Although its mechanism cannot be described accurately, its effectiveness is proportional to wind velocity and is greatest over ocean areas where wind velocities are relatively high and persistent (Fig. 3.7).

Eddy diffusion consists of random or irregular motions incorporating both horizontal and vertical components of direction and usually forming an upward-spiraling vortex. They range in size from very small eddies just a few centimeters broad and occurring only a few centimeters above a heated surface, up to larger vortices several feet in diameter, and finally those larger circulating storms like the tornado, the migrating cyclone of the middle latitudes, and the tropical hurricane. Eddy

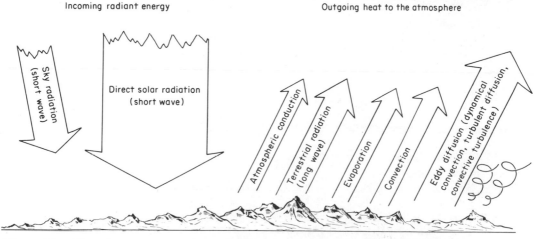

Figure 3.7. Disposition of solar and sky radiation at the earth's surface in the northern hemisphere in summer with the sun on the meridian.

diffusion is not only the chief mechanical process by which heat is transferred from earth to air, but it also plays a leading role in the transfer of moisture, dust, pollen, and other minute particles into the atmosphere.

Eddy diffusion also takes part in the process of heat transfer by evaporation and condensation. The moisture-carrying capacity of air increases with increasing temperature, and as moisture is evaporated from solid or water surfaces, it is carried upward to heights of 2000 to 7000 feet and there is condensed into visible clouds. This process takes place during warm weather in all well-watered climates and is widespread and continuous over the warm tropical oceans and hot, humid equatorial rain forests of the world. Evaporation results in the loss of heat from the surface, releasing the moisture, and when this water vapor is condensed above the earth, its heat is released to the atmosphere aloft. In this form heat is called the latent heat of evaporation and condensation.

When the sun's rays first strike the level surface of a section of dry land, that surface warms rapidly, and its increasing heat at once induces an upward pressure against the molecules of the atmosphere in contact with it. This lively molecular activity rapidly results in the formation of minute eddies that thrust upward into the still-cool overlying molecular layers. The tiny eddies release their heat at the higher level, only a few millimeters above ground, and fall back, disperse, or are maintained. They are accompanied by a complementary downward flux of cooler elements from the overlying layers. The process continues as long as increasing radiative heat is supplied by the steadily rising sun. In short, molecular conduction imparts a progressively increasing warmth to the lower film of the atmosphere in contact with the earth. Coupled with this process are long wave radiation directly from earth to air and eddy diffusion.

Solar radiation on a clear, sunny day reaches maximum intensity when the sun is highest in the sky, usually around noon. At an inland point air temperature measured about 5 feet above the ground rises rapidly during the early hours after sunrise, then warms less rapidly during the late forenoon, still less rapidly in the early afternoon, until the maximum for the

Figure 3.8. The Stevenson screen, standard instrument shelter used by the U.S. Weather Bureau. In the distance, standard 5-foot evaporation pan.

day has been reached. Five feet is about the height at which thermometers are placed for universal climatological purposes. They are housed in an instrument shelter commonly referred to as the Stevenson Screen (Fig. 3.8). The diminished rate of air temperature increase is due to the more active vertical mixing of cooler elements from above with the warmer air parcels from below the point of measurement about 5 feet off the ground. Maximum temperature for the day, when the sky is clear, or nearly so, usually occurs around two or three hours after the solar radiation maximum for the day has been reached. This is because heat stored in the ground, within just a few inches below the surface, is released gradually as the day wears on. But in the later afternoon the combination of diminishing heat from the sun and loss of stored heat in the ground brings an increasingly rapid drop in air temperature. The maximum rate of decrease for a normal day is usually reached just after sunset. On a clear night heat loss to outer space by reradiation of stored warmth in the earth's surface proceeds steadily, cooling the lower few feet of the atmosphere, and the minimum for the day is generally attained in the quiet moments just before sunrise.

The temperature pattern just described holds true for almost any inland locality in the mid-latitudes under clear sky conditions when air movement is negligible. When skies are overcast or largely cloud-covered, or during the passage of an atmospheric disturbance, or when the point of observation is very much more or less than about 5 feet above ground, the pattern differs. These variations will be considered at appropriate points in later chapters.

Moisture

Atmospheric moisture is second in importance to temperature, as a vital element in all the fundamental processes of the atmosphere. Water, as we noted in Chapter 2, is largely supplied to the atmosphere through evaporation from the surface of the seas, especially within the tropics. Lakes, rivers, marshes, and vegetation supply only a very small fraction of the over-all moisture content of the air. Atmospheric moisture is returned to the sea in a manner illustrated by the hydrologic cycle in Figure 3.9.

The amount of moisture in the air for the world as a whole does not vary greatly from time to time or from place to place and thus can be regarded as a relatively conservative property of the atmosphere. The maximum possible water vapor content of the atmosphere

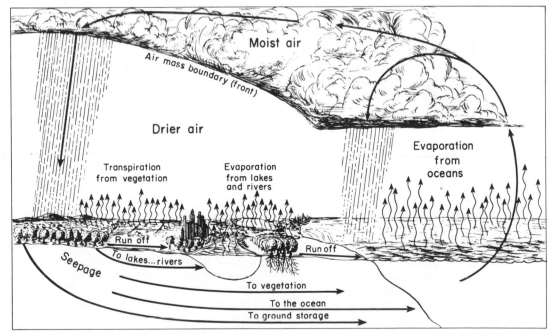

Figure 3.9. The hydrologic cycle. [After U.S. Weather Bureau.]

is a function of temperature. Where atmospheric temperatures are low, the moisture content is negligible. This is especially true of polar regions the year round and of middle latitudes in winter. It averages 0.5 per cent of volume in a mid-latitude winter, rising to 1.5 per cent of volume in summer. In tropical regions it reaches 3 per cent of volume, and in desert localities in the lower latitudes may reach 4 per cent of volume. In general, atmospheric water vapor decreases from the equator to the poles, and is three or four times greater over low-latitude deserts than over the polar oceans. In desert areas the scarcity of precipitation is not due to a lack of atmospheric moisture but to the tendency for air temperature to remain well above the dew point, the temperature at which condensation occurs. Atmospheric water vapor plays a major role in determining the relative stability and instability of the atmosphere. Atmospheric stability and instability are important properties in air mass identification and analysis (to be discussed in Chapter 5) and are vitally significant in weather forecasting.

Air which is warmed by its proximity to the earth's surface rises, and in so doing its temperature is lowered, partly because it moves away from the source of most of its warmth, and partly because of the decrease in air pressure at higher altitudes. The decrease in pressure results from a decrease in the density of air, which in turn arises from a wider diffusion of the air's component molecules, which do not strike one another as frequently as they do in the lower, denser strata. The cooling that takes place when air expands and rises with a loss of pressure is called adiabatic[1] cooling. It should not be confused with the normal lapse rate of atmospheric temperature change. Normal lapse rate is the vertical change in temperature that would be observed if one were to pass a thermometer upward or downward in the atmosphere, without any appreciable vertical motion of the air itself. Adiabatic cooling or warming, however, is brought about by the vertical motions of the air, in which air is cooled by expansion as it rises and warmed by compression as it descends.

Mean lapse rate is a statistical expression

based on countless measurements of the vertical temperature gradient under a great variety of conditions. It changes 3.6 degrees with every change of 1000 feet in altitude. It varies during the day, from day to day, and from season to season. It is usually less when air pressure is high than when it is low, and is commonly less in winter than in summer. A reverse, or negative lapse rate, called a *temperature inversion*, prevails during clear, calm nights when the ground cools rapidly, resulting in the rapid cooling of air at the surface by conduction and by heat loss through radiation, the air at ground level becoming a good deal cooler than the overlying strata.

The concept of lapse rate is based upon the supposition that air is not moving vertically. However, when air does move upward or downward, it changes temperature at a rate related to the changing pressure upon it. Unsaturated air cools as it rises at the rate of about $5\frac{1}{2}$ degrees per 1000 feet; this is called the dry adiabatic lapse rate. Saturated air cools at between 2 and 5 degrees per 1000 feet; this is called the wet adiabatic lapse rate. Adiabatic rates of temperature change are simply special kinds of lapse rate that apply to air in vertical motion (Fig. 3.10).

Let us now return to the topic of atmospheric stability and instability. Atmospheric stability is a condition in which air tends to resist vertical displacement, or, if vertically displaced, tends to return to its original position. It is a striving for a state of equilibrium in which vertical movement would be virtually absent.

When vertical movement takes place in the atmosphere, and once begun, tends to continue, convective motion is produced, and instability is said to exist. Unstable air is conducive to the formation of clouds, particularly those with pronounced vertical dimensions, and normally leads to unsettled weather, and precipitation. Fair weather with clear, cloudless, sunny skies is normally a consequence of atmospheric stability.

Let us assume that the temperature of a portion of unsaturated air is the same from the ground upward through the first 1000 or so feet of altitude. In this condition it would be called an isothermal layer. Near the ground it would be denser and slightly heavier than near the top. Its lower portions would tend to remain at the bottom, unless disturbed, through the effect

---

[1] *Adiabatic:* from the Greek *a*—not, *dia*—through, *banein*—to go; thus, without gain or loss of heat.

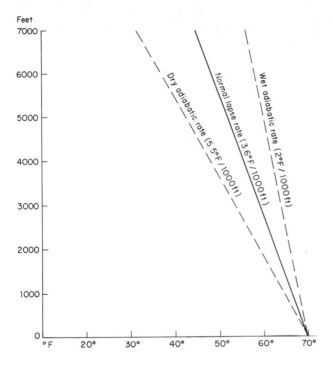

Figure 3.10. Normal lapse rate compared with dry and wet adiabatic rates (extreme cases).

of gravity. If, however, a part of this stratum of air is forced upward either by heating or by being lifted up a mountain slope (Fig. 3.11), the ascending portion would cool at the dry adiabatic rate, other things being equal, of about $5\frac{1}{2}$ degrees. Thus, at all levels during its ascent it would be cooler than the assumed isothermal strata through which it would pass. Were the cause of its ascent to be removed, it would tend to return to its original position at the bottom.

Similarly, if a parcel of air near the top of the isothermal layer (Fig. 3.11) were to be forced downward, it would gain temperature at the dry adiabatic rate of $5\frac{1}{2}$ degrees per 1000 feet and would become warmer than the air around it, and would thus tend to rise to its original position, once the cause of its descending motion were removed. In both examples air is said to have stable equilibrium, to have stability.

The examples cited above are hypothetical

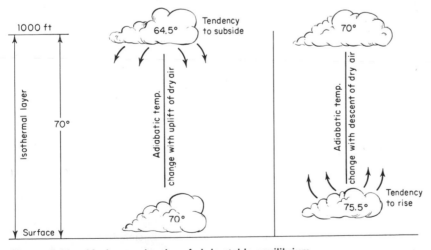

Figure 3.11. Motion tendencies of air in stable equilibrium.

extremes. Actually, air is considered stable as long as the rate of vertical temperature change is less than the adiabatic rate. If it is relatively dry, its lapse rate need only be less than $5\frac{1}{2}$ degrees per 1000 feet; if it is moist, its lapse rate need be less than 2 to 5 degrees per 1000 feet (near 2 degrees at high temperatures, near 5 at low temperatures). The main requirement is simply that a parcel of ascending air must become cooler than the surrounding air into which it rises, and thus tend to subside; if descending, it must become warmer than the surrounding air and thus tend to rise again to its former position.

When conditions opposite to the above prevail, instability results (Fig. 3.12). That is, when rising air is warmer than the surrounding strata through which it passes, it tends to continue rising; when descending air is cooler than air through which it passes, it tends to continue downward. A stimulus or a push in an upward direction may set a parcel of air in continuous, ascending motion. Such a stimulus may occur when air at ground level is heated. Passing through colder air, it is unstable because its temperature decrease with increasing height is

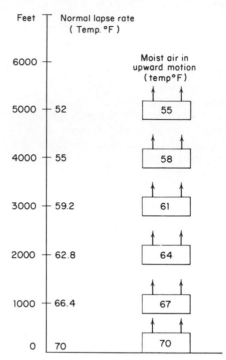

Figure 3.12. Atmospheric instability. Moist air changing temperature with increasing height at the wet adiabatic rate.

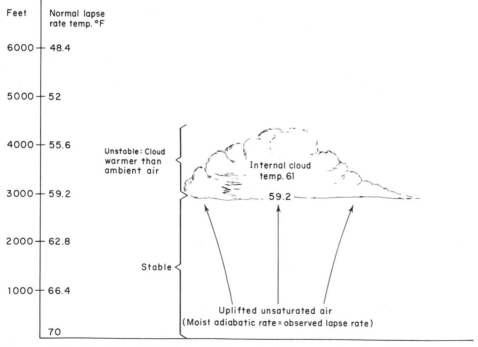

Figure 3.13. Conditional instability. Unsaturated air in upward motion is stable, becoming unstable as clouds form.

less than the observed local lapse rate. If the observed lapse rate exceeds 19 degrees per 1000 feet, a parcel of air is said to have absolute instability, and rapid, violent overturning of air results. It is said to be autoconvective, not needing an impetus to start its vertical movement. This condition, also called mechanical instability, is sometimes present during the passage of a tornado or in shallow layers of quiet air overlying highly heated ground surfaces.

In general, it may be said that dry (unsaturated) air is normally stable. Saturated air may be stable at low temperatures but is normally unstable at high temperatures.

Sometimes air is stable when unsaturated, but upon rising sufficiently for condensation to occur it becomes unstable. Condensation produces saturated air that becomes unstable when its adiabatic rate becomes less than the normal lapse rate. If condensation continues, the latent heat from this process adds to the warmth of the saturated air, lessening its lapse rate, resulting in further upward movement, and increasing its instability. This condition of stable, unsaturated air at lower levels and unstable saturated air above is called conditional instability (Fig. 3.13). It occurs quite often during a warm summer day when the air is clear and relatively dry and white cumulus clouds drift slowly across the blue sky overhead, the cloud base marking the approximate level at which instability begins.

References

GEIGER, R.: *The Climate Near the Ground*, Harvard University Press, Cambridge, Mass., 1965.

LANDSBERG, H.: *Physical Climatology*, Gray Printing Co., Inc., DuBois, Pa., 1958.

LUMLEY, J. L.: *The Structure of Atmospheric Turbulence*, John Wiley & Sons, Inc., New York, 1964.

NAWROCKI, P. J., and PAPS, R.: *Atmospheric Processes*, Prentice-Hall, Inc., Englewood Cliffs, N.J., 1963.

PFEFFER, R. L.: *Dynamics of Climate*, The Pergamon Press, New York, 1960.

chapter 4

THE GENERAL CIRCULATION
OF THE ATMOSPHERE

The primary source of weather change and climatic variety, we have discovered, is the effect of the sun's rays upon the spinning sphere of earth as it moves along its circumsolar orbit. Among the complexities of atmospheric behavior are discernible certain processes occurring with sufficient regularity to create a pattern of temperature, rainfall, pressure, and wind distribution that it is now our purpose to consider. This brings us to a study of the general circulation of the atmosphere.

The Mechanism of Wind

The general circulation of the atmosphere is simply the average movement of the world's winds. The basic mechanism by which it operates is the accumulation, transfer, and dissipation of heat from the sun. Broadly speaking, low-latitude regions, between the tropics and the equator, are constantly warm, while polar regions are always cold. Between them is a broad, undulating mid-latitude zone of interpenetration where warm tropical air meets cold polar air in an endless exchange. Were it not for such an exchange of warmth and cold, equatorial regions would become increasingly hotter, polar regions increasingly colder. Equalization of the world's excesses and deficiencies of heat is thus accomplished through a systematic north-south process (meri-

dional transfer). This is the primary tendency in the larger mechanism of the general circulation. Exactly how this process operates, and for that matter, in just what way the general circulation as a whole operates, is not at present entirely understood, nor can it satisfactorily be explained. However, we may at least approach an understanding of the general circulation through an examination of the pattern of prevailing winds and of the predominant high and low barometric pressure regions with which they are inseparably united, insofar as they have been observed, recorded, and mapped.

The traditional method of presenting the world's wind and pressure patterns is to speak of broad east-west zones or belts of wind movement and pressure values. A map is often drawn (Fig. 4.1) to show a uniform, latitudinal zoning of these average atmospheric qualities. But the picture so presented is far too generalized to suit the facts, for it fails to reveal the great contrasts within nearly all latitudinal belts, and it masks the ceaseless change that is a fundamental attribute of atmospheric behavior. Global zones of predominant wind direction and pressure values entirely girdling the earth do not actually exist, except perhaps over the southern oceans between latitudes 50° and 60°S. Here lower pressure values and westerly winds seem, on the strength of available data, to prevail in a region that completely

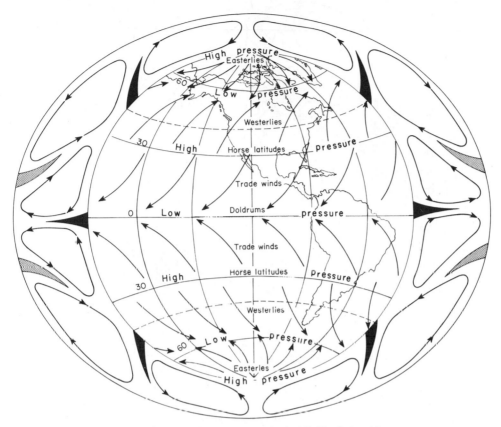

Figure 4.1. Generalized atmospheric pressure and wind field relationships.

encircles the persistent high pressures that predominate over Antarctica. Elsewhere the pattern, even of average conditions, is composed of many contrasts in all latitudes and continuously varies in response to the steadily changing declination of the sun. If it were feasible to present monthly, daily, or hourly maps of the world's pressure and wind fields, the fluctuations from which the mean annual circulation is derived would be apparent.

The world maps in Figures 4.2 and 4.3 show, for January and July, the prevailing direction of surface winds and atmospheric pressure at sea level. The pressure distribution is obtained by reducing local barometric readings taken at weather stations of many different altitudes to sea level. By so doing, the effect of altitude, a far stronger influence on atmospheric pressure than temperature, is eliminated, and a comparison of world pressure values may be made. To facilitate the comparison, a conventional device called the isobar is employed. The isobar

is a hypothetical line joining points on the map where atmospheric pressures are the same. Its usefulness is greatest in studying the larger aspects of global atmospheric pressure distribution. Isobars are really generalizations based upon data that are adequately abundant only for certain areas in the world, such as western Europe, most of the United States, the populous sections of Canada, and some well-traveled ocean areas. Antarctica and the Arctic are regions of notably meager barometric data.

Pressure is indicated in millibars. Standard sea level pressure is 1013 millibars (29.92 inches). Thus, areas marked by lower values than this are designated *low*, and those marked with higher values are designated *high*. And it should be borne in mind that it is relative pressure differences arising chiefly from relative temperature differences that create the pattern of alternate highs and lows on the map. Lower pressures over the equator, for example, are

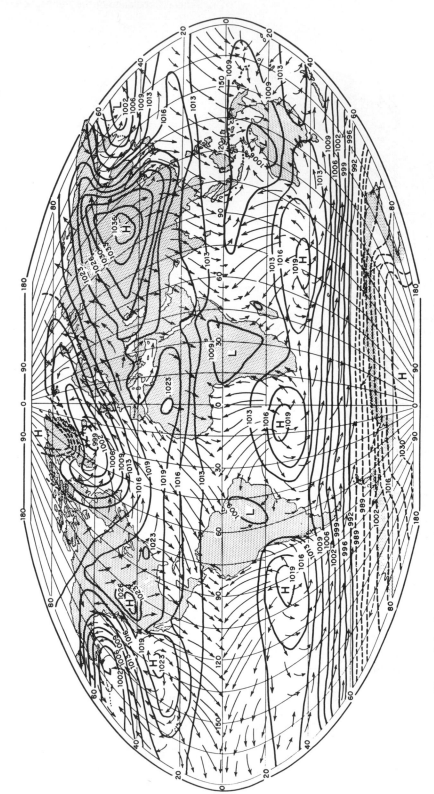

Figure 4.2. Average sea level pressure and wind fields in January. [From *Elements of Geography* by Finch, Trewartha, Robinson, and Hammond, Copyright 1957 by McGraw-Hill Book Co. Used by permission.]

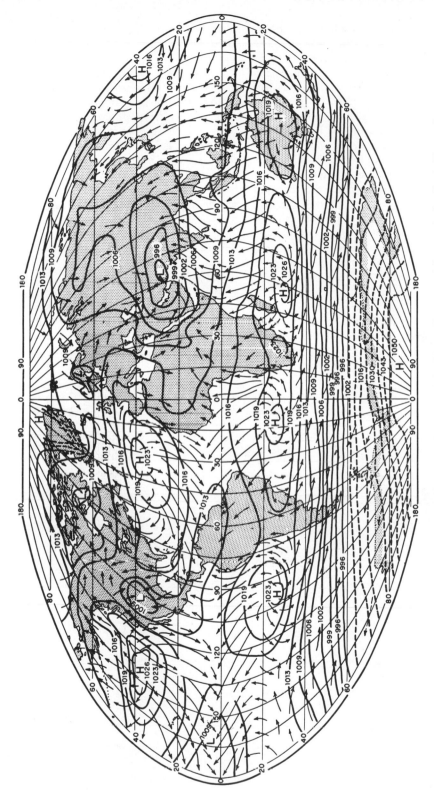

Figure 4.3. Average sea level pressure and wind fields in July. [From *Elements of Geography* by Finch, Trewartha, Robinson, and Hammond, Copyright 1957 by McGraw-Hill Book Co. Used by permission.]

related to surface temperatures in the neighborhood of 80°F, whereas wintertime low-pressure values over the North Atlantic are related to surface temperatures near and often below the freezing point (Fig. 4.2). To explain this important point further, it may be said that atmospheric pressure is not changed by changes in temperature alone. Raising or lowering the temperature of a quantity of air does not directly change its mass. It is only when the advective transfer of additional quantities of air —a shift in location—takes place that changes occur in mass, hence in weight, and in pressure registered on the barometer. One may think of higher pressure masses simply as more air, lower pressure masses as less air. Advective transfer, whether at high altitudes or near sea level, brings about these differences under the stimulus of differential heating, which is the initial action.

Arrows indicate predominant wind directions. Predominant direction is the median within the quarter (a 90 degree segment of the compass) from which winds blow and is calculated to express most clearly the general movement of surface winds.

Wind, the movement of air, is initially a gravitational response to pressure differences in the atmosphere, and pressure differentials arise mainly from differences in atmospheric temperature. A mass of air, warmed, becomes less dense, lighter, exerts less pressure upon the barometer than an adjacent air mass that is cooler. Only very slight differences in density, hence in barometric pressure, are sufficient to set the highly sensitive, fluidlike atmosphere in motion. Once set in motion, its primary tendency, in response to the force of gravity, is to flow down what is termed the barometric gradient. In short, temperature differences create differences in weight producing pressure gradients that generate initial atmospheric motion. The velocity of this primary motion depends upon the magnitude of pressure differences. The more marked the pressure difference, the steeper the resulting pressure

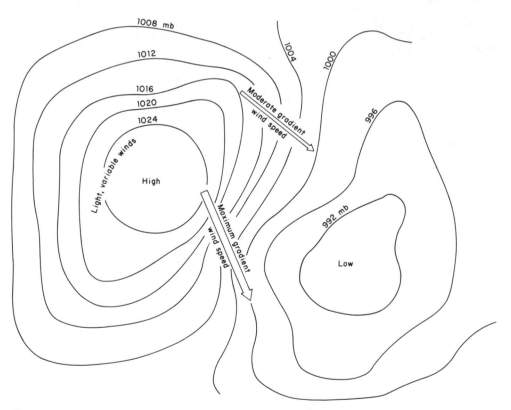

Figure 4.4. Determination of wind speeds by the steepness of the barometric gradient, indicated here by the spacing of the isobars.

gradient, hence the faster the expected gradient wind speed (Fig. 4.4). According to Kendrew,[1] a difference of only $\frac{1}{2}$ millibar (about 0.15 inch) in pressure within a distance of slightly more than 17 miles will produce a wind speed of 14.5 miles per hour, and a 1 millibar difference (about 0.03 inch) in the same distance will produce a speed of 29 miles per hour. Velocities within a given gradient increase toward the equator.

Once in motion down the pressure gradient, air responds with characteristic sensitivity to still other influences and effects that combine to steer the wind in the direction actually noted by the observer. To begin with, any moving body is diverted from a straight course by the rotation of the spherical earth. This is the Coriolis effect (also called Coriolis force, rotational deflection, deflective force, geostrophic effect, Ferrel's Law), named after G. G. Coriolis, a nineteenth century French mathematician who made the first thorough study of it. The Coriolis effect produces a tendency among all moving bodies, but particularly upon unconfined masses of air, to turn toward the right in the northern hemisphere and toward the left in the southern hemisphere.

[1] W. G. Kendrew, *Climate*, Oxford, 1930, p. 73.

A simplified explanation of the Coriolis effect, based upon the diagrams in Figure 4.5, is as follows:

When an object embarks upon a course across the rounded surface of the rotating earth, taking any direction with respect to the earth's coordinates, it is simultaneously carried eastward by the earth's rotation. In effect, the system of latitudinal and longitudinal coordinates moves out from under the moving body. Diagram A, Figure 4.5, illustrates what actually happens when an object moves in a northwesterly direction through three consecutive points, the final globe indicating the path it has followed in space, with respect to the grid pattern of meridians and parallels that has rotated beneath it during its travels. Diagrams B, C, and D illustrate the application of the principle to bodies moving in a northeast, southeast, and southwest direction.

The effect is strongest around the poles (near the axis of rotation) and diminishes with decreasing latitude and thus with increasing distance from the earth's axis, until it is absent at the equator. It is more pronounced at high velocity than at low velocity; it produces a deflective tendency in high-speed railway trains

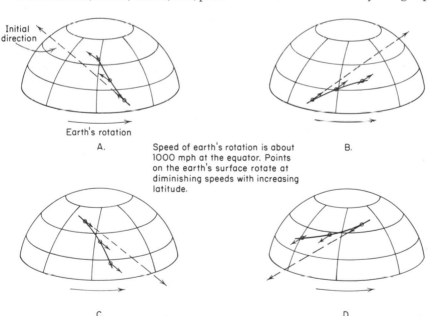

Initial direction

Earth's rotation

A.

Speed of earth's rotation is about 1000 mph at the equator. Points on the earth's surface rotate at diminishing speeds with increasing latitude.

B.

C.

D.

Figure 4.5. Clockwise deflection of moving bodies in the northern hemisphere under the Coriolis effect.

and automobiles, for example. But the effect upon trains, automobiles, bicycles, and other moving objects in constant contact with the solid earth is unnoticed, for these heavy bodies are firmly bound, for the most part, by gravity and friction to the earth's surface. The pilot of a fast-flying aircraft unconsciously adjusts his course to compensate for terrestrial deflection, in addition to the more measurable drifting due to lateral wind movement. Allowance for deflection must also be made in the firing of long-range cannon, guided missiles, and rockets. Big Bertha, the giant gun used by the German Army in World War I to fire upon Paris from a distance of 70 miles, would have landed its shells about 1 mile to the right of their target had not the ballistic experts accurately allowed for the Coriolis effect.

The light, gaseous nature of air makes it readily susceptible to rotational deflection, especially at heights of 2000–2500 feet and beyond, where friction and surface irregularities normally have little influence. Thus, the initial motion imparted to the free atmosphere at higher levels by barometric differentials is deflected toward the right in northern latitudes, toward the left in southern latitudes. But this is only one of the influences at work to alter the initial direction taken by moving air.

For the sake of simplicity let us consider the development of actual (observed) wind direction in the northern hemisphere, where clockwise deflection takes place. As air assumes its curving course toward the right and away from the approximate center of cooler, heavier air, it acquires still another sideward motion resulting from the effects of centrifugal reaction, which opposes rotational deflection and produces the wind direction actually observed at altitudes a half mile or so above the surface. Actual wind direction just above the earth is then the result of three influences: pressure gradient, Coriolis effect, and centrifugal effect. The net result of these three influences is summarized in Figure 4.6.

A fourth influence is the effect of surface friction, which is, of course, strongest at the earth's surface but is often extended into higher atmospheric levels over rough mountainous terrain where local relief—that is, the difference between valley floors and mountain peaks—may be measured in thousands of feet. Friction modifies the resultant wind direction

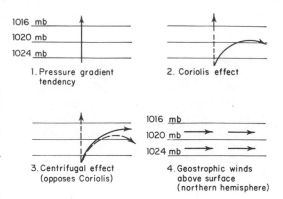

Figure 4.6. Geostrophic wind direction as a product of three effects: barometric gradient, Coriolis effect, and centrifugal effect.

in ways that are determined mainly by the magnitude and alignment of local relief features. Naturally, frictional effects are greatest over mountainous or hilly country, less over forested level lands, still less over grassy, treeless plains, and least of all over relatively level ocean surfaces.

It also appears to be true, from the countless observations of upper air made in recent years, that not only is surface friction greatly reduced at higher levels, but the diminished density of air decreases the centrifugal effect on its movement along a curving path. The result of this is a tendency toward the development of geostrophic winds at higher altitudes. These are winds that blow approximately parallel to the isobars, that is to say, at right angles to the pressure gradient (Fig. 4.6), assuming the isobars to be parallel and without curvature.

Thus far we have considered only movement outward from a mass of air that is cooler, heavier, and has higher barometric pressure than an adjacent air mass. The direction winds take as they move into air that is warmer, lighter, and has lower barometric pressure is just the opposite. They tend to swing toward the left and inward in the direction of the center of the low pressure mass in the northern hemisphere; toward the right and inward in the southern hemisphere. As they swing in toward the center, winds around a low pressure air mass increase in velocity, forming what may be thought of as a contracting spiral. The outward movement of air around a higher pressure air mass may be likened to an expanding spiral of

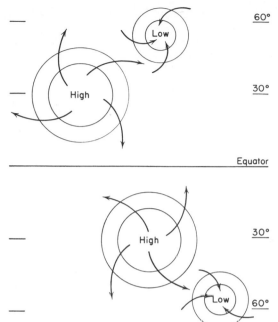

Figure 4.7. Reversal of directional tendencies around high and low pressure systems on opposite sides of the equator.

winds that increase in velocity as they approach the center of lower pressure. A schematic view

of high and low pressure circulation for both hemispheres is presented in Figure 4.7.

From the direction of surface winds the casual observer may determine the relative location of high and low pressure conditions in the atmosphere. North of the equator, with the wind at his back, the barometric pressure of air on his right is normally higher than that on his left. South of the equator the reverse is true. It is an application of Buys-Ballot's Law, which has had wide practical use since it was first proposed by the Dutch meteorologist and mathematician C. H. D. Buys-Ballot around 1850, after the careful study of air circulation related to storms.

Winds are designated by the direction from which they blow. That is, air moving from west to east is described as a west wind; from northeast to southwest, a northeast wind, and so on. Wind direction is normally given on the basis of a sixteen-point division of the compass—North (N), North-Northeast (NNE), Northeast (NE), East-Northeast (ENE), etc.—or by the compass bearing in degrees—360°, 45°, 90°, etc. (Fig. 4.8).

Wind velocity, while not accurately measurable by most means available to the ordinary observer, may be expressed according to

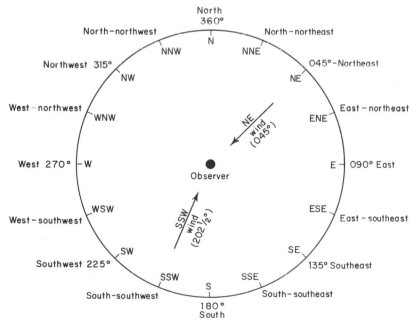

Figure 4.8. Wind directions stated according to the source of the wind approaching the observer.

another very useful device called the Beaufort Scale. This is a scheme for estimating the relative speed of wind from its effect upon familiar objects such as leaves, twigs, and branches of trees, smoke from chimneys, flags and pennants, and so on. Since it was first contrived by Admiral Sir Francis Beaufort of the British Navy in 1805, it has remained in common use, with slight modifications, to the present day and has been incorporated into the standard procedure for weather reporting employed by the United States Weather Bureau. The modern version of the Beaufort Scale is presented in Table 4-1. To illustrate its use, one might observe a wind from the southwest that keeps leaves and twigs of trees in

constant motion, causes smoke to drift at a low angle toward the northeast, and ripples a lightweight flag into full width. One would speak of this as a southwest breeze of Force 3, and would note from the scale that its probable velocity is between 8 and 12 miles per hour at about 20 feet above the ground.

Wind direction and velocity are determined by mechanical means and are often indicated by self-recording instruments that preserve the moment-to-moment variations from which average direction and velocity are computed. An examination of such continuous records reveals that winds are seldom really steady in either direction or velocity; instead, they blow with a constantly shifting gustiness that is

TABLE 4–1
The Beaufort Scale

Beaufort Number	Knots	Wind Speed MPH	Meters per Second	Seaman's Term	U.S. Weather Bureau Term	Effects Observed on Land
0	Under 1	Under 1	0.0–0.2	Calm	Calm	Calm; smoke rises vertically.
1	1–3	1–3	0.3–1.5	Light air	Light	Smoke drift indicates wind direction.
2	4–6	4–7	1.6–3.3	Light breeze	Light	Leaves rustle; wind vanes move.
3	7–10	8–12	3.4–5.4	Gentle breeze	Gentle	Leaves, small twigs in constant motion.
4	11–16	13–18	5.5–7.9	Moderate breeze	Moderate	Dust, leaves, and loose paper raised from ground; small branches move.
5	17–21	19–24	8.0–10.7	Fresh breeze	Fresh	Small trees in leaf begin to sway.
6	22–27	25–31	10.8–13.8	Strong breeze	Strong	Larger tree branches in motion; whistling heard in wires.
7	28–33	32–38	13.9–17.1	Moderate gale	Strong	Whole trees in motion; difficulty in walking.
8	34–40	39–46	17.2–20.7	Fresh gale	Gale	Twigs and small branches broken off trees; progress in walking impeded.
9	41–47	47–54	20.8–24.4	Strong gale	Gale	Slight damage to structures; slate blown from roofs.
10	48–55	55–63	24.5–28.4	Whole gale	Whole gale	Trees broken or uprooted; considerable damage to structures.
11	56–63	64–72	28.5–32.6	Storm	Whole gale	Usually widespread damage.
12	Over 64	Over 72	Over 32.6	Hurricane	Hurricane	Usually widespread damage.

After U.S. Navy Hydrographic Office, *American Practical Navigator* (H.O. 9.), 1962.

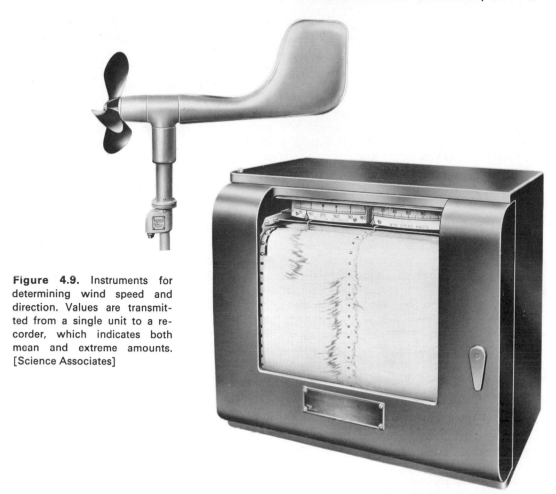

Figure 4.9. Instruments for determining wind speed and direction. Values are transmitted from a single unit to a recorder, which indicates both mean and extreme amounts. [Science Associates]

characteristic of nearly all surface winds. Self-recording wind vanes showing direction and anemometers showing wind speed (Fig. 4.9) are the standard equipment of major weather stations all over the world.

Principal Winds of the World

Only over certain sections of the globe do the surface wind patterns and related sea level pressure values tend to retain a similar relative arrangement throughout the year (Figs. 4.2 and 4.3). Our attention will be directed first to these, the regions of fairly constant atmospheric tendencies, and then to regions of marked seasonal atmospheric change, notably in the northern hemisphere, where the persistently higher pressures of winter give way to persistent lows in warm summer, accompanied by seasonal changes of average wind direction and steadiness.

There are seven regions of year-round relatively high pressure where the barometer typically registers values higher than circumjacent areas and where the air is drier, skies clearer, and surface wind speeds lower. These are the eastern Atlantic and Pacific north of the equator, the eastern Atlantic and Pacific south of the equator, the southern Indian Ocean, and also, apparently, the Arctic Ocean and Antarctica, although the data for these regions are scarce. Because they are the sources of air that moves into lower pressure regions, and hence of the atmosphere's kinetic energy, they are frequently referred to as centers of action and are commonly called semipermanent highs or semipermanent anticyclones. They are sometimes given rather loose topological designations, such as the Azores High in the eastern Atlantic and the Hawaiian High in the eastern Pacific.

There are six regions of persistently lower pressure where barometric readings of less than 1013 millibars (29.92 inches) prevail and where higher humidity and relatively higher temperatures are common. These are over the North Atlantic (the Iceland Low) and North Pacific (the Aleutian Low), the Atlantic, Pacific, and Indian oceans in a shifting zone along the equator, and the previously mentioned southern oceanic regions encircling Antarctica.

Although persistent oceanic highs and lows may be observed month after month throughout the year, it should not be forgotten that they are dynamic regions of constantly changing atmospheric qualities. Even on an average monthly basis they are not stationary, or of the same dimensions, nor do they retain the same absolute pressures from which the averages are computed. North of the equator anticyclonic areas expand and deepen (increase vertically) with summer's advance, reaching maximum development in June, July, and August, their centers shifting slightly northward and westward. At the same time, oceanic lows diminish in area, and barometric readings do not average as low as in wintertime. Winter brings a reversal of the process, with a shrinkage of higher pressure areas and an expansion of lows. And note should be taken of the change in actual barometric readings in both highs and lows. The Azores High, for example, averages 1022.5 millibars in January and increases gradually to 1025 millibars in July; the Iceland Low averages 995 millibars in January, increasing to 1007.5 millibars in July. South of the equator a similar change takes place, but here we observe the wintertime (June, July, August, and September) broadening of oceanic highs into an almost continuous globe-encircling belt that is effectively broken only by the high Andes of southern South America.

Very much in contrast with the relatively constant oceanic high and lows are those continental areas over which winter highs are replaced in summer by air of persistently lower pressure values (Figs. 4.2 and 4.3). And from these illustrations it is also evident that the alternation between cold weather high and warm weather low is much more pronounced over the broad expanses of North America and Eurasia than it is anywhere south of the equator.

In South America the greater intensity of solar radiation in December, January, and February brings a predominance of warmer, lighter air than in wintertime, and lower pressures, centered over the Amazon basin, average around 1003 millibars (29.76 inches). Winter, on the other hand, with a lowering of temperatures in southern South America, sees a gradual increase in pressure readings, with a mean of about 1020 millibars (30.10 inches) centered over Paraguay and northern Argentina.

In Africa south of the equator the summertime low, centered over the east African lake district, disappears in winter, and a higher pressure condition, averaging about 1020 millibars, prevails. Similar seasonal pressure changes are found over Australia, where the summertime low of 1005 millibars (29.7 inches) in the northwest disappears, and a winter high of about 1020 millibars appears in the southeast.

North of the equator the passing seasons bring many localized changes in average pressure values over the varied breadth of the continents, but the larger and more significant of these develop in western North America and northeastern Eurasia. In the mountainous country of the western United States an average of 1022.5 millibars (30.02 inches) occurs regularly, disappearing as summer advances to bring lower mean values of 1005 millibars over Arizona and the Sonoran region of northwest Mexico. The southwest is, in fact, almost always a region of relatively lower pressures compared with more northerly tracts, the lows simply intensifying in summer. But the most striking of all the seasonal pressure changes taking place anywhere on earth are those recorded for the northeastern and central part of Eurasia, the largest continuous land mass in the world. Mean wintertime readings, centered over eastern Siberia, are consistently in the neighborhood of 1035 millibars (30.60 inches). They become lower as warm weather approaches, and give way in June, July, and August to average values of 1005 millibars, with even lower readings of 1000 millibars (29.50 inches) centered over the plateaus of Iran and Afghanistan.

Related to the changing distribution, to the ebb and flow, of average atmospheric pressure values dealt with above are the prevailing winds, the predominant movements of air both near the earth's surface and at all levels to the very uppermost heights of the troposphere.

Characteristically, winds near the center of a high pressure air mass tend to be light and variable. Thus, where high pressures predominate throughout the year, light airs are typical, clear weather prevails, with frequent calms, and skies are seldom completely overcast. Low pressure centers tend to be stormy, with a high frequency of strong winds, cloudy, damp weather, and abundant rain. Regions of the earth where low pressure situations develop, mature, and pass on with great frequency are dominated by these conditions. From the relationship between regions of prevailing high and low atmospheric pressure values arise the prevailing wind systems of the world.

By far the most constant and most pronounced surface wind systems are found over the oceans. Let us now trace the month-by-month development of the world's major surface wind regions, with particular emphasis on the actual direction and persistence of flow.

In the summer months of June, July, and August the Hawaiian High expands to its fullest breadth and depth, and at this season produces an average clockwise wind movement, taking the form of an expanding spiral that is typical of northern hemisphere anticyclones. Air moves southward toward warmer equatorial regions of lighter air, and curving toward the west, in response to the Coriolis effect, produces the northeast trades, those winds of remarkable steadiness and moderate velocity that persist in the eastern central Pacific throughout the year. The northeast trade wind zone is latitudinally broader in summer, but at this time of year disappears in the western Pacific. Here the basically westward flow is less steady and curves northward, diverging south of Japan into two separate streams, one turning northwestward into east Asia (the summer monsoon), the other continuing its clockwise curve, flowing principally from the southwest into the upper mid-latitude zone (north of 40°) of the westerlies. Thus, the winds of the loosely termed westerly zone in the North Pacific blow for the most part in summertime from the southwest and are of only moderate persistence, alternating with winds from all quarters of the compass. Approaching North America, winds from the North Pacific turn southward with clockwise deflection, blowing most of the time from the northwest, somewhat parallel to the west coast.

Far to the north, in fact beyond the Pacific and chiefly within the Bering Sea and the southern margins of the Arctic Ocean, winds have a predominantly easterly component, although alternating with winds from many directions. The predominance of easterly winds during nearly every month of the year, here and in the northernmost Atlantic, has given rise to the term *polar easterlies* to describe the directional tendencies of air movement generally poleward of the westerlies.

With the approach of autumn and the sun's gradual declination toward the south, the westerlies become less persistent, and the North Pacific at this season is a region of variable winds. With winter's advance, however, strong and fairly steady northwest winds are seen to predominate in the western reaches of the North Pacific, blowing southeastward across the sea out of the frozen regions of eastern Siberia. Farther east the average wind flow swings toward the left in a marked counterclockwise circulation around the strongly developed Aleutian Low of wintertime. The average movement of air is roughly parallel to the Alaska coast and is chiefly from the east here and over the Aleutians. This marks a southward cold season extension of the polar easterlies in the North Pacific.

The trade wind zone during the winter season (October to April) shifts southward somewhat and narrows latitudinally, elongating westward to form a continuous belt more than 8000 miles in length, from near the coast of Mexico to the shores of French Indochina. In its western reaches the southwestward flow of the northeast trades extends across the equator, and over the East Indies, from January to March, swings counterclockwise to cross the equator from the northwest. The unusual steadiness of the trades is most marked during December, January, and February along the entire span of the tropical North Pacific.

A similar seasonal development takes place in the Atlantic north of the equator, where a pronounced summertime whorl of predominant winds develops around the expanded subtropical high pressure region. Here again, the warm summer months, when the sun is high overhead, see a northward shift and latitudinal broadening of the trades. In most of the tropical zone north of the equator, however, winds tend to blow almost directly from the east in summer and curve northward for the most part, after passing across the West Indies, to divide, as they do in the western Pacific, partly invading the Gulf coast of the United States and Mexico, and partly swinging northeastward to become the prevailing southwest winds of the upper middle latitudes. In the eastern Atlantic, north and northwest winds tend to parallel the west coasts of Spain and Portugal and northwest Africa. The polar easterlies, far to the north, are weakly developed in relation to the weakening and poleward shift of persistent low pressures around Iceland. The summer situation prevails from late in May until early September.

Autumn and winter are similar in development to the North Pacific, but it should be observed that winds from almost due west prevail, with moderate persistence, between Labrador and Norway, strengthened, no doubt, and guided in part, by the cold air from ice-covered Greenland. The polar easterlies meanwhile become more pronounced as the Iceland Low intensifies.

Both the North Atlantic and the North Pacific anticyclones—sources of air forming the trades toward the south, the summer onshore winds of east Asia and southeastern North America, and the west winds of the upper mid-latitudes, expanding, contracting, and shifting position with the passing seasons—are normally centered along the 30th parallel. These subtropical areas of repeated anticyclonic development are often called the Horse Latitudes. This name is thought to have arisen from the practice, during the seventeenth-century days of sail, of unburdening becalmed vessels by throwing overboard horses destined for the Americas who had died from lack of food and water. The name was first applied to the subtropical North Atlantic and later to the Pacific.

South of the equator seasonal changes in wind pattern are in general much less pronounced, due in part to the much greater proportion of oceanic surfaces that respond very slowly to the yearly increase and decrease of insolation.

From the anticyclonic center of action in the South Atlantic the trade winds, here from the southeast, blow with almost equal steadiness throughout the year, meeting the northeast trades in a variable zone of convergence traditionally called the doldrums. This is a zone of alternate calms, variable winds, low atmospheric pressure, high vapor content, and frequent cloudy and unsettled weather, that tends to lie north of the equator during most of the year. Spanning the Atlantic between west Africa and northern South America, it shifts farther north between June and November when the southeast trades reach farthest into the northern hemisphere, blowing parallel to the northeast coast of Brazil, bringing drought to that region, but swinging northeastward over the coast of west Africa, where they bring rain. A similar doldrums belt appears in the eastern Pacific, again just north of the equator.

In recent years the term *equatorial trough* has been applied to the fluctuating belts of repeatedly low atmospheric pressure throughout the tropics. It is a general term that includes the prevailing calms of the doldrums. Within it there is reason to expect the occasional appearance of intertropical fronts between low latitude air masses of contrasting qualities, even though the contrasts are often very slight. The mean latitude of the equatorial trough is also known as the meterological equator (about 5°N. Lat.). Its axis is sometimes marked by the convergence of the northeast and southeast trades and is thus termed the intertropical convergence zone, despite the fact that actual convergence occurs only along portions of the axis.

The characteristic counterclockwise movement of air from a southern hemisphere anticyclone produces in the average wind pattern of the South Atlantic a circulatory tendency similar to that in the northern hemisphere. The calms and variable winds associated with the central area of its development are generally characteristic throughout the year in the neighborhood of the 30th parallel. It is best developed from November to April, and in this season produces a moderately persistent eastward flow in its southernmost reaches. Thus, in latitudes from 40° to 60° south of the equator, is found the region of predominantly west winds in the southern hemisphere comparable to the higher latitude westerlies of the northern hemisphere. A high degree of directional variability prevails, however, for the continuous belt of ocean in which they develop is noted for the frequent passage of storms, and was called, in the days of sailing vessels, the Roaring Forties. While the storms are almost always from the west, they are accompanied by winds from many quarters, often of gale velocity, thus diminishing the persistence of the basically westerly winds.

Still farther south a predominantly easterly component is observable in the winds along the shores of Antarctica, insofar as the meager data available reveal, again giving rise to the term *polar easterlies*.

A repetition of this basic pattern is seen in the eastern Pacific and eastern Indian oceans south of the equator, but in both cases the counter-clockwise circulatory motion is not as strongly developed in any season. The trades in the eastern reaches, however, are again the steadiest winds of both oceans. Convergence of northeast and southeast trades in the eastern Pacific takes place north of the equator, with a northward shift like that in the Atlantic, from June to November. In the western Pacific northeast and southeast trades converge south of the equator from November to April. During the remainder of the year they move almost parallel to one another in an average flow that is slightly northwestward.

The Pacific, south of the region of trade wind development, is distinctly dominated by winds of variable direction and persistence in almost all months, with the exception of that part west of southern Chile where winds of moderate persistence approach the coast from the west throughout the year. Along the thirtieth parallel particularly one may observe a belt of marked directional variability and fairly frequent calms that is also present in the southern Indian Ocean and the South Atlantic. As it prevails pretty generally throughout the year, it marks, in the southern hemisphere, a more constant development of the Horse Latitudes than in the northern hemisphere.

The westerlies of the south Indian Ocean, poleward of 40°S. Lat., are somewhat more pronounced and steadier than in the South Pacific. This is especially true from June to December. The trades in eastern sectors of the Indian Ocean blow with more or less marked persistence at all times from the southeast. Just west of Australia they are met south of the equator by winds from the northwest from November to March, and for the remainder of the year extend across the equator, becoming somewhat less steady before joining a generally northeastward flow north of the equator.

In the western Indian Ocean south of the equator southeast trades are highly persistent from April to October, again swinging north-eastward after crossing the equator to join the southwest monsoon that approaches the Asiatic mainland during the northern hemisphere's summer months. From November to March, however, winds of the western Indian Ocean are mainly from the east and northeast.

Once again it bears repeating that seasonal, monthly, weekly, and daily averages of prevailing movement are simply the statistical result of many variations on either side of the mean. Daily weather disturbances, and weekly, monthly, seasonal, and even broader cyclical weather periods are the source of those means.

Very much in contrast to the regularity of oceanic wind pattern development are the complicated average movements of surface air over most continental areas. While oceanic winds may move steadily over the featureless sea, winds over land are typically turbulent, gusty, and unsteady in course: turned aside by projecting mountain peaks, channelled down a valley between two ridges, thrust upward to surmount a steep escarpment, or compressed with accelerated speed as they converge in a pass through a range of mountains. An indication of this variability may be seen by contrasting the smooth-flowing trail of smoke streaming off to leeward from the funnel of a ship at sea with the erratically waving smoke plume of an industrial stack on land.

Local land winds, it is true, may occur with surprising frequency from certain quarters and appear to be relatively steady. But the over-all patterns of surface movement, month by month, are seldom as distinct as those of the oceans and are very much more complex, so much so, in fact, that it is quite impossible to establish a close integration of ocean winds with interior continental winds at the surface. Only at higher altitudes do the movements of air over land and sea unite in a coherent circulation pattern.

But special mention should be made of the winds along certain continental margins that share in some degree the direct effects of oceanic circulation. There are many examples of this. The equatorward flow of air along the Lower California coast and along the coast of Peru and northern Chile brings little moisture over the land, for the prevailing movement is approximately parallel to those shores every month of the year. The predominantly onshore winds of southernmost Chile, on the other hand, bring abundant moisture every month of the year to the western slopes of those mountainous regions. And the generally eastward trend of North Atlantic air extends over northwest Europe throughout the year, bringing substantial rains every month to the windward shores of Great Britain and the continent.

Another example of the direct relationship between surface winds on land and sea is found in the seasonal development of onshore-offshore movements along certain coastal tracts. This is the monsoon, originally an Arabic term (*mausim*) meaning time or season and referring specifically to the alternate landward and seaward winds of the Indian Ocean and the Arabian Sea. It is now widely applied to coastal regions elsewhere that experience these effects.

The summer brings a period of higher sun, of more effective insolation, of warmer earth, of warmer air above, and in general, of lower prevailing barometric pressures over land areas. At this season air from adjoining oceanic centers of action moves more readily and more constantly over the land, producing in certain preferred areas a pronounced onshore movement at the surface. The summertime, rain-bearing monsoon of India, Burma, and east Asia is perhaps the best known of these seasonal winds. But fairly steady onshore winds also invade the Gulf coastal regions of the United States, the north coast of Brazil, and the Guianas, the Guinea coast of Africa, and other coastal sectors of the world where the monsoon effect has been recognized. And in fact, over most of Arctic Eurasia north (onshore) winds prevail during June, July, and August. South of the equator summertime invasions of oceanic air over the smaller land areas of those latitudes are less pronounced.

In any case, wherever summertime landward movements prevail, strong indrafts of oceanic surface air seldom continue for great distances inland. This is particularly true where high mountains, as in northern India, disrupt and divert the flow of air. It is even true in the lower Mississippi valley, where low relief might seem to permit a continuous northward movement near the ground. Instead, during the summer period of onshore movement along the coast, winds from all quarters of the compass reach only a short distance inland, a fact that is attributable largely to the interference of cyclonic systems that constantly move across North America. It is only at higher altitudes, beyond 2 miles or more, that deep penetration inland of onshore air flow commonly takes place.

A reversal, or at least a marked change of direction and persistence, takes place along monsoon coasts in wintertime. In winter the sun is lower in the sky, insolation is less effective, the earth and the air above it are cooler, and average barometric pressures are higher. In this season the cooler continents become centers of action with respect to the warmer adjoining oceans, and air in general tends to move outward over the sea. Eastern North America and eastern and southern Asia are regions of predominantly offshore movement. South winds (offshore) tend to predominate in Arctic Eurasia, whereas weaker, variable winds prevail in winter along the Gulf coast of the United States and the Guinea coast of Africa.

Upper Air Winds

Most of our present knowledge concerning the movements of air at higher altitudes has been obtained since the beginning of World War II. Interest in upper air soundings grew tremendously during the war with the development of high-flying military aircraft and continued after the war as high-altitude commercial air service was extended to all quarters of the inhabited world. The techniques of upper air exploration have also been radically improved in recent years, especially with the wider use of radio, radar, rocket, and satellite equipment for observation.

The direction and velocity of winds at high altitudes have been determined for many years by the observation of a free-floating, helium-filled balloon called a pilot balloon, to which no instruments are attached. Its movements are commonly traced to distant heights by means of a theodolite, but it is valueless, of course, when it disappears behind a cloud or passes beyond the range of visibility. The observations so made are called pibals. The disadvantages of this method were overcome during World War II when radar-tracking techniques were developed by which observations could be made at all times of day or night and in all

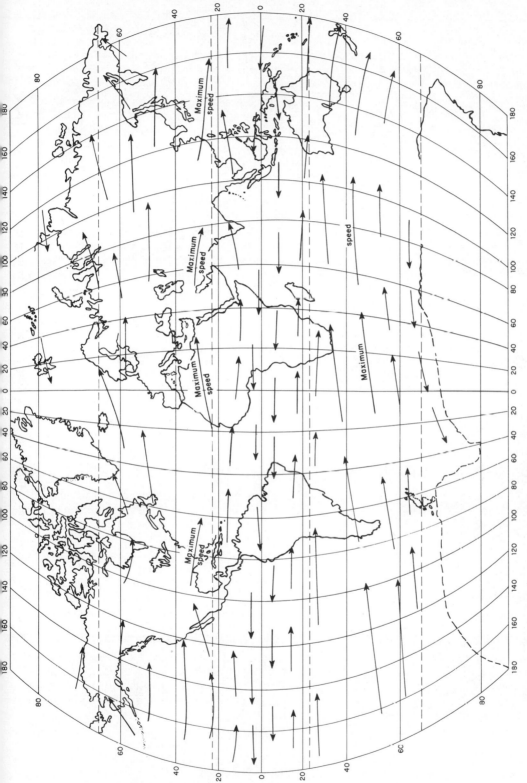

Figure 4.10. Airstreams at about 40,000 feet in January. Length of arrow denotes relative persistence; areas of maximum speed are indicated.

55

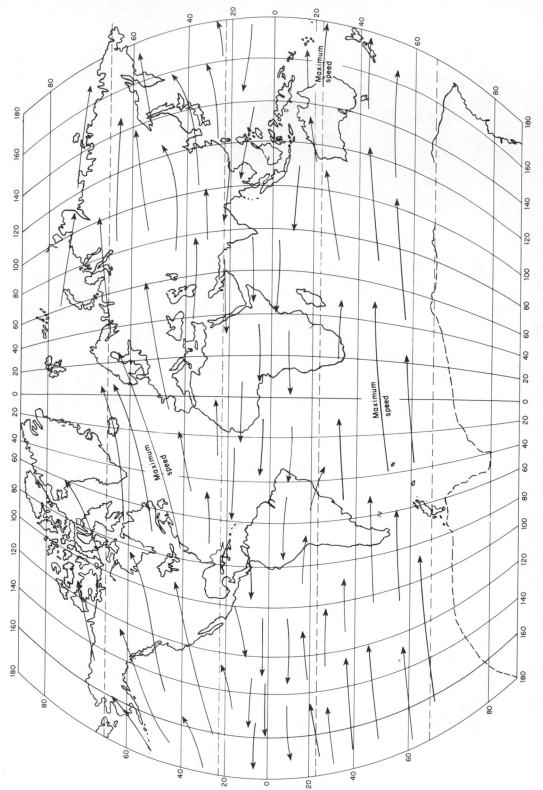

Figure 4.11. Airstreams at about 40,000 feet in July. Length of arrow denotes relative persistence; areas of maximum speed are indicated.

56

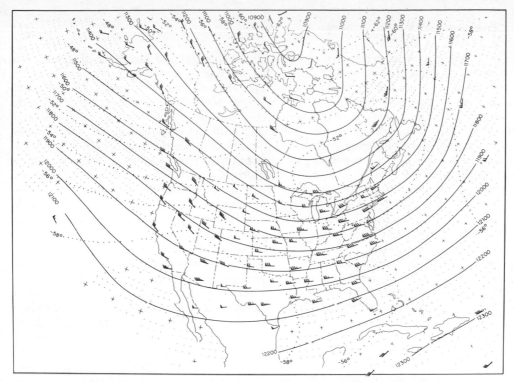

Figure 4.12. Mean wind speed and direction at 40,000 feet for January 1965. Arrows fly with the wind; flag represents 50 knots, full feather 10 knots, half feather 5 knots. Height contours in feet above sea level (solid lines); isotherms in degrees Celsius (dotted lines). [U.S. Weather Bureau]

Figure 4.13. Mean wind speed and direction at 40,000 feet for July 1965. Arrows fly with the wind; flag represents 50 knots, full feather 10 knots, half feather 5 knots. Height contours in feet above sea level (solid lines); isotherms in degrees Celsius (dotted lines). [U.S. Weather Bureau]

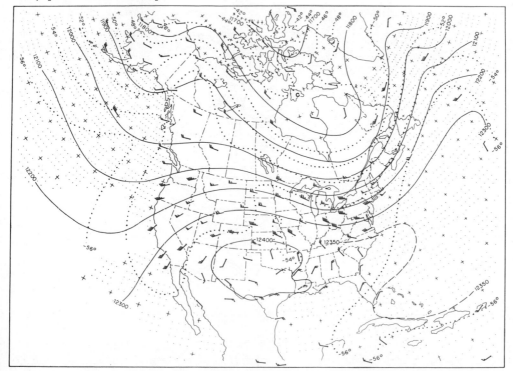

kinds of weather. A metal reflector is carried aloft by a helium-filled balloon, and the direction and speed of its movement are normally detectable until the balloon bursts. These observations are called rawins. Recent experiments with rocket-borne instruments suggest the possibility of collecting systematic data from altitudes well beyond the range of balloons and far into the stratosphere.

By these several methods an increasing body of data has become available for large segments of the northern hemisphere and certain well-populated parts of the southern hemisphere. The records apply to a short span of time, roughly since about 1940, and for many regions are lacking altogether, and therefore must be examined with reservations. Nonetheless, analyses made during the past decade have brought to light many qualities of the upper troposphere and the lower stratosphere important for the understanding of the general circulation.

With increasing altitude the movements of air become less and less confined, resulting in an increase of mean velocities and a much greater persistence of direction. The complexities of movement near the surface give way to smoother patterns of airflow, and we observe (Figs. 4.10 and 4.11) that the prevailing motion of most of the earth's atmosphere at high levels is eastward. An illustration of the way these motions actually occur over North America is seen in the maps of winds around 40,000 feet for January and July 1965 (Figs. 4.12 and 4.13). Winds at 18,000 feet, with the related pressure pattern, may be seen on the daily weather map published by the U.S. Weather Bureau, of which the map for January 27, 1966, is an example (Fig. 4.14).

Average west wind velocities increase in lower latitudes to a maximum somewhere between 20° and 35° from the equator. Maximum upper air wind speeds occur in what is now commonly called the jet stream. Yearly jet stream maxima normally develop during the winter. In the summer jet stream maxima

Figure 4.14. Mean wind speed and direction at about 18,000 feet on January 27, 1966, at 7:00 p.m. Arrows fly with the wind; flag represents 50 knots, full feather 10 knots, half feather 5 knots. Height contours in feet above sea level (solid lines); isotherms in degrees Celsius (dashed lines). U.S. [Weather Bureau]

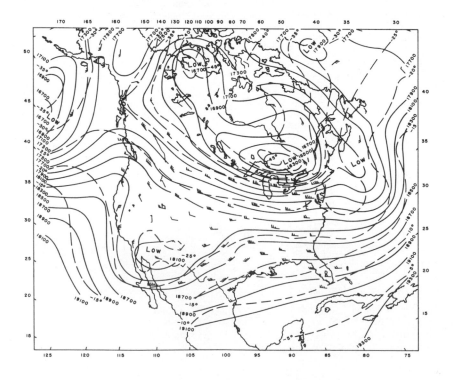

shift poleward, usually to between 35° and 50° of latitude in the northern hemisphere, and mean velocities diminish to only about half those of the wintertime maxima. Seasonal maxima tend to develop over areas where surface calms and variables prevail. Though the general movement of the upper air is dominantly eastward, there is a tendency for upper winds near the equator to move westward. Over surface polar easterlies, on the other hand, are believed to be predominantly west winds.

This, then, is a general picture of upper air movement around the world. But again it must be remembered that it is a view derived from the sum of many variable movements and is never as simply organized as this. At a given hour, high altitude movements are apt to occur in some such fashion as that portrayed in Figure 4.14.

From poles to equator the movements of air take place within an exceedingly thin layer of the atmosphere, the troposphere, that has a mean thickness of less than 10 miles. The depth of the troposphere might be expressed as roughly one six-hundredth of the distance from the equator to either pole (assuming a generous 10-mile depth compared with an approximate distance of 6000 miles from equator to pole). These proportions could be illustrated by covering the bottom of a vessel 60 inches in length with water to a depth of only one-tenth inch.

It is now generally believed that the greatest proportion of the earth's atmosphere moves eastward in two broad circumpolar whirls that are apparently driven in part by the heat expansion of tropical air and in part by the mechanical effects of the round earth's rotation on its axis.

It is known that equatorial regions receive much more solar energy than polar regions. As polar regions do not become increasingly colder, nor do equatorial regions become increasingly warmer, some mechanism exists by which warmth and cold are exchanged between latitudes and a general balance prevails. The processes of meridional exchange are not at all well understood, but are thought to include an irregular transfer of heated, expanded air at higher levels, from low latitudes toward the poles. A band of air presumed to be at rest at about 30° latitude, if moved to latitude 60° will

decrease in radius from 2200 miles to about 1500 miles. The effect is similar to that upon a weight at the end of a string whose velocity of rotation will increase if its radius is shortened. A body of air moved from latitude 30° to latitude 60° would make a gain in relative speed, if otherwise unmodified, of about 185 miles per hour.

The broad qualities of upper air movement summarized as seasonal averages in Figures 4.10 and 4.11 are marked during the year by rather well-defined expansions and contractions of the circumpolar vortices. When this happens, the eastward flow of the upper air is radically modified, and great sinuous waves or undulations develop along the zone of contact called the polar front between cold polar air and warm air from the tropics. The periods of their development, often lasting for several weeks, are called index cycles. A typical cycle is portrayed[2] in Figure 4.15. In this figure the gentle undulations of the first stage gain in amplitude in the second stage and in the third are marked by a strong equatorward movement of cold air along the western side of each polar bulge and an even stronger poleward flow of warm tropical air along the eastern side. In the final stage cells of tropical air like whirlpools are cut off, remaining for a time over middle latitudes, and cold cellular masses circle above parts of the tropics. This, as one author has expressed it,[3] results in "topsy-turvy weather, when Alaska may be warmer than Florida." Although each stage may last a week, more or less, the final stage often persists longer. Taken altogether, the two main circumpolar whirls of the atmosphere can be thought of as father to a continuous host of lesser whirlpools, of great breadth and singular shallowness, between the poles and equator.

The principal source of heat for the general circulation process, or processes, is the warmth imparted to the atmosphere within the tropics. And within the tropics the variable movements of the two gigantic circumpolar vortices are linked together in a coherent process of global atmospheric exchange. The atmosphere, in short, must be regarded as a single, organically unified whole.

[2] After J. Namias, *Scientific American*, **187**(4): 28–29, Oct. 1952.
[3] *Ibid.*

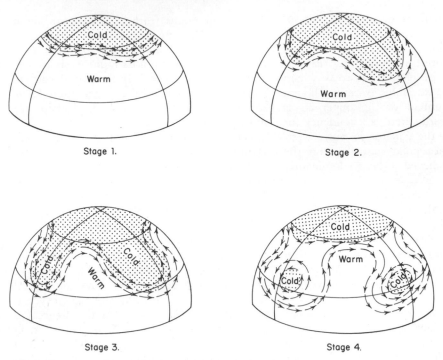

Stage 1.

Stage 2.

Stage 3.

Stage 4.

Figure 4.15. A normal index cycle in the northern hemisphere.

Surface winds over the tropical oceans, especially the steady trades, gather enormous volumes of moisture into the atmosphere through an endless process of evaporation. Borne aloft, warm, moist air is condensed at cloud level, usually from 2000 feet to between 6000 feet and 10,000 feet, the normal vertical range of trade wind cumuli. The presence of abundant microscopic salt crystals is doubtless of great importance in providing the essential nuclei of condensation.

Condensation releases warmth to the air at these levels and through the entrainment of cooler, drier high-altitude air results in a turbulent eddy motion that is characteristic of the atmosphere above the trades. When horizontal tropical eddies in the upper air are large enough and are partly drawn into the broad horizontal vortices of middle latitudes, a strong, roughly poleward flow of relatively warm air results. This is currently thought to be the primary motion of the general circulation and the chief way by which warmth is distributed from the tropics toward the poles. It is a motion that takes place at irregular, unpredictable intervals, over various changing longitudes.

A prominent feature of the general circulation is the jet stream, the generic term applied to upper troposphere winds of high velocity. Sometimes only one, other times two or more swiftly-moving currents of air may appear in mid-latitudes simultaneously, moving on a roughly eastward course more rapidly—at, say, 50 to 60 miles per hour—than the intervening air between them. Two or more may combine to reach still higher velocities, often well over 100 miles per hour, and sometimes as high as 300 miles per hour. The jet stream occurs both north and south of the equator. Its development is believed to take place normally nearer the equator in the southern hemisphere than in the northern hemisphere.

For some reason not yet understood, the jet stream's maximum velocities are reached, on the average, in the winter season and in preferred areas. Average maxima for winter are attained over southeastern United States and the western Atlantic Ocean, at about latitude 30°, over North Africa and the Arabian Sea, and over East Asia. The strongest jet stream currents have been observed east of Japan between 30,000 and 40,000 feet, often increasing to nearly 300 miles per hour. This is the subtropical jet, in contradistinction to the mid-latitude jet and the polar jet farther north, all three of which are known to occur during the winter months. In the northern hemisphere during summer a single, narrow jet stream appears to be the most common occurrence, holding a fluctuating position near 45° latitude at about 37,000 feet in altitude. The wintertime polar jet is most often spoken of as the polar night jet, occurring high in the stratosphere near the Arctic Circle. Less is known of southern hemi-sphere jet streams, but a polar night jet stream has frequently been identified near the Antarctic Circle during the winter, especially from June through August.

The presence of high-altitude, high-velocity winds was first recognized by the crews of high-flying B-29 bombers operating in the western Pacific during World War II. The pilot sometimes noted that his plane moved over the earth at less than 100 miles per hour, although his instruments indicated an air speed of around

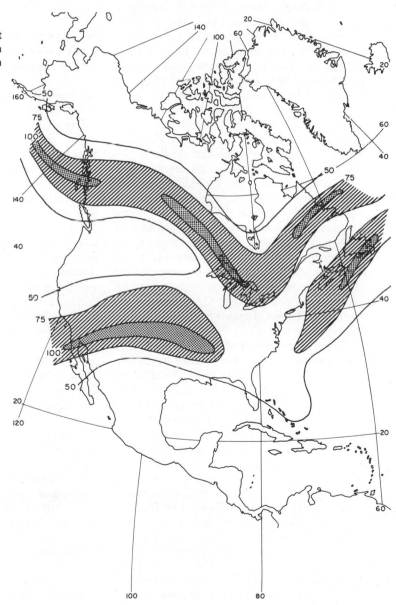

Figure 4.16. Multiple jet stream over North America on October 25, 1960. Speed in knots.

300 miles per hour. Returning to base he occasionally observed a ground speed nearly twice the air speed of his craft. At first mystified, meteorologists finally deduced the presence of swift-flowing currents in the upper troposphere over east Asia and the western Pacific. As the altitude range of aircraft was raised still higher, other regions of jet stream development were identified.

Most of the measurements of wind speed aloft have been made from the surface of the earth by means of rawin, radiosonde, and other devices. Recently, however, specially equipped aircraft have been assigned the task of "flying the jet stream," and occasional rocket sounding devices have been sent aloft to obtain further and more accurate measurements. Consequently, a more satisfactory concept of the jet stream and its relationships is now at hand.

The jet stream is essentially ribbonlike in nature, being usually quite broad, often from 300 to 500 miles, and from only a few thousand feet to perhaps 3 or 4 miles in thickness. Although at times a continuous stream may entirely encircle the globe in middle latitudes, it more often appears in detached segments (Fig. 4.16). At other times it may completely disappear. Jet streams occur at altitudes of 10,000 feet to 50,000 feet, but maximum speed is typically reached between 35,000 and 40,000 feet, in short, close to the tropopause. Recent wintertime investigations over southeastern United States revealed that 37,000 feet was the commonest height of peak wind speed development.

The speed and height of the jet stream's core of maximum velocity vary along its length. Over St. Louis, for example, it may be traveling 200 miles per hour at 43,000 feet, but at Pittsburgh the same continuous current may be observed traveling 150 miles per hour at 35,000 feet, and the intervening portion moving about 100 miles per hour at around 38,000 feet. Wind speeds diminish rapidly away from the central core, particularly with changing altitude. A 30 mile per hour change in velocity may occur with a change in altitude of only 1000 feet.

The relation of the jet stream with other atmospheric qualities is suggested in Figure 4.17, showing a schematic north–south profile of the troposphere north of the equator. From the diagram we observe that the jet stream is found where a marked change in the altitude of

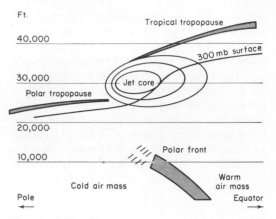

Figure 4.17. The position at which the polar front jet stream commonly forms in relation to the fractured tropopause and the surface polar front.

the tropopause exists. Sometimes this feature, called a fractured tropopause, is indicated by a difference in altitude of 30,000 feet between the higher tropical portion and the lower polar tropopause. The central core typically occurs quite well below the altitude of the tropical tropopause.

It is also evident that the jet stream develops on the equatorward side of the sloping plane of the polar front, but its high altitude position is nearly always poleward of the line of contact between the polar front and the earth's surface.[4] A strong temperature gradient is present in the vicinity of the jet stream, particularly at mid-troposphere just below it or at the surface equatorward from it, with warm air toward the equator and much colder air toward the pole.

Strong decreasing wind shear, a change in wind velocity at right angles to the direction of flow, is noted on both sides of the jet stream axis. Great turbulence in absolutely clear air, without clouds or other visible signs of its presence, is often a feature of strong high-altitude wind shear. It is referred to in meteorology as clear air turbulence. The strongly concentrated airflow of the jet stream near the tropopause appears to be the direct source of nearly all of the kinetic energy of the entire westerly (eastward) circumpolar vortex. Its energy is initially derived from density gradients that ultimately trace their origin to

---

[4] The concept of the polar front, and of frontal features in general, is dealt with at length in Chapter 5.

thermal contrasts arising from the sun's radiant heat and the motions of the earth.

In summary, the general circulation of the atmosphere is at present thought to operate in the following manner:

The main source of energy for driving the broad currents of the atmosphere is supplied to the air by the sun-warmed waters of the tropical oceans. Continuously heated and expanded, upward and poleward, the tropical atmosphere moves at irregular intervals aloft in broad horizontal whirls that occasionally merge with high-altitude vortices of middle latitudes. When this happens, the high speed poleward transfer of warmer tropical air takes place, feeding the eastward flow of air in the mid-latitudes and contributing an essential element in the formation of the major circumpolar vortices.

As for a satisfactory explanation of the general circulation and its many irregularities, we are compelled to admit at this time that none exists. A leading authority on the subject[5] has suggested that variable solar activity, particularly in the shorter, ultraviolet wavelengths such as must accompany the sunspot cycle, is the most logical and easily expressed factor in the weekly, seasonal, and longer periodical variations of the general circulation.

[5] H. C. Willet, *Transactions of the American Geophysical Union*, **29**(6): 803–9, 1948.

References

BATTEN, E. S.: "Wind Systems in the Mesosphere and Lower Ionosphere," *Journal of Meteorology*, **18**(3): 283–91, 1961.

BORCHERT, J. R.: "Regional Differences in the World Atmospheric Circulation," *Annals of the Association of American Geographers*, **43**(1): 14–26, 1953.

HARE, F. K.: "The Stratosphere," *Geographical Review*, **52**(4): 525–47, 1962.

HARE, F. K.: "The Westerlies," *Geographical Review*, **50**(3): 345–67, 1960.

LAMB, H. H.: "The Southern Westerlies," *Quarterly Journal of the Royal Meteorological Society*, **85**: 1–23, 1959.

NAMIAS, J.: "Interactions of Circulation and Weather Between Hemispheres," *Monthly Weather Review*, **91**: 482–86, 1963.

NEWELL, R. E.: "The Circulation of the Upper Atmosphere," *Scientific American*, **210**(3): 62–74, 1964.

REITER, E. R.: *Jet-Stream Meteorology*, University of Chicago Press, Chicago, 1963.

RIEHL, H. and MALKUS, J. S.: "On the Heat Balance and Maintenance of Circulation in the Trades," *Quarterly Journal of the Royal Meteorological Society*, **83**: 21–29, 1957.

VEDERMAN, J.: "The Life Cycles of Jet Streams and Extratropical Cyclones," *Bulletin of the American Meteorological Society*, **35**(6): 239–44, 1954.

chapter 5

AIR MASSES, FRONTS, AND STORMS

It is the purpose of this chapter to examine in some detail those features of atmospheric behavior that develop within the larger mechanism of the general circulation and produce the unending changes and varieties of weather observed all around the world. These processes are sometimes spoken of as the secondary circulation, and to understand them in the light of contemporary meteorology involves a concept of air masses, of fronts, and of migrating cyclones, anticyclones, and storms.

Meteorologists are constantly searching for improved methods of analysis in order to forecast the daily weather with greater accuracy. A revolutionary change in methods of weather analysis and in the outlook on the physical problems related to it was accomplished during World War I when a group of Scandinavian meteorologists, including Jacob Bjerknes of Norway and Carl-Gustaf Rossby of Sweden, developed the idea of air mass formation and the occurrence of fronts. Contemporary weather analysis and prediction now consist largely in studying the properties of individual, discrete masses of air and the changes resulting when they meet.

Air Masses

An air mass is a portion of the atmosphere having a uniform horizontal distribution of certain physical characteristics, especially of temperature and humidity. These qualities are acquired when a mass of air stagnates or moves very slowly over a large and relatively unvaried surface of land or sea. Under these circumstances surface air gradually takes on properties of temperature and moisture approaching those of the underlying surface, and there then follows a steady, progressive transmission of properties to greater heights, resulting finally in a fairly clearly marked vertical transition of characteristics. Those parts of the earth where air masses acquire their distinguishing qualities are called source regions.

The height to which an air mass is modified depends upon the length of time it remains in its source region and also upon the difference between the initial properties of the air when it first arrived and those of the underlying surface. If, for example, an invading flow of air is cooler than the surface beneath as it comes to virtual rest over a source region, it is warmed from below, and convective currents are formed, rapidly bearing aloft new characteristics of temperature and moisture to considerable heights. If, on the other hand, it is warmer than the surface of the source region, cooling of its surface layers takes place, vertical thermal currents do not develop, and the air is modified only in its lower portions. The process of modification may be accomplished in just a few days of slow horizontal drift, although it often takes longer, sometimes several weeks. Radiation, convection, turbulence, and advection are the chief means of bringing it about.

The prerequisite condition for these developments is very slowly migrating, outward-spreading, diverging air, and a very extensive surface beneath that is fairly uniform in nature. Light winds and relatively high barometric pressures characteristically prevail. Hence, most masses form within the great semi-permanent anticyclonic regions of the general circulation, where calms, light, variable winds, and over-all subsidence of the atmosphere are typical.

Four major types of source regions are recognized: Continental Polar (cP), Maritime Polar (mP), Continental Tropical (cT), and Maritime Tropical (mT). The designations *Arctic* (A), applied to the Arctic Ocean, *Antarctic* (AA), applied to Antarctica, and *Equatorial* (E), describing regions within a few degrees of the equator, are also used. Polar air masses are continental when they develop over land or ice surfaces in high latitudes, as they do over Greenland, northern Canada and Eurasia, and Antarctica. These are cold and dry. They are maritime when they form over the oceans in high latitudes, as the northern Atlantic and Pacific and the oceanic waters surrounding Antarctica. An air mass from these sources is cold and moist. Similarly, tropical air is continental when it originates along the Tropics of Cancer and Capricorn over northern Africa and northern Australia and is therefore warm and dry. It is maritime when it forms along the Tropics over the Atlantic, Pacific, and Indian oceans, where it develops as a mass of warm, moist air. A single air mass usually covers thousands of square miles of the earth's surface when fully formed.

An air mass is recognizable to the meteorologist chiefly because of the uniformity of its primary properties—temperature and humidity—and the vertical distribution of these. Secondary qualities, such as cloud types, precipitation, and visibility, are also taken into account. These qualities are retained for a remarkably long time, often for several weeks, after an air mass has traveled far from its source region, and they are thus the means of distinguishing it from other masses of air. This is especially true at upper levels, for the lower layers tend to be modified much more rapidly and more definitely by the surfaces over which the air mass

moves. Eventually, however, a migrating air mass is inevitably fully transformed, losing its original identity entirely, as the changes in its lower layers are transmitted to greater heights.

The nature of change in an air mass as it approaches any locality is of the utmost importance in forecasting the weather anticipated for that locality. For the weatherman it is essential to know whether the lower levels of an advancing air mass are cooling or warming and whether its upper layers are becoming more stable or less stable. These conditions are indicated by adding the symbols w, k, s, and u to the air mass designation.

w means that the lower levels of air are warmer than the surface beneath and are thus being cooled; k signifies the reverse; s means that air aloft is stable, that is, it is cooler than the surrounding high altitude air and hence tends to subside; u means unstable air aloft, when it is warmer than the surrounding upper air and active convection currents are present. For example, a mass of air originating over northwestern Canada in summertime drifts slowly southward over the warm central plains. Warmed as it enters lower latitudes, it is designated cPKu, signifying its source region, that its humidity is low, that it is cooler than the surface below, and that it is unstable aloft. An air mass designated mTWs, appearing over the Mississippi valley in wintertime, might be analyzed as one having originated over the Gulf of Mexico or the Caribbean, moist and warm, but cooling in its northward advance and having stability aloft. The air masses commonly affecting North America are shown in Figure 5.1, with the average trajectories they follow in moving across the continent.

For the world as a whole the generalized distribution of major air masses is presented in Figures 5.2 and 5.3, intended to serve as a guide to the location of air mass types described in Table 5-1.

Among the important advantages of air mass identification to the climatologist are the records of the frequency with which the various air mass types pass across any part of the world. From these records it is possible to diagram the basic flow patterns associated with the particular circulations appropriate for a given section of the world. Coupled with a study of the statistical record of precipitation, wind, and pressure data, this synthesis of daily air mass

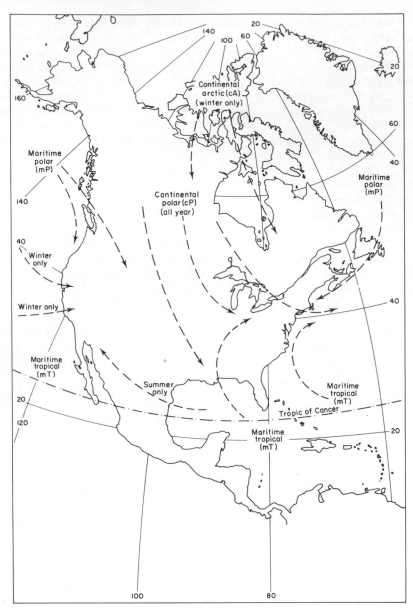

Figure 5.1.   The principal air masses affecting North America, showing their seasonal trajectories.

analyses is called dynamic climatology. It is a practicable study only where the necessary data, particularly for high altitudes, have been collected over a reasonably long period of time. This requirement is satisfactorily met only in North America, western Europe, and to some extent in southeast Asia, Australia, and New Zealand. For that reason it should be thought of as a fairly new branch of analytical climatol-

ogy that has prospects of becoming increasingly valuable as the world's weather observation network is expanded and improved.

Fronts

Two converging air masses tend to retain their individual properties after they have met, creating a zone of discontinuity between them called a front. A front is a rather narrow

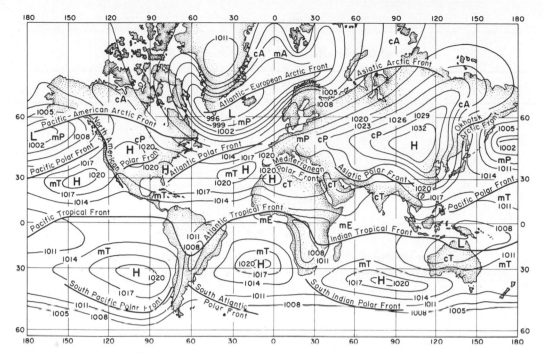

Figure 5.2.   World distribution of air masses in January. [Adapted from S. P. Chromov, 1940]

Figure 5.3.   World distribution of air masses in July. [Adapted from S. P. Chromov, 1940]

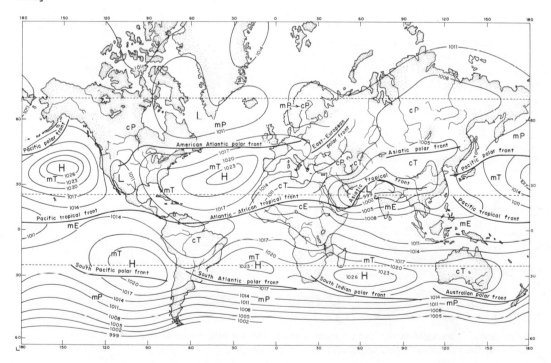

TABLE 5–1

Air Masses
Chief Characteristics of Primary Air Mass Types

Symbol		Characteristics
cP	Continental polar	Relatively cold, dry air, originating over land areas in high latitudes.
mP	Maritime polar	Relatively cold, moist air, originating over the sea in high latitudes.
cT	Continental tropical	Relatively warm, dry air, originating over land areas in low latitudes.
mT	Maritime tropical	Relatively warm, moist air originating over the sea in low latitudes.
k		Air that is cooler than the surface over which it moves, hence is warmed at its lower levels and is unstable up to around 5000 ft; e.g., cPk.
w		Air that is warmer than the surface over which it moves, hence is cooled at its lower levels and is stable up to around 5000 ft; e.g., mPw.
s		Air aloft that is stable, that is, air in which the lapse rate does not exceed the adiabatic rate and which tends to be dry and to subside. Convection is absent.
u		Air aloft that is unstable, that is, air in which the lapse rate tends to exceed the adiabatic rate and which tends to be humid and to rise. Convection is present.

transition zone, marked by lower barometric pressures, between two discrete air masses. It is usually along a front that the ordinary changes in weather evident to the casual observer take place. A front is often described as resembling an inclined plane, separating cooler air below from warmer air above, in a wedgelike fashion (Fig. 5.4). These concepts apply primarily to regions intermediate between the tropics and the poles.

Although occasional transition zones move imperceptibly and are then called stationary fronts, they nearly always move measurably over the earth, for air masses are, of course, amorphous bodies, constantly moving and changing their positions in amoebalike fashion. The leading margin of an advancing mass of cold air is called a cold front (Fig. 5.4). When a mass of warm air overtakes cooler air, its leading margin is called a warm front (Fig. 5.5). The conditions necessary for the formation of fronts are (1) the meeting of two air masses having temperatures that contrast to the extent that one is colder and hence denser than the other, and (2) circulation of the two air masses such that they are brought together by converging

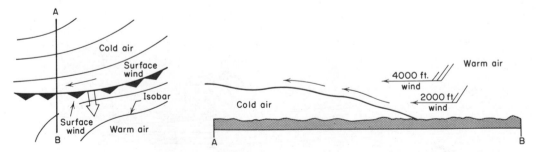

Figure 5.4. Schematic details of cold front showing surface winds and winds aloft in relation to the advancing front. Cross section along line *A–B*.

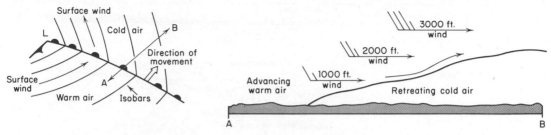

Figure 5.5. Schematic details of warm front showing surface winds and winds aloft in relation to the advancing front. Cross section along line *A–B*.

currents of air. The development and intensification of a pronounced front is termed frontogenesis; the opposite tendency, toward the degeneration or disappearance of a front, is called frontolysis. Frontolysis occurs whenever the temperature contrast between two air masses disappears or when the circulations no longer produce a convergence of air currents. Stationary front, cold front, warm front, frontogenesis, and frontolysis are features commonly appearing on the daily weather map published by the U.S. Weather Bureau.

Although the passing of a cold front may not always be detected without instruments, it is often accompanied by very pronounced changes in weather. A cold front in mid-latitude North America during the warmer part of the year commonly approaches from the northwest or west and is normally aligned in a northeast–southwest direction. As it approaches, winds begin to increase in velocity from southward, and the air is relatively warm and moist. High cirrus clouds, usually between 200 and 300 miles ahead of the front, are seen toward the west, blending into altocumulus forms near the horizon. Moving eastward, these give way to cumulonimbus or high nimbostratus clouds,

and the sky becomes well overcast. Lower nimbostratus clouds may then appear, and rain begins to fall, increasing in intensity as the approaching front nears (Fig. 5.6). At this point massive, billowing cumuli may form, towering to great heights, and bringing thunderstorms along a line of disturbance, roughly parallel to the front, called a squall line. These conditions usually develop when the air ahead of the cold front is particularly warm and moist, tending to be unstable and to nourish convectional movements. As the front passes, winds shift rather rapidly to a westerly or northerly direction, the barometric pressure rises rapidly, and a short time later clear weather appears, with cooler, drier air.

Cold fronts are sometimes many hundreds of miles in length, although often very short and fragmentary, and average anywhere from 10 to 50 miles in width. They have been known to advance at speeds up to 60 miles per hour, but the usual velocity is less than half that. The wintertime mean velocities of cold front advance are commonly higher than those of summertime.

Warm fronts are seldom as clearly marked in passing as cold fronts. Partly because of the

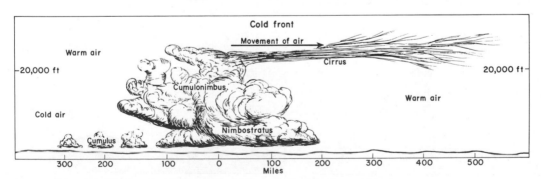

Figure 5.6. Distribution of cloud types in relation to an advancing cold front.

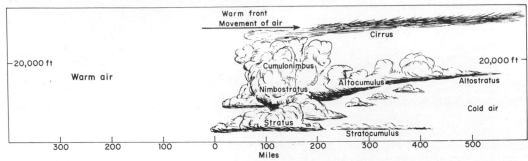

Figure 5.7. Distribution of cloud types in relation to an advancing warm front.

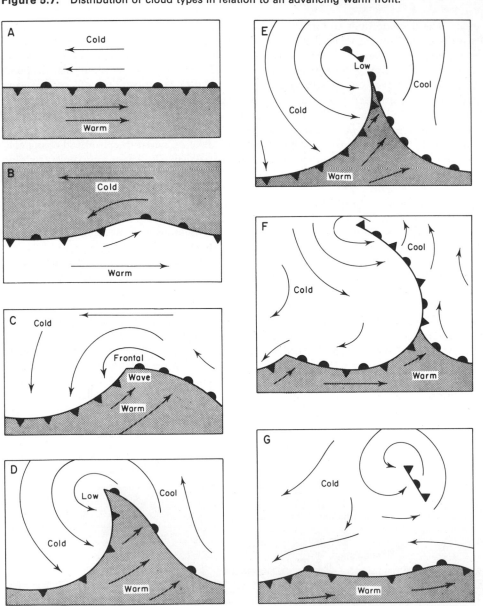

Figure 5.8. Schematic development of an occluded front in the northern hemisphere.

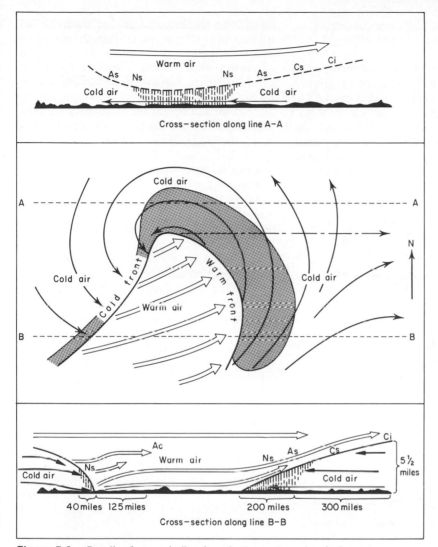

Figure 5.9. Details of an occluding front in the northern hemisphere.

relative speed of advance, the boisterous, gusty weather associated with its passage, and the bracing effect of the cooler, drier air that follows, the cold front is usually much more spectacular than the warm front. The approach of a warm front may be detected twenty-four hours or more before it arrives by the typical cloud forms that develop some 400 or 500 miles ahead of it, and the speed of its advance is normally about half that of a cold front. High cirrus clouds are first seen, merging with thin cirrostratus that sometimes produce a halo effect, and these give way to nimbostratus clouds that finally cover the sky completely. In summer light, steady rains begin to fall long

before the front passes, enduring for many hours, sometimes for several days, under an overcast of nimbostratus clouds that seem to hug the earth. Heavy fog is not unusual. Winds are normally light, blowing somewhere between east and south.

After the actual front has passed, the rain stops, temperature rises, the barometer becomes steady, the wind shifts to a northerly or westerly direction, and fairly warm, hazy air prevails in what is sometimes spoken of as the warm sector. Occasional drizzling rains may follow as the skies gradually clear. Figure 5.7 is a diagram of warm front characteristics, in which one should note the greater breadth of advancing cloud development (indicated by the scale of miles) as compared with cold front clouds (Fig. 5.6).

Another type of frontal development is one that occurs during the life cycle of a migrating cyclone and is termed an occluded front.[1] The series of maps in Figure 5.8 illustrate the way in which an occluded front is thought to develop. In some way not entirely understood at present, an undulation is thought to result from changes in the velocity of winds adjacent to the front.

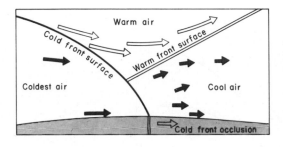

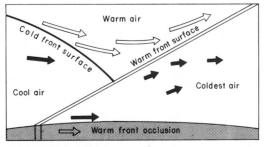

Figure 5.10. Schematic view of surface changes at occlusion.

This frontal wave then travels, very like an ocean ground swell, roughly eastward, gaining amplitude and gradually acquiring a cyclonic circulation of its own as a low pressure cell takes form. This is the meteorologist's *low, barometric depression, cyclonic storm, cyclone.*

If sufficiently well nourished with relatively warm, moist air, the migrating cyclone gradually expands in size and intensity, developing a pronounced counterclockwise circulation in the northern hemisphere, as adjoining air of higher pressure flows toward it in a process of convergence. In time the wave deepens still further,

[1] *Occlude, occlusion*: from Latin *ob*—to, against, and *claudere*—to close, shut.

interposing an elongated arm of warm air between two masses of cooler, heavier, diverging air. Thus, behind the cyclone lies a mass of advancing cold air, and ahead lies another, which in Figure 5.8 (E) has almost been overtaken. An enlargement of this situation is diagrammed in Figure 5.9. In Figure 5.8 (F) the pursuing cold front has joined the warm front, or leading edge of the cyclone, and the two fronts have closed. Occlusion has occurred. Figure 5.10 shows a profile of an occluded front in which the two masses of colder air have met beneath the cyclone. The cyclonic mass of warmer air has been uplifted, is borne eastward in the general circulation, and is finally dissipated. It must be pointed out that occlusion does not always occur in the evolution of a mid-latitude cyclone.

We have seen in the preceding paragraphs that the frontal or convergence zones between two diverging air masses are the zones of active storm development where fairly strong, shifting winds, clouds, precipitation, and generally unsettled weather prevail. We will now turn our attention to the subject of storms in general. To this end we must elaborate upon the chief distinguishing characteristics of cyclones and anticyclones discussed earlier, in Chapter 4.

Cyclones, Anticyclones, and Storms

The endless, year-round procession of cyclones and anticyclones, which may be thought of as details in the general circulation and the broader movements of air masses, is mainly responsible for the ceaseless variation of the world's daily weather. A migrating anticyclone, wherever it appears, usually brings a spell of relatively cooler, drier, bracing weather with clear, comparatively cloudless blue skies above and light, variable winds near its center where pressures are higher. Characteristically outward-spreading, diverging, the flow pattern formed by the winds of an anticyclone is essentially that of an expanding spiral, in which velocities increase toward the periphery. A cyclone[2] is the reverse, consisting of warmer, more humid, lighter air, its winds tending to

[2] The term *cyclone*, from the Greek *kyklos*—a circle or ring—was first suggested by Henry Piddington about 1850 to describe the revolving storms in the Bay of Bengal, although the whirling nature of certain storms had been recognized by Varenius two centuries earlier, in his *Geographica Naturalis*.

Figure 5.11. A small cyclonic system generated off the coast of Morocco south of Agadir on the morning of August 26, 1965, as viewed from Gemini V at an altitude of about 120 miles. [NASA photo]

form a contracting spiral of increasing velocity toward the center, which is further distinguished by its lower pressure values (Fig. 5.11). Migrating cyclones usually bring inclement weather with abundant clouds, especially stratus forms, and are responsible for much of the rain or snow that falls in all latitudes. The weather characteristic of cyclonic movement differs considerably in various parts of the world and will be discussed in subsequent chapters on regional climatology. Broadly speaking, however, there are two main types of cyclones: (1) the mid-latitude, or extratropical cyclone, and (2) the tropical cyclone.

Mid-latitude cyclones, annually more numerous than those of the Tropics, are most frequently formed in a rather wide zone of contact between polar and tropical air masses, extending from about 30° to 70°N. Lat. and from about 35° to 60°S. Lat. The situation in southern latitudes is not at all satisfactorily known because of the inadequate distribution of weather stations.

We have just seen one way in which cyclonic disturbances are thought to develop. Once developed, a cyclone in northern mid-latitudes may reach a diameter of from 100 to 2000 miles, averaging around 600 miles, and heights of from 6 to 7 miles. Approximately a hundred cyclones cross eastern North America and western Europe each year, carried eastward, as a rule, in the path of predominantly westerly winds at higher altitudes. They occur with greater frequency during winter than in summertime and normally travel across the earth at speeds of from 20 to 30 miles per hour. They often develop an elliptical form, with the longer axis oriented in a roughly north–south direction, and when considerably elongated are called troughs. The weatherman commonly speaks of troughs in contrast to the ridges formed by elongated high pressure anti-cyclones.

The average paths followed by mid-latitude cyclones are fairly well known for the northern hemisphere and are shown in Figures 5.12 and 5.13, along with the somewhat more conjectural cyclone tracks of mid-latitudes south of the equator, for February and August.

Middle latitude cyclones are responsible for most of the rain or snow that falls in all regions

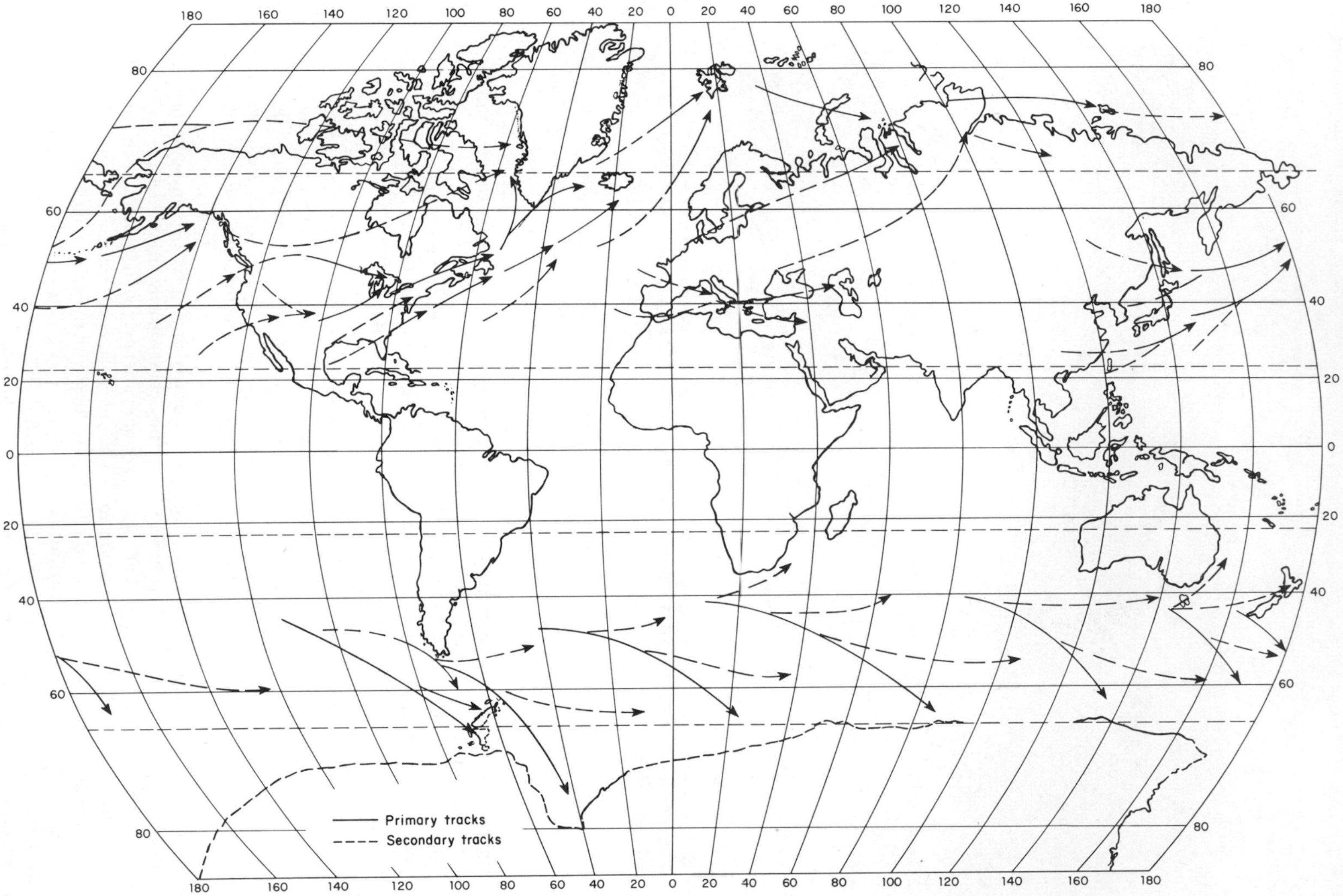

Figure 5.12. Principal tracks of lows in February.

Primary tracks
Secondary tracks

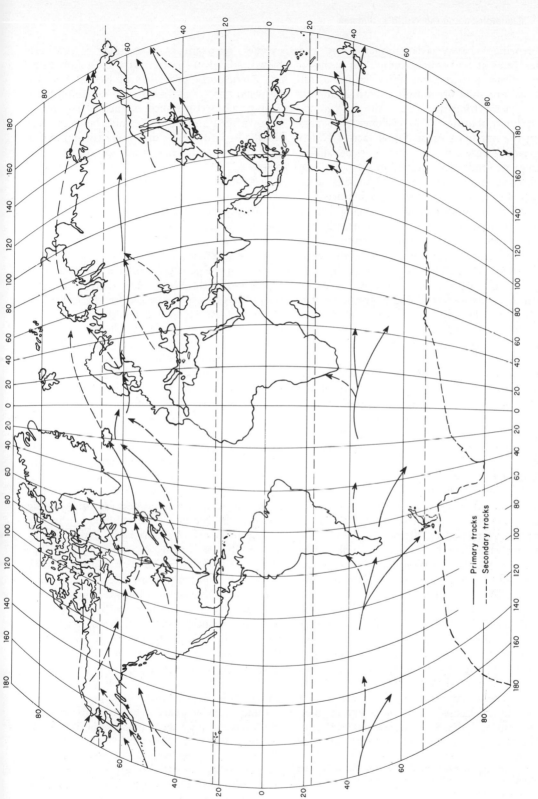

Figure 5.13. Principal tracks of lows in August.

—— Primary tracks
---- Secondary tracks

intermediate between the equator and the poles. But not everywhere along their paths do they release precipitation upon the earth, for only where they are supplied with abundant atmospheric moisture does rain fall in appreciable quantities. The cyclones that pass from the northern Pacific Ocean across North America release enormous amounts of rainfall with great regularity in rising to surmount the west coast mountains and the Rockies, after which they may travel for many hundreds of miles without precipitating. Advancing farther eastward, however, they may eventually entrain sufficient moist air from Hudson Bay or the Great Lakes in summer, or from the western Atlantic or the Gulf of Mexico at all times of the year, to produce rain. Drawn into the gigantic vortex of a traveling depression's converging circulation, moisture is cooled, condensed, and precipitated, in part by mixing with cooler air of polar origin, but mainly by the convective uprising of air that typically takes place in low pressure cells of the atmosphere. Hence a more accurate picture of the rain-producing effectiveness of migrating mid-latitude cyclones may be obtained by comparing the map of their average paths with the world map of average annual rainfall in Figure 6.11.

Although a migrating cyclone is itself often called a cyclonic storm, the common conception of "storminess" usually includes especially heavy falls of rain, snow, sleet, or hail, sometimes accompanied by thunder and lightning and almost always by high or strongly gusty winds. Storms that are typically mid-latitude in origin and development are the tornado[3] and the so-called "ice storm."

An ice storm, or freezing rain, occurs when liquid drops of rain, having a temperature slightly below freezing, fall upon solid surfaces of the earth, such as trees, buildings, and vehicles, whose temperature is well below freezing. The raindrops at least partly solidify, and a glaze of ice, sometimes as much as two inches in thickness, forms on every exposed object out of doors. Such storms are often confined to small areas but occasionally may

extend, for example, over much of southern New England and eastern New York state. They are particularly prevalent in North America between the Great Lakes and Newfoundland. The special circumstances of fairly warm, moist air overhead and frozen ground beneath exist chiefly in late winter and early spring, and it is in this season that most ice storms take place.

TORNADOES. A storm that is typically cyclonic in character and one of devastating intensity is the tornado, even more violent than the much larger and longer-lasting hurricane or typhoon.

It is a questionable distinction of the United States that the gently sloping basin of the Great Plains east of the Rocky Mountains is the most favorable place in the world for the formation of tornadoes. Here, incidentally, it is often termed a cyclone, or twister. The United States accounts for over 90 per cent of all recorded tornadoes. Most of the remainder have been observed in Australia, and others have occurred less frequently in parts of western Europe, eastern Asia, the East Indies, southern Africa, and South America.

The conditions preceding a tornado are well known in the grain-farming regions of the Midwest. The air becomes hot, sultry, and oppressive. Dark gray cumulus clouds are seen in towering masses toward the west or southwest, attended by the constant play of lightning and the rumble of distant thunder, indicating the approach of a thunderstorm. As the advancing clouds obscure the sky overhead, raindrops begin to fall, often preceded or accompanied by hailstones. Suddenly from the base of those dark, foreboding clouds a ragged fragment may appear, rotating furiously with an upward-spiraling, counterclockwise motion, not too far behind the leading edge of the disturbance. It may then become more definitely funnel-shaped, or it may develop into a sinuously twisting tube, composed mainly of rain, dust, and debris. As the tornado nears, a roaring rushing sound is heard. The powerful violence of its passing may seem to those in its path to last interminably. However, being small in diameter, a tornado usually passes any one point in about twenty seconds to two minutes. It is commonly followed by very heavy thundershowers, which, upon ceasing, give way to clear skies and cooler weather.

[3] The African tornado, of the Guinea lands in west and central Africa, is a storm or violent squall in which high, destructive winds are accompanied or followed by torrential rains, but it does not typically assume a gyrating, circulatory form.

The average width of a tornado's path is between 300 and 400 yards, although some have cut a swath across the land more than a mile wide. It commonly remains in contact with the earth for a distance of from 10 to 40 miles, but may go on for as much as 300 miles.

One of the most deadly tornadoes on record occurred on March 18, 1925, first touching the earth near Annapolis, Mo. From this point it took an almost unswerving course for the Mississippi River, crossing the river into Jackson County, Ill., and continuing eastward, severely damaging several small towns and villages in Illinois and finally disappearing near Petersburg, Ind. It had traveled about 219 miles on a path averaging less than 1 mile in width, at a speed ranging from 57 miles per hour in Missouri to 68 miles per hour in Indiana. It killed 689 persons, injured 1980, and caused property damage exceeding $16 million.

The tornado most destructive to property, however, and the worst that ever struck in the northeastern part of the United States, roared across the central part of Massachusetts in the late afternoon of June 9, 1953. Three minor tornadoes also occurred elsewhere in southern New England that afternoon. All three accompanied a passing squall line that had been moving across the Great Plains for the previous two days. On June 7 severe storms had occurred between Colorado and Iowa, taking thirteen lives and causing over $2 million-worth of property damage. On June 8 a tornado struck Flint, Mich., killing 116 persons, injuring 867, and causing property damage to the amount of $19 million. By June 9 the squall line had reached Massachusetts. Worcester, in a region where tornadoes are rare, was struck without warning. It cut an erratic path of from 300 yards to $\frac{3}{4}$ of a mile in width and traveled a total of about 25 miles between Rutland and Fayville, Mass., leaving behind it ninety dead, 436 seriously injured, 852 slightly injured, and over $50 million in property damage.

Massachusetts averaged slightly more than one tornado every year between 1916 and 1960. Other New England states experienced even fewer in the same period, although every mainland state, including Alaska, and most of the Canadian provinces had at least one. Kansas holds the record for the greatest number in that forty-five-year period, with 1167, an average of more than twenty-five annually;

Texas, Oklahoma, and Iowa are next in order. The national distribution of tornado frequencies by states is shown in Fig. 5.14.

Tornadoes occur most commonly in the late afternoon between 3 and 7 P.M., although they have been known to appear at all times of the day or night. They develop more frequently during May than in any other month, and late spring and early summer is the season of greatest concentration (Fig. 5.15). They travel over the ground at from 25 to 40 miles per hour on the average, but one is said to have sped across Kansas at 139 miles per hour on May 25, 1917.

The wind velocity within the vortex has never been measured but is estimated to be up to 500 miles per hour, far faster than any hurricane winds ever measured. Updrafts of 100 miles per hour have been estimated, and the drop in atmospheric pressure within the roaring, whirling vortex is known to be unusually great.

Closely akin to the tornado of inland regions is the twisting column of whirling, funneling cloud that appears over the sea as a waterspout. Composed almost entirely of moisture, mainly resulting from condensation in the atmosphere but to some extent from the sea, the waterspout is otherwise very much like a tornado, occurring under the same kinds of circumstances. Waterspouts are commonest over warm tropical seas, but they have also been observed in summertime as far north as Cape Cod, the Hudson River, and the warmer of the Great Lakes. Henry Seebohm in 1875 reported a violent waterspout near the mouth of the Petchora River in northern Russia at a latitude of about 70°.

In desert regions of the world whirlwinds are very common, sinuously twisting their way across a barren stretch of level land, carrying aloft upward-spiraling clouds of dust. Short-lived and not as violent as a tornado, the dusty whirlwind, or dust devil, as it is sometimes called, is rarely destructive.

THUNDERSTORMS. Thunderstorms are the most numerous of all the storms the atmosphere produces. It is estimated that about 50,000 of them occur throughout the world each day, and that around 2000 are in progress at any one time. They are much more common in rainy regions along the equator than anywhere else and occur there more frequently over land than over water. They are typically a

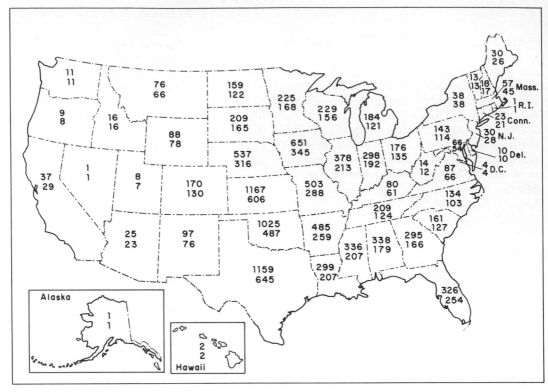

Figure 5.14. Tornado frequency in the United States from 1916 to 1960, by states. Upper figure indicates the total number of tornadoes reported during the period. Lower figure indicates the number of days during the period when tornadoes were reported. [U.S. Weather Bureau]

Figure 5.15. Tornado frequency in the United States from 1916 to 1960, by month. [U.S. Weather Bureau]

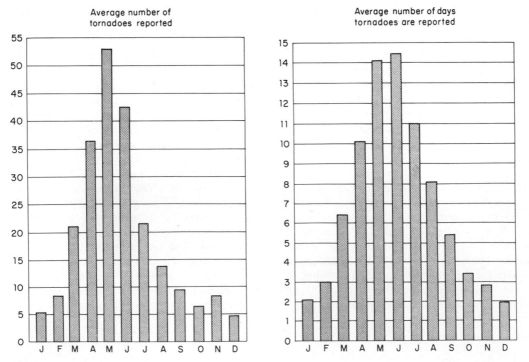

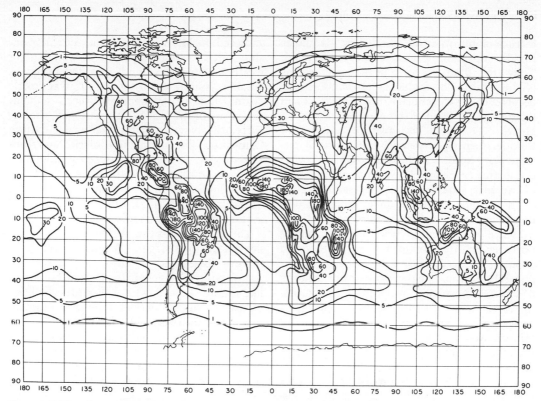

Figure 5.16. Average number of days per year when thunderstorms are reported. [After U.S. Air Force, *Handbook of Geophysics*, ed. 2, 1961]

Figure 5.17. Average number of thunderstorms each year in the United States.

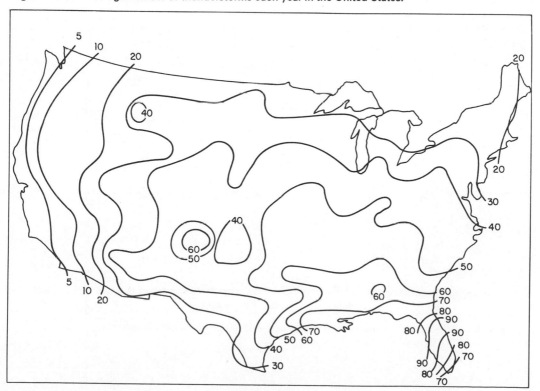

feature of summertime weather in the rainier middle latitudes, again chiefly over the land. They are seldom observed in the polar regions of the world. The frequency of thunderstorm occurrence for the entire world is portrayed in Figure 5.16. A detail of this generalized view in Figure 5.17 shows the average number of thunderstorms per year in the United States. Note that Florida and the Gulf coast, in a region dominated by relatively warm, moist air most of the year, experience the largest number.

The various conditions under which a thunderstorm may develop require at least the presence of abundant moisture and highly unstable air. A minimum relative humidity of about 75 per cent is thought to be necessary. Instability is caused either by excessive heating of lower atmospheric layers, producing strong updrafts, or by the mechanical uplifting of moist air as it moves up the slopes of a mountain or, as we have seen in the discussion of warm and cold fronts, as it is thrust upward by an invasion of cold air at ground level. Condensation of the contained moisture as air rises releases warmth to the surrounding atmosphere, increasing the tendency for convective currents to develop. Convective circulation is an important requirement for thundercloud formation, giving rise to those towering masses of ominous dark gray cumuli that are the typical cloud forms of the thunderstorms.

Since World War II a great deal of new information about thunderstorms has been gathered, mainly with the use of more dependable aircraft and improved techniques of weather observation and recording aloft. A notable concentration of effort was made during the Thunderstorm Project, a joint enterprise of the U.S. Weather Bureau, the Air Force, the Navy, and the National Advisory Committee for Aeronautics, carried on from 1946 to 1949. The results of this project, involving over 12,000 miles of thunderstorm flying, were published in a volume entitled *The Thunderstorm*,[4] on which much of the material in the following paragraphs is based.

The life cycle of a thunderstorm may be considered in three stages: (1) cumulus stage, (2) mature stage, and (3) dissipating stage. All thunderstorms develop from cumulus clouds, like those fleecy, white, harmless-looking, pillowy forms of considerable vertical dimension, typically associated with fair weather. A thunderstorm may only occur when such a cloud grows in depth, with the strengthening of updrafts that begin near the ground and sweep skyward, often at a velocity of more than 3000 feet per minute, thrusting the top of the cloud to well over 25,000 feet above sea level. Its diameter may be roughly 3 miles in the earliest stage. In this early cumulus stage, air within the cloud is everywhere warmer than the surrounding air at the same altitude. Since, even in its

[4] U.S. Weather Bureau, *The Thunderstorm, Report of the Thunderstorm Project*, 1949.

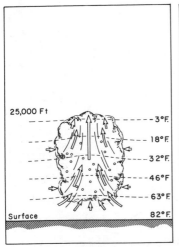
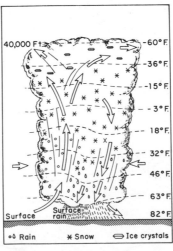
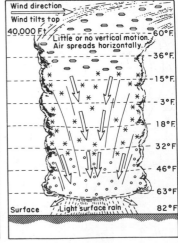

Figure 5.18. Schematic diagrams of three stages in the development of a thunderstorm cell. [U.S. Weather Bureau]

Figure 5.19. Three photographs of a burgeoning thunderstorm cloud in Arizona. Taken at five-minute intervals, beginning with the bottom photograph. [Institute of Atmospheric Physics, The University of Arizona]

beginning stage, a thundercloud reaches high altitudes where temperatures are well below freezing, condensation readily takes place and tends to produce liquid rain at lower levels and frozen flakes of snow above. Many droplets remain liquid, however, despite very low temperatures, when whirled rapidly upward in the strong convectional circulation of the thunderstorm cell (Figs. 5.18 and 5.19).

It is the continued upward sweep of warm, moist air from near ground level that nourishes the growing cumulus cloud in its first stage of development. As more and more droplets of moisture, flakes of snow, and tiny crystals of ice accumulate in the predominantly upward movement of air in the cloud at this stage, they gradually gain sufficient mass and weight to fall earthward, helping to create a downdraft of air and bringing the first few drops of rain to the ground below. Snow and ice, except in very cold weather, melt before reaching the ground.

When the first spattering of raindrops and the first gusts of cool air are felt by the observer on the ground, the mature stage is said to begin. This is a characteristic of thunderstorms well known to people of the rainy mid-latitudes. On a particularly hot afternoon it is one of the benefits a thunderstorm brings. Another is the release of nitrogen from the air by lightning. It is borne to the earth with the rain and amounts to a gain of around 100 million tons of fixed nitrogen for the entire world each year. This is important because fixed nitrogen, carried into the ground by percolating water and thus made available for absorption by the roots of plants, is essential to plant growth. These advantages are offset by the destructive effects of strong gusts of wind that frequently reach velocities in excess of 60 miles per hour at the surface, and the damage caused by lightning, which accounts for over five hundred deaths and millions of dollars in property damage in the United States alone each year.

During the mature stage an individual thunderstorm cell commonly contains liquid raindrops in its lower levels, mixed rain and snow above, and snow mixed with ice crystals at its higher levels. At this stage turbulence within the cloud is greatest, and updrafts are usually strongest, attaining a velocity of more than 5000 feet per minute and carrying minute drops of water toward the top of the cloud and hence well into the zone of subfreezing temperatures.

It is under these circumstances that hailstones may form, although they do not develop in every thunderstorm. Hailstones that fall from a thundercloud are drops of water that have been whirled swiftly upward into the farther, frigid reaches of the cloud, are then dropped, then whirled aloft again and again until they have become pellets of ice finally large and heavy enough to fall to the ground. They usually melt before they can be examined carefully, but many measure up to an inch in diameter, and some, evidently kept in rapid flight much longer than usual, have been reported as much as 3 inches.

The mature stage is distinguished, then, by swift vertical currents of air—strong updrafts buoying up the growing, multiplying particles of moisture and strong downdrafts which accompany their eventual fall to earth—by heavy showers, and by the soaring, seething growth of the dark cloud mass. Most of all, it is distinguished by a display of lightning and thunder. The thundercloud now towers up to 40,000 feet and beyond, or more than 8 miles above the earth, and may have a rough diameter of about 5 miles (Fig. 5.19).

Lightning is the consequence of a change in the normal electrical field between the earth and the atmosphere. The earth in fair weather is negative, the atmosphere positive. As a thundercloud rises to heights where its uppermost reaches are cooled to something below $-4°F$, those levels that have a temperature in the neighborhood of $15°F$ become positively charged, while just below them is warmer air (between $15°F$ and freezing) that is negative. This reverses the normal atmosphere-to-earth relationship, giving the ground a postive charge with respect to the intermediate negative layers of the thundercloud (Fig. 5.20).

The first strokes of lightning in a developing thundercloud usually take place between the two differently charged layers within the cloud itself. Later, as electrical energy increases from the accelerating turbulence and moisture accumulation of the growing cloud, it is released to the earth and to other clouds in long streaks of brilliant white or rosy fire. Thunder, which follows the flash, is believed to result from the sudden expansion of air subjected to the tremendous heat of electrical energy transmission.

During the mature stage rain, downward

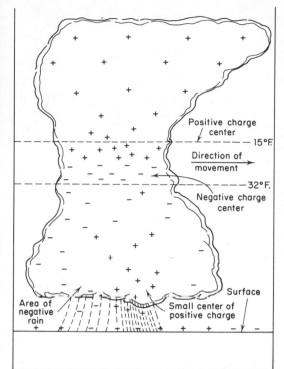

Figure 5.20. Reversal of normal electrical field between the earth and the atmosphere within a mature thunderstorm cloud. [U.S. Weather Bureau]

gusts of cool air, thunder, and lightning, occur with mounting intensity. Upward movement diminishes, and downdrafts finally predominate within the entire cell. At this point the final, dissipating stage is said to be reached. With the continuation of downdrafts rain, thunder, and lightning decrease, and the thunderstorm gradually ceases. Before the end of the dissipating stage, however, the thundercloud may extend as high as 60,000 feet. Very often it will have been tilted, and its lofty top may be swept rapidly downwind on the high speed currents of the upper air to produce the anvil-shaped cumulonimbus form that is characteristic of the storm's final stage (Figs. 5.18 and 5.19).

The life history of thunderstorms is not everywhere the same. The Thunderstorm Project revealed that such disturbances in the Midwest develop, mature, and dissipate very often within the space of an hour, although they may endure for twice this long, especially as the result of prolonged maturity. The Project also revealed that these storms seem to

develop, at least in mid-latitudes, over low mountains, regions of rugged relief, and over surface features like islands and peninsulas, which act as special sources of radiational and convective warmth for the air in contrast to the cooling influence of water surfaces adjoining them.

In general, it may be said that the latent heat of uplifted moisture is the fuel, so to speak, with which a thunderstorm must constantly be supplied. Where warm, moisture-laden air is present, therefore, along with some means of producing strong updrafts, a thunderstorm may develop. Hence the great preponderance of thunderstorms over tropical regions throughout the year, and in the humid mid-latitudes in summertime.

At this point let us return to the broader topic of cyclonic storms. Commanding far greater interest than its prosaic counterpart, the migrating cyclone of middle latitudes, is the tropical cyclone, out of which may be born the destructive hurricane of the West Indies, typhoon of the China seas, baguio of the Philippines, willy-willy of tropical Australia, and cyclone of the Bay of Bengal and the Arabian Sea. All are but different names for the same type of violent tropical storm (Fig. 5.21).

Not all tropical cyclones are violent storms, however; although some two hundred or more cyclonic disturbances are thought to occur over tropical lands and seas each year, only a fraction of these reach destructive intensity. A score or more may reach hurricane force in a single year.

Furthermore, not all storms of the tropics are large cyclonic ones, for we have seen that the smaller tornado occurs in parts of southeast Asia and Brazil and that thunderstorms, most of which are convectional, are more numerous in the tropics than anywhere else in the world.

HURRICANES.   The largest of the powerfully circulating cyclones of the tropics are the most dangerous of all the storms of the earth. The term *hurricane* has a meaning as excitingly ominous to people of eastern North America and the West Indies as *typhoon* does in the densely populated regions of the East Indies and southeast Asia. Not even the more violent tornado is as widely feared, for its effects are confined to a very much smaller area, and the loss of life and property is usually much less.

The destruction caused by a hurricane results

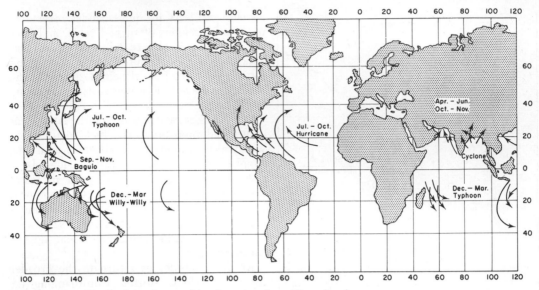

Figure 5.21. Distribution of normal hurricane tracks, with regional names.

not only from the compounded effects of its very high winds, huge storm waves, exceptionally high tides, and heavy rains, but also from its great size, which may extend over an area of 500,000 square miles when the storm has reached maturity.

It is certainly true, in contrast to most tornadoes, that a mature hurricane is far too large

Figure 5.22. A large tropical storm over the Marshall Islands, viewed from Gemini V around noon on August 27, 1965, from an altitude of about 150 miles. Storm center is about 400 miles from the spacecraft and ranges from 300 to 450 miles in diameter. [NASA photo]

to be fully visible at one time from the earth. But because of recent advances in observational technique, it is possible to isolate and discuss the salient characters of a severe tropical cyclone. The most dramatic invention for observing the hurricane is the Television and Infra-Red Observation Satellite (*Tiros*), the first of which was launched into orbit by the United States Aeronautics and Space Administration on April 1, 1960. This vehicle, about the size and shape of a large bass drum, carries two television cameras and radiation-sensing instruments at a mean altitude of about 475 miles, encircling the earth about fourteen and one-half times every twenty-four hours, taking thirty-two pictures on each orbit. By this means, man for the first time is able to view extensive areas of cloud cover from above (Fig. 5.22). *Tiros* has already detected the existence of tropical cyclonic storms that had otherwise escaped notice, simply by portraying the circular cloud patterns over remote regions of the sea where surface observations are lacking.

A hurricane is in some respects like a swirling eddy in a flowing stream of water. It is a large, circling whirlpool of the atmosphere that takes shape in the steady flow of the trades and is borne along on the currents of their westward course. Roughly circular in form, it often has a diameter of 400 or 500 miles (Fig. 5.23). Its approach is heralded by the appearance of long

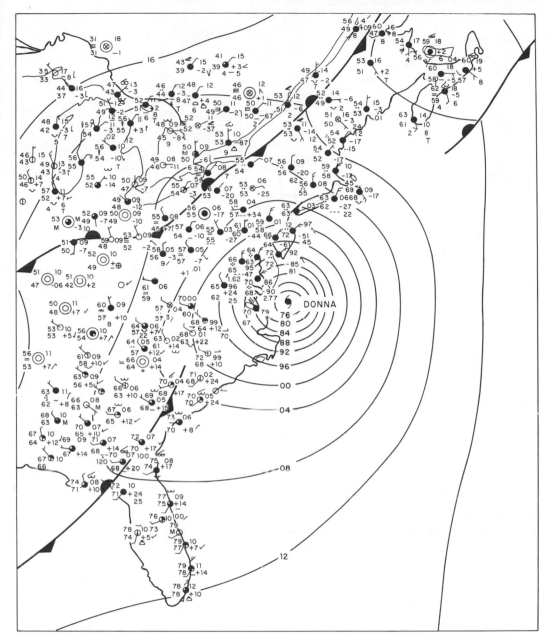

Figure 5.23. Hurricane "Donna" as it appeared on the surface weather chart for September 12, 1960. [U.S. Weather Bureau]

lines of high, divergent clouds above and more dense, altostratus clouds below that gradually merge as the storm draws nearer in a solid, sullen overcast and eventually bring heavy rains. The clouds at middle and upper levels of the hurricane are carried away from the center by outflowing winds at these altitudes (Fig. 5.24). Winds at the surface, however, blow with increasing strength from the perimeter toward the center of the storm, accelerating to speeds of 72 to 100 miles per hour[5] around the center, often blowing steadily at 150 miles per hour, with gusts up to 200 miles per hour or more. Around the center these converging winds

[5] See Beaufort Scale, Chapter 4, Table 4-1.

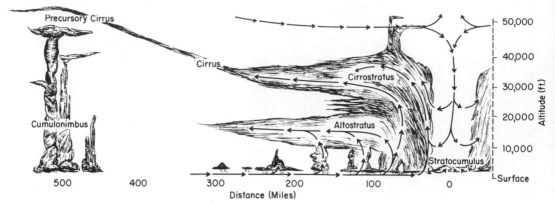

Figure 5.24. Cross section of a hurricane's internal circulation.

revolve in a tremendous upward-spiraling vortex which is the peak of the storm's intensity, producing the energy, as one author has expressed it,[6] of several thousand atomic bombs.

The center, or eye, of this huge atmospheric eddy is a roughly circular region of calms and light, variable winds, usually having a diameter of from 10 to 30 miles, sometimes more. It is funnel-shaped, its steep, cloud-banked sides rising to heights of 35,000 or 40,000 feet or more, surrounding a cloudless, roughly cylindrical space at the base of which are often broken, drifting, stratocumulus clouds that rise only a mile or so above the sea. Surface rainfall in the center is commonly light or absent, in sharp contrast to the torrential downpours of the surrounding areas. Sea level barometric pressure within the eye of the storm is very low, the lowest reading of record being 886.8 millibars (26.19 inches) made aboard ship during a typhoon east of the Philippines in 1927. Temperature within the roaring, rainy mass of the storm remains characteristically lower than that of the region through which it passes, but it rises with remarkable suddenness to a maximum within the eye. Humidity, which is typically very high throughout the storm, suddenly drops within the center, where the rains cease or at least are sharply diminished.

The eye of a hurricane seldom passes directly over a well-equipped weather station, but it has done so often enough that the atmospheric

changes of a few such storms have been observed and recorded. One of these was the passing of a typhoon across Manila on October 20, 1882. Figure 5.25 is a diagram of the changes in temperature, pressure, humidity, and wind velocity that took place.

The lull that accompanies the passing of a hurricane's calm center over populated areas is one of the truly treacherous aspects of the storm. Loss of life is often greater than it might otherwise be when a large number of persons abandon shelter to examine the damage done

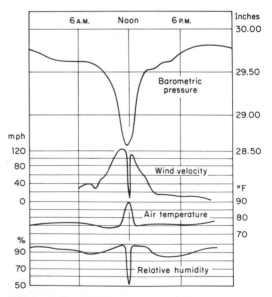

Figure 5.25. Changes in barometric pressure, wind speed, temperature, and relative humidity during the passage of a typhoon over Manila on October 20, 1882. [After Tannehill]

[6] R. H. Simpson, "Hurricanes," *Scientific American*, **190**(6): 32–37, June 1954.

in the storm's first phase, unaware that further gales are in store and will approach from a new direction. In the northern hemisphere the winds of a hurricane revolve in a counterclockwise direction. Thus, strong winds blow from the northeast and east as the center approaches. Suddenly abating with the passage of the eye, they freshen again, but now from a northwest or westerly direction as the trailing portions of the cyclone arrive, and a new threat to life and property is at hand.

Although strong winds constitute a great part of the danger from a well-developed tropical cyclone, much more destruction and a larger number of deaths result from the inundation of coastal areas by storm waves and tides. Over three quarters of the deaths in tropical cyclones are attributable to coastal inundations, especially when they have occurred along certain densely populated shores of southeast Asia. But here a distinction must be made.

The hurricane wave is a consequence of the piling up of water generally within the central area of the storm and is partly due to the confinement of water by the force of the encircling winds. As the storm center approaches a coast, it brings with it masses of water, raising the sea level along the shorelines from 10 to 20 feet above normal. High tides, on the other hand, begin long before the storm center arrives and continue until after it has passed. These are the result of the temporary currents developed over a wide area by the steady force of surface winds revolving in a huge vortex around the center. Such currents drive thousands of tons of sea water against a coast with steady, persistent force, causing particularly great damage along gently sloping shorelines like those of southern New England and the Ganges delta region of India and eastern Pakistan.

Inland, the most destructive effects of a hurricane are the floods resulting from the torrential rains that accompany the storm.

The valley lowlands of southern New England have twice in seventeen years experienced devastating floods caused by the heavy downpour of hurricane rains, once in 1938 and again in August 1955. In 1938,

New England had been experiencing heavy rainfall on September 18, 19, and 20, and streams were bank full when the rain associated with the hurricane brought the total rainfall during a 4-day period to a maximum of about 17 inches in certain limited areas and to an average of more than 11.5 inches over an area of 10,000 square miles.

Thus the great storm wave that swept inland along the shores of Connecticut and Rhode Island coincident with the passing of the hurricane on the afternoon of September 21 was followed by a wave of floods in all the stream channels on the timbered slopes of the New England hills and in the larger rivers, inundating, destroying, or damaging all within the flood plains. Generally by the evening of September 23 the flood waters had passed into the Atlantic Ocean.[7]

Estimates of the damage to property in the northeastern states caused by the August hurricane of 1955, the fourth of that season, called *Diane*, amounted to nearly $1 billion. Around ninety lives were lost. The worst damage was suffered in the heavily populated valleys of Connecticut, where about 14 inches of rain fell on the watersheds of the principal streams in a space of thirty-six hours on August 19 and 20, producing flash floods that destroyed or severely damaged the business heart of more than a dozen valley communities.

The precise causes of tropical cyclones are not known. According to recent studies, however, tropical cyclones originate only over warm water surfaces, generally between 5 and 15 degrees of the equator. A water temperature of 82° is thought to be necessary. The other special circumstances under which these storms develop are believed to include a highly unstable condition within the usually steady trades, marked by the presence of strong convectional activity, and an abundance of atmospheric moisture. It has been suggested that these conditions occur very often during the passage of a broad wave or undulation in the over-all pressure distribution at higher levels of the troposphere. The effect of local heat sources and surface frictional drag is also deemed important. The regional importance of tropical disturbances is dealt with more fully in a later chapter on tropical climates.

Once under way, a tropical cyclone that is constantly nourished by warm, moist air grows in size and intensity, moving over the tropical

---

[7] U.S. Department of the Interior, U.S.G.S. *Water Supply Paper*, No. 867, 1940, p. 2.

oceans at from 10 to 15 miles per hour, and in response to the Coriolis effect, curving gradually away from the equator. Except in the Indian Ocean tropical cyclones north of the equator often continue on a right-curving trajectory into the middle latitude zones of predominantly westerly winds, where they may recurve toward the northeast, and, with diminishing intensity, eventually disappear in the cooler regions of those latitudes. Their loss of vigor seems to arise from a diminished supply of warm, moist air. This is also true when tropical cyclones pass into the interior of North America or eastern Asia and thus leave behind the main sources of such air. The cyclones of the Bay of Bengal and the Arabian Sea, which occur chiefly during the onshore, summer monsoon, usually develop a northward trajectory that is considerably shorter than those of the storms in the Atlantic or the western Pacific.

Records indicate that the largest and most powerful tropical cyclones are the typhoons of the western Pacific. Next in size and destructive force are those of the West Indies, and third in order of violence are the cyclones of the Indian Ocean.

Tropical storms south of the equator are generally less violent than those of northern latitudes, and there is no record at all, for some reason as yet unknown, of destructive tropical storms in either the eastern Pacific or the Atlantic south of the equator. Furthermore, few if any such storms have been known to develop within 5 degrees of the equator. All seem to originate at some distance from the equator within the steady currents of the trades

and the persistent onshore flow of the summer monsoon of the Indian Ocean.

Tropical cyclones also show a strong seasonal preference. The latter part of the summer is the season when destructive tropical storms occur with greatest frequency. August, September, and October are the months when hurricanes strike most often in the region of the West Indies and the Caribbean. The frequency of occurrence diminishes rather sharply before and after this season, although violent storms have been observed as early as May and as late as December. Approximately the same seasonal preference is true of storms along the Pacific coast of Mexico and Central America, the western Pacific, and the northern Indian Ocean. South of the equator, both in the western Pacific and Indian oceans, the season extends from November or December to April or May, with greatest concentration toward the latter part of the warm period.

Despite its frequently disastrous effects, the hurricane, like the thunderstorm and tornado, is the source of large volumes of rain that fall on sometimes thirsty soil, and in this respect they may be considered beneficial. Otherwise, the violent tropical cyclone, the thunderstorm, and the tornado are the most hazardous consequences of the secondary circulation.

In this chapter we have seen that within the larger movements of the general circulation occur certain events that we can speak of as the secondary circulation, in which the development of air masses, frontal zones of contact, migrating cyclones, anticyclones, and storms are the most striking features.

References

BATTAN, L. J.: *The Nature of Violent Storms*, Doubleday & Co., Inc., New York, 1961.

FLORA, S. D.: *Tornadoes of the United States*, University of Oklahoma Press, Norman, Okla., 1953.

RIEHL, H.: "On the Origin and Possible Modification of Hurricanes," *Science*, 141: 1000–1010, 1963.

TANNEHILL, I. R.: *Hurricanes*. Princeton University Press, Princeton, N.J., 1952.

U.S. WEATHER BUREAU: *Principal Tracks and Mean Frequencies of Cyclones and Anticyclones in the Northern Hemisphere*, (Res. Paper No. 40), 1957.

————: *The Thunderstorm, Report of the Thunderstorm Project*, 1949.

chapter 6

WORLD CLIMATIC PATTERNS
AND MODIFYING INFLUENCES

The purpose of this chapter is to examine more fully the earth's fundamental relationship with the sun, particularly the manner in which this relationship is influenced by certain properties peculiar to the earth's surface. We shall examine world patterns of sunshine duration, solar radiation intensity, temperature, and precipitation and consider modifying influences that produce the actual distribution of discrete and identifiable climates. The material to follow is thus a further elaboration of the basic theme of Chapter 3, that climate is a consequence of the motions of the earth.

The earth, in its annual orbit around the sun, is exposed to a quantity of sunlight that is very nearly the same from one year to another. Were it not for the variable amounts of cloud cover and inclement weather that intervene in a random way to obscure the light of the sun, yearly amounts would for all practical purposes be exactly the same. Thus it is common practice to speak of possible sunshine as the length of day in hours and minutes from sunrise to sunset. The number of hours and minutes of actual observed sunshine during a given day is expressed as the per cent of possible sunshine. On February 23, 1963, for example, New Haven, Conn., recorded 100 per cent of possible sunshine, while on February 24, the value was 17 per cent.[1] During the entire month of February

1963 New Haven averaged 67 per cent of possible sunshine, compared with 29 per cent at Mt. Washington, N.H., whose lofty summit is frequently enshrouded in cloud when clear, sunny skies prevail elsewhere.[2] The percentage of possible sunshine actually received is the corollary of cloud amounts observed during daylight hours. It is thus useful to have a record of either one or the other for comparative purposes in climatological study. For example, at Sacramento, a station in the Central Valley of California, summer's predominantly sunny weather was recorded in 1961 by the fact that July averaged 97 per cent of possible sunshine. In January of the preceding winter, on the other hand, an average of only 41 per cent was recorded, suggesting the predominantly cloudy, rainy weather of that season.

It is plain that the amount of possible sunshine for any day at any latitude can be calculated with good accuracy. This value is commonly expressed as the length of day, in hours and minutes (Fig. 6.1). The annual amount of possible sunshine can also be worked out from these figures, an indication of the comparative potential sunshine from latitude to latitude between the equator and the poles.

[1] U.S. Weather Bureau, *Local Climatological Data for New Haven, Connecticut*, 1963.
[2] U.S. Weather Bureau, *Climatological Data for New England, February, 1963*, **75**(2): 37.

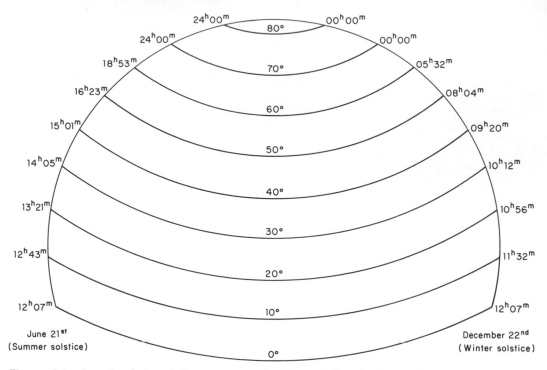

Figure 6.1. Length of day at the summer and winter solstices in the northern hemisphere.

Figure 6.2. Mean annual temperature for the world.   [After Koeppe and De Long]

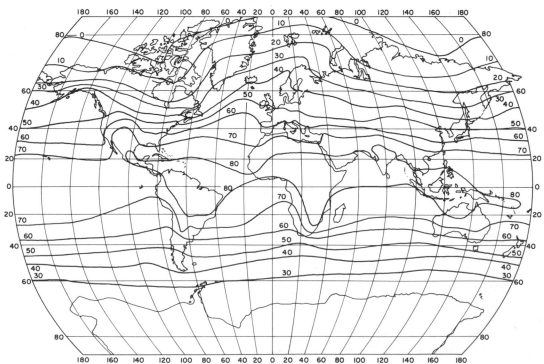

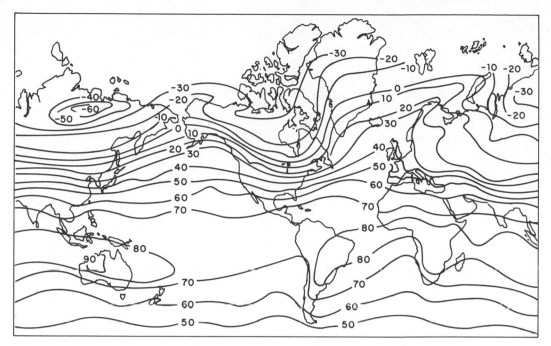

Figure 6.3.   Mean January temperature for the world.

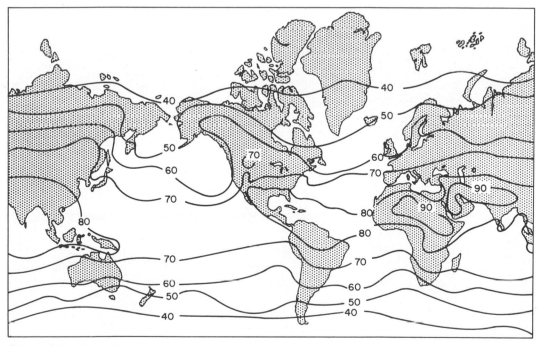

Figure 6.4.   Mean July temperature for the world.

Of even greater significance is the average amount of radiant energy from the sun received at the earth's surface. Figure 3.1 shows the amounts, in gram calories per square centimeter per day (gm cal/cm²/day), for the equator, for 40°, and for 80°, illustrating the nearly uniform intensity at the equator compared with the marked seasonal fluctuations in the middle latitudes and the polar regions.

The primary relationship thus described between the earth and the sun gives rise, as expected, to continuously high air temperatures near the equator and gradually colder conditions toward the poles. If the earth possessed a level surface composed entirely of a single, solid substance, temperatures would range evenly from hot to cold in parallel zones between the equator and the poles. In like fashion, the pattern of climates would consist of an even gradation from the equator to the poles. That such an arrangement does not exist is mainly a consequence of the following conditions: (1) The earth's surface is part land (about 29 per cent) and part water (about 71 per cent). (2) Land and water areas are unequal in size, shape, and distribution. (3) Land surfaces are diverse in altitude and configuration. (4) The earth's

rotation produces a special influence upon moving bodies called the Coriolis effect (described in Chapter 4), causing currents of air and of water to deflect toward the right in the northern hemisphere and toward the left in the southern hemisphere.

A world map of the distribution of annual temperatures (Fig. 6.2) reveals the unevenness of effective heat from the sun. Still, it should be remarked that the isotherms are approximately parallel to the equator in higher latitudes, suggesting the theoretical possibility of a uniform temperature gradation on a hypothetically uniform surface between the poles and the equator. Figures 6.3 and 6.4 portray the world distribution of isotherms for January and July, again revealing the unequal distribution of heat at the earth's surface at the times of the year when the sun is highest overhead. Figure 6.5 shows the mean annual range of temperature for the world as a whole, and once again the striking contrasts from place to place within the same latitudes are evident. Mean annual temperature range is a most important climatic value, a meaningful key to climatic character, as we shall see in the later chapters on specific climates.

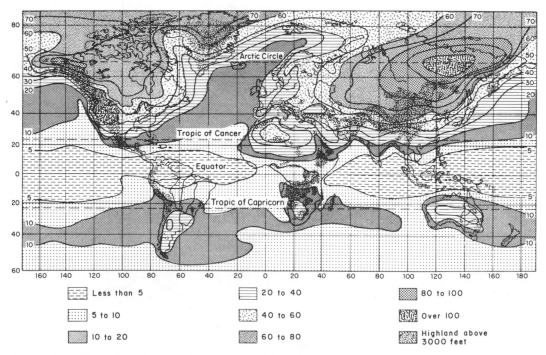

Figure 6.5. Mean annual temperature range for the world.

LAND AND WATER REACTIONS TO HEAT.   Solar energy is of such high temperature and such short wavelength that only a small amount (about 14 per cent) is taken up during its passage through the atmosphere to the earth's more substantial surface. There it is either reflected without appreciably changing the temperature of the reflecting surface or is absorbed and raises the temperature of the absorbing surface. In this process solar energy is transformed into lower-temperature, longer-wavelength energy that is then reradiated into the atmosphere, and in its changed form is the chief source of atmospheric heating.

But surfaces react differently to the effects of insolation. It seems probable that absorption takes place to an almost equal degree, although not at an equal rate, on both the land and water surfaces of the earth. Conversely, both land and water seem to have nearly equal powers of solar energy reflection. This near concordance is evident from the data in Table 6-1.

TABLE 6–1

Percentage of Solar Radiation Absorbed by Various Surfaces

Surface	Percentage of Absorption
Oceanic water	98
Bays, lakes, and rivers	90–95
Coniferous forest	90–95
Broadleaf forest	90
Green, grassy meadows	85–90
Black, dry soil	85–90
Dry, light-colored sand	80–85
Dry, grassy meadows	75–85
Dry, plowed fields	75–80
Snow	10–20

However, an examination of Table 6-1 reveals that different kinds of terrestrial surfaces— forest, green fields, plowed fields, snow—possess varying capacities for absorbing solar energy. Naturally, the angle of incidence is important, and while no set value is assumed in these computations, the sun's elevation is considered to be at least 15 degrees. The values given are, of course, approximate and hopefully will be refined by future experimentation. The most important consideration, not evident from the table, is the difference in the way water

disposes of absorbed solar energy in comparison with the reaction of solid materials on land.

Solar heat that reaches the wave-tossed surface of the world's oceans is disposed of in several ways. The largest amount of energy, variously estimated at from 50 to 65 per cent, is consumed in the evaporation of surface water and is not available for raising its temperature. This energy is borne aloft on rising currents of vapor-laden air and is released ultimately in the form of heat when moisture condenses at cloud level. Evaporation, basically a cooling process, also increases the salinity and hence the density of surface water, causing it to descend toward the depths, thereby conveying a certain amount of heat to lower levels. This process is called thermohaline convection. Especially important is the fact that the specific heat of water is greater than that of land. That is, about two and one-half times as much heat is required to raise the temperature of a volume of water 1 degree Celsius than to raise the temperature of an equal volume of dry, sandy soil by the same amount.

Another method by which the heat is distributed in water is the ceaseless turbulence of the oceans' upper layers. Most of the heat of insolation is effective in only the top few centimeters of water, despite the fact that the sun's rays may be visible at depths of several hundred feet in clear ocean water. This is simply because the longer heat rays of the solar spectrum do not penetrate transparent water even though light rays do. Rippled and wave-tossed by the wind, rising and falling with the endless rhythm of the tides, warmed surface water is constantly mixed with deeper layers by turbulence or dynamical convection, an effect thought to penetrate to a depth of around 650 feet in the open ocean, perhaps much more, and somewhat less deeply in large lakes and land-locked seas. Also important in the transfer of heat within large water bodies are the slower, more majestic movements of both horizontal and vertical currents. Thus, by its many motions, water transmits to considerable depths the heat of its sun-warmed surface. Large water bodies hence act as reservoirs of heat, their temperature rising slowly during periods of maximum insolation and decreasing slowly when insolation is at a minimum.

In sharp contrast to this is the heat response of solid substances on land. The surface of the ground, warmed by the sun's rays, transmits by conduction part of the heat it absorbs toward the cooler material beneath. But soil is a poor conductor, and normally only the top 4 inches undergo a marked daily change in temperature. Slight daily changes have been observed as deep as 3 feet, and small annual changes have been measured at the mid-latitude city of Potsdam, Germany, as deep as 47 feet. But because the effect of the sun's warmth is mainly confined to the top few inches of solid material, the volume heated is relatively small. Accordingly, the daily temperature rise of soil is relatively large. And when, as the sun drops below the horizon, its source of warmth disappears, the ground rapidly loses the heat it has gained during the day. Hence the diurnal temperature change on land is very much larger than that in water. Annual temperature change is also much greater.

Because the atmosphere is heated chiefly by the transmission of warmth from the earth's surface, the air above land also undergoes larger daily and seasonal temperature changes than air over water exposed to the same amount of insolation. These differences (Fig. 6.5) are especially noticeable between the tropics and the polar regions, where the maximum change in effective insolation takes place.

The variety of surface material on land leads to still further variations in the heating of the overlying atmosphere. Table 6-1 reveals, for example, that snow absorbs only a fraction of the solar heat taken in by the coniferous forests. Something between 80 and 90 per cent of the sun's radiant energy is reflected back into space from snow-covered surfaces as short wave light rays and is not converted into long wave radiation, hence is not available for warming the atmosphere above it.

THE UNEQUAL SIZE, SHAPE, AND DISTRIBUTION OF LAND AND WATER AREAS. North of the equator a much larger percentage of the earth's surface (Fig. 6.5) is land than in the southern hemisphere, which is mainly water, and north latitude lands converge poleward almost to surround the icy wastes of the Arctic Ocean. In contrast, the continents of Africa and South America narrow toward the south pole, and their southernmost reaches, and those of Australia, are widely separated from one another and from the ice-covered continent of Antarctica by the continuous water surface of

the South Atlantic, Pacific, and Indian oceans. Thus the greatest variety of climate, and with few exceptions the larger tracts of particular climates, are found on the broader expanses of land in North America, north Africa, and Eurasia. This is plain from an examination of a map of climatic regions (Fig. 7.1), on which may be seen, for example, the larger proportions of desert lands, mid-latitude forest lands, and mountain lands north of the equator. It should also be noted that the boreal forest and tundra are exclusively climates of the northern hemisphere, although they appear as fractional portions of undifferentiated mountain climates on both sides of the equator.

Because water bodies and hence the air above them undergo temperature changes slowly, they exert a moderating effect upon the temperature change of adjacent lands. This is true of coastal areas in all latitudes from the equator to the poles to some extent, but it is more pronounced along the shores of mid-latitude lands lying roughly between the Tropics and the polar circles. It is most evident along their western seaboards, which are constantly invaded, through the strong, generally eastward movement of the atmosphere in these latitudes, by a persistent flow of moist, temperate, maritime air. The less pronounced maritime effect upon the eastern shores of mid-latitude lands arises from the fact that westerly winds bring air from continental interiors that is drier and has considerable temperature variation both from day to day and from season to season. The moderating effects of large water bodies upon adjacent lands is usually termed marine influence, in contradistinction to the effects stemming from a position remote from large expanses of water, which, for large land masses, is commonly called a continental influence. From the widespread development of this concept, the terms *marine climate* and *continental climate* have come into common use.

In general, it may be said that maritime locations tend to receive a more equitable yearly distribution of rainfall and to experience smaller variations in both daily and yearly temperature. But one must note the great difference between east and west coast marine climates in the mid-latitudes. West coasts tend to experience much lower temperature variability than east coasts and to receive a major proportion of the year's rainfall in the winter

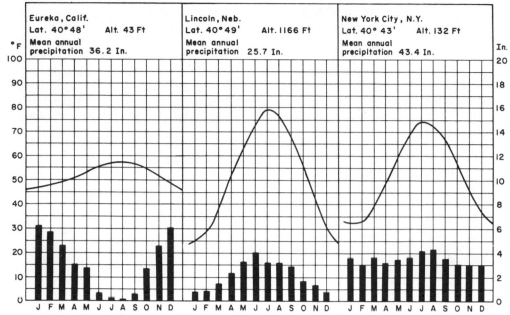

Figure 6.6. Normal monthly temperature and precipitation at a west coast marine station, a continental interior station, and an east coast marine station along the same latitude in the northern hemisphere.

months, whereas eastern seaboard areas receive a greater proportion of rain in summertime. These generalizations are illustrated in Figure 6.6, showing temperature and rainfall for Eureka, Calif., Lincoln, Neb., and New York City, all in approximately the same latitude.

It will be noted in Figure 6.6 that the mean annual range of temperature at Eureka is only 10 degrees (47° in January and 57° in August) and that the warmest month is August. At Lincoln, however, the mean annual range is 54 degrees (25° to 79°), and the warmest month is July. The modified marine/continental climate of New York is indicated by a mean annual range of 43 degrees (32° in February and 75° in July), and here the coldest month is February. Continental climatic stations normally experience a wide mean annual temperature range, and January and July are always the extreme months. At marine stations summers are cool and winters are mild (above freezing), and the moderating effect of the adjacent sea delays the cooling and warming process so that February and August are usually the extreme months. Yearly rainfall at continental stations in the mid-latitudes increases greatly during the warmer half-year, when 60 to 80 per cent of the annual increment may normally be expected.

But at west coast marine stations the regime is reversed. The mixed temperature-rainfall regimes at New York reflect the combined effects of continental influences from the west and marine influences from the nearby Atlantic.

Examples of similar climatic differences will be presented in later chapters for the middle latitude portions of Eurasia, South America, and Australia. The annual range of temperature is larger where protection from the moderating influence of oceanic air is most effective. Thus, distance from the sea is most important. We observe (Fig. 6.5) that the annual temperature range in eastern Siberia is greater than anywhere else on earth: at Verkhoyansk (67°32′N. Lat.), about 250 miles from the Arctic Ocean on the upper Yana River, a mean annual range of 118 degrees prevails, from 59° in July to −59° in January. In North America the greatest mean annual range recorded was 83 degrees, at Fort Good Hope (66°15′N. Lat.), Northwest Territories, on the lower Mackenzie River about 250 miles from the Arctic Ocean.

The lower temperature variations in the southern hemisphere are a result of the smaller size and distribution of land areas and the consequent preponderance of moderating oceanic air south of the equator.

THE DIVERSITY OF ALTITUDE AND SURFACE CONFIGURATION ON LAND. It will be recalled (Chapter 2) that a major part of the atmosphere's mass and most of the climatically significant changes in temperature, pressure, movement, and moisture content of air are found within a few miles above the earth's surface. With increasing altitude the temperature, weight, and humidity of air decrease, wind velocities increase, and the sun's rays, because they penetrate less of the air's mass, impart an increasing amount of heat by direct radiation. For these reasons differences in altitude result in a further variation of the world's climates.

A striking example of the effect of altitude upon temperature may be seen by comparing (Fig. 6.7) the average monthly temperature of

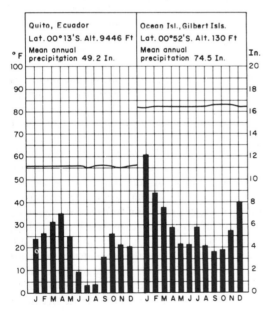

Figure 6.7. Normal monthly temperature and precipitation at an oceanic station at low altitude and an inland high altitude station, near the equator.

Quito, Ecuador (Lat. 0°13'S., Long. 78°30'W.) and Ocean Island (Lat. 0°52'S., Long. 169°35'E.). Although both stations are almost on the equator, Quito's altitude of 9350 feet explains its almost invariable monthly average temperature of 57°F, whereas Ocean Island, with a weather station elevation of 85 feet above sea level, has a nearly equitable monthly tempera-

ture of 82°F, a difference of 25 degrees. Differences in altitude also produce differences in precipitation, which are often strikingly apparent in mountainous country.

The broader influence of altitude upon climate in general is graphically illustrated by Frank Chapman's account[3] of a journey from the tropical Gulf coast of Mexico to the snowy upper slopes of Mt. Orizaba. Chapman's ascent to an altitude of more than 13,000 feet was made in April and took him through four distinct climatic belts.

Remarkable as is the railway journey from Vera Cruz to table-land, it must be remembered that the region has been settled for centuries and that the original forest has long since disappeared. To find primeval conditions one must therefore go some distance from the long-established railways. In my opinion the whole region may best be seen from Cordoba as a base. Cordoba, with an elevation of 2,700 feet, is near the upper edge of the humid Tropical Zone, and in an hour or two one may go by train to the heart of the tropics below or to the Temperate Zone above.... Finally, our work in the Tropical Zone completed, we turned our faces towards the snows of Orizaba or, to be more exact, toward the clouds of Orizaba, for in consequence of a norther which had prevailed for a week we had been surrounded by fog and drizzling rain, and the mountain had been invisible.... Mist and cloud obscured all but the nearby landscape. The trail was good, but as slippery as though soaped, and the animals fell with discouraging frequency. We were now in the Temperate Zone, a region favorable alike for man and maize, and hence so populous and cultivated that the original growth had long disappeared. The last mango trees and coffee plantations were left at 4,700 to 4,900, and at 5,000 feet the trail was bordered by great sycamores. Within the succeeding 500 feet we saw hawthorn blooming, wild ("rum") cherry trees with green fruit, poplars and oaks; and these trees, with willows, peaches, pears, apples, elderberries, huckleberries, and lupines, were characteristic of the zone through which we were travelling....

Toward mid-day the trail took the crest of the ridge between the deep Jamapa and Tlacatiopa

[3] Frank M. Chapman, "A Naturalist's Journey Around Vera Cruz and Tampico," *National Geographic Magazine*, **25**: 533–56, May 1914. By permission of the National Geographic Society.

barrancas. Dense clouds were below as well as above us. We seemed to be climbing a knife-edge through space. Reaching level ground on what might have been another planet, we camped for the night.

We awoke in the clouds, and all day they hung closely about us. Huts of hewn boards roofed with split shingles, without windows, and with an unhinged door leaning against their one opening, we passed at intervals.

At about 9,000 feet we reached the upper limit of corn, and in consequence the upper limit of human habitation. Beyond this point only goatherds and iceminers were encountered. At the same time we entered the outskirts of the coniferous forests of the Boreal Zone.

A few outlying short-leaved pines (*Pinus montezumae*) had been seen as low as 5,700 feet and the pine forests descended at least as low as 8,000 feet. At 9,300 feet we encountered the first spruce (*Abies religiosa*), convincing evidence of the boreal character of our surroundings, and at 9,500 feet we camped in a superb primeval forest of pines, spruce, and oak. The pines compared favorably in size with those of the California Sierras, while some of the oaks, locally termed "*encines*", we estimated to be 130 feet in height, with a basal diameter of six feet.

At night, enshrouded by the now chilly mist, we sat closely around our camp fire discussing the prospects of better weather, when, doubtless through a change in the direction of the wind, by us unnoticed, the clouds with surprising suddenness disappeared, and almost as quickly as one would turn on a light the once ghostly forest was brightly illuminated by the rays of a full moon!

The weather had cleared and in a manner which made the experience the most memorable one of our journey. The following morning was cloudless, and as a reminder that we were in the Tierra Fria the mercury stood at 31 degrees and ice formed in pools left by the rain. . . .

At 11,500 feet the last spruces were observed. At their timberline they were still large, vigorous trees and there was no apparent reason why they should not continue to appear for at least another thousand feet; but, if unseen, the law that controls their distribution was not the less potent. Shortly they were followed by the long-leaved pine (*Pinus liophylla*), and only the short-leaved pine reached the upper limit of tree-growth.

Camp was made at 12,600 feet, in an ill-selected spot, where, after sunset, the wind swept down off the great snowfields above us, and we could actually see the mercury in our thermometer fall. In 30 minutes it dropped 28 degrees from 48 to 20 and at 6 o'clock the following morning it registered 12 degrees. Lack of suitable clothing, though we prepared for reasonably cold weather, and the suddenness of the change, gave us, in spite of a camp fire, a realizing sense of what it means actually to suffer with cold. Six hours later the sun temperature was 112 degrees, and, suffering now from the heat, we endeavoured to adjust ourselves to a variation of 100 degrees in six hours.

. . . The men who passed our trail, it appeared, were on their way to the ice deposits near the head of the Jamapa barranca. This cutting of ice near the summit of Orizaba to take to the hot lands at its base is a primitive industry which appeals to one as an eminently practical demonstration of the effect of altitude on climate, and to see it practiced we followed the trail of the cheerful little men from the tropics.

Crossing rock slides where pikas would have been at home, we passed timberline, which on the northern slope of the barranca was at 13,000 feet, but on the southern slope appeared to be at least 800 feet higher. The short-leaved pine was the only tree occurring there, and to the last it stood erect, was symmetrical, and attained a height of about 30 or 40 feet, or about one-half of its maximum size.

In this account is suggested the vertical zoning of climates that results from differences in altitude and is a conspicuous quality of mountainous country everywhere except in the constantly ice-covered lands around the poles. But differences in altitude are not the only effects of topographic diversity on the earth. We read, in the last few lines of Chapman's account, that the timber line was at 13,000 feet on the north slope of the barranca and about 800 feet higher on the south slope. The south-facing (equatorward) slope is exposed to the direct rays of the sun in both summer and winter, but in winter the north slope is shaded. The south slope is therefore warmed directly by the sun to some extent during the entire year, thus the survival of forest trees at a higher altitude. A diversity of exposure to the sun's rays produces, in mountainous topography and even in hilly topography within high latitudes, variations in the broad pattern of vegetation and climatic zones.

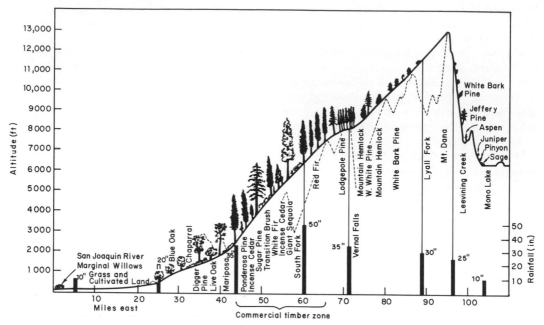

Figure 6.8. Vertical distribution of principal vegetation types on the slopes of the Sierra Nevada in California. [U.S. Department of Agriculture, *Yearbook of Agriculture,* 1949]

Another illustration of this effect is seen in the vertical arrangement of vegetation zones on the slopes of the Sierra Nevada (Fig. 6.8). Rising to more than 13,000 feet, over a dozen distinct plant zones may be identified between the base and the peak of the mountain.

Mountains also modify climates by creating what is commonly termed a rain shadow. This term is applied to the dry areas lying on the leeward side of mountains that stand in the path of rain-bearing winds. As moisture-laden air is borne up the windward side of a mountain it is dynamically cooled, and its moisture is condensed and released as orographic rain. The cooling effect of high altitude continues to produce rain even in the lee of the loftiest heights, but as air descends the leeward slopes, it brings much less rain to the earth. This is partly because it has lost most of its moisture at higher elevations, and partly because it has been warmed adiabatically during its descent and has thus increased its moisture-retaining capacity.

The rain shadow effect may be evident in any mountainous or even hilly country, but it is most striking where high mountains lie athwart

prevailing moisture-laden winds from the oceans. An example of this is found in the Sierra Nevada of California, whose gently rising flanks, intercepting the moist air from the Pacific, are well watered and heavily forested and stand out in contrast to the arid basin of Nevada in the lee of its steep, eastern slopes. On opposite sides of Mt. Olympus (el. 8150) in Washington the total annual rainfall is quite different. Quinault, 20 miles from the Pacific Ocean on the southwest flank, receives 128 inches each year, whereas Sequim, 60 miles away on the shores of the Strait of Juan de Fuca, northeast of the mountain and in the lee, has an average annual rainfall of only 16.81 inches. The mountainous island of Kauai in the Hawaiian group lies in the path of prevailing winds from the east and northeast, and though its highest peak is only 5113 feet above the sea, a rain shadow effect is created in which its windward slopes are everywhere amply watered and places southwest of its central heights are relatively dry. Kalihiwai Reservoir (el. 400), about 10 miles north-north-east of Mt. Waialeale (el. 5113), with 451.1 inches, has an annual rainfall of 100.44 inches, and at

Pali Trail (el. 850), about 12 miles southwest of Waialeale, less than 16 inches of rain is received during an average year.

Thus in many ways the surface irregularities of the earth, particularly mountainous areas, complicate the pattern of the world's climates. The scattered, unordered distribution of mountainous topography on the earth compounds the degree to which climatic diversity is present, a fact that is apparent from a comparison of a relief map of the world (Fig. 6.9) and the map of mean annual precipitation (Fig. 6.10).

THE CORIOLIS EFFECT. Like the major anticyclonic circulations that prevail much of the time over the eastern Atlantic and Pacific on both sides of the equator and the eastern Indian Ocean south of the equator, ocean currents too (Fig. 6.11) travel a circulatory course. As they are impelled primarily by the frictional force of winds against their surfaces, the ultimate cause of their sideward turning may also be traced to the Coriolis effect upon winds. Thus the broad North Equatorial Current of the Pacific is driven slowly westward by the steady effort of the northeast trades. Gradually turning northward, it flows gently past the islands of Japan and there becomes the Kuro Shio, or Japan Current, which slowly circles northeastward, bringing the warmth of tropical waters to mid-latitudes and finally, taking an eastward course, is urged on by winds from the west toward the shores of North America. Here it divides, a major branch reversing northwestward to wash the south coast of Alaska, another, losing its warmth on the way, turning southeastward along the California coast and there merging with upwelling water from the depths to form the cool California Current. These waters in turn are warmed as they enter the tropics to join the North Equatorial Current and thus complete the circle (Figs. 6.12 and 6.13).

In a similar fashion the North Equatorial Current of the Atlantic becomes the north-flowing Gulf Stream, then the North Atlantic Drift, one of whose several bifurcations eventually washes the shores of northwest Europe, moderating the air temperature of these lands, while another part of it turns southward and is lost in the cooler, upwelling water of the Canaries Current off northwest Africa.

Left-turning currents south of the equator, like the Brazil and East Australia currents, also transport warm water of tropical origin to middle latitudes, producing a corollary equatorward movement of cool water in the Peru and Benguela currents.

Climatic anomalies arising mainly from the circulatory movement of prevailing winds and ocean currents are evident in many parts of the world. An example may be taken from the sharply contrasting climates found on opposite

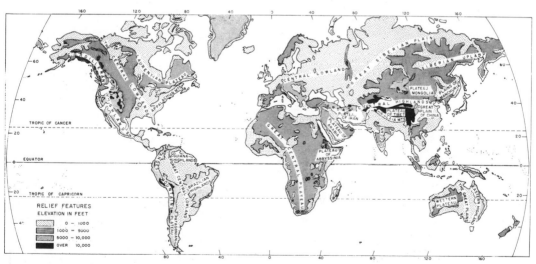

Figure 6.9. Major relief features of the world.

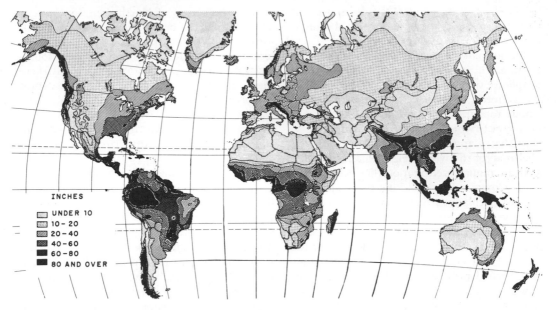

Figure 6.10. Distribution of mean annual precipitation (inches).

sides of South America in the latitude of the Tropic of Capricorn. The waterless desert of Atacama on the west coast may be compared to the humid, hot rainforest littoral of southern Brazil in the neighborhood of Rio de Janiero. Less than 1 inch of rain falls during an average year at Antofagasta (Lat. 23°31'S.), and its average temperature ranges from 57 to 70°F

(Fig. 6.14). The prevailing winds of the South Pacific circulation blow northward, for the most part parallel to the coast, over the relatively cool waters of the Peru Current that have a temperature of around 60°F. Rio de Janeiro (Lat. 23°00'S.), in contrast, receives more than 44 inches of rainfall annually, and its temperature averages about 10 degrees higher, from a

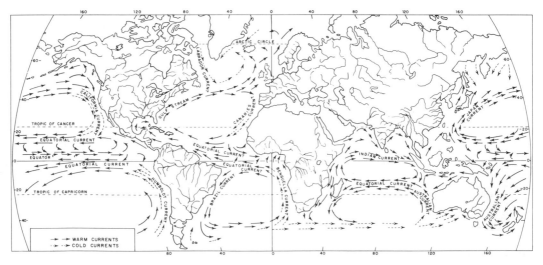

Figure 6.11. Distribution of major ocean currents.

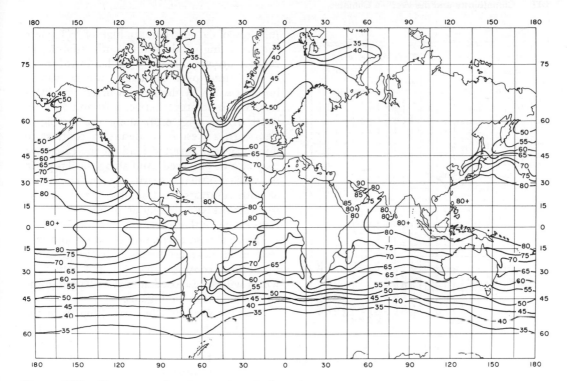

Figure 6.12. Mean sea surface temperatures in August.

Figure 6.13. Mean sea surface temperatures in February.

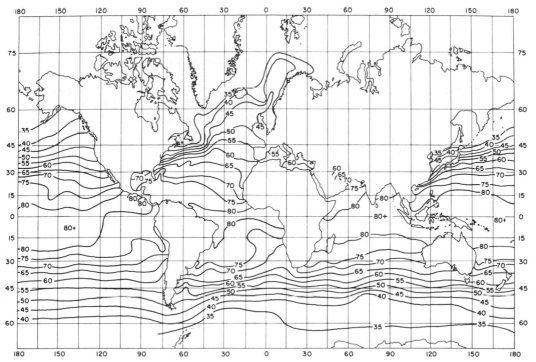

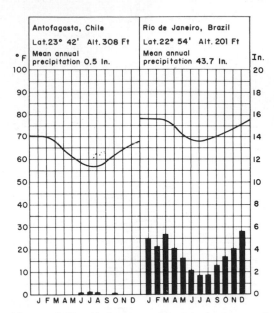

Figure 6.14. Normal monthly temperature and precipitation at stations on opposite sides of South America at the same latitude.

July low of 69° to a January high of 78°F. Here the prevailing winds of the South Atlantic circulation are variable but blow landward much of the time over relatively warm waters, brought south by the Brazil Current, having a surface temperature between 70 and 75°F. In South Africa (Fig. 6.10) along the Tropic of Capricorn a west coast desert in contrast to humid, warm, forested land on the east coast may also be observed. And along the Tropic in Australia a similar disparity is seen. The causes of both contrasts are traceable mainly to the counterclockwise circulation of winds and currents in the southern oceans.

The clockwise circulation of winds and currents in the northern hemisphere also gives rise to climatic contrasts (Fig. 7.1 in Chapter 7), which will be discussed at greater length in the chapters on climatic regions.

Thus the Coriolis effect, resulting from the earth's rotation, is another major cause of the many variations that appear within the broad pattern of the world's climates between the poles and the equator.

References

Budyko, M. I.: *The Heat Balance of the Earth's Surface*, trans. by N. A. Stepanova, U.S. Government Printing Office, 1958.

Chang, Jen-Hu: *Ground Temperature*, 2 vols., Harvard University Press, Milton, Mass., 1958.

Fritz, S.: "Solar Radiant Energy and Its Modification by the Earth and Its Atmosphere," *Compendium of Meteorology*, American Meteorological Society, Boston, 1951.

Houghton, H. G.: "On the Annual Heat Balance of the Northern Hemisphere," *Journal of Meteorology*, 11: 1–9, 1954.

Shear, J. A.: "The Polar Marine Climate," *Annals of the Association of American Geographers*, 54(3): 310–17, 1964.

chapter 7

THE CLASSIFICATION OF CLIMATES

A climate is a part of the earth where the qualities of the atmosphere, for a reasonably long period of time, are characteristic of it and more or less distinct from the atmospheric qualities of adjoining regions. The western Sahara, for example, has average temperatures ranging from the low 60s in January to the mid 90s in July; yearly rainfall is extremely variable, both in amount and time of occurrence, and when it does occur seldom totals more than 2 or 3 inches. North of the Sahara along the Mediterranean coast of the Atlas lands yearly temperatures range from the low 50s to the mid 70s, and besides being generally cooler, this region receives between 15 and 25 inches of rain that falls for the most part in winter. South of the Sahara and nearer the equator the atmosphere over the grassy savanna lands of the western Sudan has temperatures in the low 70s in January and the mid 80s in July and considerably more rain than the other two regions (from 30 to 50 inches), most of it falling in the summertime. The Guinea coast, south of the Sudan, is distinguished in many places by temperatures averaging about 80° throughout the entire year and heavier rainfall, often in excess of 100 inches. But these are only the broader varieties of climate to be found in this part of Africa. A careful study would disclose the presence of enormous complexities within the general pattern of climatic regions.

The great diversity of the world's climates has been revealed in comparatively recent times through the study of a growing body of climatological literature, especially the descriptive accounts of scientific observers and statistical data collected at thousands of weather stations throughout the world. In an effort to identify, describe, and explain the climates of the world, scholars have constantly sought a rational method of classification. Not until 1900, however, with the publication of Wladimir Köppen's first important paper on the subject (referred to in Chapter 1), did a reasonable scheme of climatic classification appear. Since then a great many systems have been presented, most of them based in some way upon Köppen's work. The more recent proposals have had the advantage of advances in the techniques of weather observation, an increased knowledge of the atmosphere, and a better understanding of its relation to the earth beneath.

Köppen and those who have followed him owe a great deal to the prior efforts of phytogeographers who sought, more than a century ago, to explain the relation between plant life and such factors as temperature, rainfall, and altitude and to map the world distribution of critical climatic qualities. Most of these studies were the products of German science.

Köppen's first major treatment of climatic

TABLE 7–1

World Climates According to W. Köppen

A	Tropical forest climates; all months average above 64.4°F (18°C).	a	Warmest month above 71.6°F (22°C).
		b	Warmest month below 71.6°F.
B	Dry climates	c	Less than 4 months above 50°F.
	BS semi-arid or steppe	d	Less than 4 months above 50°F, coldest month below −36.4°F (−38°C).
	BW arid or desert		
C	Mesothermal forest climates; coldest month averages above 32°F (0°C) but below 64.4°F, warmest month above 50°F (10°C).	f	Constantly moist; rainfall every month of year.
D	Microthermal snow forest climates; coldest month averages below 32°F (0°C), warmest month above 50°F (10°C).	h	Hot and dry; all months average over 32°F.
		k	Cold and dry; at least 1 month averages below 32°F.
E	Polar climates; warmest month averages below 50°F (10°C).	s	Dry season in summer.
	ET Tundra climate; warmest month below 50°F but above 32°F.	w	Dry season in winter.
	EF Perpetual forest; all months average below 32°F.	m	Monsoon rain; short dry season; yearly rainfall sufficient to support tropical rainforest.
		n	Frequent fog.

classification placed paramount importance on plant distribution in identifying climatic regions and helping in the identification of their boundaries. The system is thus essentially phytogeographical.

The vegetation zones, which are presented to us in the maps of Griseback, Drude, and others for the world or parts of its surface, in a large part may be traced back to the biologic groups of the plant kingdom and may supply accurate evidence of the geographic boundaries. Thus if one proceeds from the physiologic bases of that grouping and seeks for the climatic values that are characteristic of these boundaries, then one acquires gradually a fairly simple scheme of climatic regions.[1]

Recognizing five major vegetation groups, Köppen established a broad climatic classification, identified according to numerical values of temperature and rainfall, to correspond with each, and a system of letter designations to facilitate mapping their distribution. Tropical rainforest corresponds, for example, with the category *tropical forest climate* (A) in which the temperature of the coolest month is above 18°C (64.4°F). The remaining major groups, as shown in Table 7-1, are designated by the

capital letters B, C, D, and E. Additional letters are used to indicate seasonal variations in temperature, rainfall, and other qualities, and by these means a wide variety of climatic conditions can be expressed and easily mapped.

In requiring that each climatic type be defined by precise mathematical values, Köppen attempted to discipline the identification of climatic regions, with the hope that continued research would bring further refinements to his system, leading finally to a reasonably accurate, mathematically determined picture of the world's climates. He himself revised his original plan several times, the last revision appearing in 1953.

Other scholars have followed Köppen's lead, and the past half-century has seen the introduction of many alternative classification schemes, most of them based to a large degree on the Köppen system. Among the better known are the methods proposed by Thornthwaite in 1931 and 1948.[2]

The 1948 Thornthwaite system is fundamentally different from the earlier one, and also from the Köppen system, in being developed independently of other geographic features such as vegetation, soils, and land use. Six climatic types, not specifically corresponding to vegetation, soils, or other regions, are

[1] W. Köppen, "Versuch einer Klassifikation der Klimate, vorzugsweise nach ihren Beziehungen zur Pflanzenwelt," *Geographischen Zeitschrift*, **6**: 593–611, 657–79, 1900.

[2] See *Geographical Review*, **21**: 633–55, 1931, and **38**: 55–94, 1948.

employed: Perhumid, Humid, Moist Subhumid, Dry Subhumid, Semiarid, and Arid. Letter designations (Table 7-2) are used for convenience in mapping. The climatic types and the boundaries separating them are determined by the mathematical analysis of climatic data, using a formula designed to permit the comparison of precipitation with potential evapotranspiration at specific localities. Evapotranspiration is simply the reverse of precipitation, that is, the return of moisture to the atmosphere by evaporation from land and water surfaces and by transpiration from plants. Potential evapotranspiration is then the maximum of moisture return to the atmosphere that could result in a given temperature regime.

Climates are determined in both the Köppen and Thornthwaite methods by the numerical values of temperature and rainfall, the two most important climatic elements. Their successful application obviously depends upon a large number of accurate, long-term temperature and rainfall data, kept according to a universal standard and well distributed around the world. In this respect they are not entirely satisfactory, for observational methods are not uniform, the accuracy of all records is not assured, the length of record may at some places be nearly a century and at others only a few years, and the distribution of weather stations over the earth is woefully uneven. Massachusetts, for example, has sixty-three weather stations, fairly well distributed over an area of 8257 square miles, of which twenty-

seven have been in operation since 1900 or before; Nevada, over ten times larger with an area of 110,540 square miles, has sixty-five stations, only seven of which have been keeping records since 1900; Alaska, at least seventy times as large as Massachusetts, having an area of 585,400 square miles, is served by only forty-five stations, and only three have been functioning since 1900. The discrepancies revealed in this comparison, while not extreme, indicate that only in the well-populated parts of the world may we expect to find records of weather observations made over a reasonably long period of time. And even in some densely settled areas such as China and certain Latin American countries weather records are disappointingly lacking in number and accuracy. Still, despite inadequate statistical data for vast tracts of the earth's surface, climatologists have applied both the Köppen and Thornthwaite systems with enough success to produce some degree of order in the world's climatic pattern.

Certain broader defects in both systems have prompted justifiable criticism. Jones has pointed out in regard to the Köppen system that

...its research value is extremely slight; it is meaningful only on small scale maps; efforts to redefine the boundaries are a waste of time; as a teaching device it is actually harmful; to some students it is a tricky puzzle concealing the true nature and meaning of climate; to others it gives a false sense of scientific knowledge: ... any climatic classification concerned chiefly with boundary

TABLE 7–2

World Climates According to C. W. Thornthwaite			
Precipitation Effectiveness			
P-E Index		Temperature Efficiency	
A	128	Perhumid	A′	Tropical
B	64–127	Humid	B′	Mesothermal
C_2	32–63	Subhumid (moist)	C′	Microthermal
C_1	21–31	Subhumid (dry)	D′	Taiga
D	0–20	Semiarid	E′	Tundra
E	Less than 0	Arid	F′	Perpetual frost

Seasonal Precipitation Efficiency	
r	Rainfall adequate at all seasons
d	Rainfall deficient in all seasons
w	Rainfall deficient in winter
s	Rainfall deficient in summer

values on a global scale is of limited research use. The Köppen system focuses all attention on boundary values. The validity of Thornthwaite's indices, however, does not depend upon his choice of boundary values. They can be computed with precision for any spot for which data are available, whereas Köppen merely puts stations in pigeon holes.[3]

And Brooks has stated that in some ways Köppen's system is superior because it includes "indications of seasonal features and significant details (such as the fogginess of certain coastal deserts), which are lacking in Thornthwaite's over-all annual indices of moisture and temperature efficiency."[4]

Dissatisfaction seems reasonable with these or any other schemes of climatic classification in which an attempt is made to identify, describe, and systemize the fluid atmosphere in the same way taxonomists deal with plants and animals. The atmosphere is constantly in motion, ever changing, and a method of describing its qualities precisely has thus far eluded climatologists. Hence, a classification of purely atmospheric phenomena, if one is employed, must somehow take into account their transitory nature. Only an approximation of the long-range atmospheric behavior constituting climate is possible, and this is particularly true in view of the dearth, throughout most of the world, of adequate weather data.

The requirements of a strictly atmospheric classification system are met to some extent in the method introduced by Strahler,[5] which is based upon the location of air mass source regions and their zones of contact. Three major climate groups appear in this scheme. Group A includes equatorial air masses, within a few degrees of the equator, and tropical air masses, within a few degrees of the tropics of Cancer and Capricorn; Group B are zones of characteristically lively interaction between tropical and polar air masses; Group C includes climates dominated by cold polar air masses. Thirteen principal types of climate are derived from

these groups. No attempt is made to delineate boundary lines between them, and thus the system is designed to produce a rational arrangement of climates entirely within the atmosphere and independent of terrestrial phenomena. A generalized scheme such as this is probably as close as we can come to a reasonable designation of strictly atmospheric regions. But this innovation, yet to stand the test of usefulness among climatologists, is based, like most other systems, upon the actual mathematical measurement of continuously changing atmospheric elements, principally temperature and rainfall. And, as we have observed before, the numerical data available for these elements are not at all adequate for the construction of a completely satisfactory climatic classification. Until further advances in the technique of weather observation and recording have been made for the entire world, only broadly generalized schemes can be derived.

Nevertheless, in the study of natural phenomena some systematic arrangement must be employed, and it is believed by many that for this we must turn to readily identifiable features of the earth that reflect with reasonable accuracy the many varieties of climatic influence. In this volume the plan adopted for the introductory investigation of climatic regions is based primarily upon the general effect of long-range atmospheric behavior on major plant associations (Table 7-3). It is a modification of a plant distribution system that first appeared in the *U.S. Department of Agriculture Yearbook*[6] for 1941 and is used here in conformance with the principle that the presence and form of natural vegetation are mainly attributable to the qualities of the atmosphere. It is a return, of course, to the relationship upon which the Köppen system was founded, having its origins in the phytogeographic studies of the nineteenth century. Progressive advances made since 1850 in the study of ecological plant geography facilitate the use of such a scheme. Certainly the easiest way to recognize a climatic region, at least at the introductory level of investigation, is through its effect upon the predominant groupings of plants that grow on the earth's surface.

[3] S. B. Jones, "What Does Geography Need from Climatology?" *The Professional Geographer*, N.S., 2(4): 43, 1950.

[4] C. F. Brooks, "What Does Geography Need from Climatology?" *The Professional Geographer*, N.S., 3(1): 39, 1951.

[5] A. N. Strahler, *Physical Geography*, John Wiley & Sons, 1960, pp. 188–91.

[6] D. I. Blumenstock and C. W. Thornthwaite, "Climate and the World Pattern," *U.S. Department of Agriculture Yearbook*, 1941, pp. 98–127.

TABLE 7–3

World Climates as Classified in This Volume

Polar Ice Cap	Coastal Deserts
Tundra	Mid-latitude Deserts
Boreal Forest	Tropical Evergreen Rainforest
Mid-latitude Mixed Forest	Tropical Semideciduous Forest
Mid-latitude Coastal Evergreen Forest	Tropical Savanna Woodland
Mediterranean Scrub Woodland	Tropical Thorn Scrub Woodland
Mid-latitude Prairie Grassland	Mountain Climates
Mid-latitude Steppe Grassland	Oceanic Climates
Subtropical Interior Deserts	

The system is not without its weaknesses, of course, for it is quite impossible to establish a distinct boundary line between any adjoining vegetation regions. It is rather a transition zone that exists between broadly discrete plant associations, and hence between the climatic regions they help to identify. Thus the lines of separation shown on the map of the world's climates (Fig. 7.1) should be thought of as the approximate median lines of the variable interregional transition zones and are provided only as a convenience for purposes of discussion.

Not only is it impossible to be exact about these matters, even with an abundance of statistical and descriptive data, but it must also be recognized that transition zones between vegetation regions, in common with all things in nature, are constantly changing to some degree in both quality and distribution. Thus, in some degree climatic regions are eternally changing in quality and distribution. These are important principles to bear in mind in the discussion of regional climatology that follows.

Generally speaking, where regional plant species are numerically dominant and by their appearance create the essential physiognomic character of nearly every scene, a region may safely be identified. When the dominant species of an adjoining region outnumber those of the first and are intermingled in such a way as to impart a new and distinctly recognizable character to nearly every scene, the second region may be identified. The transition takes place normally through a vaguely defined zone in which the dominant species of two adjacent regions interpenetrate in no readily measurable proportions.

Seldom is a regional boundary clearly defined. Only on maps of a very small scale can lines of regional separation be drawn with confidence. The larger the scale, and the more closely one examines the terrestrial criteria, the more baffling the problem becomes. In no instance has the problem of boundary determination among vegetation regions been satisfactorily solved. Efforts to solve it have only served to emphasize the difficulties involved.[7]

Another problem arises from the fact that within a given vegetation region will be found a great variety of plant groups, partly because of the countless diverse edaphic situations that always exist in an area of considerable size. The word *edaphic* refers to the nature of the soil and of the bedrock from which it is derived, and to subterranean water relationships, which together affect the way plant associations develop. Ecologists have identified three main plant groups according to the edaphic situations in which they grow: mesophytes, hydrophytes, and xerophytes. Mesophytes are those plants that develop under well-drained soil conditions that are neither too moist nor too dry; hydrophytes grow in excessively wet situations; xerophytes persist in very dry situations.

The representative plants of a climatic region are usually found among the mesophytes, which, if undisturbed, produce a grouping called a climax plant association. These are the plants that predominate, under the influence of long-term atmospheric circumstances, over all other mesophytes. They tend to replace and outlast other mesophytes, which are often found in groups called subclimax associations, and to persist over a long period of time as the

[7] See A. W. Küchler, "Classification and Purpose in Vegetation Maps," *Geographical Review*, **47**(2): 155–67, April 1956.

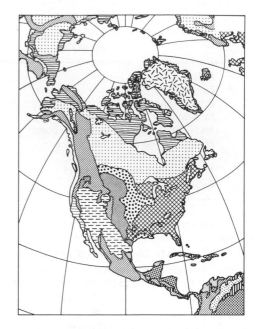

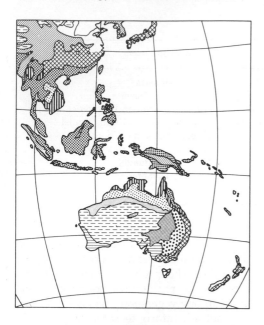

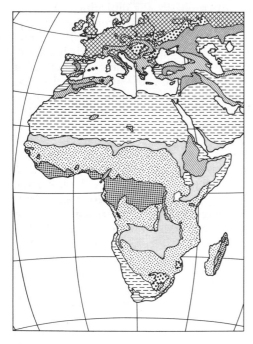

 Polar ice cap

Tundra

Boreal forest

Mid-latitude mixed forest

Mid-latitude coastal
evergreen forest

Mediterranean scrub
woodland

Mid-latitude prairie

Mid-latitude steppe

Desert

Tropical rain forest

Tropical semi-deciduous
forest

Tropical savanna
woodland

Tropical thorn scrub
woodland

Mountain

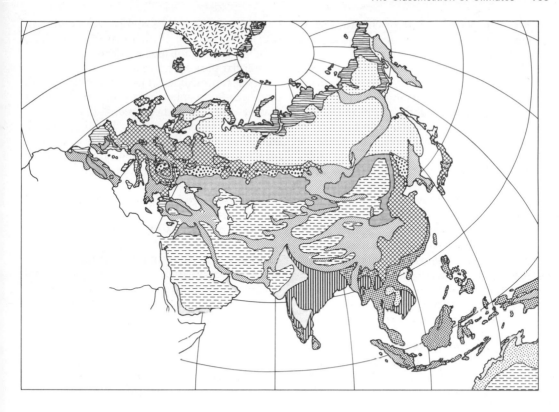

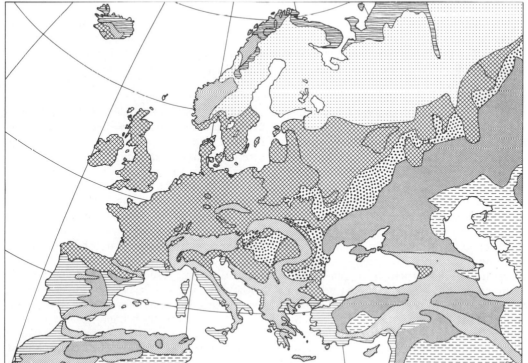

Figure 7.1. Generalized distribution of the climatic regions of the world.

characteristic plant cover of the climatic region. They are thus sometimes called climatic plant associations.

In broadest terms, terrestrial plant life (not including algae, plankton, kelp, and other oceanic forms) may be arranged in four main groups: forest, grassland, desert, and tundra.

FOREST. Forests cover about 33 per cent of the world's land surface. Trees predominate over other plant forms where sufficient water is provided to their root systems and where their roots are able to develop laterally or deeply enough for structural support of trunk and branches. They may rise to great heights, as the Douglas fir (*Pseudotsuga taxifolia*), which averages 180–190 feet under ideal conditions, redwood (*Sequoia sempervirens*), averaging 190–280 feet under favorable conditions, and other trees of the west coastal mountain regions of North America where relatively mild temperatures and abundant rainfall are characteristic of the weather throughout the year. Tropical forests of Asia, Africa, and America also include species such as teak (*Tectona grandis*), African mahogany (*Khaya nyasica*), and West Indian cedar (*Cedrola mexicana*) that rise to heights well in excess of 100 feet in response to continuously high temperatures and ample rain.

The trees of mid-latitude forests, however, as in western Europe and eastern North America, seldom exceed heights of 70–80 feet, in a climate typified by seasonal variations in both temperature and rainfall and yet, on the average, enjoying a fairly equitable distribution of rain throughout the year. Still smaller trees, 25 to 40 feet high and usually scattered in an open, park-like woodland, tend to prevail over others in many parts of the world where a prolonged dry season must be endured, as on the coastal lowlands of Mediterranean Europe and in the foothills of south coastal California. Temperatures in these areas are usually high in summer, winters are mild, and rain falls mainly in winter.

Another general distinction among trees is based upon leaf types. The leaves of some are narrow and needle-shaped, as the pine, spruce, and fir of eastern North America; others are broad and variously shaped, as the oak, maple, elm, and poplar of the same locality. Still another distinction is seen in the way leaves are shed by trees. Some are evergreen, continuously in foliage, including most of the needleleaved trees and many of the broadleaved trees,

especially in the tropics. Others are deciduous, that is, they lose all of their leaves at one time, standing bare of foliage and dormant during a substantial part of the year.

GRASSLAND. About 21 per cent of the earth's land area is occupied by a dominant cover of grasses and other herbaceous plant forms. Grasslands usually mark a broad transition zone between well-watered forests and moisture-deficient deserts. They are similar to forests in having an unbroken plant cover, distinguishing them along their drier margins from the scattered vegetation that is typical of most desert regions.

Three main kinds of grasslands are recognized: short grass steppes, and tall grass prairies, both of the middle latitudes, and the tall grass savannas of the tropics. Steppe and savanna lands comprise the greatest expanses of the earth's grassy areas. Generally speaking, grassland formations tend to dominate where the upper layers of soil are moist for a considerable part of the year but the deeper layers are too dry to provide water for the roots of trees. The long-term average moisture conditions of the soil thus govern the general distribution of grassland.

DESERT. Desert regions occupy less than one fifth of the earth's land area (about 18 per cent), and contrary to popular opinion are seldom absolutely without vegetation. The chief distinguishing feature of desert plant life is its scattered distribution, drought-resistant xerophytes appearing singly or in clumps widely separated by broad patches of bare ground. Their roots are usually well developed both laterally and in depth to take advantage of rarely available surface and deep-lying ground water. Their characteristic hardiness enables them to withstand long periods of dormancy when water from any source cannot be reached. The irregularity of rainfall, to which these qualities of the vegetation are related, is probably the most important atmospheric feature of deserts. Desert landscapes normally wear a brownish cast, resulting from long periods without rain, often lasting for several years. When rains do occur, they frequently fall in a torrential downpour, bringing plants quickly to life and in a short time imparting a sweet-scented greenness to an apparently lifeless expanse. A few desert areas in the world, such as the northern Atacama, parts of Libya, and the Tarim basin of northwest China, where little if any rainfall has ever been observed, actually approach a lifeless condition.

TUNDRA. In the far northern reaches of North America and Eurasia, between the northernmost poleward limits of continuous forest and the constantly ice-covered tracts of endless frost, is a virtually treeless landscape dominated by many varieties of mosses and lichens, called the tundra. Other plants commonly found include grasses, sedges, low shrubs, dwarfed trees, and countless flowering herbs. All are plants that must survive a long, severe winter and must accomplish their annual growth during a short, cool summer usually lasting only a few weeks. Though little rain falls, the ground remains damp and, except for a thin layer of soil at the surface thawed by the summer sun, is gripped firmly in a wintry frost throughout the year. Only about 7 per cent of the earth's land area is tundra.

The general distribution of forest, grassland, desert, and tundra, occupying about 79 per cent of the earth's land area, provides a useful key to the variety of most of the world's climates. Of the remaining 21 per cent of land surface about 9 per cent is ice-covered the year round—chiefly in Greenland, certain elevated areas around the Arctic Ocean, and in Antarctica—and about 12 per cent is mountainous, where high altitudes and a predominance of sloping land give rise to a complex vertical arrangement of plant associations.

In the next chapter begins our study of individual climatic regions. Note that the regional classification followed bears a broad resemblance to the ancient five-zone concept of the Greeks. At the same time it incorporates the most important features of contemporary climatology, especially the principle that the qualities of the land are attributable to the qualities of the atmosphere.

References

BAILEY, H. P.: "Toward a Unified Concept of the Temperate Climate," *Geographical Review*, 54(4): 516–45, 1964.

BROOKS, C. E. P.: "Classification of Climates," *Meteorological Magazine*, 77: 97–101, 1948.

CHANG, JEN-HU: "An Evaluation of the 1948 Thornthwaite Classification," *Annals of the Association of American Geographers*, 49(1): 24–30, 1959.

GLEASON, H. A. and CRONQUIST, A.: *The Natural Geography of Plants*, Columbia University Press, New York, 1964.

HARE, F. K.: "Climatic Classification," in *London Essays in Geography*, ed. by L. D. Stamp and S. W. Wooldridge, Longmans, Green and Co. Ltd., London, 1951.

KENDREW, W. G.: *Climates of the Continents*, The Clarendon Press, Oxford, 1961.

THOMPSON, B. W.: *The Climate of Africa*, Oxford University Press, New York, 1965.

U.S. DEPARTMENT OF AGRICULTURE, *Climate and Man*, Yearbook of Agriculture, 1941.

VISHER, S. S.: *Climatic Atlas of the United States*, Harvard University Press, Cambridge, Mass., 1954.

chapter 8

THE POLAR ICE CAP

Surrounding the north and south poles of the earth are regions of constant cold where vast expanses of both land and water wear an enduring mantle of ice and snow. These are the ice cap[1] regions of the world, where the atmosphere is seldom above freezing, plant life is almost entirely lacking, and most animals are creatures of the sea. The south pole lies deep within the interior of the mountainous continent of Antarctica, all but a small portion of which is fast-frozen throughout the year beneath a blanket of ice and snow. The north pole is surrounded by the ice-covered waters of the Arctic Ocean, which is in turn embraced by the northernmost coasts of North America and Eurasia. The south pole thus lies deep within a major land mass over six times larger than Greenland, the north pole within a large sea.

Around the north pole an estimated 4,390,000 square miles of ice persist through the summer season of continuous daylight in the following distribution: about 3,600,000 square miles on the surface of the Arctic Ocean, about 640,000 square miles on the Greenland ice cap, and about 150,000 square miles among the scattered

[1] The term *ice-cap* is commonly applied only to the ice-bound surfaces of Greenland and Antarctica, both of which are uplifted several thousand feet above the sea, but it will be used in this volume to designate all polar land and water surfaces, including the Arctic Ocean, that remain ice-covered throughout the year.

alpine glaciers of mountainous areas on the Arctic islands and the continental periphery. During the winter months of almost continuous darkness the north polar ice cap expands to about 6,600,000 square miles, including nearly the total area of the Arctic Ocean (about 5,500,000 square miles), most of Greenland's 800,000 square miles, and at least 300,000 square miles elsewhere (Fig. 8.1).

Around the south pole a persistent ice cap covers the massive Antarctic plateau during the southern hemisphere summer, amounting to about 5,000,000 square miles (approximately 98 per cent of the total 5,100,000 square mile area), to which may be added the marginal areas of shelf ice—an estimated 360,000 square miles—plus a variable area of unconsolidated drift ice. During the winter the ice cover expands, chiefly in the floating masses of drift ice that surround the continent, to an estimated area of about 9,112,000 square miles (Fig. 8.5).

Because of the earth's motions around the sun the length of day is six months, and of night six months, at each pole. At 80° latitude, north and south, day and night are slightly more than four months, at 70° they are two months, and so on. Figure 6.1 shows the length of the longest day for 10 degree intervals of latitude.

The fluctuating ice cap of several million square miles in each polar region indicates that subfreezing temperatures prevail for nearly the

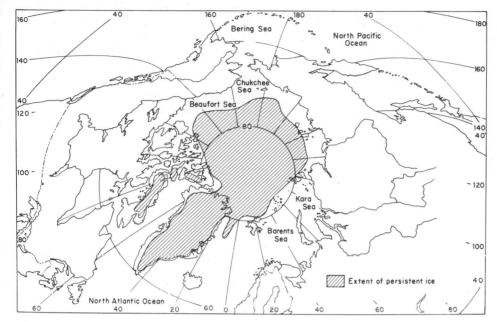

Figure 8.1.   Minimum north polar ice cap distribution (September).

entire year over these vast territories. They are major sources of chill, polar air that tends at all times to move equatorward, converging with warmer air from the subtropical anticyclones in the middle latitudes. Thus the ice cap cold sources—heat sinks, in meteorological terms—play a primary role in the ultimate generation of rain- and snow-bearing disturbances arising along the zones of contact between cold and warm air.

The Arctic Ocean

Most of the north polar ice cap is a low-lying mass of slowly drifting ice afloat on the surface of the Arctic Ocean. Viewed from a low-flying airplane, ice on the great northern sea presents a flat, seemingly featureless appearance to the limits of visibility. The actual nature of nearly all of this water-borne ice is unknown. Only from a few expeditionary reports and from observations made by weather reconnaissance aircraft, by temporary scientific stations on the ice, and by nuclear-powered submarines traveling beneath floating Arctic pack ice, may we derive some idea of the qualities of its surface, its thickness, and the atmosphere above it.

During the long, cold, dark months of winter when the continental shores embracing the Arctic Sea are white with snow and frost, sea and land are drawn together as the ice of coastal waters expands seaward to meet the main body of pack ice in the central ocean area. As temperatures steadily drop, oceanic ice increases in area, usually reaching a maximum thickness and extent in the month of April just as the long period of daylight begins.[2] In wintertime three kinds of oceanic ice have been identified.[3] Fast ice, that which is firmly anchored to the shore, occupies up to 50 per cent of the ocean area and achieves its greatest width along the Siberian coast. Pack ice, a variable zone of broken fragments of displaced ice frozen together during the winter, occupies up to 15 per cent of the ocean area between fast ice and the third type, called Arctic Pack, the main body of constantly drifting old ice composed of enormous floes, or fields, almost completely unified into a drifting mass occupying the remaining 35 per cent of the central ocean area. From a climatic standpoint, the ice surface is everywhere the same, never quite level, but nearly so, with hummocks or ridges that are

[2] Sea water of average salinity freezes at about 29°F.
[3] N. A. Transehe, "The Ice Cover of the Arctic Sea," *Problems of Polar Research*, American Geographical Society Special Publication No. 7, New York, 1928, 91–123.

piles of ice resulting from the crushing together of adjacent floes. Seldom do these have a local relief of more than 50 or 60 feet.

The growing use of aircraft for military and exploratory purposes in the Arctic has led to the closer examination, from the air, of thousands of square miles of hitherto unknown areas of the central ocean and has revealed that many "islands" of thicker, harder, relatively smooth-surfaced ice are embedded in the shallower, less solid pack. On one of the ice islands, called T-3, or Fletcher's Island, an observation base was established early in 1952, in a latitude of nearly 88° to record weather data and to examine the nature of the island. Fletcher's Island was discovered to be about 31 miles in circumference and approximately 160 feet thick (compared to an average thickness of about 12 feet in the surrounding pack ice) and to stand at an average height of 20 or more feet above the surrounding ice. Because of the presence of rock material and the skeletal remains of certain animals, and because of their resemblance to fast, or shelf, ice in some coastal areas, the ice islands are thought to have broken away from Arctic shores and to have drifted for years on the currents of the northern sea. Their life expectancy is thought to be around seventy-five to one hundred years. As they stand well above the main pack, they have been easily identified by means of radar.

The three main classes of oceanic ice endure for between nine and ten months of the year, but by the end of summer, after the sun's rays have played upon northern lands for several months, most of the fast ice has disappeared, and its remaining fragments have been carried seaward into the peripheral pack. In summertime perhaps up to 50 per cent of the ocean area, along the coasts of North America and Eurasia, becomes open water, from which open channels penetrate the edges of the water-borne pack. September is normally the month of minimum ice area. It is important to note that even in winter a certain amount of open water is present, resulting from the constant shifting of ice in response to the complex movements of Arctic tides and currents.

A consideration of temperature, rainfall, pressure, and winds in the Arctic area is greatly handicapped by a scarcity of weather records. Qualities of the atmosphere can only be determined—and are largely guessed at—from the records of a small number of weather stations established in recent years and from the reports of exploring parties that have ventured into the frozen north since the time of Henry Hudson in the early 1600s (Fig. 8.1).

The qualities of the atmosphere that give rise to continuous frost in north polar ice cap regions are a consequence of high latitude. Most ice cap areas lie north of 70° latitude and receive little warmth of solar radiation even in summer,[4] although the sun remains constantly in view for months at a time as it circles the horizon during the long period of continuous daylight (Fig. 6.1). In July and August air temperatures hover near the freezing point, for the sun's rays pass obliquely through the atmosphere, losing much heat in passage, and strike the earth's surface at such a low angle that little heat is transmitted. Because ice surfaces remain at subfreezing temperatures, the temperature of the air above them cannot rise much beyond freezing. On the Soviet expedition to the north pole in 1937–38, for example, the average temperatures within a hundred miles of the pole were 32.3°F in July and 34°F in August. Conjectural isotherms of the mean daily maximum temperatures for the warmest month in the ice cap areas are shown in Figure 8.2.

As a general rule, temperature fluctuations are much less extreme in summer than in winter. They usually reach a maximum in March or April, just before summer begins. Still, summer temperatures of up to 56° and 60°F have been made around latitude 80°. Widespread melting takes place everywhere over the Arctic Pack (chiefly through the radiational effects of solar heating) despite recurrent drops in temperatures well below the freezing point. Low summer temperatures are frequently the result of overcast skies, which appear more commonly during this season than in winter. Melting softens the outlines of ice hummocks and reduces their size, while broad pools of fresh water collect in shallow hollows, flowing together and draining ultimately into the sea. Leads and channels of open water, separating large floes of ice, are more frequently seen. Members of the Soviet expedition, noted in latitude 85° that by the end of July a

---

[4] Although there is not actually a "summer" in the Arctic as we think of it in middle latitudes, it is convenient to speak of the months of June, July, and August as summer.

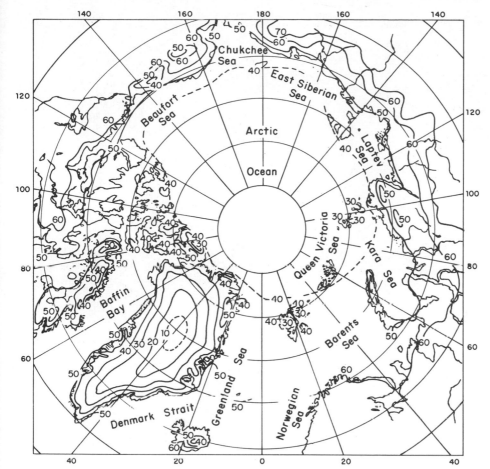

Figure 8.2. Isotherms of mean daily maximum temperature during the warmest month in the Arctic Basin.

16-inch snow cover had entirely melted, as had about 10 inches of the icy stratum beneath. Observers on T-3 reported that between June 30 and August 15 all the snow and from 1 to 2 feet of ice had melted off the island.

Temperature inversion—warmer air overlying cooler surface air below—is much less commonly observed and less pronounced in summer than in winter.

Summer is also a season of greater cloudiness than winter, of higher relative humidity, more fog, and more precipitation. Higher relative humidity is especially noticeable to human beings, whose erect bodies absorb much more heat directly from the sun's radiation than does the frozen terrain beneath. A black bulb thermometer, when exposed directly to the sun's rays, has registered 113°F while air temperature in the shade was 31.6°F.[5] The increased fogginess of summertime is particularly apparent over the warmer surface of open water, as cold air from the ice pack moves across it. In fact, fog is often concentrated near the margins of water-borne ice, where differences in temperature are more pronounced. Wherever it is seen, fog is normally confined to low strata near the surface, most often only 50 or 60 feet thick, obscuring surface visibility while clear air and sunshine prevail above.

Increased cloudiness in summer, like increased fog, is partly the result of higher temperatures in air, raising the air's moisture capacity, and partly the result of more plentiful

[5] R. N. Rudmose Brown, *Polar Regions*, London, 1927, p. 35.

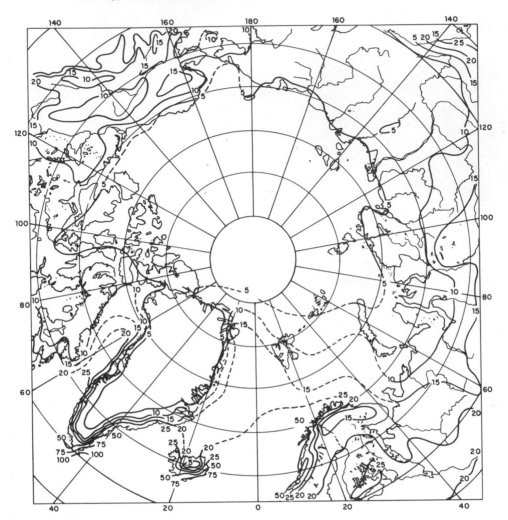

Figure 8.3. Mean annual precipitation in north polar areas (rainfall equivalents).

sources of moisture in the presence of larger open water areas and surfaces of melting. Clouds diminish the intensity of insolation, however, and an extended stratus overcast may keep air temperatures below freezing for many days in succession.

Much of summer's more abundant precipitation falls as rain, and often as sleet. Snow also appears at intervals, usually driving across the partly melted surface in a blinding blizzard. Most precipitation occurs over the Arctic Pack as the result of highly turbulent storms in which high winds drive rain or snow obliquely across the earth. Exact measurement of the quantity that falls is thus almost impossible. It is estimated that the equivalent of about 5 inches or less of rainfall accumulates over the central ocean area and central Greenland each year, with a somewhat larger amount along the southern margins near more abundant open water, in scattered places totaling 20 inches or more (Fig. 8.3). Storms over the Arctic Ocean tend to be small in area, although frequently accompanied by winds of high velocity. They are known to descend with sudden fury and little warning, drifting snow into ridges and driving man to shelter, and to vanish with almost equal suddenness, followed by the return of clear, calm, untroubled skies.

The greater storminess of summertime increases with the advance of the season, reaching a maximum during the early months of autumn. It is at this time of year that temperature contrasts between open water and ice cap are greatest. By October the Arctic coasts of North America and Eurasia have become frozen. Pack ice has ceased melting and has begun to thicken and expand, giving rise to colder, heavier air than that over the still-unfrozen waters along the coast. The stronger pressure contrasts resulting from marked temperature differences in turn give rise to steeper pressure gradients and hence to winds of higher velocity and a more turbulent condition in the affected parts of the atmosphere, mainly around the periphery of the persistent Arctic Pack.

The storm winds related to increased cyclonic activity in autumn continue into the early months of winter but diminish in frequency as winter advances toward spring. March and April are usually the months of most prolonged calm. Actually, however, all months of the year have a fairly large percentage of days during which winds of measurable velocity occur. Arctic Ocean wind velocities are generally much lower than those of winds farther south, particularly over the North Atlantic and Pacific oceans. In short, high winds over the Arctic are rare, but variable winds, in terms of both direction and velocity, are common. Nansen, for example, reports that the only real gale during his entire three-year drift in polar ice on the *Fram* took place around the end of January 1896 (Lat. 85°N., Long. 25°E.), when the wind blew steadily from the east for seven days, reaching a peak velocity of 47 miles per hour the seventh day, and then ceased.

Cold air from the Arctic Ocean flows continuously outward, equatorward, into zones of warmer, lighter air. This is true despite the recurrence of cyclonic activity around its borders, the frequent passage of storms across its central area, and the variety of locally disturbing influences along the circumjacent coasts, all of which produce wind directions that differ decidedly from season to season and from place to place.

There is also evidence of a general clockwise movement of air within the Arctic basin, centered approximately north of Alaska around 85° latitude. The wind records of travelers show a preponderance of easterly winds, and recent observations of the movement of ice islands indicate a pronounced clockwise drift that is undoubtedly related to the frictional effect of surface winds and wind-driven ocean currents. The predominance of variable winds over the central Arctic and of easterly winds around its periphery are qualities of anticyclones in the northern hemisphere. It will be recalled from Chapter 4 that the right-turning tendency of moving bodies is normal in the northern hemisphere and is especially pronounced near the pole.

After the lengthening shadows of autumn have succumbed to the continuous night of winter, storms over the central Arctic Ocean gradually diminish and are punctuated by more frequent periods of calm, clear, very cold, very dry weather, when the dark desolation of endless ice and snow is illuminated only by the stars, the moon, and the sometimes dazzling brilliance of the Aurora Borealis, visible toward the south. During this season, when temperatures are far below zero, the air can hold but little moisture, and excessive dryness is a cause of constant thirst to human beings. Moisture breathed into the air turns instantly, with a crackling sound, into frost particles that drift softly to the ground when the air is still. Frost that forms on the ground or other solid surfaces reaches extraordinary thickness, oftentimes as much as 4 or 5 inches. Snow is dry and very fine, easily raised from the surface by the slightest wind. Indeed, Arctic blizzards in which snow crystals are blown from the ground to heights of 20 or 25 feet have been observed in winds of only 15 miles per hour. Winds of 30 miles per hour have raised snow 100 feet from the ground. The drifting of snow is common in winter.

Winter temperatures become lower as the darkness continues (Fig. 8.4), minimum readings over the polar ice pack reaching −50° (Sverdrup) in some places, and in others −60° (Nansen). It is generally believed that the steady loss of heat from the frozen sea in wintertime is somewhat compensated by the moderating effect of unfrozen water beneath, which transmits warmth to the ice above and thus prevents surface air over the Arctic Ocean from reaching the low extremes that have been observed in the continental interiors of North America and Siberia where no such compensation exists.

Temperature fluctuations are greatest in April, when a variation of as much as 40 degrees (from −35° to 5°F) may be experienced in a

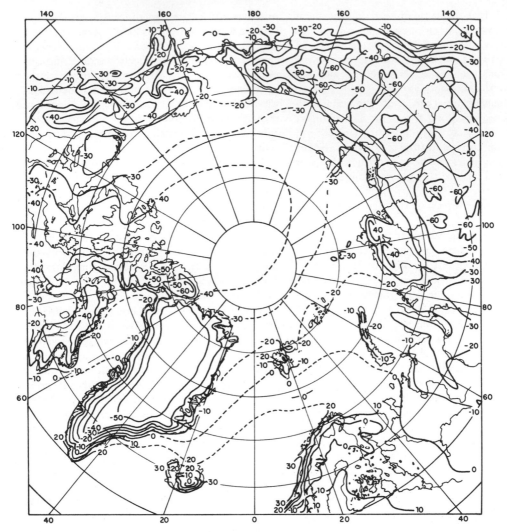

Figure 8.4. Isotherms of mean daily minimum temperature during the coldest month in the Arctic Basin (°F).

thirty-six-hour period.[6] Temperature inversions are common in wintertime. Sverdrup reported the following figures: at the surface −19.1°; at 445 feet above the surface −9°; and at 3200 feet, −4.5°. A gradual decrease began above that altitude. Similar temperature inversions have been observed in the Antarctic (see Table 8-6).

The calmer, clearer, drier air that develops over the Arctic as the cold of winter deepens is an indication of greater air density, of higher atmospheric pressure. Ice in the Arctic basin thickens and expands, attaining a maximum

[6] *Ibid.*

area nearly everywhere in April. It is at this season that the highest average air pressures develop over the Arctic Ocean. Pressure readings, although too few and too scattered to permit broad generalization, at least suggest that in April the barometer commonly registers between 1016 and 1020 millibars (30.0 and 30.1 inches). These values, while not as high as those normally reached in eastern central Asia or in the middle Mackenzie valley of North America, are considerably higher than the pressure of 1000 millibars (29.53 inches) common over the northern arms of the Atlantic and Pacific oceans at this period.

During summer the anticyclonic qualities of air over the Arctic Ocean persist, but they are less strongly developed than in winter. At the same time, barometric readings over the North Atlantic and Pacific are not as low—averaging around 1010.6 millibars (29.84 inches)—and the pressure gradients are thus less steep in summer than in winter.

Greenland

The great island plateau of Greenland is the second major region of continuous ice and snow in the neighborhood of the north pole. Its northernmost coast reaches a latitude of more than 83°, and over 1600 miles to the south, at latitude 60°, it juts a narrowing tip into the North Atlantic between Labrador and Iceland. Most of the island lies north of the Arctic Circle and in those latitudes is over 600 miles in width. Its vast, rocky bulk rises steeply from the water's edge to heights of several thousand feet above the sea; only a small fraction of its total area is lowland, appearing in discontinuous tracts along the coast. Its coastline is, in fact, distinguished mainly by the presence of steep-sided fiords, in which deep, narrow arms of the sea penetrate between lofty, snow-capped peninsulas of rocky land.

From altitudes of 3000 to 4000 feet the outer edges of the ice plateau rise toward the interior in successive terraces of great breadth, in many places reaching heights of more than 10,000 feet above sea level. From its outer margins the ice thickens toward the center, where it is well over a mile in depth. Depths of more than 8000 feet have been measured by means of the seismograph.[7]

About 82 per cent of Greenland is ice-covered throughout the year, for only near the coast, at low altitudes, are the warmth of the sun and the moderating effects of the sea sufficient to melt away ice and snow and lay bare the ground beneath for from one to three months in summertime. Much of the coast has a tundra climate similar to the coastal tundra around the Arctic Ocean. It is chiefly during the summertime that millions of tons of Greenland's ice are released into the coastal waters in the form of countless icebergs broken loose from glacial

[7] A seismograph is an electronic device used to determine the depth within the earth of strata having different densities.

tongues that reach the sea. This is thought to be the chief way in which Greenland's winter accumulation of ice and snow is diminished. Many icebergs, particularly those from the northwest coast, are large and dense enough to withstand the destructive effects of ocean waves until they have drifted far to the south, often beyond the island of Newfoundland.

In summer a certain amount of melting also takes place over much of the interior plateau in spite of an average temperature of less than 32°F for the warmest month. The inland terraces are frequently sown with countless broad, shallow lakes, and rivulets of flowing water appear everywhere as the icy meltwater seeks a lower level, coursing through innumerable troughs that are sometimes several feet deep and only a few inches wide and that wrinkle the surface and present a hazard to travel. For only a few weeks, however, do temperatures occasionally rise above freezing (see Table 8-1). Hence, relatively little surface ice is lost through the combined effects of sublimation, evaporation, melting, and percolation. Most of the year the surface remains solidly frozen, and in winter, with a growing accumulation of ice and snow around its edges, it expands downward and outward to merge with the water-borne ice along the coast and contribute to the over-all expansion of north polar ice to a wintertime area of about 6,600,000 square miles.

Latitude and altitude combined create the icy surface of Greenland that stands as a polar wedge between the oceanic arms of Baffin Bay and the Norwegian (Greenland) Sea. It endures throughout the year as a source of cold air, its air temperatures, both summer and winter, being much lower than those over the Arctic Ocean.

The Wegener expedition of 1930–31 operated a weather station at Eismitte (Lat. 70°50′N., Long. 40°42′W.; el. 9941), high on the central part of the ice cap, and the observations recorded there (Table 8-1) suggest the nature of Greenland's interior climate.

July was the warmest month, having a statistical average temperature of 12.6°F. Nine months of the year averaged temperatures below zero, the coldest of which was February, with a monthly mean of −53°F. In January, February, and March, temperatures of −84° and −85° were recorded, and on eighty-three days between October 10 and April 12 (45 per

TABLE 8–1
Climatic Data for Stations in Greenland
(Temp., °F; Rainfall, In.)

Station	Position	El. in Ft		Jan.	Feb.	Mar.	Apr.	May	Jun.	Jul.	Aug.	Sep.	Oct.	Nov.	Dec.	Year
Eismitte	Lat. 70°50′N.	9941	T	−43.1	−53.1	−39.9	−23.8	−4.2	+4.5	+12.6	+0.1	−7.8	−32.1	−45.6	−37.8	{−22.4 12.2
			R	No monthly data												
Ivigtut	Lat. 61°12′N.	82	T	19	19	24	31	40	46	50	47	41	34	27	21	33
			R	3.3	2.6	3.4	2.5	3.5	3.2	3.1	3.7	5.9	5.7	4.7	3.2	44.6
Godthaab	Lat. 64°11′N.	66	T	14	14	19	25	33	40	44	43	38	31	24	18	29
			R	1.4	1.7	1.6	1.2	1.7	1.4	2.2	3.1	3.4	2.5	1.9	1.5	23.5
Jakobshavn	Lat. 69°13′N.	102	T	0	−3	3	15	31	40	46	44	35	25	17	9	22
			R	0.4	0.4	0.5	0.5	0.6	0.8	1.2	1.4	1.3	0.9	0.7	0.5	9.0
Upernivik	Lat. 72°47′N.	59	T	−7	−10	−7	7	25	35	41	41	33	25	15	2	17
			R	0.4	0.5	0.7	0.6	0.6	0.5	1.0	1.1	1.1	1.1	1.1	0.6	9.1
Thule	Lat. 76°30′N.	23	T	−21	−21	−15	1	23	35	40	39	28	14	0	−13	9
			R	0.1	0.1	0.2	0.1	0.2	0.3	0.8	0.7	0.3	0.1	0.3	0.2	3.4
Angmagssalik	Lat. 65°36′N.	236	T	18	16	19	25	34	41	45	43	38	30	23	20	29
			R	3.3	2.0	2.4	2.4	2.4	2.1	1.9	2.4	3.7	5.7	3.3	2.8	34.4
Scoresby Sound	Lat. 70°29′N.	230	T	1	−2	2	10	24	35	40	38	32	19	9	4	18
			R	1.8	1.7	0.6	1.5	0.3	1.0	0.6	0.4	1.1	1.1	1.0	1.5	12.5
Myggbukta	Lat. 73°29′N.	10	T	−4	−6	−6	2	19	33	39	37	29	14	4	−2	13
			R	0.2	0.4	0.2	0.2	0.0	0.2	0.5	0.4	0.0	0.2	0.4	0.2	3.1
Danmarkhavn	Lat. 76°46′N.	20	T	−7	−17	−8	−3	19	34	40	36	25	6	−5	−6	9
			R	1.2	0.7	0.7	0.1	0.2	0.2	0.0	0.3	0.3	0.2	1.0	0.8	5.7

Sources: Handbuch der Geographischen Wissenschaft, *Nord- und Mittelamerika, die Arktis,* Potsdam, 1933; U.S. Hydrographic Office, *Sailing Directions for Baffin Bay and Davis Strait* (H.O. No. 76), 1952, *Sailing Directions for East Greenland and Iceland* (H.O. No. 75), 1952.

cent of the total number of days) the temperature dropped to −60°F. At the western base of the expedition, near the edge of the ice cap at an altitude of only 3100 feet, the lowest winter temperature was −60°F, the February average was −20°F, and July and August averaged 31°F.

Central Greenland is thus the coldest region year-round in the northern hemisphere. The winter cold of its coastal periphery is neither so extreme nor so persistent. Table 8-1 gives the monthly rainfall and temperatures at nine coastal weather stations, from which it will be observed, in contrast to the interior, that summer temperatures near the sea average above freezing for three to six months. The table also shows that as one travels northward along either coast, summers become cooler and shorter, winters become colder and longer, and total annual precipitation decreases. Fogs also are much more typical of coastal than of interior weather, both winter and summer, as cold air from the pleateau moves across unfrozen expanses of the adjacent seas.

On the ice cap precipitation most commonly falls as snow. At Eismitte the year's accumulation of snow amounted to somewhat more than 3 feet, the equivalent, because of its lightness and fineness, of about 12.2 inches of rainfall. This is a higher-than-average ratio. Ordinarily, about 10 inches of snow in middle latitudes is counted as the equivalent of 1 inch of rain. But the actual value depends upon the nature of the snow, and the ratio varies considerably. The light, dry, fine snow of very cold regions, as at Eismitte, has a high water content, and thus the ratio between snowfall and rainfall equivalent is higher. Total annual precipitation was also observed to increase toward the ice cap's outer edges, where it often fell as rain during the summer months, and rain was recorded at elevations of more than 6000 feet. But accurate measurements of precipitation are not possible, for the atmosphere over the ice cap is seldom still, and blizzards occur frequently. As in the Arctic Ocean, winds of even low velocity easily raise the fine, light particles of previously deposited snow from the surface, swirling it high into the air, and so mingle old snow with new that only by measuring average depths of snow accumulated by the end of winter can a reasonable estimate of the total fall be gained.

From the scanty information available, it appears that summer in north Greenland, as in the Arctic Ocean, is the season of maximum precipitation, and autumn and early winter are the seasons of heaviest precipitation in south Greenland.

Because of its elevation, its white surface of ice and snow, and an atmosphere relatively free of dust, the Greenland ice cap is thought to reflect from 80 to 90 per cent of all the insolation received (see Table 6-1). Surface loss of heat leads to almost continuous temperature inversions, when a cold layer of surface air from 100 to 1500 feet deep is overlain with warmer air aloft. Temperature inversions are more marked in wintertime.

Because air over the ice cap is very cold at all times, it has a constant tendency to flow down off the edges of the high plateau. Katabatic (gravity) winds along the margins are thus a consequent characteristic of Greenland's ice cap climate. They are intensified by the presence of much warmer air over the adjacent seas, resulting in remarkably strong temperature contrasts, hence a strong barometric gradient, between interior plateau and ocean surface. Both temperature and pressure contrasts become most marked in wintertime, when temperatures may drop to −85°F over the ice cap while the surface of the Atlantic Ocean just south of Greenland and Iceland remains unfrozen at temperatures in excess of 30°F. The notorious vigor of storms in the North Atlantic is at times augmented by outflowing air from the icy plateau.

On account of its persistently low temperatures and its elevation well above the sea, the atmosphere over interior Greenland is predominantly anticyclonic, that is, relatively much cooler, drier, and greater in density, than the air over Baffin Bay or the Norwegian Sea. Though cyclonic storms are known to pass across its broad, uplifted, ice-bound surface, they do so infrequently and are mainly occluding types, for Greenland stands as a bulwark against the passage of most of the storms that travel across the North Atlantic out of Hudson Bay or the Gulf of St. Lawrence. Low pressure disturbances commonly move up into Baffin Bay, along Greenland's western flanks, and even more often along its eastern flanks, through Denmark Strait between Iceland and Greenland, causing turbulent mixing of air over the ice cap, temporarily destroying the temperature inversion, and bringing

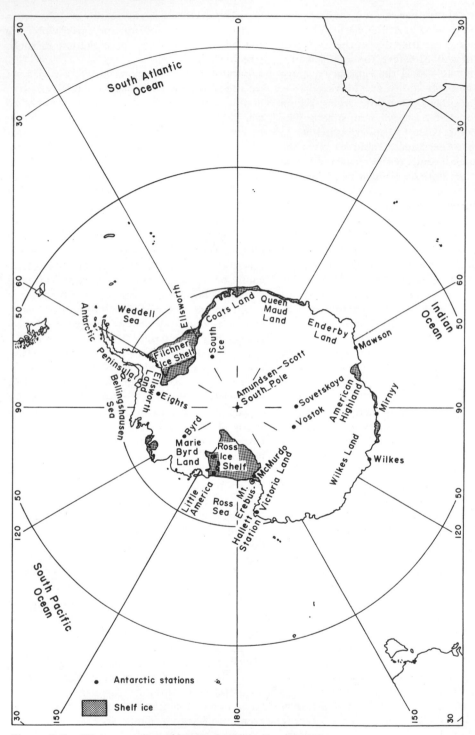

Figure 8.5.   Minimum extent of ice cap in Antarctica (March).

widespread cloudiness, precipitation, and warmer weather.

Anticyclonic conditions of cold, dense, high pressure, outflowing air prevail much of the time over Greenland, save during the brief passage of occasional weak cyclones across its interior. Anticyclonic conditions are more pronounced and more persistent over uplifted Greenland than over the sea level expanse of the Arctic Ocean. Together, however, these are the major regions of constant ice and snow, and hence of constant cold, dry air in the northern hemisphere. Their combined area is considerably less than that of the south polar ice cap of Antarctica, sole major region of enduring cold in the southern hemisphere.

Antarctica

The ice cap of south polar regions covers the vast continental plateau of Antarctica and its coastal waters to a minimum extent of nearly 5,360,000 square miles (Fig. 8.5). Each winter period of prolonged darkness it extends outward into the surrounding oceans, increasing its area by around 70 per cent to an estimated 9,112,000 square miles. It thus expands and contracts with the rhythmic alternation of continuous night and continuous day in high southern latitudes, the counterpart of glacial expansion and contraction in north polar regions.

Little is known about most of Antarctica. Only certain coastal tracts have been explored in detail, most of them since World War I, while the interior is still an enormous unknown territory, the largest remaining unexplored region on earth. It was not until 1911 that the Norwegian explorer Raoul Amundsen first reached the south pole. Since that time several expeditions have increased our knowledge of a small part of a continent two thirds again as large as Australia. One of the more recent major expeditions was undertaken by the United States Navy in 1946–47 under Admiral Richard E. Byrd, commanding thirteen ships and four thousand men. The most prolonged investigation of Antarctica was begun in July 1957 with the start of the International Geophysical Year (July 1, 1957, to December 31, 1958). A one-year extension, the International Geophysical Cooperation, ended December 31, 1959. Since then a number of scientific observation stations have been maintained by a few of the participating nations for the continued collection of data on such topics as glaciology, geology, and biology, as well as on the atmospheric studies begun in 1957. Over fifty separate stations have been manned for varying intervals in Antarctica since July 1957.

Unlike the north pole, which lies at nearly sea level in the Arctic Ocean, the south pole has an altitude of 9186 feet and is more than 800 miles from the nearest open water. Antarctica is in many respects very like the ice-covered plateau of Greenland. Its coasts rise steeply from the water's edge to elevations of 3000–4000 feet above sea level, in many places reaching altitudes of over 14,000 feet only a short distance from the coast. Many extended ranges of high mountains have been identified near the coast, others in the interior, with several peaks of over 16,000 feet.

Antarctica is a compact, mountainous plateau having only three pronounced irregularities along its coastline: the Weddell Sea facing the Atlantic, the Antarctic (Palmer) Peninsula, thrust northward in the direction of Cape Horn to latitude 63°, and farther west the deep indentation of Ross Sea, which supports on its inner reaches a broad expanse of enduring shelf ice called Ross Barrier. This is the largest area of persistent, water-borne ice, with dimensions of about 300 by 500 miles, and stands between 60 and 160 feet above sea level along its seaward margin (Fig. 8.6). Its thickness ranges from about 790 feet along the seaward edge to 1380 feet where it joins the continental mass at Beardmore Glacier. From place to place along the coast are other portions of persistent shelf ice that expand outward during the winter months of June, July, and August. And from place to place huge glaciers, tongues of inland ice, extend downward through rocky, steep-sided coastal valleys from the interior high plateau to the sea.

All of Antarctica, save a scattering of high, angular peaks and negligible, discontinuous tracts of coastal lowland, is covered with a deep mantle of enduring ice and snow. It is estimated that 90 per cent of the world's ice is concentrated in this single, enormous expanse. Most of it stands at high altitude, averaging more than 6000 feet above the sea. Only about 13 per cent of its area is lower than 3000 feet in altitude; almost a quarter (23 per cent) stands between 3000 and 6000 feet; nearly two thirds (64 per

Figure 8.6. The ice shelf of Ross Barrier in Antarctica. [U.S. Navy photo]

cent) is over 6000 feet. The thickness of the ice cap has been seismically measured to average about 8000 feet, although in Marie Byrd Land it is about 14,000 feet, and there are indications that it may exceed 16,000 feet in depth from surface to bedrock at several points.

When Admiral Byrd flew over the south pole in 1947 he described that part of the interior between Ross Barrier and the pole as a rolling, spotless white, and essentially featureless surface. He was flying about half a mile above the ice in clear weather at an air temperature of $-40°F$ in the summer month of February. From this low altitude he also observed innumerable sastrugi, the long, low, narrow ridges of wind-blown firn (consolidated snow particles) that lie almost parallel to one another and are characteristic of all ice cap regions. They are especially important as indicators of prevailing wind direction. From their position Admiral Byrd determined the prevailing wind direction between Ross Sea and the pole to be southeast, a conclusion later confirmed by meteorological observations.

The Antarctic is a continent almost devoid of lakes,[8] without rivers, marshes, or swamps,

having no soils, no forests, no grasslands, nor any deserts of the sort found in milder latitudes. Its fauna are creatures of the sea, such as certain varieties of whales, or of the coastlands with an affinity toward the sea, such as the giant Weddell seal, the flightless penguin, and flying birds like the albatross, petrel, fulmar, and skua. Plant life includes over a hundred species of lichens and less than a hundred species of mosses found on bare rock areas along the coast. Algae often color the snows of coastal tracts and are found in a few freshwater lakes. Three species of flowering plants have been identified, two grasses and one herb, on the northward projection of Antarctic Peninsula.

The size, latitude, altitude, and comparative compactness of Antarctica, the height and steepness of its coastal margins, the broad embayments of Ross Sea and Weddell Sea, and

---

[8] In an ice-free area of about 300 square miles on the Queen Mary coast of Wilkes Land (between 90 and 100°E. Long.) were found three lakes of open water each at least 3 miles long, and twenty smaller lakes. They are blue or green, from the presence of algae of those colors, and are surrounded by bare brown areas of rugged, exposed bedrock. Still another, although smaller, ice-free area was found about 600 miles farther west. Several small lakes were discovered in the open that were entirely frozen to the bottom, and there was every indication that they had not thawed in recent years.

the tapering projection of a single large peninsula, all surrounded by the unfrozen sea, combine to establish the essential climatic character of the south polar ice cap. A remote region of continuous cold, its craggy, ice-fringed coasts inaccessible save where occasionally breached by rocky tracts of lowland, ice-scoured sloping bedrock, and shingle beach, Antarctica has remained uninhabited by man. Hence weather records are scarce and are available only for a small number of widely scattered places where temporary stations have been established near the sea, on the adjacent shelf ice, or, since 1957, at a few points on the interior plateau. The scant scientific observations of solar radiation, cloud cover, temperature, humidity, precipitation, atmospheric pressure, and wind have been supplemented to some extent by the reports of seafaring men who annually venture into the Ross and Weddell seas in search of whales and seals during the less severe weather of November, December, and January. All in all the data are meager. Yet the meagerness of the data has been offset somewhat by an intensive and exhaustive study of all available information, from which a general idea of climate in Antarctica may be derived. The continuing evaluation of older, historical records has been immeasurably bolstered by new data made available since 1957 and by the application of machine methods of data-processing.

In time, no doubt, a variety of polar climates will be identified and their character specified for the entire continent. For the moment, however, we must accept, with caution, certain basic assumptions concerning broad-scale tendencies, still in the realm of speculation, and consider some of the available short-run data that appear to support them.

Because most of Antarctica lies within 20 degrees of the south pole, the sun remains constantly above the horizon nearly everywhere for at least two months (six months at the pole) during the long period of continuous daylight. The long winter night has a period of at least two months without any light or direct heat from the sun. The icy surfaces of this polar land receive but little warmth from the sun's slanting rays even in summertime. When viewed from the pole, the sun stands at a maximum elevation above the horizon of $23\frac{1}{2}$ degrees on December 22. At latitude 70° on this date it stands $43\frac{1}{2}$ degrees above the horizon at noon and sinks to an elevation of $3\frac{1}{2}$ degrees at midnight. Thus, because of its high latitude and its general altitude of more than 1 mile above the surrounding seas, plus its geographical remoteness from other continental expanses, it is nearly free of dust particles and micro-organisms. The brilliant purple color of the sky observed on many occasions in clear weather is doubtless attributable to the low incidence of atmospheric impurities.

TEMPERATURE. Antarctic weather may be described as a combination of very cold air, high winds, and blowing snow. Thus it is very much like that of Greenland, but more severe, possessing longer, colder winters and shorter, colder summers than the north polar plateau. Temperature records are available mainly for the regions around Ross Sea, Weddell Sea, and the Antarctic Peninsula. From these and the more recent IGY and post-IGY records of about ten interior stations, we may gain a meaningful impression of thermal experience for the continent as a whole.

In the south latitude summer of 1911–12 Scott reported at the pole a mean temperature for December of −8.6° (Max. 5.5°, Min. −19.3°), and a January mean of −18.7° (Max. −3.2°, Min. −29.7°). These should be compared with the summer readings for Eismitte, Greenland (June and July, Table 8-1). The sharp drop in average temperature from December to January suggests a rapid response of the thin, high altitude polar air to reduced insolation that results from the decreasing elevation of the sun above the horizon after the summer solstice on December 22. The low density of dry, nearly dust-free air at an altitude of more than 9000 feet does not permit the absorption of much of the large amount of solar radiation reflected from the snow and ice surfaces. Snow is a particularly poor conductor of heat and absorbs little insolation, reflecting (Table 6-1) up to 90 per cent or more of the insolation received. And it is interesting to recall that the earth is much nearer the sun during this period of the year and receives a larger increment of insolation than at any other period.

The American IGY Amundsen-Scott South Pole Station (el. 9186), where observations have been continued since July 1957, has reported a maximum of 5.5°F in the summer period of continuous daylight and a winter low of −110°F. The prevailing wind is NNE at a mean annual speed of 12.7 knots. On March 1, 1964,[9] increasingly lower temperatures set in. On the average, values dropped 3 degrees per day. A 30-degree change was observed on March 8, from −64° to −34°, and visibility was reduced to zero in blowing snow when winds increased in gusts to 36 miles per hour. On March 15 the thermometer reached −61°. With the annual setting of the sun on March 21, extremely low temperatures occurred with increasing frequency, and less than twenty-four hours after the equinox the thermometer plunged to −96°. Weather conditions in April fluctuated considerably, with mainly clear skies, good visibility, moderate winds, some blowing snow, and ice fog. The temperature rose slightly early in the month but dropped during the second week to the low −90s. A record high for April was set on the 14th when the thermometer read −25°. May continued cold, with a maximum reading of −47° on the 12th.

At Byrd Station, about 450 miles from the sea with an elevation of 5012 feet, a maximum temperature of 30.6° has been observed and an extreme low of −82°. The prevailing wind is NNE at a mean annual speed of 16.5 knots. During the second week of March 1964 the temperature ranged from 0 to −22°, in the third week from 5° to −38°, and during the last week of the month dropped to −60°. April was the warmest on record, the thermometer rising to 11° at one point. Over 2 inches of snow fell during the month. Unlike the South Pole station, no drastic temperature changes followed the last sunrise on April 17. But in May a new record low was established when the thermometer dropped to less than −65° from the 17th to the 23rd, with winds up to 42 knots and much drifting snow. The first two weeks had been very windy with a great deal of ground fog. During the final week the weather cleared somewhat and temperatures rose, producing a high of −5° and a low of −35°.

At Eights Station on the base of Antarctic Peninsula at an elevation of 1380 feet, the temperature has been up to 29° and as low as −60°. Wind direction is not available, but wind speeds appear to average about 10 knots during the year. In 1964 on the 9th and 10th of March

occurred a severe storm that lasted for a little over twenty-four hours, the temperature averaging −5° and the wind gusting up to 51 knots, blowing much snow about the station. It was the first storm since January. A second storm battered the station on March 20 and 21, bringing much snow and winds up to 39 knots. Colder weather ruled during April, a storm on the 4th bringing light snow and gusts to 21 knots, followed by temperatures down to −48°. On April 16 a violent storm brought winds of up to 70 knots, followed by quieter, colder weather when the thermometer ranged from −53° to −17°. Cloudy weather prevailed in May with moderate to strong winds and some snowfall, the temperatures ranging between −15° and −45°.

At McMurdo Station on Ross Island at the inner edge of Ross Sea, with an elevation of 79 feet, the thermometer has risen to 42° and dropped to −59°. The prevailing wind is east at a mean annual speed of 12.2 knots. During the early part of March 1964 the weather was relatively stable, the temperature hovering around zero. During the third week a storm lasting two and a half days brought wind gusts to 48 knots and reduced visibility to zero in the blowing snow. With it came the month's lowest temperature of −31°, a new record low for March at the station. When the wind abated, the low temperatures froze the adjacent waters of McMurdo Sound almost immediately, marking the start of the annual freezeover. The highest temperature for the month was 14°, the lowest −46°. During the first three weeks of May the thermometer fluctuated between 8° and −41°. The minimum for the month was reached on the 24th (−48°), but four days later the maximum of 16° for the month was reached, at the same time that peak winds up to 55 knots were recorded.

Extremely low temperatures have been observed since July 1957 at a number of stations high on the interior plateau. The lowest recorded value was reached on August 24, 1960, at the U.S.S.R. station of Vostok, about 800 miles inland from Shackleton Ice Shelf in Eastern Antarctica at an elevation of 11,440 feet. On this date the thermometer stood at −127°F. The validity of this reading is supported by the occurrence of similarly low values around the same time of the month during the preceding two years: −122° on August 23–24, 1959, and

---

[9] *Bulletin of the Antarctic Projects Officer*, **6**(6): 2–4, April 1965, is the source of the recent data cited for Antarctic stations here and the paragraphs immediately following.

TABLE 8-2
Temperature and Wind Speed Data for Vostok (1958)
Lat., 78°27'S.   Long., 106°52'E.   El. 11,400 ft

	Jan.	Feb.	Mar.	Apr.	May	Jun.	Jul.	Aug.	Sep.	Oct.	Nov.	Dec.	Year
Mean temperature (°F)	−24	−48	−69	−83	−81	−90	−86	−97	−87	−74	−46	−28	−68
Maximum temperature	−9	−20	−53	−45	−45	−53	−47	−67	−49	−42	−29	−15	−9
Minimum temperature	−42	−76	−89	−99	−108	−113	−114	−125	−116	−96	−76	−47	−125
Mean wind speed (knots)	9	7	10	8	10	10	10	9	11	8	8	7	
Mean wind direction	180	180	220	240	240	270	240	220	250	220	220	260	

Source: G. D. Cartwright and M. J. Rubin, "Inside Antarctica No. 6—Meteorology at Mirny," *Weatherwise*, **14**(3): 114, June 1961.

TABLE 8-3

Temperature Observations in Antarctica

Station and Dates	Position	El. in Ft	Jan.	Feb.	Mar.	Apr.	May	Jun.	Jul.	Aug.	Sep.	Oct.	Nov.	Dec.	Year	Av. Range	Abs. Max.	Abs. Min.	Extreme Range
Gauss 1902–03	66°02'S. 89°38'E.	0	30	26	17	4	7	1	-1	-7	0	9	20	30	11	37	41	-41	82
Cape Denison 1912–13	67°00'S. 142°40'E.	20	30	24	12	2	-1	-4	-3	0	-1	5	17	27	9	34	41	-28	69
Cape Adare 1899–1900	71°18'S. 170°09'E.	20	31.6	27	19	9	-2	-14	-12	-14	-7	-1	19	30	7	46	49	-43	92
McMurdo Sound (Ross Island) 1902–04, 1908–09, 1911–12	77°42'S. 166°29'E.	66	24	16	5	-9	-11	-12	-15	-15	-12	-2	15	25	1	40	41	-47	88
Framheim 1911–12	78°38'S. 163°37'W.	36	15	4	-7	-18	-32	-30	-34	-49	-36	-12	4	20	-14	69	32	-74	106
Belgica Drift 1898–99	70°35'S. 86°21'W.	16	30	30	16	11	20	4	11	-2	18	20	28	28	15	32	37	-46	83
Port Charcot (Wandel Island) 1904–05	65°04'S. 64°02'W.	33	33	31	30	23	13	12	-3	21	26	19	32	31	22	36	43	-29	72
Pedermann Island 1908–09	65°10'S. 64°14'W.	115	34	35	34	23	23	20	20	22	21	28	30	34	27	15	48	-11	59
Snow Hill 1902–03	64°22'S. 57°00'W.	39	30	26	14	7	-1	-4	-5	-3	4	15	17	28	11	35	48	-38	86
Paulet Island 1902–03	63°35'S. 55°50'W.		30	28	18	12	5	3	8	10	8	26	25	30	17	27			
Endurance Drift 1915	72°43'S. 44°27'W.		25	7	1	-2	-9	-13	-10	-7	6	20	26	4	39	37	-34	71
Deutschland Drift 1911–12	69°05'S. 38°22'W.		28	22	13	3	-8	-15	-15	-9	9	14	20	28	8	43	38	-34	72
Little America III 1940–41	78°30'S. 163°50'W.	50	17	10	3	-13	-32	-25	-28	-32	-43	-11	6	19	-11	60	43	-75	118
Maudheim 1950–52	71°03'S. 10°55'W.	123	25	21	12	1	-8	-15	-17	-17	-13	-6	7	18	1	42			

Sources: W. Köppen and R. Geiger, *Handbuch der Klimatologie*, **4** (Part U), Table 1, pp. 110–12, and U.S. Weather Bureau, *Monthly Weather Review*, Supp. No. 48, Table 20, p. 117, 1949.

−125° on August 25, 1958. The highest temperature reported from this station in 1958 was −9°F. The station is situated on a gentle slope of the high central plateau of Eastern Antarctica,[10] where downslope winds apparently control general weather experience, and the extremely low temperatures may thus be a product of downgrade movement augmented by radiative cooling that lowers the surface air temperature of the moving air mass. Advection at the time the low temperature was observed was about 11 miles per hour. Details of monthly temperature and wind speed during 1958 at Vostok appear in Table 8-2.

The general severity of Antarctic climate is further illustrated by weather records kept for brief intervals at the coastal stations listed in Table 8-3. Only two (Wandel Island and Pedermann Island), within a few miles of one another and both at approximately the same relatively low latitude of 65°, experienced summer mean temperatures a degree or two above freezing. At Framheim in 1911–12 the mean temperature for December, the warmest summer month, was 20°. The highest temperature recorded that year was 32°, the lowest reached was −74°, and the average temperature of the coldest month was −49°. At Little America III, only a few miles from Framheim on the eastern side of Ross Sea, the warmest month of December

[10] It has become the practice to speak of Eastern and Western Antarctica. These two unequal parts—Eastern Antarctica occupying the section that extends roughly from Ross Sea to Weddell Sea, and Western Antarctica the remainder—are separated by a great system of ranges, the Transantarctic Mountains, that stretch from the western side of Ross Sea to the eastern side of Weddell Sea.

averaged 19°, and the coldest month, September, averaged −43°. The maximum reading at this station was 43°, the minimum for the year −75°. It should also be noted that mean winter temperatures differ from place to place more widely than do mean summer temperatures, and the intensity of winter cold seems to vary from year to year at any one point of observation. The long, dark winter normally lasts from April to October, and the example of Framheim indicates that winter temperatures may remain below zero for as long as eight months. Summer is not a season of warmth but more of an astronomical period in which prolonged daylight is the principal characteristic.

Temperature ranges, both average and extreme, vary from season to season. The monthly averages and the extreme ranges of temperature at Little America, computed from observations made during three separate seasons, are indicated in Table 8-4. The results are in general accordance with observations made at other stations and reveal that winter is the season of maximum temperature variation, when the amplitude between extreme high and extreme low may be over twice the amplitude in summer. Random synoptic changes are responsible for broad-scale temperature fluctuations throughout the year. The alternation between relatively quiet, stable anticyclonic subsidence, producing extreme cold, and the turbulent upsetting of low-level thermal strata by transient linear and cyclonic frontal disturbances determines these fluctuations.

Temperature inversions are as typical over the frozen surface of Antarctica as they are over the ice cap regions around the north pole and

TABLE 8–4

Monthly Range of Temperatures at Little America (°F)

	Jan.	Feb.	Mar.	Apr.	May	Jun.	Jul.	Aug.	Sep.	Oct.	Nov.	Dec.
Mean monthly range (Feb. 1940–Jan. 1941)	11.8	16.0	19.8	19.0	24.5	25.5	23.5	26.4	19.6	20.5	14.8	12.0
Absolute monthly range (computed from records of 3 separate seasons)	43.8	54.0	84.7	80.6	93.4	74.0	93.3	78.0	89.6	67.6	58.1	40.5

Source: U.S. Weather Bureau, *Monthly Weather Review*, Supp. No. 48, Tables 21a and 21b, p. 118, 1949.

TABLE 8–5

Temperature Inversions at Little America III, Apr. 1940–Jan. 1941 (°F)

Altitude in ft	Apr.	May	Jun.	Jul.	Aug.	Sep.	Oct.	Nov.	Dec.	Jan.
16,400	−38.6	−48.5	−46.3	−48.1	−49.0	−48.3	−40.7	−35.3	−23.6	−22.9
13,000	−27.0	−37.5	−34.6	−35.9	−36.4	−35.5	−28.1	−24.9	−12.3	−12.8
9800	−14.6	−26.9	−24.5	−25.4	−24.9	−24.7	−16.8	−13.2	−1.5	−0.9
8200	−8.1	−22.5	−19.8	−21.1	−20.4	−20.2	−11.9	−7.1	2.7	3.9
6400	−3.3	−18.9	−17.1	−18.0	−17.0	−17.7	−6.9	−2.0	7.2	8.1
4800	0.9	−15.5	−13.5	−16.4	−14.8	−15.9	−3.5	1.8	12.0	12.0
3200	3.9	−15.5	−12.5	−16.2	−14.4	−14.3	−2.2	5.4	16.9	14.4
1600	1.2	−17.5	−13.5	−18.4	−14.6	−18.0	−0.4	8.2	20.8	17.1
Surface	−10.7	−35.1	−32.4	−29.9	−31.4	−49.7	−18.8	−9.7	18.1	18.3

Source: U.S. Weather Bureau, *Monthly Weather Review*, Supp. No. 48, Table 6, p. 37, 1949.

probably persist throughout the year over most of the interior. Some idea of Antarctic inversions may be gained from the record of air temperatures (Table 8-5) observed by radiosonde at Little America III between April 25, 1940, and January 15, 1941, from the surface to an altitude of 16,400 feet. Overlying warmer air may extend as high as 3 miles above the earth, as in September 1940; it commonly averages more than 2 miles deep from May to October. From Table 8-5 it should be noted that air temperature 1600 feet above the surface may be nearly 32 degrees higher, as in September, than that within only a few feet of the surface. Inversions were absent or only slightly developed at this station in summertime. This is chiefly due to strong radiation from the white surface during continuous exposure to the sun's rays. Warming of the lower atmospheric strata by reradiation gives rise to a gradual decrease in temperature with increasing altitude, and thus an absence of temperature inversions.

In wintertime inversions are momentarily destroyed by the turbulent air of passing blizzards. Thus, locations exposed to frequent storms have at least the partial advantage of occasional rising temperatures. But the advantages to human beings may be slight indeed. At Little America, for example, in the winter of 1930, the wind increased in velocity from 2 miles per hour at 2 P.M. on July 23 to 49 miles per hour at the same time on the following day, and the temperature rose from −59°F to only −17°F in the twenty-four-hour period.

PRECIPITATION. The cold, dry air of Antarctica releases little moisture to the surface beneath. Almost all of it falls as snow, or in the form of minute crystals of clear ice, or more rarely, as very fine, icy mist. Rain has been known to fall in summertime along the coast, but these observations have only been made at a few widely scattered places for brief and often unrelated periods of time. Snow occasionally falls in large, soft, wet flakes, especially in summertime, and may even appear as graupel, which is somewhat massive and globular, very much like hail. Most of it is fine, light, and dry, however, and the actual amounts that reach the central plateau have the water equivalent of precipitation occurring in desert regions of the world. Wide variability in year-to-year amounts is also characteristic of desert precipitation and is a probable feature of Antarctic weather, indicated by the records by Byrd Station for three years: in 1957, 16.88 inches (water equivalent), in 1958, 1.75 inches, and in 1959, 1.21 inches.

The most striking form of Antarctic precipitation is called ice crystals—tiny, elongated needles of transparent ice. They have been observed during every month of the year but occur with greatest frequency during the colder months of winter. Ice crystals are thought to be present in the air much more of the time than records indicate, for they are sometimes too fine to be visible unless observed against the beam of an artificial light or against the light of the sun. They often fall when there is not a trace of cloud in the sky and are then easily seen by their shimmering reflection of the sun's rays. At times they occur with sufficient density to produce a halo effect around the sun or moon, an effect characteristically common in Antarctica.

In the opinion of experienced Antarctic travelers, precipitation measurements within the normal limits of accuracy are impracticable, for the fine, light flakes of snow and crystals of ice in which it most commonly falls are easily drifted by the lightest winds. Furthermore, most snowfalls are accompanied by winds of considerable velocity, which easily raise old snow from the ground, whirling it aloft to mingle with fresh snow from the air. The measurement of periodic accumulation is also difficult because of the ceaseless rearrangement of drifts by winds of remarkable frequency. Drifts are usually only a few inches to a few feet high, but may reach a height of between 50 and 100 feet.

Most of the surface of the great continental ice sheet is composed of loose snow and hard-packed firn. Firn is a consolidation of tiny, angular fragments of snow shattered under repeated buffeting by the wind. It differs from the loose amalgamation of rounded, granular particles known as névé. Névé has been found in a few localities near the coast, especially on the plateau in Eastern Antarctica near the Prince Charles Mountains.

TABLE 8–6
Estimated Annual Precipitation at Certain Coastal Stations in Antarctica

	In. of Rainfall
Port Charcot	15.0
Pedermann Island	9.8
Maudheim	14.3
Laurie Island	16.3
Deutschland Drift	4.2

From recent investigations of accumulation and depletion the ice sheet appears to be relatively static, due chiefly to the small amount of precipitation. Estimates of snow and ice accumulation for certain Antarctic stations are shown in Table 8-6. The figures are rainfall equivalents, for purposes of comparison with other regions outside Antarctica.

The Norwegian-British-Swedish Antarctic expedition of 1950–51 determined the average annual accumulation of ice at Maudheim to be about 14.3 inches.[11] This figure was obtained by digging a pit 38 feet deep exposing seventeen annual layers of ice accumulation. Each layer approximately equaled the mean annual precipitation in rainfall. From the variations in ice density it was also concluded that some melting of surface ice had taken place at Maudheim every summer since 1935. A field party that traveled 300 miles inland from the coastal station of Maudheim found no such signs of summer thaw on the interior plateau and great variability in the amount of annual accumulation from place to place between the coast and the interior. Windward slopes, normally facing east, gained much more ice each year than leeward slopes. Further examination of the exposed flanks of nunataks (peaks of bare rock, projecting as islands above the surrounding ice and snow) revealed polishing striations and erratic boulders nearly 1000 feet above the ice surface, which indicated the presence of glacial ice in times past at those much greater heights.

Cloud and fog are reportedly common at all points of observation, alternating with frequent periods of calm, clear weather. Most cloud forms are a variation of stratus, although stratocumulus are often seen in summertime, as are cumulus clouds over open water. Fog or mist has been observed along the coast almost every month of the year. Records show a greater preponderance in summer, however, and fog almost always freezes upon exposed surfaces, forming a coating of hard, clear ice as much as an inch thick. At other times, when the air is drier and colder, frost or rime accumulates to a great thickness and often imparts a white coating several inches in depth.

A unique condition, described by meteorologists as "milky," is created in the atmosphere on certain foggy and cloudy days. This condition prevails when low cloud, perhaps combined with fog, imparts a fleecelike wooliness to the atmosphere, in which light is so diffused that no shadows may be seen. Objects on the landscape, particularly figures dressed in white, may suddenly vanish, without moving, and as suddenly reappear. Elevations and depressions, ordinarily used as landmarks, merge into an endless amorphic whiteness. This condition,

[11] Valter Schytt, "Glaciology in Queen Maud Land," *Geographical Review*, 44(1): 70–87, 1954.

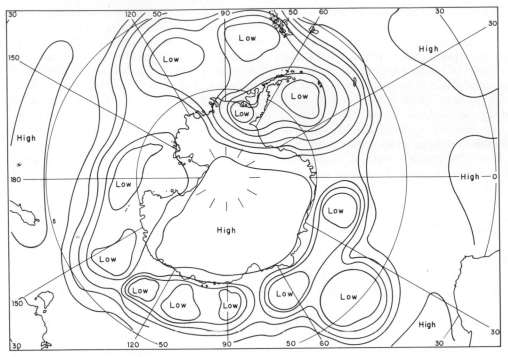

Figure 8.7. Surface synoptic chart at 0600 on February 17, 1958.

similar to the "white-out" familiar in the Arctic, is thought to be due to the multiple reflection of sunlight from below, from above, and from all sides where white surfaces are overlain with cloud or fog.

Most precipitation in Antarctica occurs with the passage of frontal storms that are thought to exert their greatest effect along the coasts (Fig. 8.7). Three areas of semipermanent cyclonic activity have been identified: Ross Sea, Weddell Sea, and Bellinghausen Sea on the west side of Antarctic Peninsula. Many migratory cyclones move toward these areas with notable frequency, merging with and reinforcing the semipermanent circulations. Typical of the southern hemisphere, cyclonic circulations maintain a clockwise vorticity. Traveling cyclonic systems appear to originate over the warmer, open seas in the middle latitudes, move in a generally eastward direction, but curve poleward toward the continent (Fig. 8.8). They do not entirely encircle Antarctica several times, as might be supposed, but tend to enter one of the three preferred areas mentioned above, there to halt before a blocking anticyclone, and from time to time to move up onto the great plateau and continue across the

continent. This is apparently a year-round process. Their eastward paths coincide as a rule with the northern edges of continuous ice, shifting equatorward during the polar night and poleward during the summer season of continuous daylight and higher temperature.

General air movement in Antarctica is a product of several geographical circumstances:

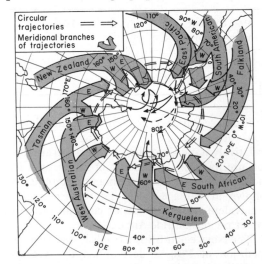

Figure 8.8. Tracks of cyclonic depressions in 1958.

(1) the presence of the large mass of persistent polar ice, (2) the elevation of most of the mass a mile or more above sea level, (3) the much warmer ocean surfaces surrounding the ice cap at sea level, (4) the Coriolis effect.

Air temperatures over the interior of Antarctica remain below zero throughout most of the year. Constantly cold surface air thus tends at all times to move outward and downward over the warmer, unfrozen waters of the southern Atlantic, Pacific, and Indian oceans. (See Table 8-7 for temperatures of scattered oceanic stations beyond the frozen realms of Antarctica.) Deep within Antarctica air movements are certainly much more gradual, wind velocities much lower as a rule, than along the coasts, where steep declivities intensify the outflow, causing katabatic acceleration, especially down the slopes of glacial tongues of ice that reach the sea. A semipermanent anticyclonic circulation seems to exist over Eastern Antarctica, just above the surface at about 10,000 feet (the 700 millibar level). Here an accumulation of subsiding air repeatedly forms, playing a major role in the counterclockwise divergence toward the coast and thus influencing the prevailing direction of general winds for the continent as a whole.

Along the coast the winds are mainly westward, the polar easterlies thus prevailing, as far as the assessment of short and incomplete records can reveal. Their ruling effect is indicated partly in the direction taken by coastal currents, in turn revealed through the movement of icebergs. The tabular iceberg, virtually unknown in the Arctic, is particularly characteristic of Antarctic waters. Detached at some point from one of the many masses of shelf ice, these large, flat-topped slabs with perpendicular sides, sometimes 20 miles or more in length, move very slowly and majestically northwestward, then northward, and finally eastward as they enter the westerly drift of the southern oceans, a circumpolar current impelled eastward by the prevailing westerlies of the higher middle latitudes.

The wind in Antarctica, the driving fury of the blizzard, is the dominant, overwhelming feature of atmospheric behavior. The Antarctic explorer Frank Debenham describes it this way:[12]

[12] Frank Debenham, *Antarctica*, The Macmillan Company, New York, p. 126, 1961.

The traveller in the Antarctic, therefore, brings back with him the lasting impression that it is nearly always blowing, from the ferocity and shriek of a blizzard to the nagging breeze that drives snow against his face and hastens frostbite to his nose and cheeks. Yet against that background of constant pitiless wind he will also have a memory of a calm day, perhaps only two or three of them in a whole summer which will stand out clearly and gloriously because of its very rarity.

A really calm day in the Antarctic is nothing less than startling. The sudden change from the noise and hurly-burly of a blizzard or from the soft susurrus of the snow driving over the surface in the lightest breeze has something of the awed pleasure of a gnawing toothache that has miraculously stopped, but is almost certain to come on again. . . . Perhaps most startling is the silence because it is so utter, so complete, that one can hear a man talking half a mile away, one can hear the tiny crackle of one's breath freezing, or the high piping of a seal miles out on the ice.

Air over the ice cap at temperatures far below zero is very much colder and gains relative densities far greater than those of air over the open sea, where temperatures are usually more than 30°. As it flows seaward in the normal tendency for fluid air to strive for pressure equilibrium, it sweeps down off the plateau, gaining speed with the influence of gravity, to blow in a gale out across the shelf ice and the open sea. Any slight increase in temperature due to compression as it loses altitude is apparently negligible.

At all points of observation high velocity winds have occurred. Records indicate, however, that wide differences exist in both average and extreme wind velocities from season to season and from place to place. At Little America, for example, the average wind speed during three separate years of observation was 11 miles per hour, the extreme maximum (persisting for a period of at least five minutes) was 62 miles per hour. At another station not too far distant from Little America, also on the east side of Ross Sea, winds were measured on one occasion at 88 miles per hour and were estimated to reach 150 miles per hour, when an airplane was torn loose from its moorings, carried a distance of one-half mile, and dropped to the earth a total wreck. At Cap Denison, in Adelie Land, the mean wind speed for one year of continuous observation was almost 45 miles per hour with frequent gusts of 80–100 miles

TABLE 8–7
Temperature at Islands in Oceans Surrounding Antarctica (°F)

Station and Dates	Position	El. in Ft	Jan.	Feb.	Mar.	Apr.	May	Jun.	Jul.	Aug.	Sep.	Oct.	Nov.	Dec.	Year	Av. Range	Abs. Max.	Abs. Min.	Extreme Range
Laurie Island (South Orkneys) 1903–34	66°44′S. 44°39′W.	23	32	32	31	26	19	13	12	14	20	24	28	31	23	20	47	−28	75
Gruytviken (South Georgia) 1903–34	54°13′S. 36°33′W.	13	41	41	40	36	32	29	29	29	32	35	37	39	35	12	69	9	60
Kerguelen 1902–03	49°25′S. 69°53′E.	53	44	45	39	39	35	37	33	34	33	34	39	41	38	12	67	17	50
Heard Island 1902–03	53°08′S. 73°34′E.		38	38	33	31	29	30	28	28	28	29	34	37	32	10			
Macquarie Island 1912–15	54°30′S. 158°57′E.	13	43	43	42	41	39	37	37	38	38	38	40	42	43	6	51	24	27

Source: W. Köppen and R. Geiger, *Handbuch der Klimatologie, 4* (Part U), Table 1, pp. 110–12.

per hour, and on one occasion reaching a maximum of more than 200 miles per hour. Adelie Land has indeed been referred to as the "home of the blizzard," for blizzards rage almost constantly along that section of the Antarctic coast. For days, even weeks, the wind varies between gale and hurricane velocity, blowing from the southeast with such regularity that travelers may confidently determine direction with respect to it. Objects weighing hundreds of pounds, and men themselves, have frequently been swept through the air for yards. Even seals avoid resting on the shelf ice of the immediate shoreline, for they are invariably blown into the water when they do. At Commonwealth Bay in Adelie Land a gale in July 1913 produced winds averaging 89 miles per hour for twelve consecutive hours. The average velocity for July was 55.6 miles per hour. In August the same year the wind averaged 80.6 miles per hour during one twenty-four-hour period, with gusts reaching more than 100 miles per hour. The calmest month from 1911 to 1914 was February 1912, when mean wind speed was 26.2 miles per hour. Blizzards occur with greatest frequency during the winter months, although they have been observed at various times throughout the year. They may last for only a few hours or for several days.

The normal pattern of weather is dominated at most interior stations by a continued alternation of strong and light winds, with only occasional calms. But at a few stations a preponderance of calms has been reported (Table 8-8). Ross Barrier, for example, is said to have more calm days than stormy ones during the year, with the result that temperatures remain very low. The Barrier, although standing between 60 and 160 feet above the sea along its outer edges, is a relatively level expanse of more than 150,000 square miles. Storms at nearly all stations on the Barrier bring a rise in temperature as warmer, overlying air is mixed in the general turbulence with colder air from the surface. The change from clear, cold calm to violent, stormy blizzard may take place very suddenly and with little warning and then, just as suddenly, give way once again to calm on Ross Barrier. Calms appear to be more frequent here during the winter period of continual darkness.

Storm winds of high velocity are often of limited extent, as though hemmed in on all sides by a wall. Smaller storms have been called "whirlies" and may be remarkably distinct from surrounding calms. Mecking reports[13] that "Laseron one day was skinning at one end of a seal and remained in perfect calm, while McLean, at the other extremity, was on the edge of a furious vortex." Whirlies that travel over the open sea have been seen to raise columns of water, frozen spray, and ice in the form of a waterspout to heights of from 200 to 400 feet.

At all stations surface winds from all points of the compass have been observed. The mean direction of predominant offshore winds is generally east or southeast, mainly in response to the Coriolis effect, which deflects outflowing winds toward the left. This is a natural quality of anticyclonic air movement in the southern hemisphere.

The direction of surface winds is usually at variance with wind directions aloft, and surface winds are often quite shallow. At Little America, for example, on the morning of September 30, 1930, when the surface wind was easterly and moving at 9 miles per hour, the wind generator 65 feet overhead was being propelled at a fair speed by a wind from the west.

The direction of higher altitude winds is determined by observation of clouds between 10,000 and 15,000 feet in height, of smoke from Mt. Erebus (el. 12,360) on Ross Island, and in recent years, of pilot balloons that are visible in clear weather by theodolite at heights of more than 10 miles. From such observations it is evident that air at higher levels constantly invades Antarctica from lower latitudes to replace that which flows out near the surface. These higher altitude invasions take place at frequent, though irregular, intervals and are probably related to the development of peripheral cyclonic storms. Because they originate as warmer air, they are thought to bring a certain amount of the moisture that falls on the interior in moderate quantities as crystals of ice or flakes of fine, dry snow. There thus exists, to a marked degree, an exchange between warmer oceanic air in lower latitudes and the cold, dry air of Antarctica, an exchange that is integrally related to a prevailing equatorward pressure gradient, which in turn is the

[13] O. Nordenskjold and L. Mecking *The Geography of Polar Regions*, American Geographical Society Special Publication No. 8, New York, 1926.

TABLE 8-8
Frequency of Surface Wind Directions (%)

Station	Lat.	Long.	Jan.									Jul.								
			N	NE	E	SE	S	SW	W	NW	Calm	N	NE	E	SE	S	SW	W	NW	Calm
Gauss 1902–03	66°02'S.	89°38'E.	0	4	50	16	5	2	11	3	9	0	0	64	5	1	2	7	3	18
Cape Denison 1913	67°00'S.	142°40'E.	2	0	2	86	6	1	2	1	0	0	0	0	16	83	0	1	0	0
Cape Adare 1899–1900	71°18'S.	170°01'E.	3	2	20	27	7	2	2	3	34	0	2	11	25	11	0	2	3	46
McMurdo Sound (Ross Island) 1908–09	77°42'S.	166°29'E.	9	17	0	48	13	2	4	3	4	20	9	3	27	6	0	0	3	31
Framheim 1911–12	78°38'S.	163°37'W.	1	3	32	9	11	18	3	0	23	0	3	39	8	11	15	3	1	20
Little America III 1940–41	78°30'S.	163°50'W.	2	3	29	25	24	13	3	1	0	6	5	32	11	30	11	2	3	0
Belgica Drift 1898–99	70°35'S.	86°21'W.	2	28	30	18	9	5	2	0	6	4	1	8	14	14	11	17	7	24
Port Charcot 1904–05	65°04'S.	64°02'W.	10	40	10	5	5	16	3	3	8	1	7	1	6	63	7	0	6	9
Pedermann Island 1908–09	65°10'S.	64°14'W.	10	25	6	6	5	8	3	3	34	14	29	4	10	14	8	1	3	17
Snow Hill 1902–03	64°22'S.	57°00'W.	7	25	4	2	16	27	7	1	11	3	8	3	1	16	42	4	0	23
Endurance Drift 1915	72°43'S.	44°27'W.	4	22	26	7	11	11	8	3	8	7	1	4	6	22	36	11	5	8
Deutchland Drift 1911–12	69°05'S.	38°22'W.	10	33	6	1	5	25	9	11	0	8	4	6	13	16	33	11	8	1

Sources: W. Köppen and R. Geiger, *Handbuch der Klimatologie, 4* (Part U), Table 7, pp. 115–18; and U.S. Weather Bureau, *Monthly Weather Review,* Supp. No. 48, Table 262, p. 134.

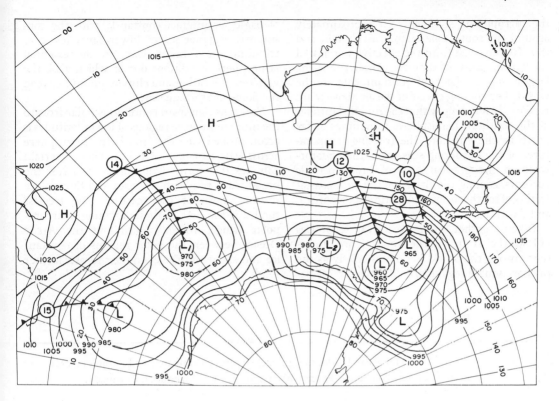

Figure 8.9. Synoptic chart for the south Indian Ocean for June 12, 1958.

result of exceedingly strong pressure contrasts between the Antarctic and the southern oceans (Fig. 8.9).

But the repeated development of steep pressure gradients takes place only between the continental periphery and the surrounding seas. This is mainly because the Antarctic anticyclones are shallow, although very cold. In fact, as most of interior Antarctica is over 6000 feet in altitude, it lies above the over-all mass of the cold, clear, dry anticyclones with their characteristic northward flow. Thus, most of interior Antarctica reaches upward into the variable, though generally poleward, drift of air from lower latitudes.

Sea level pressures along the coast average somewhat higher in summer than in winter, the season when wind velocities are greater. At Little America in 1940 the average barometric readings from June to October were 974 millibars (28.751 inches), and from November to May 988 millibars (29.152 inches). The lowest reading in the Ross Sea area between 1899 and 1940 was 933 millibars (27.54 inches) in 1940, and the highest 1030 millibars (30.43 inches) in 1912.

Northward, between latitudes 55° and 65°S., is a zone of repeated low atmospheric pressures and variable strong winds that are related to the eastward passage of frequent, tempestuous cyclonic storms. The northern side of this zone is a region of prevailing west winds, famed among seafaring men as the Roaring Forties because of their gale velocities and almost unrelieved persistence. The latter arises chiefly from the fact that they develop over the virtually unimpeded surface of an oceanic belt that passes entirely around the world in the upper middle latitudes. Their predominantly eastward movement within these latitudes is mainly traceable to the hydrodynamic effect of the earth's rotation upon north-flowing air from Antarctica and south-flowing air from the subtropical, semipermanent oceanic highs farther north. This is the principal locus of cyclogenesis from which revolving disturbances then curve southeastward toward the Antarctic coasts, where they may join resident depressions in one of the three major cyclonic areas referred to earlier.

Vast in area, elevated well above the level of

the surrounding seas, centered approximately around the south pole of the earth's axis, and thus far removed from the effective warmth of the sun for most of the year, Antarctica is the largest single region of constant cold in the world. The cooling effects of the air above it are repeatedly felt deep within the middle latitudes of the southern hemisphere, sometimes as far north as the equator. The freezing temperatures of the bordering seas are borne equatorward in the gradual drift of broad oceanic currents, cooling the air above the west coastal waters of southern South America, South Africa, and Australia.

Taken together, the polar ice cap territories of both the Arctic and the Antarctic are important among the world's climates chiefly as the primary source regions of cold, polar air. Masses of frigid air interact constantly with the consistently warmer air of lower latitudes, contributing, in a broad way, to the essential atmospheric conditions out of which arise the varieties of weather and climate found between the poles and the equator.

The transition from continuous polar frost to the more temperate regions of lower latitudes is accomplished in the southern hemisphere across vast expanses of ocean. Hence, certain climates that form significant belts across the broad tracts of North America and Eurasia are missing south of the equator. The treeless tundra is the first of these, forming a circumpolar fringe, roughly encircling the Arctic Ocean, between the polar regions of constant ice and snow and the evergreen forests farther south.

References

BAIRD, P. D.: *The Polar World*, Longmans, Green & Company, Ltd., London, 1964.

DEBENHAM, F.: *Antarctica, The Story of a Continent*, The Macmillan Company, New York, 1961.

DORSEY, H. G.: "Arctic Meteorology," *Compendium of Meteorology*, American Meteorological Society, Boston, 1951.

LAMB, H. H.: "South Polar Atmospheric Circulation and the Nourishment of the Antarctic Ice Cap," *Meteorological Magazine*, 81: 79–98, 1952.

MEINARDUS, W.: "Klimakunde der Antarktis," *Handbuch der Klimatologie*, 4 (Part U), Berlin, 1938.

PRIESTLEY, SIR R. E., ed.: *Antarctic Research*, Butterworth, Washington, D.C., 1964.

SYMPOSIUM ON ANTARCTICA: *Antarctic Meteorology*, The Pergamon Press, New York, 1960.

U.S. ARMY, QUARTERMASTER RESEARCH AND ENGINEERING COMMAND: *Atlas of Arctic Environment*, Natick, Mass., 1961.

U.S. NAVY: *Marine Climatic Atlas of the World*, Vol. 7, Antarctica, 1965.

———: *Marine Climatic Atlas of the World*, Vol. 6, Arctic Ocean, 1963.

chapter 9

THE TUNDRA

The tundra[1] of northern North America and Eurasia is a zone of transition between the frost-bound, barren polar ice cap and the wooded tracts of the boreal forest toward the south. It is a region of subtly varied landscapes, a rolling, nearly level terrain that is almost completely devoid of trees. Its climate is also varied, but again, like the floristic features to which it gives rise, it is unique, distinguishable from other climates by the regular occurrence of long, very cold winters, short, cool summers, and a low annual fall of rain and snow. Ice cap and tundra together are often spoken of as the polar lands, or the Arctic.

Only in the northern hemisphere is the tundra a fully developed region, although it is represented in a fragmentary way in small, isolated patches along the coast of Antarctica and on certain islands in the South Atlantic, South Pacific, and Indian oceans. It also appears in warmer latitudes, even along the equator, on the upper slopes of mountains above the tree line, where it forms part of the complex mountain climates of the world (Chapter 24) and is there called alpine tundra. Tundra landscapes that appear in rugged territories of strong relief and high elevations are more apt to be a consequence of altitude and slope than of latitude. In this chapter the term *tundra* is applied, as a

[1] From the Finnish *tundren*, meaning a rolling, treeless plain.

means of regional distinction, to lands of gentle relief that generally lie at less than 1500 feet above sea level.

The North American tundra (Fig. 9.1) extends in an almost unbroken belt from the Alaskan shores of the Bering Sea to the coast of Labrador. Beginning south of the Yukon River, where a broad and uneven tract stretches inland for more than 100 miles, it becomes narrower northward around the perimeter of Seward peninsula and the western end of Brooks Range until, along the Arctic shores of Alaska, it widens again to a breadth of about 200 miles between the foot of Brooks Range and Point Barrow. Where mountain and sea coast converge near the Alaska boundary, it is confined to a narrow coastal strip and then, beyond the Mackenzie delta, expands in an ever-widening band northeastward across the lower slopes of the many islands in the Canadian archipelago and southeastward across the mainland districts of Mackenzie and Keewatin to the shores of Hudson Bay. It appears east of Hudson Bay in the northern part of Ungava and Labrador. The tundra reaches a maximum north–south extent of nearly 2000 miles between James Bay at 55°N. Lat. and the poleward tip of Greenland at around 83°N. Lat.

While more than four-fifths of Greenland's mountainous bulk is ice-covered the year round, tundra landscapes appear along the

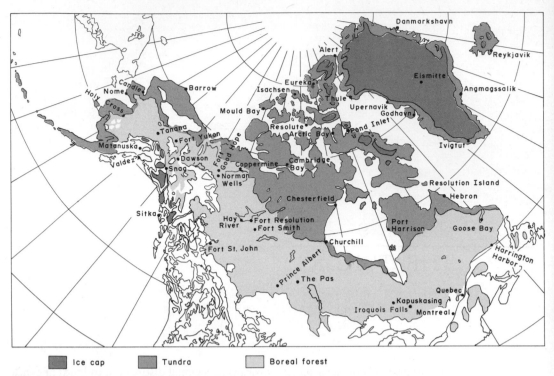

Figure 9.1. Ice cap, tundra, and boreal forest in North America.

Ice cap   Tundra   Boreal forest

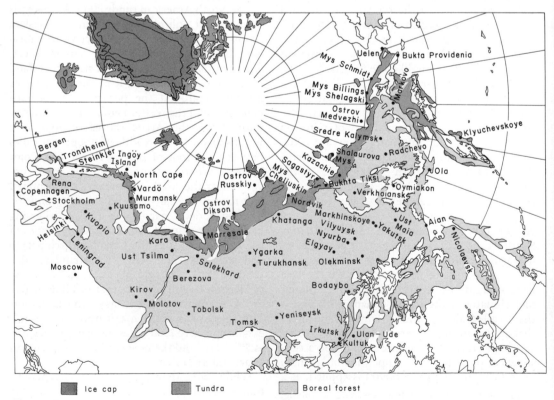

Figure 9.2. Ice cap, tundra, and boreal forest in Eurasia.

Ice cap   Tundra   Boreal forest

margins of the frost-bound plateau. Where its jagged coasts are low and are washed by the waters of the unfrozen sea in summertime, there are scattered patches of seasonally ice-free barrens in many places along the water's edge and in notable expanses around Scoresby Sound and the far north coast of Peary Land.

Tundra is present on at least the coastal lowlands of the islands of Iceland, Spitzbergen, Novaya Zemlya, Franz Josef Land, Northland, the New Siberian Islands, and Wrangel Island, where the winter mantle of ice and snow disappears for several weeks in summertime. On the Eurasian mainland it is an almost continuous belt extending from the north coast of Norway to the Siberian coast of the Bering Sea, and thus in its over-all distribution nearly encloses the polar ice cap regions of the Arctic Ocean and Greenland.

The Eurasian tundra is narrower than that of North America and is confined to higher latitudes, most of it lying north of 65° (Fig. 9.2). It begins along the Arctic coast of Norway and the Kola peninsula as a band less than 100 miles in width, reappearing northeast of the White Sea and broadening toward the east into a belt between 300 and 400 miles wide from the Ob River to the Taimyr peninsula. Between the Khatanga River and the Lena delta it is generally less than 200 miles wide, and its uneven breadth diminishes still further beyond the Lena, becoming a narrow coastal strip along the poleward flanks of the Anadyr Mountains and the ranges of the Chukotski peninsula. Along the northeast coast of Siberia it appears in unequal patches from Bering Strait to the Kamchatka peninsula, occupying considerable areas along the lower valleys of the Anadyr and Penzhina rivers.

The poleward limits of the tundra coincide approximately with the edge of the sea, along the coast of the Arctic Ocean and its adjoining seas and bays. Inland, however, and generally southward, where it merges with the boreal forest or with mountainous terrain, its boundaries are much less definitely determined by the northern limits of forest tree growth. It is plainly quite as impossible to establish a definite boundary line between tundra and taiga[2] as it is between the adjacent climates of milder latitudes.

[2] The boreal forest, northern coniferous forest, sub-Arctic forest.

Plant Life

The most striking feature of the tundra is the absence of forest trees. Except in certain localities favorable for the development of root systems sufficiently strong to support tall tree forms and sheltered from icy winds, arctic plant life is dominantly low-growing and densely matted on the damp, cold ground. Still, some woody plants, including species of willow, birch, and heather, are found. The arctic willow (*Salix arctica*) and white heather (*Cassiope tetragona*) have been identified as far north as Ellesmere Island, beyond the latitude of 80°; here they are usually low, creeping forms, however, seldom rising much more than a foot above the surface. The willow in particular grows laterally along the ground rather than vertically, and in this recumbent, vinelike form appears in many places on the tundra as an extensive mat of dense vegetation.

The treeless nature of the tundra arises in part from the fact that only a very shallow layer of surface soil is released from winter frost during the brief summer growing season. The subsoil remains solidly frozen, sometimes from within a few inches of the surface to depths of 1000 feet or more. This condition is commonly called permafrost and extends southward in many places well into the boreal forest (Fig. 9.3).

The depth to which tundra surfaces thaw in summertime is, of course, variable, ranging from only a few inches in many areas to 2 or 3 feet or more, especially along the banks of the principal streams. But even when frost-free, tundra soils tend to remain cold and waterlogged throughout the summer, particularly in poorly drained sections, for meltwater and occasional summer rains cannot percolate downward into the permafrost layer. Nor can the rootlets of plants penetrate the permafrost. Hence, by their shallowness tundra soils prevent the development of root systems strong enough to provide mechanical support for trees of forest size. And shallow soils that are sodden a good part of the time cannot adequately anchor the roots of tall, exposed plants against the strength of high-velocity winds over much of the tundra.

Saturated soils, underlain by solidly frozen substrata, also contribute to the levelness of the tundra. By virtue of their somewhat fluid state, the soils on slopes containing a good proportion of clay and other fine materials commonly tend

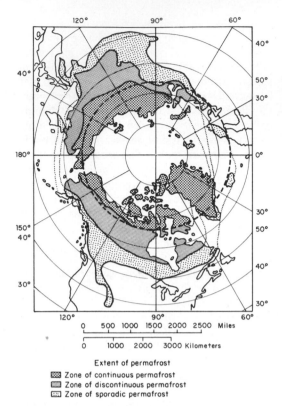

Figure 9.3. Permafrost distribution in North America and Eurasia. [U.S. Air Force, *Handbook of Geophysics*, ed. 2, 1961]

to slide downward in a process described as solifluction or soil creep. In this manner a general tendency toward leveling prevails, by the reduction of heights and filling in of depressions.

Quite the opposite effect is seen, however, from the disturbance of the soil by severe frost action. This produces, where the overburden is deep, features known as frost mounds, or pingos, that may stand as high as 200 feet or more above the surrounding terrain and may be several hundred feet in diameter. Peaty tussocks or hummocks and the curious sorting of clay and stony materials that form soil polygons and stone rings are other features of frost action in tundra soils.

The main reason for the typical absence of trees is the shortness of the growing season and the fact that the warmest month averages no more than 50°F. In temperatures like these woody plants tend to remain dwarfed, often prostrate. It has long been generally accepted

that the theoretical position of the 50°F isotherm for the warmest month may serve as a guide to the placement of the boundary between tundra and taiga. But it is useful only as a rough rule of thumb, for in many places it does not at all coincide with the southern limits of forest-free areas.

Another important temperature relationship to note is that most woody plants undergo vegetative growth only when air temperatures around them are 43°F or higher. They begin growing when this value is reached and cease when temperatures drop below it. In this it should be noted that the actual temperature of the plant's immediate environment (the surface soil, water, and air close around it) may, on sunny days and on sunny slopes, be 20 or 30 degrees higher than the air temperature several feet above the ground. The dark surfaces of the plants and soils take radiant heat directly from the sun. Under these circumstances, plus the advantage of continuous sunlight at very high latitudes in summer, plants might be expected to grow luxuriantly. But their actual growth is very slow, for temperatures all summer long repeatedly drop below the freezing point. Many species, especially among the woody plants, require a developmental period of several years before bearing flowers or fruit for the first time. At the same time they are often very long-lived; in the trailing stems of juniper and Lapland rhododendron over four hundred annual growth rings have been counted.

Insufficient summer rain, low atmospheric humidity, and high winds are unquestionably other important deterrents to tree growth often combining together to cause physiological drought, that is, an excess of moisture loss by evaporation and transpiration from the plant's foliage over moisture intake through its roots.

A preponderance of exposed bedrock in many areas, overlain with only scattered patches of thin, immature soils, also precludes the ready development of higher plants. Such a dearth of soils in the Arctic regions of North America and Eurasia is largely a consequence of ancient glaciation, when masses of north polar ice expanded southward over these lands and eroded away much of the loose surface material. Continental ice sheets are thought to have advanced and receded several, perhaps many times over these northern regions.

Generally speaking, the number of plant

Figure 9.4. Moss-lichen heath in the tundra of northern Norway. [Photo J. M. Aitken]

species in the Arctic is relatively small, whereas the number of individuals within a species is commonly very large. Those hardy forms capable of surviving the rigors of the tundra climate often occur in such dense profusion as to form a thick cushion of vegetation wherever growing conditions are favorable. And their conspicuous luxuriance is accomplished without the protective qualities found on the plants of more temperate regions, for there are no stinging or poisonous plants, and none with spines or thorns. Such protection is not needed. Many, however, have drought-resistant properties such as small, thick, leathery leaves or leaves and stems that are densely covered with hairs, reducing transpiration and enabling the plants to withstand the loss of moisture due to low atmospheric humidity and high winds.

TUNDRA LANDSCAPES. When the deep frost of winter settles in, the tundra becomes a bleak and lonely region of monotonous whiteness, seemingly without life and incapable of supporting life. As the sun dips lower toward the southern horizon and is seen at most for only a few hours each day (Fig. 6.1), darkness prevails, relieved chiefly by a dim twilight arising from the pale gleam of the moon, starlight of unusual brilliance, and the scintillating colors of the Northern Lights.

Summer is the season when the tundra, despite a general appearance of apparently endless and unrelieved emptiness, quickly and briefly breaks into life. Out of the first pools of open water emerge millions of mosquitoes, which hover, with hordes of gnats and other trouble-

some insects, in quivering clouds even over the remaining patches of unmelted snow, and upon these feed countless flocks of birds newly arrived from more temperate regions far to the south. Plant life, too, responds with almost equal suddenness to the warming effect of the higher sun and the lengthening day, creating a diversity of vegetational landscape that reflects not only a variety of atmospheric properties but the influence of local conditions of drainage, the depth and friability of the soil, the slope and exposure of the ground as well.

Discernible in the disordered patterns of vegetation are broad regional divisions that may be said to mark stages in the general transition from ice cap to boreal forest. These landscapes, arranged from north to south, roughly from seacoast to forest, are the rocky barrens, moss and lichen heath, shrub tundra, and wooded tundra.

Perhaps the dreariest of all tundra landscapes are the rocky barrens, or rock deserts, seemingly without any plant life whatever. They are chiefly seen wherever the weathered face of exposed bedrock stands elevated above the surrounding terrain in low, flat-topped tablelands or in rough and irregular knolls and ridges. They are also present on unstable rocky slopes or screes and on the shifting, gravelly tracts of beaches and alluvial lowlands that are annually ground beneath moving masses of water-borne ice.

The rock desert is distinguished from other tundra landscapes by having only an incomplete cover of plant life, if any, which arises in the main from the virtual absence of soil. Soil-forming processes, weathering and decomposition, are inactive for most of the year on the frozen lands of these high latitudes. Hence, despite the annual work of frost-shattering, the reduction of bedrock into small particles proceeds very much more slowly than in warmer regions. This is one reason for the widespread presence of bare, exposed bedrock in many sections of the tundra. Another is the erosive action of ancient continental glaciers, which are thought to have removed much soil material that may have been present a very long time ago.

A virtually complete plant cover is characteristic of the remaining tundra landscapes. On the drier, better-drained interfluvial areas (Fig. 9.4) moss and lichen heaths are seen. On these vast, rolling plains flowering herbs, grasses, and low shrubs are submerged in a deep carpet of lichens such as the so-called reindeer mosses (*Cladonia spp.*) and Iceland moss (*Cetraria islandica*). These are pale yellow and white in color and dominate the landscape to such a degree that it often seems from a distance to be covered with snow.

On lower ground and generally in wetter circumstances the moss-lichen heath merges gradually into the dwarf shrub tundra. This landscape is perhaps the closest to a typical tundra, although it has many competitors. Here are found several varieties of woody plants, including the ground birch (*Betula glandulosa*), Labrador tea (*Loedum spp.*), Arctic willow (*Salix arctica*), various berry bushes (*Vaccinium spp.*), Arctic heather (*Cassiope spp.*), and certain rhododendrons. Beneath these more prominent forms, which are seldom more than knee high (Fig. 9.5), is a thick, damp, resilient carpet of mosses and lichens into which the traveler may sink ankle-deep. The shrub tundra is somewhat more plentiful nearer the southernmost wooded tundra into which it imperceptibly merges, and there it is often seen as a ground cover beneath the small, widely scattered forest trees.

The last of the general landscape types, the wooded tundra, is distinguished from the truly treeless tundra by the presence of innumerable, although widely scattered trees. Appearing individually or in clumps (Fig. 9.6), they are erect and fairly tall, usually more than 6 feet in height. In North America the white spruce

(*Picea glauca*), black spruce (*Picea mariana*), larch (*Larix laricina*), various poplars (*Populus balsamifera*, *P. tremuloides*), birches (*Betula spp.*), alders (*Alnus spp.*), and juniper (*Juniperus communis*) are common. In Eurasia the Scots pine (*Pinus sylvestris*), Siberian larch (*Larix sibirica*), poplars, birches, and willows are among the common woody plants. The wooded tundra is distinct from the boreal forest in having a much larger percentage of its area occupied by moss-lichen-shrub forms than by trees. In fact, large interfluvial areas often are entirely free of forest forms, and only in stream valleys and in other protective depressions are forest trees found. Along the banks of north-flowing streams in particular the wooded tundra extends its poleward distribution into the more distinctly treeless realms. Along its southern margins, where the percentage of land occupied by trees becomes greater than that occupied by mosses, lichens and shrubs, the boreal forest may be said to begin. The line on the map (Fig. 9.1) approximately marking this separation thus indicates the southern extent of the tundra region as a whole.

Other significant landscape features include bogs, sedge-grass meadows, the ubiquitous flowering herbs, and innumerable lakes and rivers.

Bog, or marsh, is common in low, level areas where the drainage is poor. It is typically dominated by hygrophytic plants that frequently cluster together in tussocks or *têtes de femmes*. Among the common species are sphagnum mosses, sedges, and equisetum, bordered on their drier margins by dwarfed, water-tolerant shrubs like the Labrador tea, bilberry, crowberry, and cloudberry. Marshy tracts become more widespread toward the southern reaches of the tundra, occupying as much as half the lowland areas in the wooded tundra and penetrating in significant proportions into the zone of continuous forest. A conspicuous region of plentiful marshland extends over thousands of square miles of the broad, low-lying basin of the Ob River, reaching southward from its mouth deep into the Siberian forests. The proportion of marshland decreases from west to east in the tundra of Eurasia; it seems to have a more general distribution throughout the tundra in North America.

Arctic meadows or prairies of predominantly grass and sedge are oftentimes encountered on

Figure 9.5. Low shrub tundra. [Photo J. M. Aitken]

Figure 9.6. Wooded tundra. [Photo J. M. Aitken]

somewhat drier lowlands, especially the plains of ancient lake beds, notably in the district of Keewatin west of Hudson Bay. Both meadow and marshland are thought to occupy a transitory or subclimax position in the Arctic, for their margins are actively invaded by species of plants from among the main vegetation groups described earlier in this chapter. This again suggests the instability of plant associations in the tundra.

Among the more strikingly colorful features to be seen within the tundra are the countless gaily blossoming herbs that provide startling and welcome relief to the generally dreary and monotonous landscape. Well over one hundred species of flowering herbs are known. Clustering closely together in rounded, cushion communities or extending widely over the sunny slopes of low hills are many varieties resembling those of warmer latitudes. The yellow buttercup (*Ranunculus spp.*) and arnica (*Arnica spp.*), white or purple saxifrage, blue lupine (*Lupinus spp.*), and the blue-white Arctic crocus (*Pulsatilla spp.*) are typical varieties.

A final distinguishing feature of tundra landscapes is the presence of thousands of lakes and rivers, very often linked together in a complex, disrupted drainage pattern that is traceable to the effects of ancient continental glaciation. Though not uniformly distributed, they are abundantly present in the arctic regions of both North America and Eurasia.

Climatic Conditions

Much of what is commonly expressed about the atmospheric behavior of tundra regions is conjectural, just as it is for most of the ice cap regions. In relation to total area, weather stations are few, widely scattered, located principally along the edges of the Arctic Ocean and its adjoining seas and bays. Only a few lie at any distance from the coast, with the result that little information is available specifically relating to the broad inland tracts that make up the greater part of the tundra landscapes. The records of observation at many stations are of short duration and are often discontinuous and fragmentary as well. Thus the conclusions based upon existing data will have to remain tentative for some time to come. The generalizations in the paragraphs that follow must be taken in this light and will, it is hoped, gradually be improved upon as more accurate and more plentiful data become available. Weather observation facilities have been expanded more in the Arctic during recent years than in any other part of the world. Around two hundred weather stations of various classes are now in operation, where fewer than fifty existed before World War II. At most of the stations only surface data on temperature, rainfall, wind, and pressure are collected, but many of the newer ones conduct upper air observations as well, marking a notable advance in the study of high altitude atmospheric levels. This is related in part to the operational needs of military preparedness, in part to the expansion of commercial polar air travel, and in part to the need for development of more accurate weather forecasting for mid-latitude regions in North America and Eurasia.

The climate of the tundra is mainly a consequence of high latitude, resulting in a short polar summer[3] of continuous daylight that alternates with a long winter of continual twilight and darkness. The seasonal rhythm arising in consequence of these astronomical relationships produces intense cold that settles over most of the tundra in wintertime and a summer warmth sufficient to melt away most of the winter's ice and snow. But other conditions vary the effect of latitude. Most important among these are the influence of the sea and the presence of mountain barriers in northwestern North America, northwestern Europe, and eastern Siberia, barriers that stand in the way of warm currents of air from the unfrozen surfaces of the North Pacific and the North Atlantic.

North America and Eurasia are separated by polar arms of the Atlantic and Pacific oceans, whose relatively warm waters penetrate the Arctic regions through the Bering Sea, Davis Strait, and the Norwegian Sea. The moderating effect of this marine influence is seen in the lower annual range of temperature and in the more abundant precipitation of stations in relative proximity to the Atlantic and Pacific.

The mean annual temperature range at Nome is 46 degrees, and at Resolution Island

[3] A summer season, as we think of it in the mid-latitudes, is absent in the tundra just as it is in the polar ice cap regions. The term is used, along with the terms *spring, fall,* and *winter,* as a convenience of exposition in the discussion of annual changes in atmospheric conditions.

TABLE 9-1

Climatic Data for Tundra Stations in North America and Eurasia
(Temp., °F; Rainfall, In.)

Station	Lat.	El. in Ft		Jan.	Feb.	Mar.	Apr.	May	Jun.	Jul.	Aug.	Sep.	Oct.	Nov.	Dec.	Year
North America																
Arctic Bay	73°00'	36	T	-20	-27	-17	-4	20	36	43	41	30	14	-6	-17	
			R	0.4	0.5	0.4	0.3	0.6	0.6	0.7	1.5	0.7	0.7	0.5	0.4	7.3
Cambridge Bay	69°07'	45	T	-25	-28	-19	-7	15	35	47	45	31	12	-9	-21	
			R	0.3	0.2	0.2	0.2	0.3	0.5	0.8	0.9	0.6	0.7	0.5	0.3	5.5
Chesterfield Inlet	63°45'	4	T	-27	-26	-17	1	21	37	48	46	38	24	0	-17	
			R	0.4	0.6	0.7	0.7	0.5	0.9	2.4	1.8	2.0	1.2	0.8	0.9	12.9
Hebron	58°13'	25	T	-6	-5	6	18	32	40	47	48	41	31	20	4	
			R	0.9	0.7	0.9	1.1	1.6	2.2	2.7	2.7	3.4	1.6	1.1	0.6	19.4
Nome	64°30'	13	T	4	6	8	20	34	46	50	49	42	30	16	7	
			R	1.1	1.0	0.9	0.7	0.7	1.1	2.6	3.6	2.7	1.7	1.1	1.1	18.4
Point Barrow	71°23'	25	T	-16	-17	-15	0	20	35	40	39	32	17	0	-11	
			R	0.2	0.2	0.1	0.1	0.1	0.3	0.9	0.7	0.5	0.6	0.3	0.3	4.3
Resolution Island	61°18'	127	T	-3	-4	7	15	28	34	39	41	37	30	21	6	
			R	1.2	1.5	1.0	1.3	1.6	1.4	2.4	1.8	2.1	0.9	1.3	1.6	18.1
Eurasia																
Chelyuskin Mys	77°43'	23	T	-14	-12	-19	-7	15	30	35	34	29	14	-2	-12	
			R	0.1	0.1	0.1	0.1	0.1	0.7	1.1	1.1	0.4	0.3	0.2	0.1	4.4
Ingöy	71°04'	13	T	27	26	27	31	37	43	48	49	44	37	32	28	
			R	2.8	1.4	3.3	1.0	2.2	1.5	1.4	1.1	1.0	1.6	1.8	2.1	21.2
Marresale	69°43'	56	T	-1	-4	-5	10	23	35	43	44	39	26	14	1	
			R	0.2	0.2	0.2	0.1	0.3	1.0	1.4	1.6	1.4	0.8	0.3	0.2	7.7
Medvezhi Ostrov	69°37'	98	T	-23	-16	-19	1	16	39	44	43	34	15	-3	-9	
			R	0.2	0.2	0.1	0.0	0.0	1.1	0.9	0.6	0.8	0.2	0.1	0.2	4.4
Ostrov Dikson	73°30'	66	T	-10	-7	-12	2	19	33	41	41	35	20	3	-7	
			R	0.2	0.1	0.2	0.2	0.2	0.7	0.8	1.6	1.6	0.5	0.3	0.2	6.6
Shalaurova Mys	73°11'	26	T	-23	-24	-20	7	15	32	38	37	31	14	-9	-19	
			R	0.1	0.1	0.1	0.0	0.2	0.4	0.5	0.7	0.5	0.2	0.1	0.1	3.0
Tiksi Bukhta	71°35'	23	T	-20	-18	-20	-1	24	39	48	47	36	14	-10	-16	
			R	0.1	0.1	0.1	0.1	0.1	1.2	1.3	1.1	0.8	0.2	0.2	0.1	5.4

Sources: U.S. Naval Oceanographic Office, *Sailing Directions for Northern Canada* (H.O. 15), 1954, *Sailing Directions for the Northern USSR* (H.O. 137), 1954.

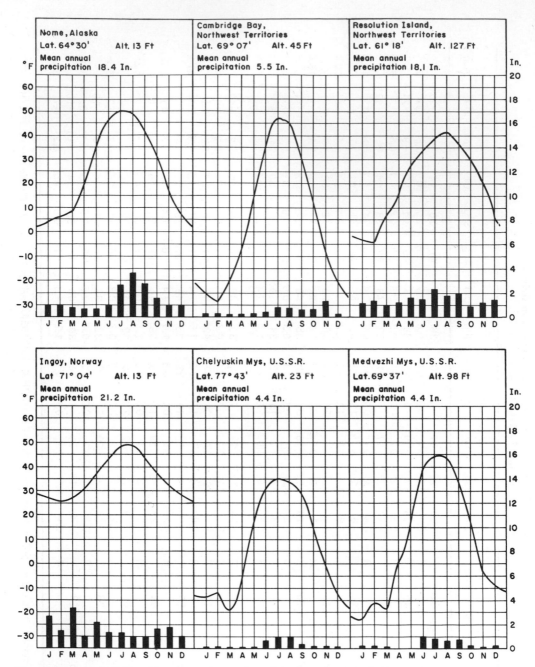

Figure 9.7. Normal monthly temperature and precipitation at stations in the tundra.

45 degrees, as opposed to 75 degrees at Cambridge Bay and Chesterfield Inlet (Table 9-1.) It is about 22 degrees at Ingöy and 42 degrees at Provideniya Bukhta, as opposed to 68 degrees at Tiksi Bukhta and 67 degrees at Medvezhi Ostrov. The extreme range between highest and lowest recorded temperatures is also more moderate under the marine influence, Nome

having 117 degrees, and Resolution Island, 97 degrees, in contrast to Cambridge Bay with 138 degrees and Chesterfield with 146 degrees; Ingöy, 82 degrees, and Provideniya Bukhta, 111 degrees, in contrast to Tiksi Bukhta with 148 degrees and Medvezhi Ostrov, 124 degrees. Thus, the influence of the sea renders the annual changes of temperature in the eastern and western sections of the tundra more moderate than in those territories remote from the waters of the Atlantic and Pacific.

From the data in Table 9-1, moreover, it appears that the moderating influence of warmer water from the Atlantic is more pronounced and more far-reaching than is that of the Pacific. This is primarily because of the narrowness of Bering Strait in contrast with the great breadth of the Norwegian Sea that allows a much broader sweep of ice-free water to enter the basin of the Arctic Ocean. This influence extends eastward into the Barents Sea and the Kara Sea regions of Eurasia, whereas the warming effects of the Pacific scarcely extend beyond Nome, Alaska. The northern half of the Bering Sea is usually ice-bound by the end of winter (March or April), but open water persists throughout the winter at least in the southern part of the Barents Sea. A practical result is seen in the fact that the ice-free port of Murmansk, on the Kola peninsula, lies well within the Arctic basin at latitude 68°50′N., whereas the northernmost ice-free port in Alaska is Valdez, on the south coast, at latitude 61°05′N.

The influence of the sea also retards the progression of the seasons in eastern North America and western Eurasia. August is the warmest month at Hebron and Resolution Island and at many stations around the shores of the Barents and Kara seas, whereas July is the warmest month throughout most of the remaining tundra regions. The coldest month of winter is also delayed, until March at many coastal localities in western Siberia, in contrast to February at places in eastern Siberia near the sea. Throughout most of the North American tundra February is the coldest month, except along the northern and western margins of Hudson Bay where the frigid blast of winter winds from the frozen barrens toward the west almost always brings extreme cold earlier in the season, during January (Fig. 9.7).

The oceanic influence upon annual precipitation is also evident in Table 9-1. Most tundra stations show a mean value of considerably less than 10 inches, but many places in the eastern and western reaches of both continents receive much more than this amount. In North America Nome, with 18.4 inches, Resolution Island with 18.1 inches, and Hebron with 19.4 inches offer a marked comparison with Point Barrow, having only 4.3 inches, Cambridge Bay, 5.5 inches, and Arctic Bay, 7.3 inches. In Eurasia the Norwegian stations of Ingöy, 21.2 inches, and Vardö, 25.9 inches, and of the east Siberian stations Provideniya Bukhta, 14.1 inches, may be compared with Tiksi Bukhta, having 5.4 inches, and Medvezhi Ostrov, having 4.4 inches.

A notable feature of tundra climate is a concentration of heaviest rainfall in summer. July is the rainiest month at most of the drier continental stations remote from the Atlantic and Pacific, but at marine stations August is usually the rainiest month. At the marine stations of Ingöy and Vardö in Norway, however, most of the year's total rainfall comes in winter, the heaviest amounts occurring in March or February.

Air masses responsible for much of the weather variety in Arctic regions are of three general types: continental Arctic (cA), which is very cold and relatively dry, continental polar (cP), which is less severely cold but still dry, and maritime polar (mP), which is still less cold and relatively humid. Continental Arctic air originates in the poleward reaches of the Arctic, over the Arctic Ocean, the Canadian archipelago, and northern Greenland, and generally forms only during the polar night. Continental polar air tends to form somewhat farther south over the continental interior, appearing with about equal frequency during both winter and summer. Maritime polar air that affects the tundra regions originates over the North Pacific and North Atlantic during the winter months, but in summertime it also develops frequently over the Arctic Ocean north of Bering Strait and also over the Barents Sea and the Kara Sea around the Soviet island of Novaya Zemlya.

As a general rule, either continental Arctic or continental polar air prevails over the tundra during the winter months. But, as we noted in the preceding chapter, winter weather in the far north is occasionally modified by the passage of variable weather, usually in the form of cyclonic storms of small dimension and short duration. In summertime the frequency of weather dominated by relatively milder, humid maritime polar air is considerably increased and thus tends to alternate between periods of clear, bracing air and somewhat longer intervals of damp, chill, rainy conditions.

During the winter months the ice- and snow-mantled tundra of both North America and

Eurasia joins the Arctic Ocean and Greenland, creating a circumpolar surface of ice and snow over twice the summertime area. Thus the Arctic regions as a whole are a much expanded source of larger masses of cold, dry air in wintertime. The sources of warmer, more humid air are contracted and lie farther south, and hence the zone of conflict between strongly different air masses, the mean frontal zone of cyclonic storms, also lies farther south. Nonetheless, some relatively warm, humid, maritime polar air originates over the North Pacific, the Norwegian Sea, and the North Atlantic between Labrador and southern Greenland and enters the circumpolar circulation—the wintertime procession of alternate storms and fair weather in the tundra.

As winter continues and deepens, the intervals of calm, clear weather gradually increase and lengthen toward spring; at the opposite time of year storms tend to increase with the advance of autumn. Partly because air over the northern continents becomes even colder than that over the Arctic Ocean, surface winds are commonly observed to flow seaward from the interior, a condition that is approximately reversed in summer, when the land is warmed and the air masses that travel across it develop unstable characteristics and sufficient convectional tendencies to attract an inflow of onshore winds from the Arctic Ocean.

Most storms of the Arctic arise from the overriding of colder, heavier air by maritime polar air that is lighter, warmer, and more humid, producing precipitation mainly of a frontal type. During the months of summer and early autumn, when the waters of the polar seas are largely unfrozen, the relative warmth and moisture they provide lead to instability and a certain amount of convectional turbulence in the lower layers of passing air masses. Thus, maritime polar air gains some nourishment in these seasons over the open polar seas, whereas at other times of the year when the seas are ice-covered, a tendency toward stability of the lower air results, and precipitating storms do not develop as fully or as frequently.

Let us now consider the qualities of the atmosphere as they vary from season to season, beginning with summer.

Summer. In summer mean monthly temperatures are above 32°F but below 50°F. Above-freezing averages may occur during only

two months at very high latitude, as along the northern shores of the Taimyr peninsula, at Ostrov Russkiy and Chelyuskin Mys, or they may persist for as long as six months, as at Ingöy and Vardö, or five months, as at Nome. In most localities above-freezing temperatures prevail for three to four months.

Summer is usually damp, raw, and chilly despite the prolonged period of daylight, for even at noon the sun remains low in the sky, resulting in low effective insolation. It is the season when the weather of all tundra lands is most nearly uniform. The mean temperature of the warmest month for North American stations having at least a ten-year period of record is between 40° and 50°F, a difference of only 10 degrees.[4] In Eurasia the warmest month may have a mean temperature of from 35° to 50°, a difference of only 15 degrees. The relative uniformity of mean summer temperatures stands in sharp contrast to the variety of mean values for the winter months (see Table 9-1), when in North America, Cambridge Bay averages −28° in contrast to Nome, averaging 4°, and in Eurasia, Shalaurova Mys averages −24° in contrast to Ingöy with 26°, a difference of 32 and 50 degrees respectively.

Although average temperatures during the warmer part of the year are above freezing, there is no complete freedom from frost, for subfreezing values may be expected at any time during the summer months at most stations. Indeed, in at least one summer season at Resolution Island, the longest period entirely free from frost lasted for only one week. Plants of the tundra are frost-tolerant. The severity of the weather to which they are often subjected during their normal growing season is indicated in Figure 9.8, showing the daily temperatures at Alert for July 1963. At this truly Arctic location the temperature dropped to freezing or below on eighteen out of thirty-one days. The thermometer rose to a maximum of 57° for the month on the 29th, but two days later registered a minimum of 23°.

The mean daily range of temperature at most

●[4] Weather records for certain Arctic stations are either incomplete or of such short duration as to have doubtful value in these generalizations. However, it should be noted that the temperature of the warmest month at Alert (Lat. 82°30′) is 41°; Eureka (80°00′) is 39°; Isachsen (78°47′) is 35°; Mould Bay (76°17′) is 38°; Resolute (74°43′) is 38°.

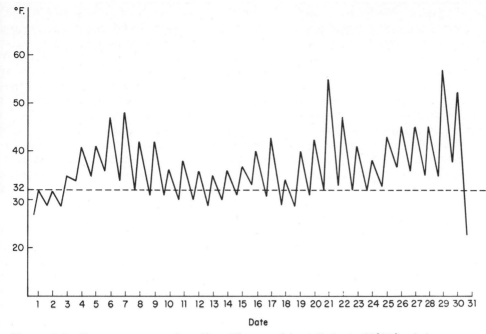

Figure 9.8. Temperature record at Alert, Ellesmere Island (latitude 82°30′), during July 1963.

North American stations is not much less in summer than in winter. In the Eurasian tundra, however, it is ordinarily only about half the daily range of winter, except at marine stations as in northern Norway. Diurnal temperature variations in summertime are quite often brought about by changes in humidity, cloud cover, and other transitory properties of migrating air masses that bring alternating types of weather. In many situations this is a more important factor than the changing position of the low summer sun.

Temperature inversions are usually most strongly developed when both sea and land are frost-bound and covered to a maximum extent with ice and snow, a condition that prevails chiefly during March or April. Thus they are not common in summertime, although they occasionally occur even in July when warm air passes over very cold water or tracts of persistent ice and snow. Air of considerable warmth quite often enters these far northern margins of the Arctic seas. At Nome and Coppermine, for example, summer maxima of 84° have been observed, at Chesterfield 86°, Hebron 87°, Kara Guba 80°, Nordvik 87°, and Tiksi Bukhta, with what seems to be a record for the tundra, 91°.

It will also be observed in Table 9-1 that the mean temperature of the warmest months at many stations, although above freezing, does not rise above 43°, the temperature at which vegetative growth normally begins. And along the east Siberian coast, Billings Mys, Shelagski Mys, and Schmidta Mys, the mean temperature of the warmest month does not even rise to 40°.

The annual precipitation of most tundra regions is characteristically light, a condition that arises in the main from the predominantly low temperatures of the atmosphere in all seasons. The resulting low moisture-retaining capacity of the atmosphere produces an absolute humidity that is very much lower than even that of tropical desert regions. The surface temperature of the seas, lakes, and rivers is seldom far above freezing even in summer, an important factor in creating a low evaporation rate in that season, while in wintertime most land and water surfaces are solidly frost-bound and are thus capable of releasing little if any moisture to the atmosphere. However, because most water surfaces are unfrozen during July, August, and September, and because at this time of year the tundra is repeatedly invaded by warmer air from lower latitudes, the largest percentage of annual precipitation occurs during the summer and early autumn seasons.

The zone of contact or conflict between cold polar air and warmer air from the south or from the open polar seas, sometimes referred to as the polar belt of storms, moves northward in summertime. Although snow is not unusual, most of the precipitation is rain, of frontal or cyclonic origin, that falls most commonly in a light, steady drizzle. Often, for a day or two or more clouds of driving, soaking, misty rain may sweep across the rugged plains, blotting out the horizon, and drenching the already water-logged ground. Along the courses of northward flowing rivers bearing warmer water from the south, mist and rain are sometimes locally intensified, and fog may occur in the valleys far more frequently than over the interfluvial barrens. Thunderstorms are rare, although the strong convective turbulence necessary to produce them must occasionally develop in interior areas that are well heated when they are overlain with air that is especially moist.

The total annual precipitation varies from place to place (see Table 9-1), and in both North America and Eurasia is heaviest at those localities close to the sea. Nome, with 18.4 inches of annual rainfall, and Hebron, having 19.4 inches, are examples of marine situations in North America. Both of them experience about five months of above-freezing temperatures, during which time Nome receives 58 per cent of its annual precipitation and Hebron 65 per cent. Point Barrow, on the other hand, receives a total of only 4.3 inches, 56 per cent of it occurring in a four-month above-freezing period, and Cambridge Bay, with 5.5 inches, receives 40 per cent of it in a three-month frost-free period.

An exception to the general rule is seen at the Norwegian stations of Ingöy and Vardö, where at least half the year's mean precipitation of 21.2 inches and 25.9 inches respectively occurs during the winter months when average temperatures remain below freezing. This condition results mainly from the frequent polar penetration of winter storms from the North Atlantic and the fact that these are nourished by the moisture made available from the surface of the continuously unfrozen seas. The Bering Sea coast stations of Provideniya Bukhta and Uelen demonstrate the effects of marine influence in having a heavier annual

rainfall than is usual for tundra stations (14.1 and 11.4 inches respectively) and, in contrast to northern Norway, receive 49 and 57 per cent of the total during only four months of above-freezing temperatures.

From the shores of the Kara Sea eastward an increasing percentage of the year's rainfall comes during the brief frost-free spell of summer. Ostrov Dikson receives 71 per cent of a 6.6 inch total during a frost-free period of only two months, and Tiksi Bukhta receives 81 per cent of a 5.5 inch total during a four-month above-freezing period.

Though the absolute humidity of tundra lands is lower than that of all other regions save the polar ice cap, the relative humidity is noticeably higher in summer than in winter. This conclusion is based more upon the hearsay reports of travelers than upon instrumental measurement, for the devices at present available for determining precise humidity values at low temperatures are not reliable. This is generalization established chiefly from the facts that atmospheric dampness is more noticeable and that both fog and cloud are more abundant during summer and early autumn. Advective fog in coastal regions is common when warm air is chilled as it moves out over the unfrozen seas, waters that are seldom more than a few degrees above the freezing point.

With the onset of autumn the lengthening night and the fading warmth of the sun together allow land areas to cool rapidly and become a source of cold air to the air above. Water, slower to cool, remains unfrozen long after rock, soil, and plant life are brittle with cold and is a source of relative warmth for the atmosphere. The contrasts in air temperature that result during this transitional period make it the tundra's stormiest season in all sections save the Norwegian coast, where winter brings the year's severest storms. It does not, however, resemble the autumn of middle latitudes, for temperatures at most stations average well below freezing (see Table 9-1); Cambridge Bay and Tiksi Bukhta, for example, show mean temperatures for October that are less than the mean temperature at Montreal for January, the winter's coldest month in that more temperate locality.

Largely because of the moderating effect of the sea, autumn is a warmer season than spring, for September, three months after the summer solstice, averages only a few degrees lower than June, and the mean temperature in October at most stations is considerably higher than in April, which is three months after the winter solstice. At Point Barrow April is about 0°F, October almost 17°; Chesterfield averages 1° in April and 24° in October; Marresale is 10° in April and 26° in October; Russkiy Ostrov is −6° in April and 16° in October. The difference is less, of course, at places nearer the year-round influence of the Atlantic and Pacific oceans. After October temperatures drop rapidly, and November in many places is 20 degrees or more lower than the previous month.

The mean daily range of temperature at most stations is lowest in late summer, just before the autumn storms begin. Then, when thermal contrasts strengthen between air masses of continental or ice cap origin and those originating over the sea, sudden and violent changes in weather occur with mounting frequency. The yearly peak of storm intensity is commonly reached in the tundra during October or November. In November a wind velocity of 83 miles per hour has been recorded at Arctic Bay and of 67 miles per hour at Port Harrison. Winds of gale force have also been observed in winter and late spring at several stations and are not at all uncommon at any time of the year except, perhaps, in midsummer.

Winter. Winter in the tundra broadly resembles the conditions observed over the polar ice cap described in Chapter 8. Thoroughly ice-bound, almost all localities average temperatures below zero, and the air is remarkably dry. Winter temperatures in marine situations, however, average above zero, as at Nome, and at Ingöy and Vardö average higher than 20°. Cold season precipitation, chiefly snow, is unusually heavy for the tundra at these stations.

The long, cold winter reaches a climax of intensity in February at most North American stations and March at most places in Eurasia. The lowest mean values in the North American tundra are found at Cambridge Bay (−28.1°), Chesterfield (−27°), Arctic Bay (−27°), and Pond Inlet (−29°). Cambridge Bay and Chesterfield are near midcontinent and are thus remote from the invasion of moderating air from the oceans, while Arctic Bay and Pond Inlet have a poleward exposure in northern Baffin in positions that are locally sheltered by prom-

inent highlands from warmer air of oceanic origin. Extreme low temperatures of −63° and −60° have been observed at Cambridge Bay and Chesterfield respectively; extreme minima of −57° and −60° have been recorded at Arctic Bay and Pond Inlet.

The winter temperatures of record for tundra stations in Eurasia are not as low as those for the western hemisphere. The mean value of the coldest month at Nordvik is −22°, at Shalaurova Mys, −24°, at Medvezhi Ostrov, −23°, and at Schmidta Mys, −20°. An extreme minimum of −59° has been observed at Marresale, Preobrazheniya Ostrov, and Nordvik, and −64° at Sagastyr. As we shall see in the next chapter, stations in the boreal forest, deeper within the continents, have recorded temperatures much lower than these.

Temperature inversions are prominent wintertime phenomena over the frosty wastes of the tundra. Air is warmer only a short distance above the frozen surface, and temperatures continue to increase upward for about a mile, the greatest differences occurring in sheltered situations, where warmer strata tend to overlie pockets of cold, still air.

The lighter precipitation of winter is extremely difficult to measure with accuracy, for most of it falls as fine, light, dry snow or tiny crystals of ice, similar to the winter precipitation of the ice cap regions. Small in amount, and easily transported even by very gentle winds, it is constantly being piled into drifts, which are then torn down, swept away, and driven furiously over the plains to collect in depressions or in the lee of hillocks or other obstructions, leaving wide areas of the frozen ground completely bare. Blizzards of the tundra, the dreaded purga of northern Siberia and Alaska, often last for days, and the light, swirling, driving snow fills the air, blending earth and sky together in undistinguishable whiteness.

George W. Melville, describing a winter on the Lena delta, reported that gales had blown constantly with scarcely a day's let-up, from November to the end of February.

February 27th. The storm rages more furiously, if possible, than yesterday.... No one willingly forsakes the shelter of his hut, and those unfortunates who are forced to expose themselves to the pitiless weather must either cling to some support or sit down. There is no compromise. An old native started from our hut to reach another not more than one hundred yards distant. So blinding was the snow, and so fierce the wind, which lifted and whirled him around, that he lost his head, and consequently his way . . . in a few seconds all the men were getting into their boots and furs . . . to set forth on the search. . . . Noting the direction of the wind and their present location, they all set squarely down on the snow and then crawled away before the wind, shouting vigorously for the lost one; and they found him but a little distance off under the lee of a storehouse crying aloud for help.[5]

Although the inclement weather of winter sometimes endures continuously for days, sudden changes take place frequently. One explanation of this is the fact that cyclonic storms and frontal disturbances in general are often small in size and move rapidly over the surface in quick succession, bringing alternate periods of furious storm and clear, cold calm. A blizzard is usually followed by weather in which the brilliant sparkle of starlight, the bright gleam of the moon, and the colorful play of aurora borealis appear with startling clarity against the deep, violet blue of the dust-free sky.

As the end of winter approaches with the lengthening day, storms diminish in frequency and intensity, cloudiness and fog become rare, and the weather is more and more clear, cold, dry, calm, and often very, very still. The chief difference between winter and spring is at first only an increase in light, for temperatures remain well below freezing at most stations until the end of May, when small creeks begin to run, foretelling the arrival of summer. Maud D. Haviland, describing the advent of summer on the Yenesei delta, writes as follows:

On the Yenesei tundras snow melts around the beginning of June, and for three to four weeks the country is almost impassable. Ice in the rivers, often six or seven feet thick, breaks up at the same time, and great blocks, hurtled by the current against the unbroken sheet beyond, are piled into barricades which dam up the waters already swollen by thaw, and cause extensive floods over the land. By the end of the month, summer has come. Birds begin to breed and vegetation to grow. From May to July the sun never sets below the

horizon and perpetual daylight reigns. . . . The first impression of the "Big Low Tundra" in June is one of utter desolation. River banks are flanked either by swamps or by snow-ribbed mud hills. Sandy beaches at the water's edge are strewn with iceblocks, and bleached, shattered timber brought down from the forest zone by floods. The whole landscape, immense though it is, seems repellent, bleak and formless, without beauty or dignity of any kind. Even the river is so muddy and cumbered with flotsam that it looks more like the titanic scourings of a continent than a noble water-course. And when the disillusioned traveller lands and wades through the frozen marshes to the mud hills which bound the valley, the scenery seems still more desolate and inhospitable. Once at the summit, the tundra rolls away from him into the misty horizon, apparently without a single feature to afford a landmark, or to relieve its grey monotony . . . the untrodden ways of the earth.[6]

Thus, to a certain extent a seasonal progression of weather variety may be observed in the tundra. A season's actual weather, however, may be at considerable variance with the mean weather patterns we have been discussing. In the experience of Arctic sea-faring men, for example, certain summers have been much colder than usual, and bays and seas that are normally open to navigation have remained continuously ice-bound through July and August. Travelers across the frozen barrens of the Siberian tundra have reported winters that were unusually stormy at times, with much more than the ordinary accumulation of snow and a persistent repetition of high winds and the intolerable purga.

The tundra shares its winters with the ice cap regions toward the north and its vegetative summers with the boreal forest toward the south. In wintertime its rolling, lifeless landscapes are dark, bleak, severely cold and dry. Its summers—chill, damp and frequently rainswept—are sunlit and become warm enough in sections to support a densely matted moss-lichen heath, a shrub tundra, or a stunted growth of small forest trees. These are the features that portray its position in the northern hemisphere as a transitional zone between perpetual ice and snow and the evergreen landscapes of the boreal forest.

[5] George W. Melville, *In the Lena Delta*, Houghton Mifflin Company, Boston, 1896, pp. 298–99.

[6] Maud D. Haviland, *Forest, Steppe, and Tundra*, Cambridge University Press, Cambridge, 1926, pp. 152–53.

References

BERG, L. S.: *Natural Regions of the USSR*, The Macmillan Company, New York, 1953.

HAVILAND, M. D.: *Forest, Steppe, and Tundra*, The University Press, Cambridge, 1926.

HUSTICH, I.: "The Boreal Limits of Conifers," *Arctic*, 6(2): 149–62, 1953.

KIMBLE, G. H. R., and GOOD, D.: *Geography of the Northlands*, The American Geographical Society and John Wiley & Sons, Inc., New York, 1955.

MELVILLE, G. W.: *In the Lena Delta*, Houghton Mifflin Company, Boston, 1896.

POLUNIN, N.: *Arctic Unfolding*, Hutchinson and Co., New York, 1949.

————: "Aspects of Arctic Botany," *American Scientist*, 43(2): 307–22, 1955.

U.S. ARMY, QUARTERMASTER RESEARCH AND ENGINEERING COMMAND, *Climatic Analogs of Fort Greely, Alaska, and Fort Churchill, Canada, in Eurasia*, Natick, Mass., 1957.

chapter 10

THE BOREAL FOREST

Along the southern margins of the somber, treeless tundra, where those vast and lonely spaces give way to a more luxuriant growth of trees, the boreal forest begins. Like the tundra almost completely encircling the pole, this great northern woodland is the third climatic region in the gradual transition from polar cold to equatorial warmth. Also in common with the tundra, it is exclusively a region of the northern hemisphere, for land surfaces are lacking in the appropriate latitudes south of the equator (Figs. 9.1 and 9.2).

The boreal forest is a region where coniferous trees and shrubs tend to outnumber other species on the mesophytic sites of northern landscapes, at elevations generally below 3000 feet. Species of spruce, fir, larch, and pine are numerically dominant throughout most of its vast extent. These, by virtue of their typically pyramidal profiles, their dark needle-leaved foliage, and their penetrating, astringent fragrance, create the essential character of the region, a character that is recognizable from coast to coast across the great breadth of both continents. One is impressed with the physiognomic uniformity of the region and with the fact that only a few tree species are dominant, particularly in view of its great length and latitudinal breadth.

In North America the boreal forest extends from the Bering Sea coast to Alaska southeast-ward for approximately 4400 miles to the shores of the Gulf of St. Lawrence and has a tremendous breadth in latitude of some 24 degrees, from around 69° in the lower Mackenzie valley to around 45° in northern New England. In Eurasia it reaches eastward from the fjord coast of Norway to the Pacific shores of Siberia for a distance of more than 5000 miles, with a latitudinal breadth of around 25 degrees, from about 72° in the lower Khatanga valley to 45° on Sakhalin Island.

The qualities of the atmosphere chiefly responsible for the vegetational features of the region are also reasonably uniform, as revealed in the records of temperature and rainfall kept at a fairly large number of weather stations somewhat unevenly scattered through the region. Short, rather warm summers and long, severe winters are typical, with a rapid transition from one to the other in spring and fall. Mean summer temperatures rise to more than 50°F for at least one month and usually prevail for from three to four months each season. This is at least one requirement for the development of forest trees—for vegetative growth seldom takes place at temperatures below 43°F. Mean values of more than 60°F are recorded for one to three months at many inland stations, although means at very few places exceed 65°F. Prolonged hot spells are very rare, but high temperatures are not. Readings in excess of

80 or 90°F are not uncommon during the warmest month, and many stations have recorded extreme maxima above 100°F. The growing season is commonly in the neighborhood of seventy-five days, but may vary from around fifty to 125 days, depending upon such factors as the amount of insolation received, location with respect to the sources of warm air, and proximity to large lakes, seas, and bays.

The length and severity of winter is an important quality of the boreal forest, where below freezing temperatures prevail for from five to seven months, and many stations record subzero averages for several months during the season. Deep cold is characteristic. Fort Good Hope, in the Northwest Territories of Canada, has a January mean of −24°F, and Verkhoyansk, Siberia, a January mean of −58°. The lowest temperature reported anywhere in North America has been   81° at Snag, Yukon Territory, and in Eurasia the absolute minimum of −94° has been observed at Verkhoyansk.

Thus the high mean temperatures of summer and the very low averages of winter produce a mean annual range of more than 80 degrees in the interior valleys of northwestern North America and more than 100 degrees in eastern Siberia. Coupled with this singularly wide range of normal yearly values is the range between absolute extremes of record. Fort Yukon, Alaska reports a spread of 178 degrees (−78° to 100°), and greater still is the range of 188 degrees at Verkhoyansk, between an absolute maximum of 94° and an absolute minimum of −94°. Nowhere else on earth have ranges of these amplitudes been reported, although these examples are exceptional. Strong contrasts between summer and winter temperatures are typical of the boreal forest. It is then, more than anything else, a region of remarkable continentality. Temperature in all its aspects, is the most significant climatic element of the region and the primary control of its distribution.

Precipitation varies considerably in amount between interior and coastal sections. A total annual fall of 10 to 20 inches is widely characteristic, although in milder sections near the sea, and in closer proximity to the favored paths of rain-bearing storms, it amounts to between 20 and 30 inches or more. Summer is the season of greatest intensity.

In summary, the typical boreal forest develops in those areas where below-freezing temperatures prevail for about six months, where the coldest month averages less than 10°, where mean summer temperatures are above 50° for about three months but usually no more than 65° in the warmest month, and where annual precipitation averages between 10 and 20 inches. These are the chief regional criteria. A wide annual temperature range and a wide variation between the observed extremes of temperature, as well as relatively low yearly precipitation, should be emphasized. The farther mean values depart from these criteria, the more closely the boreal forest approaches an adjoining region.

As in the tundra, the number of plant species is small, the individuals within a species are numerous. Hence, scarcely a dozen species of coniferous pine, larch, spruce, and fir are the dominant trees of the region. Actually, most of the species of these genera are found within more temperate regions at lower latitudes. Pine, for example, is represented by only five widespread northern species (Scots pine, Siberian cembra pine, Siberian dwarf pine, lodgepole pine, and jackpine) although at least ninety species are known, some of which are found in tropical forests.[1] A single tree species, the common juniper (*Juniperus communis*, including *J. communis var. montana*, *J. communis var. nana*, and *J. sibirica*), is the only one whose distribution is almost completely circumpolar. Although typically a low-growing shrub, it must be included among the very small number of significant ligneous plants of the nothern forests. Its distribution extends to the poleward reaches of boreal forest and continues northward as a dwarf shrub in the wooded tundra. Its significance as a boreal conifer is enhanced by the fact that it is the only one native to Greenland, Iceland, and Novaya Zemlya and the only one found in the Torngat region of Labrador and in the vicinity of North Cape, Norway.[2]

The dominant trees of the northern forest are coniferous and needleleaved, but they are not all evergreen. The larch (also called tamarack in North America) is deciduous, and by

[1] F. K. Hare, "The Boreal Conifer Zone," *Geographical Studies*, 1(1): 4–18, 1954.

[2] I. Hustich, "The Boreal Limits of Conifers," *Arctic*, 6(2): 149–62, July 1953.

appearing widely in both North America and Eurasia, prevents our terming the region an evergreen forest. Certain broadleaved deciduous species are also present everywhere in the forest, and as a general rule are members of the poplar, birch, alder, and willow genera. They most commonly appear as subdominant, subclimax associations, playing a transitory part in the ceaseless ecological tendency of the conifers to dominate.

The variety of natural landscapes in the boreal forest includes four clearly recognizable types: deciduous thickets that are chiefly transitory; swamps, bogs and marshy lowlands; open lichen woodland; and close-crowned coniferous forest. The first of these is composed mainly of subdominant species of birch and poplar that grow rapidly and are short lived, developing quickly in areas that have been cut over or swept by fire. In such areas they appear for a time in extensive groves, sometimes in pure stands of a single species, where they perform an important ecological function by providing a temporary protective canopy beneath which the coniferous seedlings are sheltered, in their early years, from the direct rays of the sun. After several years the rising conifers project their tapering forms skywards into the leafy crowns of the small-to-medium-sized birches and poplars. The deciduous trees lose their vitality within perhaps two or three decades, after which they decay, fall, and lie rotting on the gound. Again and again their dead, decaying, topless trunks may be encountered throughout the boreal forest (Fig. 10.1).

In some areas, as in northern Scandinavia, birch-aspen stands seem to be persistent locally, dominating in the drier edaphic situations where coniferous species do not easily take hold. Whether clearly transitory or seemingly dominant, these rather small, broadleaved deciduous trees create one of the typical regional landscapes widely seen in the boreal forest.

Poor drainage conditions are extremely common in these cold northern woodlands, giving rise to another of the important landscapes of the region—swamp, marshland, or peat bogs, loosely termed muskeg[3] in North America. More than any other region in the world the boreal forest provides optimum climatic conditions for the formation of peat from the decomposition of organic materials.

[3] The exact meaning of *muskeg* is disputed among plant ecologists, but it is fairly well accepted as a designation for sphagnum bogs that are interspersed with sedge-grass tussocks and often with scattered tree species such as black spruce and tamarack.

Figure 10.1. Subclimax deciduous thickets in boreal forest. Birch-aspen stands provide protective cover, beneath which black spruce crowds upward. [American Geographical Society photo]

Figure 10.2. Open lichen woodland in boreal forest. [American Geographical Society photo]

Generally speaking, the tundra is too cold and the rate of decomposition too slow, more southerly regions are too warm and the rate of decomposition too rapid, for successful peat formation. But even in the innumerable bogs and marshes can be seen the assertive tendencies of the dominant conifers.

One of the truly distinctive landscapes of the boreal forest is the open lichen-woodland, which has its widest development in the poleward sections of the region where, in a sense, it blends into the wooded tundra. The latter it will be remembered, is a tundra landscape in which forest trees are found chiefly along the valley floors and are generally absent from the lichen-dominated interfluves. The lichen-woodland, on the other hand, is distinguished by the presence of forest trees on all the mesophytic interfluvial sites, spreading outward from the valley in an open distribution. The 30–40-foot larch, spruce, or pine stand several yards apart on a surface that is completely covered with a dense matting of reindeer moss, lichens, and occasional shrubby plants. In North America the subtle shades of pale green, yellow, and violet of the lichen ground cover contrast with the dark spires of spruce trees above to create one of the more beautiful forest landscapes on the continent (Fig. 10.2).

Last of the principal landscape types is the closecrowned forest, the prototype of all the boreal forest lanscapes. It is recognizable as a dense stand of close-growing conifers that raise their spirelike crowns in an impenetrable phalanx of intertwined branches. Beneath it the deeply shaded forest floor is cool and damp, occupied by a few types of mosses, lichens, ferns, and herbs, and the seedlings of the dominant trees that readily take hold in the welcome shade. This lanscape is climatically controlled, tending to assert and reassert itself on all mesophytic sites (Fig. 10.3).

In addition to the four chief landscape types, there is still another characteristic terrestrial feature that is climatically controlled. This is the presence of an underlying zone of permanently frozen subsoil (permafrost), a feature that the boreal forest holds in common with the tundra. It appears in generally continuous distribution, however, only in northern sections of the region, for the forest soils thaw to greater and greater depths with increasing distance from the northern treeless zone. Thus it is found only in patches in the southern portions of the region. With the deepening thaw zone farther south, the presence of more luxuriant plant life, and the occurence of warmer summers and more effective precipitation that give rise to these conditions, mature acidic soils called podsols are developed in the better-drained situations that are regionally typical of the boreal forest.

Boreal Forest in North America

In North America the boreal forest is dominated almost entirely throughout its great length and breadth by three conifers: white and black spruce (*Picea glauca* and *P. mariana*), and tamarack (*Larix laricina*). East of the Rockies

Figure 10.3. Close-crowned boreal forest. [American Geographical Society photo]

jackpine (*Pinus banksiana*) and balsam fir (*Abies balsamea*) become important codominants. Also present throughout the entire region are certain of the transitory, subdominant deciduous species: white birch (*Betula papyrifera*), trembling aspen (*Populus tremuloides*, and balsam poplar, along with various alders (*Alnus spp.*), wild cherries (*Prunus spp.*), and willows (*Salix spp.*).

The North American taiga[4] extends in a vast and virtually unbroken belt of woodland from the low-lying coast of the Bering Sea in Alaska southeastward to the rock-bound shores of the

---

[4] This term has been traditionally applied to the boreal forest as a whole, especially in Eurasia, where it originated as a Russian designation for the swampy northern coniferous forests of Siberia. Its traditional application is retained in this text, although in recent years it has been proposed as a term applying only to the lichen-woodland, or open transition belt of the boreal forest, south of the wooded tundra.

Gulf of St. Lawrence. In Alaska it merges with the tundra on the north and west, with the humid coastal coniferous forest along the southeastern shores, and with alpine vegetation at higher levels on the innumerable mountain slopes. The actual pattern of distribution in Alaska is exceedingly difficult to map because of its great complexity, arising from the constant intermingling of polar maritime air from the Pacific Ocean with the colder, drier invasions of polar and arctic continental air masses over this northern area of the continent, whose surface is dominated by features of strong relief.

Although appearing in the Matanuska valley at the head of Cook Inlet and in thinly scattered stands of stunted trees along the inner edges of Seward peninsula, the main development of the boreal forest in Alaska is found in the valleys of the Yukon River and its tributaries, generally at altitudes below 2500 feet. The Yukon is the principal drainage feature of Alaska and the Yukon Territory of northwestern Canada, where its tributaries cut deeply into the northern Rockies (Fig. 9.1). Along the lower and intermediate mountain slopes overlooking these streams the taiga extends eastward across the divide at altitudes between 2000 and 4000 feet, descending into the lower reaches of the Mackenzie valley. In the low, swampy floodplains of these rivers stunted larch and black spruce appear, and toward the timberline at around 4000 feet, below the open, mountain meadows, alpine fir (*Abies lasiocarpa*) becomes dominant, with some scattering of lodgepole pine (*Pinus contorta*) and Alaska white birch (*Betula papyrifera* var. *humilis*).

At several points east of the Mackenzie delta the boreal forest thrusts out attenuated fingers of stunted spruce and tamarack to mark its northernmost extent in North America. There is evidence that large north-flowing streams like the Mackenzie, whose headwaters lie some 15 degrees south of its delta, locally moderate the climate of their lower valleys in the process of transporting warmer water from milder latitudes. The presence of fingerlike extensions of the boreal forest along the banks of streams flowing into the tundra regions of both continents supports this belief, and so, to some extent, does the meteorological record.

Southward along the eastern flanks of the

Rockies the boreal forest continues to within about 300 miles of the Montana border, rising to altitudes of around 4000 feet in the upper valleys of the Liard, Peace, and Athabaska rivers, western tributaries of the Mackenzie. Above 4000 feet alpine fir becomes the dominant tree, along with the lodgepole pine, an alpine species very similar to jackpine both in appearance and in its character as a widespread subdominant. Southeastward up the broadly winding valley of the Mackenzie, and embracing the large northern lakes (Great Bear, Great Slave, and Athabaska), the forest spreads a dark-green mantle of conifers over the central plains and the rounded, rocky knolls and ridges of the Canadian Shield. It attains a maximum north–south breadth of nearly 1000 miles between the Rockies and the shores of Hudson Bay, north of Churchill.

Almost pure stands of white birch or balsam poplar will be found at frequent intervals, often with a heavy growth of young spruce and fir seedlings developing beneath their protective cover. In drier situations pure stands of jackpine are also seen, and these too sometimes occupy a subclimax position in the regional trend toward the dominant spruce-fir climax. In the numerous moist, low-lying situations, especially where continental glaciation has disrupted the drainage pattern, muskeg landscapes appear. These are extremely common between the Rockies and the Atlantic coast and frequently contain a generous scattering of tall, gaunt, black spruce or tamarack trees, largely devoid of living branches, surmounting a dense ground cover of sphagnum moss and certain shrubs like the leatherleaf and labrador tea.

Between the Rockies and Lake Winnipeg the southern margins of the taiga are gradually interpenetrated by poplar, oak, and willow, giving way to the drier, warmer regions of the grasslands through a rather variable transition zone that in North America is known as an open parkland, or aspen-grove. The Eurasian counterpart of this transition zone is called a forest-steppe. An approximate balance exists between precipitation and evaporation during the growing season, and any lessening or increase of the long-term average fall of rain, under a normal temperature regime, causes fluctuations in the generalized boundary between this section and the boreal forest.

In recent years the direction of movement has seemed to be from boreal forest into grassland, resulting from increased precipitation effectiveness.

The white spruce attains its largest size just north and northwest of the aspen-grove section. Here it commonly averages between 80 and 100 feet in height and between 2 and 3 feet in diameter. Still, it maintains dominance over poplars with difficulty, for many groves of aspen and Balm of Gilead (*Populus candicans*) are found in this part of the region.

East of Lake Winnipeg the boreal forest occupies nearly all the land between Hudson Bay and Lake Superior, stretching eastward from here to the Gulf of St. Lawrence. One of the larger tracts of muskeg is found in this area, west and southwest of James Bay, where the water of many streams converge to cross a broad, low, level coastal plain to the shores of the bay. The boreal forest merges unevenly with the tundra in northern Labrador-Ungava, where spruce and larch are the principal dominants. Particularly dense close-crowned forest is found in the sheltered valleys of the Hamilton River and Lake Melville, which empty into the Atlantic, and the middle reaches of the Kaniapiskau River, flowing northward into Ungava Bay. The taiga does not reach the Atlantic shores of Labrador, for it is separated from the sea by a narrow, almost continuous strip of coastal tundra. This cold, wet, broken tract has remained treeless, apparently from a condition of physiological drought, excessive transpiration, that is partly due to the high frequency of strong coastal winds. Tundra flora, and low, shrubby forms of typical taiga plants dominate the scene.

Outliers of the region appear in Newfoundland, the mountainous interior of the Gaspé peninsula, and northern New England, where it meets the milder, wetter environment of the coastal Acadian forest. Here, higher temperatures, an annual rainfall in excess of 30 inches, and frequent invasions of fog from the sea create a more diversified forest with a strong penetration of hardy deciduous species.

The southern margins of the boreal forest, roughly between Lake Winnipeg and the Gaspé peninsula, are very indistinctly blended with a temperate, well-watered region called the Great Lakes–St. Lawrence forest. This is the northernmost division of the middle latitude

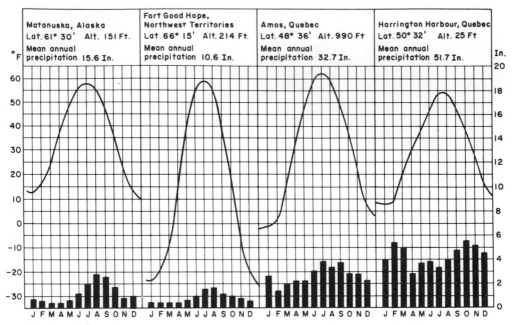

Figure 10.4. Normal temperature and precipitation at boreal forest stations in North America.

mixed forest in eastern North America. White pine (*Pinus strobus*), red pine (*P. resinosa*), sugar maple (*Acer saccharum*), yellow birch (*Betula lutea*), hemlock (*Tsuga canadensis*, and species of beech, oak, and ash dominate in varying associations. Deep interpenetration of these species with the spruce-fir dominants of the boreal forest takes place within the drainage basins of Lake Superior, Lake Huron, the Ottawa River and other tributaries of the St. Lawrence, and the Lake St. Jean lowland. Higher year-round temperatures, a longer, much wetter growing season, and an annual rainfall in excess of 30 inches are characteristic of the Great Lakes–St. Lawrence region, making it readily distinguishable from the taiga toward the north.

Spanning the continent in a single broad belt that reaches virtually from coast to coast, the boreal forest constitutes a transition southward from the treeless tundra into four quite distinct regions: the humid coastal evergreen forest; the highlands of Alaska, Yukon Territory, British Columbia, and Alberta; the grasslands of the prairie provinces; and the mid-latitude mixed forests of eastern Canada and northeastern United States. The atmospheric qualities with which these terrestrial features are inseparably united are also discrete and characteristic of the region.

We have noted that temperature is the most important climatic element in the boreal forest region and that both mean and extreme annual temperature ranges are unusually wide. Long, severely cold winter gives way to moderately warm summer. Precipitation is relatively light and falls most abundantly during the warm season. It is a region of distinctly continental qualities that are typical throughout its length and breadth. These important qualities in turn arise primarily from a location in high latitudes, producing a pronounced seasonal change in the duration and intensity of solar radiation, and from the great breadth of the continent, over which the interplay of maritime and continental polar air produces strongly contrasting seasonal circulations.

The amplitude of the mean annual temperature range is assuredly continental everywhere in the boreal forest (Fig. 10.4). But we should observe that stations near the sea experience a considerably lower range than do those of the interior. In Table 10-1 are the temperature and rainfall data for weather stations in the North American boreal forest. From this table we note that Matanuska,[1] for example,

---

[1] Matanuska is included here to indicate the transition to Coastal Evergreen Forest.

TABLE 10-1

Climatic Data for Boreal Forest Stations in North America
(Temp., °F; Rainfall, In.)

Station	Lat.	El. in Ft		Jan.	Feb.	Mar.	Apr.	May	Jun.	Jul.	Aug.	Sep.	Oct.	Nov.	Dec.	Year
Matanuska, Alaska	61°30'	151	T	13	18	24	36	47	55	58	55	48	36	23	14	
			R	0.9	0.7	0.5	0.4	0.7	1.3	2.0	2.8	2.6	1.7	0.9	1.0	15.6
Fort Yukon, Alaska	66°34'	394	T	−22	−14	0	20	42	59	61	56	42	21	−7	−23	
			R	0.5	0.6	0.4	0.4	0.6	0.8	1.1	1.0	0.6	0.8	0.3	0.4	7.1
Fort Good Hope, N.W. Terr.	66°15'	214	T	−24	−19	−10	14	38	54	59	56	40	21	−6	−20	
			R	0.5	0.5	0.5	0.5	0.7	1.0	1.6	1.7	1.2	1.1	0.8	0.6	10.6
Beaverlodge, Alta.	55°13'	2500	T	7	13	21	37	50	55	59	57	48	38	25	11	
			R	1.4	0.8	1.2	0.8	1.6	2.1	2.2	1.7	1.7	1.1	1.2	1.3	17.1
Prince Albert, Sask.	53°13'	1414	T	−4	2	15	37	50	59	63	60	50	39	20	5	
			R	0.7	0.6	0.9	0.9	1.5	2.8	2.2	2.0	2.1	0.8	0.9	0.8	16.1
Churchill, Man.	58°45'	115	T	−19	−17	−6	14	30	43	54	52	42	27	6	−11	
			R	0.5	0.6	0.9	1.0	0.9	1.9	2.2	2.7	2.3	1.4	1.0	0.7	16.0
The Pas, Man.	53°49'	890	T	−8	−2	11	33	48	59	65	61	49	35	17	1	
			R	0.6	0.5	0.7	0.8	1.4	2.2	2.2	2.1	2.0	1.2	1.0	0.8	15.4
Moosonee, Ont.	51°16'	34	T	−7	−2	9	27	41	53	60	59	50	37	19	3	
			R	1.9	1.7	1.2	1.7	2.4	3.3	2.6	3.7	3.6	3.3	2.5	2.5	30.4
Timmins, Ont.	48°30'	1100	T	2	5	16	32	46	58	63	61	52	39	24	9	
			R	1.8	1.3	1.5	1.7	2.0	2.7	3.5	2.6	2.8	2.5	3.1	1.6	27.1
Amos, Que.	48°36'	990	T	−1	1	15	31	46	57	62	59	51	39	24	7	
			R	2.7	1.4	2.0	2.2	2.2	3.1	3.8	3.5	3.8	2.9	2.9	2.2	32.7
Harrington Harbour, Que.	50°32'	25	T	8	9	20	30	38	46	53	54	48	39	28	16	
			R	4.1	5.6	5.0	2.9	3.7	3.8	3.4	4.0	4.9	5.6	5.2	4.6	51.7
Goose Bay, Lab.	53°19'	144	T	−1	6	15	27	40	51	62	59	51	38	25	7	
			R	1.8	2.5	1.9	1.6	1.9	2.5	3.2	2.7	2.2	2.6	2.2	2.4	27.6

Source: Canada, Department of Transport, Meteorological Division, *Climatic Summaries*, Vol. 1, Toronto, 1956.

has a mean range of 45 degrees, and Harrington Harbor, on the Gulf of St. Lawrence, has 46 degrees, both of which stand in marked contrast to the values reported from Fort Yukon, 84 degrees, Fort Good Hope, 83 degrees, and Dawson, 81 degrees. At the latter stations and other inland points in the northwest the mean annual range of temperature is greater than anywhere else in the world, save in eastern Siberia (Fig. 6.5). Between the northwestern valleys and Lake Winnipeg it is generally between 70 and 80 degrees, and stations between Lake Winnipeg and Labrador from 60 to 70 degrees.

The range between absolute maxima and minima is also considerable everywhere, but again is less in marine than in continental situations. Thus, Matanuska and Harrington Harbor record 132 degrees and 120 degrees respectively, whereas in the upper Yukon valley and generally from the Rockies east to Lake Winnipeg, 160 degrees or more is common Fort Yukon reports 178 degrees, which seems to be the maximum extreme range of record for the continent. Other examples are seen at Fort Smith, 168 degrees, Prince Albert, 166 degrees, and The Pas, 154 degrees. East of Lake Winnipeg values are only slightly less.

Precipitation is evidently a less significant quality of regional distinction, for we observe an appreciable difference in the total annual amounts from one section to another. In the general view, precipitation increases from northwest to southeast. Northwest sections of the boreal forest lie for the most part in the lee of fairly high mountain ranges that stand at altitudes of 5000–10,000 feet. Most of the moisture borne toward the land by air of oceanic origin is released upon their seaward flanks, and thus, diminishing amounts are available with increasing distance from the sea. Sitka, for example, a station in the much more temperate coastal coniferous forest, is on an island of the Alaskan archipelago, at 15 feet above sea level, and receives annually about 87 inches of rain. Fort St. John, at almost the same latitude but east of the Rockies, receives only 15 inches. In the westernmost reaches of the taiga in Alaska, Holy Cross, Matanuska, and Tanana, receiving 19.5 inches, 15.6 inches, and 13.2 inches respectively should be compared with Candle, having 7.5 inches, and Fort Yukon, 7 inches. The first three stations are fairly well

exposed to indrafts of moist, oceanic air, whereas the latter two lie in the shelter of low mountain ranges.

Between the Rockies and Lake Winnipeg annual amounts gradually increase, ranging from 15 inches to 20 inches in that central section, and from 20 inches to 35 inches from there to the Gulf of St. Lawrence. In places along the north shore of the Gulf values of more than 40 inches are reported, Harrington Harbor, about 150 miles from the Straight of Belle Isle, receiving nearly 52 inches. The eastward increase of mean annual precipitation is partly attributable to increasing proximity to the Atlantic Ocean and to the presence of large bodies of water, principally Hudson Bay and the Great Lakes. The presence of innumerable smaller lakes and of countless streams and sodden boggy areas means an additional quantity of moisture released to the air through evaporation. Even more important, however, is the fact that in summer, when more than half the yearly precipitation is received, the paths of cyclonic storms and other rain-producing disturbances of frontal origin converge in this general area.

Winter. Because the boreal forest lies generally between 45° and 75°N. Lat. the amount of warmth received directly from the sun is very much less in winter than in summertime. At 45° latitude the sun is low above the southern horizon for about nine hours each day during December and January and rises to an angular elevation of only $21\frac{1}{2}$ degrees on December 21st. At 70° it is not visible at all in December, and for less than two hours in January. At noon in this latitude its elevation does not exceed 10 degrees from November to January. Between the latitudes of 45° and 70° the sun's elevation and the total possible duration of sunlight is intermediate between these values (Fig. 6.1). Light rather than heat is the chief advantage derived from the winter sun.

As autumn gives way to approaching winter, the sun sinks lower in the southern skies, and hours of daylight steadily diminish. The diminishing warmth of direct solar radiation and an increasing proportion of darkness over daylight result in an increase of heat loss over heat gain, and a rapid cooling of the earth's surface takes place. Ice begins to fringe the shores of lakes and streams during the first cold nights of September, frost returns to the upper layers of soil during October, and in time the region becomes almost as one with ice cap and tundra, a vast snow- and ice-covered surface that is a constant source of cold. This frigid surface extends from the upper Mississippi valley northward across Canada, widening over the polar basin and southward from there into Eurasia as far as the Ukraine, Turkestan, and northern China.

These wintertime conditions give rise to polar continental air masses over northern Eurasia, the Arctic Ocean (Arctic continental), and northern North America. Clear, cold, dry, stable air recurrently develops over the northern Rockies and the Mackenzie valley. Thus, northwestern North America becomes in winter a source region of cold, dry polar continental air, a center of action typically producing well-developed anticyclones of appreciable breadth and depth. The Alberta High is a well-known example. Cold, dry, subsiding air becomes increasingly prevalent in northwestern sectors of the boreal forest as winter progresses. Air masses having these properties grow and intensify during the winter months and repeatedly extend their influence far beyond their region of origin. The distinction between continental polar air originating over the northwestern interior, the eastern Canadian archipelago, or the Arctic Ocean is difficult to make. Cold, dry, initially stable air from either of these sources, but most frequently from the interior northwest, typically moves southward and then southeastward across the continent. Bending eastward between Hudson Bay and the Great Lakes, it continues toward the Atlantic, where it normally loses its identity at surface level as it is warmed by the unfrozen seas. Several such masses often pass southward across the boreal forest in quick succession, producing surges of increasingly colder air.

Outbreaks of polar air, called polar outbursts, are often felt along the British Columbia coast, the lower valleys of Alaska, and in eastern Canada and the United States, where their arrival is termed a cold wave. On occasion, a polar outburst may extend in an elongated ridge of high pressure air southward to the Gulf of Mexico and the Mexican highlands, to bring damaging frost to these subtropical regions.

From time to time the cold dry weather of the interior northwest is interrupted by invasions of warmer, more humid air from the North Pacific. This maritime air tends to override the colder, more stable indigenous masses, supplying most of the moisture to these sections and giving rise to the formation of traveling cyclones. The main belt of migrating storms from the North Pacific, the zone in which cyclonic disturbances travel with greatest intensity and frequency from west to east, lies, in wintertime, well to the south of its summer position, generally along the southern margins of the boreal forest. This zone of transient storm systems, arising from contact between polar continental and maritime polar air from the Pacific, is depressed southward primarily by the expansion and intensification of the continental highs over the northwest. Extending eastward, the paths of these storms converge over the Great Lakes and the St. Lawrence with the accustomed tracks of cyclonic storms from southwestern United States and the Gulf of Mexico, bringing to eastern sectors of the boreal forest a much greater frequency of changeable weather and more abundant precipitation, especially in number of days with snowfall, than one finds in the northwest (Fig. 10.5).

Migrating cyclones arising from contact between polar continental air from the northwest and polar maritime air from the North Atlantic to the east are not common and only occasionally extend westward into the basin of Hudson Bay, usually following a southward advance of cold, dry air in the interior, farther west. The waters of Hudson Bay are frozen over during the latter part of winter and at this time provide a surface that tends to perpetuate to some extent the properties of expanding anticyclones from the northwest, to reinforce their initial stability rather than to destroy it, and thus to depress southward the paths of cyclonic storms from the west.

Atmospheric pressures associated with the repeated development of anticyclones in the northwest are higher in winter (mean value of 1022.5 millibars in February) than at any other time of the year. Mean pressure gradients are steep, diminishing westward into the enlarged Aleutian Low and eastward into the greatly enlarged Iceland Low of the North Atlantic, where mean values of about 1000 millibars prevail. The predominant wind pattern arising from these conditions is clockwise over the interior of the continent west

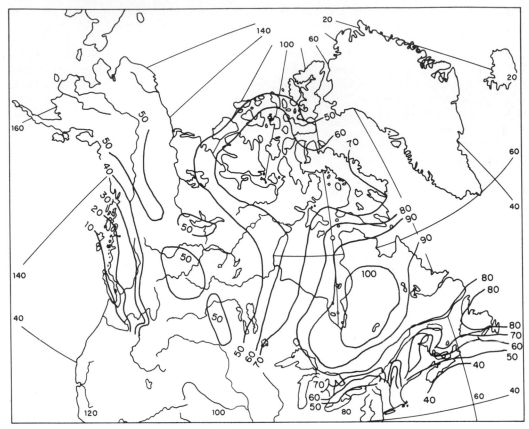

Figure 10.5. Mean annual number of days with measurable snowfall in northern North America.

of Hudson Bay, although winds from every point of the compass are experienced with the alternate passing of cyclones and anticyclones. Southerly winds are common along the eastern front of the Rockies, west and northwest winds along the Arctic east, and north to northwest winds along the western shores of Hudson Bay.

The approach of winter is normally heralded by the first frosts early in September. But winter does not actually arrive with the first snow flurries and the earliest appearance of an icy film along the shores of the lakes and rivers. The waters of countless thousands of lakes and rivers cool much more slowly than the surrounding land and exert a moderating effect upon the air above, holding back the development of continuous cold. Furthermore, autumn is the cloudiest season of the year, and either October or November is usually the cloudiest month, when extensive banks of stratus clouds become widespread, confining whatever warmth exists to lower atmospheric strata near the surface. The fact that the mean daily range of temperatures is lowest in October or November is a further consequence of these conditions. Finally, when land and water are firmly bound in frost, the severe cold of winter develops rapidly. Thus we note in Table 10-1 that the drop in mean monthly temperature is greatest for the entire season from October to November in all sections northwest of the Great Lakes, commonly amounting to around 20 degrees. East of the Great Lakes, however, the greatest mean monthly temperature drop takes place from November to December and amounts to around 15 degrees. Compare Fort Vermilion, Alta., with Amos, Que.

Subfreezing temperatures prevail for approximately six months nearly everywhere from October or November to March or April. With few exceptions, January is the coldest month, and mean values are generally below zero. Above-zero temperatures in January are observed at stations near the sea, as at Matanuska and Harrington Harbor, and along the north shore of Lake Superior and the lower St. Lawrence valley. Subzero temperatures persist for two or three months as a rule northwest of the Great Lakes and for four or five months along the northern tundra margins of the region. East of the Great Lakes a more lenient winter is indicated by the fact that usually no more than one month averages below zero, a consequence, in part, of the frequent westward invasions of warmer air from the Atlantic entrained in the passing cyclonic disturbances, appearing at the surface in the form of cold, damp, persistent east winds.

Winters along the eastern slopes of the Rockies are somewhat less severe than elsewhere in the interior, chiefly in consequence of the frequent passage of warm west winds in the southern sectors of cyclones traveling eastward from the Pacific. Gathering warmth and moisture over the sea, maritime air crosses the Rockies, is cooled, and releases most of its moisture before entering the interior of the continent. Descending the eastern slopes of the mountains, it acquires föhn characteristics from time to time, that is, it remains relatively warm after losing its moisture and gains further heat dynamically on its descent, raising air temperatures well above freezing in a remarkably short space of time, melting the thin blanket of snow, and exposing the vegetation beneath. These warm west winds of winter are called, in Alberta, the Chinook. A rise of as much as 40 degrees in fifteen minutes has been recorded, and although the thermometer seldom rises above 45°, the sudden warmth contrasts sharply with the intense cold of anticyclonic weather.

Although persistent cold is characteristic of the boreal forest, winter temperatures vary widely around the mean values shown in Table 10-1. Consider Fort Good Hope, for example, where January has averaged about −24° over

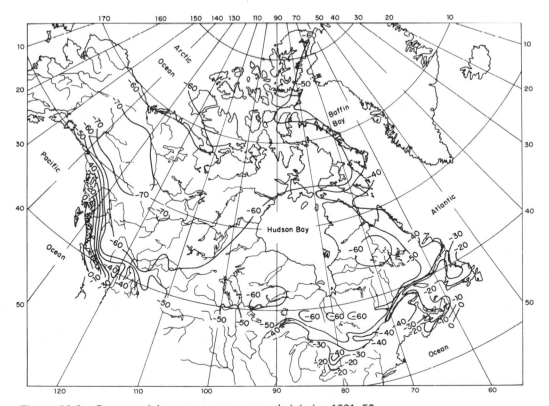

Figure 10.6. Extreme minimum temperature recorded during 1921–50.

several decades. The highest temperature in January 1953 was − 4°F, the lowest − 51°. Mean temperature for the month was − 30.6°F. For eleven days the thermometer rose no higher than − 25°. In January 1947, however, the maximum reading was 28°, the minimum − 60°, and for nine consecutive days the thermometer rose no higher than − 32°F. The mean temperature for January of that year was 25°F. In eastern sectors of the region deviations from the normal and the general severity of winter are considerably less (Fig. 10.6).

When polar continental air predominates over sections of the boreal forest in winter, its cold, dry, stable qualities lead to the development of strong temperature inversions. This is true of all winter months, but especially so of January. At Norman Wells, for example, mean radiosonde readings for January 1945 were − 12.8°F at the surface, − 9.0° at 1600 feet, 6.1° at 3200 feet, and 11.5° at 4800 feet, diminishing above that elevation. Extremely low readings are obtained in areas of rough topography where colder strata collect in pockets during the night and warmer air rests on the intervening highlands. Differences amounting to 20 degrees may be observed in a distance of only a few miles. The air in the colder pockets has been reported to be filled with visible ice particles or dense white fog. "In the case of a minimum of − 58°F at Iroquois Falls in northern Ontario, evidence was given by men ascending a hydro-electric transmission tower during the night that up to seven or eight meters the visibility was extremely low, but above that height the air was perfectly clear and calm, and the temperature sensibly much higher." [5]

As winter progresses, the mean daily range of temperature increases in most places from an annual minimum in autumn to a yearly maximum in early spring. It should be noted, however, that the maximum is often reached in summer and that mean daily ranges of large magnitude persist for a longer continuous period during the summer season than in winter.

The moisture content of the atmosphere, its absolute humidity, is less in winter than at any other time of year. Paradoxically, however, low temperatures raise the relative humidity,

that is, the apparent or sensible dampness of the air, to its highest values. Cloud cover also diminishes in most interior sections with the advance of winter, reaching a minimum in early spring. The occurrence of fog is not definitely known over most of the region but seemingly is least during the winter months in eastern sectors and greatest in the mountain valleys of the northwest. Radiation fog is to be expected in valley situations like those on the rugged surface of the Canadian Shield, especially in the presence of repeated temperature inversions.

Winter is characteristically the dry season in the boreal forest. In the northwest less and less precipitation is recorded with each successive month, and April is commonly the driest one. East of Lake Winnipeg, however, February is most often the driest month. Only about one third of the total annual precipitation falls during the winter period throughout most of the region, although in the valleys of the northwest where the season is longer this value increases to nearly one half. Except in the vicinity of the Great Lakes and the St. Lawrence where occasional rains occur almost all of the winter precipitation falls in the form of snow.

The mean annual fall of snow increases strikingly from northwest to southeast (Fig. 10.7). From the Yukon valley to Lake Winnipeg the yearly total amounts to between 3 and 4 feet with considerable variation from year to year. In these sectors the maximum depth of accumulated snow on the ground during the period 1941–50, was between 30 and 40 inches. From the vicinity of Lake Winnipeg eastward the boreal forest receives copious volumes of snow. The average winter fall increases from around 60 to 100 inches across northern Ontario and from 100 to 200 inches across central Quebec and southern Labrador. Measurable amounts of snow come to northeastern Ontario and north central Quebec on an average of one hundred days during the winter months each year (Fig. 10.6). It is the highest value in all of Canada. This means that one may expect to find it snowing in these sections during more than half the days of the winter season. Blizzards of dry, light, driving snow are common. Unlike the tundra, where the sweep of winter gales is virtually unimpeded, in the boreal forest dense, luxuriant stands of tall coniferous trees prevent widespread drifting of the winter's

[5] A. J. Conner, "The Climates of North America, II, Canada," in W. Köppen and R. Geiger, *Handbuch der Klimatologie*, **2** (Part J), p. 1348.

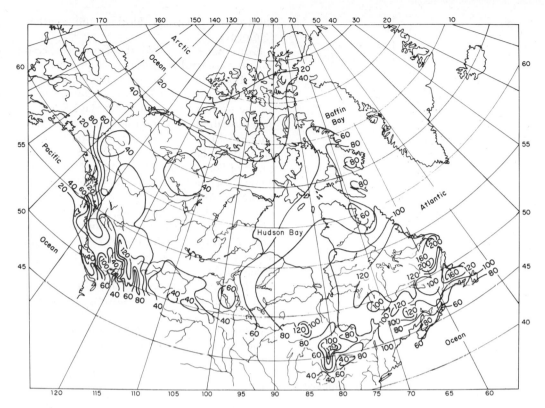

Figure 10.7. Mean annual snowfall in northern North America (inches).

snow. This protective cover also delays the progress of melting and evaporation in spring, when patches of snow may remain on the ground, particularly on north-facing slopes, until the latter part of May or early June.

Spring in the boreal forest is a season of rapid transition from the deep cold of winter to the pleasant warmth of summer. The most rapid change in temperature usually takes place from March to April, with a rise in the neighborhood of 20 degrees. As the sun appears higher and higher in the southern skies, the dark coniferous forest absorbs more and more heat of insolation from week to week. Streams begin to flow, swollen by meltwater from the vanishing snows, and the annual breakup of winter is on. Precipitation increases, and more of it falls in the form of rain. With these changes an increase in cloudiness also takes place. Cool, damp weather is characteristic as the ice-bound lakes and bogs are slowly released from the grip of frost. Mean monthly temperatures rise above 32° in April along the southern

margins of the taiga, and by May above-freezing values prevail everywhere. The approach of summer is universally delayed by the slow melting of thick ice in lakes and streams. It takes place most rapidly northwest of Lake Winnipeg with the rapid increase of effective solar radiation on the broad land surface of the interior, while it is retarded in Quebec and Labrador to a large extent by the lingering ice of Hudson Bay.

Summer. The fact that mean warm season temperatures are above 50° typically for three to four months indicates that summer as we think of it in mid-latitudes occurs also in the boreal forest, a condition that is not true of either tundra or polar ice cap. Summer days are as a rule only moderately warm, however, and are subject to a wide daily range of temperature. The mean daily range at most stations is in fact continuously greater during this season than any other period of the year. The monthly average of mean daily ranges for Dawson is graphically portrayed in Fig. 10.8, showing a

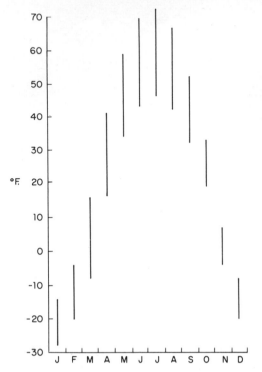

Figure 10.8. Monthly mean daily temperature range at Dawson, Yukon Territory.

gradual increase in amplitude from lowest in November to highest in July. To further clarify the seasonal differences in these values, Fig. 10.9 shows a diagram of actual maximum-minimum temperatures recorded at Dawson during July 1964 and January 1965. Mean daily range for the summer months, like mean annual range, of course, reaches greater amplitudes in continental interior situations like that of Dawson than at stations near the sea. At most inland stations mean daily range is between 20 and 30 degrees, commonly around 25 degrees, whereas at coastal stations it is usually less than 20 degrees.

Generally speaking, the typically wide range of daily temperature indicates an ever-present threat of frost during the growing season. Thus the boreal forest in which the frost-free season lasts in the neighborhood of seventy-five days, and is often no more than fifty, is a region hazardous for the profitable growing of all but the hardiest cereals and root crops. It is interesting to note that here the threat of damaging summer frost contrasts with the threat of occasional damaging winter frost in such

sub-tropical areas as Florida and southern California.

From place to place the frost-free season varies considerably. Locally, a proximity to large bodies of water extends the length of the growing season. Fort Resolution, for example, on the southern shore of Great Slave Lake, has an unusually long period of ninety-three days, and Hay River, just 70 miles west on the same lake shore, has eighty-seven, but Fort Smith, south of Fort Resolution and 90 miles from the water, has only fifty-six days of frost-free weather. At Haileyburg, on the northwest shores of Lake Temiskaming, a mean frost-free period of 123 days is recorded, but at Heaslip, only 25 miles north, the period is around seventy-one days, a difference of more than seven weeks.

Whereas the broader changes in temperature that occur during the summer months are attributable to the alternate passage of contrasting air masses and intervening disturbances, most of the daily variations result from the normal diurnal movements of the sun. In this the qualities of the land are undoubtedly important as well. The dark coniferous forest absorbs a large percentage of the solar radiation received by day (90 to 95 per cent), and the cool, damp, humus-covered soil beneath the dense, needle-leaved crowns combined with widespread permafrost below the surface provide a marked cooling effect at night.

Although summers are in general only moderately warm in the taiga, maximum temperatures have reached or exceeded 100°F at many places, including Fort Yukon (100°), Fort Smith (103°), The Pas (100°), Kapuskasing (101°), and Goose Bay (100°). Absolute maxima in excess of 100°F are not at all uncommon along the southern margins of the boreal forest in the continental interior where the region gives way to grassland, in which high intensities of summer warmth are typical. This is to be expected, and it is more significant to note that stations near the tundra margins much farther north have also reported very high extremes—Churchill with 96°, and Fort Good Hope with 95°.

July is almost without exception the warmest month, when the thermometer ranges on the average between 55° and 65° (Fig. 10.4). Usually only one month averages above 60°, but in a section west of Lake Winnipeg two months, July and August, normally exceed this value at several stations. Near the sea, and also in the lichen-woodland sections approaching the tundra, mean values for the warmest month seldom rise above 60°.

Summer is the season of most abundant precipitation everywhere save on a slender coastal strip along the north shore of the Gulf of St. Lawrence, where a winter maximum occurs. Harrington Harbor, for example, receives around 53 per cent of its total yearly amount during winter. Normally, nearly two thirds of the yearly total comes during the summer season. The heaviest monthly fall is ordinarily recorded in July, although either June or August may be the wettest month (Table 10-1).

The intensity of summer rainfall varies from year to year and from decade to decade most noticeably in the drier northwest. From Lake Winnipeg eastward greater reliability becomes characteristic, and the boreal forest of eastern Quebec and Labrador has been described as a territory less threatened by drought than almost any other part of the world.

Convective showers are not uncommon in the boreal forest, and thunderstorms are by no means rare, although few places experience more than five each year, and in northwestern

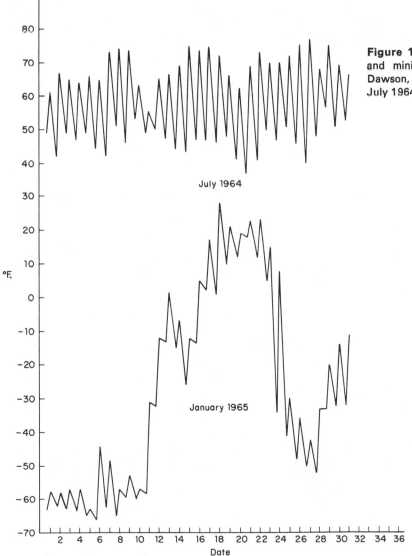

Figure 10.9. Daily maximum and minimum temperatures at Dawson, Yukon Territory, during July 1964 and January 1965.

sections the frequency is even less. Most of the summer's rain falls in the form of a light, steady drizzle of cyclonic origin.

Cyclonic storms in summer are weaker than in winter and move much more slowly, following less direct, more uncertain paths. Northern sections of the boreal forest are affected much more frequently by cyclonic storms, especially in the Mackenzie valley and the border lands of Hudson Bay. Maritime polar air, originating over the Bering Sea, enters Alaska, moving up the Yukon valley across the northern Rockies and into the Mackenzie lowlands, where it typically overrides colder Arctic air originating over the Arctic Ocean or the Canadian Archipelago, producing frontal rains. Cyclonic storms develop here under these conditions, and along the eastern front of the Rockies, where maritime air that has crossed the mountains from the Pacific comes into contact with drier, highly heated air over the interior plains. The paths followed by these and by storms from the northwest tend to converge in the general area of Hudson Bay. Hudson Bay and the archipelago remain relatively cold during summer, however, and are often overlain by masses of cold, dry air from the north. When this happens, the paths of eastward-moving cyclones are depressed southward toward the Great Lakes and the St. Lawrence valley, there to join the preferred paths of cyclones originating in the south from contact between maritime tropical air from the Gulf of Mexico or the South Atlantic and drier, continental air from the interior. A certain amount of the more plentiful rain that comes to eastern sections of the boreal forest is thought to be precipitated from moisture transported at high levels from maritime tropical sources south of the United States. Only rarely do tropical cyclones developing at the surface bring rain directly to eastern sectors of the boreal forest.

The northward shift of cyclonic activity, the increased occurrence of cyclonic disturbances in higher latitudes, arises mainly from the remarkable heating of the continental interior that takes place in summer. During most of the period from March to September the sun is above the horizon more than twelve hours each day throughout the latitudinal breadth of the region, and during at least part of May, June, and July may be visible for twenty-four

hours per day along the narrow fringe that lies beyond the Arctic Circle. On June 21 it stands 47 degrees above the southern horizon at $66\frac{1}{2}°$ latitude, and about 68 degrees above the horizon at $45°$ latitude (see Chapter 8). Polar continental air masses no longer develop, and cold, dry, stable air originates only over the polar basin. The interior lowlands of the northwest become regions of characteristic inflow from the Arctic Ocean and, more commonly, from the North Pacific. Counterclockwise circulations prevail, bringing north and northeast winds to the Arctic coast and northwest winds to the northern Rockies.

Gradually, as the sun swings across the southern skies at increasingly lower altitudes, nights lengthen, days become shorter, and the chill, damp autumn approaches.

Boreal Forest in Eurasia

Turning to the boreal forest of Eurasia, we observe a similar transition from tundra barrens to mid-latitude mixed forests, grasslands, and complex mountainous country. The pattern of distribution, however, is quite different (Fig. 9.2).

Extending in an unbroken belt of forest from the Atlantic to the Sea of Okhotsk, from the Scandinavian peninsula to Kamchatka, the Eurasian taiga is the largest tract of continuous woodland in the world. For more than 5000 miles it spreads a dark green mantle over the drainage basins of many north-flowing streams, including three of the world's largest, the Ob, the Yenesei, and the Lena. It preserves its identity as a truly boreal woodland up to elevations of around 3000 feet in western sections, up to around 5000 feet farther east. The dominant conifers differ somewhat from east to west, but Scots pine (*Pinus sylvestris*) and Norway spruce (*Picea excelsa, Picea obovata*) are important through almost its entire length and breadth.

In its westernmost margins the boreal forest faces the Atlantic along the deeply dissected coast of Norway, where it lightly fringes the lower, steep-sided slopes of countless fjords in discontinuous tracts of spruce, pine, and boreal hardwoods. Here Norway spruce and Scots pine are the principal species, present in varying proportions along with a generous admixture of birch, aspen, and alder. Subalpine stands of birch-aspen are persistent and widespread at the uppermost levels, especially in northern areas. The altitudes reached by the boreal forest in Norway vary with exposure to the sun, with latitude, and with proximity to the sea. In southern areas they appear from sea level to more than 3000 feet, but in the far north, beyond the Arctic Circle, they are seldom seen more than 1000 feet above sea level, where lower temperatures and lower effective precipitation produce a tundra series of landscapes. Generally speaking, the forest reaches higher elevations in localities deep within the fjords than in those exposed to the sea and rises higher on southern than on north-facing mountain slopes.

The boreal forest in Norway merges on the south with the mid-latitude mixed forests of western Europe, not far north of Bergen and Oslo. Ten degrees farther north, beyond latitude 70°, it gives way to the tundra, and on the upper slopes of the mountainous interior yields to alpine meadow and tundra. The Norwegian taiga is almost cut off from the main body of the Eurasian forest. It is linked by a slender, transalpine band of wooded country just north of Oslo and the central lowlands of Sweden.

From around latitude 60° the region extends northward in a belt of well-developed woodland some 200 miles or more in width, between the alpine tundra of the interior highlands and the waters of the Gulf of Bothnia. Reaching as far north as the Kola peninsula, it continues in luxuriant development throughout most of Finland. South coastal Finland and the southern part of the Scandinavian peninsula are occupied by segments of the main mid-latitude mixed forests of western Europe. The presence of oak, ash, linden (basswood), and other deciduous hardwoods indicates a transition into the warmer latitudes of the British Isles and the north European plain.

The boreal forest touches the shores of the White Sea and the Gulf of Finland before expanding eastward toward the Ural Mountains in a continuously wooded territory some 700 miles in breadth. East of the White Sea the Siberian larch (*Larix sibirica*) and Siberian fir (*Abies sibirica*) join with Scots pine and Norway spruce as the dominant conifers of the forest. White birch (*Betula verrucosa*), common birch (*B. pubescens*), and aspen (*Populus tremula*) are also plentiful. Pure stands of white birch are common and are called the white taiga, in contrast to the black taiga, composed of predominantly coniferous trees.

Between the Gulf of Finland and the southern end of the Urals the boreal forest merges gradually toward the south with the mid-latitude mixed forests of the north European plain. The presence of deciduous dominants from this region, such as the Norway maple (*Acer platanoides*), ash (*Fraxinus excelsior*), oak (*Quercus pedunculata*), and linden (*Tilia cordata*), in increasing proportions southward marks the change into a milder environment of less severe winters, longer, warmer summers, and more effective precipitation. Beyond the Urals only the linden remains important, where it is seen to form part of the forest-steppe transition zone, extending well into the Ob River valley. The deciduous forests come to an end along the western slopes of the southern Urals, and the more sparsely wooded forest-steppe forms the southern margin of the taiga east of the mountains, reaching beyond the Ob and well into the Yenesei valley.

This climatic change results partly from the fact that the Urals, rising to heights of 3000 and 4000 feet above the surrounding plain (many peaks clothed in alpine tundra formations are more than 5000 feet in elevation), interpose a low barrier to the eastward movement of rain-bearing storms from the North Atlantic. Hence, the westward slopes bear a more luxuriant and more diverse vegetation cover than the eastern slopes, clearly indicating a change in prevailing atmospheric properties. East of the Urals the taiga becomes a region of increased aridity and greater climatic severity, with a notable increase in mean annual and extreme ranges of temperature. These changes are reflected in the addition of the Siberian stone pine (*Pinus sibirica*) and the greater proportion of Siberian larch among the dominant conifers east of the mountains. East of the Urals a remarkable expanse of lowland, conspicuous for its nearly unrelieved flatness, is subjected to widespread flooding every spring when the Ob and its tributaries overflow their ice-dammed banks. Hence, over much of the area, edaphic conditions that are dominantly hygrophytic lead to the development of vast tracts of marsh and bog. This section extends eastward approximately as far as the Yenesei.

Beyond the Yenesei the Dahurian larch (*Larix dahurica* and *L. gmelinii*), a shallow-rooted species that survives where only a thin layer of soil thaws in summertime, replaces the Siberian larch, and still farther east the Japanese stone pine (*Pinus pumila*) becomes an important dominant. Generally speaking, the taiga becomes increasingly dominated by the deciduous larch east of the Yenesei, although the evergreen Scots pine, Norway spruce, Siberian fir, and stone pine remain in evidence in southern areas.

The boreal forest continues well into eastern Siberia in the valleys of the Yenesei, the Lena, the Yana, Indigirka, and Kolyma. High mountains, rising to elevations of more than 5000 feet and mantled by a complex vertical zoning of vegetation, form the southern borders of the taiga in the tributary regions of these rivers. The forest attains its greatest breadth in Eurasia roughly between Lake Baikal and the Taimyr peninsula, extending in a north–south direction for more than 1800 miles.

Between the Yenesei and the Lena is a rugged, dissected tableland called the central Siberian plateau, approximately 1000 to 2000 feet above sea level, that is heavily mantled with forest. East of the Lena, higher and more deeply dissected mountains, including the Verkhoyansk, Cherskogo, and Kolymski ranges, whose higher slopes commonly rise more than a mile above the sea, disrupt the continuity of the forest distribution. Alpine tundra is widespread at higher levels, and the taiga is found chiefly on the lower and intermediate slopes of the valleys, generally below 4000 feet. In these remote sections of eastern Siberia we are handicapped by a shortage of descriptive accounts and weather data. In general, however, we observe that though tundra landscapes predominate, the taiga continues into the upper valleys of the Lena and the Kolyma rivers, reappearing as outliers in the middle valleys of the Penzhina and the Anadyr. It also appears on the coastal lowlands of the Kamchatka peninsula, around the shores of the Sea of Okhotsk, on Sakhalin Island, and on the shores of the Gulf of Tartary. In all these easternmost coastal situations a milder form of the boreal forest climate is found, resulting from proximity to the moderating influence of the sea. Additional species such as Erman's birch (*Betula ermani*), Yeddo spruce (*Picea jezoensis*),

and Khingan fir (*Abies nephrolepis*) indicate the environmental change.

The dominant conifers of the boreal forest may be traced in areas somewhat south of Lake Baikal, at elevations below 5000 feet, and eastward into the upper Amur valley. There, and in general along the Pacific coast, the region comes to a gradual end with the increasing interspersion of species representing the mid-latitude mixed forests of eastern Asia. These include the Korean pine (*Pinus koraiensis*), Mongolian oak (*Quercus mongolica*), Amur linden (*Tilia amurensis*), Amur maple (*Acer ginnala*), and Manchurian ash (*Fraxinus mandshurica*).

Thus, from the Atlantic to the Pacific the Eurasian taiga marks a transition zone of reasonable uniformity between the polar tundra and four fairly distinct regions toward the south: the mainly deciduous forests of the north European plain, the grassy steppe lands of the interior, the diversified highlands of central and east Asia, and the mid-latitude mixed forests of China, Korea, and Japan. In essential respects the regional relationships of the boreal forest in North America are the same, differing chiefly in locational arrangement.

The seasonal weather patterns in the boreal forest of Eurasia resemble very closely those of North America. The same marked contrast exists between the extreme cold of winter and the mild warmth of summer, and a low mean annual rainfall with a summer increase in volume is also characteristic. But these qualities of a typically continental climate are more intensified, apply to a much larger area, and produce a somewhat different geographical distribution and relationship with adjoining regions in Eurasia. These differences arise mainly from the enormous size and continuity of the Eurasian land mass and the arrangement of prominent relief features. As we shall see, the general pattern of all the climates in Eurasia is to a large extent a consequence of the great east–west breadth and latitudinal span of the continent, coupled with the presence of mountain barriers along certain coastal sections that seriously hamper the deep inland penetration of moisture-bearing, moderating air from the sea.

Much more so than North America, most of interior Eurasia, with the exception of the western seaboard, lies remote and sheltered

TABLE 10-2
Climatic Data for Boreal Forest Stations in Eurasia
(Temp., °F; Rainfall, In.)

Station	Lat.	El. in Ft		Jan.	Feb.	Mar.	Apr.	May	Jun.	Jul.	Aug.	Sep.	Oct.	Nov.	Dec.	Year
Rena, Norway	61°08'	738	T	12	16	23	35	45	56	59	55	47	36	25	15	
			R	1.5	1.3	1.6	1.7	2.2	2.3	3.3	4.0	2.6	2.8	1.9	2.3	27.6
Malaa, Sweden	65°11'	1050	T	9	11	19	31	41	52	58	53	43	31	18	12	
			R	1.2	1.0	0.7	0.9	1.1	2.6	2.9	3.6	2.4	2.0	1.9	1.3	21.5
Archangelsk, U.S.S.R.	64°28'	20	T	8	10	17	30	41	53	60	55	46	34	21	12	
			R	0.9	0.8	0.9	0.8	1.4	2.0	2.4	2.5	2.2	1.8	1.3	1.1	18.0
Kirov, U.S.S.R.	58°36'	594	T	5	10	19	35	50	59	65	59	48	34	20	10	
			R	1.3	1.3	1.0	1.0	1.9	2.5	2.4	2.8	2.3	2.0	1.4	1.4	21.9
Salekhard, U.S.S.R.	66°31'	86	T	-14	-8	0	13	28	45	57	52	41	24	2	-7	
			R	0.3	0.3	0.2	0.3	0.7	1.3	1.8	2.0	1.5	0.7	0.5	0.4	10.0
Tobolsk, U.S.S.R.	58°12'	355	T	-4	4	16	33	49	60	65	60	49	33	14	3	
			R	0.8	0.7	0.7	0.6	1.7	2.1	3.0	2.6	1.9	1.2	1.2	1.1	17.6
Turukhansk, U.S.S.R.	65°55'	131	T	-19	-10	1	14	30	48	61	54	41	19	-5	-18	
			R	0.5	0.4	0.4	0.5	1.0	1.6	2.0	2.3	2.0	1.1	0.8	0.5	13.1
Irkutsk, U.S.S.R.	52°16'	1532	T	-6	-1	14	33	46	58	63	59	46	32	13	-1	
			R	0.4	0.3	0.3	0.2	1.5	2.2	3.5	3.1	1.7	0.7	0.7	0.6	15.2
Verkhoyansk, U.S.S.R.	67°33'	400	T	-58	-48	-24	9	36	56	60	52	36	6	-34	-51	
			R	0.2	0.1	0.1	0.2	0.3	0.9	1.0	1.0	0.5	0.3	0.3	0.1	5.0
Yakutsk, U.S.S.R.	62°01'	354	T	-46	-33	-9	17	41	60	65	59	43	17	-20	-40	
			R	0.2	0.2	0.1	0.2	0.5	1.1	1.3	1.6	0.9	0.5	0.4	0.3	7.3
Markova, U.S.S.R.	64°45'	85	T	-20	-14	-9	5	30	51	58	51	38	16	-3	-16	
			R	0.3	0.2	0.3	0.1	0.3	0.8	1.5	1.9	1.0	0.5	0.4	0.3	7.6
Nikolaevsk, U.S.S.R.	53°08'	66	T	-12	-4	9	27	39	53	62	61	53	36	14	-4	
			R	0.7	0.5	0.7	1.2	1.2	1.3	1.9	3.2	2.8	2.4	1.3	1.0	18.2

Source: American Institute of Crop Ecology, *Agricultural Climatology of Siberia*, Washington, D.C., 1950.

from the influence of the sea, a source of warm, moist air in winter and cool, moist air in summer. Oceanic air, whatever its origin, is rapidly modified as it moves inland over the continent, speedily changing its properties and losing its moisture and its moderating capacity. Moreover, the prevailing movement of the general circulation is eastward, guided by the dominant flow of the circumpolar whirl. Thus, cyclonic storms and other migrating weather systems affecting the northern region of forests tend for the most part to originate over the North Atlantic and those arms of the Arctic Ocean called the Barents and Kara seas. They are much more frequent in summer than in winter and are typically transported eastward with diminishing intensity and effectiveness as they range farther and farther from their sources. The inland penetration of maritime air from the North Pacific is slight in summer and scarcely evident at all in winter. The results of these conditions are an increase in mean annual temperature range and a decrease in total annual rainfall from west to east (Fig. 6.5 and 6.10). Table 10-2 provides climatic data for boreal forest stations in Eurasia.

The eastward decrease in total annual rainfall within the Eurasian taiga is, of course, opposite to the general distribution of yearly rainfall in North America. Western Europe is especially well watered, but the inland portions of eastern Siberia are relatively dry. This arises mainly from the fact that storms originating over the North Atlantic, principal source of moisture for the region, are scarcely impeded during their eastward progress over the land. Save for the steeply sloping western flanks of the Scandinavian plateau in Norway, northwestern Europe is free of high mountain barriers like those of Alaska and British Columbia. Moisture-laden air masses thus penetrate more deeply into Eurasia than into North America before releasing all their available moisture and otherwise undergoing change. Actually, a mean annual rainfall of more than 20 inches is common to the western sectors of the region, all the way from the Atlantic shores to the Ural Mountains, a distance of approximately 2000 miles.

Norwegian stations, directly exposed to the onshore movements of storms, receive more than 25 inches; stations in Sweden, Finland, and the western U.S.S.R. receive 20 inches or more

as far east as the Urals. Amounts are somewhat less than 20 inches toward the north in the direction of the drier tundra. The Ural Mountains provide a certain degree of orographic uplift to migrating storms, with the result that their western slopes are better watered and are mantled with a more diversified vegetation than are the leeward slopes on the east. A slight rain shadow effect is seen in the lower rainfall totals east of the Urals compared with those on the windward side, latitude for latitude. Compare Salekhard (10 inches) and Berezovo (13.6 inches) with Ust Tsilma (15.8 inches), and Tobolsk (17.6 inches) with Molotov (24 inches) and Kirov (21.9 inches). The Urals may be thought of as a weak climatic divide, for nearly everywhere east of their low-lying ranges all the way to the Pacific coast less than 20 inches of rainfall is annually received (Fig. 10.10).

Along the southern margins of the taiga, in the tributary regions of the Ob and the Yenesei and where the boreal forest extends into the middle reaches of the Amur, values in the neighborhood of 18 inches prevail. Toward the north and the colder, drier tundra, annual amounts diminish strikingly, often to less than half this value. Exceptionally small quantities for a boreal forest region are received, for example, at Verkhoyansk (5 inches), Oymiakon (5.2 inches), and Ust Maia (6 inches), places far from the Atlantic, well removed from summertime sources of moisture over the Arctic Ocean and sheltered from the Pacific by mountain ranges toward the south and east.

Among the wooded valleys in northeastern Siberia rainfall remains generally below 10 inches, even in coastal sections of the Bering Sea and along the northern shores of the Sea of Okhotsk. Along the western shores of the Sea of Okhotsk, however, annual rainfall is again relatively high, amounting to 18.2 inches at Nikolaevsk and 34.8 inches at Aian. These coastal stations are affected by more frequent invasions of maritime polar air from the North Pacific in summertime than are stations farther north. The fact that only a narrow belt of the Pacific coast receives appreciable amounts of annual rainfall, diminishing sharply toward the interior, indicates the weakness of the summertime onshore monsoon in these high latitudes of east Asia. Farther south in Japan, Korea, and China, on the other hand, a considerable

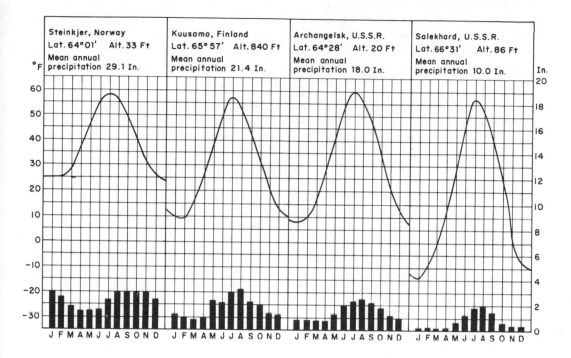

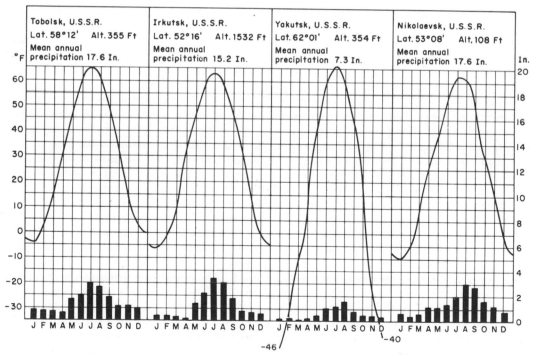

Figure 10.10. Normal temperature and precipitation at boreal forest stations in northern Eurasia.

summertime increase in rainfall is typical. For the Eurasian taiga as a whole most stations receive more than two thirds of their total annual precipitation during the months when temperatures average above freezing. In short, only in the neighborhood of 30 per cent of the mean annual total falls in wintertime. Thus, the summer intensity of precipitation is somewhat greater than in North America (compare Figs. 10.4 and 10.10).

The mean annual range of temperature is lowest along the coast of Norway, where, as at Steinkjer (34 degrees), the moderating effect of the North Atlantic Current is most strongly felt. Values are relatively low in the boreal forest over all of Norway, Sweden, and Finland, being generally less than 50 degrees. Eastward, however, a gradual rise to 60 degrees or more may be noted with increasing distance from the sea. Kirov (60 degrees) and Molotov (61 degrees) are examples. As with rainfall, we note again the effectiveness of the Urals in the creation of temperature contrasts between eastern and western slopes. East of the mountains amplitudes of mean annual temperature range are 10 degrees higher (Berezovo 71 degrees, Salekhard 70 degrees, and Tobolsk 70 degrees) and gradually increase eastward to the regions of greatest values in the upper reaches of the Lena, the Yana, and the Indigirka valleys. Here are seen the most extreme variations between mean summer and mean winter temperatures that have been recorded anywhere on earth. The greatest amplitude is 121 degrees at Oymiakon, a station lying within less than 300 miles of the Sea of Okhotsk.[6] Although the records from which this statistical mean is derived are for only a seven-year period, the mean ranges of 118 degrees at Verkhoyansk (thirty-five-year record), of 115 degrees at Markhinskoe (twenty-one-year record), and 112 degrees at Yakutsk (seventy-seven-year record) strengthen the probability that the value for Oymiakon is representative. All in all, a section of eastern Siberia about 600,000 square miles in area—extending between Nyurba and Sredne-Kolymsk, between Kazachie and Ust Maia—seems to experience a mean annual temperature range in excess of 100 degrees. Neither the tundra toward the north

nor the mountain border lands on the south have recorded values of this magnitude. And eastward along the shores of the Pacific values diminish to less than 60 degrees for places like Aian (58 degrees), Ola (58 degrees), and Klyuchevskoe (59 degrees) that are favored by the moderating effect of the sea.

The range between the highest and lowest temperatures ever recorded is also greatest in the remote interior of eastern Siberia. Maximum values of 178 degrees at Elgyai (near Nyurba), 180 degrees at Oymiakon, 184 degrees at Yakutsk, and 188 degrees at Verkhoyansk are examples. They should be compared with those for North America of 178 degrees at Fort Yukon and 174 degrees at Fort Good Hope. The exceptional range of mean yearly and extreme temperatures in eastern sectors of the Eurasian taiga arises principally from the very low readings for the coldest month of January, for winters are colder here than anywhere else in the world. Summer means, and for that matter summer extremes, differ less than 10 degrees at most stations throughout the entire region. During winter, on the other hand, January averages more than 60 degrees colder in eastern Siberia than at stations west of the Ural Mountains, and available reports of extreme minima show values that are 40 or 50 degrees colder in eastern than in western areas.

Winter. In wintertime at these high latitudes, whatever warmth may be derived from the sun during the brief periods of daylight is far outweighed by an excessive loss of heat during the long, cold hours of darkness. Thus, with winter's advance, this tremendous, unbroken mass of land, from the Baltic Sea to the Pacific, gradually becomes a vast source of extreme cold. In eastern Siberia especially, mean winter temperatures in the boreal forest drop far below those observed even in the tundra and the frozen Arctic Ocean farther north. The great size, particularly the enormous west-to-east extent of the region, is of primary importance in this. So much of the vast area east of the Urals lies remote from the moderating influence of the Atlantic that both cloudiness and snowfall are much less prevalent in eastern than in western sections of the region.

Late winter and early spring are usually the time of least cloud development and minimum

---

[6] Its elevation of 2625 feet places it very near the upper altitudinal limits of the boreal forest in east Asia.

precipitation for the entire year. Late summer brings maximum cloudiness and maximum precipitation. Winter in general, however, is hardly less cloudy than summer save in the easternmost section between the Lena valley and the Pacific coast, where observed cloudiness in January is oftentimes only half that of areas farther west, especially west of the Ural Mountains. During those prolonged periods when the atmosphere remains free of passing disturbances, northeastern Siberia is dominated by weather that is singularly clear, dry, and calm. Under these circumstances radiational loss of heat from the earth's surface proceeds surely and steadily to lower the readings on the thermometer far below the zero mark. Time after time the slender column of mercury stands rigidly frozen in the glass (below $-40°F$), and human activity out of doors is virtually brought to a stop.

Mountainous relief evidently plays an important role in determining the exceptional severity of winters in northern sectors of eastern Siberia. The Dzhugdzhur Mountains, rising steeply along the Pacific coast, and the somewhat less precipitous slopes of the Cherskogo and Kolymski ranges present effective barriers more than 3000 feet in elevation to the inland invasion of maritime air from the sea. Westward and northward of these ranges the valleys of the Lena, Yana, Indigirka, and Kolyma rivers, sloping gently toward the Arctic coast, lie at elevations considerably less than 1000 feet above sea level. It is in these valleys that the lowest mean and extreme temperature readings have been recorded. Sheltered from the North Pacific, the nearest source of moderating influences, and overlain by calm, clear, stable, subsiding air for long periods of time, they accumulate the colder elements of the lower atmospheric strata. Verkhoyansk, for example, a place that has never recorded a January temperature higher than $-13°F$, with a January mean of $-58°F$, has an elevation of only 400 feet, with mountains rising to the west, east and south of the Yana valley to heights of 5000 feet or more. Similar conditions should be noted for Yakutsk, Markhinskoe, Ust Maia, Kazachie, and Rodchevo. Oymiakon, although seeming to confute this rule by lying at an elevation of 2635 feet, nonetheless occupies a sheltered situation in the upper Indigirka valley, above which are mountains that rise

more than 5000 feet over sea level. The valleys in which extremes of winter cold are commonly observed are sometimes spoken of as frost hollows. The mean daily range of winter temperatures is undoubtedly great, for although comprehensive data are lacking for the region as a whole, we may note in Berg[7] "that the thermometer has risen, in the middle of February at Yeniseysk, from $-40°F$ to $1°F$ in a short period of time, and that in one day, at the same place toward the end of January, it dropped from $9°F$ to $-44°F$, a 24-hour range of 53 degrees."

Temperature inversions are common and well developed throughout the entire region but are more pronounced and more persistent in eastern sections. It is generally believed that temperatures increase up to around 4500 feet, decreasing above that level.

Winter, when monthly mean temperatures remain below freezing, commonly lasts for seven months, from October to April, in most sections of the boreal forest. The period may be anywhere from five to eight months in length, depending on nearness to the chief sources of warmer air over bodies of open water (Fig. 10.10). At northern stations east of the Urals, such as Turukhansk, Sredne-Kolymsk, and Markova, that lie near the borders of the tundra, the season is eight months long. It is shorter in coastal areas, as at Rena (five months), Kuopio, Finland (five months), and Nikolaevsk at the mouth of the Amur on the Pacific coast (six months), as well as at stations near the deep waters of Lake Baikal, such as Irkutsk and Kultuk (five months) and Ulan Ude (six months).

Generally speaking, winters are shorter and less severe west of the Ural Mountains, where continuous frost seldom prevails for more than six months, and the coldest month usually averages above zero. At most stations east of these low mountains at least one month of subzero readings is the rule. With increasing distance eastward, mean subzero readings often prevail for several months running. In northeastern Siberia many stations regularly record mean temperatures below zero for five months in succession. Elgyai and Vilyuisk in the valley of the Ilyui, a western tributary of the

[7] E. S. Berg, *Natural Regions of the U.S.S.R.*, The Macmillan Company, New York, 1950, p. 25.

Lena, Olekminsk and Yakutsk in the Lena valley, and Verkhoyansk on the banks of the Yana are examples of places where the exceptional severity of a bitterly cold winter is marked by such prolonged periods of below-zero temperatures. In almost all situations in the boreal forest January is the coldest month.

Winter endures for at least half the year throughout most of the boreal forest, but less than one third of the total annual precipitation is received during the season of subfreezing temperatures. Nearly all of it falls during the passage of cyclonic storms originating over the North Atlantic. Migrating cyclones are usually deeper and travel more rapidly in winter than in summer. The east, northeast, and north winds usually accompanying these migrating storms bring the purga, or winter buran (described in the preceding chapter on the tundra) that is the Siberian counterpart of the North American blizzard. Such winds often blow with gale force at temperatures well below zero, and even in the forested taiga commonly drift the light, dry snow into ridges and hillocks many feet in depth, often rising to the rooftops of one-story dwellings. In the account given by Sawicz[8] of a forty-day march from Irkutsk to a prison camp southwest of Yakutsk during December and January 1940–41, three heavy blizzards occurred. Each lasted for more than twenty-four hours, and each brought the marching force of several thousand men to a complete standstill in impassable drifts of deep, dry, crunching snow. Drifting is less characteristic of the boreal forest than it is of the treeless border regions, however. The shelter afforded by the forest permits the winter's snow to accumulate in depths of 2 feet or more over most areas, with perhaps something less than 2 feet along the northern and southern margins.

Snow falls on many more days of winter here than anywhere else in northern Eurasia, save on the windward slopes at upper levels of the Scandinavian plateau. Note for example, that Turukhansk has recorded snow on an average of 104 days during winter, Vilyuisk ninety-two days, Yeneseysk eighty-six, and Verkhoyansk and Yakutsk seventy-five days. Average duration of the snow cover is from seven to eight months (220 to 240 days) over northern areas, and around six months (180 days) along the southern margins (Fig. 10.11).

Though overcast skies and snowstorms are common enough during winter, clear, clam, dry, subsiding air predominates over most of the taiga. After every driving blizzard, when the snow has ceased falling and the wind has died away, the clear, dry air under cloudless, violet-blue skies becomes remarkably quiet. One of the special qualities of Siberian winters is the absolute silence that frequently reigns in those desolate frost-bound forests. Atmospheric pressure values increase with winter's advance, and January, the coldest month, also sees the highest mean readings on the barometer. High atmospheric pressures intensify and expand over much of the boreal forest, and most of the region becomes a wintertime source of polar continental air that is unusually dry and intensely cold. Mean atmospheric pressure values are highest in the mountainous region south of Lake Baikal, outside of the boreal forest, where the general level of the land is more than a mile above the sea. Here the mean barometric readings for January exceed 1035 millibars (30.56 inches), and from this central area persistently high values are recorded in winter toward the northeast and west to create a region of anticyclonic development larger and more intensified than any other part of the earth. The reading of 1076 millibars (31.77 inches) at Irkutsk is perhaps the world's highest value of record.[9]

Pressure gradients established between the Asiatic anticyclones, the predominantly cold, dry air over the interior, and the expanded Icelandic and Aleutian lows of wintertime give rise to recurrent outbursts of cold winter gales into those milder climatic regions of western Europe and eastern Asia that are nearer the sea. The over-all surface wind pattern related to the repeated development of anticyclonic systems produces predominantly southwest winds over eastern Europe, southwesterly and westerly winds along the Arctic coast, northwesterly winds along the Pacific coast, and northeasterly winds that sweep down out of Siberia across the desert interior of central Asia.

[8] Slavomir Sawicz, *The Long Walk*, Harper & Row, Publishers, New York, 1956, pp. 48–56.

[9] Kendrew, *Climates of the Continents*, 5th ed. The Clarendon Press, Oxford, 1961, p. 261.

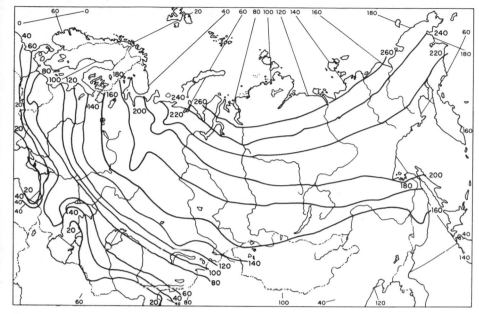

Figure 10.11. Average duration of snow cover in northern Eurasia. [After Berg]

The long, cold winter, when the rivers are covered with a heavy thickness of ice and the ground lies deeply mantled in snow, persists until May in most areas, and even into June in those northern sections near the Arctic Circle. The transition from a season of deep, relentless cold into a summer of considerable warmth takes place during a short spell of stormy, changeable weather that is typical of the boreal forest but scarcely deserves the name *spring*. Henry Seebohm, wintering at Ust Tsilma in 1875 on the banks of the Pechora, a few degrees south of the Arctic Circle, gives this account:

On the 8th of May summer seemed farther off than ever. On the previous day the weather had been very changeable—alternately warm, snowing, hailing, sleeting, with an occasional gleam of sunshine, and a cold wind, but on the whole a thaw. The next day the morning was bitterly cold, with a north wind blowing hard. In the afternoon the wind veered to the west, with a heavy fall of snow. At midnight the wind dropped, the sky became clear, and the thermometer went down to 16°F. The landscape was again white and frost-bound. It looked exactly like mid-winter, except that at that hour of night we could see to read a newspaper out of doors. The climate of these regions is very curious at this time of year. The change is sudden and violent—a leaping from mid-winter into summer, without any intervening spring.[10]

He later reported that by May 30, about three weeks later, the Pechora was free of ice for the first time the steady march past of its shattered winter surface having occupied a span of just one week.

The most dramatic effect engendered by the approach of summer's warmth is the annual spring breakup of ice in Siberia's great north-flowing rivers. The Ob, more than 3000 miles long, and the Yenesei and the Lena, about 2800 miles long, rise in the mountain border regions south of the boreal forest. With the first prolonged thaws of early spring the waters of their tributaries swell and rapidly course their way northward into the broad, still-frozen valleys far downstream. The ice at first refuses to yield to the pressure of increasing volumes of water, with the result that rivers overspread their lower shores and flood the surrounding countryside. Where the banks are high and steep, however, the rivers rise many tens of feet with the oncoming deluge of the

[10] Henry Seebohm, *The Birds of Siberia*, John Murray, Publishers, Ltd., London, 1901, pp. 70–71.

swirling, ice-laden torrent. Here again we shall turn to a description by Seebohm, this time from an account of late-winter conditions in the lower Yenesei valley, at a point almost exactly on the Arctic Circle, near the mouth of the Kureika River, which flows into the Yenesei from the northeast.

Noting the tempestuous variability of the weather during the preceding two weeks, he states that a revolution began to take place in the ice of the Yenesei on June 1st. Huge blocks of river ice, measuring 20 feet or more in length, were piled into floating mountains 50 to 60 feet high at the Kureika's mouth. They were clear as glass and bright blue in color to a thickness of 3 feet, overlain by a hard white layer about 4 feet thick, and then surmounted by about 18 inches of fresh snow.

The battle of the Yenesei raged for about a fortnight, during which the Kureika alternately rose and fell. Thousands of acres of ice were marched upstream for some hours, then the tide turned and they were marched back again. This great annual battle between summer and winter is the chief event of the year in these regions, like the rising of the Nile in Egypt. Summer in league with the sun, fights winter and the north wind, and is hopelessly beaten until she forms an alliance with the south wind, before whose blast the forces of winter vanish into thin water and return to the Pole. . . . Although the river frequently fell for a few hours, it was constantly rising on the whole, and in ten days the rise where we were stationed was 70 feet. . . . On several occasions we stood on the banks of the river for hours, transfixed with astonishment, staring aghast at icebergs, 20 to 30 feet high, driven down the river at a speed of from 10 to 20 miles an hour. . . . At last, after fourteen days' battle, the final march-past of the beaten winter forces took place, and for seven days more the ragtag and bobtail of the great Arctic army came straggling down the Kureika. . . . Winter was finally vanquished for the year, and the fragments of his beaten army were compelled to retreat to the triumphant music of thousands of song-birds, and amidst the waving of green leaves and the illumination of gay flowers of every hue.

In these remarks one finds an example of the rapidity with which the turbulent upheaval of the long, cold winter takes place under the influence of a renewed and more vigorous

interaction between cold, dry polar air and warmer, humid maritime air as the sun climbs higher in the southern sky. During a few weeks in May and June the winter's ice and snow are melted away by more frequent invasions of oceanic air masses and the northward advance of milder, sun-warmed air from lower latitudes. Polar continental air withdraws to the Arctic Ocean, and with it the polar frontal zone of air mass convergence. Anticyclonic circulations no longer predominate over the continental interior; they are replaced by the more frequent passage of migrating cyclones, chiefly from the North Atlantic, but, during summer, from the Barents and Kara seas, and from the North Pacific to some extent.

Mean monthly temperatures (Table 10-2) increase rapidly, more so at interior stations, of course, and one finds, for example, that April is 35 degrees warmer at Verkhoyansk than March, and May is 27 degrees warmer than April, while at Yakutsk figures for the same months are 26 and 25, respectively.

Summer. Monthly temperatures average above freezing for about five months over most of the boreal forest in Eurasia. West of the Ob River valley, however, although not in northern sections, the period may be six or seven months long. Everywhere, from coast to coast, mean monthly values above 50°F prevail for three months, rarely more and rarely less, except near the tundra margins, as at Turukhansk and Igarka. In those sections west of the Ob where much milder winters are typical, the warmest month of summer seldom averages more than 60°F. East of the Ob, however, at least one and sometimes two months average temperatures above 60°. Values above 65° are not uncommon in the middle reaches of the Yenesei and Lena valleys. In general, summers become slightly warmer in the Eurasian boreal forest east of the Urals than anywhere in the North American taiga.

Although records of mean daily range are not available for most Eurasian stations, values are undoubtedly at least as high as those for North America. Certainly the records of maximum observed summer temperatures, as for Gallivare (94°), Kuopio (93°), Tobolsk (95°), Tomsk (96°), Ulan Ude (100°), Yakutsk (100°), and Verkhoyansk (94°), indicate a wide variation

[11] *Ibid*, pp. 332–34.

around the monthly mean. Near Yakutsk the thermometer has dropped from 95°F to 41°F in one day, a range of 54 degrees. These readings were taken in July, the warmest month for the region as a whole, with the exception of Pacific coast stations such as Aian and Okhotsk, where August is the warmest month, indicating the maritime retardation of the progress of summer's warmth. Both average and extreme summer maxima are lower west of the Ob River valley and the Urals, where the cooling effect of frequent invasions of maritime air from the North Atlantic is most pronounced. The frost-free season varies in length from year to year but in general tends to be shorter in the lichen-woodland nearer the tundra margins and in the eastern interior, than on either the Atlantic or Pacific coasts. Compare, for example, the average of eighty-three days at Kuusamo, sixty-five at Verkhoyansk, and eighty at Bodaybo, with 139 days at Steinkjer on the Norwegian coast and 106 at Okhotsk on the Pacific.

Long hours of daylight in summer, warming the earth's surface and the lower levels of the atmosphere, coupled with the more frequent passage of migrating cyclones, obviate the development of temperature inversions during this season. Instead, convective activity is increased, and summer showers arising from convective turbulence are common throughout interior sections of the region. These, and traveling storms originating over the North Atlantic and along the western Arctic coast bring most of the summer's rainfall. Cyclonic storms originating over the Pacific invade eastern sections of the region to some extent, releasing additional amounts of rain to the mountainous eastern seaboard, aided by orographic uplift, especially over the watershed of the Amur River.

All in all, around two thirds of the annual precipitation falls at most stations during the months when temperatures average above freezing. The rainiest month is most commonly August, although at many places it is July. Actual amounts are not great, however, seldom exceeding 3 inches except at coastal stations. The wettest month at Molotov (Perm) and Tobolsk brings 3 inches, for example, at Yakutsk 1.6 inches, and at Verkhoyansk 1 inch. At Olekminsk in the Lena valley, where July temperatures average nearly 67° and the summer's maximum monthly rainfall of 2.1 inches comes in August, irrigation is necessary for successful crop production. Adding further to the hazards of farming in eastern Siberia is the fact that precipitation varies considerably from year to year.

The marked warmth and increased humidity of the summer lead to the development of atmospheric pressures that are very much lower than those of the expanded anticyclones of the North Atlantic and North Pacific and the colder, drier air over the Arctic Ocean (Fig. 4.3). The result of these conditions is a general inflow from adjoining oceanic regions and a reversal of the wintertime anticyclonic circulation (Fig. 4.2). East and northeast winds tend to prevail along the Arctic coast, southeast winds along the Pacific coast (usually considered part of the east Asiatic onshore monsoon), west winds over south central regions, and northwest winds over western sections of the region.

The boreal forest, with its variety of wooded landscapes, the striking contrast between its dry, bitterly cold winters and its warm, rather rainy summers, is the northernmost woodland on earth. Below it lie the mid-latitude mixed forests, the subject of the next chapter.

References

BORISOV, A. A.: *Climates of the USSR*, trans. by R. A. Ledward, Aldine Publishing Company, Chicago, 1965.

GORDON, A. R., Jr., and WOODWORTH, W. C.: "Some Inter-Relationships of Snow and Ice Conditions and Weather in the Arctic," *Bulletin of the American Meteorological Society*, **31**(8): 271–78, 1950.

HALLIDAY, W. E. D.: *A Forest Classification for Canada*, Canada, Department of Resources and Development, Ottawa, 1952.

Hare, F. K.: "The Boreal Conifer Zone," *Geographical Studies*, 1(1): 4–18, 1954.

Nuttonson, M. Y.: *Agricultural Climatology of Siberia, Natural Belts, and Agro-Climatic Analogues in North America*, International Agro-Climatological Series, Study No. 13, Washington, D.C., 1950.

Platt, R. R.: *Finland and Its Geography*, Duell, Sloane & Pearce, New York, 1955.

Suslov, S. P.: *Physical Geography of Asiatic Russia*, trans., by N. D. Gershevsky, W. H. Freeman and Co., San Francisco, 1961.

chapter 11

MID-LATITUDE FORESTS
OF NORTH AMERICA

From our study of the world's climates thus far, we have observed that ice cap, tundra, and boreal forest are arranged in a relatively simple pattern of nearly circumpolar distribution. South of the boreal forest, however, we find, in the middle latitudes of North America and Eurasia, a complex arrangement of climates that is somewhat more difficult to identify. Here, roughly between 25 and 60 degrees north of the equator, is a great variety of forest and woodland types, of grassland formations and deserts. Extending from coast to coast across both northern continents, they are interrupted here and there and rendered more complex by an irregular distribution of mountainous terrain. Within the same latitudes south of the equator similar relationships are found, although to a very much smaller extent, in South America, southern Africa, Australia, and New Zealand (Fig. 7.1).

It will be remembered that the polar ice cap is a region of continuous winter, the tundra a region of prolonged winter briefly interrupted by a cool season, and the boreal forest a realm of long, cold winters alternating with short, warm summers.

The middle latitude climates, lying intermediate between poles and equator, tend to share more equally the qualities of both polar and tropical environments. Nearly all experience an annual program of four fairly distinct seasons—summer, fall, winter, and spring. As each season waxes and wanes, it produces frequent variations of weather experience. Thus, perhaps the prime characteristic of all mid-latitude climates is the certainty of changing weather, from season to season, and within each season as well. This feature sets them apart from climates toward the north that are definitely influenced for a major part of the year by polar cold, and from those lower latitude climates that are mainly dominated by tropical warmth.

Considerably broad in latitude, all middle latitude climates possess a generally north–south modulation of temperature regimes. The geographic thermal gradient, in turn, depends primarily upon latitude.

Within the mid-latitudes climates are chiefly differentiated on the basis of contrasting moisture conditions. One finds, as a general rule, that abundant precipitation gives rise to forest, less plentiful amounts produce grassland, and arid desert arises where the moisture supply is not only much smaller but much less reliable as well.

The somewhat bewildering variety of wooded landscapes in the middle latitudes must be grouped in a highly simplified fashion to provide a manageable, understandable key to the pattern of climates. Setting aside the complexities induced by mountainous terrain, the simplest grouping reveals three main types: the mid-latitude mixed forest, the coastal evergreen forest, and the Mediterranean scrub woodland. Mediterranean scrub woodlands are dealt with in later chapters; in this and the next chapter we shall consider the mid-latitude mixed forests and coastal evergreen forests of the northern hemisphere.

MID-LATITUDE MIXED FORESTS. Abundant and reasonably reliable year-round precipitation, coupled with pronounced seasonal changes in temperature, are basic characters of the mid-latitude mixed forests. A normal yearly precipitation consisting mainly of rain and amounting to 20 inches or more, with ample amounts during the growing season, is typical. Snow accounts for most of the winter precipitation in poleward sections, often alternating with sleet and freezing rain. It is significant of the temperate mixed forests as a whole that snow is not unknown anywhere within their reaches, even toward their limits in the lower latitudes. Frontal disturbances, chiefly cyclonic storms, are responsible for most of the precipitation, although in summertime convective showers become a major source of rain, arising from the intensified heating of lower atmospheric layers under a higher sun.

Frost occurs in most mixed forest areas at least briefly nearly every winter, even in areas near the tropics. The frequency and duration of subfreezing temperatures depend mainly upon latitude but also upon proximity to major bodies of water, particularly the sea. These same circumstances, of course, also govern the length of the growing season, which may be no more than one hundred days in poleward areas, or well over three hundred days near the tropics.

Summers may be hot, averaging more than 80° for the warmest month, or warm, averaging around 65°. Winter may be a season of pronounced cold, the coldest month averaging 10° or less, or quite mild, lowest mean monthly values remaining above 50°.

The mid-latitude mixed forests, wherever they are found, bear evident signs of their transitional position intermediate between tropical and polar environments. Evident everywhere is a general intermingling of broadleaf and needleleaf, deciduous and evergreen trees of good size, ranging in height from around 75 feet to well over 100 feet, and in diameter from 3 to 4 feet or more. Broadleaf trees, many of them evergreen as in the tropics, indicate a relationship with tropical regions; needleleaved species provide a link with the great coniferous forests of the northern continents.

These forests are transitional in still another way. We recall that the vast breadth of the boreal forest is dominated by scarcely a dozen coniferous species. The opposite is true, as we shall see, of many tropical forests, where a great diversity of species is typical. The mid-latitude mixed forests are dominated by a moderate number of important species. In eastern North America, for example, some two hundred broadleaf species and a score or more of conifers can be counted. Among the remnant stands of a once magnificent primeval wooded region more than two dozen tree species are widespread and characteristic, providing a key to the size and distribution of the temperate mixed forest in eastern North America.

The mid-latitude mixed forest is most fully developed in eastern North America, western Eurasia, and east Asia, with much smaller segments to be found near the Pacific coast of North America, and in the southern hemisphere in southern middle Chile, southern Brazil, southern Africa, and parts of Australia and New Zealand.

MID-LATITUDE COASTAL EVERGREEN FORESTS. On the west coasts of the continents in middle latitudes a uniquely equable climate is found. Relatively mild and humid, this forest climate is generally confined to a narrow, elongated zone near the sea, for it owes its existence to the frequent, sometimes constant, invasion of moist air of oceanic origin. Seldom found more than 100 miles from the coast, it is often much narrower than this, but it usually extends for several hundred miles in a north–south direction. Except in western Eurasia, vegetation is dominantly coniferous or broadleaf evergreen.

The mean annual range of temperature is low, rarely more than 25 degrees, for summers are only moderately warm, the warmest month averaging between 60 and 70°, and winters are mild, from about 35 to 50°. The frost-free season is long, usually in the neighborhood of two hundred days or more. Precipitation is ample during summer and increases in the winter, a distinctive feature of the region. It is chiefly in the form of rain of cyclonic origin.

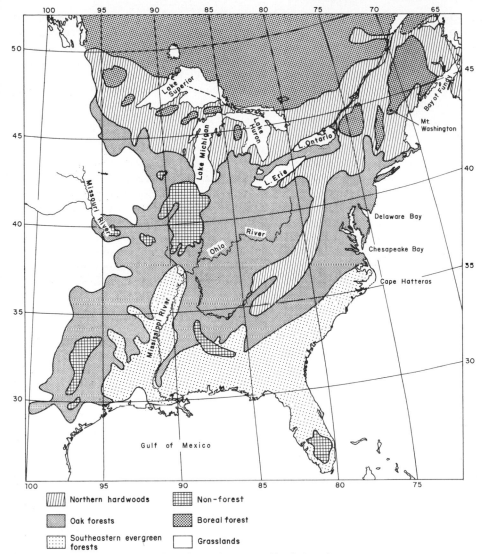

Figure 11.1.   Mid-latitude mixed forest in eastern North America.

The high incidence of systematic, precipitating disturbances arises mainly from the position of these regions athwart the preferred paths of frontal storms, whose high frequency is a noteworthy feature of oceanic areas in the upper middle latitudes.

Mid-Latitude Mixed Forests of Eastern North America

From the Great Lakes and the St. Lawrence valley to the Gulf of Mexico, from the Atlantic seaboard westward beyond the banks of the Mississippi, the mid-latitude mixed forest spreads a nearly unbroken mantle of arboreal foliage over uncleared portions of the varied surface of eastern North America. Principally a broadleaf, deciduous forest, it is transitional between the mainly needleleaved evergreen forms of the boreal forest and the near-tropical, subtropical broadleaved evergreens common in the southeast (Fig. 11.1).

Extending for some 1200 miles from north to south and for about 1100 miles inland from the Atlantic coast, it seems at first glance to be a rather homogeneous mixture of broad-crowned trees. The apparent homogeneity of the vegetation arises in part from the physiognomic similarity among many of its components

(Fig. 11.2). Of the two-hundred-odd broadleaf species, more than two dozen are very widely distributed and can be seen almost anywhere from the shores of Lake Huron to the Gulf coast. They include flowering dogwood, red maple, green ash, sycamore, yellow poplar, American elm, eastern cottonwood, black willow, black cherry, beech, black tupelo, bitternut hickory, and white oak. Local variety arises from the addition of other species of these genera and of still different deciduous genera like the basswood, locust, walnut, cypress, and the root-sprouting remnants of the once-thriving chestnut.

Intermingled among the summer-green, winter-bare varieties are innumerable stands and scattered clumps of needleleaved evergreens and a smaller number of broadleaved evergreens. The largest number of evergreen species are to be found among the pines, although cedar and hemlock are also well represented. It is interesting to note, as we shall in the next chapter, that many of the prominent genera in eastern North America are also the leading genera in the temperate forests of Eurasia.

TYPES OF MIXED FORESTS. When the predominant species are grouped into major plant associations, a pattern unfolds that provides a tangible link with the climatic variations of eastern North America. Perhaps the most useful arrangement for our purposes is the highly simplified one appearing in Figure 11.1, which indicates only three chief divisions of the mixed forest extending southward from the spruce-fir forests farther north: the northern hardwoods, oak forests, and southeastern evergreen forests.

As one turns southward from the boreal forest into the region of the Great Lakes and the St. Lawrence, from northern Minnesota eastward across northern Wisconsin, northern Michigan, southern Ontario, and northern New England to Nova Scotia, the climax forest shows a response to longer, warmer summers and shorter, less severe winters and more abundant rainfall. These are the northern hardwoods, dominated by maple, especially sugar maple (*Acer saccharum*) and red maple (*Acer rubrum*), black ash (*Fraxinus nigra*), yellow birch (*Betula lutea*), and beech (*Fagus grandifolia*), intermingled with hemlock (*Tsuga canadensis*), white pine (*Pinus strobus*), and red pine (*Pinus resinosa*) from Lake Michigan to the Atlantic.

An attenuated fingerlike projection of this subdivision extends down the upper slopes of the Appalachians as far south as the Blue Ridge Mountains in western North Carolina, where it is found at elevations of around 4500 feet in discontinuous stands among the more prevalent oak forest formations. At higher altitudes along the Blue Ridge are occasional stands of red spruce that represent outliers of the maritime variation of the boreal forest seen in some profusion in northern New England, Nova Scotia, and New Brunswick. Thus, at the altitudes attained by the southern Appalachian ridges (up to 6684 feet at Mt. Mitchell in the Blue Ridge), are found climates that favor the development of plant associations typical of lower altitudes in northern areas.

A variety of edaphic situations produce many apparent anomalies in the northern hardwood section. Extensive tracts of pine, for example, are found from Minnesota to Nova Scotia on lighter, especially well-drained soils. In low-lying boggy areas, larch, black spruce, and eastern white cedar (*Thuja occidentalis*) are often present in almost pure stands.

Intermingled among the dominant hardwoods are intrusive species from the oak forests to the south, such as silver maple (*Acer saccharinum*), certain ashes (*Fraxinus spp.*), walnut (*Juglans spp.*), hickory (*Carya spp.*), basswood (*Tilia spp.*), and elm (*Ulmus spp.*), in addition to several kinds of oaks (*Quercus spp.*).

Oaks of several species, in combination with a variety of codominant trees, create a distinctive character to the forest vegetation from the northern hardwoods section to the pineries of the southeast. White oak (*Quercus alba*), black oak (*Quercus velutina*), and northern red oak (*Quercus borealis*) may be seen almost anywhere within the section, although more than a score of species are found in more restricted distribution.

In oak forests the endless variety of vegetation types is a natural consequence not only of varied exposures to the mean weather patterns occasioned by topographic diversity, but also of diversity in underlying bedrock, soils, and drainage. Certain broad groupings may be identified. From southern Minnesota to southern New England is an important subdivision composed of oak, tulip tree (*Liriodendron tulipifera*), basswood (*Tilia americana*), sourgum or black tupelo (*Nyssa sylvatica*), and the vestiges

Figure 11.2. Mid-latitude mixed forest landscape in eastern Tennessee. [American Airlines photo]

of former stands of chestnut (*Castanea dentata*). This association also extends an arm southwestward along the lower slopes and valleys of the Appalachians, mingling with the beech and maple that prevail at higher levels. In the Ohio valley, ash, beech, maple, and sycamore are prominent members of the forest complex, and from northern Indiana to eastern Iowa and central Texas, hickory (*Carya spp.*) is the leading codominant, producing a climax association of once-widespread oak-hickory stands. From central Texas to Delaware Bay a curving band of oak-pine forest marks a gradual transition into the southeastern evergreen forest.

Certainly the most prominent feature of the southeastern evergreen forest, and an important reason for its designation *evergreen*, is the seemingly universal presence of several species of pine. The entire section is, in fact, most commonly referred to as the southern yellow pine forest, in which the longleaf pine (*Pinus palustris*), loblolly (*Pinus taeda*), and slash (*Pinus caribea*) pines are perhaps the most important of a half-dozen dominant species of pine. But some ecologists believe that except on poorer, lighter, excessively drained soils, pines are to a large extent temporary, subdominant forms. From a long history of frequent forest fires, followed by the rapid reappearance of pine, the term *fire subclimax* has been suggested for existing pineland.

Broadleaved trees, some deciduous and some evergreen, are thought to represent the ultimate climax, the ultimate vegetational response to climate, of forest succession on mesophytic sites. A number of deciduous oaks indigenous to the southeast, such as southern red oak (*Quercus falcata*), water oak (*Quercus nigra*), and laurel oak (*Quercus laurifolia*), along with sweet gum (*Liquidambar styraciflua*), are prominent members of persistent forest communities. A special quality is imparted to the southeastern evergreen forest by the presence of certain broadleaved evergreen trees. Conspicuous examples are the shiny foliage of the southern magnolia (*Magnolia grandiflora*), the spiny leaves of American holly (*Ilex opaca*), and the small, elliptical leaves of the massive, long-lasting live oak (*Quercus virginiana*). Magnolia, with its large, showy blossoms, its broad, dark green, shiny foliage, is considered a climax tree in association with various co-dominants such as beech, maple, oak, and holly, and thus, in the minds of ecologists, contributes a definitive element to the true climax forest of the southeast.

Bottomland vegetation, in which cypress is the most prominent tree, often in combination with tupelo, cottonwood, and sweet bay (*Magnolia virginiana*), extends up the broad, shallow stream valleys of the southeast, from North Carolina southwestward beyond Galveston Bay and up the valley of the Mississippi to its junction with the Ohio. Bald cypress (*Taxodium distichum*) is the most widespread species, with pond cypress (*Taxodium ascendens*) appearing east of the Mississippi.

The outward appearance of the southeastern evergreen forest is further distinguished from the rest of the mid-latitude mixed forest region by the presence of Spanish moss (*Tillandsia usneoides*), whose slender, gray-green, grasslike strands hang festooned and garlanded in tattered, waving pennants from the branches of trees. An epiphyte, Spanish moss subsists on the moisture and chemical properties of air and is found from North Carolina to Texas and to some extent along the Gulf coast of eastern Mexico, thriving in this region of long, tropically hot, humid summers and short mild winters.

The Florida peninsula extends to within a few degrees of the Tropic of Cancer, sufficiently far equatorward to come under the influence of a purely tropical climate at its southernmost tip and along the Florida Keys. Frost, for example, has never been recorded at Key West. In Florida the mid-latitude hardwoods, one by one, reach the southern limits of their range, and physiognomically tropical types of vegetation become dominant. The transition from mid-latitude to tropical environment is suggested by the increasing importance of the broadleaved evergreens. The presence, in wide distribution, of a great many plants introduced from the tropics, such as the coconut palm, Royal palm, and sugar cane, and of the native cabbage palm (*Sabal palmetto*) are convincing evidence of the dominantly tropical milieu. The hydrophytic mangrove (*Rhizophora spp.*) of tropical coastal areas appears in dense thickets from place to place along the more southerly coasts of the peninsula, and in special abundance southwest of Lake Okeechobee.

From east to west a gradual gradation of the

mixed forests into grassland takes place with increasing distance from the Atlantic coast. The forest becomes less luxuriant and less varied as important species one by one reach the western limits of their range in the increasingly drier environments of the interior. Fewer species, smaller in size and more scattered in distribution, are characteristic of the forest beyond the Mississippi River. Oak, hickory, ash, elm, and willow are common. Tall grass prairie occupies a larger and larger proportion of the landscape, finally superseding the woodlands on interfluvial watersheds from central Texas to southern Canada. Only slender ribbons of riparian forest are to be seen reaching westward and gently upward toward the Rocky Mountains along the banks of the Missouri, the Platte, the Arkansas, and the Red rivers and their tributaries.

Throughout the middle latitude mixed forests of eastern North America landscapes everywhere, except in densely populated areas, are dominated by forest vegetation. True, in the low-lying, coastal marshes from southern New Jersey to the Louisiana bayous, in certain extensive tracts of swamp land such as the Dismal Swamp of eastern Virginia and North Carolina, and in the natural grassy meadows of Alabama, Mississippi, Kentucky, and Tennessee, other forms of vegetation outnumber forest trees. Still, in the background on every hand the forest can be seen. Its tendency to prevail is evident everywhere.

Little of the earth's surface is left bare in a region like this where, over a long span of time, rainfall is plentiful all the year long, where no month is typically dry. The contours of hilly country are typically rounded in gently sloping curves that show the effects of conservative surface modification by rainfall runoff and the settling of saturated soil processes, that have been reasonably constant for thousands of years. Such landscapes are quite unlike the harsh, angular features that distinguish the surface contours of drier regions.

This eastern forest has developed where the qualities of the atmosphere have tended, presumably for the past thousand years or more, to vary within a rather narrow range, producing extremes of weather generally tolerable to the plant associations that dominate nearly every scene. From a relatively brief record of measured temperature, rain-

fall, sunshine, wind, humidity, and cloudiness we are able to learn approximately what the mean weather has been like and to acquaint ourselves with some of the extremes from which the mean, statistically average conditions have been computed.

CLIMATIC CONDITIONS. All sections of the region are well watered, receiving at least 20 inches of annual rainfall. All experience a rhythmic program of four seasons, all are at least touched by frost each year, all experience both freezing temperatures and snow. The growing season is sufficiently long (one hundred to more than three hundred days) to permit the cultivation of a wide variety of crop plants and the rearing of many kinds of livestock and poultry. Cyclonic storms are important features of the year's weather everywhere, although much more so in northern than in southern sections. The pronounced seasonal variations in temperature, with at least a slight summer increase in rainfall, are characteristic of a continental climate; thus, the northern hardwood and oak forest sections are often described as a humid continental region. The southern evergreen forests, on the other hand, being definitely transitional into tropical environments and possessing many qualities of weather common to tropical lands, are often called humid subtropical.

Let us consider first a résumé of atmospheric qualities for the year as a whole, turning then to a season-by-season development of important weather varieties and their effects upon various sections of the region. The number and distribution of weather stations and the length of observational record are somewhat more satisfactory here than in any other part of North America. Temperature and rainfall records have been kept continuously for over sixty years at more than one thousand stations in these eastern woodlands. From Toronto, Ont., to Charleston, S.C., more than a dozen stations have continuous records for over a century. At New Haven, Conn., an exceptional record of 178 years is available, dating from 1779.

Annual range of temperature, length of frost-free season, and total annual rainfall are seen to change from northwest to southeast in a manner roughly corresponding to changes in dominant plant groups. (See Table 11-1 and Fig. 11.5.)

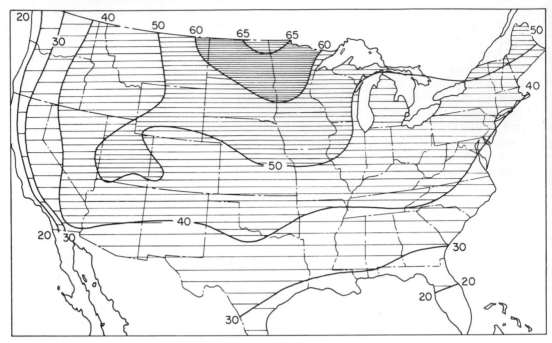

Figure 11.3. Mean annual temperature range in the United States (°F). [By permission of the publishers from Stephen S. Visher, *Climatic Atlas of the United States*, Cambridge, Mass.: Harvard University Press, Copyright, 1954, by the President and Fellows of Harvard College.]

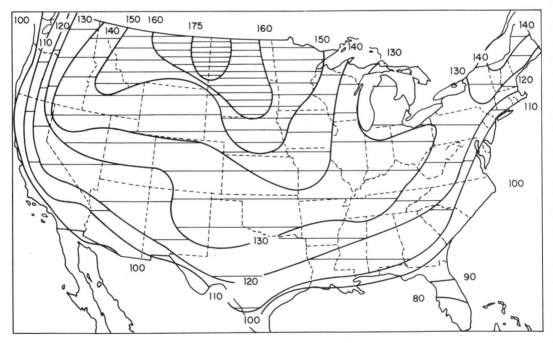

Figure 11.4. Range between the highest and lowest recorded temperatures in the United States (°F). [By permission of the publishers from Stephen S. Visher, *Climatic Atlas of the United States*, Cambridge, Mass.: Harvard University Press, Copyright, 1954, by the President and Fellows of Harvard College.]

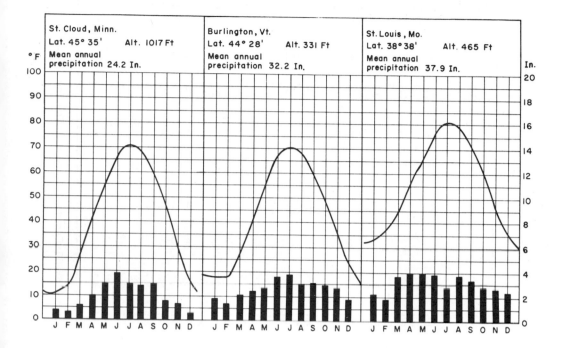

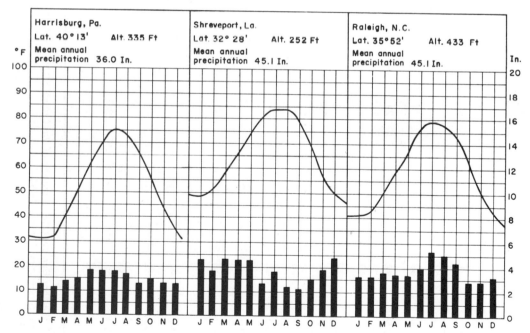

Figure 11.5. Normal temperature and precipitation at stations in mid-latitude mixed forest in eastern United States.

TABLE 11-1
Climatic Data for Mid-Latitude Mixed Forest Stations in North America
(Temp., °F; Rainfall, In.)

Station	Lat.	El. in Ft		Jan.	Feb.	Mar.	Apr.	May	Jun.	Jul.	Aug.	Sep.	Oct.	Nov.	Dec.	Year
Northern Hardwoods																
St. Cloud, Minn.	45°35'	1017	T	11	14	27	43	55	65	71	68	59	47	29	16	
			R	0.8	0.7	1.2	2.0	3.1	3.9	3.1	2.9	3.0	1.6	1.4	0.7	24.2
Grand Rapids, Mich.	42°54'	681	T	24	24	33	45	56	67	72	70	62	50	38	27	
			R	1.9	1.7	2.4	2.9	3.5	3.4	2.7	2.6	3.4	2.5	2.5	2.2	31.5
Toronto, Ont.	43°40'	379	T	23	22	30	42	53	63	69	67	60	48	37	27	
			R	2.7	2.4	2.6	2.5	2.9	2.7	3.0	2.7	2.9	2.4	2.8	2.6	32.2
Burlington, Vt.	44°28'	331	T	18	18	29	42	55	66	70	68	60	48	36	23	
			R	1.9	1.5	2.2	2.6	2.9	3.6	3.8	3.0	3.1	2.9	2.9	1.9	32.2
Oak Forests																
St. Louis, Mo.	38°38'	465	T	33	37	45	57	66	76	81	79	71	61	46	36	
			R	2.3	1.9	3.6	4.0	4.1	3.8	2.9	3.8	3.4	2.9	2.7	2.4	37.9
South Bend, Ind.	41°42'	768	T	25	26	36	47	58	69	73	71	65	53	39	28	
			R	2.0	1.6	3.0	3.4	3.8	3.8	3.0	3.3	3.7	3.0	2.7	2.3	35.6
Nashville, Tenn.	36°07'	577	T	40	42	50	60	68	77	80	79	73	62	49	42	
			R	4.9	4.2	5.3	3.7	3.8	3.2	4.0	3.3	2.7	2.5	3.4	4.1	45.0
Harrisburg, Pa.	40°13'	335	T	31	32	41	51	62	71	75	73	66	55	44	34	
			R	2.6	2.2	2.9	3.0	3.7	3.6	3.6	3.3	2.6	3.1	2.7	2.6	36.0
Southeastern Evergreen Forests																
Shreveport, La.	32°28'	252	T	49	52	58	67	74	81	84	84	79	69	56	50	
			R	4.7	3.8	4.7	4.6	4.6	2.6	3.7	2.4	2.2	3.1	3.9	4.8	45.1
Montgomery, Ala.	32°18'	198	T	49	52	57	65	73	80	81	81	77	66	55	49	
			R	4.6	4.7	6.5	4.8	3.5	4.7	5.8	4.8	3.5	2.4	4.0	4.5	53.7
Augusta, Ga.	33°22'	143	T	47	49	56	63	72	79	81	80	76	65	54	48	
			R	3.5	3.7	4.3	3.5	3.3	3.7	5.2	4.1	3.2	2.5	2.4	3.7	43.2
Raleigh, N.C.	35°52'	433	T	41	43	50	59	67	76	79	77	73	61	50	42	
			R	3.3	3.3	3.6	3.5	3.4	4.1	5.5	5.0	4.5	2.8	2.9	3.3	45.1

Source: U.S. Weather Bureau, *Climatography of the United States, Climates of the States*, 1959–60; Canada, Department of Transport, Meteorological Division, *Climatic Summaries*, Toronto, 1956.

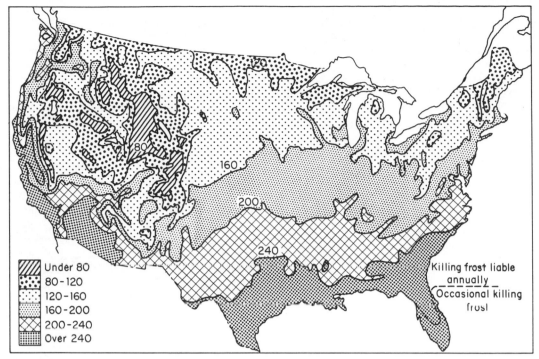

Figure 11.6. Average length of the frost-free season in the United States (days). [By permission of the publishers from Stephen S. Visher, *Climatic Atlas of the United States*, Cambridge, Mass.: Harvard University Press, Copyright, 1954, by the President and Fellows of Harvard College.]

In northern Minnesota and the lower Ottawa valley of Ontario and Quebec one observes a mean annual range of around 60 degrees, from about 5° in January to about 65° in July. Then, southeastward across the Great Lakes, the Ohio valley, and the Appalachians and out over the coastal plain this value diminishes, until along the Gulf coast it is only about 27 degrees, from around 55° in January to about 82° in July (Fig. 11.3). The greater severity of northern winters is chiefly responsible for the differences observed. In like manner, the range between extreme temperatures of record decreases from more than 170 degrees to only about 110 degrees from northwest to southeast (Fig. 11.4).

Understandably, the frost-free growing season increases in a southeasterly direction, from about one hundred days in northern Minnesota to more than three hundred days in central Florida (Fig. 11.6). Yearly variations in the length of the growing season range widely and unpredictably on either side of these means. Certain portions of northern Minnesota may experience frosts several times during the

summer period or may escape freezing temperatures for as long as four months or more, and central Florida may have a frost-free season of only 240 days one year and, not long afterward, be entirely free of damaging frost for 365 days.

The total annual rainfall of the region increases from the prairie margins to the coastal plain, amounting to around 25 inches in northern Minnesota, eastern Nebraska, central Oklahoma, and Texas and to more than 40 inches along the eastern seaboard (Fig. 11.7). It also increases southward, from about 40 inches in the lower Great Lakes and St. Lawrence valley sections to more than 60 inches along the Gulf coast. The general pattern is appreciably modified, however, by the presence of mountains, for considerably more rain falls on the upper slopes of the Ouachitas, the Appalachians, the Adirondacks, and the New England ranges than in the nearby valleys.

In western Arkansas at higher elevations on both the Boston and Ouachita mountains up to 60 inches of annual precipitation is recorded, whereas in the Red River valley of the southern foothills, some 1000 feet lower in elevation, most localities receive around 40 inches. Many places in the southern Appalachians, especially in the Great Smoky Mountains, receive more than 60 inches of yearly rainfall, and occasional amounts of more than 100 inches have been recorded. At the small town of Highlands, N.C. (el. 3817 ft) on the southern slope of the

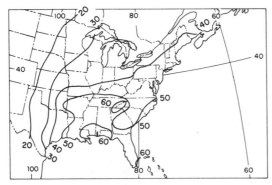

Figure 11.7. Mean annual precipitation in eastern United States (inches).

Smokies, an annual amount of more than 85 inches is normal. By contrast, less than 50 inches is normal for most of the upper Tennessee valley, less than 100 miles northwest.

In northeastern United States and south-eastern Canada from 40 inches to 45 inches is common at lower elevations, but in the Adirondacks and mountainous northern New England amounts in excess of 50 inches are typical. Mount Washington, N.H. (el. 6288 ft) annually receives around 70 inches. Topography, therefore, imparts a virtually unmappable complexity to the general distribution of rainfall in the mid-latitude mixed forests of eastern North America.

The seasonal distribution of precipitation throughout the year also varies from place to place within the region. All along the western margins, from 60 to 70 per cent of the year's precipitation falls during the six-month period of milder weather. In western sections the rainiest period is in late spring and early summer. At Duluth, Minn. and St. Louis, Mo., June is the wettest month; from southern Missouri to central Texas the wettest month is May. The yearly distribution is much more nearly uniform in the northern hardwoods section, from the Great Lakes to the Atlantic coast, where winter and summer precipitation

are about equal. From Long Island southward along the east coast, however, a marked increase in summer intensity is again observed, especially south of Chesapeake Bay. Here, however, late summer rather than late spring is the rainiest season. Even at New York City, July and August are slightly wetter than other months, each having a normal fall of more than 4 inches.

At Norfolk, Va., the rainiest period extends from June through August, both July and August having more than 5 inches of normal rain. From Wilmington, N.C., to Tampa, Fla., the summer period of increased rainfall intensity lasts from June through September. At Tampa, for example, this four-month period accounts for about 60 per cent of the year's rainfall, and from Norfolk to Jacksonville, about 50 per cent of the yearly total. There is a less pronounced seasonal concentration of rainfall along the narrow strip of the Gulf coast from the vicinity of the Mississippi delta to northwestern Florida. Summer maxima are typical, but the seasonal concentration is lessened. Every month except October and November averages at least 5 inches of rain. Convective showers are the main source, and these increase in number and intensity during the summer heating of land surfaces, which brings about a greater inflow of moist oceanic (mT) air from the Gulf of Mexico and the South Atlantic.

Northeastward from Long Island the seaward margins of New England, the maritime provinces, and all of Newfoundland normally record maximum precipitation during the cooler half of the year. At Nantucket December, January, and February account for 11.44 inches, compared with 9.23 inches for June, July, and August; at Provincetown on the tip of Cape Cod, 10.96 inches vs. 8.94 inches; at Portland, Me., 12.47 inches vs. 9.20 inches; at Grand Manan Island in the Bay of Fundy, 13.12 inches vs. 9.22 inches; at Halifax, 15.14 inches vs. 12.21 inches; and at St. John's, N.F., 15.70 inches vs. 10.74 inches.

Heavier winter precipitation over these coastal areas arises mainly from an increase in the number of cyclonic storms originating along the Atlantic coast of the United States from the Carolinas northward, and to a lesser extent over the Gulf of Mexico, storms which then follow a normal trajectory northeastward along the coast. They develop chiefly in consequence of the fact that cold, continental air masses from the interior are often subjected to rapid modification on nearing the sea; thus the coastal zone is an important wintertime locus of cyclogenesis. The storms developing here add their moisture output in winter to the precipitation of cyclonic storms originating east of the Rockies, which are the main source of precipitation for all the eastern woodlands during the winter months. Compare the storm track distribution for the winter and summer months in Figures 5.12 and 5.13.

The normal yearly pattern of rainfall over the mixed forests of eastern North America, where no season is ordinarily dry, is one for which migrating storms are mainly responsible. The alternation of rain-bearing storms with spells of fair weather and the frequent alternation of cold and mild weather through the year are mainly traceable, as we have seen for the boreal forest, to the seasonal changes in the general circulation and to the consequent advance and retreat of the polar frontal zone of contact between air masses of polar and tropical origin.

Summer. During the summer months of June, July, and August the climate of the entire region is more nearly uniform than at any other season of the year. July is the warmest month, except along the Atlantic and Gulf coasts where August is as warm or somewhat warmer.

July can be called hot, averaging 68° or more, from north central Minnesota, southern Ontario and Quebec, and southern New England southward to the Gulf coast (Fig. 11.8). Travelling southward from the lower Great Lakes or St. Lawrence valley during a normal July, one would expect to pass from temperatures averaging just under 70° through increasingly warmer and more humid air, reaching temperatures of around 82° near the Gulf of Mexico. Mean maximum temperatures in midafternoon would be about 80° in the north but 90° or more in southern sections. Around dawn each day the thermometer would be expected to drop to about 60° in the north but usually not less than 70° in the south. Thus, the mean daily range of temperature is about 20 degrees throughout the region, with the exception, once again, of coastal tracts where minimum temperatures tend to remain very near those

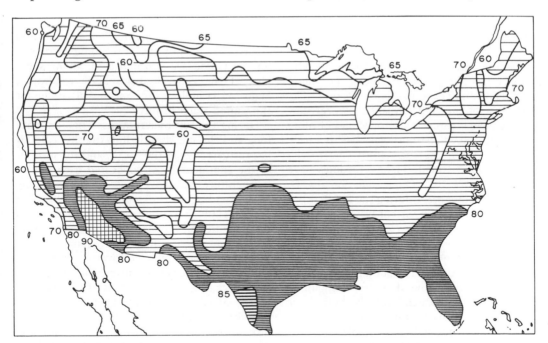

Figure 11.8. Surface temperatures in July in the United States (°F). [By permission of the publishers from Stephen S. Visher, *Climatic Atlas of the United States*, Cambridge, Mass.: Harvard University Press, Copyright, 1954, by the President and Fellows of Harvard College.]

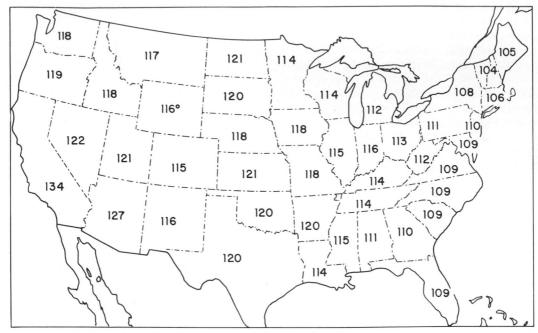

Figure 11.9. Extreme maximum temperatures in the United States, reported by state (°F). [By permission of the publishers from Stephen S. Visher, *Climatic Atlas of the United States*, Cambridge, Mass.: Harvard University Press, Copyright, 1954, by the President and Fellows of Harvard College.]

of the adjacent waters, thus lowering the mean daily range.

Extreme maximum temperatures of 120° or more have been observed along the prairie margins from Texas to South Dakota (Fig. 11.9). East of the Appalachians, however, few stations have recorded extreme values of more than 110°, and in the northeast 100° is rarely exceeded. Along the coast from Chesapeake Bay to the Rio Grande highest readings have not been above 105°. Often, but not always, extreme maxima occur during the familiar but unwelcome heat wave, or hot wave, of eastern North America. This is a period of three or more consecutive days when maximum temperatures reach 90° or above, usually when anticyclonic conditions remain for several days over southeastern United States, bringing a steady supply of warm, initially humid air from the south over most of the region. Relatively clear skies and calm, stable air allow the high sun to warm the earth and the air above it to an unusual degree.

The maximum and minimum temperatures at St. Paul, Minn., New Haven, Conn., Little Rock, Ark., and Jacksonville, Fla., are shown in Figure 11.10 for July 1965. Prevailing air masses for the period are also indicated, giving some idea of the general atmospheric conditions. Figure 11.11 indicates the mean daily range for the United States in July.

During the summer months, when days are long and the sun rises high in the sky, cold air has retreated far to the north, and the interior of the continent becomes heated each day to temperatures far above those of the bordering oceans and seas. The tendency develops for moist, relatively cool air to move inland from the Atlantic and the Gulf of Mexico repeatedly throughout the season, as anticyclonic air from the North Atlantic expands over the continent. An onshore monsoon movement of oceanic air, especially apparent along the Gulf coast and south Atlantic coast of the United States, is a prominent feature of the summer circulation. It resembles the summertime onshore monsoon of southeast Asia but is interrupted many times by the irregular passage of cyclones and anticyclones, moving along in the dominantly eastward flow of the general circulation in

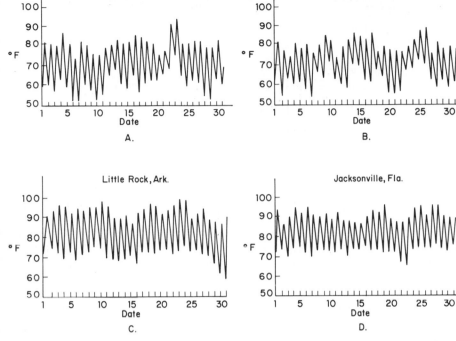

Figure 11.10. Daily maximum and minimum temperatures recorded at four stations in eastern United States during July 1965.

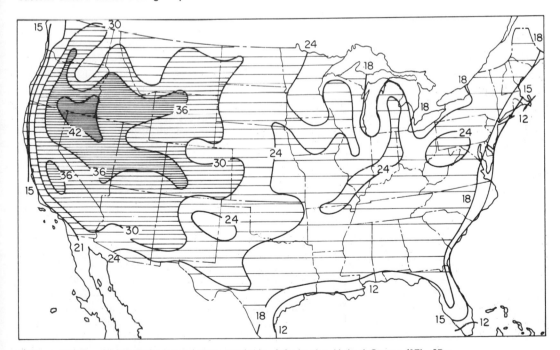

Figure 11.11. Mean daily temperature range in July in the United States (°F). [By permission of the publishers from Stephen S. Visher, *Climatic Atlas of the United States*, Cambridge, Mass.: Harvard University Press, Copyright, 1954, by the President and Fellows of Harvard College.]

middle latitudes. Evidence of the general movement of air is found in the fact that the dominant wind direction at nearly all stations in the mixed forest region is southwest in July. Wind velocities are greatest, on the average, at Cape Hatteras and Cape Cod, where mean values are twice what they are at interior lowland locations. The upper slopes of the Appalachians and the mountains of northern New England also receive much higher wind velocities, and the weather station at Mt. Washington, N.H., has recorded gusts in excess of 100 miles per hour in July.

Although relative humidities are lower in summer than in winter, the repeated invasion of maritime tropical air from the south brings very moist air whose absolute humidity, or actual water content, is greater in summertime than in winter. In spite of more moisture in the air, the number of cloudy days and the average amount of cloud cover is less in summer than in winter. As a general rule, nearly all of the mid-latitude mixed forest region is less foggy in summer, except in sections adjacent to cold bodies of water. Examples of these are found in the northeast, such as Nantucket, the coastal waters from Portland to Newfoundland, and the cold waters of Lake Superior, where, as at Marquette, Mich., and Duluth, Minn., heavy moisture condensation occurs over wide areas along the margin between land and water when the warm, moist air of a stable air mass overrides the colder surface below.

Abundant moisture-laden air above and strong, almost daily heating of the land below give rise to frequent thermal convection resulting in a warm season increase in brief showers and thunderstorms, which account for much of the summer rain. Damaging hailstorms are a special feature of well-developed convective storms in summer. Particularly in the early part of the summer, tornadoes occur more frequently than at any other season.

Departures from the season's normal precipitation can be expected from year to year over the entire region except the extreme northeast, particularly the maritime provinces, where rainfall reliability is akin to that over eastern Quebec and Labrador in the boreal forest. Excesses of summer rainfall are not as greatly damaging as are deficiencies. Although drought is not nearly as frequent in this region as it is in the grasslands of the central plains, it has

occurred with ruinous effect in parts of the east. The summer of 1957 was a notoriously dry season, when, from Chesapeake Bay to southern New England, only about 50 per cent of the normal monthly fall of rain appeared during June and July. Certain sections of New Jersey, eastern Pennsylvania, New York, and southern New England were declared disaster regions for want of sufficient water for crops, livestock, and household use. Lasting relief did not come until well past the end of summer when, in October, a revival of cyclonic and frontal weather activity brought substantial rains.

While the mean weather patterns of summer continue through August, an increase in the frequency of tropical cyclones takes place, and thus we find with the approach of autumn a mounting threat of hurricanes along the Atlantic and Gulf coasts. (See Chapter 5.)

Autumn tends to bring slightly clearer weather over inland sections of the region, and calms prevail at this time more than during any other season. Diurnal convective activity decreases, for days become shorter and daily maximum temperatures are lower. Temperatures at night drop to increasingly lower values. Nocturnal inversions occur with increasing frequency under calm, clear skies, especially in the north, bringing frosts to the ground as early as September 15 in central Minnesota, northern New England, and the maritimes, and frequent radiation fogs in the protected valleys of hilly and mountain areas. Less frequent rains and the gradual desiccation of summer foliage, along with periods of protracted calm, allow dust particles to accumulate in the lower layers of air, creating a hazy condition known in most of the region as Indian Summer. At most locations the drop in mean temperature is greatest from October to November.

Winter. As the continental interior receives less and less warmth from the lowering sun, the land becomes steadily cooler. Periods of darkness lengthen with the approaching winter solstice, and ground frost creeps gradually southward from the boreal forest. Polar continental air masses enlarge and intensify and repeatedly surge toward the equator, bringing strong blasts of frigid air deep into the southern reaches of the mixed forest region (Fig. 5.1).

During the winter months of December,

January, and February mean monthly temperatures remain below freezing over the entire northern hardwoods section and as far south as the northern drainage of the lower Missouri and Ohio valleys, the Susquehanna valley, and southern New England, and somewhat farther south along the higher Appalachians. January is the coldest month throughout the region, except in northern localities adjacent to the waters of the Atlantic or in the eastern portions of the Great Lakes, where February is the coldest. Cape Cod and most of Nova Scotia and Newfoundland experience lowest mean monthly temperatures during February, as well as the eastern shores of the Great Lakes and most of southern Ontario.

Average January temperatures are between 5° and 10° in central Minnesota, between 20° and 25° over the lower Great Lakes, southern Ontario, and the coastal maritimes, and 10° or less in the interior of Maine and New Brunswick, but they increase to just below freezing south of the Great Lakes and Long Island Sound (Fig. 11.12). Average monthly temperatures are 32° or below at places as far south as St. Louis, Cincinnati, and Wheeling, W.V., in the interior, Long Island and the Susquehanna valley along the seaboard, and at scattered places high on the Appalachians as far south as Mt. Mitchell in the Smokies of western North Carolina. South of these localities, generally over the entire oak forest section, winters may be described as cool, with mean January temperatures increasing from slightly above freezing in the Ohio valley and the Chesapeake Bay area to around 50° within about 100 miles of the Gulf coast. Along the coast over all of Florida and southern Georgia winters are warm, with January averaging 50° or more. The normal penetration of frost (Fig. 11.13) decreases sharply south of the northern hardwoods.

The thermometer rarely rises above freezing during the day in January from the Great Lakes to the Atlantic coast, although the average daily maxima are above freezing south of the Ohio valley and along the coastal plain, reaching more than 60°, as a general rule, near the Gulf of Mexico. Minimum temperatures, on the other hand, are normally in the low 40s along the Gulf coast and below freezing northward from southern Tennessee and Virginia. In central Minnesota daily minima average around zero, but elsewhere in the north they range between 10 and 15°. Thus, the mean daily range of temperature over nearly all the region is about 20 degrees, although it is about 15 degrees in the Atlantic coastal sections and in the eastern Great Lakes (Fig. 11.14).

Below-zero temperatures have been experienced at some time in all sections of the mixed forest region, including northern Florida. Many places from eastern Texas to South Carolina have recorded values of −10° or lower; from eastern Oklahoma to Virginia, −20° or lower; from Missouri up the Ohio valley and across Pennsylvania to New Jersey, −30° or lower; and from Michigan across southern Ontario to northern New England and the maritimes, −40° or lower. Many places in Minnesota and Wisconsin have experienced −50° or lower, although this exceedingly low value has not been reached south of the northern hardwoods section (Fig. 11.15).

Very low wintertime temperatures are most commonly experienced when an enlarged and intensified polar continental air mass expands southward over the interior of North America, usually accompanied by strong northerly winds in eastern portions and bringing subfreezing temperatures to the Gulf coast and central Florida. In the wake of such a cold front advance, when calm, clear, dry, cold air settles over the eastern woodlands, temperatures may drop sufficiently to produce what is commonly termed a cold wave. In sections west of the Great Lakes and in northern New York and New England temperatures must drop at least 20 degrees in twenty-four hours to zero or less, in Florida 16 degrees in twenty-four hours to 32° or less, the requirements established by the U.S. Weather Bureau for designation as an official cold wave. Requirements vary throughout the United States; Figure 11.16 shows the changes of temperature necessary in various sections.

In wintertime polar air masses expand southward, especially the dry, cold polar continental type from northern Canada, unimpeded by major relief features and undeterred by the diminished radiation of the sun. The average zone of conflict between polar and tropical air masses, the polar front, is thus deflected farther south in winter, and frontal disturbances, particularly cyclonic storms, move with greatest frequency over the mixed forest region at

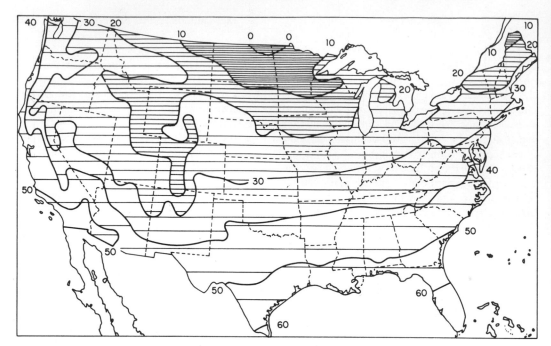

Figure 11.12. Surface temperatures in January in the United States (°F). [By permission of the publishers from Stephen S. Visher, *Climatic Atlas of the United States*, Cambridge, Mass.: Harvard University Press, Copyright, 1954, by the President and Fellows of Harvard College.]

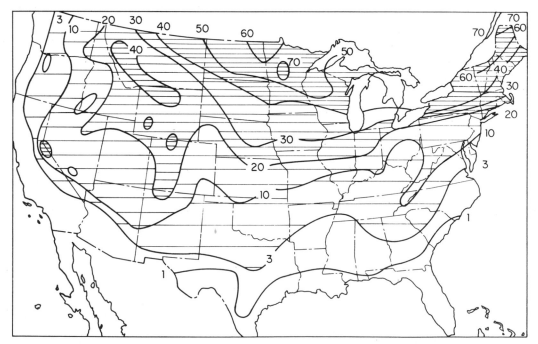

Figure 11.13. Depth of frost in the United States at the end of winter (inches). [By permission of the publishers from Stephen S. Visher, *Climatic Atlas of the United States*, Cambridge, Mass.: Harvard University Press, Copyright, 1954, by the President and Fellows of Harvard College.]

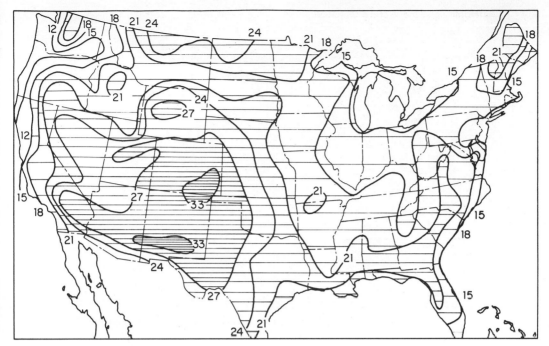

Figure 11.14. Mean daily temperature range in January in the United States (°F). [By permission of the publishers from Stephen S. Visher, *Climatic Atlas of the United States*, Cambridge, Mass.: Harvard University Press, Copyright, 1954, by the President and Fellows of Harvard College.]

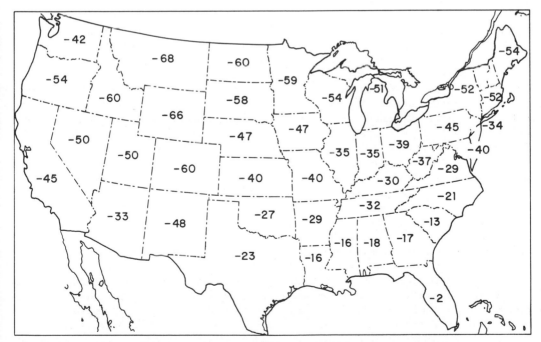

Figure 11.15. Extreme minimum winter temperatures in the United States, reported by state (°F). [By permission of the publishers from Stephen S. Visher, *Climatic Atlas of the United States*, Cambridge, Mass.: Harvard University Press, Copyright, 1954, by the President and Fellows of Harvard College.]

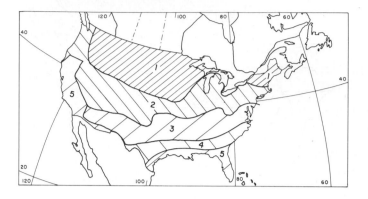

Zone	Temp. drop in 24 hrs. required (°F)	Min. temp. required (°F) Winter	Min. temp. required (°F) Other seasons
1	20	0	16
2	20	10	24
3	20	20	28
4	18	25	32
5	16	32	36

Figure 11.16. U.S. Weather Bureau definition of cold wave by zones in the United States.

this season (Fig. 5.2). Winter weather is dominated by the alternate passage of cyclones and anticyclones moving along rather well-defined paths in a general easterly direction. Winter precipitation results to some extent from orographic uplift over the low mountains of the east, to a greater extent from elongated frontal zones of convergence between contrasting air masses, but most of all from the frequent passage of cyclonic storms.

The principal paths of winter cyclones are shown for December, January, and February in Figure 5.12. The chief centers of cyclonic development are found along the eastern front of the Rockies in Canada and the United States and in the Great Basin of the southwest, where more winter storms form, or re-form after crossing the western mountains from the Pacific, than in any other area. Cyclonic storms originating in Texas or the lower Ohio valley, in the Gulf of Mexico, and along the south Atlantic coast, also contribute to the winter precipitation of the eastern woodlands. Most of the paths taken by storms developing in the west converge over the eastern Great Lakes and proceed northeastward over the Gulf of St. Lawrence. More southerly storms tend to follow the Atlantic coast, where the thermal contrast between land and sea favors cyclogenesis, but the paths of these, too, tend to converge toward the northeast, near Newfoundland.

Most of the winter's precipitation falls as snow from the Ohio valley and Delaware Bay northward. From the Great Lakes region to the Atlantic coast more than 40 inches of unmelted snow falls annually (Fig. 11.17). Over northern Michigan, northern New York State, and northern New England the amount is in excess of 60 inches, and in especially favored situations, such as the Lake Superior shores of Michigan and the Adirondacks, more than 120 inches of snow falls each year. From the Ohio valley and Delaware Bay southward annual amounts are less than 20 inches, and the southern evergreen forest section usually receives less than 1 inch. Here, snow falls on only one day during a normal winter, and generally on not more than twenty days from the Ohio valley and Delaware Bay southward (Fig. 11.18). In the regions of heavier snowfall, from the Great Lakes to northern New England, snow falls on forty days or more.

The alternate passing of cyclones and anticyclones continues to dominate the weather of the eastern woodlands into early spring, when, in April, a climax of cyclonic development takes place over western sections and along the Atlantic coast. This is when most of the central and northern Mississippi valley begins to receive the year's heaviest fall of rain, May and June often being the rainiest months.

Spring is generally a cooler season than

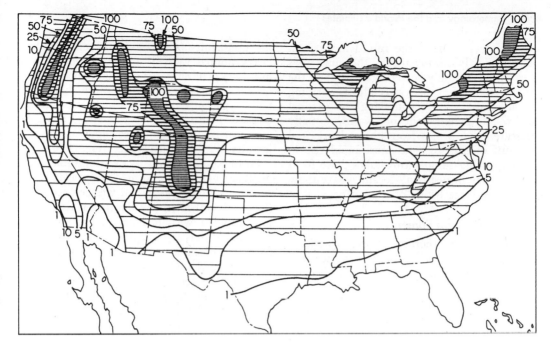

Figure 11.17. Annual snowfall in the United States (inches). [By permission of the publishers from Stephen S. Visher, *Climatic Atlas of the United States*, Cambridge, Mass.: Harvard University Press, Copyright, 1954, by the President and Fellows of Harvard College.]

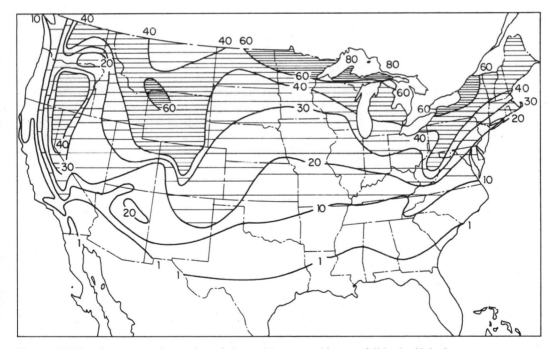

Figure 11.18. Average yearly number of days with measurable snowfall in the United States. [By permission of the publishers from Stephen S. Visher, *Climatic Atlas of the United States*, Cambridge, Mass.: Harvard University Press, Copyright, 1954, by the President and Fellows of Harvard College.]

autumn over most of the mixed forests, advancing slowly northward as the sun's rays exert an increasingly powerful effect upon the land, melting away the winter's frost, warming the air above, and encouraging the gradual northward penetration of warm, usually moisture-laden winds from the Atlantic and the Gulf of Mexico. The most rapid rise in mean monthly temperature takes place from April to May in nearly all localities save those adjacent to large bodies of water (Fig. 11.5).

Coastal Evergreen Forest

On the western shores of North America a coastal evergreen forest extends from near the entrance to San Francisco Bay to Kodiak Island,

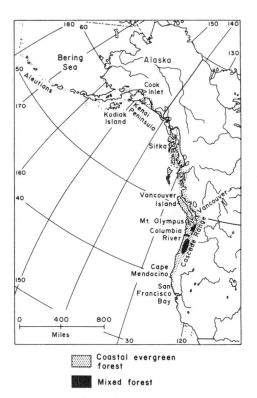

Coastal evergreen forest

Mixed forest

Figure 11.19. Distribution of coastal evergreen forest in western North America.

Alaska, a distance of more than 2000 miles (Fig. 11.19). This region, confined to within 50 miles of the sea for most of its enormous length save in the lowland areas of southwestern British Columbia and the Puget Sound–Willamette valley, is remarkable for

the uniformity of its moderate temperatures, heavy annual rainfall, and continuously high humidity. The climate near the sea is singularly uniform from about 38° to more than 60°N. Lat., a span of 22 degrees. Chiefly a coniferous forest, it is also remarkable for the great size of many of its important trees and for the uniformity of its outward aspects (Fig. 11.20).

From Kodiak Island to the Columbia River western hemlock (*Tsuga heterophylla*), Sitka spruce (*Picea sitchensis*), and western red cedar (*Thuja plicata*) form the dominant association, intermingled with less prominent species of fir, pine, alder, and poplar. Along the south coast of Alaska the forest is found on well-drained lowlands and up to elevations of around 1000 feet, gradually rising to loftier heights, generally from 2000 to 3000 feet, in southeastern Alaska and up to 4500 feet in southwestern British Columbia. Southward from Queen Charlotte Sound at the north end of Vancouver Island, Douglas fir (*Pseudotsuga taxifolia*) becomes the most important single species over mainland sections of the region, often accounting for 90 per cent of the stands, although heavily intermingled with western hemlock, western red cedar, Sitka spruce, grand fir (*Abies grandis*), and amabilis fir (*Abies amabilis*). The Douglas fir association is dominant along the coast from near the mouth of the Columbia River to northern California, where it gives way south of Cape Mendocino to continuous tracts of California redwood (*Sequoia sempervirens*), mixed with less important species such as California bay (*Umbellularia californica*), wax myrtle (*Myrica californica*), and other broadleaf forms. The presence of several deciduous species like broadleaf maple (*Acer macrophyllum*), Douglas maple (*Acer douglassi*), Oregon oak (*Quercus Garryana*), and several alder, birch, willow, and poplar species in the southern part of the region tends to develop a mixed forest in sheltered, interior sections. This is a point of resemblance to west Eurasian deciduous-evergreen mixed forests. It is particularly evident in the Puget Sound–Willamette lowland, where rainfall and moisture conditions in general favor forest development but where in places a modified continental temperature regime encourages mixed rather than coastal evergreen forest.

Just how well forest trees can thrive under constantly moist, temperature climatic con-

Figure 11.20. Coastal evergreen forest in Washington. Virgin forest near Olympic National Forest. [U.S. Bureau of Land Management]

ditions of the coast is suggested by their enormous size. Western hemlock is commonly 160 feet tall and 4 feet in diameter; western red cedar 175 by 8 feet, and up to 200 by 16 feet; Sitka spruce 175 by 6 feet, occasionally 250 by 12 feet; Douglas fir often 200 by 6 feet, sometimes 300 by 15 feet; redwood 190 to 280 by 12 feet or more, and sometimes up to 350 feet high and 20 feet in diameter.

Although very narrowly confined to the coastal fringe by high mountains whose lofty slopes in all but a few places plunge steeply down to the water's edge, this region is an important feature of the climatic pattern of North America. It merges with the boreal forest in the interior of southern Alaska, although for most of its great length it yields to undifferentiated highlands along its inland margins, and finally makes a transition along its southern extremity into the mediterranean scrub woodland of California. Certain broad-leaved evergreens typical of the scrub woodland are present in the south, such as Pacific madrone (*Arbutus menziessi*), California bay or

TABLE 11–2

Climatic Data for Stations in Coastal Evergreen Forest of North America
(Temp., °F; Rainfall, In.)

Station	Lat.	El. in Ft		Jan.	Feb.	Mar.	Apr.	May	Jun.	Jul.	Aug.	Sep.	Oct.	Nov.	Dec.	Year
Anchorage, Alaska	61°10'	92	T	13	19	25	35	46	54	57	56	48	36	22	14	
			R	0.8	0.6	0.6	0.4	0.5	0.9	1.6	2.6	2.7	1.9	1.0	0.8	14.3
Sitka, Alaska	57°03'	90	T	33	33	36	41	46	51	55	56	52	46	39	33	
			R	8.4	6.4	7.1	5.2	4.6	3.6	5.0	7.7	11.8	15.6	11.7	9.3	96.3
Masset, B.C.	54°02'	10	T	36	37	39	42	48	53	57	58	53	47	41	38	
			R	5.6	4.4	4.0	4.6	4.1	2.4	3.1	2.7	4.2	6.7	7.2	6.9	55.7
Vancouver, B.C.	49°17'	10	T	37	39	43	48	55	60	64	64	58	50	43	40	
			R	8.6	5.8	5.0	3.3	2.8	2.5	1.2	1.7	3.6	5.8	8.3	8.8	57.4
Eureka, Calif.	40°48'	43	T	47	48	49	51	53	56	56	57	56	54	51	49	
			R	6.2	5.7	4.6	2.9	1.8	0.7	0.1	0.1	0.7	2.7	4.6	6.1	36.2

Source: U.S. Weather Bureau, *Climatography of the United States, Climates of the States,* 1959–60; Canada, Department of Transport, Meteorological Division, *Climatic Summaries,* Toronto, 1956.

laurel, and tanoak (*Lithocarpus densiflorus*). (See Fig. 11.19.)

The coastal evergreen forest is a truly temperate region in spite of its high latitudes. Cool, damp summers with appreciable rain give way gradually to mild winters with increased cloudy weather, rain, and much fog. These familiar qualities of a marine environment are not surprising, as the prevailing easterly flow of the free atmosphere moves over unfrozen water the year round, bringing cool, moist, maritime polar air to the northwestern shores of the continent (Figs. 4.2 and 4.3). The eastern Pacific in February averages around 37°F off the south coast of Alaska and 52°F near Cape Mendocino; in August sea water temperatures in these localities average around 54°F and 59°F respectively (Figs. 6.12 and 6.13). But mountainous topography abruptly modifies oceanic air that invades the interior, and only a short distance from the coast are encountered the intricate varieties of environment typically found in highland regions. Consequently, important contrasts are found between coastal stations and those within the protection of the Kenai peninsula, the Alaskan archipelago, Vancouver Island, the Olympic peninsula, and the Cascade Mountains. Table 11-2 presents climatic data for stations within the region.

Summer. Temperatures in summer are more nearly uniform, as they are everywhere in the mid-latitudes, than at any other season. The average July temperature at Kodiak is about 54°, at Yakutat 53°, at Sitka 55°, and at Eureka 56°. Thus, for nearly 2000 miles along the coast there is a difference of only 2 or 3 degrees among places with a seaward exposure. Mean temperatures in July and August are nearly the same at coastal stations, although July is usually slightly warmer in the south, and August is the warmest month along the Alaskan coast (Fig. 11.21). The effect of an inland, protected situation is evident in the July temperature of 57° for Anchorage at the head of Cook Inlet, of 64° for Vancouver, 63° for Seattle, and 67° for Portland. A further point of contrast is the fact that extreme maximum temperatures at coastal stations have rarely exceeded 85°, whereas most inland stations of the Puget Sound–Willamette valley have recorded maxima of more than 100°. The growing season is around 240 days long in most low-lying areas from Eureka to Vancouver, but diminishes to about 150 days along the Alaskan coast.

Summer is the period of least rainfall over

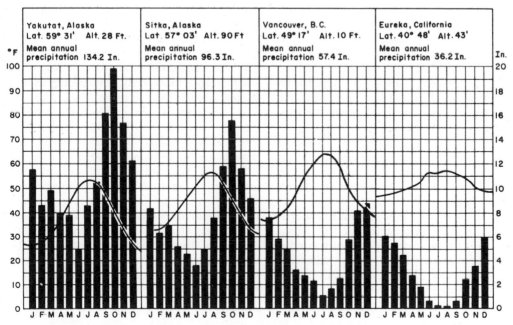

Figure 11.21. Normal temperature and precipitation at stations in coastal evergreen forest of North America.

the entire region, for the cyclonic storms mainly responsible for precipitation decrease in frequency over the Gulf of Alaska as the principal storm tracks shift farther north along with the poleward shift of most features of the general circulation (Fig. 5.13). In August principal storm tracks are farther north than in any other month, and cyclonic activity is less in the Gulf of Alaska than in any other month. Accordingly, the North Pacific anticyclone expands northward, bringing winds from west and northwest roughly parallel to the entire northwestern coast. Still, some rain falls during every month of summer, average amounts increasing from south to north. We observe that Eureka receives less than 1 inch during the three-month period of June, July, and August, Portland receives 2.6 inches, Seattle 2.66 inches, Vancouver 5.36 inches, Sitka 14.67 inches, Yakutat 22.52 inches, and Kodiak 13.51 inches.

Winter. In December more lows or depressions occur over the Gulf of Alaska than anywhere else in the northern hemisphere at any time of the year (Fig. 5.12). Consequently, December is the rainiest month at nearly all stations in the coastal evergreen forest region, except in the southernmost sections near Eureka. Most of the year's rain comes during the winter season everywhere, but the actual percentage of the year's total decreases considerably from south to north. From October 1st to March 31 Eureka receives about 83 per cent of annual precipitation, Portland 77 per cent, Seattle 75 per cent, Vancouver 73 per cent, Sitka 60 per cent, Yakutat 59 per cent, and Kodiak 53 per cent. Snow accounts for a good percentage of the season's precipitation, but long, steady, drizzling rains are the principal source. Cloudiness is at a maximum for the year, and damp, persistent fogs occur frequently. The increased frequency of cyclonic storms results in repeated changes of wind direction. However, the generally counter-clockwise circulation over the Gulf of Alaska brings winds that are predominantly parallel to the coast from Oregon to the Aleutians. From December through February south-easterly and southerly winds tend to prevail along the coast from northern California to

Alaska, and easterly winds predominate along the south coast of Alaska.

Winter temperatures are unusually mild all along the shoreline, compared with interior locations in the same latitude. Kodiak, for example, averages around 30° in January, which is the same as the much more southerly station at Boston, Mass., Yakutat averages about 29°, Sitka about 32°, Clayoquot, on the west coast of Vancouver Island, about 40°, and Eureka 47°. The mean annual range is about 24 degrees along the south coast of Alaska, diminishing to 18 degrees at Clayoquot and to only 9 degrees at Eureka.

Inland stations experience a greater range, for in addition to higher summer temperatures these stations also have lower winter temperatures than those near the sea. Vancouver has a mean January temperature of 36°, thus an annual range of 28 degrees; Seattle a January mean of 40°, an annual range of 27 degrees; Portland a January mean of 39°, an annual range of 28 degrees.

Occasionally in winter a mass of cold, dry continental air from the deep-frozen interior expands out over the sea to bring much lower than usual thermometer readings to places along the coast. Extreme minimum temperatures in January have been as low as −12° at Kodiak, 5° at Yakutat, −5° at Sitka, 2° at Vancouver, 3° at Seattle, and −2° at Portland.

Winter snow seldom amounts to more than 10 inches along the coast from Cape Mendocino to Queen Charlotte Sound. North of here snow-fall increases appreciably, amounting, even at sea level, to 60 inches or more. These values are small in comparison to those recorded for interior valleys in the mountain region just a short distance inland, where up to 140 inches of snow is normal in many localities.

From the north coast of California to southern Alaska the total annual precipitation is generally over 80 inches. On the seaward-facing slopes of mountains only a short distance inland more than 100 inches is normal from the Columbia River northward beyond Yakutat, and in a good many places exceeds 200 inches. In this same section departures from normal are rarely more than 15 per cent, indicating a high degree of rainfall reliability.

References

BRAUN, E. L.: *Deciduous Forests of Eastern North America*, The Blakiston Co., Philadelphia, 1950.

CANADA, DEPARTMENT OF TRANSPORT, METEOROLOGICAL DIVISION: *Climatic Summaries*, Toronto, 1956.

KIMBLE, G. H. T.: *Our American Weather*, McGraw-Hill Book Company, New York, 1955.

U.S. WEATHER BUREAU: *Climatography of the United States, Climates of the States*, 1959–60.

VISHER, S. S.: *Climatic Atlas of the United States*, Harvard University Press, Cambridge, Mass., 1954.

chapter 12

MID-LATITUDE FORESTS OF EURASIA

Mid-Latitude Mixed Forest in Western Eurasia

In western Eurasia a temperate marine climate, closely similar to that of the North American coastal evergreen forest, gives way imperceptably, a short distance inland from the sea, to a more continental mixed forest climate that spreads eastward and southeastward continuously for some 3000 miles. Unhindered by high mountain ranges along the coast, most of western Europe is favored by marine atmospheric influences for hundreds of miles into the interior. This contrasts noticeably with the presence of high mountains near the sea in North America within the same latitudes. The forests of western Europe are dominantly broadleaf deciduous, but the presence of coniferous evergreens and a luxuriant growth of broadleaf evergreens like holly, box, and strawberry tree as far north as the British Isles gives a somewhat evergreen character to sections along the west coast. This is a response to climatic qualities resembling very closely the climate along the northwest coast of North America. Because of their contiguity, we shall treat mid-latitude forest climates of western Eurasia as a single unit.

The mid-latitude forests extend eastward from the shores of the Atlantic Ocean to the Ural Mountains and southward from southern Norway, Sweden, and Finland to central Spain,

the Appennines of Italy, the Balkan peninsula, and the hilly countryside of the Ukraine. They also appear to some extent in fragmentary tracts on the slopes of the Anatolian highlands in Turkey, the mountain ranges of the Caucasus, and northern Iran. The climatically transitional nature of the region is indicated by the widespread presence of both deciduous broadleaved and needleleaved evergreen trees, contrasting with the dominantly needleleaved evergreens of the northern coniferous forest and the dominantly broadleaved evergreens of the mediterranean scrub forest (Fig. 12.1).

The continuous stands of virgin forest that existed in Roman times were largely cleared for cultivation by the seventeenth century, with the result that present-day impressions of their original nature and extent must be gleaned from the occasional references found in early writings and from the presence of scattered vestiges of a once abundant woodland.

PLANT LIFE. Some eighty important tree species are known in all of Europe, and more than a dozen are widespread and regionally significant of the mid-latitude mixed forest. Broadly speaking, deciduous forms tend to prevail on low, rolling terrain and conifers in the highlands. Of the deciduous species oak, beech, hornbeam, ash, elm, linden, maple, birch, and alder are found, at least in scattered distribution, throughout the length and breadth of the

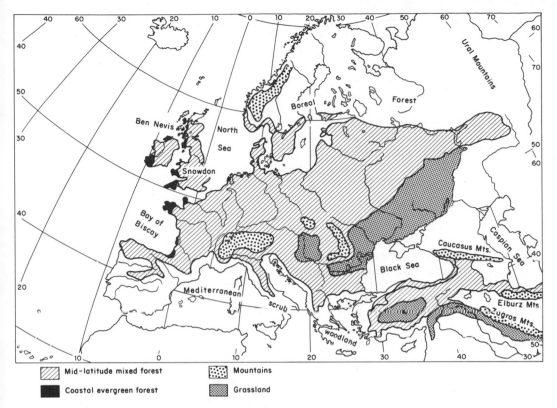

Figure 12.1. Mid-latitude mixed forest and coastal evergreen forest in western Eurasia.

region. Of these, two species of oak, the English oak (*Quercus robur*) and sessile oak (*Quercus petraea*), and a single species of beech (*Fagus silvatica*) are numerically superior to others, creating a predominant deciduous complex commonly referred to as the oak-beech forest of the Eurasian plains and low plateaus.

Hornbeam (*Carpinus betulus*), ash (*Fraxinus excelsior*), elm (*Ulmus spp.*), linden, also called lime and familiar in North America as basswood (*Tilia spp.*), Norway maple (*Acer platanoides*), "sycamore" (*Acer pseudo-platanus*), alder (*Alnus spp.*), and silver birch (*Betula alba*) may be sighted almost anywhere within the region and occasionally in nearly pure stands. They are, however, subordinate in numbers and density to oak and beech for the region as a whole, simply contributing to the over-all deciduous nature of these forested tracts.

In highland areas a variety of coniferous species is found. Only three are widespread, however: the Scots pine (*Pinus sylvestris*), familiar to us also as an important member of the European taiga, silver fir (*Abies alba*), and

Norway spruce (*Picea excelsa*), which is a distinctly European tree, yielding in northeastern Europe to the Siberian spruce of the boreal forest. Conifers now are more commonly seen in the lowlands than in earlier times; they grow more rapidly, have straight, clear trunks, and, especially the pines, are adaptable to inferior, light, sandy soils, and for these reasons are often preferred for reforestation programs. A good example is the maritime pine (*Pinus pinaster*), introduced in the lumber and turpentine plantations of the lands in southwestern France.

The southwestward limits of the mid-latitude mixed forest are found in the Castillian highlands of central Spain and the mountainous interior of Portugal, north of the Tagus River. Spreading northward from here to the rugged hills of Galicia and the Cantabrian Mountains of northern Spain, but skirting the grasslands in the lower valley of the Ebro, the oak-beech-pine forest is repeatedly seen, chiefly in broken, less populous country, continuing along the middle slopes of the Pyrenees into southern

France. Northward from the Pyrenees it expands over all of France save the Mediterranean coast and the lower Rhône valley. Predominantly coniferous over the Massif Central, the French Alps, the Jura, and the Vosges, it is mainly an oak-beech-hornbeam woodland in the plains and rolling hillsides below, with the exception of the pineries in the Landes and Gascogne facing the Bay of Biscay. Sweet chestnut (*Castanea sativa*) is a prominent member of the mediterranean forest associations, interspersed among the temperate deciduous forest in south central France.

Across the English Channel the mixed forest is found in all of Great Britain and Eire save in the rugged highlands of northern Scotland, whose treeless heaths and meadows remind us of the polar tundra. The coastal evergreen character of the forest near the Atlantic is evident as far north as the British Isles, where at least three native broadleaf evergreens are found, outliers of the Mediterranean flora, adapted to the year-round humidity and equable temperatures of Britain: the holly (*Ilex aquifolium*), box (*Buxus sempervirens*), and strawberry tree (*Arbutus unedo*).

Beyond the North Sea and the Baltic the mixed forest merges with the boreal forest along the narrow lowlands of Norway's indented coast almost as far north as Trondheim, occupying much of the area around Oslo and most of Sweden south of Stockholm and fringing the south coast of Finland. The dominant hardwood is beech, although the two important oaks, Norway maple, ash, elm, and linden are plentiful.

From northern France and the Low Countries the mixed forest spreads a continuous and ever-widening mantle eastward over the north European plain to the Ural Mountains. Oak, pine, linden, maple, ash, and hornbeam, in various combinations with aspen, birch, spruce, and fir, are the principal trees. Beech, east of the Pripet marshes, tends to disappear, hornbeam fades from the scene beyond the Dneiper, and ash becomes rare almost 500 miles west of the Urals. The linden, however, along with diminishing numbers of oak, elm, and maple, continues eastward beyond the Urals into the valley of the Ob. East of the Urals the forest steppe replaces the Eurasian mixed forest as the regional dominants become increasingly rare, and aspen, birch, and willow, with a variety of hardy shrubs, are the principal forms in the scattered woodlands. Forest steppe is, in fact, an open grassy woodland that begins well to the west along the Danube in southern Rumania and from here continues eastward for more than 2500 miles to the mountains of central Asia, providing a nearly unbroken transition zone between the forests of the north and the treeless, grassy steppe along its southern borders.

Though it is comparatively uniform and continuous across the north European plain, the mixed forest in central and southern Europe is interrupted and complicated by the presence of many mountain systems. East of the Rhine it continues in typical character as an oak-beech forest across the Bavarian highlands and down the valley of the Danube to the fringes of the broad Hungarian plain. There it encircles the virtually treeless prairie land of central Hungary along the lower and middle slopes of the Carpathians, the Austrian Alps, the low mountains of northern Yugoslavia, and the Transylvanian Alps of Rumania. Here, among the mountainous countries of central Europe, the mixed forests form part of the rather well-marked vertical zoning of plant associations typically found in areas of strong relief.

Mountain peaks rise steadily higher from west to east. In the Bohemian Mountains of western Czechoslovakia they are somewhat less than 5000 feet, in the Carpathians of eastern Czechoslovakia and northern Rumania they are more than 6000 feet, and in the Transylvanian Alps of middle Rumania many a summit attains a height in excess of 8000 feet. Oak, maple, ash, linden, and elm are dominant at lower levels, and spruce, pine, beech, and fir become more plentiful from around 2500 feet to 4000 feet above sea level. Beech often alternates in pure stands with fir in the middle elevations below 4000 feet, beyond which spruce forests, occasionally mixed with larch (*Larix decidua*), mark the presence of alpine outliers of the boreal forest farther north.

Descending the eastern slopes of the Transylvanian Alps in Rumania, the mixed forest gradually merges with the forest steppe, where oak (*Quercus petraea*, *Quercus cerris*, and *Quercus frainette*), hornbeam, linden, elm, willow, and ash are found chiefly in the stream valleys, and these, in turn, yield to the treeless steppe of Moravia and the Ukraine.

From the complex mountain region of the Swiss Alps the mixed forests extend southeastward across the Po valley, along the middle and upper slopes of the Appennines in Italy, and then over the rugged mountains of the Balkan peninsula. The plain of the Po was originally forested with oak (*Quercus robur*), elm, ash, and other deciduous hardwoods, revealing its affinity with the non-mediterranean climate of central and western Europe. Peninsular Italy south of the Po valley, however, possesses a deciduous hardwood forest only from about 2500 to 4500 feet above sea level, below which a Mediterranean environment prevails, giving rise to evergreen broadleaved species along the Adriatic and Tyrrhenian coasts. Above the deciduous zone are mainly spruce, fir, larch, and pine, notably Cembrian pine (*Pinus cembra*). In the lower levels of the deciduous range oak and chestnut predominate, and beech is the principal species above. A southward detachment of pine, oak, chestnut, and beech forest is found in scattered fragments on the upper slopes of the lofty mountains in Sicily.

Except along the coasts of Yugoslavia, Albania, Greece, Bulgaria, and European Turkey, where the Mediterranean environment prevails, the Balkan peninsula is dominated by oak-beech forests from 2500 to 4500 feet or more, with oak, ash, chestnut, hornbeam, plane (*Platanus orientalis*), walnut, and poplar occupying lower levels of the range.

Across the Sea of Marmora the mid-latitude mixed forest is again seen on the middle slopes of the Pontic Mountains overlooking the Black Sea coast of northern Turkey, where relict stands of Oriental beech (*Fagus orientalis*), chestnut, and fir (*Abies nordmanniana*) are found above thinly scattered oaks at lower levels. Continuing eastward, the mixed forests occupy much of the Caucasus Mountain region between the Black and Caspian seas. Naturally enough, a vertical zoning of vegetation occurs, with oaks dominating from about 1000 to 2000 feet, beech from about 2000 to 4500 feet, and fir and spruce from about 4000 to 7000 feet. Admixtures of hornbeam, ash, maple, elm, birch, aspen, and alder are common at lower and intermediate elevations.

The southeastern extremities of the mid-latitude mixed forest in western Eurasia are found in northern Iran, along the seaward slopes of the Elburz Mountains facing the Caspian, and on the higher flanks of the Zagros ranges as far south as Shiraz. Although only an open woodland of gnarled scrub oak prevails in the upper Zagros, whose impoverished species are mainly foreign to the vegetation of southeastern Europe, the Caspian forests are rather abundantly varied. Over forty species of timber trees are believed to occur here, with oak and beech forming the dominant associations. Here, beech (principally *Fagus orientalis*) attains higher altitudes than we have noted heretofore, predominating between 5000 and 7000 feet, with oak (chiefly *Quercus castanaeifolia*) leading from 2000 to 5000 feet. Hornbeam, maple, ash, linden, and other deciduous hardwoods are intermingled to some extent throughout the oak-beech range of distribution.

CLIMATIC CONDITIONS. We have noted the importance of a coastline unobstructed by high mountains in allowing the deep penetration of maritime influences in the interior of western Eurasia. From southern Norway to northern Spain the western exposure of the continent is freely open to the invasion of oceanic air borne eastward from the Atlantic on the prevailing winds of higher altitude. Even the Pyrenees, which rise to heights of more than 10,000 feet in several places, lie approximately parallel to the prevailing currents of air from the west (Fig. 12.2). Only the lofty Alps interpose an important barrier to the movement of air above the friction layer, and here, in south central Europe, one finds a large area of complex highland environments. Lesser relief features like the mountains of Bohemia, the Carpathians, and the Balkans simply introduce a moderate variety of landscapes within the general context of the mid-latitude mixed forest.

Still another important geographical aspect of western Europe is the pronounced interpenetration of land and sea. Europe is very like a large peninsula of western Asia, bordered on the north, west, and south by major bodies of water. Its countless islands and peninsulas, which are in turn indented and further compounded into an endless number of smaller projecting capes and promontories, are embraced by the many lesser arms of the sea, bringing the moderating effect of a marine environment eastward for many hundreds of miles into the continent. Moreover, the Atlantic Ocean is extremely warm for these latitudes,

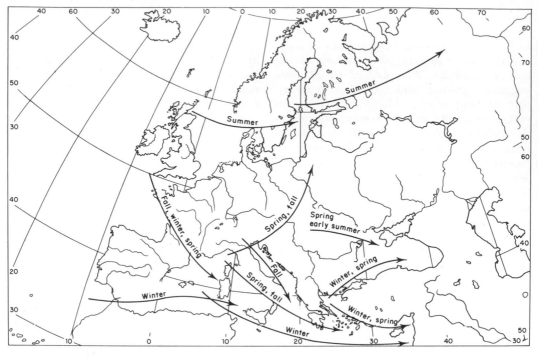

Figure 12.2. Mean storm tracks by season in western Eurasia.

having a February temperature around 40° off the southern coast of Norway, increasing to 54° off Corunna, and in August warming up to about 57° off the Norwegian coast and 68° off the north Portuguese coast (Figs. 6.12 and 6.13).

In spite of plentiful evidence that maritime air dominates the year-round weather of the mid-latitude forests of western Eurasia as far east as the Ural Mountains, those distinctly marine qualities that distinguish the coastal evergreen forest are confined to the seaward margins of the continent and give way, a short distance inland, to a normal weather regime that is essentially continental in nature. Thus, mild winters, cool summers, abundant cloudiness and fog, and a winter maximum of rainfall are typical of the fiord coast of southwestern Norway, all the British Isles (save for the territory around Edinburgh and east central England), the coastal margins of Belgium and the Netherlands, France inland for a hundred miles or more from the coast, the narrow seaward slopes of the Cantabrian Mountains in northern Spain, and the coast of north Portugal.

From southern Norway to northern Portugal, the yearly range of average temperatures is rarely more than 20 degrees at places immediately facing the sea. At Ona Lighthouse, Norway, it is 17; Rothesay, Scotland, 17; Edinburgh, 20; Valencia, Eire, 14; Falmouth, England, 17; Brest, France, 17; Corunna, Spain, 16; Oporto, Portugal, 20. Places near the coast but somewhat sheltered from the open sea experience a slightly greater range, as at Trondheim, about 50 miles inland, with 30 degrees; Bergen, also about 50 miles inland, with 24 degrees; Bordeaux, about 30 miles inland, 27 degrees; and Bilbao, Spain, about 10 miles inland, 30 degrees. The frost-free season along the coast varies from about six months in length in southern Norway to ten months or more in northern Spain and Portugal. (See Table 12-1.)

The year's total precipitation averages more than 40 inches in almost all coastal areas with direct exposure to the sea, except in Denmark and most of the French coast, where annual amounts between 30 and 40 inches are normal (Fig. 12.3). Well-exposed places, especially in the low mountains of the British Isles, receive much heavier precipitation. Snowdon, north Wales, at 3560 feet, is said to be the rainiest point in Europe, receiving an estimated 200 inches or

TABLE 12–1

Climatic Data for Mid-Latitude Mixed Forest Stations in Western Eurasia
(Temp., °F; Rainfall, In.)

Station	Lat.	El. in Ft		Jan.	Feb.	Mar.	Apr.	May	Jun.	Jul.	Aug.	Sep.	Oct.	Nov.	Dec.	Year
Bergen, Norway	60°24'	141	T	35	35	38	44	52	58	61	60	55	48	41	37	
			R	7.9	6.0	5.4	4.4	3.9	4.2	5.2	7.3	9.2	9.2	8.0	8.1	78.8
Edinburgh, Scotland	55°55'	441	T	39	39	41	45	49	55	59	58	54	49	43	40	
			R	2.5	1.6	1.6	1.6	2.2	1.9	3.1	3.1	2.6	2.9	2.4	2.1	27.6
Brest, France	48°19'	56	T	45	45	47	51	55	60	63	64	60	55	49	46	
			R	3.5	3.0	2.5	2.5	1.9	2.0	2.0	2.2	2.3	3.6	4.2	4.4	34.1
Paris, France	48°49'	164	T	37	39	44	51	57	63	66	65	60	52	49	38	
			R	1.5	1.3	1.5	1.7	2.0	2.1	2.1	2.0	2.0	2.2	2.0	1.9	22.3
Corunna, Spain	43°22'	177	T	50	50	52	54	58	62	65	66	64	59	54	51	
			R	4.4	3.3	3.9	3.2	2.2	1.5	1.3	1.7	2.8	3.9	4.5	5.2	37.9
Oslo, Norway	59°56'	308	T	25	26	33	42	53	60	65	61	53	43	38	28	
			R	1.7	1.3	1.4	1.6	1.8	2.4	2.9	3.8	2.5	2.9	2.3	2.3	26.9
Copenhagen, Denmark	55°41'	43	T	33	32	36	44	53	59	64	62	56	48	39	35	
			R	1.6	1.3	1.2	1.7	1.7	2.1	2.2	3.2	1.9	2.1	2.2	2.1	23.3
Berlin, Germany	52°27'	187	T	31	33	39	47	56	61	65	63	57	48	38	33	
			R	1.9	1.3	1.5	1.7	1.9	2.3	3.1	2.2	1.9	1.7	1.7	1.9	23.1
Munich, Germany	48°09'	1739	T	28	31	38	46	54	60	63	62	56	47	38	31	
			R	1.7	1.4	1.9	2.7	3.7	4.6	4.7	4.2	3.2	2.2	1.9	1.9	34.1
Milan, Italy	45°27'	341	T	35	40	47	56	63	70	74	73	67	57	45	38	
			R	2.2	2.0	2.1	2.4	3.4	2.6	2.3	2.2	2.8	3.9	3.3	2.4	31.6
Stockholm, Sweden	59°21'	146	T	27	27	32	39	49	57	63	60	52	44	35	30	
			R	1.5	1.1	1.1	1.5	1.6	1.9	2.8	3.1	2.1	2.1	1.9	1.9	22.4
Warsaw, Poland	52°13'	394	T	26	28	35	46	58	63	66	64	57	48	36	29	
			R	1.2	1.1	1.3	1.5	1.9	2.6	3.0	3.0	1.9	1.7	1.4	1.4	22.0
Belgrade, Yugoslavia	44°48'	453	T	32	36	44	55	64	69	73	72	66	56	46	35	
			R	1.6	1.3	1.6	2.2	2.6	2.8	1.9	2.5	1.7	2.7	1.8	1.9	24.6
Moscow, U.S.S.R.	55°46'	505	T	15	17	25	39	55	62	66	62	52	40	27	18	
			R	1.5	1.4	1.1	1.9	2.2	2.9	3.0	2.9	1.9	2.7	1.7	1.6	24.8
Kiev, U.S.S.R.	50°27'	600	T	22	24	32	45	60	66	68	66	58	46	34	26	
			R	1.3	1.0	1.6	1.7	1.9	2.6	3.1	2.3	1.8	1.8	1.5	1.5	22.1

Source: "World Weather Records," *Smithsonian Miscellaneous Collections*, Vol. 79, 1927, Vol. 90, 1934, Vol. 105, 1947; U.S. Weather Bureau, *World Weather Records, 1941–50,* 1959.

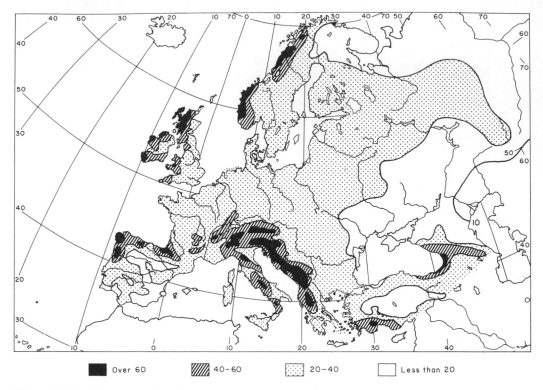

Over 60   40-60   20-40   Less than 20

Figure 12.3.   Mean annual precipitation in western Eurasia (inches).

more; Ben Nevis, north Scotland, at 4406 feet, about 165 inches; and the lower hills of the English lake district, at between 1500 and 2000 feet, up to 185 inches. Except in Norway, the low mountains near the Atlantic coast are high enough to intercept, uplift, and hence to cool the invading air from the sea, but at the same time they are not high enough to create drought conditions in low-lying tracts to leeward, such as one finds in western North America at the same latitude.

More than half the annual precipitation falls during the six-month period from October 1 to March 1 over coastal sections. Trondheim receives 56 per cent in this period, Bergen 58 per cent, Rothesay 55 per cent, Valencia 59 per cent, Falmouth 63 per cent, Brest 59 per cent, and Corunna 67 per cent.

Snow contributes only a small fraction of the year's precipitation at low altitudes, and when it falls, does not often exceed a few inches in depth, seldom remaining on the ground for many days. Along the coast the average number of days with snow during the year decreases from north to south, Trondheim having

seventy-four, Bergen forty-two, Rothesay fourteen, Falmouth and Valencia five, Brest six, Bilbao five, and Corunna less than one. The first flurries are usually seen in October at northern localities, continuing until April, but farther south the season is much shorter and is variable from month to month. At higher points, such as Ben Nevis, and Snowdon, snow has been recorded in some quantity every month of the year.

The coastal margins of northwest Europe are among the very cloudy regions of the world, particularly in the British Isles and Norway. For the year as a whole 7.6 tenths of the sky is cloud-covered at Trondheim, 6.8 at Bergen, 7.5 at Rothesay, 7.2 at Valencia, 6.6 at Brest, 6.1 at Bilbao, decreasing to 5.4 at Corunna, and 5.0 at Oporto. The winter half of the year, from October through April, is usually the period of most abundant cloud, and some month of summer is normally least cloudy, such as April at Trondheim, June at Bergen, April at Rothesay and Valencia, May at Falmouth and Brest, and August at Bilbao, Corunna, and Oporto. Conversely, the annual amount of sunshine actually received is small in proportion to the amount it would be possible to receive from dawn to dusk through completely clear skies each day, ranging from about 25 per cent in southwestern Norway and northern Scotland to 35 per cent or more in southern England and northern France and to more than 50 per cent in northern Spain and Portugal.

Though winter, as a rule, is the season of greater cloudiness along the coast, the occurrence of fog is greatest in late spring and early summer, when warm, moist, tropical air spreads over the cooler sea. This is advective fog that seldom penetrates far inland. Interior sections receive most fog during winter. This is radiation fog arising from the pronounced cooling of land surfaces on calm, clear, cold nights and is especially noticeable in valleys.

As one turns eastward from the sea, the temperate marine climate of the coastal evergreen forest gives way gradually to the humid continental climate of the mixed forest. The change becomes evident in several conspicuous ways as one advances farther eastward into the interior. Winters become colder, as a result of which mean annual temperature range increases from less than 20 degrees on the seaboard to more than 50 degrees around Moscow and more than 40 degrees in the Balkans and the Po valley. Most of the year's precipitation falls during the summer half of the year, from April 1 to September 30, largely as a result of increased convective showers. Snow falls on an increasingly larger number of days, accumulates to greater depths, and remains on the ground for longer periods (Table 12-1). Relative humidity, cloudiness, and fog decrease, and the yearly percentage of possible sunshine gradually increases to more than 50 per cent near the grassland margins of southeastern Europe.

From west to east the annual range of temperature increases steadily at places in approximately the same latitude. Bergen, with 24 degrees, may be compared with Oslo, having 39, Stockholm 35, and Stalingrad 45 degrees, all at nearly 60°N. Lat. Rothesay, having 17, may be compared with Edinburgh, having 20, Copenhagen 32, Riga, Estonia, 40, and Moscow 52, all between 55° and 57°N. Lat. Valencia, with 14 degrees, compares with Cambridge 23, Utrecht 27, Berlin 33, Warsaw 40, and Kiev 46. Brest, having 18, compares with Paris 28, Munich 35, Vienna 39, and Vaslui, in eastern

Rumania, 45. Summer temperatures at most of the places mentioned are very little different from one another, as reference to Table 12-1 will reveal. It is the increasing cold of the winter months that accounts for the steadily widening range of mean annual temperature toward the east.

An important quality of the mid-latitude forests of western Eurasia is the absence of a rainfall deficiency at any time under normal conditions. June or July is usually the rainiest month. Total annual precipitation decreases toward the east, but in a highly irregular fashion, principally as a result of the orographic effect of the complex mountain systems in central Europe. Generally speaking, along the north European plain annual precipitation averages between 20 and 25 inches, and in southeastern Europe slightly higher amounts, between 25 and 30 inches, are common (Table 12-1). At higher elevations, however, an annual amount of 40 inches or more is often the normal total, creating the irregular rainfall pattern revealed in Figure 12.3. Puy de Dome in the Massif Central, at 4815 feet, with 66 inches; Pic du Midi in the Pyrenees, at 9380 feet, with 64 inches; Freudenstadt in the Black Forest, at 2395 feet, with 58 inches; Santis, in northeastern Switzerland, at 8216 feet, with 110 inches; Trauenstein, Bavaria, at 1960 feet, with 59 inches; and Petrohan in northern Bulgaria, at 4593 feet, with 45 inches, are examples of elevated locations receiving more than the normal rainfall of the adjacent lowlands.

Evidence is available at many mountain situations in the interior that marine conditions penetrate far inland. Not only is precipitation more abundant at higher altitude, but there is also here a higher winter maximum and a lower annual range of temperature than at lowlying places nearby. Puy de Dome, at 4815 feet, is 10 miles west of Clermont-Ferrand, at 1280 feet. Puy de Dome receives 52 per cent of the year's 66 inches of rain between October 1 and April 31, and the mean annual temperature range is about 24 degrees, while in the same period Clermont-Ferrand receives only 37 per cent of its annual 25 inches of rain and has a mean annual temperature range of about 31 degrees. Freudenstadt, at 2395 feet, is 40 miles southwest of Stuttgart, at 876 feet. Freudenstadt receives 53 per cent of its 58 inches of annual rainfall between October 1 and April 31 and has a mean annual temperature range of about 31 degrees, but Stuttgart receives only 37 per cent of its annual rainfall of 26.5 inches during the same period and has a mean annual temperature range of about 34 degrees.

Snow accounts for an increasingly larger proportion of the year's precipitation eastward over the north European plain. Although it normally falls on fewer than twenty days over most of France and the Low Countries, it falls on an average of eighty-three days around Moscow, but on about thirty days in most of southeastern Europe.

The growing season decreases from around nine months along the coast of France to less than five months east of the Baltic Sea, but southward from the vicinity of Moscow it increases to more than six months over most of the Balkan peninsula.

The year-round weather of western Eurasia results from the endless interplay of air masses from three main source regions and the modification they undergo as they move alternately over land and water surfaces and are either warmed or cooled from below (made less stable or more stable) and either gain moisture or become drier. As many as twelve different air mass types have been distinguished that regularly affect the weather of western Eurasia. All, however, are some variation of three main types: (1) maritime polar air from the North Atlantic, poleward of about 45°, (2) maritime tropical from the Atlantic south of 45°, and (3) polar continental from northern Eurasia and the Arctic (Figs. 5.2 and 5.3). Of these, the two types of maritime air appear most frequently and are responsible for the dominantly marine character of the mid-latitude forest climates in western Eurasia. These contrasting air mass types tend to meet along two favored zones of conflict: the Atlantic polar front, extending in a northeast–southwest direction between eastern United States and northern Europe, and the Arctic front, lying somewhat farther north between Greenland and the Barents and Kara seas of the Arctic basin. The ceaseless parade of cyclones and anticyclones developing along these axes brings a variety of weather that varies from warm to cool, from humid to dry, and is occasionally extremely cold. Passing disturbances engender surface winds from all quarters of the compass, but most of the time the main stream of atmospheric movement is

eastward from the sea, and the air it brings is dominantly moist and cool.

Summer. During the summer months, when the higher sun warms the land surfaces of the mid-latitudes, the buoyant, unstable air is readily moved eastward in the prevailing westerly currents at higher altitude and is replaced by strong indrafts of oceanic air from the west. The prevailing wind direction is west across the north European plain, but generally northwest along the Norwegian coast, northern Spain, and the Balkans. At this season the primary tracks of cyclonic storms are eastward across the North Sea and the Baltic, a bit to the north of the British Isles, as the Azores High expands northward and eastward and the Iceland Low diminishes in size and intensity.

Along the coast August is generally the warmest month at seaside locations from Norway to Spain, although average temperatures during both July and August are often the same. The monthly mean for both July and August is 57° at Rothesay, 59° at Valencia, and 61° at Falmouth. Nearly everywhere else throughout the region July is the warmest month, and mean values gradually increase eastward from the sea. From around 65° in western sections away from the coast, the warmest summer month averages nearer 70° west of the Urals and around 75° in many parts of the Po valley and the Balkans (Table 12-2). The mean daily range of temperature is about twice that of the coldest month of winter. At Berlin it is 19 degrees in July compared with 9 degrees in January, at Vienna 18 degrees in July compared with 9 degrees in January, and at Milan 21 degrees compared with 11. Occasionally, very high temperatures have been observed, such as 105° at Paris, 95° at Oslo, 96° at Berlin, 100° at Vienna and Milan, and 107° at Belgrade.

Summer is the season of maximum precipitation at nearly all places remote from the sea. Along the west coast, however, winter is usually the rainy season. In the British Isles, around Dublin, Edinburgh, and central England north of the Thames, eastern France except the Rhône valley, most of the Low Countries and Denmark, southeastern Norway and southern Sweden, and in nearly all the remainder of the region to the Ural Mountains and the Balkan peninsula, June or July is usually the month of heaviest rain. It is at this time that thunderstorms occur with greatest frequency. Inland stations in regions of strong relief experience the violent, crashing effect of strong convective uplift, producing lightning, thunder, heavy showers, and hail more often than lowland stations on broad plains or near the sea. Munich, in Bavaria, for example, normally records about thirty-two thunderstorms each year, more than twice the number at Bremen, on the north German plain, which usually has about fourteen. Brest, on the French coast, has an average of slightly more than seven, in contrast to Paris, with twenty-eight.

Winter. As the result of a dominantly marine situation, winter approaches slowly over most of the region, particularly in western sections. The coldest month is delayed until February along the coast, but inland it is usually January, although the difference in mean monthly values for December, January, and February is seldom more than 3 degrees. The temperature of the coldest month is between 35° and 40° in southern Norway and the British Isles, and between 40° and 50° from the English Channel to northern Portugal. Eastward, however, where January is normally the coldest month, temperatures are very much lower. At Bergen the mean January temperature is 34°, at Stockholm 27°, and at Leningrad 18°. An eastward traverse a little farther south indicates a similar trend. Rothesay averages 40° in January, Edinburgh 38°, Copenhagen 31°, Riga 24°, and Moscow 14°. In southeastern Europe winter temperatures average generally between 25° and 35°, and in the Po valley and the Apennines January means remain above freezing at about 35° (Table 12-1).

At this time of year the decreasing warmth of the sun allows cold air to expand and intensify over the vast interior of northern Eurasia, in consequence of which polar continental air masses develop into large and vigorous sources of cold, dry air that frequently expands westward over the continental coast and the British Isles, to bring clear skies and low temperatures to much of the region. The winds blow from the southeast in eastern Europe, from the southwest in western sections (Fig. 5.2). The zones of conflict between polar continental and maritime air from the Atlantic become more complicated during winter, and the cyclonic storms that develop tend, at this time, to move along three principal tracks (Fig. 12.2). The two main tracks are along the Arctic coast eastward beyond the Kara Sea and through the Mediterranean Sea. The third is across the North Sea and the Baltic into the interior. Many of these storms originate along the east coast of North America, notably near Newfoundland, and simply intensify as they enter the region of the Icelandic Low, certainly one of the world's stormiest oceanic areas. Few of the storms entering western Eurasia advance beyond the Urals with any considerable intensity, for they most commonly are dissipated or blocked by the excessively powerful winter anticyclone of central Eurasia. Rarely does a cyclonic storm entirely traverse the continent to the Pacific coast in wintertime (Fig. 5.12).

Eastward into the heart of central Eurasia the diminishing breadth of the mid-latitude mixed forest is an indication of its increasing remoteness from the moisture-bearing, moderating air of the North Atlantic. Toward the Urals the boreal forest on the north and the grassy steppelands on the south tend to converge, finally drawing together beyond the Urals in a broad transition zone of wooded steppe. East of the Urals the mixed forest appears only in scattered patches, and it finally disappears among the mountains of central Asia.

Mid-Latitude Mixed Forest in East Asia

Far to the eastward the mixed forest region reappears in southeastern Siberia, Korea, China, and Japan, where its general distribution is farther south than in western Eurasia. Here, on the Pacific side of the world's largest land mass, it reaches a broader latitudinal range and possesses a richer variety of species than anywhere else in the world (Fig. 12.4).

Merging with the boreal forest in southeastern Siberia, it extends from the lower Amur valley for nearly 2000 miles to the hill lands of south China, where it mingles with the mainly tropical and subtropical vegetation that predominates along the south China coast. One may think of the Nan Ling Mountains, north of the Si Kiang valley, as marking the approximate dividing zone between the mixed forest and the subtropical and tropical region of south China. Having a north–south span from about 52° to 25°, nearly 10 degrees greater than in eastern North America (where it is about 48° to 30°), the region occupies a greatly varied terrain that, unlike other mixed forest sections

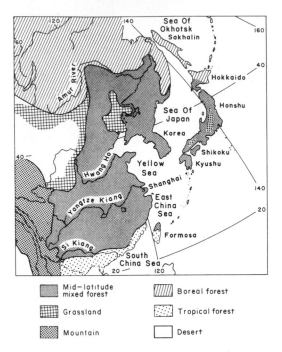

Mid–latitude mixed forest
Grassland
Mountain
Boreal forest
Tropical forest
Desert

Figure 12.4. Mid-latitude mixed forest in east Asia.

in the northern hemisphere, has never been modified by continental glaciation.

PLANT LIFE. The variety of species is impressive. More than two thousand deciduous and coniferous tree species are known in China alone, compared with some two hundred in eastern North America and eighty important species in western Europe. Even more remarkable is the presence of at least 1100 of largely the same species in Japan, an area of around 142,000 square miles, smaller than the state of Montana.

Almost all the important genera known in North America and western Eurasia are found here. Many species endemic here have been introduced to the temperate zones to the west and have long been as familiar to Americans and Europeans as their native vegetation: weeping willow (*Salix babylonica*), ailanthus, or tree of heaven (*Ailanthus altissima*), white mulberry (*Morus alba*), ginkgo (*Ginkgo biloba*), Chinese elm (*Ulmus parvifolia*), Japanese maple (*Acer palmatum*), and others.[1] A host of flowering

[1] Perhaps not so familiar are Tallowtree, Siberian elm, Chinese parasoltree, Royal Paulownia, Amur corktree, Chinese scholartree, and panicled goldenrain.

shrubs and succulent plants, too numerous to mention here but long familiar to American gardeners, originated in the temperate regions of China and Japan and have been brought into the hospitable environments of western Eurasia and eastern North America over the past several hundred years.

Little of the original temperate forest remains in east Asia today. These heavily populated areas have been occupied for centuries by a diligent agricultural people who long ago cleared the woodland from the fertile plains for cultivation. The north China plain, one of the world's older regions of sedentary settlement, has been continuously cultivated for more than four thousand years. The composition and extent of the original vegetation is thus a matter of speculation, based upon the study of ancient descriptions, remote relict stands, and a thin distribution of village and roadside plant growth. Only in the less accessible mountain areas that have resisted complete deforestation does one now find persistent tracts of wooded country. In China these are mainly in the southwest in the tributary watersheds of the Yangtze and Si rivers, in the northeast in Manchuria, in the contiguous mountain country of southeastern Siberia and Korea, and in the mountainous islands of Japan. The peninsula of Korea and the four main islands of Japan are largely mountainous, with the result that some two thirds or more of each is uncultivated and thus under forest or brushland.

Mid-latitude mixed forest occupies most of the central Amur valley from the approximate locality of Blagoveshensk to the vicinity of Komsomolsk, about 150 miles from Tatar Strait. Mantling the lower slopes of the Bureya Mountains on the north and the Lesser Khingans in Manchuria on the south, mixed forests of oak, maple, ash, linden, elm, birch, pine, spruce, and larch form the dominant vegetation up to elevations of around 2000 feet. Generally above 2000 feet coniferous elements of the boreal forest predominate. Mongolian oak (*Quercus mongolica*), Manchurian ash (*Fraxinus mandshurica*), Mono maple (*Acer mono*), Amur linden (*Tilia amurensis*), Amur cork (*Phillodendron amurense*), and Korean pine (*Pinus koraiensis*) are important species, along with a profusion of shrubby undergrowth and many vines of grape, honeysuckle, and magnolia. Manchurian walnut (*Juglans mandshurica*) is common on well-drained flood plains, and swamp vegetation and considerable stands of larch (*Larix dahurica*) occupy large tracts of less well-drained land.

From the middle Amur the mixed forest extends southward up the Ussuri valley and on the lower slopes of the coastal ranges to the Korean peninsula, along whose extreme south coast it merges with a narrow band of subtropical evergreen broadleaf forest. Southwestward up the Sungari it expands into the interior basin of central Manchuria, where it all but encircles a broad, grassy lowland of virtually treeless mid-latitude prairie and steppe. Remaining generally below altitudes of from 2500 to 3000 feet in the Sikhote-Alin Range northeast of Vladivostok, the Chang Pai Mountains north of Korea, the Lesser Khingan of northern Manchuria, and the Greater Khingan Mountains of northwestern Manchuria, the forest becomes more dominantly deciduous with increasing distance southward. The many species of oak, along with ash, birch, and elm, outnumber others wherever the forest has endured, except that pine, spruce, hemlock, larch, and fir are important at higher elevations well into the central part of the region, at least as far south as the Tsing Ling Mountains. South of this important mountain barrier, which lies between the valleys of Hwang Ho and the Yangtze Kiang, oak, maple, poplar, laurel, chestnut (*Castanopsis spp.*), boxwood (*Buxus spp.*), tulip (*Liriodendron chinense*), locust (*Gleditsia* and *Gymnocladus spp.*), and softwoods of pine, cypress (*Chamaecyparis spp.*), and cedar (*Libocedrus spp.*) are among the principal species. Chinese fir (*Cunninghamia lanceolata*), considered the most valuable tree in China, appears widely in the southernmost part of the mixed forest region.[2]

Among the south China hills between the valleys of the Yangtze Kiang and the Si Kiang the mid-latitude mixed forest of deciduous broadleaf and evergreen needleleaf trees intermingles with a subtropical vegetation in which evergreen broadleaf plants, including oaks, pine, lichee (*Litchi chinensis*), camphor (*Cinnamomum camphora*), palm, banyan, tree fern, and bamboo are present in great profusion. In general composition, the subtropical vegetation

of southern Korea and the islands of Kyushu, Shikoku, and southern Honshu in Japan is similar, and similar in external appearance and internal variety to the subtropical forests of northern Florida, parts of southern Europe, the Caucasus, and the Caspian littoral of Iran.

Most of Korea is occupied by temperate forests, the proportion increasing southward from the Chang Pai Mountains, which rise rather steeply from the Pacific coast to heights of more than a mile and a half above the sea. On the seaward slopes of this lofty range the mixed forest is rarely seen beyond 1800 feet above sea level, but as one proceeds southward, almost continuous stands of oak (*Quercus glandulifera*, *Quercus dentata*, *Quercus acutissima*, and *Quercus variabilis*), Japanese red pine (*Pinus densiflora*), maple, linden, chestnut, walnut, poplar, and elm are found at increasingly higher elevations, reaching up to around 4500 feet in south Korea. Beyond these heights are detachments of boreal forest that include Yeddo spruce (*Picea jezoensis*), fir (*Abies nephrolepsis*), larch (*Larix koreana*), and pine (*Pinus Koraiensis*).

In Japan the mid-latitude mixed forest occupies the southwestern part of Hokkaido, which is otherwise a region of coniferous boreal forest, and most of Honshu north of the latitude of Tokyo (about 36°). In northern Honshu it begins to recede from both east and west coasts just south of Ishiomaki and Niigata respectively, and southward from these points is found chiefly on mountain slopes overlooking the coastal lowlands. The remainder of Honshu and most of Shikoku and Kyushu are dominantly evergreen broadleaf forests where live oak (*Quercus spp.*, *Lithocarpus spp.*, *Shiia spp.*), laurel, camphor, pine, momi fir (*Abies firma*), southern Japanese hemlock (*Tsuga sieboldii*), and sugi or cedarwood (*Cryptomeria japonica*) are important species. The vertical zoning of vegetation typical of mountain regions is again seen in the mountainous islands of Japan, where it is a conspicuous feature of the forest distribution. On Kyushu, southernmost of the four main islands, the mixed deciduous and evergreen forest is observed in discontinuous tracts above 2500 feet, from 2100 to 5000 feet in Shikoku, from about 1500 to 4000 feet in central Honshu. Subtropical evergreen forest prevails from its lower limits to sea level, from sea level to about 2800 feet in northern Honshu, and generally

---

[2] Bamboo, over four hundred species of which have been identified, is much more important, but it is a grass.

below 1500 feet in southwestern Hokkaido. Predominantly deciduous in type, these carefully preserved woodlands include beech, oak, maple, ash, chestnut, magnolia, walnut, alder, elm, cherry, birch, hinoki, Japanese cedar or cypress (*Chamaecyparis obtusa*), pine, Japanese larch (*Larix kaempferi*), fir, spruce, and hemlock.

THE MAINLAND CLIMATE. Before discussing the qualities of the atmosphere in the mid-latitude mixed forests of east Asia, it is necessary to take note of a number of important geographical circumstances.

Because the region lies approximately midway between the equator and the north pole, there is a mean easterly transport of air at altitudes far above the earth, from about 15,000 to 50,000 feet above sea level. The generally eastward flow of the north circumpolar whirl persists at high levels throughout the year, although at lower altitude and farther south in winter than in summer. (Compare Figures 4.10 and 4.11.) It embodies at frequent intervals those singularly high speed currents of the upper air described in Chapter 4 as the jet stream. These currents of concentrated eastward movement are common over southern China in winter, but in summertime are found chiefly over eastern Siberia and Manchuria.

A second meaningful circumstance is the location of the mixed forest region on the eastern side of the vast Eurasian continent. This is the world's largest land mass, and here it extends from within a few degrees of the equator to about 70°N., a distance of approximately 4000 miles. It stretches away to the westward for some 7000 miles. These two conditions—the mean easterly flow of the upper air, and a location on the eastern, hence lee, side of Eurasia—are of primary significance in the climate. Yearly weather patterns are strongly influenced by the seasonal changes that take place within the continental interior.

Another important geographical circumstance is the enormous area of the Eurasian land mass. Because of its vast dimensions, much of the continental interior lies remote from the influence of the sea. The qualities of the atmosphere over most of central Eurasia are primarily controlled by the periodic increase and decrease of solar radiation that produces excessive heating in summer and excessive cooling in winter. Nonperiodic occurrences, particularly in the form of cyclonic storms, are of negligible importance over most of the interior. The weather variety occurring from the alternate passage of cyclones and anticyclones is a minor feature of the climate, in contrast with the mixed forests of eastern North America and western Eurasia, where rain-bearing cyclones alternating with dry anticyclones are important climatic features. Thus, we find that the main feature of the mixed forest climate in east Asia is a reasonably regular, monsoonlike, periodic shift in circulation each year. During the winter months when strong anticyclonic conditions prevail over the interior, a generally offshore, southward flow of cold, dry air takes place (Fig. 4.2), whereas in summer, when the continent is warmed excessively, the North Pacific anticyclone expands westward over the edge of the land mass to bring a generally onshore, northward flow of moist air into the region (Fig. 4.3).

A fourth geographic condition of some importance is the presence of many tremendously high mountain ranges in central Asia that block the movement of air near the earth's surface, uplifting, deflecting, and adiabatically modifying the air that moves over them. Many snow-capped peaks in the Himalayas tower above 25,000 feet, fringing the southern margins of the huge, lofty pleatau of Tibet, which averages more than 2 miles above sea level. Northward from Tibet an almost unbroken series of magnificent mountain systems stretches toward Siberia, including the Altyn Tagh, the Pamirs, and the Tien Shan, embracing the Tarim basin and thrusting many a snow-topped peak to 20,000 feet or more, and the Altai Mountains of Outer Mongolia and southern Siberia, rising to more than 15,000 feet in many places. From the high mountain systems of the interior to the Pacific coast, the surface of the east Asiatic mainland descends in a disordered array of lower mountains, extensive plateaus, elevated basins, and broad, low-lying plains, to the level of the sea.

South of the Yangtze Kiang, broken hill country, with many ridges rising to elevations of more than 5000 feet, extends to the shores of the East China Sea, ending in a narrow, crenelated coastal plain. In the upper Yangtze valley, the Red Basin of Szechwan, at 1500 to 3000 feet above sea level, is almost entirely surrounded by mountains. On the west are the towering, snow-capped heights of eastern Tibet, on the south the Yunnan plateau, toward the east the

TABLE 12–2
Climatic Data for Mid-Latitude Mixed Forest Stations in East Asia
(Temp., °F; Rainfall, In.)

Station	Lat.	El. in Ft		Jan.	Feb.	Mar.	Apr.	May	Jun.	Jul.	Aug.	Sep.	Oct.	Nov.	Dec.	Year
Blagoveshensk, U.S.S.R.	50°10'	440	T	-12	-1	15	36	51	63	70	66	54	35	12	-7	
			R	0.1	0.1	0.3	0.9	1.6	3.3	4.4	4.5	2.7	0.7	0.3	0.1	19.0
Aigun, Manchuria	49°58'	446	T	-14	5	13	37	51	63	69	67	53	37	11	-11	
			R	0.1	0.1	0.2	0.3	1.2	3.6	3.9	5.3	3.1	0.8	0.6	0.2	19.4
Mukden, Manchuria	41°45'	144	T	9	14	28	46	60	70	76	74	62	48	29	14	
			R	0.2	0.2	0.8	1.1	2.3	3.6	6.4	6.1	3.0	1.6	0.9	0.3	26.6
Peiping, China	39°54'	361	T	24	29	41	57	68	76	79	77	68	55	39	27	
			R	0.1	0.2	0.3	0.6	1.3	3.3	9.8	5.7	2.3	0.7	0.3	0.1	24.7
Kaifeng, China	34°48'	328	T	30	37	47	58	70	79	83	79	70	60	47	36	
			R	2.7	1.8	1.8	5.5	3.9	3.9	7.9	7.1	3.9	2.8	2.5	2.8	46.6
Chungking, China	29°38'	754	T	48	50	58	67	74	79	84	85	76	67	59	50	
			R	0.7	0.8	1.5	3.9	5.7	7.2	5.5	5.0	5.8	4.3	1.9	0.8	43.1
Vladivostok, U.S.S.R.	43°07'	95	T	7	14	26	40	49	57	65	69	62	49	31	15	
			R	0.3	0.4	0.8	1.2	2.1	2.9	3.3	4.8	4.5	1.9	1.2	0.6	24.0
Inchon, Korea	37°29'	231	T	26	29	38	50	60	69	75	78	69	58	44	31	
			R	0.8	0.7	1.2	2.6	3.3	3.9	10.9	8.8	4.3	1.6	1.6	1.1	40.8
Tsingtao, China	36°05'	243	T	31	33	41	51	61	68	74	77	70	61	47	35	
			R	0.4	0.3	0.7	1.2	1.7	3.5	5.8	6.0	3.4	1.4	0.8	0.7	25.9
Shanghai, China	31°12'	23	T	40	41	48	58	67	75	82	83	75	65	54	44	
			R	1.9	2.3	3.3	3.7	3.7	7.1	5.8	5.6	5.1	2.8	2.0	1.4	44.8
Nanking, China	32°07'	52	T	38	40	47	58	69	76	82	82	74	64	52	41	
			R	1.6	1.9	2.6	3.9	3.2	6.5	7.8	4.3	3.3	1.7	1.6	1.4	40.0
Hankow, China	30°35'	118	T	40	43	50	62	71	80	85	85	77	67	55	43	
			R	1.8	1.9	3.6	5.8	7.0	9.0	7.0	4.1	3.0	3.1	1.9	1.2	49.4

Source: M. Y. Nuttonson, Ecological Crop Geography of China, International Agro–Climatological Series, Study No. 7, Washington, D.C., 1947.

Pa Shan and Wu Shan, rising to 5000 feet or more, and on the north is the Tsinling Shan, which at many points is more than 8000 feet in elevation. The Tsinling Shan is an important barrier not only to overland travel but to the northward and southward flow of air near the surface as well.

North of the Tsinling Shan and Tibet is the vast, interior Gobi Desert of Mongolia. Having a general elevation of 3000 feet or more, the Gobi Desert is bordered on the north by the complex mountains around Lake Baikal and the upper drainage of the Amur, rising at many points to heights of more than a mile and a half above sea level.

Farther east the valley of the lower Amur, the interior basin of Manchuria, the north China plain, and the lower Yangtze valley are separated, to some extent, from interior regions by low mountain ranges like the Greater Khingans of western Manchuria, the Jehol Mountains, and the Shensi and Shansi Mountains bordering the middle, south-flowing reaches of the Hwang Ho.

The complicated surface features of the east Asiatic mainland are to a large extent responsible for the climatic complexity that prevails within that region we have broadly termed the mid-latitude mixed forest.

Finally, the warm waters of the north-flowing Kuro Shio (Japan Current), the Pacific counterpart of the Atlantic Ocean's Gulf Stream, moderate air temperatures along the east China coast, the Pacific coast of Korea, and the islands of Japan (Fig. 6.11).

An assessment of the qualities of the atmosphere in the east Asiatic mixed forest region is hampered by a great scarcity of adequate weather data. Large segments of the region are without representative records of weather behavior, and the reliability and length of record at many stations are not satisfactory.

Most of the region on the mainland is distinguished from other segments of this region in the northern hemisphere by a yearly mean weather regime of strongly contrasting extremes. Summers are unusually warm for the latitude, and winters unusually cold. Most of the year's precipitation is concentrated in the six-month warm season of the year, and very little occurs in winter. A monsoon reversal of prevailing winds is a major feature of the climate as a whole.

Between the boreal forest margins in the Amur valley and the tropical environment of the south China coast the mean annual range of temperature decreases from around 85 degrees to less than 30 degrees, chiefly in consequence of the lessening severity of winter in the 2000-mile distance from north to south. At Chernyaevo it is 86 degrees, at Blagoveshensk 82, diminishing southward to 77 degrees at Harbin, 67 at Mukden, 55 at Peiping, 44 at Nanking, 39 at Kweilin, and 28 in subtropical Canton. These are inland stations at relatively low altitude. At places near the sea and inland stations a half mile or so above sea level values are somewhat lower. (See Table 12-2.)

The frost-free season is actually less than one hundred days in the Khingan Mountains of northwestern Manchuria, between 125 and 150 days in the middle Amur valley and along the lower Sungari and Ussuri rivers, increasing to about 175 days in southern Manchuria and the

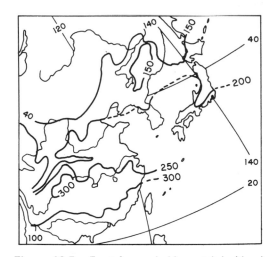

Figure 12.5. Frost-free period in east Asia (days).

north China plain around Peiping and Tientsin. From the lower reaches of the Hwang Ho to the Yangtze it increases from about two hundred days to 250, and to more than three hundred days in the valley of the Si Kiang in subtropical south China. The growing season is generally longer near the sea and shorter at higher elevations, compared with inland stations at low altitude (Fig. 12.5).

The Red Basin of Szechwan, a productive and heavily populated region, experiences a lower mean annual temperature range and a longer

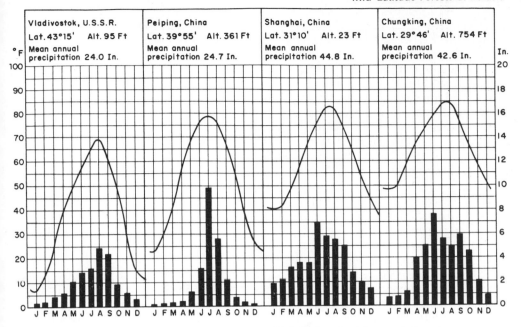

Figure 12.6. Temperature and precipitation at mid-latitude mixed forest stations in east Asia.

growing season than low-lying areas east of it, partly as a result of being sheltered by the Tsinling Shan from the severity of winter's outbursts of cold, dry continental air from the north. The mean annual temperature range at Chengtu is 34 degrees, at Chungking 35, and Ipin 37, compared with 49 degrees at Changte and 47 at Kiukang, farther east and in approximately the same latitude. The growing season is between three hundred and 350 days for low-lying areas within the Red Basin, compared with 250 to three hundred days in areas toward the east (Fig. 12.6).

Normal yearly precipitation increases southward from about 20 inches in the Amur valley to more than 60 inches in eastern portions of the south China hills. It amounts to less than 40 inches north of the Tsinling Shan barrier and more than 40 inches south of it. Actual amounts vary considerably from place to place, however, in consequence of the irregular relief pattern and the larger irregularities of the coast line, such as the peninsula of Korea and the Liaotung and Shantung peninsulas that embrace the northern part of the Yellow Sea. The distribution of statistical averages for specific localities can be observed in Table 12-2 and Figure 12.7.

The Amur, Ussuri, and Sungari valleys generally average around 20 inches, but the eastern mountain area of Manchuria receives between 25 and 30 inches, and most of Korea receives 50 inches or more. The territory around

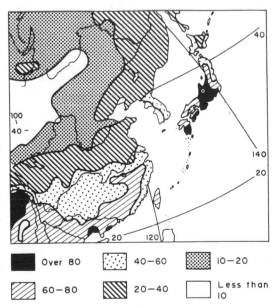

Figure 12.7. Mean annual precipitation in east Asia (inches).

Peiping receives between 20 and 25 inches, but from Peiping to the Hwang Ho less than 20 inches is common. Places near the coast, especially on the Shantung peninsula, receive around 25 inches or more. From the Hwang Ho southward annual amounts increase to 40 inches or more, and south of the Yangtze Kiang to more than 50 inches. A number of localities in eastern sections of south China normally report 80 inches or more, and this is also true of tropical situations along the coast, as at Hong Kong and Pakhoi.

The fact that a very large percentage of the annual precipitation occurs during the warmer season of the year is an important distinguishing feature of the mixed forest in east Asia. These are the rains of the summer monsoon, made possible by the prevailing onshore flow of moist oceanic air from the Pacific and the South China Sea and brought about chiefly by the frequent occurrence of cyclonic disturbances having a frontal origin. Thermal convection, weak frontal, and orographic uplift are also important in this season, thunderstorms accounting for about 10 per cent of the rainfall for the period in the south and up to 15 per cent or more north of the Hwang Ho. Along the southern and southeastern coasts the tropical cyclone (typhoon) accounts for a percentage of the annual rainfall, perhaps as much as 20 per cent of the total. Migrating cyclones are the principal source of the summer's rain, as they are of the scant precipitation in winter as well.

Summer. With the exception of the lower Yangtze valley and east coastal sections of south central China, most of the region receives at least 75 per cent of its annual precipitation from May 1 to October 31. Along the lower Yangtze, however, the summer concentration is less than elsewhere, for between 60 and 65 per cent of the year's precipitation occurs, and along the coast between Shanghai and Amoy it is about 67 per cent. Percentages vary from place to place under the influence of topography and exposure; Canton receives 75 per cent, and Chungking and Ichan receive 77 per cent during this period, with increasing values toward the north. Note that Peiping, Tientsin, and Chinwangtao receive more than 90 per cent of the year's precipitation during this period, as is also true of places farther north, like Harbin, Blagoveshensk, and Aigun. Even along the coast, where one naturally expects to find more conservative climatic qualities, 80 per cent or more of the year's precipitation occurs between May 1 and October 31 from the Shantung peninsula northward. Tsingtao receives 84 per cent, Inchon 81 per cent, Dairen 83 per cent, and Vladivostok 81 per cent.

Rainfall reliability, a vital matter in a predominantly agricultural region, is difficult to determine statistically in the absence of sufficient data. The wide range of rainfall intensity is indicated for some stations by the extremes of rain recorded for July. Along the Amur, Aigun has received as much as 11 inches and as little as 0.2 inches, Harbin has recorded a maximum of 13.9 inches and a minimum of 0.8 inches, Mukden 12.2 inches and 1.2 inches. The section of the east Asiatic mixed forest where greatest rainfall is most uncertain is the north China plain from the Shantung peninsula to the Jehol Mountains north of Peiping. Peiping has received as much as 32.5 inches of rain during July and as little as 0.3 inches, Tientsin 14.9 inches and 1.6 inches, and Tsinan 16.5 inches and 2.4 inches. As much as half the year's rainfall normally comes during July and August, often resulting from the heavy downpour of only a half-dozen passing storms. Occasionally up to 10 inches of rain have fallen in a single day. Floods are the result, unusually destructive here where streambeds in many places are many feet above the bordering plains, which slope downward from the river banks. When less than an inch of rain falls during a single summer month, drought becomes severe. Thus, the north China plain has been alternately threatened by an excess or a deficiency of adequate rainfall, making it, with a population always near the limit of the land's capacity to support, one of the major disaster regions of the Orient. South of the Shantung peninsula and the Tsinling Shan divide annual precipitation is considerably more reliable. The most uniform yearly distribution is along the lower Yangtze valley from near Changsha to Hangchow on the coast.

Heaviest monthly rains occur somewhat earlier in the season over southern sections where the monsoon first begins to gain strength. Hence, June is commonly the rainiest month from near Hankow and Wuhu on the lower Yangtze Kiang southward. The very heavy rains that accompany the hot, humid, equatorial air and the heavily depressing effect of leaden skies in June are called the Plum rains, as they are said to occur at the ripening of plums. July is the wettest month north as far as the Sungari River valley, but along the middle Amur and the coast north of Wonsan, Korea, August is the wettest month. The August rainfall maximum coincides with the August maximum of cyclogenesis in northern Manchuria, an area where cyclonic storms originate, frequently entering the Bering Sea, strengthening there, but weakening later as they move along the Arctic shores of North America. Along a short section of China's coast between Hangchow and Foochow two periods of increased rainfall intensity normally occur. It is here that the late summer typhoons play a more substantial role in bringing rain to the mainland, although they are not considered to add appreciably to the total annual precipitation of inland stations very far from the sea.

With the sizable increase of moisture supply during summer, cloudiness and relative humidity are greater over interior sections. In some coastal sections advective fog also increases during summer, but the distribution is quite irregular.

The summer monsoon brings a predominantly northward flow of moist equatorial air from the South China Sea and the open Pacific (Fig. 4.3). Prevailing winds are onshore, responding to the pressure gradient between the expanded North Pacific High and the lower barometric values of the strongly heated interior. Mean barometric values are generally less than 1005 millibars over land and more than 1010 millibars over the western Pacific. The resulting winds are not nearly as strong nor as steady as those that respond to the very much steeper pressure gradients of wintertime. Predominantly from the southwest along the south coast as far north as Formosa, they become more southerly along the coast of the East China Sea, shifting to southeasterly around the Shantung peninsula, Korea, and southeastern Siberia.

In summertime the sun-warmed surface of interior east Asia gives rise to high atmospheric temperatures that are augmented by the import of warm, dry air from farther west. The vast, summer-heated regions of central Asia supply the atmosphere with large amounts of highly heated air, which, when transported eastward across the intervening mountain

heights toward the Pacific, is further warmed adiabatically as it descends to lower levels.

Highest mean summer temperatures are usually reached during July at most inland stations in the mixed forest region, with the exception of places at higher altitude like Chungking, where the warmest month is August. Along the coast north of Shanghai August is usually the warmest month, as at Tsingtao, Dairen, Antung, all of coastal Korea, and southeastern Siberia. At Vladivostok the statistical mean for August is 69.1° in contrast to 64.6° for July. From Shanghai southward along the coast, and in fact at a number of inland stations south of the Tsinling Shan and the Shantung peninsula, the normal mean temperatures for July and August are about equally high. At Canton mean statistical values are 82.8° and 82.9° for July and August respectively, at Hankow 85.4° and 85.4°, Shanghai 80.2° and 80.2°, Kiukiang 85.3° and 85.3°, Ichang 84.2° and 84.2°, and Changsha 86.4° and 86.4°.

As these values suggest, low-lying areas south of the Shantung peninsula and the Tsinling Shan (Fig. 12.8), experience temperatures during the

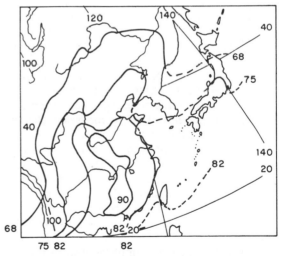

Figure 12.8. Mean July temperature in east Asia (°F).

warmest summer months in the middle 80s; north of the Shantung peninsula the warmest month averages in the high 70s, Peiping averaging 79°, Mukden 78°, Dairen and Antung 77°, and Changchun 75°. In the lower Amur and Ussuri valleys values average between 68 and

70°, and from Vladivostok northward along the coast 69° or less.

The mean daily temperature range is considerably greater at inland stations than along the coast, where it is between 12 and 14 degrees. Absolute maxima of more than 100° have been recorded at most interior stations from Peiping southward. High summer temperatures at Peiping have reached 107°, at Kaifeng 113°, at Ichang and Chungking 111°, at Changsha 105°, and at Kweilin 103°. In the lower Yangtze valley the thermometer frequently rises to 100° or more during summer, more so than in sections farther north, indicating the intensity of summer's heat in the more southerly portions of the mixed forest region.

The change from summer to winter takes place more rapidly over the east Asiatic mainland than in any other section of the mid-latitude mixed forest. Autumn comes on earlier and more rapidly in the Amur valley and interior Manchuria than in more southerly sections. There September temperatures average from 10 to 15 degrees lower than those of August, and from the north China plain southward the monthly change is between 6 and 8 degrees. October in the north is from 16 to 19 degrees colder than September, and the change from October to November—from 20 to 25 degrees—is the greatest of all during this season. Aigun is 25.4 degrees and Hailar is 25.6 degrees colder in November than in October. Farther south the change is between 14 and 18 degrees in the same period. Coastal stations, of course, experience a more moderate change into the cold, dry season of winter.

Autumn is considered by some to be the pleasantest time of the year throughout most of the region. Skies are clear, the land is still warm, and the frequency of cyclonic storms has diminished to a yearly minimum.

Winter. During the winter months the daily net loss of heat from the surface of a large land area such as northern interior Asia results in excessive cooling of enormous volumes of air that tend to move outward and downward into warmer surrounding areas. Atmospheric pressure increases to its greatest value in this season, and mean barometric readings of 1036 millibars are repeatedly observed over the territory south of Lake Baikal. From this intensely developed anticyclone clear, cold, dry surface air makes its chief escape eastward

toward the Pacific, where mean winter barometric values average around 1010 millibars not far from the east Asiatic coast. Surface wind velocities in northern sections of the mixed forest are commonly double the values of summertime onshore winds. Northward from the Yellow Sea and Korea, the prevailing wind direction is northwest; south of here it is chiefly northeast (Fig. 4.2).

The dominantly eastward flow of surface air in winter is augmented most of the time by the strong easterly movement of upper air currents, which at this season are observable from around 10,000 feet upward.

December, January, and February are the heart of the winter season. A very marked difference between northern and southern sections in winter is one of the striking qualities of the mixed forest region on the east Asiatic mainland. Over the north China plain temperatures during these three months are below freezing. In interior Manchuria, however, and the valleys of the lower Amur, Sungari, and Ussuri rivers, and also in northern interior Korea, average below-freezing temperatures prevail for the five months from November through March. South of the Shantung peninsula and the Tsinling Shan mean monthly temperatures are above freezing, but the thermometer frequently drops below 32°, and frosts and occasional snow are normal occurrences of winter.

January is usually the coldest month, except along the coast from Foochow southward, where the fullness of winter is delayed until February by the slow cooling of the South China Sea. Mean January temperatures are below zero at many places in northern parts of the region (Fig. 12.9). In the Amur valley Blagoveshensk averages −12°, Aigun −14°, and Khabarovsk −10°; in interior Manchuria, Hailar averages −19°, Tsitsihar −5°, and Harbin −4°. Tyukotin, in the steep-sided valley of the Upper Yalu in northern Korea, averages −6°. Most localities on the north China plain average between 25° and 30°. From the Shantung peninsula, where the coldest winter month averages around 30°, south to the lower Yangtze valley, mean January temperatures increase to about 40°. Mean January temperatures in the middle 40s suggest the mildness of winters in the south China hills. This is also true in Czechwan, where Chengtu and Ipiir, with 44°, and Chungking, with 49°,

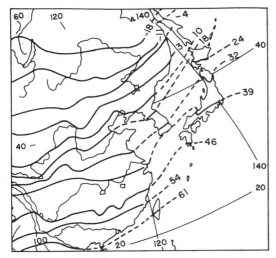

Figure 12.9. Mean January temperatures in east Asia (°F).

represent the general temperate situation of the sheltered valleys of the Red Basin.

Coastal stations experience milder winters, but nearly all points bordering the Yellow Sea, including Tsingtao, Chinwangtao, Antung, Inchon, and Taikyu, are beyond the moderating influence of the Kuro Shio and experience average temperatures well below freezing in January. Temperatures over the entire south coastal region of Korea, however, remain well above freezing during the coldest month (Fig. 12.6).

Extreme minima of −41° at Blagoveshensk, −46° at Khabarovsk, and −44° at Aigun have been observed, and slightly less severe extremes are reported for Harbin (−40°), Mukden (−27°), Kamen Ribolov (−33°), and Kinkow (−24°). Peiping and other stations on the north China plain have recorded extreme values of a few degrees below zero, but such low readings are very rare south of the Shantung peninsula and the Tsinling Shan. Freezing temperatures have affected south China all the way to the shores of the South China Sea, although this is a rare occurrence along the coast.

Winter north of the Tsinling Shan and the Shantung peninsula is not only very cold but also unusually dry. The actual moisture content of the air flowing out of the frost-bound interior is much lower than that of the oceanic air brought in during the summer. At most inland stations in the north from December through February less than 1 inch of precipitation is

normally received, and either January or February is statistically the driest month. Precipitation is commonly in the form of snow, and occasional blizzards add to the rigors of the season. Although clear skies prevail through most of the winter, the air is frequently filled with dust raised from the desert expanses of interior Sinkiang and Mongolia, swept down over the basin of Manchuria and the north China plain. To a certain extent the overworked soils of these regions are replenished in this way, but the dust-laden air is a menace to health, and in being carried far out to sea, lowers the visibility for navigators many miles from the coast.

Coastal areas in the north and nearly all the region south of the Shantung peninsula are favored by more plentiful precipitation in wintertime, which is partly due to the fairly frequent occurrence of cyclonic storms along the coastal meeting ground of the cold continental polar air masses with warmer, more humid air over the sea. Cyclonic disturbances originate with considerable frequency over the coastal waters of southern Japan in wintertime, and also in the upper Yangtze valley, the latter storms following a fairly normal path down the valley to the sea. At least 1 inch of rain is received each winter month, on the average, in southern sections of the mixed forest, usually from the passage of shallow depressions originating as part of the recurrent disturbances along the polar front. During winter this variable zone of contact between continental polar and maritime tropical air masses is displaced equatorward to a mean position south of the Tsinling divide.

Cyclonic activity, the main source of precipitation, increases with the approach of spring, reaching a maximum usually in March, the month when the winter monsoon begins to weaken. Snow persists in northern areas, continuing in Manchuria and along the lower Amur until around the middle of May.

JAPAN. It will be expedient to consider the climates of the four main islands as a whole. This will take us from the interesting transition of boreal forest on most of Hokkaido into mid-latitude mixed forest over southwestern Hokkaido and northern Honshu, and then into the humid subtropical environment of the remainder (Fig. 12.10). On the four main islands we find, as on the mainland, that the rhythmic

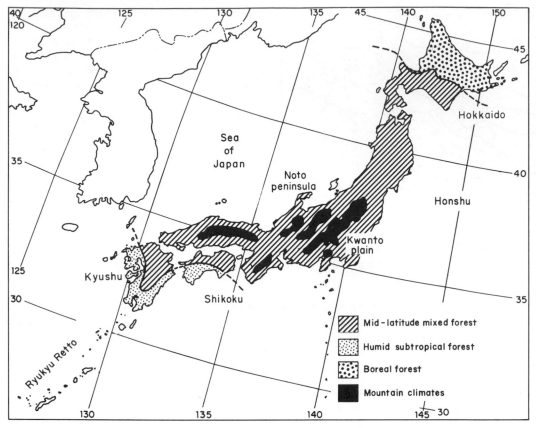

Figure 12.10. Mid-latitude mixed forest and contiguous climates in Japan.

shift of the monsoon circulation plays a leading role in the mean weather. But a number of additional features must be considered. Japan is surrounded by the sea, which exerts a moderating effect on all events of the weather. The islands lie, for the most part, several hundred miles from the continental shores. Southwestern Honshu, nearest the mainland, is 100 miles from Korea. The northern tip of Hokkaido is about 150 miles from the Siberian coast. Japan is thus well within the realm of oceanic influence and appreciably removed from the direct effects of continental influence. These are chiefly mountainous islands, rising to more than a mile above sea level in many places on every island, and to 2 miles above the sea in central Honshu. The distance from southern Kyushu to the northern tip of Hokkaido is a bit more than 1000 miles, only about half the span from the Amur valley to the Nan Ling Mountains in south China. The warm waters of the Kuro Shio modify the tempera-

ture of nearly all the coastal lowlands, giving most of populated Japan a much more temperate climate than sections of the mainland within the same latitudes.

The prevailing effect of the marine environment is reflected in the normal yearly weather of most of Japan. The mean annual temperature range in the north is generally around 45 degrees, diminishing to around 35 degrees in southern sections, as contrasted with 75 degrees or more in central Manchuria and 55 degrees or more on the north China plain, areas within equivalent latitudes. Slightly cooler summers and considerably milder winters make the difference. The range between extreme maxima and minima is also appreciably lower in Japan.

The frost-free season on most coastal sections of Hokkaido is more than 150 days, and in northern Honshu more than 175 days, compared with 125 to 150 days in central Manchuria. From central Honshu southward the growing season increases in length from around two hundred to more than 250 days over most of lowland Shikoku and Kyushu, in contrast to 175 to two hundred days over the north China plain. Thus, latitude for latitude, Japan enjoys nearly a month more of growing weather each year (see Table 12-3).

Normal yearly rainfall over most of Japan is much greater than that over the mainland mixed forest areas, many stations reporting more than 100 inches annually. Even during the driest months less than 1 inch of rain is rarely reported. Mean annual rainfall increases from north to south, with lowest values of less than 35 inches applying to the north and south coastal sections of the taiga of east central Hokkaido, and more than 100 inches typical of the Pacific coasts of Kyushu and Shikoku and the west coastal area of central Honshu. High relative humidity prevails the year round nearly everywhere.

The intensities of annual rainfall, and also the yearly temperature range and the length of the frost-free season all vary considerably within very short distances. This is chiefly in consequence of the complex relief pattern, which includes a high mountainous interior, a number of relatively broad plains areas, innumerable coastal valleys, and interior depressions. The largest coastal plain area is the Kwanto plain, immediate hinterland of Tokyo, having an area of about 5000 square miles, approximately the size of the state of Connecticut (see Fig. 12.10 and Table 12-3). As an example of local weather variety, Takada, within 5 miles of the Sea of Japan in central Honshu, receives an average of 112.3 inches of annual rainfall, while Nagano, only about 35 miles inland and separated from it by a low mountain range—and thus subjected to a rain shadow effect—normally receives 39 inches, less than one third as much. Asahigawa, in the western interior of Hokkaido, has a mean annual temperature range of about 55 degrees, compared with about 41 degrees for Nemuro, facing the Pacific on the eastern end of the island.

Despite the ever-present influence of a marine environment, continental aspects are strongly developed everywhere except along the extreme south coasts of Kyushu, Shikoku, and Honshu. Evidence of this is found in a number of ways, among them the mean annual temperature range, which is rarely less than 35 degrees at any point. This is quite a bit more continental than the values over much of the southeastern coastal plain of the United States. Another continental aspect is the marked warm season increase in yearly precipitation, with the notable exception of the coast of central Honshu facing the Sea of Japan. Still another is the frequent cold of winter, for no part of Japan's four main islands has been spared entirely from freezing temperatures, although they are rare along the southern coasts.

Summer. August is the warmest month of summer in virtually every corner of Japan. Delayed by the thermal lag of the surrounding sea, August at most stations attains a mean temperature comparable with that of places at the same latitudes in eastern United States, where July is the warmest month.

Over most of Hokkaido August temperatures average between 65 and 70°, the lowest at Nemuro (63°), the highest at Hakodate (71°). Values are generally higher over most of northern Honshu, averaging between 75 and 80° on the lower side of this range near the sea, and on the higher side at inland locations. Temperatures tend to be higher on the west coast than on the east coast of northern Japan, for the warm Kuro Shio passes across the Sea of Japan, whereas the colder Oya Shio (Okhotsk Current) from the north affects the east coast. The mean daily range is also higher at inland stations. Extreme maximum temperatures of record are, on the whole, less than 100°, although at least one station on each of the four main islands has reported a value of 100° or slightly higher at least once.

The approach of summer is heralded about two months earlier in southern than in northern Japan. Cherry trees bloom in southern Kyushu late in March, but snow remains on the ground until nearly the end of May in central Hokkaido. Summer also lingers longer in the south, the first frosts usually occurring toward the end of November, almost two months after the thermometer has dipped below freezing in Hokkaido.

As the northward and northwestward flow of the expanding North Pacific anticyclonic circulation increases in strength and frequency, the monthly rainfall also increases along the southern and eastern coasts of Japan. From 65 to 70 per cent of the year's precipitation is received on the Pacific side of Japan from May 1

TABLE 12–3
Climatic Data for Mid-Latitude Mixed Forest Stations in Japan
(Temp., °F; Rainfall, In.)

Station	Lat.	El. in Ft		Jan.	Feb.	Mar.	Apr.	May	Jun.	Jul.	Aug.	Sep.	Oct.	Nov.	Dec.	Year
Asahigawa, Hokkaido	43°47'	370	T	14	16	25	39	51	60	68	69	59	46	34	22	
			R	2.9	2.2	2.1	2.0	2.6	3.1	4.6	4.9	5.7	4.3	4.4	4.1	42.9
Hakodate, Hokkaido	41°17'	10	T	26	28	33	43	51	58	66	71	64	54	42	31	
			R	2.7	2.5	2.6	2.7	3.4	3.5	5.4	5.1	6.8	4.6	4.2	3.3	46.8
Akita, Honshu	39°43'	33	T	29	30	35	47	56	65	72	75	67	55	44	34	
			R	5.2	4.1	4.0	4.5	4.4	4.7	7.7	7.0	7.9	7.0	7.6	6.4	70.5
Niigata, Honshu	37°55'	84	T	35	35	40	50	58	67	75	78	70	59	49	39	
			R	7.1	5.1	4.4	4.1	3.6	4.2	6.5	4.3	7.2	6.5	7.8	9.0	70.1
Tokyo, Honshu	35°41'	19	T	38	39	45	55	62	69	76	78	72	61	51	42	
			R	2.3	3.0	4.3	5.2	5.9	6.7	5.6	7.1	10.1	7.9	3.5	2.2	63.8
Osaka, Honshu	34°39'	10	T	40	40	46	55	64	71	79	81	74	63	53	44	
			R	1.6	2.3	3.7	4.8	4.8	7.8	6.0	4.5	6.8	5.2	2.8	1.9	52.2
Nagasaki, Kyushu	32°44'	340	T	42	42	48	57	64	71	79	80	73	64	55	46	
			R	2.7	3.2	4.8	7.1	6.4	13.0	10.2	6.6	10.9	4.6	3.6	3.1	76.2
Kagoshima, Kyushu	31°34'	18	T	44	45	51	59	66	72	79	80	75	66	57	48	
			R	3.4	4.0	6.4	8.7	8.2	17.0	12.2	7.4	8.7	5.2	3.7	3.4	88.3

Source: M. Y. Nuttonson, *Agricultural Climatology of Japan*, International Agro-Climatological Series, Study No. 9, Washington, D.C., 1949.

to October 31. At most localities having a good exposure to the south, June is commonly the rainiest month of the year, as in southern Kyushu where, for example, Kagoshima normally receives 17 inches in June, and southwestern Honshu, where Shimonoseki at the western end and Wakayama at the eastern end of the Inland Sea receive 11.5 inches and 8.2 inches respectively. The cloudiness, humidity, and generally oppressive conditions accompanying the start of the warm season's heavy rains in southern Japan combine to create a period of depressing, gloomy weather called here, as in south China, the plum rains (*Bai-u*). Fortunately, in Japan a diurnal windshift, the familiar daytime sea breeze alternating with a nocturnal land breeze, relieves the unpleasantness of weather in early summer.

Elsewhere throughout Japan, with a single important exception, the summer monsoon brings a maximum of rain in September, when cyclones of tropical origin, the type that occasionally gain the intensity of the destructive typhoon, occur with greatest frequency. Thus, tropical cyclones rather than mid-latitude cyclones are responsible for the heaviest rains of the year in this region, although they combine with weak, slow-moving depressions originating over the Chinese mainland during the earlier part of the season. Typhoon rains at Tanabe in southern Honshu brought 35.4 inches on August 29, 1889, and at Nagasaki in western Kyushu, 3.5 inches of rain fell in one hour on September 5, 1923.

At many stations June provides a secondary maximum to September's primary maximum, both, however, occurring as part of the summer's concentration of yearly precipitation. Tokyo, for example, normally receives 10.1 inches in September and 6.7 inches in June. Along most of the Pacific seaboard from 45 to 50 per cent or more of the year's total precipitation occurs during the four-month period from June through September.

The single important exception referred to above is the section of central Honshu facing the Sea of Japan, where winter is the season of heaviest precipitation and December the wettest month of the year. This situation arises from frequent and heavy winter snowfalls along the coast on either side of the Noto peninsula, brought by the northwest winds of the winter monsoon, which are warmed and provided with moisture as they sweep across the 400–500 mile breadth of the Sea of Japan. Niigata, with 9 inches (water equivalent of snows, which, of course, total much greater depths) and Kanagawa and Fukui with 13.4 inches illustrate the normal precipitation amounts recorded for the maximum month of December. May is the driest month at these stations, when less than half the December amount is commonly received. Cloudiness and relative humidity are usually at a maximum during the season of heaviest precipitation, whatever the time of year.

The summer rainfall pattern is irregular at many places. Osaka, for example, has experienced a rainless period of forty-three days in the wet summer season when rain normally falls every third day of each month. Cyclonic activity, the main source of Japan's rainfall, is reasonably regular, as a rule, and migrating storms travel rather well-defined paths whose mean location is northeastward across some part of the four main islands and the Sea of Japan toward the Bering Sea. Orographic uplift and thermal convection are responsible for many of the local variations in rainfall intensity by rendering the moist oceanic air unstable in its progress over the land.

Winter. The transition from summer to winter takes place rather rapidly in the north, where frosts are experienced, as noted above, in late September or early October. Over most of Japan, where seasons change gradually from one to another, autumn is a fairly long period and, like spring, is considered a pleasant season. From September to November days become shorter, temperatures lower, and rains diminish over most of Japan. With southward displacement of mean mid-latitude storm tracks, increased cyclonic activity takes place over the East China Sea, and increased cyclogenesis occurs over the warm waters south of Japan. At this season tropical cyclone tracks are usually confined well to the south. By January two primary storm tracks have usually developed, one off the east coast of Hokkaido and the other in the East China Sea, converging south of Alaska in the region we recognize as the Aleutian Low.

January is the coldest month at most stations in Japan, but the effect of a marine environment means that February remains about as cold as January in a great many places. This is especially so in the mixed forest and subtropical portions of Japan. Note that Akita averages 29° in January and February, Niigita 35°, Kanazawa and Fujui 37°, and Osaka 40°. At a few localities in central Honshu February is the coldest month. The lowest January means are, of course, to be found in interior Hokkaido, Asahigawa recording 14° and Obihiro 13° for this month. January averages below freezing at every station in Hokkaido, and at many inland stations in Honshu as far south as the mountainous section west of the Kwanto plain. South of here, however, mean January values range between 35 and 40°. Most places in Shikoku and Kyushu average about 40° in January, except sheltered interior localities at higher elevation.

Extreme minimum temperatures are lowest in Hokkaido, Asahigawa having recorded − 42° and Obihiro − 37°. Subzero values are rare elsewhere, even in northern Honshu, but − 10° has been recorded as far south as Takayama in the central interior of I Ionshu, about 150 miles west of Tokyo. In Kyushu and Shikoku the extreme minimum of record is nowhere lower than 10°, and few stations have recorded less than 20°.

Winter being the driest season of the year over most of Japan, except, of course, for the west central part of Honshu, January is most commonly the month of least precipitation. The situation varies considerably from place to place, however. At Tottori, for example,

August is the driest month, with 4.2 inches preceding the wettest month, September, with 9.2 inches. The December normal is also 9.2 inches. In west central Honshu the spring months are usually driest.

Despite the lower amounts of winter, the number of days with precipitation is almost as great in winter as in summer in a great many places. The cloudy, damp, disagreeable weather of winter often is less frequently relieved by clear, sunny skies than the rainy periods of summer.

Snow is known everywhere on the four main islands and usually falls, at least briefly, a few times every winter, even in southern areas. It falls, on the average, on between fifteen and twenty days during winter in northern Kyushu and Shikoku, and with increasing frequency northward along the western coasts, normally appearing on thirty days at Hamada, seventy-one days at Niigata, and ninety-four days at Akita. Over most of northern Honshu and Hokkaido almost all the winter's precipitation falls as snow; Hakodate experiences 105 days of snowfall as a rule, Haboro 126 days. Snow usually lies on the ground all winter in these areas, commonly attaining depths of a foot or more, much more than this during a heavy blizzard. As much as 3 feet of snow have accumulated on western mountain slopes during a particularly severe blizzard in a single night.

References

BROOKS, C. E. P.: *The English Climate*, English University Press, Ltd., London, 1954.

EDLIN, H. L.: *British Woodland Trees*, B. T. Batsford, Ltd., London, 1945.

HADEN-GUEST, ed.: *A World Geography of Forest Resources*, The Ronald Press Company, New York, 1956.

HADLOW, L.: *Climate, Vegetation and Man*, The Philosophical Library, New York, 1953.

HESKE, F.: *German Forests*, Yale University Press, New Haven, 1938.

MANLEY, G.: *Climate and the British Scene*, Collins, London, 1952.

NUTTONSON, M. Y.: *Ecological Plant Geography of Albania, Its Agricultural Crops and Some North American Climatic Analogues*, International Agro-Climatological Series, Study No. 6. Washington, D.C., 1947.

————: *Ecological Crop Geography of China and Its Agro-Climatic Analogues in North America*, International Agro-Climatological Series, Study No. 7, Washington, D.C., 1947.

————: *Agricultural Climatology of Czechoslovakia and Its Agro-Climatic Analogues in North America*, International Agro-Climatological Series, Study No. 3, Washington, D.C., 1947.

————: *Ecological Crop Geography of Germany and Its Agro-Climatic Analogues in North America*, International Agro-Climatological Series, Study No. 8, Washington, D.C., 1949.

————: *Ecological Crop Geography of Greece and Its Agro-Climatic Analogues in North America*, International Agro-Climatological Series, Study No. 5, Washington, D.C., 1947.

————: *Agricultural Climatology of Japan and Its Agro-Climatic Analogues in North America*, International Agro-Climatological Series, Study No. 9, Washington, D.C., 1949.

————: *Agricultural Climatology of Poland and Its Agro-Climatic Analogues in North America*, International Agro-Climatological Series, Study No. 2, Washington, D.C., 1947.

————: *Agricultural Climatology of Yugoslavia and Its Agro-Climatic Analogues in North America*, International Agro-Climatological Series, Study No. 4, Washington, D.C., 1947.

U.S. Air Force, Weather Division: *Weather and Climate of China* (Report 890), 1945.

chapter 13

MEDITERRANEAN SCRUB WOODLAND IN THE NORTHERN HEMISPHERE

Unique among the mid-latitude forests and woodlands of the world is the mediterranean scrub woodland, whose climate is distinguished chiefly by its very warm, dry summers, its mild, wet winters, and a large amount of clear, sunny weather throughout the year. Broadly speaking, it is transitional from the humid forests on its poleward margins to the treeless steppes and deserts toward the equator.

It is mainly a coastal lowland climate, seldom found more than 100 miles from the sea, often much less, and normally at altitudes less than 2500 to 4000 feet above sea level. It is uniquely confined to west coastal situations on the world's major land masses, where it extends from about 30° to about 45°N. Lat. and from 30° to 35°S. Lat. Appearing most extensively along the shores of the Mediterranean Sea, a circumstance topologically responsible for its designation *mediterranean*, this climate is also found in five smaller, widely separated areas: central California, middle Chile, southwestern Africa, and the Perth and Adelaide districts of Australia (Fig. 13.1).

Vegetation is typically broadleaved evergreen, whose forest trees are commonly of low to moderate height, with broad, rounded crowns supported on short, heavy trunks having rather thick bark, and fed by deep and extensive root systems. Foliage usually consists of small leaves, often elliptical in outline, and not uncommonly provided with such drought-protective devices as a hard, shiny or waxy surface, hairs, thorns, and relatively few stomata. These features are necessary to plants that must endure warm, prolonged summers of little or no rain. Many areas also include a large number of taller broadleaved and needle-leaved forms. Trees are not always present, but when they are, they appear in scattered clumps or individually, separated by wide tracts of brushland of varying density, and occasionally of grassland. Except in unusual edaphic circumstances, vegetation of some kind is to be seen everywhere across the landscapes of the region.

The most widely characteristic vegetation of mediterranean regions is a shrubby thicket of woody plants, best known as maquis (chaparral in the United States, mallee in Australia).

The normal weather occurrences typical of a mediterranean climate are traceable to the annual changes in solar radiation, giving rise to periodic shifts of the mean pressure pattern and resultant wind fields of the general circulation. These periodic changes, described in Chapter 4, arise from the alternate increase and decrease of effective solar radiation received on either side of the equator from one end of the year to the other.

The heating of land surfaces in the summertime gives rise to a weakening of anticyclonic

238

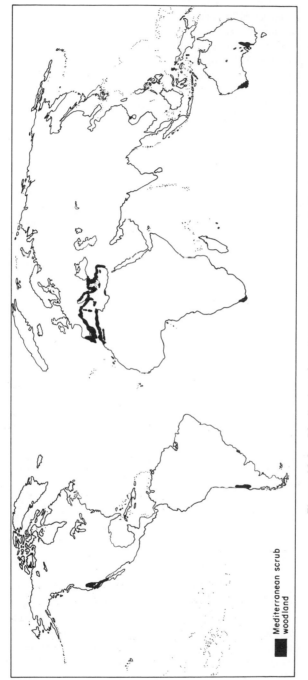

Figure 13.1. Distribution of mediterranean scrub woodland climates.

Mediterranean scrub
woodland

activity overland and a relative strengthening of those oceanic subtropical anticyclones that tend to persist over the warm waters of the sea in lower middle latitudes. Expanding eastward and poleward in summer, they are responsible for the dominantly clear skies, light, variable winds, and calms of mediterranean climatic areas at this season. The prevailing movement of surface air over these areas is equatorward. At the same time, the polar frontal zone of precipitating storms also moves poleward, with the result that precipitation is typically light or entirely lacking.

Winter brings a relative weakening of subtropical oceanic highs. Simultaneously, the polar frontal zone of storms shifts equatorward, providing mediterranean areas with fairly frequent rains that are the main source of the year's precipitation.

In spite of the yearly meridional shift of normal pressure patterns over the oceans, there is a tendency for surface air to flow constantly toward the equator the year round along the continental west coasts at lower middle latitudes. Thus, the predominant wind direction is roughly parallel to those coasts, diverging only in the zones of the trades relatively near the equator. The wind-driven ocean currents that move in response to this circulation in turn transport cool surface water into tropical latitudes, exerting a profound effect upon coastal weather. Coupled with the horizontal transport of cool surface water is the upwelling of still-cooler water from the ocean depths adjacent to the shoreline, where surface currents diverge from the coast.

Summers in general tend to be long and hot, temperatures even a short distance from the sea averaging between 70 and 80° for two months or more. Where coastal stations lie well exposed to the air moving shoreward over cool ocean currents, however, the warmest months average between 60 and 70° and are thus warm rather than hot. The growing season averages some three hundred or more days in length, depending chiefly upon latitude, and in a great many instances continues the year round, allowing the uninterrupted growing of a great variety of subtropical crops.

The sunny skies of summer are among the best-known characteristics of the mediterranean climate. For weeks on end the sun's bright rays blaze down from a nearly cloudless sky to warm and parch the earth beneath. In this region a much higher percentage of possible sunshine is typical than of any other mid-latitude forest climate. Twice as many hours of sunshine are recorded here than in the very much wetter, cloudier coastal evergreen forests at higher latitude. The very edge of the sea is an exception, for in many such localities fogs are a frequent feature of early morning weather, reducing the number of sunny hours on many days of the year.

A high percentage of possible sunshine prevails even in winter, the season of rain, for precipitating storms tend to be short and intense, approaching rather rapidly, releasing heavy showers during their passage, and then moving on to be replaced by fairly long periods of clear weather. Something like 65 to 75 per cent of yearly rainfall occurs during the winter. Yearly totals average from about 15 to 35 inches, with considerable variation from place to place and from year to year. Snow is rare in the low-lying mediterranean areas, although it is often a frequent occurrence in nearby mountain country and there may accumulate to a depth of several feet and lie unmelted through the entire winter. At this season cloudiness is greatly increased, and relative humidity also reaches a maximum nearly everywhere.

Killing frosts are infrequent, are about as rare as snowfall, for the coldest month in most mediterranean areas commonly averages above 40°, often even milder.

The transitional nature of this region is expressed in the annual regime of mean weather. In summer the region takes on the aspects of desert lands equatorward from it, losing much of its winter greenness to assume an appearance of brownish, dusty dessication, and frequently to experience the large daily range of temperature typical of desert situations. Thermometers often register more than 100° under cloudless, sun-bright skies, only to drop rapidly after sunset to 65 or 75°, producing a daily range of 30 to 35 degrees. In winter the region comes under a distinctly marine set of influences, with increased cloudiness and relative humidity and a lowering of the daily temperature range to 15 or 20 degrees. These are qualities shared with the humid forest regions poleward of most mediterranean areas.

Mediterranean scrub woodland areas are far from uniform, however, and as they are widely separated and thus related to separate systems of mean weather activity, they possess certain points of difference, to which must be added their many points of contrast in geographical detail. Hence, each requires a separate description and analysis.

The Mediterranean Sea Region

The Mediterranean Sea, lying between north Africa and southern Europe from about 30 to 45°N. Lat., is influenced along its entire coastline by the seasonal oscillations between dry anticyclonic and wet cyclonic weather. Because of its deep indentations, the estimated length of this coastline is more than 8000 miles, most of which, except for the northwestern shores of the Adriatic and the desert coast of Egypt and Libya, possesses the climate for which the region is famous. Adding to this the scores of islands in the Mediterranean and along the Atlantic shores of Portugal and Morocco, the region is many times larger than any of its climatic counterparts elsewhere in the world. (See Fig. 13.2.)

A number of important features contribute to the variety and extent of the mediterranean climate in this part of the world. The large, ice-free Mediterranean Sea reaches eastward for some 2400 miles from the Atlantic, within latitudes dominated by anticyclonic weather in summer and by a succession of frontal disturbances in winter. Secondly, as most precipitating storms travel eastward, the western windward shores of land areas have the better exposure to advancing storms. Thirdly, several sizable peninsulas and many large islands lie athwart the main paths of migrating weather disturbances. Finally, the varied topography of the lands bordering the Mediterranean includes mountains, plateaus, and rolling hills that often reach to the water's edge; the intervening low-lying plains are thus scattered and discontinuous, only a few of them more than a few hundred square miles in area.

The combined effect of these features gives rise to certain general characteristics of climate. The Mediterranean Sea exerts a cooling effect upon air masses in summer and is responsible

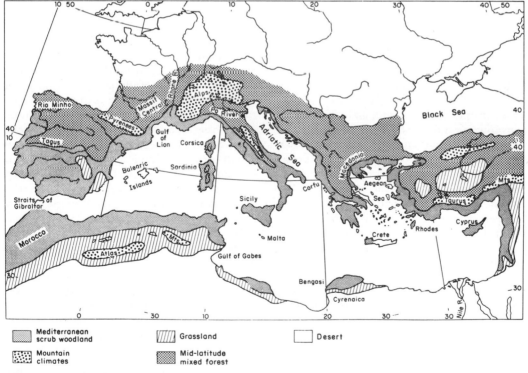

Figure 13.2. Mediterranean scrub woodland and contiguous climates in the Mediterranean Basin.

Figure 13.3. Scrub woodland aspect near Valencia, Spain. [American Geographical Society photo]

for the welcome sea breeze that is often a daily feature of its sun-bathed shores. A source of warmth in winter, the sea moderates the severity of the season and also acts as an important source of nourishment for migrating storms. Its great length allows rain-bearing disturbances to continue eastward to the Levantine coast of southwest Asia and often beyond. Land areas in the paths of such storms tend to receive more precipitation on their western than on their eastern leeward shores. This condition is rendered more pronounced by the rugged relief of peninsular and island interiors, for the loftier slopes intercept rain-bearing winds, creating a rain shadow in the lee. Land of higher elevation leads to a vertical zoning of climates in mountainous areas. On the higher, cooler slopes, generally above 2500 feet, the mixed forest climate of northwest Europe, with summer rain, is found, and when mountains tower a mile or so above the sea, these in turn give way to even cooler climates. Where rugged topography extends to the water's edge, projecting headlands and promontories in many instances confine the strictly mediterranean climate to a discontinuous scattering of small embayments, differing from one another and from the broader stretches of coastal lowland in one or more details of the mean climatic situation.

In a more general way, from north to south and from west to east the region becomes sunnier, the temperatures of any season higher, the frequency of storms less, and mean annual rainfall amounts lower. Such a loose generalization cannot be applied to particular localities, for the great irregularity of land and water distribution, along with marked contrasts in topography, create an almost indeterminate variety of deviations from the broader pattern of the mediterranean climate.

The Mediterranean Sea may be divided, around Sicily, Malta, and Tunisia, into eastern and western sections. Such a distinction is geographically and climatologically sound, for each section possesses reasonably discrete terrestrial and atmospheric characteristics and relationships.

PLANT LIFE. The distinctive vegetation of the Mediterranean basin is far from simple or uniform in nature. Many varieties of plant associations and a wide assortment of locally dominant species are characteristic. This is due partly to the geographical advantage of a location beyond the reach of destructively expanding ice sheets from the far north during prehistoric periods of glaciation, thus allowing a broad variety of plant forms to persist here in contrast to northwestern and central Europe, where vegetation was repeatedly wiped out. More than 250 genera are found here, as many as half of them endemic. Over twenty species of pine and over thirty species of oak are known. Mediterranean plant associations also owe their great variety to the complex configuration of the coastlines, uneven topography, varieties of soils, and local differences in the seasonal qualities of mean weather in the Mediterranean basin.

Three readily recognizable types of vegetation are widespread and dominant: scrub woodland, maquis, and garigue.[1]

The scrub woodland, dominated by forest trees, is (Fig. 13.3) typically rather open, its low-

[1] Much of the material on plant associations comes from M. Rikli, *Das Pflanzenkleid der Mittelmeerländer*, 3 vols., Verlag Hans Huber, Bern, 1943.

crowned trees standing individually or in scattered clumps and averaging a height between 30 and 40 feet, but occasionally more than 50 feet. It is chiefly represented by olive, oak, and pine. Three species can be found over the entire extent of the region: olive (*Olea europea*), evergreen oak (*Quercus coccifera*), and Aleppo pine (*Pinus halepensis*), in addition to less widely distributed species of oak and pine, along with cypress, sweet chestnut, pistachio, alder, acacia, arbutus, tamarisk, and zizyphus. Many mediterranean plants, although dominant within the region, are frequently found outside it as subordinate members of other climax associations. Although representative trees, however sparsely distributed, can be seen within the entire region, the percentage of land they actually occupy is considerably less than that occupied by maquis.

Maquis is typically a dense, shrubby evergreen type of vegetation, from about 6 to 12 feet in height, with a foliage of small, hard-surfaced leaves and frequently an impenetrable tangle of tough, woody branches and stems (Fig. 13.4). This is often considered to be the most characteristic climax vegetation of the Mediterranean basin. The most typical species are heath (*Erica arborea*), the strawberry tree (*Arbutus Unedo*), and rockrose (*Cistus spp.*, especially *Cistus monspeliensis* and *Cistus salviifolius*), although the chaste tree (*Vitex Agnus castus*), oleander (*Nerium oleander*), and sweet bay (*Laurus nobilis*) are also highly representative and widespread. Where the tall, woody shrubs that compose the dense thickets of maquis become considerably shorter and more widely spaced, one often observes a transition into the third type of vegetation, the garigue.

Garigue is an open association of low shrubs, frequently rich in fragrant oils, that commonly stand between 3 and 4 feet high. Intervening spaces are usually covered with low-growing ground plants, particularly flowering herbs that include many species of anemone, iris, gladiolus, poppy, salvia, and germander. The much greater abundance of small flowering plants is a distinguishing point in contrast with the maquis. The surface on which garigue typically develops is usually stony or rocky, without humus and without an accumulation of water at any time of year. Many different associations of plants combine to create the garigue landscape of the Mediterranean basin, but several species can be found nearly everywhere: the sparrowbush (*Thymelaea (Passerina) hirsuta*), rosemary (*Rosmarinus officinalis*), lavender (*Lavendula Stoechas*), globe daisy (*Globularia Alypum* and *spp.*), palmetto (*Chaemerops humilis*), phillyrea (*Phillyrea media*), euphorbia (*Euphorbia spinosa*), and varieties of rockrose (*Cistus spp.*).

Although the mediterranean environment is generally confined to lowlands well below 2500 feet, its upper limit increases from north to south in the Mediterranean basin, as suggested by the mean upper limit of such trees as the olive, Aleppo pine, cork oak (*Quercus suber*), and palmetto. In north central Spain, for example, the mean upper limit of these plants is around 1600 feet, rising to around 3300 feet in the Sierra Nevada of southern Spain, in contrast

Figure 13.4. Maquis aspect in mediterranean scrub woodland in middle Chile, near Santiago, here known as matorral. [American Geographical Society photo]

to the even greater range of around 4000 feet in the Atlas Mountains of Algeria and Morocco. Along the Dalmatian coast of Yugoslavia the vertical range increases from around 650 feet in the north to 1000 feet near the Albanian border, 2000 feet in Albania, and more than 2200 feet in the Peloponnesus of Greece. Across the Mediterranean on the Cyrenaican plateau of Libya the upper limit is over 2600 feet. The mean upper limit of mediterranean vegetation also increases somewhat from east to west, averaging around 1600 feet along the Mediterranean coasts of Asia Minor, around 1700 feet in Greece, around 1900 feet in southern Italy, and 2500 feet in southern Spain. Beyond the upper range of mediterranean vegetation in southern Europe are usually found southern outliers of the mid-latitude mixed forest, including deciduous species of oak, maple, and beech and evergreen spruce and fir.

Most of the natural vegetation has been cleared from areas accessible for cultivation, but its original distribution can be inferred from the presence of relict growths in remote localities and from descriptions of landscapes preserved from antiquity.

A mediterranean climate prevails over most of Portugal and the southern half of Spain, except at higher elevations where more abundant, year-round rainfall supports a mixed forest and in certain localities of east central and southeastern Spain where numerous enclaves of grassy steppe respond to much less rain, higher summer temperatures, and a large annual range of temperature.

Where the lower Minho River forms a boundary between northern Portugal and northwestern Spain, the temperate mixed forest is replaced by more open mediterranean vegetation; for example, beech is replaced by olive, Scots pine by stone pine (*Pinus Pinea*), and the maquis, composed of such species as rockrose, heath, strawberry tree, and boxwood, begins to dominate the uncultivated landscapes on every side. Forest trees here include not only olive and stone pine but also the valuable cork oak (*Quercus suber*), holm oak (*Quercus ilex*), and maritime pine (*Pinus pinaster*). Actually, maritime pine is most plentiful north of the Tagus River, and cork oak most abundant southeast of the Tagus River and highly conspicuous southeastward from here to the Malaga coast of Spain. Here, also, the maquis becomes more

richly varied and includes rosemary, lavender, sparrowbush, and palmetto.

Mediterranean landscapes, maquis predominating but with scattered stands of olive, oak, and pine and frequent rocky tracts of sparse garigue, reach as far north as the vicinity of Madrid in central Spain and eastward to the sea. Northeastward, along the coast, the region extends in a band that is rarely more than 50 miles wide, skirting the foot of the Pyrenees into the coastal plain of Languedoc in southern France. Up the valley of the Rhone it reaches its northern limit, about 100 miles from the river's mouth, near where the foothills of the French Alps reach out toward the Massif Central in the vicinity of Valence. East of the Rhône the region occupies most of the hilly countryside of Provence, where maquis and garigue are especially prominent.

Along the Riviera, from Nice beyond Genoa to Pisa on the plain of the Arno, the region is narrowly confined to the lower seaward slopes of the Maritime Alps and the northern Apennines, whose steep-sided flanks press close to the water's edge. A much broader expanse of evergreen hardwood mediterranean vegetation occupies most of the hilly country between the Arno and the Tiber as far inland as Perugia, continuing southward from Rome to prevail over most of southern Italy up to elevations of 1900 to 2600 feet. The dominant association here is maquis, including the strawberry tree, heath, evergreen oak, mastic tree (*Pistacia lentiscus*), myrtle (*Myrtus communis*), and the cactuslike Euphorbia (*Euphorbia dendroides* and *Euphorbia spinosa*). Northwestward along the Adriatic shores of Italy the region gradually loses its identity beyond Ancona, giving way to the mid-latitude mixed forest climate of the Po valley. The environment of the Balearic Islands, Corsica, Sardinia, Sicily, and Malta is predominantly mediterranean, except at higher elevations.

From Fiume southward the mediterranean environment dominates Yugoslavia's rugged, mountainous shores and offshore islands, prevailing over the enlarged coastal plain of Albania and expanding over most of Greece. Eastward along the Aegean coast of Macedonia the region continues to the shores of the Sea of Marmora southeast of Istanbul. In the hills around Bursa, an inland town across the Marmora from Istanbul, one encounters, above

2500 feet, the temperate mixed forest that is dominant toward the east and expresses the general character of the Black Sea region of Turkey.

An alpine forest of mediterranean character extends over the higher mountain slopes eastward in Turkey almost without break into the Zagros Mountain region of southwestern Iran, reaching as far southward as Shiraz. It also appears above the deciduous forest of Iran's Caspian lowlands, but at these altitudes, generally over 5000 feet above sea level, it no longer represents the mediterranean climate of the coastal lowlands.

Along the Aegean coast of Turkey a series of interrupted coastal plains extends well inland, allowing the mediterranean climate to penetrate as much as 100 miles from the sea. Along the rugged, broken south coast, however, the region is more narrowly confined. The islands of the Aegean, including Crete, Rhodes, and Cyprus are for the most part mediterranean in nature, except where a more mixed forest responds to cooler, more humid conditions at higher levels.

Southward from Turkey all that remains of a once abundant forest are scattered individual trees or clumps in out-of-the-way places. Maquis and garigue are the commonest types of vegetation, and maquis is hard-pressed to survive. Closely restricted to seaward slopes of coastal ranges like the mountains of Lebanon, the mediterranean environment extends into northern Israel, but rapidly gives way to steppe and desert south of the Dead Sea.

In the eastern Mediterranean basin additional species impart further variety to the surviving plant associations. Among those especially noticeable on the Asiatic mainland are the Judas tree (*Cercis Siliquastrum*), storax gum tree (*Styrax officinalis*), cypress (*Cupressus sempervirens*), Carob (*Ceratonia siliqua*), jujube (*Zizyphus lotus*), and several indigenous oaks. A common maquis formation frequently seen on the slopes of hills in Palestine is an oak-gum vegetation composed chiefly of *Quercus calliprinos* and *Pistacia palaestina*. In the mountains of Syria and Lebanon, above the vertical range of mediterranean species, are very small relict stands of the famous Cedar of Lebanon (*Cedrus Libani*), along with juniper (*Juniperus excelsa*) and fir (*Abies cilicica*).

From Israel to southern Tunisia the north coast of Africa is principally desert or semi-desert steppe for some 1500 miles. Only on the Achaar plateau of Cyrenaica east of Bengasi and the Nefusa plateau of Tripolitania about 50 miles southwest of Tripoli is sufficient rainfall received to support mediterranean vegetation. At altitudes above 600 feet mediterranean tree species include cypress (*Cupressus sempervirens*), Aleppo pine (*Pinus halepensis*), evergreen oak (*Quercus coccifera*), holm oak (*Quercus ilex*), strawberry tree (*Arbutus unedo*), and olive (*Olea europea*), amid a dominant maquis composed of such species as sweet bay (*Laurus nobilis*), myrtle (*Myrtus communis*), oleander (*Nerium Oleander*), phillyrea (*Phillyrea media*), rockrose (*Cistus salviifolius*), sparrowbush (*Thymelaea* (*Passerina*) *hirsuta*), euphorbia (*Euphorbia dendroides*), rosemary (*Rosmarinus officinalis*), mastic tree (*Pistacia lentiscus*), carob (*Ceratonia siliqua*), and laurustine (*Viburnum tinus*).

The portion of the Barbary Coast from the Gulf of Gabes in Tunisia to the Atlantic shores of Morocco possesses a broad, well-developed variety of mediterranean landscape, virtually uninterrupted for 1200 miles. Here the qualities of the mediterranean environment are extended inland about 100 miles in Tunisia and up to 200 miles in Morocco, by virtue of the Atlas Mountains. Two roughly parallel systems of interrupted, folded ranges lie approximately parallel to the coast. The southern one (Grand Atlas, High Atlas, Sahara Atlas) is the larger and forms a mountain border overlooking the Sahara Desert. The northern one (Middle Atlas, Tell Atlas), nearer the coast, is separated from the southern by a region of high plateaus in Algeria and Morocco. General elevations decrease from west to east. Peaks of more than 12,000 feet in Morocco, more than 6000 feet in Algeria, and more than 4000 feet in Tunisia are common.

Over the coastal plains cork oak, holm oak, olive, and Aleppo pine, along with juniper (*Juniperus phoenicia* and *Juniperus thurifera*) and the sandarac tree (*Callitris quadrivalvis*), are important scrub forest species. On the lower mountain slopes other species like the zeen oak (*Quercus faginea*) combine with the more common members of maquis formations. On the upper slopes of mountains near the sea in Algeria, Spanish Morocco, and French Morocco, but not in the Grand Atlas, are found the commoner mediterranean oaks (cork, evergreen,

TABLE 13–1

Climatic Data for Mediterranean Scrub Woodland Stations in the Mediterranean Basin
(Temp., °F; Rainfall, In.)

Station	Lat.	El. in Ft		Jan.	Feb.	Mar.	Apr.	May	Jun.	Jul.	Aug.	Sep.	Oct.	Nov.	Dec.	Year
Oporto, Portugal	41°08'	328	T	48	50	53	56	59	65	67	68	66	60	54	49	
			R	6.0	4.6	5.4	4.1	3.3	1.7	0.9	0.7	2.1	4.3	5.9	6.5	45.5
Seville, Spain	37°29'	98	T	50	53	58	62	69	76	82	83	77	68	58	52	
			R	2.2	2.9	3.3	2.3	1.3	0.9	0.1	0.1	1.1	2.6	3.7	2.8	23.3
Fez, Morocco	34°02'	1368	T	50	51	56	59	66	73	80	81	75	67	57	51	
			R	2.0	2.5	2.5	2.4	1.4	0.6	0.0	0.2	0.5	1.9	2.8	3.1	19.9
Avignon, France	43°55'	66	T	39	43	49	56	63	71	75	73	66	57	47	40	
			R	1.5	1.5	1.6	2.0	2.4	2.0	1.1	2.0	2.9	3.5	2.6	1.8	25.4
Marseilles, France	43°17'	246	T	43	45	49	55	61	68	72	71	66	58	50	44	
			R	1.9	1.5	1.9	2.0	2.0	1.0	0.6	0.9	2.7	3.7	3.1	2.2	23.5
Valencia, Spain	39°28'	79	T	50	52	55	59	65	71	76	76	72	65	57	47	
			R	0.9	1.5	0.9	1.2	1.1	1.3	0.4	0.5	2.2	1.6	2.5	1.3	15.4
Algiers, Algeria	36°46'	194	T	54	55	58	61	66	72	77	78	75	68	61	55	
			R	4.5	3.3	2.9	1.6	1.8	0.6	0.1	0.2	1.6	3.1	5.1	5.4	30.0
Setif, Algeria	36°11'	3546	T	41	43	48	53	60	69	77	76	69	59	49	42	
			R	2.4	1.8	1.7	1.4	2.0	1.1	0.4	0.6	1.5	1.5	2.1	2.1	18.5
Genoa, Italy	44°24'	177	T	44	48	51	57	63	69	74	75	70	61	53	47	
			R	4.1	4.3	4.2	3.9	3.4	2.8	1.7	2.4	4.9	7.9	7.1	5.0	51.7
Ajaccio, Corsica	41°56'	7	T	49	50	51	57	62	69	74	75	70	63	56	51	
			R	3.0	2.0	2.4	2.0	1.6	1.1	0.2	0.8	2.0	3.6	4.6	2.8	26.1
Tunis, Tunisia	36°47'	216	T	51	52	56	60	66	74	79	80	76	68	59	52	
			R	2.5	2.1	1.6	1.4	0.8	0.4	0.1	0.3	1.3	2.0	1.9	2.4	16.5
Rome, Italy	41°48'	377	T	47	48	52	57	65	71	76	76	72	63	55	49	
			R	2.7	2.3	1.5	1.7	2.0	1.0	0.6	0.9	2.7	3.7	3.8	2.8	25.7
Syracuse, Sicily	37°03'	72	T	52	52	55	59	65	73	78	80	75	68	60	54	
			R	3.7	2.4	1.6	1.4	1.7	0.2	0.2	0.3	2.0	3.3	5.0	3.9	24.7
Bengasi, Libya	32°06'	82	T	56	57	60	65	71	75	77	78	76	73	67	59	
			R	2.7	1.6	0.8	0.2	0.1	0.0	0.0	0.0	0.1	0.7	1.8	2.6	10.5
Athens, Greece	37°58'	351	T	47	48	53	59	67	75	80	80	74	66	57	51	
			R	2.2	1.5	1.3	0.9	0.9	0.6	0.3	0.4	0.6	1.7	2.8	2.6	15.8
Salonika, Greece	40°31'	23	T	42	46	51	58	68	75	80	79	72	64	53	47	
			R	1.5	1.4	1.6	1.9	2.4	1.7	1.0	1.2	1.6	2.1	2.7	2.4	21.5
Izmir, Turkey	38°27'	92	T	47	49	53	60	68	75	81	81	74	66	58	50	
			R	4.4	3.3	3.0	1.7	1.3	0.6	0.2	0.2	0.8	2.1	3.3	4.8	25.5
Beirut, Lebanon	33°54'	121	T	57	58	61	66	72	78	82	83	81	76	68	61	
			R	7.2	6.4	3.5	2.3	0.7	0.1	0.0	0.0	0.3	1.9	5.0	7.4	34.8

and holm), along with chestnut oak (*Q. castaneaefolia*), cedar, fir, and pine. On the high plateau between the two main mountain systems are principally regions of grassy steppe where mediterranean vegetation is only sparsely represented. The steppe in turn disappears where the shifting sands and rocky plateaus of the drought-ridden Sahara begin.

CLIMATIC CONDITIONS. Annual changes in the duration and intensity of solar radiation typical of middle latitudes bring to the Mediterranean basin two sharply contrasting periods of mean weather experience. Summer is a time of little or no precipitation and high daily temperatures, when the region resembles the arid desert to the south, and when the rhythmic alternation of strong sunlight in daytime and marked radiational heat loss at night give rise to weather with many unique qualities of local origin. Winter is the period of weakened insolation when most varieties of weather result from invasions of atmospheric qualities from outside the region, among which is the frequent passage of migrating cyclones, bringing rain (Fig. 12.2).

For the year as a whole, the mean annual range of temperature is roughly between 25 and 30 degrees over most of the Mediterranean basin. Along the Atlantic coast, however, milder winters and cooler summers produce a range of only about 20 degrees. On the shores of the Aegean Sea, hemmed in on three sides by land, hotter summers are chiefly responsible for the increased mean range of between 30 and 35 degrees. Places removed from the sea experience a wider annual range temperature than nearby localities on the coast. In central Portugal, Coimbra, 25 miles inland, has a mean range of 23 degrees, compared with 16 degrees for Figueira de Foz, on the coast. Seville, 40 miles from the sea, has a range of 33 degrees, in contrast to the coastal station of Cadiz, which has 22 degrees. In southern France, Avignon experiences a mean annual temperature range of 36 degrees, compared with Marseilles, 29 degrees. And in northern Algeria the inland station of Setif has 36 degrees, Algiers only 24 degrees.

The extreme range between the highest and lowest temperatures on record is also much less at coastal than at interior stations. At Oporto, Cadiz, Tripoli, and Kythera, for example, it is 74 degrees. Inland it is often more than 100 degrees, as at Seville (102), Madrid (102), and Geryville (107). (See Table 13-1.)

The growing season free of frost lasts for nearly the entire year in most coastal areas, between 360 and 365 days. The chief exceptions to this are the Mediterranean coast of France and the north Adriatic and north Aegean coasts, where an average period of from 330 to 340 days is common.

Yearly precipitation is distinctive in a number of ways. It occurs mainly in winter, is largely of cyclonic origin, consists almost entirely of rain, varies considerably in amount from place to place and from year to year, and falls, as a general rule, on a comparatively small number of days.

Summer. After the vernal equinox the land surfaces of the northern hemisphere are warmed rapidly by the sun's direct rays, giving rise to recurrent low pressure situations of thermal origin over certain sections of the continents. At the same time, over the more slowly warming surfaces of the intervening seas oceanic subtropical anticyclones move northward and expand zonally over the bordering lands. Thus the Azores High gradually extends the influence of its light, variable winds and clockwise circulation over western Europe and northwest Africa. This brings to the western half of the Mediterranean Sea a typical pattern of normally light north and northwest winds, clear skies, and dry air remarkable for its persistence from about May to September. Occasional summer gales, however, are reported in the Gulf of Lion, the northern Adriatic, and the Aegean.

Over the eastern half of the Mediterranean light north, northwest, and west winds persist at this season, but they are only partly related to the expanded circulation of the Azores High. Instead, they arise primarily in response to the large, intensively developed thermal low pressure situations that prevail over southeastern Iran and West Pakistan. These persistent lows comprise the chief element of the south Asian summer monsoon (Fig. 4.3). Air currents in the main tend to move southwestward out of west central Asia over the Anatolian plateau of Turkey, acquiring a southward trajectory over the Aegean, curving eastward over the eastern Mediterranean toward the shores of Syria, Lebanon, and Israel and southeastward over the Arabian peninsula as they respond to the generally counterclockwise circulation of the dominant monsoonal low. A secondary depression often develops over the island of Cyprus in summer, augmenting the larger circulation and occasionally sending northward, onshore winds against the southern shores of Turkey that bring sporadic rains to the upper slopes of the Taurus Mountains.

An important feature of the summertime circulation in the eastern Mediterranean is the rather frequent occurrence of warm, dry north winds in the Aegean. These are the Etesian winds of ancient Greece, *Meltemi* in modern Greek. Although warm, they are quite dry and thus tend to produce a welcome invigorating effect. They frequently blow at velocities up to 40 miles per hour near sea level, necessitating the planting of tall cypress windbreaks for orchards and olive groves. Near the summits of mountainous islands they are sufficiently strong and persistent to prevent the growth of trees. Blowing down off the lee of the higher islands, the *Meltemi* often produce sudden, short-lived gales called white squalls because of the flurry of whitecaps they send scudding along the surface of the sea. Strong north winds are also common in summer in the north Adriatic and

around Corsica and Sardinia, where they are called maestral. But the Etesian wind of summertime is only one of a great many locally notorious winds in the Mediterranean basin (Fig. 13.5), most of which occur during the stormier season of winter.

The most notable characteristic of summertime circulation everywhere around the Mediterranean is the sea breeze of coastal localities. The sea breeze is mainly a function of daily variations in local surface thermal gradients of the littoral. Intensified summer insolation raises the temperature of coastal land surfaces in contrast to the neighboring sea. By August the sea surface normally attains temperatures ranging from about 70° in western areas to more than 80° in the east (Fig. 13.6), whereas adjacent land surfaces commonly rise to 100° and often to over 130° by the midafternoon. Rapid warming of air over land takes place daily, resulting in lower atmospheric pressures as air aloft diverges and is displaced seaward. Cooler, higher density air from the sea moves shoreward at the surface to equalize the temporary pressure differences, accompanied by an offshore flow at higher levels. The reverse takes place at night when the

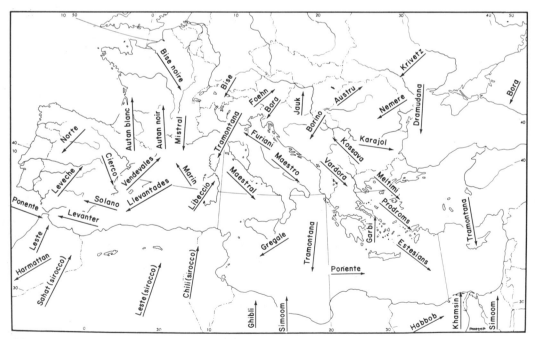

Figure 13.5.   Local winds in the Mediterranean Basin.

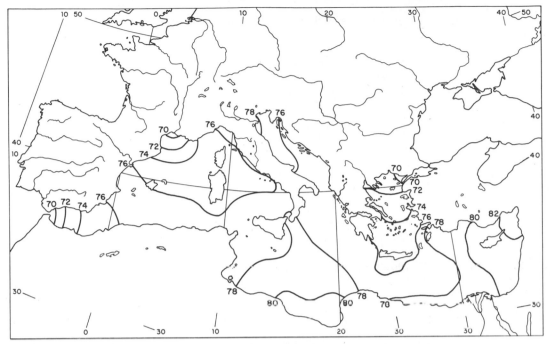

Figure 13.6. Mean sea surface temperatures of the Mediterranean Sea in August (°F).

sun has set and air over land cools below the temperature of the thermally conservative sea. Although the schedule of these processes varies from place to place, it tends toward a pattern somewhat as follows:[2]

Sunrise to 0900	Calm
0900	Sea breeze
1400	Sea breeze maximum
1800	Sea breeze ends
1800 to 2000	Calm
2000	Land breeze begins
Sunrise	Land breeze ends

The sea breeze affects a shallow layer of the atmosphere averaging about 1500 feet in depth, although at times extending to around 3000 feet. The offshore nocturnal drift seldom exceeds 500 feet in depth. In general, the daily onshore component tends to reach as far inland as the first prominent ridge or range of hills and is frequently felt up to 50 miles from the sea. If the coastal lowland is narrow, the slopes of the coastal highlands confine the sea breeze to the shoreline and usually increase the maximum

velocities of both onshore and offshore components, the steepness and height of the slopes determining the intensity of each. Also important in varying the nature of the diurnal windshift is the curvature of the shoreline, for concave coastal lowlands as a rule intensify the offshore land breeze, while convex shorelines intensify the onshore sea breeze. The Coriolis effect may cause the onshore breeze to veer gradually during the day from the perpendicular to an angle of around 55° with the coast at maximum velocity. The onshore flow continues to veer as evening approaches and finally moves nearly parallel to the coast before ceasing at the end of day.

Heat, drought, blue skies, and blazing sunlight are the ruling qualities of summer weather in general. The return of moisture to the air by evaporation and transpiration far exceeds in amount whatever moisture is produced by precipitation and dewfall. Even the Mediterranean Sea itself loses more moisture than it receives, both from rainfall and stream runoff, a fact attested to by the prevailing eastward flow of water through the Straits of Gibraltar and the very high salinity of more than 37 parts per thousand for most surface waters. Over 39 parts per thousand is the value in easternmost

[2] U.S. Navy, *Operational Weather of the Northern Hemisphere*, Navaer 50–1C–527A. 1955, pp. 1–13.

portions of the sea. (Mean surface salinities for the world's oceans as a whole average 35 parts per thousand.)

During the summer months the sun-baked earth, unrelieved by occasional sudden, drenching showers, becomes hard and dry, the warm air frequently filled with a dusty haze. The desert seems to advance northward as the season progresses, its arid breath turning the foliage of deciduous plants brown and brittle, bringing to an end the cool spring season of gaily blossoming herbs like the poppy, salvia, germander, iris, and gladiolus. Even the evergreen oak, pine, cypress, arbutus, oleander, and bay take on a dull, lustreless aspect, and the small grey leaves of the olive blend into the background.

During May the thermometer begins to rise regularly above 70° almost every day, and mean monthly temperatures in general average more than 60° throughout most of the Mediterranean basin. Mean monthly values increase steadily as the sun's rays reach the earth through cloudless or only partly cloudy skies, attaining a maximum at most stations in August. July, however, is often only a degree or two cooler, and in some places both months are equally hot, as at Livorno, Naples, Malta, Athens, and Candia. The warmest month in most localities averages between 75° and 80°, although values are higher in Spain's interior (Seville 83°), and the inland valleys of Morocco (Qued Zem 84°, Fez 81°), and at many points in the eastern reaches (Izmir 81°, Kyrenia 84°, Beirut and Haifa 83°). Summers tend to be increasingly hotter and longer from west to east and from north to south, partly because of increasing remoteness from the Atlantic's cooling influence, and partly because of increasing proximity to the intensified desert heat of north Africa and southwest Asia. Note that southern France experiences a less extreme summer warmth, as suggested by the mean temperatures for July, the warmest month, of 72° at Marseilles and 73° at Narbonne and Montpellier (Table 13-1).

With few exceptions the mean daily range of temperature reaches a maximum during the warmer months of summer, for under the predominantly clear skies the thermometer reaches well into the 80s during the day and drops into the upper 60s at night in western areas. In the eastern Mediterranean and in interior Algeria and Morocco it rises well into

the 90s by day, lowering to around 70° before dawn. Temperatures above 100° are common at nearly all stations and occur with some frequency every summer. Seville has reported an extreme maximum of 124°, Madrid 112°, Athens 109°, Candia 114°, and Tunis 122°.

Nocturnal temperatures are prevented from dropping much below 70° by the fact that the Mediterranean Sea in July and August has a surface temperature of over 70°, ranging from about 70° at the Straits of Gibraltar and the Gulf of Lion to about 77° near Sicily and southern Italy, and increasing eastward to 81° in the Gulf of Sidra and 83° northeast of Cyprus.

The abundance of summer sunshine is indicated by the records of cloud cover for July and August. The skies of Mediterranean Europe are rarely obscured more than 20 per cent by cloud cover, and those over north Africa and the eastern Mediterranean rarely by more than 10 per cent. Athens, for example, averages 360 hours of sunshine in July, compared with 125 hours in December, and Rome reports around 350 hours in July, compared with 107 hours in December.

In places the dry sand may heat to over 150°, the air temperature in the shade rising to over 100°, and when the air is calm, a shimmering radiation of heat from the sun-baked land creates a mirage like that of the Sahara and southwest Asia. Many streams diminish in size, some cease flowing altogether, leaving only stagnant muddy pools. But the air is seldom sultry and oppressive. It is typically dry, and is usually in motion near the sea. Only in the interior valleys and depressions does it often attain a stifling quality that may remain unrelieved until nightfall.

Relative humidity is characteristically low during summer in most localities that lie sheltered from the sea. Readings as low as 4 per cent in midafternoon have been reported from points in Greece. In contrast, however, a number of coastal cities experience a summer increase in observed relative humidity, and an intolerably sweltering mugginess develops, especially where coastal mountain ranges confine the moisture brought in by the sea breeze to the littoral. Such a situation typically arises at Beirut, where a mean maximum temperature of about 90° is accompanied by an average relative humidity of 70 per cent or more in August. Here, and at a number of coastal stations where summer humidity is unusually high for the region, as at Alicante and Barcelona in Spain, Ajaccio in Corsica, Naxos in the Aegean, and Malta, nocturnal dew is often heavy enough to cause the rooftops and city streets to stream with tiny rivulets of flowing water in the early light of daybreak.

In spite of the normal summer decrease in relative humidity, light fog and mist tend to increase from April onward, reaching a maximum in June. This is the season when the air is decidedly warmer than the sea, when light fog occurs in early morning and mist during the day, augmented very often by the presence of dust and minute salt particles in the air. From early evening throughout most of the night the air is normally calm and becomes increasingly clearer toward dawn. A pronounced decrease in mist and fog takes place from September onward, when the air generally becomes cooler than the sea. For the entire year it may be said that fog occurs more frequently over relatively cold water coastal areas, especially in winter, as along the west coast of Spain and Portugal. Lisbon, for example, reports an average of five days with fog in December and only 0.3 days in July. This is also true in the Gulf of Lion, along the Riviera, and at the head of the Adriatic. Genoa reports an average of 6.4 days in January and only 1.0 days in July.

Summer drought, although attributable in part to the powerful evaporative effect of persistently high temperatures and intensive solar radiation, arises primarily from a pronounced scarcity of rainfall. As spring advances, showers fall on an ever diminishing number of days and bring successively smaller amounts of rain when they do occur. Lisbon reports an average of two days with rain in July and two in August, compared with thirteen rain days each in November, December, January and March. Cadiz averages less than one rain day each in July and August, compared with nine days per month from December through February. Marseilles, Genoa, Naples, and Athens average three rain days in July and between nine and twelve days during at least one month of the winter season. Haifa, Bengasi, and Tripoli record no rain days from June through August, compared with eleven to fourteen days during one or more winter months.

July is commonly the driest month, when an average of much less than 1 inch of rain is re-

corded at most stations, and none at all at Gibraltar, Malta, Candia, Beirut, Haifa, Bengasi, and Tripoli. Haifa reports no rain whatever for the period June through September, and Bengasi is normally rainless from June through August. Yearly variations are common at many stations, however, and Lisbon, for example, received 1.1 inch in July 1941 but none at all in July the following year; Madrid recorded only a trace in July 1946 but 2.2 inches in July 1947. Jerusalem, on the other hand, has received no rainfall whatever in either July or August for over one hundred years, from 1848 to 1950.

Convective showers are the principal source or irregular summer rains, although seldom do they develop sufficient energy to produce thunderstorms. Indeed, the rain they produce is quite often evaporated from the parched soil within a few minutes after it falls. Thunderstorms are rarely experienced in most of the low-lying lands of the mediterranean region throughout the year.

Summer continues well into September, a maritime climatic feature traceable to the influence of the Mediterranean Sea, and on the west coast of Spain, Portugal, and Morocco to the influence of the Atlantic. Toward the end of September, however, the first of winter's disturbances usually arrives, often presaged by an unwelcome increase in sensible atmospheric humidity as temperatures continue high. But cool weather comes on at last, and with it the welcome season of short, frequent rains alternating with bracing, sunny intervals, reawakening of plant life and returning the flush of green to the land.

Winter. With the southward retreat of the sun, the great Eurasian land mass, cooling rapidly in contrast to the neighboring seas, becomes a source of well-developed anticyclones. Continental polar air—clear, cold, and dry—again and again advances over the oceanic margins, and the polar front is depressed progressively farther southward as winter intensifies. Oceanic subtropical anticyclones contract and shift equatorward, as a result of which the influence of the Azores High over the western Mediterranean is steadily weakened, and cyclonic storms begin to occur with increasing frequency (Fig. 12.2). To a certain extent, then, the Mediterranean basin shares the inclemency of its winters with northwest Europe.

A certain number of winter's traveling

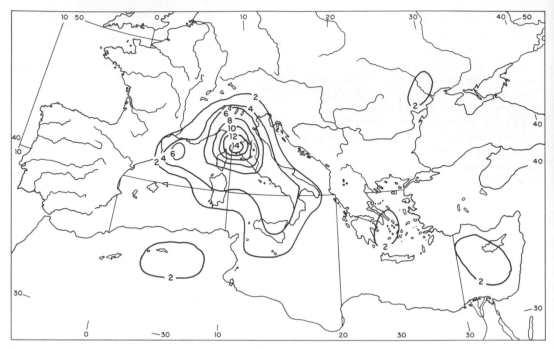

Figure 13.7. Frequency of cyclogenesis during January and February in the Mediterranean Basin.

cyclones enter the Mediterranean region from the North Atlantic, advancing over southern France or northern Spain or through the Straits of Gibraltar, intensifying as they take up warmth and moisture from the surface of the sea. The great majority of migrating disturbances, however, chiefly cyclonic in nature, originate within the Mediterranean basin itself and tend to develop in preferred areas of cyclogenesis (Fig. 13.7).

Cyclogenesis usually begins weakly in the northern Mediterranean in September, but with the more pronounced decrease in insolation after the autumnal equinox, it takes place with increasing frequency over two particular points of origin, the Gulf of Genoa and the north Adriatic. The Gulf of Genoa is in fact one of the more prominent cyclogenetic centers in the entire northern hemisphere from October through March (Fig. 13.7).

By January the Mediterranean basin has normally become one of three major storm tracks in northwest Eurasia. Most of the depressions follow a trajectory over water, moving along preferred paths roughly east-southeastward toward southwest Asia. During midwinter they either recurve northeastward over the Aegean

and into the Black Sea or else southeastward toward Iraq, Iran, and India. Later in the season a number of lows often follow a more southerly path across Arabia and out over the Persian Gulf. In wintertime Cyprus becomes the center of a notable area of intensified cyclonic activity and of fairly frequent cyclogenesis. Cyprus lows are typically small, fast-moving storms that develop rapidly and advance over the mainland, often along the front of the Taurus Mountains in southern Turkey, toward the Caspian Sea. Two other centers of cyclogenesis are along the southern flanks of the Atlas Mountains and over the Gulf of Sidra off the Libyan coast. Here storms tend to appear chiefly toward the end of winter.

Migrating cyclones in the Mediterranean are usually generated where clear, cold, dry air flows out from an arm of the continent over the coastal plains and the persistently warm sea. Initial fields of motion are often katabatically accelerated from the highlands. It is during the first four months of the year, from January through April, that the sea's surface warmth is in greatest contrast with the cold aridity of land surfaces toward the north (Fig. 13.8). Once formed, depressions gain warmth and moisture from the sea, and the cold dryness of invading air from the land provides the necessary supply of potentially unstable air and sets up initial advection. A lee depression is often formed on the sheltered sides of higher mountains, as on the south side of the Alps and the Atlas ranges. And another localized feature is the small, individual anticyclonic system that frequently forms over the major peninsulas. When such circulations take shape, southerly winds are induced along the west coasts of Iberia, Italy, Greece, and Turkey, and northerly winds down the appropriate east coasts. Such occurrences may either augment or diminish broad-scale synoptic circulations affecting much larger portions of the Mediterranean basin.

In the Mediterranean, unlike northwest Europe, inclement weather normally lasts only a few hours, to be followed by the return of clear, sunny skies and bracing air, for indigenous depressions are typically smaller and shallower than those of higher latitudes. Furthermore, whereas the warm sectors of a normal polar front depression farther north bring extensive cloud cover and higher relative humidity, the warm sector in the Mediterranean is often clear and dry. And the north winds of the trailing

cold sector in the Mediterranean usually bring clear, bright weather unlike the unsettled storminess elsewhere in Europe.

Surface winds are often well defined and bring spells of winter weather that are among the prominent features of the region's climate. They are normally of short duration and are commonly restricted to small sections of the basin. They thus appear as brief, local aberations in the generally eastward flow of surface air during the winter season (Fig. 13.5).

The mistral of southern France is a cold, dry north wind that often blows for days, bringing clear skies and good visibility. It normally attains a blustery peak velocity in the lower Rhône valley, where speeds of 35 to 40 miles per hour are common, and where, as it rushes out across the delta, records of 80 mph winds are known. Trees have a permanent set to southward, and many houses are built without windows on their northern sides. The counterpart of the mistral along the east coast of the Adriatic and in northern Italy is the bora, a northeast wind that has reached a maximum velocity of more than 100 miles per hour. The north to northwest winds of the winter season in the northern Aegean are called the Vardarac

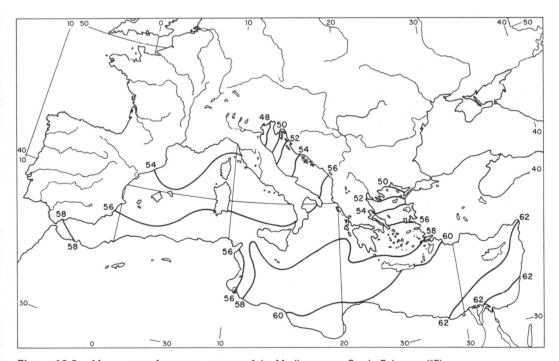

Figure 13.8. Mean sea surface temperatures of the Mediterranean Sea in February (°F).

because they blow down out of the Vardar valley. Such winds normally develop when a strong barometric gradient prevails in consequence of an intensified anticyclone over the land in contrast to lower atmospheric pressures over the adjacent sea.

A great many winds of local importance are well known in the Mediterranean (Fig. 13.5), but we shall consider only one widespread type, the sirocco. A typically warm, dry wind originating over desert tracts, the sirocco, under one or another of its many local names, commonly forms as part of the advance warm sector of an east-bound wintertime disturbance. It is not experienced in the eastern half of the basin during the summer. Maximum intensities usually develop in spring. The sirocco frequently picks up considerable moisture on its passage across the sea, bringing high humidity to European shores. It is often identified with mud rains, occasionally called blood rains, that discolor the snows on the mountain slopes of southern Europe. The sirocco is known as the *khamsin* in Egypt, *leveche* in southeastern Spain, where it is usually quite dry, *garbi* in the Aegean, *samoom* in Algeria, *sahat* in Morocco, and *ghibli* in Libya, where, with the help of adiabatic warming, it is reputed to be the hottest wind known on the globe.

The marked increase in cyclonic disturbances normally beginning in September ushers in the rainy season of winter. Plentiful rains of relatively short duration and occasional snow are the chief distinguishing features of the season. Along the south European coasts and in Tunisia the latter part of September usually sees a pronounced increase in rainfall. In most sections of the eastern Mediterranean and in Algeria and Morocco the onset of recurrent rains is delayed until October. October, in fact, is normally the month of maximum precipitation in eastern Spain, southern France, western Italy, and the eastern Adriatic. Along the Atlantic coast of Spain and Portugal, in southern Spain and Italy, the eastern Mediterranean, and north Africa the wettest month is more commonly November or December, and is occasionally delayed until January (Fig. 13.9).

A point of contrast with the wetter mixed forest regions of Europe to the north is the common occurrence of two yearly rainfall maxima, usually in October and again in March. This is true of the central part of Spain, southern France, and the north coast of the Aegean, illustrated in the records for Seville, Madrid, Avignon, and Salonika (Table 13-1). The spring maximum is normally less than that of autumn, a feature consistent with the rule for the rest of the Mediterranean basin of a single autumn maximum.

Mention has been made of the general decrease in yearly rainfall from west to east and from north to south, and of the fact that the western shores of island and peninsula alike are usually wetter than eastern shores in the lee of prevailing storm paths. Thus Barcelona on the east coast of Spain is seen to receive less than half (21.4 inches) the annual rainfall of Oporto, Portugal (47.6 inches), and Cartagena, with 15 inches, receives only slightly more than half the amount recorded for Lisbon (27.1 inches). Naples, with 33.4 inches, compares with Bari in southeastern Italy, which has 23.3 inches. Corfu off the northwest coast of Greece records 48.7 inches in contrast to Salonika, with 21.5 inches (Table 13-1).

The mean number of days on which rain falls is another point of contrast with northwest Europe. Rain-bearing disturbances of short duration occur on the average of eighty-one days in Marseilles, compared with 160 days at Paris, and in still drier areas, as along Spain's southeast coast, even fewer rain days are experienced, as at Cartagena (forty-three days), and Valencia (fifty-six days).

Snow is a rare component of winter's precipitation, especially near the sea. However, it may occur anywhere throughout the region during any winter, even at low altitudes along the coast, in small amounts that quickly fade from the ground. On the northernmost reaches of the strictly mediterranean environment the mean number of days in winter when any snow is likely to fall seldom exceeds ten, and in southern Spain and Italy and along the north African coast the probability of a snowfall is considerably less. However, elevation above sea level plays an important role in this. Above 4000 feet, which is usually above the elevation attained by a true mediterranean weather program, some snow mantles the ground for several weeks during a normal winter, and above 8000 feet commonly endures for as long as six months. This is especially true of the Pyrenees, the Apennines, the uplands of interior Greece, Turkey, the Lebanon Mountains,

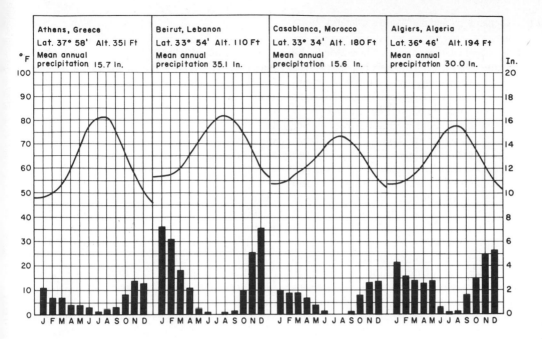

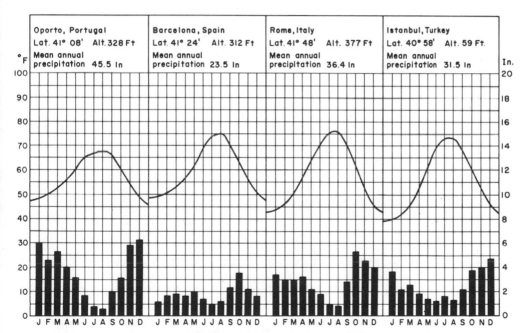

Figure 13.9. Temperature and precipitation at mediterranean scrub woodland stations in the Mediterranean Basin.

and the Atlas region of Algeria and Morocco. Local differences in altitude within short distances produce many sharp contrasts in normal snowfall amounts. Jerusalem, for example, at 2485 feet, receives some snow nearly every winter, but Jericho, at 820 feet below sea level

but only 20 miles away, has reported snow no more than twice in one hundred years.

Despite the occurrence of most of the year's precipitation during the winter months, skies are surprisingly free of cloud cover most of the time. Even in the cloudiest month, which is

April in northeastern Spain, May along the Riviera, and December through February over most of the remaining area, the mean cloud cover rarely amounts to more than 60 per cent of the sky during the day. The Aegean is an exception, most stations averaging over 60 per cent cloud cover from December through February. Typical cloudiness is created by the gradual appearance of scattered cumulus, increasing to a maximum in later afternoon and disappearing around dusk. Prolonged periods of stratus-covered skies, usually associated with passing systematic disturbances, and steady rain are comparatively rare.

Relative humidity increases in wintertime most noticeably at inland stations where daily temperatures often drop below the dew point after dark. Fog and mist thus occur during the night with considerable frequency, a feature notably true of interior river valleys and wet, marshy tracts.

With the advent of the rainy season during the latter part of September, cool weather sets in and temperatures generally average 7 or 8 degrees lower during October. The onset of cooler winter weather normally occurs somewhat more abruptly as well as slightly earlier at inland stations than along the coast. Thus, at Seville and Setif the drop in average values from September to October is 10 degrees. The greatest change is usually between 8 and 9 degrees from October to November at coastal stations. Winter's coldest month is January almost everywhere, although February is often only a degree or two warmer and may be just as cold at coastal sites in the central Mediterranean, as at Malta, Syracuse, and Candia. It is not surprising to note that many coastal stations experience very nearly the same mean monthly temperatures from December through February under the moderating influence of the sea. Oporto, Lisbon, Gibraltar, and Nice vary only 1 degree during those three months.

Nearly everywhere along the south European coast January temperatures average between 45° and 50°, although interior localities record values around 40°, as at Madrid (41°), Avignon (39°), Aleppo (42°), and Istanbul (41°). In the southern and eastern parts of the Mediterranean basin, however, January values average above 50°, with a few exceptions at higher elevation reporting lower values (Setif, at 3486 feet, averaging 41°). The mean daily range of

temperature during the winter months is generally between 5 and 10 degrees less than that of summer, occasioned in the main by the increase in transient disturbances and the higher atmospheric moisture content. Lower daytime temperatures and diminished nocturnal reradiation heat loss are chiefly responsible.

Frost is known in most sections, even near the sea, for the thermometer has registered values as low as 9° at Marseilles, 11° at Izmir, 17° at Istanbul, 20° at Livorno and Athens, 21° at Rome, and 30° at Beirut. Although frost is extremely rare at seaside points along the north African coast, inland stations in the Atlas Mountains frequently experience freezing temperatures. The Mediterranean Sea cools very much more slowly than the neighboring land areas, and from January through April its surface temperatures remain above the atmospheric temperatures over the encircling land. This is the principal reason for the moderate winter weather of the region. By February, when its surface is usually coldest, sea water temperatures range between 50° and 60° nearly everywhere, except in eastern sections where values are above 60° along the coast of Syria, Lebanon, and Israel (Fig. 13.8). Only at the head of the Adriatic are temperatures below 50° commonly reported. Here, and in the Gulf of Lion and the head of the Aegean, wintertime outbreaks of cold air have been known to freeze the coastal waters during occasional spells of unusually severe winter weather.

By May, when surrounding land areas have once again become warmer than the sea, the mean temperature gradients are reversed, the frequency of migrating storms diminishes, the sea breeze once again becomes a dominating feature of coastal weather, and the drier, warmer weather of summer begins.

North America

The North American counterpart of the Old World's mediterranean environment appears in a somewhat fragmentary distribution from the interior of northern California into northwestern Mexico. It lies roughly between 32° and 41°N. Lat. Although primarily determined by latitude, both its general distribution and its internal complexities are in part the result of its geographic setting. Three principal features are to be noted: the alignment of the coast, the types and distribution of the principal land forms, and the temperature of the adjacent sea (Fig. 13.10).

The alignment of the coast from Cape Mendocino into Lower California is approximately northwest–southeast, a fact of special significance with respect to the mean circulations of both the atmosphere and the sea. Also important are the character and arrangement of the major physiographic features of the land. From northern California, which is almost entirely mountainous, two separate mountain systems extend southeastward to embrace the Central Valley, a block-faulted basin about 450 miles long and 120 miles wide. The nearly level floor of the valley, about 50 miles in breadth, is drained by two main rivers and their tributaries: the south-flowing Sacramento and the north-flowing San Joaquin, which join before entering the northern arm of San Francisco Bay.

The eastern side of the valley, south of Lassen Peak, is flanked by the Sierra Nevada, which average between 5000 and 10,000 feet in elevation, culminating in Mt. Whitney at 14,495 feet. Along its western side the Central Valley is almost entirely separated from the sea by the Coastal Ranges, virtually rising from the water's edge, which are somewhat more than 50 miles in breadth. They are lower than the Sierra Nevada, only 2000 to 5000 feet in elevation. A single conspicuous break in the coastal ranges appears where San Francisco Bay empties into the Pacific. Northwest from the bay an elongated lowland divides the inner from the outer series of low, coastal mountains, reaching well into the valley of the Russian River. Southeastward a similar depression, again parallel both to the coastline and the Central Valley, also separates the inner from the outer coastal ranges, extending into the upper San Benito valley.

Where the shoreline bends almost directly eastward at Point Conception, the coastal mountains join the Transverse Ranges northwest of the Los Angeles lowland. The Transverse Ranges, which have an east–west alignment, are joined by the southern end of the Sierra Nevada. An elongated, unbroken system of low mountains extends from here southward all the way to the southern tip of the peninsula of Lower California, at many points attaining elevations of more than a mile above sea level.

In only a few places are the coastal ranges far enough inland to be separated from the shore by extensive coastal lowlands. One of these borders the shallow indentation of Monterey Bay and from here extends southeastward in a narrow attenuated form up the Salinas valley for over 100 miles. Another is in the Santa Maria valley north of Point Conception, and another is the Oxnard lowland between Santa Barbara and Los Angeles. In southern California the largest coastal lowland is the semi-enclosed basin around Los Angeles. This is continuous with the narrow, slightly elevated coastal plain that extends southeastward beyond Tijuana, just south of the Mexican border, a rather

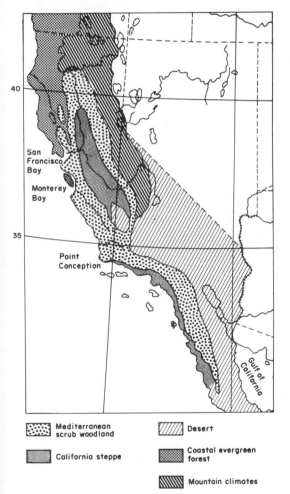

Figure 13.10. Mediterranean scrub woodland in western North America.

deeply dissected extension from 10 to 20 miles wide that lies between the inner ranges and the sea.

Finally, the temperature of the offshore waters of California plays an important part in determining the climate over the adjacent land, especially as weather along the west coast of the continent is dominated by the onshore invasion of maritime air from the sea. Systematic disturbances and the air streams of the atmospheric circulation in general over the eastern Pacific provide the main variation in weather. The California Current, south-flowing branch of the North Pacific Current that advances eastward from Asiatic waters as a warm surface flow, is relatively cold as it moves equatorward into lower latitudes. It intrudes a band of cool surface water from 200 to 300 miles wide between the coast and the warmer water farther out at sea.

The direction of surface ocean currents depends upon several factors, especially wind speed, fetch (distance of wind travel), and latitude. Surface currents tend to flow at about 45 degrees to the right of the prevailing wind direction. With increasing depth the clockwise deflection becomes greater. Thus the general mass of water moving in the California Current tends to shift seaward at about 90 degrees to the prevailing surface wind direction, or roughly southwestward. This induces a tendency for deeper, cooler water to rise up and replace it, creating a belt of constantly upwelling waters that extends perhaps 80 miles from the shore opposite the entrance to San Francisco Bay. For about 100 miles north of the Golden Gate surface waters are colder in summer than anywhere else along the west coast of the United States. From June through August temperatures range from about 60° near Cape Mendocino to 70° beyond Ensenada. During the period December through February the values range from 53° near Cape Mendocino to 60° beyond Ensenada (Figs. 6.12 and 6.13).

PLANT LIFE. In all essential respects the qualities of the vegetation and of the atmosphere in this North American fragment of the mediterranean climate are closely comparable to those of the Mediterranean basin. A scrub woodland of dominantly broadleaved evergreen and deciduous trees, with an occasional admixture of needleleaves, plus a flourishing chaparral (the maquis of Mediterranean

shores), are the chief vegetation types. A distinct vegetational transition exists between well-watered forest toward the north and drought-ridden desert toward the south, reflecting a climatic transition like that between northwestern Europe and the deserts of north Africa.

A distinctively open mediterranean scrub woodland, in which broad-crowned oaks are the leading species, reaches from the foothills of Mt. Shasta into southern California. From the upper Sacramento valley this vegetation predominates over the western foothills of the Sierra Nevada and the lower slopes of the inner coastal ranges at altitudes mainly between 400 and 3000 feet. Prominent species include the evergreen canyon oak (*Quercus chrysolepis*), coast live oak (*Quercus agrifolia*), interior live oak (*Quercus Wislizensii*), the deciduous blue oak (*Quercus Douglasii*), and California white oak, or roble (*Quercus lobata*), with which are variously associated the madrone (*Arbutus Menziesii*), California bay (*Umbellularia californica*), chestnut (*Aesculus californica*), Judas tree (*Cercis occidentalis*), walnut (*Juglans spp.*), and a wide variety of both deciduous and evergreen shrub forms. The principal trees range in height from 15 to 75 feet and include many very large oaks, such as the roble, which is often majestically proportioned, attaining a height of over 100 feet and a diameter of more than 12 feet.

Reaching up the tributary valleys, the open woodland often rises above its normal range to altitudes of around 5000 feet, where it mingles with more humid forests in which conifers like yellow pine (*Pinus ponderosa*), digger pine (*Pinus Sabiniana*), and Coulter pine (*Pinus Coulteri*) predominate. Over the floor of the Central Valley it becomes a more open parkland where the dominant cover is grass or low shrub and trees are very widely scattered. Passing from the Sacramento valley southeastward into the San Joaquin drainage, the proportion of grass and shrub forms increases, finally yielding to desert in the southwestern corner of the valley.

West of the city of Sacramento the woodland, varying considerably in both density and composition, spreads in narrow fingerlike projections into the small interior valleys northwest of San Francisco Bay. Although it extends well up the Russian River valley, it rarely reaches to within 10 miles of the sea. From the Golden Gate southward, however, it commonly spans the breadth of the coastal ranges from the shoreline to the Central Valley, interrupted from time to time by relatively small tracts of contrasting vegetation, especially those containing redwood trees. The redwood forest flourishes north of San Francisco from near sea level upward, but farther south it usually appears only on the seaward slopes of the coastal ranges, from 10 to 2000 feet, both north and south of Monterey Bay. Redwood (*Sequoia sempervirens*), Douglas fir (*Pseudotsuga Menziesii*), the evergreen narrow-crowned tan-bark oak (*Lithocarpus densiflora*), and smaller evergreen forms dominate, and on Monterey peninsula two distinctive forms are confined to this small area, the Monterey pine (*Pinus radiata*), and Monterey cypress (*Cupressus macrocarpa*). A portion of the Santa Maria valley near the sea is a more arid enclave of grassland and shrub vegetation.

Scrub woodland continues through the Transverse Ranges north of Los Angeles, diminishing in density and distribution southward into the low mountains of northern Lower California. Here it is only faintly evident, appearing for the most part in disrupted distribution, well removed from the coast along the seaward slopes for a short distance beyond Ensenada on the Bay of All Saints, giving way gradually to those subtropical desert forms that predominate over most of the southern part of the peninsula.

Chaparral, second of the two main vegetation types, is even more widely distributed than the oak woodlands and hence may be regarded as the most distinctive vegetation of the mediterranean region, like the maquis of the Mediterranean basin. Chaparral is chiefly a broadleaved, evergreen, sclerophyllous (drought-resistant) type of vegetation, ranging in height from 3 to 10 feet. A number of deciduous plants appear in its composition, and leaves are typically small, thick, and leathery. It is often very dense, its hard, stiff branches making it nearly impenetrable, and toward the end of the long, dry summers it is often highly subject to fire. If burned over, it commonly reasserts itself through the vigorous stump-sprouting of many of its component species.

This vegetation is frequently intermingled with scrub woodland, although it chiefly appears on the drier slopes and ridges at somewhat higher elevations. It often reaches altitudes of 5000 feet or more, and in the Sierra Nevada especially it tends to occupy the more xerophytic sites, forming a separate zone between the open woodland of the foothills and the luxuriant coniferous forest above. It is primarily an interior formation, rarely appearing on the sea coast proper, although it is common on the seaward slopes of the coastal ranges south of the Golden Gate. From the Transverse Ranges north of Los Angeles southward into Lower California, it tends to replace the scrub woodland as the dominant vegetation.

The principal evergreen species of the chaparral include chamise or greasewood (*Adenostoma fasciculatum*), toyon or Christmas-berry (*Heteromeles arbutifolia*), coffeeberry (*Rhamnus californica*), buckthorn (*Rhamnus crocea*), scrub oak (*Quercus dumosa*), mountain mahogany (*Cercocarpus betuloides*), Spanish bayonet (*Yucca Whipplei*), flamebush (*Fremontia californica*), holly-leaved cherry (*Prunus ilicifolia*), many wild lilacs often known by other names, such as buck brush (*Ceanothus cuneatus*), and numerous manzanitas (*Arctostaphylos spp.*). Wild lilacs are chiefly evergreen, or at least have persistent foliage in which the leaves remain attached despite a brownish, dessicated aspect during the dry summer. Liberally mixed among the dominant shrubby vegetation of maquis, and also in the more open woodland, are a great many brightly flowering herbs native to the region, among them purple lupine and golden California poppy, and a variety of introduced species, all of which impart a highly colorful quality to woodland, chaparral, and grassland, and to desert as well, during the flowering season of late winter and early spring.

CLIMATIC CONDITIONS. The essential characteristics of the normal yearly weather pattern in mediterranean North America closely resemble those of the Mediterranean basin. Warm, dry summers, mild, wet winters, and sunny skies are the principal features.

The shrub and wooded areas in the Central Valley, the Sierra foothills, and the coastal ranges coincide fairly closely with the normal occurrence of an annual precipitation of between 15 and 35 inches and temperatures for the warmest month ranging between 60° and 80°, for the coldest month between 40° and 50° (see Table 13-2).

For the year as a whole, normal mean annual ranges of temperature are generally less than

TABLE 13–2

Climatic Data for Mediterranean Scrub Woodland Stations in Western North America

(Temp., °F; Rainfall, In.)

Station	Lat.	El. in Ft		Jan.	Feb.	Mar.	Apr.	May	Jun.	Jul.	Aug.	Sep.	Oct.	Nov.	Dec.	Year
Yreka, Calif.	41°43'	2631	T	34	38	43	50	57	63	72	71	64	54	42	36	
			R	3.1	1.9	1.5	1.0	1.1	0.9	0.2	0.0	0.5	1.5	2.0	3.6	17.6
Red Bluff, Calif.	40°09'	341	T	45	50	54	60	68	76	83	81	75	65	55	47	
			R	3.7	3.5	2.6	1.8	1.1	0.5	0.0	0.1	0.3	1.5	2.3	4.2	23.6
Ukiah, Calif.	39°09'	623	T	46	49	52	57	62	67	73	73	69	61	53	47	
			R	7.2	5.5	4.5	2.4	1.1	0.5	0.0	0.1	0.2	2.0	4.1	8.1	35.6
Sacramento, Calif.	38°31'	17	T	44	50	54	58	64	70	75	73	70	63	53	46	
			R	2.7	2.8	2.1	1.4	0.5	0.1	0.0	0.0	0.1	0.9	1.5	3.0	15.0
San Francisco, Calif.	37°37'	8	T	48	51	53	54	57	60	60	61	62	59	54	49	
			R	3.5	3.4	2.4	1.3	0.4	0.1	0.0	0.0	0.1	0.9	1.6	3.6	17.4
Berkeley, Calif.	37°52'	299	T	49	52	54	56	58	61	61	61	63	61	56	51	
			R	4.7	3.7	3.3	1.6	0.7	0.2	0.0	0.1	0.1	1.2	2.5	4.8	22.7
Stockton, Calif.	37°58'	11	T	45	49	53	58	64	70	74	73	70	62	52	46	
			R	2.6	2.5	2.3	1.1	0.5	0.1	0.0	0.0	0.1	0.6	1.3	3.1	14.3
Santa Cruz, Calif.	36°59'	125	T	49	51	53	55	58	61	63	63	63	60	55	50	
			R	6.5	5.6	4.3	2.1	1.0	0.2	0.0	0.1	0.1	1.4	3.1	7.6	31.9
Mt. Hamilton, Calif.	37°20'	4206	T	40	41	43	48	54	61	71	70	66	57	49	43	
			R	5.5	4.9	4.2	2.3	0.9	0.2	0.0	0.0	0.1	1.3	2.9	6.2	28.5
Camp Pardee, Calif.	38°15'	658	T	45	49	53	59	65	71	79	77	74	65	55	48	
			R	3.8	3.7	3.3	1.8	0.8	0.2	0.0	0.0	0.1	1.1	2.2	3.8	21.0
Auberry, Calif.	37°05'	2003	T	43	46	49	56	63	69	79	77	72	62	51	45	
			R	4.4	4.9	4.1	2.2	0.8	0.2	0.0	0.0	0.1	1.3	2.4	5.6	25.9
Santa Maria, Calif.	34°57'	224	T	51	52	54	57	59	60	63	63	63	61	56	52	
			R	3.0	2.3	2.5	1.0	0.2	0.2	0.0	0.0	0.1	0.6	1.2	3.0	14.2
Santa Barbara, Calif.	34°26'	100	T	52	54	56	58	61	63	67	67	66	63	58	54	
			R	3.7	3.6	3.0	1.2	0.3	0.1	0.0	0.1	0.1	0.5	1.3	4.0	17.8
Burbank, Calif.	34°12'	699	T	53	54	57	61	64	68	73	74	71	65	60	55	
			R	2.4	3.1	2.3	1.2	0.3	0.1	0.0	0.0	0.3	0.5	1.0	2.9	13.9
Santa Ana, Calif.	33°45'	115	T	53	54	57	60	64	67	72	72	71	65	59	55	
			R	2.8	3.2	2.4	1.2	0.3	0.0	0.0	0.1	0.2	0.5	1.3	3.2	15.1
Escondido, Calif.	33°07'	660	T	51	53	56	60	63	67	73	73	71	64	57	53	
			R	2.8	3.3	2.7	1.3	0.3	0.1	0.0	0.2	0.2	0.9	1.4	3.6	16.8
Ensenada, Mexico	31°52'	43	T	55	56	58	60	63	65	68	70	67	64	61	57	
			R	3.1	2.6	1.3	1.2	0.4	0.2	0.1	0.0	0.1	0.7	0.8	2.5	13.1

Source: U.S. Weather Bureau, *Climatography of the United States, Climates of the States, California,* 1959; F. L. Wernstedt, *World Climatic Data, Latin America and the Caribbean,* Pennsylvania State University, 1959.

40 degrees but above 35 degrees in many sections of the Central Valley and the Sierra foothills. In the upper Sacramento valley, for example, the normal range at Redding Fire Station is 36.8 degrees, at Red Bluff 38.1, in the upper San Joaquin drainage at Auberry 35.6, at Fresno 37.4, and farther south at Bakersfield 37.3. These values are mainly the result of considerably higher mean temperatures for the warmest summer months at these locations, for winter temperatures tend to be much more nearly uniform. In the valleys within the coastal ranges mean annual variations tend to be less than 30 degrees. Along the coast and in the San Francisco Bay area the mean annual temperature range at many stations is less than 15 degrees, as at Berkeley where it is 14 degrees, San Francisco airport, 14.1 degrees, at Santa Cruz on the north side of Monterey Bay, 14.2 degrees. At Salinas, southeast of Monterey Bay, it is 13.7 degrees, at Santa Maria, north of Point Conception, 12.3 degrees, and at Ensenada, 14.9 degrees.

The range between the extreme temperatures of record is also notably greater in interior sections than along the coast, being near or above 100 degrees in most localities. At Chico Experiment Station east of the middle Sacramento River and at Placerville in the foothills east of Sacramento it is 106 degrees; at Red Bluff, Stockton, and Fresno it is 98 degrees. By comparison, the extreme range in downtown San Francisco is 67 degrees, at Santa Cruz 88, Santa Maria 85, and San Diego 75. The general decrease in mean annual temperature range from north to south that one observes in interior sections of the mediterranean region are brought about principally by the tendency toward increasingly milder winters with decreasing latitude.

The annual growing season is longest, as one would expect, along the coast, particularly from San Francisco Bay southward. On either side of the Golden Gate it averages around 340 days, about eleven months, and from Monterey Bay to the Santa Maria lowland it is about three hundred days, increasing to 365 days along the coast around San Diego. Within the sheltered valleys of the coastal ranges south of San Francisco the normal growing season is in places around 220 days, a little more than seven months in length, a condition that holds for the barren Mojave desert as well. The Central

Valley is somewhere between these extremes, ranging from around 240 days, about eight months, in the north, to 280 days over most of the remainder (Fig. 11.6).

The most striking characteristic of the region is a decided concentration of normal annual precipitation within the cooler season of the year. At most stations about 95 per cent of the yearly rainfall occurs in the seven-month period from October through April (Table 13-2). Only negligible amounts are received at other times. It is also evident that the rainy season is really only about five months long in southern sections.

A gradual lessening of normal yearly amounts is observed from the humid coastal evergreen forests north of San Francisco southeastward into the desert areas of the interior and along the coast into Lower California (Fig. 13.11). The rain- and fog-drenched forest region of the north coastal ranges is illustrated by

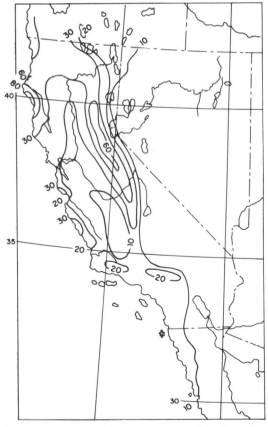

Figure 13.11. Mean annual precipitation in mediterranean North America (inches).

several long-range records, as at Happy Camp, 1090 feet above sea level east of the Klamath Mountains, where some rain falls every month of summer, and the yearly mean total, based upon more than forty years of record, is 54.19 inches. Also representative are Eureka, near the sea on Humboldt Bay, where records of more than seventy years reveal a mean annual amount of 36.15 inches, and Upper Mattole, about 10 miles southeast of Cape Mendocino, where a mean amount of 79.6 inches is based upon a record of more than seventy years. Shorter records indicate that other areas in the north coast ranges receive mean annual amounts of more than 110 inches. At Monumental in the Klamath Mountains at 2750 feet 153.5 inches were reported for 1909. Contrasted with the humid coastal forest and, indeed, with the upper slopes of the Sierra Nevada are the deserts of southeastern California, where less than 4 inches of annual rainfall is typical of a wide section from Death Valley to the Gulf of California. The mediterranean sections are transitional between these extremes.

Mean annual precipitation within the mediterranean region is extremely variable, not only from year to year, but most particularly from place to place. Topography plays a major role in creating many local variations. Two sets of parallel coastal ranges, and north of the Salinas valley three sets, with their related valleys, are in parallel alignment with the seacoast. Because most of the rain-bearing storms approach these shores from the Pacific, the seaward slopes and ridgetops tend to be wetter than the lower lee slopes of the coastal ranges. Annual amounts tend to diminish with increasing distance from the sea. Only at relatively high elevations are inland areas favored by substantial amounts of precipitation, as on the upper slopes of the Sierra Nevada, the Transverse Ranges, and the low mountains northeast of San Diego. Latitude also plays a part in establishing the local climatic variety, that is, northern sections are commonly visited by many more migrating disturbances than areas farther south, and north-facing exposures are often wetter than those facing south.

Examples of these generalizations are not hard to find. Compare, for instance, Ukiah in the Russian River valley, with 35.6 inches, and Cloverdale, with 39.2 inches, with two stations about 40 miles farther inland and in the lee of the coastal ranges, Stony Gorge Reservoir, reporting 19 inches, and Brooks Farnham Ranch, 20.5 inches. Across the Central Valley, just below the Sierra foothills, Chico Ranger Station and Rocklin show an increase, with amounts of 26.4 and 23.6 inches repectively. The increase is due partly to their proximity to the rising slopes of the Sierra Nevada and partly to the more frequent occurrence of thermal convective showers over the eastern side of the valley.

In southern California and northern Lower California, where the mediterranean environment is confined to a narrowing inland section on the western slopes of the mountains, contrasting rainfall values are again significant. Santa Ana Fire Station, 115 feet above sea level about 35 miles southeast of Los Angeles and 15 miles from the coast, reports a mean yearly rainfall of 15.1 inches, and Escondido, about 60 miles southeast and the same distance from the sea, at an elevation of 660 feet, records 16.8 inches. Still farther south, Bellvista, 20 miles northeast of Ensenada and 20 miles from the sea, at 958 feet, reports 13.7 inches. These stations gain both by orographic influence and better exposure to thermal convective activity, and compare as mediterranean sites with the drier, steppelike situations illustrated in the rainfall records for San Diego airport, with 10.9 inches, and Ensenada, with 13.1.

Another example of contrasting climatic situations within the region is a comparison of Santa Cruz, a shore station on the north side of Monterey Bay, with Salinas, about 10 miles from the sea and only 46 feet in elevation, in the lower Salinas valley, and with King City, about 50 miles farther up the valley and more deeply sheltered from invasions of moisture-laden air from the sea. Santa Cruz records a mean annual precipitation of 31.9 inches, Salinas 14.5, and King City 10.4, placing it well within a distinctly grassland environment.

Within the redwood area north of San Francisco are many sunny openings on the leeward, south-facing slopes of minor valleys. Here the tall conifers are withdrawn to higher elevations, giving way to oak, laurel, and shapely madrone, beneath which are often open pastures of colorful herbaceous plants—a local enclave of mediterranean environment.

Altitude is another factor in yearly precipitation. Mt. Hamilton, about 50 miles southeast of

San Francisco at an elevation of 4206 feet, receives 28.5 inches of annual precipitation, which is more than any of the stations in the Bay area. Similarly, at Big Pines Park, about 30 miles northeast of Los Angeles in the Sierra Madre Mountains at an elevation of 6860 feet, there is a normal yearly precipitation of 25.6 inches, and Squirrel Inn, more than 50 miles east of Los Angeles in the San Bernardino Mountains, altitude 5733 feet, receives 42.3 inches. These are alpine sites well outside the mediterranean region, and most of the winter's precipitation arrives in the form of snow.

Most of the year's precipitation in the mediterranean region is rain, although snow is not entirely unknown, even in San Diego, where at least a trace has been observed in January on rare occasions. Whereas the heavier rainfall areas of the north coastal mountains receive a substantial proportion of precipitation in the form of prolonged drizzle and protracted storms of some intensity, the mediterranean region with which we are concerned tends, even in the rainy winter season, to experience a high proportion of sunny weather interrupted by rather short rain spells. These are mainly brought on by migratory lows from the general area of the Aleutian Low, which shifts southward during the winter months from the Gulf of Alaska.

Thunderstorms are relatively rare in this region, are usually very weak, and may develop almost any time of the year. They occur on the average on only three or four days per year north of San Francisco, and perhaps one or two days yearly farther south. Much higher thunderstorm frequencies are known in the upper Sierra Nevada, where ten to fifteen may occur annually, chiefly during the summer. Here, in fact, they may develop without rain. The lightning from such dry thunderstorms has caused severe forest fires, as many as five hundred in two or three days.

The chief feature of the general circulation governing the weather situations that arise in this section of North America is the eastern Pacific High and its changing relationships with the Aleutian Low over the Gulf of Alaska. Also significant is a summertime thermal low that develops over the lower Colorado River valley. Usually by November the winter pattern of sea level pressure and wind fields has been established. The Pacific High has by this time weakened, contracted, and withdrawn southward, until it is scarcely more than a belt of higher pressure averaging about 1021 millibars (30.15 inches) about 600 miles west of Los Angeles (Fig. 4.2). Along the northern margins of this diminished clockwise circulation frontal disturbances occur with moderate frequency. The expanded Aleutian Low at this time averages about 1002 millibars (29.6 inches) for about four months. Migrating storms move eastward along trajectories that bring them well into mediterranean sections more and more often as winter continues. In March the summer circulation pattern begins to emerge, the Aleutian Low diminishing slightly in intensity, and the Pacific High recurrently takes position farther west, although its mean barometric pressure remains near 1021 millibars. By April the Aleutian Low has contracted still further, and migrating storms have become less frequent and begin to cross the coastline at points further and further toward the north. In May and June the Pacific High expands northward, reaching a maximum poleward position in July, when it is centered about 1500 miles west of San Francisco, at which time central pressure values average the highest of the year at 1026 millibars (30.30 inches) (Fig. 4.3). The Aleutian Low has by July virtually disappeared from the daily weather map. Prevailing winds are northwest, nearly parallel to the California coast, and skies dominantly sunny. Increasing the tendency for southeastward flow from the Pacific is the steepened pressure gradient toward the desert interior north of the Gulf of California, where mean atmospheric pressures in July are around 1006 millibars (29.7 inches). By September the east Pacific High begins to contract and the Aleutian Low begins to form over the Bering Sea, leading to an increasing formation of disturbances that find their way southward into the mediterranean region and usher in the winter rainy season.

Summer. Summertime, the season which the mediterranean region shares to a certain extent with the interior desert areas, is a time of predominantly anticyclonic weather when hot, dry, sunny days and clear, often very cool nights are the rule for inland sections. Along the coast summer days are rarely hot; indeed, they are generally quite cool, and although as nearly rainless as interior stations, experience a high incidence of fog from the sea.

When in March the east Pacific High shifts position westward, prior to expanding northward during the months that follow, the sun's effect on land surfaces over northwestern Mexico and southeastern California brings rising temperatures over the desert areas. It is in the early part of March that the thermal low over the head of the Gulf of Mexico and the lower Colorado valley begins to appear. Pressure values drop from around 1020 to 1017 millibars. By mid-March mean atmospheric pressure again drops to about 1014 millibars and eventually attains a normal yearly minimum of 1005 in July. It is an enduring feature of the general circulation in summertime, persisting until around the end of October. The increasing dominance of airflow from the northwest, responding to the rising pressure gradient toward the continental shores, is accompanied by a marked increase in the proportion of clear weather, with rising temperatures and diminishing precipitation. More than half the days in the summer are clear, cloudless, and sunny in interior sections and in many coastal valleys. July is normally the most cloud-free month; for example, Red Bluff reports clear skies for an average of twenty-eight days, Sacramento twenty-nine days, Los Angeles twenty days, and Santa Maria sixteen days.

The greatest decrease in mean monthly amounts of precipitation at most stations takes place from March to April. At Red Bluff April precipitation is about 68 per cent of that in March. At Sacramento it is 66 per cent, Stockton only about 49 per cent, Burbank 53 per cent, and Escondido 49 per cent (Table 13-2). In April, near the end of the rainy season, mean monthly temperatures nearly everywhere are between 55° and 60°. By May interior temperatures generally average between 60° and 65°, and coastal stations tend to remain below 60°.

After the equinox the gradual gain in the proportion of daylight to darkness and the increase in radiant warmth from the sun bring a spring season of colorful bloom to the flowering shrubs of the chaparral. In the more open areas the countless blossoming herbaceous plants for which the region is famed also come into brief flower. Viewed from a distance, the mediterranean landscapes are mantled in varied shades of blue, purple, red, and gold in such flourishing forms as lupine, clover, golden poppy, buttercup, and sunflower. With the advent of dry summer weather blossoms fade and most flowering plants enter a period of rest, and the landscape on nearly every side becomes brownish, withered, and seemingly lifeless.

In most interior situations the warmest month of summer is July (Fig. 13.12). This is chiefly due to the diurnal input and output of radiant heat from the sun, the primary influence on the temperature experience of all localities sufficiently sheltered from direct exposure to the heavy, moisture-laden air from the sea. Day after day the bright, hot sun transmits its warmth through the clear, blue air of the dominantly anticyclonic weather. Temperatures average in the upper 70s all the way from the middle Sacramento valley (Stony Gorge 79°, Chico Experiment Station 79°) to the upper San Joaquin drainage in the southern Sierra foothills (Auberry 79°, Three Rivers 80°). In the upper Sacramento valley mean values are higher, as at Redding (82°) and Red Bluff (83°). Here the northern mountains offer more effective shelter from northwesterly winds, and the area is also more remote from invasions of cooling air that frequently move northward up the Central Valley during the afternoon, coming in from the sea through the Golden Gate.

The Golden Gate is the main pass through which maritime air invades the interior, although it also enters less vigorously at a few other points like Bodega Bay, about 50 miles northwest of San Francisco, and Monterey Bay farther south. Through the main break in the coastal ranges oceanic air penetrates a fairly large segment of the interior to moderate the temperatures and relative humidities of the warmest month.

As interior valleys heat up during the day, the thermal gradient increases, thus steepening the pressure gradient between sea and land. Foggy, saturated air streams in. Maximum wind speeds are commonly reached in the middle or late afternoon, at or a little past the very time when temperature maxima occur. The resulting depression of the mean daily maximum is in turn responsible for lowering the mean temperature for the day as a whole. Thus, those inland stations affected by maritime air experience mean July temperatures significantly lower than stations not directly exposed to airflow from the sea. For example, Ukiah and Cloverdale in the upper Russian

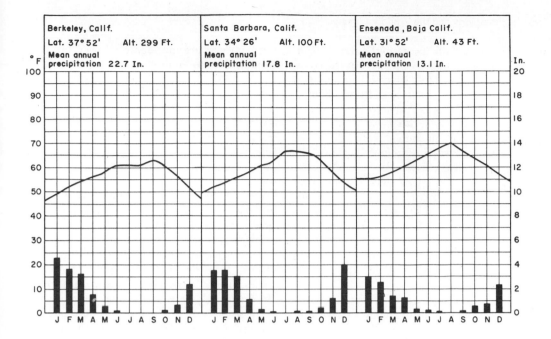

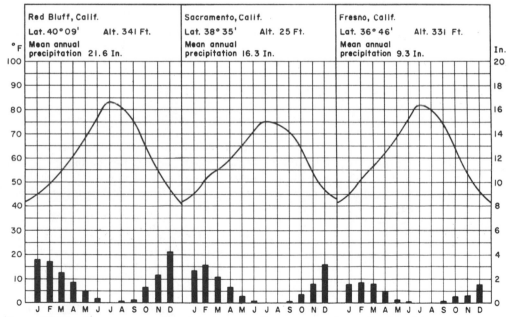

Figure 13.12. Temperature and precipitation at mediterranean scrub woodland stations in western North America.

River valley record July means of 73°, but Graton, in the lower part of the valley open to the sea, and Petaluma, several miles closer to San Francisco Bay, average values about 7 degrees lower (66°) for July, the warmest month. Similarly, July mean temperatures at Antioch (74°), Stockton (74°), and Sacramento (75°), each successively farther inland from the bay, indicate a diminishing maritime influence.

The effect is also seen east of Los Angeles where several stations in the lee of the Santa Ana Mountains, ranging between a half-mile and a mile or more above sea level, record a mean summer maximum for July. This value gradually rises with increasing distance from the sea. Corona, about 25 miles from the coast, has a July mean of 74.3°, Riverside at about 35 miles records 75.7°, and San Bernardino at about 50 miles records 77.1°. By contrast, the station at Santa Ana on the seaward side of the mountains about 10 miles from the coast attains a summer maximum in August of 72.1°.

Farther south the effect is also seen at Barrett Dam about 30 miles inland, where a statistical mean of 77° is reported for July and 76° for August. These contrast significantly with values reported from San Diego on the coast, where a summer maximum of 70° is reached in August. Barrett Dam lies at an elevation of 1623 feet in the lee of a ridge a few miles west that rises to more than 3100 feet.

The mean daily range of temperatures at most inland stations also reaches a maximum in July, amounting to around 35 degrees in the Central Valley. The highest mean monthly values for the summer months are recorded at inland stations as well, where the normal values are in the 90s, compared with the low 70s along the coast. At the same time, nocturnal cooling induces the development of low-lying radiation fog under a fairly frequent inversion. In fact, of the two main kinds of fog that occur in the region, radiation fog is the chief one affecting most inland valleys and develops with maximum frequency during the late autumn and early winter.

Relative humidities at most interior locations decrease with the advance of summer, reaching a minimum in July. Mean relative humidity at Red Bluff for 4 P.M., normally the driest time of day, is 18 per cent. At Sacramento, influenced by frequent advection from the sea, it is 28 per cent. Coastal stations reveal very different values for the same time of day in July, San Francisco airport reporting 68 per cent, Santa Maria 64 per cent. Actually, at many stations along the coast recorded relative humidities are measurably higher in summer than in winter, quite in contrast to inland stations. Increasing summer fog along the coast is the chief cause, although it must be admitted that seasonal differences in coastal humidities are not large, for damp, maritime air is almost constantly present.

Along the coast in July, when inland stations with mean temperatures in the high 70s are experiencing a maximum of summer warmth,

temperatures are considerably lower. From the Golden Gate to Point Conception values are in the low 60s or less, as at San Francisco airport (59°), Berkeley (61°), Santa Cruz (63°), Salinas (62°), San Luis Obispo (65°), and Santa Maria (both August and September 63°). The month of highest mean temperatures is delayed until September over most of this coastal section and averages are less than 65°. From month to month during the summer the change in mean value is slight, and the mean daily range is often less than half the amplitude at inland stations. These temperatures and the monthly rate of change very closely approximate the temperature changes of the cool, upwelling coastal waters over which the onshore flow of air passes. Here atmospheric temperatures are almost entirely determined by the temperature of the sea.

From Point Conception southeastward into Lower California, August is the warmest month, and averages are higher than those farther north. Santa Barbara, for example, shows an August mean of 67°, and reports from stations in the Los Angeles basin that are well-exposed to the sea are similar. August in Burbank averages 74°, in Pasadena 74° and Long Beach 71°. Farther down the coast values for this month are somewhat lower, usually around 70°, as at San Diego and Ensenada. Southeast of Point Conception warm water eddies disrupt the general cooling effect of the sea and partly account for the higher maxima observed. Summer onshore winds tend, during the day, to blow from a slightly more westerly, quite often southwesterly direction, and prolonged daytime fogs are much less frequently seen (Fig. 13.13). Instead, night and early morning fogs are characteristic. The foggiest period is usually from September to February. High humidity, fog, delayed summer temperature maxima, and conspicuously cool summer weather are qualities of the definitely marine aspect in mediterranean California, an aspect typically true only of shoreline situations.

Although advection fog from the sea is a distinctive feature of the mediterranean environment along the coast, a special modification of oceanic fog has become important over industrial areas where very damp, misty air from over the cool coastal waters mixes with smoke, vehicular exhaust, and other products of incomplete combustion. This form of murky,

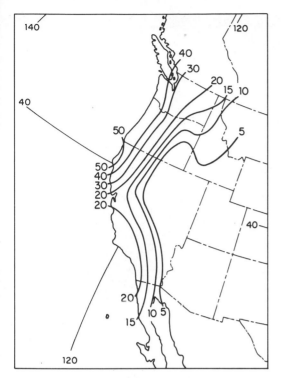

Figure 13.13. Mean annual number of days with dense fog in western North America.

over the Central Valley, in conjunction with a well-developed east Pacific High. This amounts to a pronounced aberration from normal summertime wind and pressure fields. Wind speeds up to 75 miles per hour have been observed at Point Reyes, 30 miles northwest of the Golden Gate, in every month from January to May.

Föhn types of wind, warming as they descend the slopes of mountains into the valleys below, are represented by the northers of the Sacramento valley appearing when a strong southward barometric gradient develops toward the valley. These are hot, dessicating winds that bring heat waves into the Central Valley and sometimes along the coast, augmenting the normal summer drought and thus increasing the hazards of forest fire and water shortage. In southern California föhn winds known by the name *Santa Ana* occur in the Los Angeles basin whenever a strongly developed high over the Great Basin and the resultant pressure gradient gives rise to northeasterly or easterly winds over the interior of southern California. High winds, dust, and very low relative humidities result (a relative humidity as low as 5 per cent has been recorded), and from these characteristics the breadth, fetch, and duration of the air stream of the Santa Ana can easily be identified. From the Mojave desert it streams through the Cajon Pass, about 50 miles east-northeast of Los Angeles, down the canyon of the Santa Ana River, sometimes spreading southward down the Santa Ana Mountains but normally following a well-defined path to the sea near Newport. Although it shifts position slightly from time to time, it usually changes little in width or velocity, continuing out to sea for as far as 100 miles offshore, and may persist for two or three days in succession. Good visibility and low humidity normally precede its arrival, which is heralded by a low, advancing, dark brown cloud of dust-laden air at the surface. It is reported to occur at any time of day or night, although it is reinforced by the nocturnal land breeze and opposed, hence diminished in speed, by the daytime sea breeze. Highest velocities have been noted between 0700 and 0900, dropping off after 1000. A side effect is the development of electrostatic charges on insulated objects, which are believed to cause explosions where the concentration of fuel vapor or other sensitive conditions exist.

miasmic, unpleasantly irritating air is commonly described by the portmanteau term *smog*. It occurs with especially troublesome and often hazardous intensity in the Los Angeles basin, where topography and atmospheric circumstances peculiar to the locality combine to produce it with particular frequency during the months of summer and early autumn. The presence or absence of smog is determined largely by certain variations in the normal diurnal windshift pattern.

Strong winds of gale force occasionally blow from the southeast along the coast in midwinter north of San Francisco. They occur as a rule when a strong high pressure area prevails over the Great Basin east of the Sierra Nevada, from which a powerful flow of continental polar air surges northwestward in the normal clockwise circulation toward a well-developed cyclonic storm approaching eastward over the Pacific. During late spring and early summer strong northwesterly winds up to 75 miles per hour are frequently experienced when the thermal depressions over southern interior California become elongated to form a trough

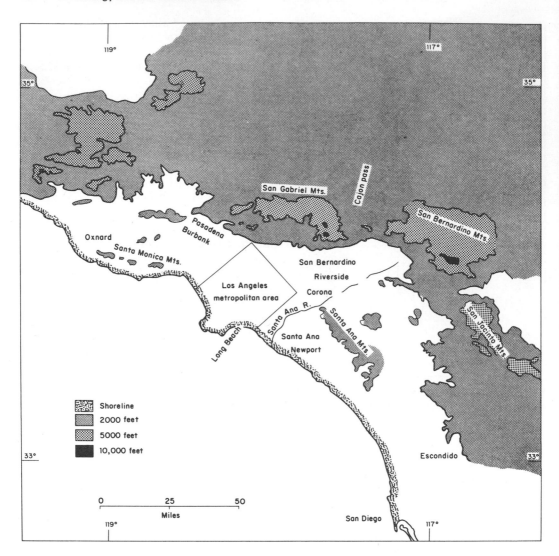

Figure 13.14.   The Los Angeles Basin and adjoining areas in California.

The daily reversal of onshore and offshore winds known as land and sea breezes is a prominent feature of summertime weather from the Los Angeles basin southward along the coast into Lower California. From April through October it is common for the first breath of cool, damp sea air to cross the shoreline a little before 0900, gaining strength as the day progresses, although rarely averaging more than 10 miles per hour by midafternoon, lessening after that but continuing after dark until around 2200. The air stream of the sea breeze tends to remain within about 2000 feet above the surface, often traveling beneath an opposing flow of air aloft, and develops appreciable turbulence, with vertical mixing rising in the nearby mountain tops to 5000 feet or more. Vertical motion is commonly evident from the formation of convective cumulus clouds a few miles inshore. The offshore land breeze, developing after the normal nocturnal inversion has formed, sets up around midnight, moving in an even shallower layer than the sea breeze, generally under 1000 feet, and at lower velocities, and continues until after dawn, extending an estimated distance of up to 50 miles from the coast under favorable circumstances. It is in connection with the nocturnal inversion, arising from normal clear sky radiation heat loss coupled with certain aspects of the land and sea breeze effect that Los Angeles smog most commonly occurs.

The Los Angeles basin is rimmed by low mountains from northwest to southeast but is otherwise open to the Pacific (Fig. 13.14). The fumes and minute particles produced by various kinds of combustion accumulate readily during the night and early morning under an inversion layer that averages about 1000 feet thick. This relatively stable, cool, damp air, polluted by the atmospheric sediment of combustion, tends to hug the surface in comparatively thin layers alternating with levels of clear air in a complex stratification that is readily observable in the valleys around Los Angeles just at dawn. Once the sea breeze has set in, some time before 0900, the ensuing turbulence causes considerable vertical mixing very rapidly, and the smog soon intensifies for the basin as a whole. On occasion, when onshore winds are strong enough to mix pollutants with moisture particles but not strong enough to carry off the noxious mixture over the bordering mountains, and the land breeze is correspondingly weak, smog may settle over the Los Angeles metropolitan area for several days in succession. It occurs on the average of at least thirty times yearly. It also develops, although less frequently and with less intensity, over certain sections of the metropolitan areas around San Francisco Bay and San Diego.

Winter. As summer begins to draw to an end with a return of longer, cooler nights and shorter, although still very warm, days, residents in the mediterranean region look forward to the first autumn rains to bring relief from both heat and drought, but especially drought. Water shortage becomes a critical problem, and the danger from severe brush fires is at its height for the year. By the end of summer the dense chaparral has become dusty, brittle, and exceedingly dry. Nearly every year at this season brush fires break out at many points. The worst of these conflagrations in Los Angeles history developed in November 1961, after an unusually long period—since the preceding April—without any substantial rain. It burned out of control through the chaparral in several areas, but particularly on the south slopes of the Santa Monica Mountains, where it destroyed more than five hundred houses. Not until

November 20 did the first effective rain appear.

July and August are statistically the driest months, although September is almost equally dry nearly everywhere. Mean rainfall totals for July or August are usually less than one tenth of an inch. Ordinarily, the winter rainy season begins before the end of October, and monthly amounts increase toward a maximum that is reached in December at most stations, but is delayed until February within the Los Angeles basin and the San Fernando valley. In these areas December is commonly a time of secondary maximum, and the differences in amount between December and February are usually very small (Fig. 13.15).

The average precipitation for the wettest month (December at most places) tends to be greater in northern sections and also well up in the Sierra foothills, as well as in exposed situations on the coast. Redding, far up the Sacramento valley, averages 7.93 inches, and Ukiah, Cloverdale, and Graton in the Russian River vally range between 8 and 9 inches. Placerville, at an altitude of 1890 feet in the Sierra foothills,

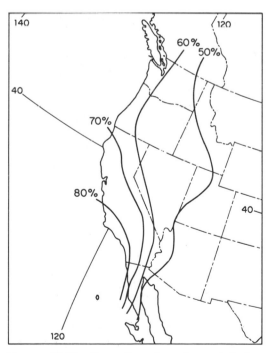

Figure 13.15. Proportion of yearly precipitation normally received December through April in western United States (per cent).

averages 7.72 inches, and Santa Cruz and Big Sur Park, both of which are seaside stations, average 7.56 inches and 9.12 inches respectively. Elsewhere, normal amounts for December are on the order of half these values.

Winter rains are often heavy and prolonged, contributing to flood conditions when accompanied by higher temperatures that melt the alpine snows. In the Sacramento valley especially, the annual spring melting of snow in the high Sierra, coupled with the last of the winter's rains, creates some flooding almost every year, although damaging floods seldom occur. In southern sections, although flooding is less frequent, heavy flood damage tends to occur more often. From 1861 to 1960 severe floods occurred in southern California in eighteen winter seasons in consequence of unusually heavy rains. During the winter of 1961–62 very heavy rains from a slow-moving frontal storm occurred in southern California in February, lasting almost without letup from February 7 to 12, causing considerable local flooding, a great many landslides of saturated, fluid mud, a large loss of property, and twenty deaths. Over 7 inches of rain fell in some areas in five days, and at certain foothill sites 14 inches fell. Temperatures in the 40s and 50s melted snow on the nearby mountain slopes to augment the runoff. All this was a startling contrast to the unusually dry, hot summer, the shortage of water, and the heavy outbreak of brush fires that had plagued the same general area in the autumn of 1961.

From year to year annual precipitation varies widely around the arithmetic mean values shown in Table 13-2. At Red Bluff, for example, total precipitation in 1940 was 67.85 inches, but in 1946 only 10.71 inches, compared with the mean amount of 25.36 inches.[3] San Francisco and San Diego provide similar examples, the former receiving 35.19 inches in 1941 and 9 inches in 1917, compared with a mean of 20.37 inches, the latter 24.93 inches in 1941 and only 4.14 inches in 1924, in contrast to a mean of 10.1 inches.

Occasionally, prolonged dry winter weather prevails when a large, intensive area of clear, cold anticyclonic air extends over most of the United States west of the Rocky Mountains.[4] For sixty consecutive days no rain whatever fell at San Francisco from November 16th to January 16th during the winter of 1876–77. The worst drought on record for this general area of the United States was in the winter of 1850–51, when only 7.5 inches of rain fell at San Francisco and only 5 inches at Sacramento.

Snow seldom falls in the mediterranean sections of the west except high in the coastal mountains, where it is a common feature at elevations of more than 4000 feet. Even here it rarely remains long on the ground. Red Bluff in the upper Sacramento valley averages no more than 3 inches of snow per year, but Sandberg, less than 50 miles northwest of Los Angeles at an elevation of 4517 feet records a mean of 27 inches of snow each winter. High level winter snow is reported as far south as central Lower California. High in the Sierra Nevada heavy winter snows are normal each winter, and these are most important for the success of agriculture, and indeed of life in general, in the mediterranean region. Snow accumulates there in a heavy blanket that creates an annual reserve of water used during the ensuing summer through streamflow and surface runoff for irrigation and municipal water supply.

Despite the high frequency of precipitating disturbances in winter, the sun shines much of the time. Clear, cloudless weather occurs on an average of eleven days each month from December through February at Red Bluff and on twelve days in the same interval at Los Angeles. In general, about one third of the days each month of winter are sunny, dry, and pleasant.

Under clear sky conditions between the autumnal equinox in September and the vernal equinox in March, when a net loss of radiative heat from the sun arises from the greater proportion of darkness to daylight, it is not surprising to observe that nocturnal temperatures can occasionally drop well below freezing. At Red Bluff, for example, a temperature of 17° has been recorded in both December

[3] John Leighly, "Weather and Climate," in C. M. Zierer, ed., *California and the Southwest*, John Wiley & Sons, Inc., New York, 1956.

[4] Information in the following paragraphs has been obtained mainly from U.S. Weather Bureau, *Climatography of the United States*, No. 60–64, *Climates of the States, California*, 1959.

and January, Sacramento has recorded 22° in January, and San Diego has reported 29° in January. Subfreezing temperatures are extremely rare along the coast, however, except at places a few miles back from the shore and sheltered to some extent, such as Santa Maria, which has reported temperatures of 26° in December, 22° in January, and 24° in February. These are extreme values. Otherwise, the mean minimum for the winter months remains above 35° in colder northern areas and above 40° for the region as a whole. The mean daily range of temperature is 20 degrees or less throughout the region, and along the water's edge approaches half this amount during the winter months.

Without exception, January is the coldest month, when mean temperatures at most interior stations are in the upper 40s and along the coast in the south are in the low 50s. From San Pedro to Ensenada mean January temperatures are near 55°.

Winter begins to wane in February in many localities, especially on the south-facing slopes in the coastal ranges, when early-blooming plants first begin to flower. The increasing length of day and warmth from the sun as it steadily rises higher in the southern sky raise temperatures month by month. The winter's rains begin to diminish. Over the sun-warmed waters of the Pacific the east Pacific High begins to intensify, to expand westward, and eventually to shift northward, bringing a return of strongly developed anticyclonic weather offshore and of northwest winds to the land along the west coast. The polar frontal zone of recurrent disturbances withdraws northward as well, and the warm, dry summer returns to this small segment of mediterranean climate in western North America.

References

Birot, P., and Dresch, J.: *La Méditerranée et la Moyen-Orient*, Presses universitaires de France, Paris, 1953–56.

Court, A.: "Thunderstorm Frequency in Northern California," *Bulletin of the American Meteorological Society*, **41**(8): 406–9, 1960.

Fisher, W. B.: *The Middle East*, Methuen & Co., Ltd., London, 1957.

Gleeson, T. A.: "Cyclogenesis in the Mediterranean Region," *Scientific Report No. 1*, Department of Meteorology, Florida State University, Tallahassee, Fla., 1952.

Ives, R. L.: "Climate of the Sonoran Desert Region," *Annals of the Association of American Geographers*, **39**(3): 143–88, 1949.

Munz, P. A., and Keck, D. D.: *A California Flora*, University of California Press, Berkeley, 1959.

Patton, C. P.: "Climatology of Summer Fogs in the San Francisco Bay Area," *University of California Publications in Geography*, **10**(3), University of California Press, Berkeley, 1956.

Rikli, M.: *Das pflanzenkleid der Mittelmeerländer*, Verlag Hans Huber, Bern, 1943–48.

Semple, E. C.: *The Mediterranean Region*, Henry Holt and Co., New York, 1931.

Stevenson, R. E.: "The Marine Climate of Southern California," *Oceanographic Survey of the Continental Shelf Area of Southern California*, State Water Pollution Control Board, Sacramento, Calif., 1959, pp. 1–58.

U.S. Naval Oceanographic Office: *Sailing Directions for the Mediterranean* (H.O. 52–56), Vols. 1–4, 1951–63.

U.S. Navy: *Operational Weather of the Northern Hemisphere*, Part I, *Climatological Charts*, Section A, *Mediterranean Area*, 1955.

Zierer, C. M., ed.: *California and the Southwest*, John Wiley & Sons, Inc., New York, 1956.

chapter 14

MID-LATITUDE FOREST AND WOODLAND CLIMATES OF SOUTH AMERICA AND SOUTHERN AFRICA

It is necessary to recall certain geographical conditions of primary significance among the climates of southern latitudes. First, the seasons are reversed on the calendar, summer spanning the months of December through February, and winter from June through August. Second, the earth's surface south of the equator is preponderantly water. This creates climatic regimes in all mid-latitude situations that are much more moderate than the regimes of the much larger land areas in the middle latitudes of the northern hemisphere. Seasonal variations in general atmospheric behavior take place within considerably narrower limits than in the northern hemisphere. Climatic rhythms are more constant and details of the weather experience from place to place more reliably predictable. Land masses being very much smaller than in the northern hemisphere, a third point to bear in mind, is that every climatic region in the mid-latitudes is smaller than its counterpart north of the equator.

South America

In South America are two distinctly separate areas of mid-latitude mixed forest. One occupies a large interior section of the south Brazilian highlands, extending into parts of eastern Paraguay and northeastern Argentina. The other is in the southwestern part of the con-

tinent, appearing mainly in Chile but also to some extent in the Andean portions of southern Argentina at moderate elevations (Fig 14.1). In middle Chile it yields, in a northward direction, to mediterranean scrub woodland (Fig. 14.2).

THE SOUTHWEST COAST. Along the west coast of southern South America may be seen a poleward climatic transition from open, arid desert to dense, wet forest. It is comparable to the meridional transition along the west coast of North America and the Atlantic shores of western Europe and North Africa. In both northern hemisphere situations we have observed how a humid coastal evergreen forest in high latitudes merges equatorward with a less humid mixed forest, which in turn yields to a dominantly evergreen mediterranean scrub woodland, and this dry summer region in its turn gives way to an even drier steppe grassland border grading into desert. Exactly the same climatic relationships are seen from Tierre del Fuego to the Atacama Desert. The South American transition most closely resembles that along the west coast of North America.

A mediterranean scrub woodland begins just north of the Rio Aconcagua, less than 100 miles northeast of Valparaiso, at around the latitude of 32°S., and extends southward for some 350 miles. A short distance south of the

Figure 14.1. Mixed forest and grassland on the east slopes of the Andes in western Argentina near latitude 38 degrees. [Pan American Photo]

Rio Bio Bio a more humid mixed forest begins, extending southward for about 300 miles before giving way to a heavier, wetter vegetation that is dominantly evergreen and reaches all the way down the coast to Tierra del Fuego, at a latitude of about 55°S.

In this part of South America the west coast preserves an almost north–south alignment from latitude 30° (about 200 miles north of Valparaiso) to latitude 50°, where an easy, graceful, eastward curve begins, terminating at Cape Horn around latitude 56°. Between La Serena, just north of 30°, and Puerto Montt, at about 41°30', the coastal configuration is almost without prominent indentations or projections. A few exceptions are noteworthy as points of reference, as at Punta Lengua de la Vaca, southwest of La Serena, Punta Caraumilla, southwest of Valparaiso, Punta Lavapie, southwest of Concepcion, and Punta Galera, southwest of Valdivia. From Puerto Montt to the Cape, however, a totally different configuration appears. This, the Chilean archipelago and fiord coast, is quite like the North American

273

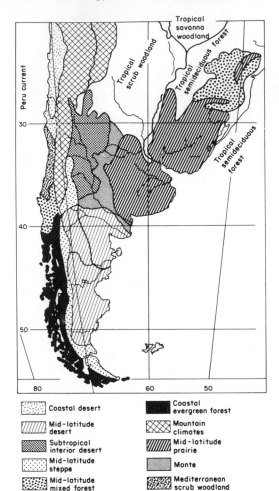

Figure 14.2. Climatic regions in southern South America.

coast north of Vancouver. Here are hundreds of islands, mostly small, but some large, like Chiloe, southwest of Puerto Montt, that is about as large as the Caribbean island of Puerto Rico. Many deep, narrow, steep-sided fiords intrude sinuously into the flanks of the lower Andes on the mainland. At the head of many a fiord south of 46° the tongue of an alpine glacier meets the sea at points some 100 miles or more from the open Pacific.

From about 100 miles north of Valparaiso to Puerto Montt, a distance of some 700 miles, the dominant physiographic features are the high Andes, the coastal mountains, and a series of small, connected valleys between. The crest line of the Andes averages about 100 miles from the Pacific in these latitudes, gradually lowering in elevation from its greatest height of 22,834 feet on Mount Aconcagua, to over 11,000 feet east of Puerto Montt. From here altitudes continue to diminish to between 5000 and 6000 feet but rise again east of the Taitao peninsula to more than 13,000 feet, thereafter declining gradually to around 3000 feet near Cape Horn. Mountain passes between Concepcion and Valdivia are as low as 3500 feet and south of Puerto Montt are often less than 1500 feet above sea level. Year-round alpine glaciers and enduring snowfields are found at increasingly lower elevations from north to south. Northeast of Santiago permanent snow extends down to about 13,000 feet, east of Valdivia to about 5000 feet, and between the Taitao peninsula and the Cape down to 2300 feet at many points, and alpine glaciers in southern Chile project tips of solid ice into the sea. Throughout the entire area the Andes stand as a barrier to the eastward movement of air streams from the Pacific. Thus, orographic rain and snow are accountable for much of the year's precipitation at higher levels on both sides of the Andes. East of the Andes at lower levels extensive desert is in part the result of a rain shadow effect produced by the high mountain barrier.

The deeply dissected ranges of terraced hills and plateaus that hug the coast of middle Chile reach heights of more than 3200 feet north and south of Valparaiso but become increasingly lower toward the south, attaining heights of around 1600 feet northwest of Puerto Montt. Although they occasionally recede from the shoreline where incised stream valleys widen out into small, often marshy coastal lowlands, they are always in sight from the beaches. Most often they rise steeply from the water's edge. The small, scattered lowlands along the shore are overshadowed by the coastal ranges, and a continuous coastal plain does not exist.

Between the high Andes and the flat-topped coastal plateaus lies an irregular structural depression called the Central Valley. It is really a connected series of small valley floors that are separated from one another by westward-reaching spurs of the Andes and eastward extensions of the coastal ranges. Thus, a variety of small, localized settings is characteristic of the interior. Most of the interior valleys are small, often less than 15 miles across, and generally appear in the form of flat or gently sloping alluvial plains drained by swift-flowing streams that pour down from the western flanks of the Andes toward the Pacific. The Central Valley, like the Andes and the low mountains along the coast, descends in a gentle gradient toward the south. Around Santiago the floors of the valleys are generally more than 1500 feet above sea level. The altitude of Santiago, for example, is 1706 feet, of Rancagua, 1640 feet, of San Fernando, about 80 miles south, 1122 feet, of Linares, about 100 miles farther south, 515 feet, of Los Angeles, 125 miles beyond, 426 feet, and of Temuco, 85 miles farther, 374 feet. Beyond Puerto Montt, which is only a few feet above sea level, the Central Valley subsides beneath the sea and is replaced by the gulfs, bays, straits, and canals of the archipelago.

The drainage features of the Central Valley are quite unlike the integrated Sacramento–San Joaquin system of California's Central Valley. In Chile the terrain is latticed by a great many west-flowing streams and their tributaries that rise high in the slopes of the Andes. Coursing rapidly downward, they cut deeply into the foothills before crossing the valley at slackened speed, and then wind steeply down to the sea. Rarely are they more than 100 miles in length, and many that originate in the coastal ranges are less than half this long. Nearly fifty small streams pursue their separate ways toward the Pacific, nourished in part by meltwater from the Andean snows, and thus maintaining a persistent, year-round flow in spite of summer's diminished rains and, in the mediterranean woodlands, summer drought.

South of Temuco and the Rio Tolten, at about 39° of latitude, is the Chilean lake district along the well-watered lower slopes of the Andes. Here a series of small lakes, embraced by the forested foothills of the high mountains and generally less than 500 feet above sea level, reaches almost to Puerto Montt. The largest of them, Lago Llanquihue, west of Osorno's volcanic peak, is more than 25 miles from shore to shore. On the opposite side of the Andes are many small, alpine lakes at higher altitude that continue southward in both Argentina and Chile all the way to the southern limits of the mainland.

The Pacific shores of Chile are washed by the cold, north-flowing waters of the Peru Current, a largely wind-driven stream of surface water originating in the icy southernmost reaches of the Pacific north of Antarctica. It continues cold in every latitude it enters on its path toward the equator, and its temperature throughout the year governs the temperature of the air in contact with its surface. During the summer season south of the equator average sea surface temperatures in February are around 60° about 100 miles north of Valparaiso, about 57.5° just south of the island of Chiloe, and only about 48° around Tierra del Fuego (Fig. 6.13). The coldest month of winter, measured in sea surface temperatures, is August, and values drop to 55° for some 100 miles north of Valparaiso, to 50° around Chiloe, and to about 40° in the vicinity of Tierra del Fuego (Fig. 6.12).

SOUTHWEST COASTAL PLANT LIFE.   The north-to-south transition from desert to dense, humid forest is marked by a succession of dominant vegetation types. The aridity of the Atacama Desert in northern Chile begins to yield to the persistent grass cover of a slightly wetter, cooler environment near Copiapo some 400 miles north of Valparaiso. But mean yearly rainfall amounts remain well below even 5 inches for more than 150 miles farther south. Copiapo records a mean of 1.1 inch, for example, and Vallenar 2.5 inches. Beginning in the valley of the Rio Elqui, which enters the Pacific at La Serena, annual rainfall in the amount of 5 inches or more supports a widespread and nearly continuous grass cover that is the dominant vegetation southward from here to the mediterranean vegetation complex starting in the valley of the Rio Aconcagua, north of Valparaiso. The change is a gradual and intermittent one, however, for outliers of shrub and low-crowned scrub woodland vegetation can be seen in the sheltered valleys and on the southern slopes along the coast, where cooler, shaded circumstances and a better exposure to the prevailing southerly winds from the sea favor their development. And grassland continues southward as a prominent feature, well beyond the Aconcagua, in both mountain and valley situations. It appears in extensive alpine meadows beyond the tree line at 4000–5000 feet in the Andes, and along the coast sometimes mantles the hillsides from summit to sea level.

Mediterranean vegetation prevails from the Rio Aconcagua valley for about 350 miles southward to the drainage of the Rio Bio Bio.

This is about half the extent of the comparable region in North America, but the essential elements are the same. In spite of the fact that most of the accessible valley floors and hillsides have been cleared for cultivation, enough remnants of the native cover remain to determine its original character. A chaparral or maquis, locally called matorral, a very thinly scattered scrub woodland, and intervening grassland are the principal elements, plus a great many beautiful flowering herbs that color the landscape in spring.

Here, as in the northern hemisphere, the maquis consists of a thick growth of small trees and shrubs, seldom more than 10 feet high, in which stiff-branched, often thorny plants with small, brittle leaves are the reigning forms. Among the more common species is a small, tough, shrubby tree, seldom more than 15 feet high, known as maqui (*Aristotelia maqui*). Fragant in both flowers and foliage, other indigenous species of such geners as *Baccharis*, *Acacia*, *Adesmia*, and *Proustia* are common. In sheltered situations where moisture is conserved and moisture-loss from evaporation is reduced are relict clumps of trees that include many species of a once more widely distributed woodland. Among them are litre (*Lithraea caustica*) and boldo or peumo (*Boldea fragrans*), which is noted for its fragrant bark and closely resembles California live oak. The latter species and several others with which it is commonly associated are usually less than 40 feet in height, and bear evergreen, leathery leaves in a low, rounded crown. In settled areas a number of introduced species like Lombardy poplar, weeping willow, and eucalyptus have generally replaced the native trees, particularly along the banks of rivers and canals and in the landscaping of farmsteads. Native trees and shrubs in the mediterranean region stand out wherever they are present as an evergreen background against which are contrasted the deciduous members of the many exotic species.

From north to south during the summertime in the mediterranean region one observes a number of striking changes in the appearance of the landscape. In the broad valleys that begin north of Santiago and continue south to the Rio Maule the land is mainly cleared, and the deep, rich soil is planted to crops in various stages of vigorous growth under irrigation. The brighter green fertility of cropland and irrigated pastures stands out against a backdrop of dull gray-green and tones of brown on the bordering hills of unwatered chaparral. Beyond the Rio Maule, however, cultivated land becomes less extensive in a terrain that is more rolling and wears a deeper, more intense shade of green, suggesting the occurrence of more frequent and more abundant summer showers. Stream margins and uncultivated depressions become increasingly marshy, and scattered stands of evergreen beech (*Nothofagus Dombeyi*), cipres (*Libocedrus chilensis*), manio (*Podocarpus salignus*), and pino (*Saxegothea conspicua*) become more and more common. Finally, just beyond the Rio Bio Bio a close-crowned forest of mixed deciduous and evergreen broadleaved and coniferous trees begins. Most of both broad-leaved and coniferous types are evergreen, but three very prominent deciduous species of the southern beech, the nire (*Nothofagus antarctica*) roble (*Nothofagus obliqua*), and lenga (*Nothofagus pumilio*), lend variety to the forest.

The mixed forest begins where summers are cooler and where a year-round precipitation brings summer rain in amounts that increase with increasing latitude. It is not strikingly different from the wetter, more luxuriant coastal evergreen forest with which it merges farther south, and it is relatively small in area. Thus, beyond Valdivia the mixed forest region takes on all the aspects of a dripping rain forest and is occasionally referred to as a temperate rain forest, a region that projects southward along both sides of the Andes to the Straits of Magellan. This is the richest forest in the southern part of the continent and includes a good many indigenous species that thrive in the constantly cool, moist atmosphere and survive the frequent buffeting of mid-latitude storms that are typical of this part of the world.

From the Rio Maule southward to the lake district and beyond, the heaviest forest appears along the middle and lower slopes of the Andes. Rarely does the forest rise to elevations above 6000 feet. Prominent species include such of the smaller conifers as the manio (*Podocarpus salignus*), llengue (*Podocarpus andinus*), which are usually under 30 feet high, and pino (*Saxegothea conspicua*), from 30 to 60 feet high. One of the more distinctive conifers is the monkey puzzle tree (*Araucaria araucana*), also called Chilean pine, which is confined to a section of the Andes roughly between the Rio Bio Bio and Lago Llanquihue and for a short distance south of Concepcion along the coast. This tall conifer, with drooping branches that recurve upward toward the tips, with very stiff, sharp-pointed leaves and with cones as large as a man's head, attains a height of 90 to 135 feet, sometimes reaching 150 feet, with diameters of 4–5 feet. Alerce (larch) (*Fitzroya cupressoides*) is considered the finest timber tree in Chile and is very like the California redwood. It commonly develops a small, pyramidal crown high up at the top of a tall straight bole and averages heights of between 130 and 150 feet near Puerto Montt, with a diameter of as much as 9 feet. One specimen towers up to 240 feet.

Among the species that range nearly all the way from the Rio Bio Bio to the Straits of Magellan and thus give some consistency to the coastal evergreen forest are the conifers cipres (*Pilgerodendron uviferum*), maniu (*Podocarpus nubigenus*), and the broadleaved beeches, the evergreen guindo (*Nothofagus betuloides*) and the deciduous lenga (*Nothofagus pumilio*) and nire (*Nothofagus antarctica*). Also typical throughout the long north–south range of this region is the ground cover, an often impenetrable tangle of vines and shrubs, as well as ferns, mosses, and other lowly plants in the spongy litter on the forest floor.

SOUTHWEST COASTAL CLIMATIC CONDITIONS. We have observed the gradual change in vegetation between arid desert in the north and rain-soaked forest in the south. This is the tangible evidence of a climatic transition between the extremes of excessive drought in the Atacama and excessive moisture in the Chilean archipelago. Actually, five distinct climates are successively encountered on a traverse from Copiapo to the Straits of Magellan: desert, steppe, mediterranean scrub woodland, mid-latitude mixed forest, and mid-latitude coastal evergreen forest, to say nothing of diversified mountain climates along the Andes.

Thus, in an exceedingly narrow band along the southwest coast of the continent a striking array of related, although contrasting climates extends for about 2000 miles. Twenty-five degrees of latitude are spanned; the primary effect of latitude on climatic distribution is nowhere better illustrated than here. But

other circumstances are fundamentally significant as well. The entire complex of latitude, west coast exposure, major relief features, cold coastal waters, and the mean circulation of the atmosphere must be taken into account as we examine the atmospheric properties of this elongated portion of South America.

The mean atmospheric circulation at the surface of the eastern Pacific is governed mainly by the pressure and wind fields of the semi-permanent subtropical high that lies at all times west of northern Chile, by the stormy turbulence of the convergence zone south of it, and by the dominantly eastward flow of the high altitude westerlies above both these sections, beginning around 15,000 feet (500 millibars). Actually, the prevailing flow of air over southern Chile, both at the surface and aloft, is generally eastward, a part of that great circumpolar surface circulation of the westerlies over unbroken stretches of the southern oceans called the Roaring Forties. With increasing distance northward the predominant surface direction becomes more southerly, with southwest, south, and finally southeast winds outnumbering others as one progresses along the Chilean coast into Peru.

Two types of air mass are involved: maritime tropical, originating in the persistent anticyclone west of northern Chile, and maritime polar (polar Pacific), arising in the higher latitudes south of this (Fig. 5.2 and 5.3). Between these two air mass source regions is a frontal zone of conflict, aligned in a slightly west-northwest to east-southeast direction. Powerful disturbances that arise in the secondary circulation between the latitudes of 40° and 60° invariably take the form of migrating cyclones combining the qualities of the westerlies of middle latitudes and the polar easterlies off the coast of Antarctica. One of the really striking characteristics of the mean circulation over southern Chile, south of about latitude 40°, is the high frequency of violent, precipitating storms from the Pacific that batter the islands of the archipelago and the western slopes of the Andes throughout the year.

The primary control of seasonal variations in the climates of southwestern South America is the periodic displacement of the east Pacific anticyclone, centered about 1000 miles west of northern Chile. As winter approaches, this persistent high pressure area contracts and

TABLE 14-1
Climatic Data for Stations in Southwestern South America
(Temp., °F; Rainfall, In.)

Station	Lat.	El. in Ft		Jan.	Feb.	Mar.	Apr.	May	Jun.	Jul.	Aug.	Sep.	Oct.	Nov.	Dec.	Year
La Serena, Chile	29°54'	115	T	65	65	63	59	56	54	53	54	55	58	60	63	
			R	0.0	0.1	0.0	0.1	0.8	1.4	0.9	0.7	0.2	0.1	0.0	0.0	4.3
Valparaiso, Chile	33°01'	134	T	64	64	62	59	56	54	53	54	55	57	60	63	
			R	0.1	0.1	0.2	0.7	3.8	5.1	3.4	2.7	1.2	0.7	0.3	0.1	18.2
Santiago, Chile	33°27'	1706	T	68	67	63	57	51	47	47	49	53	57	62	66	
			R	0.1	0.1	0.2	0.6	2.5	3.3	3.0	2.3	1.2	0.6	0.3	0.2	14.1
Los Andes, Chile	32°50'	2676	T	70	70	66	60	53	48	49	51	55	60	65	70	
			R	0.1	0.2	0.2	0.5	2.6	3.2	2.1	2.0	0.9	0.5	0.2	0.2	12.3
Constitucion, Chile	35°20'	16	T	65	64	61	57	54	51	47	47	53	56	60	63	
			R	0.3	0.5	0.6	2.2	6.9	8.5	7.5	5.2	2.0	3.0	0.8	0.6	38.8
Talca, Chile	35°26'	318	T	72	70	65	58	52	48	47	49	53	59	64	69	
			R	0.2	0.3	0.5	1.5	5.5	6.8	5.4	3.5	2.2	1.0	0.8	0.4	28.2
Concepcion, Chile	36°40'	49	T	65	63	60	55	52	50	49	49	51	55	59	63	
			R	0.6	0.7	1.7	3.5	9.3	9.9	8.9	6.9	4.3	2.3	1.9	1.2	51.2
Temuco, Chile	38°45'	374	T	62	62	59	54	50	46	46	47	50	53	56	60	
			R	1.4	1.6	2.8	4.4	8.6	8.1	7.6	6.3	3.9	2.9	3.0	2.3	52.1
Valdivia, Chile	39°48'	16	T	62	61	58	53	49	46	46	47	49	53	56	60	
			R	2.6	2.7	4.5	8.4	14.8	16.3	14.7	11.9	8.4	4.7	4.8	4.2	98.0
Puerto Montt, Chile	41°28'	3	T	59	59	59	52	49	46	46	46	48	51	54	57	
			R	3.5	4.1	5.5	7.1	9.3	10.1	8.3	7.8	6.2	4.7	5.1	4.9	76.6
Cabo Raper, Chile	46°50'	131	T	51	52	50	49	46	44	42	43	44	45	47	49	
			R	6.8	5.8	6.7	7.1	7.5	7.3	7.7	6.6	5.4	6.3	6.4	6.7	80.3
Evangelists' Island, Chile	52°24'	16	T	48	48	47	45	43	41	40	40	41	42	44	46	
			R	9.4	9.0	10.3	10.1	8.6	8.3	8.7	8.3	8.5	8.0	8.5	9.0	106.6

Source: F. L. Wernstedt, *World Climatic Data, Latin America and the Caribbean*, Pennsylvania State University, 1959.

loses intensity, and its central area shifts northward and westward to a latitude of around 25°, allowing the belt of storms to move northward bringing the great bulk of the year's precipitation to mediterranean Chile and the regions beyond.

The factor that really dominates the climates of southwestern South America the whole year long is the sea. The qualities of the atmosphere over the narrow edge of the continent between the Andes and the Pacific are derived almost constantly from the sea. Only occasionally does dry, continental air spill over the crest of the Andes onto the Pacific slope. The prevailing program of successive atmospheric situations originates over the sea, and the climates between the Atacama and Cape Horn are dominantly marine climates.

Without doubt, one of the more monotonously unpleasant marine climates in the world is that section of the Chilean coast between the Taitao peninsula and Cape Horn. Throughout the year changes in sunshine, cloudiness, relative humidity, precipitation amounts, and temperature span only very narrow limits. Available records indicate a mean cloud cover here of about 80 per cent, varying less than 10 per cent from season to season. The sun shines at most for only a few hours on those days when it appears at all; for most of the year the sky is either very cloudy or entirely overcast. Relative humidity changes very slightly, averaging between 80 and 95 per cent from one end of the year to the other. Although substantial differences appear in the mean precipitation amounts for the rainiest and driest months at the few stations of record, abundant precipitation falls every month of the year (Table 14-1). The mean range of temperature between the warmest and the coldest months averages less than 10 degrees at most locations. Heavy rain, in winter mixed with sleet and snow, alternating with prolonged drizzle, mist, and fog, and all occurring at relatively low temperatures, rule the weather within these latitudes. North of the Taitao peninsula, however, seasonal rhythms become increasingly apparent the farther one retreats from the southern hemisphere's notorious belt of storms.

Mean annual precipitation decreases northward (Fig. 14.3), with Bahia Felix at the western end of the Straits of Magellan recording an average of nearly 200 inches, the Evangelists' Island about 50 miles northwest, 106.6 inches, Cabo Raper on the southern end of the Taitao peninsula, 80.1 inches, Punta Corona on the northern end of Chiloe, 80 inches, Punta Galera, 77 inches, Puente Tumbes, 35 inches, Punta Caraumilla, 13.5 inches, and Punta Lengua de Vaca, 4.5 inches. The Evangelists' Island averages twenty-five days with rain during the least rainy month, June, and from November through April averages twenty-eight rain days per month. Valdivia, much

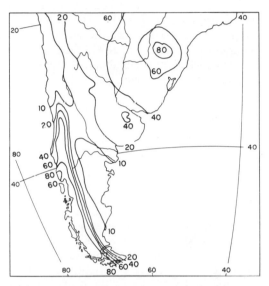

Figure 14.3. Mean annual precipitation in southern South America (inches).

farther north, records an average of twenty-one days during June, the rainiest month, nineteen days in May, July, and August, and during the summer months of January and February only seven days. At Valparaiso the highest mean number of rain days is nine in June, and either one or less than one per month from November through March.

The well-exposed points and peninsulas along the coast cited in the preceding paragraph were purposely selected to illustrate the south-to-north transition from excessively rainy to excessively dry conditions. Actually, a great deal of variation is seen within the general distribution. San Pedro, for example, about 50 miles southeast of Cabo Raper, records 176.3 inches, Isla Guafo, about 25 miles southwest of

Chiloe averages 41.1, Valdivia north of Punta Galera averages 102, and Valparaiso averages 18.2. In these instances orographic uplift, coupled in some cases with better exposure to the brunt of rain-bearing storms, is largely responsible for the differences in amount observed within roughly the same latitudes.

The importance of orographic uplift is particularly evident along the lower and middle slopes of the Andes, adding substantially more precipitation there than is normally received at interior localities nearer the coast. Note that whereas Osorno, about 30 miles from the coast at an elevation of 79 feet, records a mean annual precipitation of 52.5 inches, Ensenada, about 50 miles southeast on the shores of Lago Llanquihue at an altitude of 175 feet, averages 75.8. Similarly, Traiguen, about 50 miles from the coast at 558 feet, averages 47.5 inches, and Longuimay, about 75 miles farther east at 2952 feet, averages 73.5. Heavy precipitation continues up into higher elevations and for a short distance down the eastern slopes of the Andes into Argentina. But a well-developed rain shadow effect is plainly evident all along the eastern side of the mountains starting just a few thousand feet below the crest line. At San Carlos de Bariloche on the southeast shore of alpine Lake Nahuel at an elevation of 2798 feet, some 60 miles east of Ensenada, mean annual precipitation is 41.8 inches. Mountain heights between the two stations reach up to 8000 feet. And at Las Lajas, about 40 miles east of Longuimay at elevation 2339 feet, and again in the lee of 8000-foot mountain crests, yearly precipitation is only 8.7 inches. Stations farther south repeat the illustration: at the town of Lago Argentina on the southeast shore of glacier-fed Lago Argentina in the lee of 8000-foot mountain peaks, mean yearly precipitation is 7.5 inches, and at Elturbio, about 100 miles farther south, it is 16.2 inches; at Punta Arenas (Magallanes) on the Straits of Magellan about 150 miles east of Bahia Felix, which receives almost 200 inches of annual precipitation, the average is only 17.2 inches. Along the Argentine side of the Andes mid-latitude forests are generally found only at elevations of 3000 to 5000 feet, where sufficient precipitation occurs, although on the scores of mountainous islands around the Straits of Magellan they reach down to the high water mark. Here effective precipitation is much greater because of constantly low temperatures and high atmospheric humidity.

The season of heaviest precipitation also varies from south to north. Around the Straits of Magellan it is the summer period from December through April. Between here and Cabo Raper it is autumn, from April through July, and north of that it is the winter months of April through October. From Cabo Raper to Punta Corona between 60 and 75 per cent of the year's precipitation is recorded during the seven-month period of April through October. Between Punta Corona and Concepcion from 75 to 85 per cent is received during these seven months, and from Constitucion northward between 91 and 97 per cent is concentrated in the same period. At interior stations percentages for this period are slightly lower, for the rainy season is a trifle longer, but the proportional change from south to north is the same (Table 14-2).

TABLE 14–2

Per Cent of Annual Precipitation Received from Apr. through Oct. from North to South

La Serena	91
Valparaiso	96
Constitucion	91
Concepcion	87
Valdivia	81
Pta. Corona	74
Cabo Raper	57
Evangelists' Island	57

Most of the year's precipitation is in the form of rain, even in the southernmost areas. North of Valdivia snow rarely whitens the ground, and even south of here it rarely remains on the ground for more than a few days at lower elevations, despite the fact that snow falls on an estimated thirty days or more in the southern part of the archipelago. At higher altitudes, however, snow covers the ground during most of the winter and is commonly seen during a normal cold season at elevations of around 3000 feet from the Rio Bio Bio southward.

Thunderstorms are not at all common in either the mediterranean section or the archipelago. A slight increase in the average number of thunderstorms per year is recorded south of

Concepcion, especially between Valdivia and Isla Guafo, where thunderstorms tend to develop on an average of about five days per year, for the most part in winter. In the interior valleys they occur most frequently in the summertime, although the mean number is small. Thermal convection combined with orographic effects are responsible for a moderate thunderstorm frequency along the lower slopes of the Andes. Longuimay, at an elevation of 2952 feet, records an average of about thirteen days with thunderstorms per year.

The mean annual range of temperature between the warmest and coldest months reveals no systematic change with changing latitude along the water's edge. At the Evangelists' Island it is 9 degrees, at Cabo Raper 10 degrees, at Isla Guafo, Puerto Galera, and Isla Santa Maria 9 degrees, and at Valparaiso 10 degrees. Inland stations between Puerto Montt and Santiago do indeed show a meridional change in annual temperature range. At Puerto Montt it is about 14 degrees, increasing to 16 degrees at Valdivia, 18 degrees at Traiguen, and 20 degrees at Angol in the drainage basin of the Rio Bio Bio. From here to the Aconcagua valley mean yearly temperature ranges are between 22 and 24 degrees. The contrast between this mediterranean section and the far south is understandable from the fact that summers are sunny, with little cloud cover and very little rain, thus allowing a summer temperature rise well above that in the stormy south. It is this season that brings the strongest temperature contrast between north and south, for most mediterranean stations average 70° or above during the warmest month, compared with the Evangelists' Island, where it is only 48°, and from San Pedro to Puerto Galera, where it is between 52° and 57°. During winter, on the other hand, mean temperatures of the coldest months are almost the same in both coastal and interior situations, from the latitude of Puerto Montt to Santiago, averaging between 46° and 48° (Table 14-1).

The range between extremes of recorded temperature is considerably greater in the interior valleys, especially north of the Bio Bio, amounting to 77 degrees at Temuco and Talca, 75 degrees at Santiago, and 76 degrees at Los Andes. The extreme range at coastal stations such as the Evangelists' Island is, on the other hand, only 36 degrees, at Cabo Raper 41 degrees, and Isla Guafo 37 degrees.

Summer. The approach of the summer months in the mediterranean region is heralded by a springtime of increasing light and warmth from the sun, during which a new blush of fragrant, blossoming plant life adorns the valleys and hillsides. October is the month of maximum bloom in central Chile, from Concepcion to the Aconcagua.

During the summer period of December, January and February, the most striking feature is the withdrawal of storm activity toward the south (Fig. 5.12), allowing warm, dry, sunny weather to prevail from near Concepcion and the Rio Bio Bio northward through the mediterranean region and on into the grasslands between Valparaiso and La Serena (Table 14-3).

TABLE 14–3
Average Precipitation Dec.–Feb.
from North to South (In.)

La Serena	0.1
Valparaiso	0.3
Constitucion	1.4
Concepcion	2.5
Valdivia	9.5
Puerto Montt	12.5
Cabo Raper	19.3
Evangelists' Island	27.4

North of Rio Aconcagua from November through March the long-range means indicate at least one month without any rain at all. From the Aconcagua to the Bio Bio summer may occasionally be entirely without rain, but records show that on the average some rain falls during every month of the summer season, mainly in the form of short, convective showers. In this section of middle Chile monthly means range between only about 0.2 and 0.5 inches, increasing southward. The least rainy month in this region may be either December, January, or February. Beginning about 100 miles north of the Bio Bio mean rainfall for the driest month increases from about 0.5 to 1 inch or more around 30 miles south of the Bio Bio. In short, beginning north of Contulmo on the coast and at Traiguen in the interior, reliable summer rains are characteristic, and here, where summers are also cooler, the mixed forest begins. Mean amounts for the least rainy month increase with increasing latitude toward the south, and one observes that at Temuco in January, the driest month, the average is 1.4 inches, at Valdivia the driest month is again January and averages 2.6 inches, and at Puerto Montt January averages 3.5 inches. The last two stations are well within the temperate rain forest. Far to the south, however, the period from November through March is the season of heaviest precipitation. The rainiest month at Bahia Felix is March, with 21.5 inches, and at the Evangelists' Island it is also March, with 10.3 inches.

The bright sunny days of summer north of the Bio Bio are not often interrupted by heavy cloud cover. In interior valleys the estimated mean cloud cover for the period November through March is between 30 and 40 per cent of the visible sky area. But the change toward the south is clearly suggested in the following values: November through March at Valparaiso 40–43 per cent, at Valdivia 46–59 per cent, at Punta Corona from December through March 59–69 per cent, and at Isla Guafo from November through April 75–79 per cent. From October through April at Cabo Raper and for most coastal sites to the Evangelists' Island and beyond, the sky is 80 per cent cloud covered, and here, when the sun shines, it often appears through a heavy, watery veil of cold, drifting mist.

Fog appears to be fairly common along the entire coast, according to the small number of records available, with only slight differences between summer and winter. However, reports indicate a little higher frequency of days with fog towards the end of summer and early autumn, from January through April, especially north of Chiloe. The number of days per year increases from around forty between La Serena and Valparaiso to between fifty and sixty from Valdivia southward. Nocturnal inversion fogs are apparently fairly common in interior valleys under clear sky radiation.

Relative humidity is high all year long at well-exposed points on the coast, averaging well above 80 per cent. From Valdivia northward, especially in the mediterranean region, a definite decrease is typical of summertime. At Santiago it is about 55 per cent in December

and 56 per cent in January, and at Los Andes in the Aconcagua valley it is only 52 per cent from December through February. Higher values are reported at coastal stations, Valparaiso recording a yearly minimum of 66 per cent in December. Very low relative humidities have been observed even along the coast, however, commonly associated with very warm weather and off-shore winds blowing down from the Andes, warming adiabatically as they sweep toward sea level, producing a föhn effect. On one occasion a relative humidity of 7 per cent was observed in January at Concepcion.[1]

Land and sea breezes are an almost daily occurrence in the mediterranean region north of Concepcion, blowing inland and up the western flanks of the lower Andes during the day and downslope to seaward at night. A south or southwest sea breeze called the surada is well known from central Chile northward. It sets in at about 10 A.M., increasing in velocity until the middle of the afternoon, diminishing as evening approaches. At Valparaiso the southerly sea breeze often blows in squalls off the neighboring heights of a summer afternoon with such strength that people are compelled to take shelter.

January is normally the warmest summer month at inland stations. This is comparable with July in the northern hemisphere, also following the month of the summer solstice. One observes a steady increase in the mean January temperature of interior stations that are only a few hundred feet above sea level from Puerto Montt to Los Andes, values ranging in the low 60s as far as the Bio Bio but rising to the low 70s from there to the Aconcagua (Fig. 14.4). Even relatively small increases in altitude lower the mean temperatures for the warmest month, for we note that Longuimay at 2952 feet records 59°, compared with Traiguen at 558 feet, which records 64° (Table 14-1).

Mean maximum temperatures remain almost as high in February as for January, but the nocturnal minima at dawn are lower, with the result that February at most inland stations is the month recording the greatest mean daily range for the entire year. It is about 34 degrees at Los Andes, 33 degrees at Santiago, 38 degrees

[1] U.S. Navy, Hydrographic Office, *Sailing Directions for South America*, Vol. 3 (H.O. 25), 1960, p. 59.

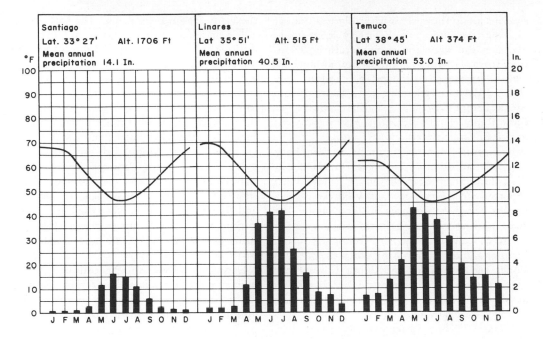

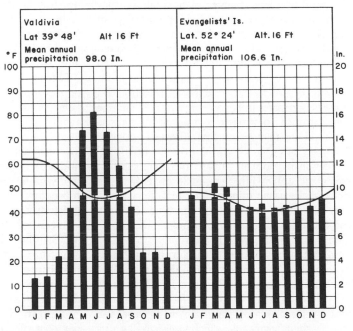

Figure 14.4. Normal temperature and precipitation at stations in mid-latitude forest and woodland in southern Chile.

at Talca and Longuimay. These amplitudes drop sharply south of the Bio Bio, as illustrated by the value of 28 degrees at Temuco about 125 miles south of that river. The mean daily temperature range of coastal stations is, of course, considerably moderated by their proximity to the thermally conservative waters of the sea. The maximum mean daily range at Valparaiso

is only 18 degrees, for example, and develops in December. It is 22 degrees at Valdivia in February and then drops to half this amount or less from Punta Corona southward. At the Evangelists' Island the mean daily range of temperature from November through March is only 6 degrees.

The temperature of the warmest month at

stations along the coast is naturally less than at interior stations, and February commonly averages the same mean temperature as January from Valparaiso to the Straits of Magellan. Values diminish, understandably, and we note that at Valparaiso January, and February are 64°, at Punta Corona 57°, at Isla Guafo 54°, at Cabo Raper (January through March) 52°, and at the Envangelists' Island 48°.

Maximum summer temperatures have reached 100° or more at several interior localities, and extremes of 91° and 97° have been reported at Valparaiso and Valdivia respectively. These occurrences are rare along the coast and usually arise from an invasion of warm dry air from the east, frequently in the form of a föhn wind moving down the western slopes of the Andes. At Punta Corona the highest recorded temperature has been 82°, at Isla Guafo 70°, at Cabo Raper 69°, and at the Evangelists' Island only 60°.

Winter. As one season gives way to another, the most striking changes in normal weather behavior take place in the mediterranean region. Here the approaching end of summer first becomes evident in the lowering of maximum temperatures attained during the warm part of the afternoon, as the radiant heat from the sun begins to decrease. Mean minima also become lower, but the downward change from month to month is only about half as great. These changes are first observed between February and March and continue until June, after which monthly mean maxima begin to rise noticeably while very little increase takes place in the mean minima (Fig. 14.4).

A second symptom of approaching winter is the more fitful behavior of winds, particularly along the seaboard. The largely southerly winds that prevail during the summer months in central Chile persist through March. Toward the end of April, however, as the axis of disturbed weather begins to move northward and cyclonic storms are driven against the coast, their typically clockwise circulations bring a high frequency of gusty, turbulent weather and winds dominantly from the opposing directions of northwest and southeast. This condition continues in varying degrees into July, when in the depth of winter northwest to northerly winds predominate along the coast of central Chile.

Meanwhile, as temperatures gradually lower, the rainy season begins, with the first appreciable gain in monthly precipitation taking place during the latter half of April. Monthly amounts increase steadily as the cooler weather of winter intensifies, reaching a maximum during June in almost all situations except in the southern section of the archipelago. Proceeding from north to south average precipitation for June is increasingly greater from the Aconcagua valley to Puerto Montt. Los Andes records a value of 3.17 inches, Santiago 3.31, Rancagua 4.70, Talca 6.8, Linares 8.3 (July averages slightly more in this case), Chillan 8.5, Traiguen 8.6, and Puerto Montt 10.1. Note that June precipitation at Puerto Montt is more than three times that of Los Andes, 600 miles north (Table 14-1).

Enduring snows are generally confined to higher elevations in the interior, occurring fairly commonly at altitudes as low as Longuimay at 2952 feet in the lower Andes south of the Rio Bio Bio. Snow is rare along the coast north of Valdivia but is a common occurrence at sea level from the Taitao peninsula south to Cape Horn. In the higher Andes snow often blocks the mountain passes for weeks during late winter and early spring.

During the sometimes intensely developed depressions that cross the shoreline in winter, gales of dangerous force are known to beat against the coast, bringing north winds averaging between 35 and 45 miles per hour and lasting for between twenty-four and thirty-six hours. Although usually not more than one or two such heavy storms occur per year, they are most apt to appear in midwinter, during June, July, or August.

In central Chile winter is the season of higher relative humidity and much more cloud cover than during the dry season, with a seasonal maximum occurring in June, the month of maximum precipitation. At this time average daily relative humidities are above 80 per cent, and mean cloud cover is between 60 and 80 per cent of the observable sky at most inland stations (Table 14-4).

The coldest period of winter is, as a rule, during both June and July at most interior locations. Average values between these two months differ only very slightly (47.1° and 46.6° at Santiago, 47.7° and 47.3° at Talca, 46.2° and 45.9° at Temuco), and from Puerto Montt to Cape Horn mean temperatures remain within a degree or two of equality for three or four months in the heart of winter. In the month of June the normal range between mean maximum and mean minimum temperatures decreases from north to south, with Los Andes recording a mean daily range of 25 degrees, between a mean maximum of 61° and 36°, Santiago 21 degrees between 58° and 37°, Talca 18 degrees between 56° and 38°. Temuco 15 degrees between 53° and 38°, Valdivia 10 degrees, Punta Corona 8 degrees, and the Evangelists' Island 7 degrees. The governing change takes place in the value of the mean maxima, for the mean minima are no more than 6 degrees apart the entire 2000 mile distance from the Aconcagua valley to the Straits of Magellan. Valdivia and Punta Corona indicate mean minima of 42°, and Los Andes and the Evangelists' Island mean minima of 35°.

SOUTHERN BRAZIL. The southwest coastal section of South America on which our interest has been centered has revealed a most interesting gradation of mid-latitude climates from steppe grassland to mediterranean scrub woodland, to mixed forest, and finally to coastal evergreen or temperate rain forest. The section of South America to which we now turn our attention possesses a very different kind of mid-latitude climate in an entirely different setting. This is the segment of mild, mid-latitude mixed forest that is found almost completely within southern Brazil.

Although the massive territory of Brazil lies mainly within the tropics, a relatively narrow portion extends southward beyond the Tropic of Capricorn into higher latitudes between the Atlantic Ocean and the borders of Argentina and Paraguay (Fig. 14.2). Here the Brazilian highlands come to an end about 200 miles north of Uruguay. This vast, westward-sloping plateau reaches nearly 2000 miles, from northeastern Brazil to the central part of the state of Rio Grande do Sul. The rugged, deeply dissected highland surface stands in the main at elevations of between 1800 and 4000 feet and is drained in its southern portions by the west-flowing waters of the Parana and the Uruguay river systems.

From the valley of the Paranapanema west of Sao Paulo southward for a distance of about 400 miles to the southern edge of the Brazilian highlands, some 50 miles north of Porto Alegre,

is a region of dominantly mixed forest vegetation that resembles in appearance the pine and oak forests of southeastern United States. In its fullest regional development it is confined chiefly to the states of Parana and Santa Catarina, between the Rio Paranapanema and the Rio Uruguay. Outliers extend northward in very small scattered patches at higher elevation in the eastern part of the state of Sao Paulo, southward into Rio Grande do Sul, and westward into the Missiones territory of northeastern Argentina. Its approximate breadth averages about 200 miles, and thus the entire region occupies an area of about 80,000 square miles, nearly the size of the state of Kansas (Fig. 14.2).

This part of Brazil is widely known as the region of the Parana pine (*Araucaria angustifolia*), very similar to the Chilean pine (*Araucaria araucana*). Although not a pine—it is actually a member of a more primitive family of conifers, the *Araucariacaea*—this tall, straight softwood is the most important lumber tree in Brazil. Where the forest is most luxuriant, as in central Parana, it appears in association with a variety of broadleaved species as the uppermost stratum of four rather well-defined vegetation levels, or stories. Commonly reaching heights of between 80 and 120 feet, with a diameter of 2 to 3 feet (and occasionally rising to 140 feet with a 10-foot diameter), its shallow, flat-topped crowns stand well above the second story of evergreen broadleaved trees, ranging in height between 60 and 80 feet. Most of these lower trees are hardwoods, members of the laurel family (*Lauracaea*), including a number of canellas (*Nectandra spp.* and *Ocotea spp.*), embuia (*Phoebe spp.*), and a locust (*Gleditsia amorphoides*). A single species of embuia called the Brazilian walnut (*Phoebe porosa*) is believed to account for more than half of all the trees in the second story.

A third story ranges between 30 and 60 feet in height and is dominated by members of the laurel and myrtle families, although immature specimens of the taller trees are also important. The best known species in the third vegetation level is the evergreen *yerba mate* (*Ilex paraguariensis*), a member of the holly family, which appears in mature stands that attain an average height of around 45 feet. This tree spreads westward across the Parana into eastern Paraguay, where it is abundant in a forest of more tropical character than the Parana pine forest. The fourth vegetation story is composed chiefly of tree ferns, bamboos, and many young, immature specimens of the taller trees, including an often dense undercover of *Ilex paraguariensis* ranging in height between 10 and 30 feet.

The Parana pine is known for its exacting climatic requirements. It is said to thrive only where frost occurs regularly each year and has not been found where below-freezing temperatures occur any less frequently than once every ten years. Its distribution also coincides with those upland areas where abundant year-round rain occurs quite reliably without the interruption of a dry season. This distinguishes the mid-latitude mixed forest region of southern Brazil from the tropical semideciduous forests and grassy savannas north of the Tropic of Capricorn with which it interpenetrates in northern Parana. Actually, tropical forest extends down the narrow, interrupted lowlands along the Atlantic coast, curving westward into the interior along the foot of the great escarpment west of Porto Alegre, as well as down the Parana river valley into northern Argentina, bracketing the cooler temperate forest at higher altitude.

Throughout the mixed forest region are scattered areas of unmixed mid-latitude prairie grassland, composed chiefly of frost-tolerant species sharply separated from the tropical members of the savanna grassland communities in southern Sao Paulo to the north. South of the Rio Uruguay the proportion of prairie grassland to forest increases rapidly in Rio Grande do Sul, so dominating the landscapes from here into Uruguay that only along the river banks are extensive stands of forest trees to be found. Rainfall in these southern areas is ample for the support of forest, and the predominance of mid-latitude grassland there is not climatically explainable. Undoubtedly, the depth and fertility of the soil as well as the character of the surface drainage and levels of the ground water table play an important part in determining the nature of the vegetation cover. Satisfactory conclusions on this point await further study of both soils and hydrology.

Long-range weather records for most of the mixed forest region are too meager to permit firm generalizations on many essential aspects of the climate. Mean values and known devia-

tions of weather experience are available for only a small number of weather stations in eastern sections. It is from the records for these scattered points and from a few published studies of Brazilian weather that the following remarks are mainly derived.[2]

The mid-latitude mixed forest region of southern Brazil annually receives ample rain for the support of forest vegetation. In most localities mean yearly amounts are between 55 and 70 inches. A somewhat drier section in the general area of Curitiba about 50 miles from the Atlantic coast receives yearly totals of between 50 and 55 inches, but in the western part of the region on the intermediate slopes leading down toward the Parana river, a much wetter section averages above 80 inches. Ruy Barbosa, for example, reports about 97 inches. The region is distinguished by the absence of a dry season, although the annual rainfall distribution is far from even. In northern areas about 60 per cent of the year's precipitation comes in the warmer season from October through March. In the tropical forest and grassland regions farther north an even higher percentage of yearly precipitation occurs in that season. Toward the southern portions of the mid-latitude forest yearly rainfall distribution becomes more equitable, and beyond the Rio Uruguay more than 50 per cent of the year's precipitation occurs during the winter season, from April through October. At Passo Fundo, for example, 55 per cent is received in this period, at Alfredo Chaves 56 per cent, and at Caxias 61 per cent (Table 14-4).

The mean annual range of temperature also distinguishes this section from tropical regions farther north, where a small amplitude of annual temperature variation prevails. Increasing from north to south, it averages around 14 degrees near the Paranapanema (14.6 degrees at Jaguariaiva), 15.3 degrees at Ivahy, 16.5 degrees at Palmas, 17.9 degrees at Ruy Barbosa, and 17.2 degrees at Passo Fundo. Still farther south, beyond the forested region, the mean annual temperature range continues to increase in those predominantly open, grassland areas where the normal input and

---

[2] See especially James R. Coyle, *A Practical Analysis of Weather Along the East Coast of South America*, Rio de Janeiro, 1945, and A. B. Serra, *Atlas Climatologico do Brasil*, Rio de Janeiro, 1955.

TABLE 14-4
Climatic Data for Mid-Latitude Mixed Forest Stations in Southern Brazil
(Temp., °F; Rainfall, In.)

Station	Lat.	El. in Ft		Jan.	Feb.	Mar.	Apr.	May	Jun.	Jul.	Aug.	Sep.	Oct.	Nov.	Dec.	Year
Ivahy, Brazil	24°54'	2519	T	71	71	69	65	59	57	56	58	61	64	67	70	
			R	7.4	6.1	4.8	4.0	5.6	5.9	3.7	4.8	6.7	6.5	6.0	6.7	68.0
Jaguariaíva, Brazil	24°16'	2942	T	70	70	69	65	59	57	56	58	61	64	67	70	
			R	9.8	6.3	4.2	2.9	2.8	4.2	2.3	3.3	4.2	4.7	5.7	5.9	56.1
Curitiba, Brazil	25°25'	3113	T	68	68	67	63	58	55	54	56	58	61	64	67	
			R	7.2	5.9	4.2	3.0	3.5	4.1	2.7	3.3	4.9	4.8	4.7	5.4	53.6
Palmas, Brazil	26°29'	3572	T	67	66	65	59	54	52	50	53	56	59	63	66	
			R	7.8	5.9	5.9	6.7	7.4	8.3	4.2	5.8	7.8	7.3	5.6	6.7	79.6
Ruy Barbosa, Brazil	26°51'	2627	T	69	68	66	60	56	54	52	57	59	61	64	71	
			R	9.3	7.3	8.8	8.0	7.8	8.8	6.3	8.0	8.5	9.8	6.7	7.7	96.9
Curitibanos, Brazil	27°17'	3411	T	67	66	65	60	55	52	52	54	56	59	62	66	
			R	6.7	5.4	5.6	4.6	4.9	6.1	3.9	5.5	6.6	6.4	5.3	5.4	66.3
Lages, Brazil	27°49'	2985	T	68	68	66	61	56	53	52	54	56	60	63	66	
			R	5.9	4.8	4.4	4.2	4.8	5.7	3.4	6.0	6.4	5.8	4.8	5.0	61.1
Passo Fundo, Brazil	28°16'	2230	T	72	71	69	64	58	55	55	57	59	63	67	71	
			R	5.2	5.0	4.7	4.8	6.4	7.5	5.5	6.2	7.3	5.8	4.6	5.1	68.2
Alfredo Chaves, Brazil	28°58'	2352	T	71	70	68	62	57	55	54	56	57	60	65	69	
			R	6.0	5.1	5.1	5.8	6.5	7.7	6.5	7.0	7.5	5.4	4.4	5.3	72.3
Caxias, Brazil	29°10'	2447	T	69	68	66	61	56	53	52	55	57	59	63	67	
			R	8.5	10.2	11.7	11.2	3.4	1.2	0.4	0.2	0.7	1.0	1.9	3.2	53.3

Source: F. L Wernstedt, *World Climatic Data, Latin America and the Caribbean*, Pennsylvania State University, 1959.

output of radiative heat from the sun is unmoderated by the presence of trees.

A surface elevation of between 1800 and 4000 feet is the primary reason for the presence of a mid-latitude forest climate in this subtropical section of South America. At these altitudes air is not only cooler but also tends to be clearer and drier (in terms of absolute humidity) than at lower levels. Its heat capacity is thus lessened, and the possibility of radiative heat loss during the hours of darkness, leading to lower nocturnal minimum temperatures, is considerably increased. The relationship between altitude, frequent wintertime frost, and the distribution of the Parana pine and its associates is plainly established.

The main source region of air passing over southern Brazil throughout the year is the South Atlantic. Maritime tropical air flows in from an east to northeast direction around the western periphery of anticyclonic circulations over the sea (Figs. 4.2 and 4.3). The surface water of the western Atlantic in these latitudes ranges in temperature between about 78° in summer to about 70° in winter, and the advected air from the sea is thus warm and humid (Figs. 6.13 and 6.12). The basically onshore flow appears to prevail up to levels of around 10,000 feet, above which the upper air is believed to maintain a dominant flow from west and southwest, particularly southwest.

Unlike the eastern Pacific south of the equator, where a semipermanent anticyclone endures all seasons of the year, the South Atlantic's anticyclonic circulation is relatively persistent only in summer. In wintertime it alternately appears and disappears, usually taking the form of moderately well-developed highs traveling eastward toward the shores of southern Africa.

Winter. During the winter season of the year, chiefly June through August, the dominant motions of the general circulation over the entire southern hemisphere are in the zonal, eastward flow of the westerlies over the unbroken ocean surface between the southern continents and Antarctica. An equatorward shift of these westerlies takes place in wintertime, with the intensity of heat from the sun, advecting colder air over most of southern South America. Indirectly, the barrier of the Andes augments the amplitude of northward pulsations in the otherwise comparatively

smooth eastward flow. It does so by its effect on the dynamic motions of the general circulation, through the repeated formation of lee waves in the mean eastward air stream. In short, air over southern South America east of the Andes tends to move northeastward throughout the year in a succession of northward-advancing cold fronts that reach well into the tropics of northeastern Brazil.[3] In wintertime they are usually stronger and more frequent than in summer, and reach to within 6 or 7 degrees of the equator near the northern end of the Brazilian highlands.

Occasional outbursts of unusually cold, relatively dry air (low absolute moisture content), originating over the expanded frozen surfaces around Antarctica, make their way much farther north than is normal and sometimes actually cross the equator. Such an outburst brought a strong northward flow of cold air at the surface up the Parana-Paraguay valley in July 1953 and again in 1955. On the latter occasion freezing temperatures were recorded as far north as Cuiaba at 15°36'S. Lat., and in the Amazon valley temperatures were in the low 60s. Such weather in Brazil is called a friagem.

Over the forested highlands in southern Brazil winter weather is often ruled for several days at a time by air that is cool, clear, and bracing. During early morning hours the chill air is usually calm and the sky cloudless. As the morning advances, winds freshen from the southeast, and scattered cumulus clouds begin to form toward the eastern edge of the upland. By midafternoon winds normally reach a moderate maximum, slightly more than half the sky will be cloud-covered, and the thermometer will stand in the 60s or low 70s. Toward evening the wind subsides, the sky clears, and temperatures drop rapidly into the 50s after sunset, gradually lowering toward the freezing point at the approach of dawn.

Winters in the mid-latitude forest are usually short and mild (Fig. 14.5). July is the coldest month, normally averaging between 50° and 55° at most stations (Table 14-5). The mean daily temperature range at this season is not appreciably different from summer amplitudes

[3] J. A. Boffi, "Effect of the Andes Mountains on the General Circulation over the Southern Part of South America," *Bulletin of the American Meteorological Society* **30**(7): 242–47, 1949.

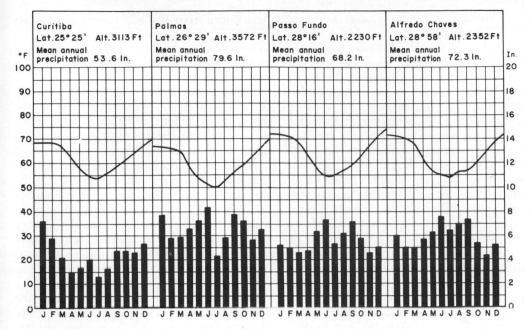

Figure 14.5. Normal temperature and precipitation at mid-latitude mixed forest stations in southern Brazil.

in northern sections but is commonly lower than in summer toward the south. Curitiba, for example, records a minimum mean daily range of about 19 degrees in March, and Curitibanos, about 150 miles farther south, reports a minimum range of about 11 degrees in the winter month of June.

Frost occurs each winter on at least ten days throughout the highland forested region, and between ten and twenty-five days in central and southeastern sections. It is much less likely to occur at elevations lower than 1800 feet, even within the same span of latitude, notably along the Parana river on the west and the Atlantic coast on the east. Frost is also a much rarer experience and is less severe on the upper highland surfaces farther north. Toward the northern limits of the mid-latitude region, in northern Parana and southern Sao Paulo, frost can be seen every winter only in shallow valleys and depressions on the upland and is absent in the deeper water courses of the larger rivers such as the Paranapanema. Thus, in agricultural areas where the temperate forest begins to disappear, such as the expanding settlement around Londrina, farmers grow coffee, cotton, oranges, and pineapples on the warmer, north-facing slopes and wheat, barley,

maize, and potatoes, along with other typically mid-latitude crops, on the colder, south-facing slopes and in the frost pockets, places that are well-marked by the presence of the Parana pines.[4]

Another distinctive feature of the cooler season in the temperate forest of the interior uplands is the length of the period during which mean monthly temperatures remain below 60°. Throughout the region average monthly temperatures are less than 60° for at least five months, from May through September, and at some stations for six months, April through September. In contrast, all the adjoining regions, tropical highlands on the north, coastal and valley lowlands on either side, and even the prairie grasslands farther south in Uruguay, experience these values for only three months.

Whereas scattered convective showers provide a large share of the year's normal precipitation, in wintertime migrating storm systems are the principal source. This is the season when stronger, more frequent penetrations of cold air from the south advance over southern

[4] P. E. James, *Latin America*, The Odyssey Press, New York, 1959, pp. 495–96.

Brazil. Modified by their passage over the unfrozen surface of the southern oceans, successive waves of cold air usually possess the character of cold, damp maritime polar air when they enter the continent. They are normally shallow and hug the surface, undercutting the warmer, resident air as they approach. Most of the disturbances that develop are of a semilinear frontal type, for very few completely cyclonic systems have been observed. When an invading mass of maritime polar air is relatively shallow in depth, it commonly effects only interior sections, remaining west of the Serra do Mar, which is the edge of the great escarpment south of Sao Paulo. When it is deep and intensive enough, however, a cold front often divides to form separate frontal disturbances on either side of the Serra do Mar, one over the interior upland and another near sea level along the coast (Fig. 14.6). In the latter section rains may last for four or five days while the temperature hovers in the 50s. In the interior the approaching disturbance is commonly heralded by brisk east to northeast winds and is often accompanied by hard thunderstorms and damaging hail. It is usually followed by a windshift to southward, a change to cold, fairly damp air, and often by subnormal temperatures and frost.

Migrating storms tend to occur on an average of about one every four days each year, with a higher frequency in winter. Average duration of individual storms varies considerably but seems to be somewhat less than twenty-four hours. Snow whitens the ground for brief intervals each winter in southern sections of the region and from time to time is heavy enough to break the weaker branches off trees.

Relative humidities are high throughout the year, reflecting the dominating influence of maritime tropical air from the Atlantic, mean daily values being near 80 per cent. During autumn and early winter, from March through June, averages are higher, between 80 and 85 per cent, in contrast to the remainder of the year, when values range between 75 and 80 per cent. Fog also increases during the winter season, appearing in part as frontal, advection fog and in part as nocturnal radiation fog that tends to settle in small, shallow pockets on the upland. In spite of the fact that more than half the year's precipitation in southern areas comes in winter, mean cloud cover, as far as can be determined from available records, diminishes to around 50 per cent of the observable sky. In summer, on the other hand, average cloud cover ranges between 50 and 70 per cent in most localities.

Summer. The short, cool winter is mainly concentrated in the period beginning in the second week of June and ending in the third week of July. By the end of July temperatures begin to rise and continue to do so at the rate of around 3 degrees per month until the maximum is reached in January. Though January is the warmest month within the region, December and February are almost as warm, differing by scarcely more than 1 degree from the January normal. The mean daily range of temperature is generally at a maximum in summer, amounting to between 25 and 30 degrees during the early part of the season in December.

Differences in altitude, exposure, and the effects of slope on air drainage create a variety of mean temperatures for the warmest month. In general, it may be said that localities between 1800 and 3000 feet in altitude tend to experience values of between 70° and 72°, and above 3000 feet the range is between 67° and 69° (Table 14-5). At similar elevations farther north and at lower elevations in the same latitudes and for some distance farther south, mean temperatures for the warmest month are everywhere several degrees higher (Fig. 14.5).

Under the influence of highly intensified solar radiation at this time of year, the interior of most of South America becomes extremely warm, and thermal low pressure prevails all the way into northern Argentina. This strengthens the movement of oceanic air from the northeast over the eastern part of the country. Warm, humid air from the sea is often made unstable over the heated land surface as the day progresses, and heavy convective showers during late afternoon and evening are a common summer occurrence. Though fogs are less frequent than in winter, relative humidities are not much lower, and mean cloud cover, as mentioned above, increases, largely in the form of cumulonimbus types that result from the effects of thermal convection.

Southern Africa

Another segment of mid-latitude mixed forest and mediterranean scrub woodland fringes the southernmost edge of the African

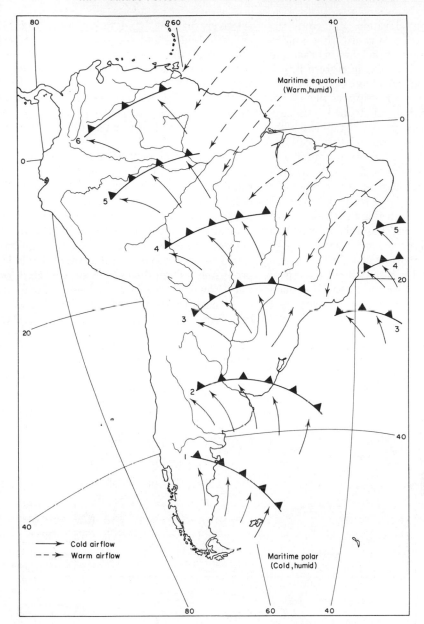

Figure 14.6.   Northward advance of a cold front across South America on six successive days, crossing the equator on the sixth day (6). Division of the front along the Brazilian Escarpment begins on the third day (3).

continent. Substantially confined to within 50 miles of the shoreline are a mediterranean environment and a mild variation of mid-latitude forest in juxtaposition, blending a dry summer climate on the one hand with a climate of year-round rainfall on the other.

Unlike South America, the greater part of Africa's bulky land mass lies north of the equator. At the equator Africa is about 2400 miles in breadth, but at the Tropic of Capricorn it is 1800 miles, tapering gradually south to a bluntly rounded end at nearly 35°S. Lat. Possessing the character of a great continental plateau, much of the interior upland is well above 3000 feet in elevation and from the Tropic of Capricorn southward rises saucer-like around its edges to heights of 4000 and 6000 feet above sea level. As in eastern Brazil, the interior highlands terminate quite abruptly in the Great Escarpment. In places the escarpment is interrupted or ill defined, but elsewhere it is a prominent physiographic feature that often establishes a well-defined climatic divide. Although it approaches to within less than 50 miles of the Atlantic shores south of the Orange river, it tends in general to remain at a distance of 100 to 150 miles from the coast. Its greatest heights are reached in the Drakensberg Mountains of northern Basutoland, where a dozen peaks rise to more than 10,000 feet above sea level, and several are 11,000 feet or more.

It is in the coastal region of southern Africa below the Great Escarpment that the main areas of mid-latitude forest and woodland are found (Fig. 14.7). They are confined to a

relatively narrow band rarely more than 50 miles in width, and together extend a linear distance of approximately 500 miles between the middle Olifants River valley in the southwest and Algoa Bay at the eastern end of the south coast. This is the Cape region of folded mountain ranges that rise from the shoreline in series toward the edge of the interior plateaus.

The main area of mediterranean climate is confined to a small section between the coastal mountains and the sea from the middle Olifants valley to the lower Breede River valley, a distance of about 150 miles. Along the coast its limits reach from near Saldanha Bay, north of Cape Town, to the vicinity of Cape Agulhas. It is thus chiefly found on that small, irregular projection of southwest Africa centered on Cape Town. The main area of temperate forest is a narrow stretch of coastland roughly between Mossel Bay and St. Francis Bay,

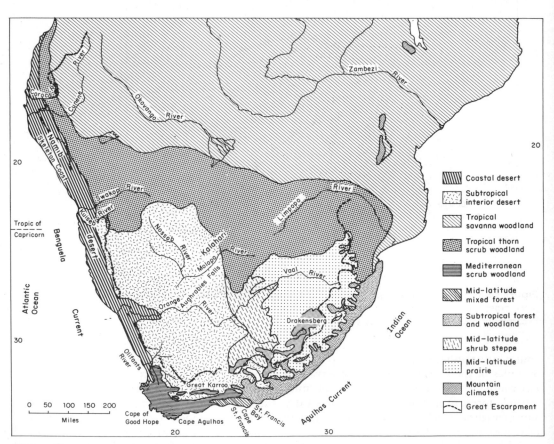

Figure 14.7. Distribution of climates in southern Africa.

again about 150 miles in length. These two climatic regions interpenetrate valleys and mountain spurs of the south coast, but eastward and northward give way to other climates that will be dealt with in later chapters.

The presence of these regions along the southernmost fringe of Africa is primarily attributable to three circumstances: latitude, coastal position on the southern shores of the land mass, and the effects of the general circulation of the atmosphere in these latitudes. Details of their distribution are, however, strongly influenced by the character and arrangement of major land forms and the surface water temperatures of the sea along the coast.

From the escarpment toward the coast the land at first falls away into a large elevated basin called the Great Karroo. This is an arid region about 400 miles in length from east to west whose floor averages between 2000 and 3000 feet above sea level. It terminates along its southern and western margins in the first of a series of prominent, narrow, elongated mountain ranges that lie roughly parallel to the coast. For about 400 miles west of Great Fish River the two most prominent coastal mountain series of ridges are actually slightly concave toward the south and thus converge with the shoreline at several points. They terminate in several prominent features of bold relief at the water's edge, rocky headlands that drop steeply down to the sea. South of the Langeberg line of mountains is an elevated, dissected peneplain that reaches west for about 150 miles from Mossel Bay. It broadens to a width of more than 60 miles between Cape Agulhas, southernmost point on the continent, and the Breede River valley.

The mid-latitude climates with which we are concerned occupy an area of considerable physiographic complexity. High, elongated mountain ranges and intervening valleys rising toward the Great Escarpment from the elevated coastal peneplain present a series of obstructions to the movement of transient weather systems, creating a great many local climatic variations.

Two major oceanic currents also exert an influence on the character and distribution of climatic qualities along these shores. The westward-flowing Agulhas Current, an extension of the Mozambique Current that drifts southward between Madagascar and Mozambique, brings a flow of relatively warm water as far west as False Bay, south of Cape Town. From Algoa Bay westward the main stream of warm water diverges from the coast, and only attenuated filaments approach the shore. Thus, the warming effect diminishes westward. Surface water temperatures reported from Bird Island on Algoa Bay average 69.1° for the warmest month, February, and 60.6° for the coldest month, August, a mean annual range of 8.5 degrees. In contrast, Muizenburg on False Bay reports 67.4° in the warmest month and only 55.9° in the coldest month, June, a mean annual range of 11.5 degrees.

Flowing northward along the west coast from around Cape Town to the equator is a relatively cold stream of surface water called the Benguela Current. Its effect on inshore water temperatures is indicated by the surface values reported for Cape Town harbor, where in December, January, and April mean amounts reach a yearly maximum of 56.5° and lower to 54.3° during the coldest month of September, a mean annual range of only slightly more than 2 degrees. Year-round air temperatures over this current thus tend to stabilize within very narrow limits.

The temperature and moisture content of the air moving in contact with the contrasting waters of these two major coastal currents are significantly different and profoundly influence the nature of the climates along the adjacent shores. The mild, humid forest climates of the southeast and south coasts are related to the warm Agulhas Current, and the dry summer scrub woodland climate into which these blend along the south and southwest coasts is related to the colder waters beyond Cape Agulhas, particularly the Benguela Current.

A dry summer mediterranean climate extends in some measure from the Cedarberg and Olifants River mountains first southward and then eastward to the lower Breede valley, a distance of about 150 miles. For about 150 miles east of Mossel Bay along the coast is an isolated stretch of mild, humid temperate forest, scarcely more than 25 miles in width, related to a year-round supply of rainfall. From St. Francis Bay west of Port Elizabeth a warmer temperate forest extends northeastward. More tropical in nature, and again confined to a narrow strip of coast, it reaches for about 400 miles before giving way to a yet more tropical forest that continues northward beyond Durban. This represents the southward extension of a strictly tropical forest-woodland along the coast of Portuguese East Africa.

PLANT LIFE. In proportion to its size the Cape region of southern Africa from near Clanwilliam in the middle Olifants valley to Port Elizabeth may possess the richest flora in the world.[5] Its botanical richness is contained in four principal types—bulbs, succulents, heaths, and proteas. On the Cape peninsula alone, an area of about 400 square miles, are some 2500 species of plants, 750 of which are among the grasses, sedges, lillies, and irises, as well as several hundred species of profusely flowering shrub and heathlike forms. Over five hundred species of the flowering heatherlike shrub *Erica*, from 1 to 3 feet tall, are known for this region. Many indigenous Cape species of tulip, gladiolus, hyacinth, iris, and lily have long been known among gardeners in the northern hemisphere, where they have been widely introduced as popular cultivated plants.

But the Cape region possesses very few native trees. Those that are native to this environment are considered closely related to tropical species and not as in California and Chile, to the temperate species of higher latitudes. Thus, the mediterranean vegetation of southern Africa is dominantly a maquis consisting principally of low evergreen shrubs with stiff branches and small, hard, drought-resistant, heathlike leaves.

Sclerophyllous, shrubby maquis is the ruling vegetation from sea level to more than 7000 feet, and wherever it is found, its presence invariably indicates a distinctly winter rainfall regime in which more than 50 per cent of the year's precipitation occurs between April and October. But the character of the maquis changes with altitude, and so do its climatic relationships. At levels above 3000 feet an alpine climate prevails, where abundant cloud cover and precipitation, plentiful mists, and more equable temperatures are characteristic, resulting in a dense, fairly low, relatively soft, heathlike shrub vegetation. At altitudes from sea level to about 3000 feet, however, especially on the coastal peneplains and in the foothills of the mountain ridges, the maquis generally

coincides with the mediterranean climate and thus provides a guide to its general distribution.

Typical structure and composition of the maquis are particularly well developed within the somewhat wetter sections of its vertical range where mean annual rainfall is between 20 and 30 inches. Here the climax vegetation called sclerophyll bush (also cape macchia)[6] is a relatively dense, three-layered plant community. The uppermost layer is composed of large bushes, usually 5 to 8 feet in height, among which a few small trees standing only a little taller are occasionally interspersed. Leaves of the dominant shrubs are medium in size, flat, hard or leathery, and most often lustreless. Prominent species include the honey flower (*Protea mellifera*), whose large pink and white terminal flower heads overflow with sweet fluid, the silver tree (*Leucadendron argenteum*), with nearly white bark and 6-inch-long, lance-shaped leaves of silvery gray. Normally a small tree, it can attain a height of 75 feet. More than seventy species of *Leucadendron* are found here. Also important are species of *Gymnosporia* and *Leucospermum*, a well-known example of the latter being the low shrub *Leucospermum nutans*, 3 to 5 feet tall, with broad, short leaves and brilliant red and orange terminal flowers.

The uppermost layer frequently fails to form a continuous crown cover, and this allows the development of a second, denser stratum of small shrubs having more flexible, slender stems and smaller, shiny, heathlike leaves. It includes many species of the prolific *Erica*. Below the second layer are low-growing shrubs and often a ground cover of a great many herbaceous plants, among which are brightly flowering bulbs and creeping succulents with thick, fleshy leaves. As a general rule, however, the ground under the maquis is rarely completely covered, remaining about 15 per cent bare. A typical scarcity of dense grass cover is characteristic. The three-layered structure has become increasingly rare as a result of frequent fires, and the most typical appearance of the sclerophyll bush is a simple one-layered or two-layered community, often quite open in character. In narrow, sheltered canyons it also

[5] Ronald Good, *The Geography of the Flowering Plants*, Longmans, Green & Company, Ltd., New York, 1947, p. 173.

[6] R. S. Adamson, *The Vegetation of South Africa*, London, 1938. Most of the material on the vegetation of South Africa has been obtained from this source.

appears sometimes as a close-crowned vegetation between 12 and 15 feet high.

In drier sections of the region where mean annual rainfall is between 15 to 20 inches the vegetation is typically more open and is not distinctly stratified. Dominant species are fewer in number than in the wetter maquis and include members of the drought-tolerant communities in the not-too-distant deserts. Where mean annual rainfall drops below 12 inches and is less predictable, mediterranean maquis comes to an end, giving way to the scattered, incomplete plant cover and high proportion of succulent plants typical of semidesert vegetation, as in the Great Karroo, the lower Olifants River valley, and the coast north of Cape Town. Semidesert vegetation also appears in patches along the coast between Mossel Bay and Cape Town, where rainfall is deficient or where sandy soils produce xerophytic edaphic conditions.

Distribution of the maquis along the coast from north of Cape Town to Algoa Bay is almost unbroken, with the important exception of that 150 mile stretch of temperate forest east of Mossel Bay. Inland, however, where steep-sided folded mountain ranges that lie nearly parallel to the coast disrupt the flow of rain-bearing winds from the sea, its distribution is frequently interrupted. Here it is principally found along the margins of the interior valleys and on the lower and middle seaward slopes of the mountains. The inner lee slopes of the mountain ranges, as well as the valley floors, are commonly occupied by a semidesert shrub vegetation like that of the Great Karroo. Notable areas of this more xerophytic plant cover are found in the Little Karroo, an interior basin in the Gamka-Gouritz drainage area between the Langeberg and Swartberg ranges, and the middle Breede River valley, southwest of the Little Karroo.

A change in the character of the maquis into a denser, less brittle vegetation with softer foliage and more flexible stems is seen in the eastern sections of its distribution. The wetter maquis is found where the soil is permanently moist, under a year-round rainfall distribution, beginning near the mouth of the Breede River, and thus from here to Algoa Bay no longer indicates a strictly mediterranean climate. The transition, represented by the wetter maquis, into forest along the coast and into a temperate grassland away from the coast primarily reveals the change in rainfall—in amount, distribution, and reliability—to which these adjoining regions are related. In an easterly direction maquis of all types come to an end in the low mountains around Grahamstown south and west of the Great Fish River.

In striking contrast to the summer-dry shrub vegetation of the maquis are the well-watered forests of the south and southeast coasts. A dense, complex evergreen forest representing a very mild, frost-free form of mid-latitude mixed forest somewhat akin to that of southern middle Chile and generally known as the Knysna Forest occupies a narrow belt of coastal territory between the mountains and the sea. In this small tract, approximately from Mossel Bay to St. Francis Bay, rarely more than 25 miles wide and limited to elevations under 2000 feet, the temperate forest has attained its maximum development. The predominant trees are evergreen with small, elliptical leaves, usually less than 3 inches long, that are firm, dark green, and have shiny upper surfaces. The "mixed" nature of the forest is established by the fact that no single species dominates among the score or more present. Yellow wood (*Podocarpus spp.*) is considered the most important tree, in addition to black ironwood (*Olea laurifolia*), and Cape beech (*Myrsine melanophloeos*), stinkwood (*Ocotea bullata*), sneezewood (*Pteroxylon obliquum,*) and white ironwood (*Toddalea lanceolata*).[7] A shrub layer commonly appears beneath the canopy of tree crowns, and the ground below is often carpeted with mosses and ferns, in wetter situations including the tree fern (*Hemetelia capensis*).

Viewed from a distance, the external appearance of the tree crown canopy is irregular but averages close to 70 feet in height. Several species of *Podocarpus* attain heights of around 100 feet, and the largest may reach 150 feet. Associated with these tall forms are numerous lianas, and epiphytes reminiscent of Spanish moss in southeastern United States and related species in southern middle Chile.

Although the main area of temperate forest is the small Knysna Forest, it is not strictly confined to this locality. It is represented in

---

[7] John H. Wellington, *Southern Africa, A Geographical Study*, Cambridge, 1955, 1, 302.

small fragments throughout most of the winter rainfall region, where it usually appears in moderately moist ravines facing the sea, and in very small outliers at higher elevations in southwest Africa as far north as the Cedarberg Mountains, where, at 3000 to 5000 feet, the endemic cedar (*Widdringtonia juniperoides*) forms a scrubby, open-crowned tree cover on rocky, forbidding slopes. Toward the northeast fragments of the temperate forest are found on the upper seaward slopes of interior mountains, some fifty miles from the sea and usually at elevations of 3000 to 4000 feet or more. Northeast of Algoa Bay forest of the same general character—well-watered throughout the year, frost-free, and chiefly evergreen—continues in patches along an exceedingly narrow band of the littoral, less than 20 miles in width. It may be designated warm temperate forest simply for comparison with the temperate forest proper where temperatures at all seasons are consistently lower. It receives more rain than the latter, and up to 75 per cent of the annual mean amount occurs in summer. Winter mists and high relative humidities compensate for the shortage of rain in this season. The warm temperate forest gradually gives way to a subtropical forest in which a variety of palms becomes important, leading to the name *palm belt*, applied to the coastal stretch from Port Shepstone northward into Mozambique.

CLIMATIC CONDITIONS. The qualities of the atmosphere to which the mediterranean maquis and the temperate forest owe their presence arise mainly from the ever-changing circulations of the subtropical anticyclones in these latitudes. Oceanic high pressure cells prevail throughout the year over the South Atlantic and the south Indian oceans, shifting position slightly with the seasons but generally remaining centered near 30°S. Lat. These are not static features but consist chiefly of an almost unbroken succession of anticyclones repeatedly forming, changing size and shape, and from time to time moving off eastward under the primary influence of the general circulation. They are of dynamic origin, believed to arise from the confluence of air streams at altitudes of 30,000 feet or more, producing an accumulation of relatively colder, denser air at those levels that subsides, becomes warmer adiabatically, and diverges to bring high pressure anticyclonic effects to the surface (Fig. 4.3).

Dynamic high pressure cells are understood to prevail throughout the year over southern Africa, in wintertime reaching from the stratosphere to the surface. In summertime, however, they only occasionally reach the surface when a shallow but very strong thermal low pressure condition develops under the high summer sun (Fig. 4.2).

Also important are the westerlies of the Roaring Forties that sweep over the seas at higher latitude well to the south of the continent, and the disturbances that frequently pass along their northern margins. Rarely do the westerlies advance far enough north to affect the continent directly, but migrating low pressure cells from time to time originate along their northern flanks and play a part in the yearly weather program.

Although the surface circulations are mainly determined by the features just noted, at higher levels, from about 10,000 feet upward, the general flow of air is eastward the entire year long. This holds true for southern Africa as far north as about 20°S. Lat. These high level westerlies are part of the southern hemisphere's circumpolar whirl, a fundamental feature of the general circulation, and exert a primary influence on the speed and trajectories of surface weather systems.

Three types of air mass affect the weather of southern Africa: maritime tropical from the Atlantic and Indian oceans, maritime polar from the Atlantic south of the continent, and in summertime small, weakly developed masses of tropical continental air from the interior plateau (Figs. 5.2 and 5.3). Southern Africa is too far north to be visited by cold, dry continental polar air from Antarctica, and air masses of this type originating far to the south are modified into maritime polar air on their long journey over the unfrozen waters of the Atlantic separating the two continents. It is possible that during the winter months small, weak masses of continental polar air develop identifiable character over the interior upland through the net radiation heat loss taking place during the period of lessened insolation.

Turning now to the climatic characteristics of the regions under discussion in this chapter, it should first be noted that details of sharply contrasting climatic situations within a short distance of one another are not available through want of sufficient statistical material.

TABLE 14–5

Climatic Data for Mid-Latitude Forest and Woodland Stations in Southern Africa
(Temp., °F; Rainfall, In.)

Station	Lat.	El. in Ft		Jan.	Feb.	Mar.	Apr.	May	Jun.	Jul.	Aug.	Sep.	Oct.	Nov.	Dec.	Year
Clanwilliam,	32°11′	249	T	79	79	75	70	61	57	55	58	61	67	73	76	
Union of S.Af.			R	0.1	0.2	0.3	0.6	1.0	1.7	1.2	1.1	0.7	0.4	0.3	0.2	8.0
Cape Town,	33°56′	39	T	71	71	69	65	60	57	55	57	59	62	66	69	
Union of S.Af.			R	0.7	0.6	0.9	1.9	3.7	4.3	3.7	3.3	2.3	1.6	1.0	0.8	24.7
Caledon,	34°13′	800	T	68	69	66	63	59	54	52	54	57	61	64	67	
Union of S.Af.			R	0.9	0.9	1.4	1.7	2.2	2.8	2.6	2.4	2.2	1.7	1.6	0.9	21.3
Cape Agulhas,	34°50′	62	T	69	69	67	64	60	58	56	57	58	61	64	66	
Union of S.Af.			R	0.8	0.7	1.3	1.5	2.0	2.3	2.1	1.9	1.6	1.5	1.1	0.7	17.5
Mossel Bay,	34°11′	197	T	70	70	68	66	63	60	59	60	60	62	65	68	
Union of S.Af.			R	1.1	1.3	1.5	1.5	1.4	1.2	1.2	1.3	1.7	1.6	1.4	1.2	16.4
Montagu,	33°47′	731	T	75	75	71	64	58	53	52	55	58	64	68	72	
Union of S.Af.			R	0.5	0.5	0.8	1.1	1.5	1.3	1.5	1.4	1.2	1.0	1.0	0.6	12.3
Riversdale,	34°06′	344	T	71	72	69	65	59	55	54	56	58	62	66	69	
Union of S.Af.			R	0.9	1.3	2.0	1.5	1.4	1.2	1.5	1.3	1.7	1.8	1.9	1.1	17.6
Hermitage,	33°31′	400	T	73	74	72	66	61	57	56	58	61	65	67	70	
Union of S.Af.			R	0.9	1.3	1.7	1.1	1.2	0.7	1.0	0.6	0.8	1.9	1.9	1.1	14.2
Cape St. Francis,	34°12′	26	T	68	68	66	64	61	59	58	59	59	61	63	66	
Union. of S.Af.			R	1.2	1.1	1.9	2.1	2.9	2.6	2.8	2.7	2.7	2.5	2.1	1.6	26.2
George,	33°58′	725	T	67	68	67	63	60	57	55	57	57	60	62	65	
Union of S.Af.			R	3.0	3.3	3.6	2.6	2.4	1.9	1.9	2.3	3.3	3.2	3.3	3.1	33.9
Deepwalls,	33°57′	1702	T	65	66	65	64	59	56	54	55	56	58	61	63	
Union of S.Af.			R	4.2	3.9	4.1	3.1	4.0	2.6	3.5	3.3	4.9	4.9	4.9	4.4	47.8
Port Elizabeth,	33°59′	190	T	70	70	68	64	61	57	56	57	59	62	64	67	
Union of S.Af.			R	1.2	1.3	1.9	1.8	2.4	1.8	1.9	2.0	2.3	2.2	2.2	1.7	22.7
Bird Island,	33°50′	13	T	69	70	68	66	65	62	61	62	62	64	66	68	
Union of S.Af.			R	1.0	1.0	1.9	1.2	2.0	1.5	1.5	1.5	1.5	1.8	1.8	1.4	18.2
East London,	33°02′	410	T	71	71	70	67	64	60	60	61	62	64	66	69	
Union of S.Af.			R	2.9	3.0	3.8	2.7	2.2	1.4	1.4	1.7	2.7	3.6	3.4	3.0	31.8
Durban,	29°50′	16	T	75	75	74	71	66	63	62	64	66	68	71	73	
Natal			R	4.3	4.8	5.1	3.0	2.1	1.3	1.1	1.5	2.8	4.3	4.8	4.7	39.7

Source: F. L. Wernstedt, *World Climatic Data, Africa,* Pennsylvania State University, 1959.

Hence we must bear in mind that a great many local climatic variations exist within the general scheme of things presented in the paragraphs that follow (Table 14-5).

Mean annual precipitation along the southwestern and southern fringes of the continent is highest on the upper slopes of the coastal mountain ranges below the Great Escarpment. Indeed, the greatest precipitation in these parts is found on the higher mountainsides of the mediterranean region in the southwest (Fig. 14.8). Orographic uplift of moisture-laden air

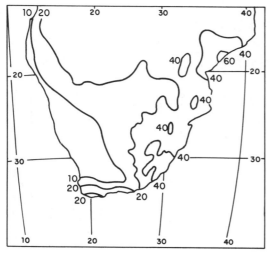

Figure 14.8. Mean annual rainfall in southern Africa (inches).

currents is the mechanical agent upon which these special intensities mainly depend. Unofficially, annual amounts of about 200 inches have recently been collected at points in the Drakenstein Mountains about 40 miles east of Cape Town, and it is believed that many parts of both the Drakenstein and Hex River ranges receive more than 100 inches.[8] Amounts in excess of 60 inches are considered likely for the higher slopes from the Hottentots-Holland to the Cedarberg ranges. An official record from the coastal station at Maclear's Beacon, the highest point on Table Mountain overlooking Cape Town about 3 miles from the sea at an elevation of 3567 feet, provides an annual average of 75 inches.

From the Breede River valley eastward the

[8] *Ibid.*, p. 239. Much of the material on precipitation characteristics is derived from this source.

coastal ranges between the Great Karroo and the sea again act as baffles to the passing air streams and, with one exception, receive much heavier precipitation than the adjoining lowlands. Actual amounts are considerably lower than those in the southwestern mountains, however, generally ranging between 30 and 40 inches. The one exception is the Knysna Forest, which in the main is wetter than the nearby mountain slopes, averaging between 40 and 50 inches yearly.

Amounts fall away rapidly from these extremes. One example is the comparison of Maclear's Beacon at 3567 feet, recording a mean value of 75 inches, with Cape Town Hospital, only $2\frac{1}{2}$ miles northeast of here at about 300 feet, averaging 21 inches. Another is the comparison of two rain-recording stations in the small, narrow valley southeast of Stellenbosch where observations were made for over fourteen years. The valley is about 5 miles long, and its floor is scarcely more than 1 mile wide, hemmed in on all sides save the northwest by spurs of the Hottentots-Holland system that rise 5000 feet above the valley floor. Annual rainfall during the period of record on the valley floor averaged 41 inches, but up on the slopes one station averaged about 80 inches. Similar contrasts can be detected from the map of mean annual rainfall for this part of southern Africa all the way from the Olifants valley to the valley of the Gamka-Gouritz, notably in a section of the Olifants valley from Clanwilliam (8.8 inches) southward, in the middle Breede valley from Worcester (9.4 inches) for about 50 miles southeastward, and in the Little Karroo (Oudtshoorn 9.6 inches). Such local contrasts in mean precipitation amounts are especially typical of the mediterranean region where most of the year's supply arrives during the winter months of April through September. Between here and Algoa Bay, in the region of year-round precipitation, the orographic influence on rainfall intensities is not at all marked.

In the mediterranean region winter precipitation accounts for at least 60 per cent of the annual total. Cape Agulhas, for example, receives 65 per cent of a 17.5 inch total, and Montagu, 75 miles north of Cape Agulhas and about 40 miles east of Worcester on the north side of the Langeberg Mountains, receives 64 per cent of a 12.3 inch mean. Most of the region west of the Hex River range, however, receives more than 75 per cent of the yearly total during the six-month period (Fig. 14.9). Ceres, about 60 miles northeast of Cape Town on the north side of the Hex River range, records 78 per cent of a 41.5 inch total; Elgin, about 35 miles southeast of Cape Town, records 79 per cent of a 47.9 inch total; Darling, about 35 miles north of Cape Town, records 82 per cent of a 21.1 inch total; and Cape Town itself, 77 per cent of a 24.7 inch

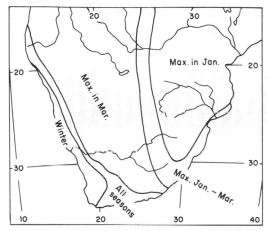

Figure 14.9. Seasonal rainfall distribution in southern Africa.

total. Actually, the great bulk of the winter's precipitation in the mediterranean region occurs during only four months from May through August, and thus summers are long and very dry.

East of Cape Agulhas, on the other hand, where yearly precipitation is more evenly distributed, at most stations only from 40 to 50 per cent occurs in the six-month winter season. And with the exception of a few well-exposed points that receive more than half the year's rainfall in winter (Mossell Bay 51 per cent, Cape St. Francis 60 per cent, Port Elizabeth 54 per cent, and Bird Island 51 per cent), the actual amounts received in the temperate forest region during the winter months are very much less than in the mediterranean region. Apparently the eastward-traveling storms in winter expend most of their precipitable moisture over the broad southwest cape and its mountains. Note, for example, that Elgin receives an average of 37.9 inches during April through September and only 10.1 inches in summer, but Riversdale, about 50 miles west of Mossell Bay

and well within the year-round rainfall region, receives only 8.7 inches during April through September and almost exactly the same amount (8.4 inches) in the summer period of October through March. A similar comparison of Cape Town (19.6 inches in winter, 5.7 inches in summer) with Port Elizabeth (12.2 inches in winter, 10.5 inches in summer) again illustrates the fact that actual amounts of winter rainfall are appreciably larger and less evenly distributed seasonally in the mediterranean region than in the temperate forest region.

For the year as a whole, however, the temperate forest is a good deal wetter and mean annual amounts higher than for most of the mediterranean region. Four stations in the temperate forest, all within less than 15 miles of the sea, illustrate the contrast. From west to east, George, at 725 feet, reports 34.2 inches; Deepwalls, higher on the peneplains at 1702 feet, reports 47.3 inches; Harkersville, at 550 feet, reports 39.3 inches; and Storms River, at 735 feet, reports 44.5 inches. In the warm temperate coastal forest northeast of Algoa Bay, where 75 per cent or more of the mean yearly precipitation occurs in the summer period from October through March, representative amounts are reported from East London of 31.8 inches, from Port St. John of 46.1 inches, from Port Shepstone, Natal, of 41.5 inches and from subtropical Durban of 39.7 inches (Fig. 14.10).

The main sources of winter rain are migrating cyclonic storms advancing east-northeastward from the main belt of the westerlies farther south in the Atlantic. Most of the rain falls in the form of light showers, a warm front rain, during the passage of the warm sector of the depression, as mild, moist air from the tropical Atlantic in the northwest flows into the clockwise circulation of the storm system (Fig. 14.11). Rains are typically of low to moderate intensity, rarely reaching more than 2 inches in twenty-four hours except on the mountain heights, where an increase in both amount and intensity is common. Snow regularly occurs in the mountains at elevations above 4000 feet in wintertime but rarely remains on the ground for more than a few days.

The main sources of summer rainfall that contribute more than half the yearly total along the south coast east of the mediterranean region are migrating depressions of mid-latitude

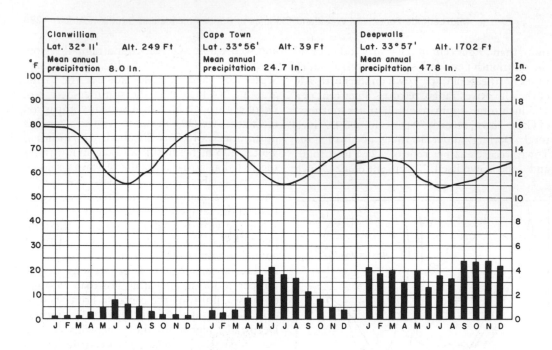

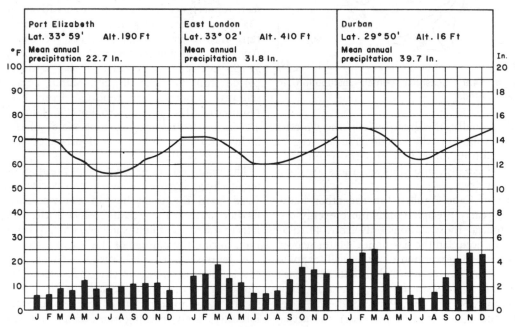

Figure 14.10. Normal temperature and precipitation at stations in mid-latitude mixed forest and mediterranean scrub woodland in southern Africa.

origin, supplied by strong indrafts of maritime tropical air from over the surface of the Indian Ocean to the northeast when anticyclonic conditions spread westward over the eastern part of southern Africa. These traveling storm cells that normally skirt the mediterranean southwest are from time to time augmented by a southward extension of the thermal lows that develop over the interior (Fig. 14.12). Thermal convective storms are rare near the sea along the southwest and south coasts but fairly frequent during the summer in the interior, where thunderstorms, accompanied by hail, contribute to the season's total, especially toward the end of summer in February and March. In wintertime thunderstorms occasionally develop as a frontal phenomenon on the southwesterly winds of a retreating disturbance and may affect both the southwest and south coastal regions.

The reliability of annual precipitation is high for both the mediterranean and temperate forest regions. During any one year at least 85 per cent of the statistical normal can be expected, and between Cape Town and Mossell Bay, along the coast, at least 90 per cent is expected. On the average, precipitation occurs about every three days in both regions through the winter season and continues at this frequency during summer on the south coast, dropping off to very infrequent and uncertain occurrences in the mediterranean region.

A high percentage of possible sunshine prevails throughout the year in these regions, commonly remaining above 60 per cent (Fig. 14.13). The cloud cover associated with transient weather disturbances does not usually persist for more than a day or two at a time. Maximum sunshine normally prevails in the summer months of December to February in the

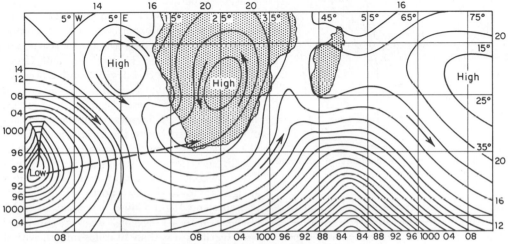

Figure 14.11. Representative synoptic situation in winter leading to precipitation along the south coast of Africa (values in millibars).

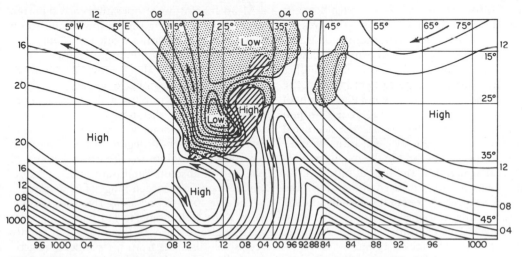

Figure 14.12. Representative synoptic situation in summer leading to precipitation in southeastern Africa (values in millibars).

mediterranean southwest, when it increases to 70 per cent or more and cloud cover is at a minimum, and maximum sunshine prevails in the winter month of July along the south coast, when it is around 70 per cent and cloud cover is at a minimum. Conversely, relative humidities increase to a maximum in June, July, and

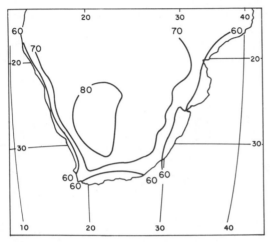

Figure 14.13. Annual percentage of possible sunshine in southern Africa.

August in the mediterranean region and to a maximum in the late summer months of March and April in the temperate forest region.

In wintertime transient disturbances frequently bring a certain amount of fog with the wind-blown rains. March is the month of maximum fog for the entire coastal stretch between Cape Town and Algoa Bay, and the greatest proportion occurs in the six months of March through August. Generally, the number of days per year when fog may be expected diminishes from the southwest cape eastward, with Cape Town averaging sixteen days and Port Elizabeth nine days. Low radiation fog is a common feature of inland valleys under the nocturnal inversion during spells of clear, calm weather in late autumn and winter in the mediterranean region, at which time the tops of hills and distant mountains may be seen rising above the fog banks. Such fogs are readily dispelled by the warmth of the morning sun and rarely persist through the day. They are much less common east of the mediterranean region.

The mean annual range of temperature is greatest in the drier maquis of the mediter-

ranean region (Clanwilliam 23.6 degrees, Montagu 22.5, Oudtshoorn and Willowmore 23), and least along the coast all the way from Cape Columbine, about 80 miles northwest of Cape Town, to Durban. There is really very little difference in the mean temperature range at well-exposed stations along the entire shoreline. Cape Columbine reports about 8 degrees, Dasseineland Light House, between here and Cape Town, 7, Cape Agulhas 13, Cape St. Francis 10, Bird Island on the east side of Algoa Bay 8.4, East London 11.3, Port Shepstone 12.6, and Durban 13.4. The principal differences appear in a comparison of actual summer and winter temperatures.

Most of the mediterranean region at any distance from the sea experiences a mean annual range of 16 to 20 degrees: Cape Town and Caledon 16 degrees, Langgewens and Groot Drakenstein about 20.5 degrees, and Worcester 20 degrees. Within the temperate forest the range is much lower, as at George, 12.2 degrees, and Deepwalls, 12 degrees. With the exception of the temperate forest, the mean annual range of temperature tends to increase with increasing distance from the sea. An example is provided by comparing three stations along a line at right angles to the coast north of Cape Town. Dasseineland Light House, less than 10 miles offshore, with a range of 7 degrees, compares with Darling, less than 10 miles inland, with a range of 18 degrees, which, in turn, compares with Laggewens, about 30 miles inland, with a range of 20.5 degrees.

Mean maximum temperatures are reported to be about 90° along the southwest and south coasts, increasing within a few miles inland to about 100°. Mean minimum temperatures average about 40° along most of the same coasts, giving a mean extreme range of about 50 degrees. Mean minima a short distance inland, except in the temperate forest, are reported to be about 30°, producing a mean extreme range of 70 degrees. Cape Town has recorded an absolute maximum in January of 104° and an absolute minimum of 32°, producing an extreme recorded range of 72 degrees.

The frost-free period along the water's edge, from Cape Columbine to Durban and northward, is almost the entire year long. But at only very short distances from the seashore, as little as a mile or two, light frosts have touched the ground in the coastal section between Cape

Town and Algoa Bay. In general, the frost-free period ranges in duration from three hundred to 330 days in most inland sections of the mediterranean and temperate forest regions, beginning only a few miles from the sea.

Summer. During the summer months, particularly December through February, when the southern part of Africa experiences maximum insolation, the highly heated continental surface warms a shallow layer of the atmosphere resting on it, creating a thermal low pressure condition that primarily governs the weather program of the season. At the same time, the oceanic anticyclones over the Atlantic and Indian oceans shrink, diminishing in intensity to around 1020 millibars, and their central areas shift away from southern African shores. In short, the almost unbroken belt of subtropical high pressure over the South Atlantic, the southern part of Africa, and the southern Indian Ocean in winter disappears from lower levels over land during summertime. It is displaced southward over the coastal waters, where it appears in the form of small traveling anticyclones that pass eastward along the south coast between the continental low and the oceanic depressions associated with the westerlies at higher latitudes farther south.

The most frequent feature of summertime weather (occurring normally about fifty times during the season) is a combination of an interior thermal low over the northern Kalahari and a secondary, migrating low of westerlies origin in the southeast, separating anticyclones off the southwest coast and off the coast toward the northeast (Fig. 14.12). Along the southwest coast winds are mainly from a southerly quarter, blowing approximately parallel to the shoreline, but slightly onshore. In this area there is no precipitation. Along the southeast coast, however, from the temperate forest eastward, this synoptic situation brings rain about 70 per cent of the time. On such occasions north and northeast winds bring a moderately strong flow of maritime tropical air southward from the Indian Ocean into the clockwise circulation of the moving depression. After the coastal low has moved off northeastward over the sea, sometimes to the accompaniment of strong southeast gales, anticyclonic air moves against the coast, and clear, fair weather returns.

From time to time (about twenty-two times during a normal summer), thermal low pressure conditions prevail over the entire southern end of the continent poleward of the Tropic of Capricorn. On these occasions an inflow of air from the sea is normally felt during daylight hours in all coastal sections, often leading to local convective showers and thunderstorms farther inland.

Summer is the season of little or no rain in the mediterranean region of the southwest. Statistically, the region is not entirely rainless at this time, but its occurrence is extremely uncertain in both time and amount, and over the years monthly amounts have averaged less than 1 inch from October through March (Fig. 14.10).

From the lower Breede River valley eastward the more equitable distribution of yearly rainfall begins. This is typical of the temperate forest. Riversdale, about 30 miles northeast of the river's mouth, reports between 1 and 2 inches for every month of the year except January (0.91 inch). March is the month of maximum precipitation, averaging 2.01 inches. Monthly values range between 1.06 and 1.65 inches at Mossel Bay, between 1.14 and 2.87 inches at Cape St. Francis, between 1.18 and 2.40 inches at Port Elizabeth, and between 0.98 and 2.01 inches at Bird Island. At the last three stations the early winter month of May is the wettest. At George and Deepwalls, both well within the temperate forest, a moderate summer increase in rainfall is reported: 3.58 inches at George in March, and 4.92 inches at Deepwalls in both October and November.

East of Algoa Bay the late summer month of March is commonly the wettest for the year. At Grahamstown and King Williamstown, both about 25 miles from the sea and at moderate elevations, March is the month of maximum rainfall and at both stations averages 3.3 inches. At East London in the warm temperate forest March averages 3.8 inches, and at Port Shepstone and Durban within the subtropical forest farther north averages for March are 5.6 and 5.1 inches respectively. These stations are, of course, within the region of pronounced summer rainfall increase, where more than 60 per cent of the annual increment comes from October through March. Actually, a secondary maximum occurs in the spring season of October and November from Algoa Bay northeastward to Durban. This is a consequence of the conflict between relatively rapid temperature rise over land areas under the influence of increased solar radiation intensity, and the lingering chill of winter over the adjacent seas.

An occasional feature of summer weather along the entire coast from Cape Town to East London is a southeasterly gale. Winds from the southeast, setting in when the barometer is comparatively high, rise to velocities of around 60 miles per hour and bring powerful drafts of cool, damp air to the coastal regions. Such gales are most common during the beginning and again toward the end of the summer, October and November being the months of maximum occurrence. At Cape Town the approach of the southeaster is usually indicated when skies are clear and the flat top of Table Mountain bears a low cloud cap that hangs part way down the slope and is popularly called the table cloth. When the cloud on Table Mountain becomes a rain-bearing nimbus cloud, a black southeaster, as it is locally known it often brings light rain and cold weather.

Summer temperatures most commonly attain a maximum in February in the entire coastal mountain section from the Olifants valley to the Great Fish valley and thence along the coast to Durban. The temperature lag is clearly understandable for climates that are so strongly dominated by air from the sea. The maritime influence is also expressed in the fact that mean January temperatures at all stations of record are less than 1 degree cooler than February and in many instances are statistically the same. Throughout the mediterranean region, and also in the warmer coastal temperate forest northeast of Algoa Bay, mean values for the warmest months range between 69° and 75° (Table 14-5). February temperatures at Cape Town average 71°, at Montagu 75°, Riversdale 72°, Port Elizabeth 70°, East London 71°, and Durban 75°. Within the main area of the warm temperate forest between Mossel Bay and St. Francis Bay summers are not as warm, averaging between 65° and 68°. George, for example, reports 68°, and Deepwalls 66° (Fig. 14.14).

Coastal stations, well exposed to the sea, report the lowest values and generally reflect the influence of the surface sea water temperature offshore. The February temperatures of 63° at Cape Columbine and of 62° at Das-seineland Light House arise chiefly from the fact that the Benguela Current brings surface water temperatures of around 56° to these

shores. On the other hand, February averages of 70° at Bird Island and Great Fish Point Light House, as well as the fact that from here north-eastward along the coast to Durban mean values are gradually higher, indicate the influence of the warmer water of the Mozambique and Agulhas currents, the Agulhas Current averaging 69° at Bird Island in January.

Inland stations are warmer in summer. Cape Town reports 71° in February, and Great Drakenstein, about 35 miles inland, 73°; Cape

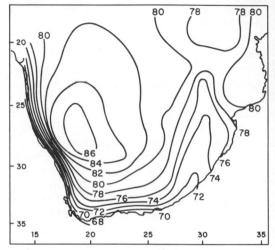

Figure 14.14. Mean summer temperatures in southern Africa in January (°F).

Agulhas 69°, Montagu, 65 miles inland, 75°; Port Elizabeth 70°, Hermitage, 30 miles inland, 74°.

The mean daily range of summer temperatures is also greater inland, where nocturnal clear sky radiation is less moderated by air from the sea, and averages 30 degrees or more in sheltered valleys, except, of course, in the Knysna Forest. Here, nearness to the sea results in a moderating maritime influence, in addition to which daily temperatures do not fluctuate as widely under forest as they do under more open vegetation. In the mediterranean region of the southwest summer has the greatest daily temperature range, when skies are clear most of the time, allowing both a high input of heat from the sun during the day and a rapid rate of outgoing heat loss through reradiation at night. Cape Town, for example, averages a mean daily range of 19 to 20 degrees from November through March and only 12 or 13 degrees in wintertime. There is little seasonal change in mean daily range in the temperate forest of year-round rainfall, but in the warmer forested regions northeast of Algoa Bay winter, the drier season, is the time of maximum mean daily range (Fig. 14.10).

The maximum recorded temperatures in these regions of southern coastal Africa are well over 100°. They occur most often when warm, dry winds known as Berg winds blow down off the vast, highly heated interior plateau. Warmed adiabatically as they descend toward sea level, they may occasionally blow for two or three days at a time. The temperature at Cape Town has been raised to 105° by a Berg wind in the late summer month of March. Berg winds, however, are mainly a feature of wintertime weather.

Winter. As late summer advances, temperatures begin to drop slowly, a gradual increase in cloudiness is noticed over the mediterranean southwest where rains begin to increase, and anticyclonic conditions begin to appear with increasing frequency over the interior of all of southern Africa. By the month of June the oceanic highs over the South Atlantic and Indian oceans have once again been united by the return of predominantly anticyclonic weather over the intervening land.

The most common synoptic situation is one in which a continental high is centered along the southeastern side of the continent inland from Durban. It normally occurs about fifty-three times each winter. Air movement under the subsiding divergence of the high pressure cell is mainly seaward over most coastal sections, although an afternoon sea breeze usually intervenes briefly in most areas. Over inland sections the sun shines brightly down through cloudless skies. The air is clear and dry, and at any distance from the sea days are usually quite warm and nights become moderatley cold.

Continental anticyclones usually originate as small segments of the South Atlantic highs detach themselves, and move toward the continent. Now and then one may merge with a thermal anticyclone moving northeastward from the colder part of the Atlantic farther south and may enter southern Africa from the southwest to establish itself over the interior plateau.[9] By displacing the comparatively warm

air normally over the plateau, a modified continental polar mass of air forms, bringing unusually deep cold and heavy frost to the interior. Excessive cold, under these circumstances, even reaches the coastal regions, especially the unforested areas, although it is considerably offset by the moderating effect of the sea.

The second most frequent weather occurrence in winter, one that normally comes about twenty-six times during the season, is the combination of a depression over the south coast while anticyclonic conditions prevail over the interior plateau. Stimulating the outflow of air from the continental anticyclone, northwest winds bring moist, warm air from the Atlantic to the southwest cape, and in an average of 70 per cent of such situations moderately heavy rains fall on the mediterranean region.

Along the Namib coast north of the Olifants River, Berg winds off the plateau often so raise the air temperature in winter (as much as 20 degrees above normal) that a small low pressure situation results, causing rains that frequently affect the southwestern cape. This, and the conditions described in the preceding paragraph are the main sources of winter precipitation along the south and southwest coasts. Sometimes uniting with a migrating low of higher latitude origin in the westerlies, such a system eventually moves southeastward and then eastward, bringing rain to the temperate forest region as well, and occasionally to stations northeast of Algoa Bay.

The winter rains that are such a prominent characteristic of the mediterranean region vary in amount from place to place, depending on exposure to the prevailing rain-bearing winds of the season and also on topography. By and large, stations in mountainous situations, even those at rather low altitude, gain from the more frequent and more vigorous turbulence of rugged terrain. Jonkershoek at an altitude of 899 feet receives 42 inches of rain yearly, and Elgin at 919 feet receives 47.9 inches. Both stations lie in the high mountain zone of the Hottentots-Holland ranges on the southwest cape and are much wetter than stations on the peneplains or nearer the sea. The wettest month throughout the mediterranean region is June, with only rare exceptions, one of which is Jonkershoek where the month of maximum rainfall is July. East of the mediterranean

[9] Wellington, *op. cit.*, p. 194.

region, with the exception of the Knysna Forest, winter is the time of least precipitation (Table 14-5).

The coldest month of winter is July throughout the entire coastal margin of southern Africa from Cape Columbine to Durban. Values remain relatively high and in both the mediterranean and temperate forest regions generally average from 52° to 55°, the lower temperatures being characteristic of interior locations (Fig. 14.15). Some locations facing the sea, even

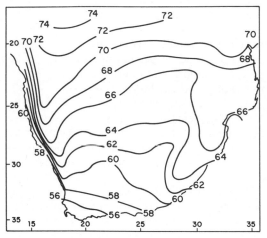

Figure 14.15. Mean winter temperatures in southern Africa in July (°F).

at some distance from the coast, are sufficiently favored by the moderating affect of maritime airflow to be warmer in winter than localities sheltered from the sea. Langgewens, for example, lies at some 35 miles from the coast but on the inner edge of the rising peneplain, and it averages 54° in July, whereas Groot Drakenstein, only 25 miles from the shore of False Bay in the pass where the upper Berg River cuts through the Drakenstein Mountains, averages 53°. And Caledon, only 20 miles from the sea but within the shelter of the 3000–4000-foot ridges of the Babylons Toren and Klein River ranges, averages 52° in July, compared with 54° at Riversdale, about 25 miles from the

seashore toward the inner edge of the well-exposed peneplain.

From Algoa Bay northeastward along the frost-free, forested shoreline mean temperatures in July range between 56° and 61°, increasing to more than 61° from the vicinity of Port St. Johns northward (Table 14-5).

Frost may occur at any time during the coldest month and more rarely at other times in the winter season in open inland areas sheltered from the influence of the sea, even within just a few miles of the coast. This is especially true of interior valleys in the mediterranean region and of the inner temperate grasslands toward the east and northeast. Frost occurs largely during intervals of clear, calm weather when the dry, stable air is still, allowing nocturnal radiation to reduce ground temperatures to subfreezing levels.

The mean daily range of temperature in the mediterranean region is only about 12 or 13 degrees during this season, whereas in the forested regions toward the east it is between 16 and 17 degrees, the maximum for the year. Minimum temperatures in July average between 35 and 40 degrees over most of the mediterranean region, increasing to between 40 and 45 degrees from Algoa Bay northeastward.

In the preceding pages we have dealt with the mid-latitude forest-woodland climates in a small coastal mountain zone of southern Africa: a mediterranean scrub woodland, mainly on the southwest cape, a temperate evergreen rainforest, between the Olifants valley and Algoa Bay, and a true temperate forest, the Knysna Forest. We have seen how, with increasing distance northward—in other words, with diminishing latitude—temperatures at all seasons are higher, and a marked seasonal distribution of annual rainfall with the maximum in summertime is typical. Along the inner margins of this zone are more arid mid-latitude grassland regions having wider ranges of temperature experience and more frequent and more severe frosts; these will be discussed in a later chapter.

References

ADAMSON, R. S.: *The Vegetation of South Africa*, Cape Town, 1938.

BOFFI, J. A.: "Effect of the Andes Mountains on the General Circulation Over the Southern Part of South America," *Bulletin of the American Meteorological Society*, **30**(7), pp. 242–47, 1949.

COYLE, J. R.: *A Practical Analysis of Weather Along the East Coast of South America*, Rio de Janeiro, 1945.

GOODSPEED, T. H.: *Plant Hunters in the Andes*, University of California Press, Berkeley, 1961.

OLASCOAGA, M. J.: "Some Aspects of Argentine Rainfall," *Tellus*, **2**(4): 312–18, 1950.

RUBIN, M., and VAN LOON, H.: "Aspects of the Circulation of the Southern Hemisphere," *Journal of Meteorology*, **11**(1): 68–76, 1954.

SERRA, A.: *Atlas climatologico do Brasil*, Rio de Janeiro, 1955.

Wellington, J. H.: *Southern Africa*, Cambridge University Press, Cambridge, 1955.

chapter 15

MID-LATITUDE FOREST AND WOODLAND IN AUSTRALIA AND NEW ZEALAND

Continuing our survey of the mid-latitude forest-woodland climates south of the equator, we again find segments of these regions between 30° and 45°S. Lat. in southern Australia and New Zealand. A mediterranean scrub woodland climate appears in two sections of southern Australia, one in the southwest generally poleward of Perth and another about 1000 miles east in the district around Adelaide. A modified mid-latitude mixed forest climate is found in eastern Australia from the Tropic of Capricorn southward to Tasmania, and also in New Zealand. A coastal evergreen or temperate rainforest climate appears in southeastern Australia, Tasmania, and New Zealand.

Australia

It is necessary to consider the climates of any part of Australia within the general context of the continent's geography and its relationships with the fundamental tendencies of the general atmospheric circulation. Australia's size, shape, position on the earth, and principal geomorphic features, coupled with the major oceanic currents that wash its shores and the prevailing circulation of the atmosphere, are important factors in the variety and distribution of its climates.

A compact, continental expanse of 2,974,581 square miles, Australia lies between the South Indian and South Pacific oceans roughly astride

the Tropic of Capricorn, remote from other major land masses. Cape York, the northernmost tip of the continent, is almost within 10 degrees of the equator. From this point to Wilson's Promontory, the southernmost point, is a distance of over 2000 miles. It is about 300 miles farther to the southern tip of Tasmania. Longitudinal extent, measured from Brisbane to the west coast, is about 2500 miles. About three fifths (61 per cent) of the total area lies poleward of the Tropic of Capricorn; thus, although its lesser, northern section is tropical in character, the continent's southern reaches are far enough poleward to experience the seasonal rhythms of mid-latitude climates during the annual orbit of the earth around the sun (Fig. 15.1).

The primary influence of latitude upon climate is nowhere in the world any better illustrated than here, for Australia is almost entirely lacking in features of striking relief. Hence, latitude coupled with position in relation to the seaward margins of the land mass are geographical circumstances of primary significance in the distribution of Australia's climates. However, where inconspicuous land forms rise to moderate heights above the general surface level, some advantage is gained by the local increase in precipitation, a most important factor in a predominantly dry land. Save for the low mountains in the southeast,

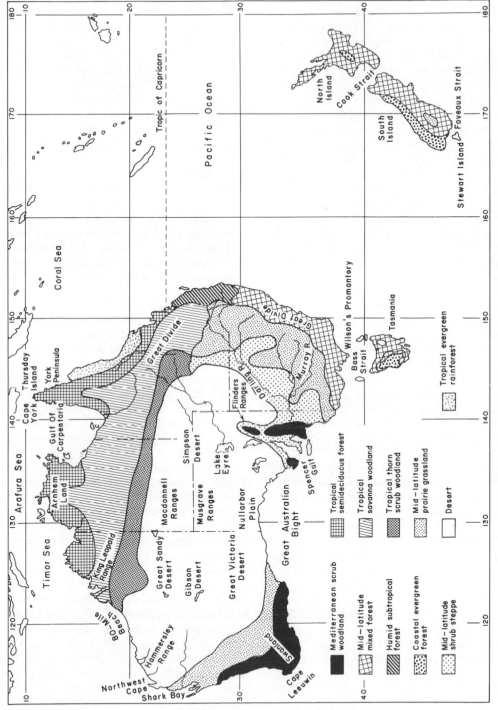

Figure 15.1. Distribution of climates in Australia and New Zealand.

Legend (left column):
- Mediterranean scrub woodland
- Mid-latitude mixed forest
- Humid subtropical forest
- Coastal evergreen forest
- Mid-latitude shrub steppe

Legend (right column):
- Tropical semideciducus forest
- Tropical savanna woodland
- Tropical thorn scrub woodland
- Mid-latitude prairie grassland
- Desert
- Tropical evergreen rainforest

Map labels: 80-Mile Beach, Northwest Cape, Hammersley Range, Shark Bay, Cape Leeuwin, Swampland, Great Victoria Desert, Gibson Desert, Great Sandy Desert, King Leopold Range, Timor Sea, Arafura Sea, Arnhem Land, Gulf Of Carpentaria, Cape York, Thursday Island, York Peninsula, Coral Sea, Great Divide, Macdonnell Ranges, Musgrave Ranges, Simpson Desert, Lake Eyre, Nullarbor Plain, Great Australian Bight, Spencer Gulf, Flinders Ranges, Darling R., Murray R., Great Divide, Wilson's Promontory, Bass Strait, Tasmania, Tropic of Capricorn, Pacific Ocean, North Island, Cook Strait, South Island, Stewart Island, Foveaux Strait

Australia's geomorphic features consist chiefly of low plateaus, peneplains, extensive basins or lowlands, and occasional sections of small to moderately hilly country. There are three main topographic divisions: the western peneplain (Western Shield), the eastern highlands, and the interior eastern lowlands or Geosyncline.[1]

About a million square miles of the western half of the country are dominated by an extensive arid peneplain, averaging about 1200 feet above sea level but rising in broad, very gradual stages, consisting of several sections of moderately hilly terrain, to heights of from 3000 to 5000 feet. From north to south are the Hammersley (highest point Mt. Bruce, el. 4024), Ashburton, and Wiluna ranges, and in the central part of the country, toward the eastern limits of the peneplain, the Macdonnell and Musgrave ranges. In the Macdonnell Range, along the Tropic, elevations rise very gently to a maximum of 4955 feet at Mt. Ziel, and in the Musgrave Range about 200 miles toward the south the highest point is Mt. Woodroffe, at 4970 feet. Around most of its perimeter the peneplain falls gently away into fairly broad, peripheral basins of lower elevation, but in the southwest around Perth it drops down more abruptly along a 200 mile escarpment to a relatively narrow coastal plain.

East of the great peneplain the eastern lowlands extend in a series of interior basins generally less than 500 feet above sea level from the Gulf of Carpentaria for about 1200 miles to the south coast. Between the Tropic and gulf the hilly terrain of the Selwyn Range attains elevations of over 1000 feet, even so scarcely interrupting the over-all continuity of the interior lowlands. From the south coast near Adelaide, however, the Flinders Ranges reach northward for about 400 miles, rising in many places to more than 3000 feet to interpose features of significant relief in that locality. East of the Flinders Mountains is the semi-arid Murray River basin, drained by the Murray-Darling system of partly persistent, partly intermittent streams, the largest stream system in the country, emptying into Victoria Harbour south of Adelaide.

The eastern highlands reach from York

[1] Griffith Taylor, *Australia*, E. P. Dutton & Co., Inc., New York, 1943. Most of the geographical material presented here has been obtained from this and other writings by Professor Taylor.

Peninsula to the south coast, reappearing in the compactly mountainous island of Tasmania. Confined for the most part to within about 200 miles of the east coast—except northwest of Brisbane, where they recede to around 300 miles from the coast—this series of isolated plateaus and gentle hills has been inaptly named the Great Dividing Range. Northwest of Brisbane its moderate slopes remain generally under 3000 feet above sea level, and from here southward it is between 3000 and 6000 feet, rising gradually to a maximum height in Mt. Kosciusko at 7328 feet about 200 miles northeast of Melbourne. Tasmania is a thoroughly mountainous island where rugged terrain exceeds 5000 feet in elevation in several localities and commonly extends to the coast to form a great many bold headlands overlooking the sea.

Three oceanic currents affect Australia's extratropical shores: the East Australia Current, a southward flow of warm water down the east coast, the West Australian Current, a variable but generally northward flow of cool water along the west coast, and the east-flowing West Wind Drift, which moves well to the south of the continent. The main stream of this cool water tends to remain rather far offshore, actually forming a westward countercurrent inshore along the Great Australian Bight from time to time. In Bass Strait, however, it converges with the shoreline of the mainland and washes the shores of Tasmania and southeastern Australia (Fig. 15.1).

Coastal sea water temperatures are affected in part by these currents and in part by the seasonal variation in solar radiation intensity. Warm water persists throughout the year along the north coast, where the variable direction of the South Equatorial Current is guided mainly by seasonal and temporal changes in wind direction, ranging between 75° in August and 80° to 84° in February. Along the south coast summer temperatures in February are moderately high, from around 70° near Cape Leeuwin to about 65° in Bass Strait. In August mean values drop to around 61° to 63° near Cape Leeuwin and around 57° in Bass Strait. The constantly cooler waters in the vicinity of Bass Strait are, of course, primarily due to the West Wind Drift.

Australia's position astride the Tropic of Capricorn places it well within those latitudes where atmospheric cells of high pressure repeatedly form. Although these subtropical highs are more persistent and more typical of oceanic regions, they occur with sufficient frequency over large land masses in the same latitudes to play a dominant role in the year's normal sequence of weather variations. Australia possesses the largest land area south of the equator within these latitudes. Thus, we find a tendency for the weather throughout the year to be influenced primarily by a succession of anticyclonic circulations. The internal motions of these subsiding, diverging air masses are basically counterclockwise, transporting air westward on their northern margins as part of the southeast trade wind flow, and eastward on their southern margins where they contribute to the mean flow of the westerly circulations.

A seasonal north–south shift in mean circulation takes place, however. In winter anticyclonic air prevails over most of the continent, centered over the southeastern interior (Fig. 4.3), and at this season the southeast trades blow approximately parallel to the northeast coast but are mainly offshore along the north coast. At the same time, the westerlies, now farther north than at other seasons, reach their maximum frequency along the south coast, particularly in southwestern and southeastern sections. In summer the main area of anticyclonic development is displaced southward (Fig. 4.2), generally centering off the south coast, and is very much smaller in size. At this season the predominant surface airflow is onshore for most of Australia, although subject to frequent disruption with the passage of transient weather systems. All along the north coast the prevailing direction is northwest, resulting in typically heavy summer rains. Northwest weather extends down the east coast a short distance, normally as far as Cairns just north of the Atherton plateau. From Cairns to Brisbane winds of the summer season are chiefly easterly, representing a slight southward deflection of the southeast trades. From Brisbane to Bass Strait winds are often onshore but are more variable than those farther north, with the alternate passage of cyclones and anticyclones. Along the south coast summer winds are mainly southerly and, therefore, onshore. Southerly winds also predominate along the west coast under the strengthened influence of the south Indian Ocean High, which at this

season shifts eastward toward the Australian coast. At higher altitudes of a mile or so mean air movement is principally eastward over southern Australia the year round. In northern sections where the trade winds dominate, surface airflow movement of the upper air is consistent with this in the summer months, moving westward toward the Indian Ocean. In wintertime, however, upper airflow is mainly eastward over nearly all of Australia.

PLANT LIFE. A last important consideration of Australia's general geographical setting concerns the unique character of the indigenous plant life. The most noteworthy fact is that most of the woody plants, from the mid-latitudes to the tropics, belong to one or the other of only two genera, the eucalypts and the acacias. Although many other genera are represented, not a single one is numerically important. Three fourths of the total vegetation is composed of evergreen hardwood trees and shrubs belonging to the genus *Eucalyptus*. These range in size from dwarfed and stunted shrubs less than 6 feet high, of the sort one sees scattered over desert landscapes, to giant timber trees of certain well-watered coastal and hilly areas. Many of the latter are equal in height to the sequoias and redwoods of California. The tallest eucalypt accurately measured was a specimen of *Eucalyptus regnans* in Victoria that was 374 feet high and 25 feet in diameter 6 feet above the ground. (The tallest tree in North America, a redwood, was 364 feet high when measured in 1947.) Eucalypts belong to the myrtle family (*Myrtaceae*), and thus far no fewer than 520 species and 138 varieties have been identified, nearly all of them endemic to Australia.

Acacias comprise the largest genus in Australia, for over six hundred species of shrubs and small trees, both deciduous and evergreen, are known, accounting for more than half the total number of this species known in the entire world. So abundant are the acacias that they form the familiar landscape of bright yellow that is widely seen over the interior. Australia's national emblem is an acacia bearing the name *wattle*. As a general rule, acacias tend to dominate the more open woodland and scrub vegetation of the interior between the barren desert and the wetter forest areas nearer the coast. In the latter regions the eucalypts tend to dominate.

The forest-woodland regions of southwestern and southeastern Australia stand out from the desert interior and from the tropical environments in the north as regions with relatively plentiful rainfall and pronounced seasonal rhythms of solar radiation input and temperature variation. Admirably suited for human habitation and agricultural productivity, these regions are the most populous parts of the country. In outward appearance their distinctive vegetation is climatically controlled and is in many respects similar to the mid-latitude forest-woodland areas in other parts of the world.

Mean annual rainfall sufficient in amount and reliability to support extensive tree growth in edaphic situations that are neither poorly drained and excessively wet nor extremely well drained and excessively dry is the controlling meteorological element by which the distribution of the regions is determined (Fig. 15.2). Close-crowned forest in mid-latitude Australia is generally confined to areas within 100 miles of the sea receiving a reliable 30 inches or more of annual rainfall, a more open, parklike woodland tends to prevail under 20 to 30 inches of annual rain, and a mainly shrubby scrub vegetation called mallee predominates where annual amounts average less than 20 inches. There is much interpenetration of these dominant types of vegetation, and mallee (Australian term for the maquis of other parts of the world) is by no means confined to the forest-woodland regions but enjoys a considerable distribution in semi-arid grassland regions between forest-woodland and desert.

The distinction between the mediterranean environment and the temperate mixed forest and rainforest environments is established primarily on the basis of the normal seasonal rainfall distribution for the year. Comparative amounts and types of normal yearly precipitation, as well as sunshine, cloud cover, temperature regimes, and other considerations are important, but the main influence is seasonal rainfall distribution. Of the two mediterranean areas of winter rainfall and summer drought, the larger is in the southwest around Perth and the smaller around Adelaide.

A mediterranean environment is found in southwestern Australia from around Geraldton, some 230 miles north of Perth, to the vicinity of Esperance on the south coast about 380 miles southeast of Perth. It is confined for the most part to within 50 to 100 miles of the coast. It reaches about 400 miles from near Geraldton to Cape Leeuwin, southwesternmost point on the continent, and about 400 miles from there to Esperance.

In this part of Australia the great western peneplain falls away toward the sea rather more sharply than elsewhere, yielding to hilly topography that is dissected and eroded by a number of short streams that mainly flow at right angles to the shoreline. This is especially true of the section from near Perth to Esperance. For a distance of around 200 miles south of Moora, a small town about 90 miles north of Perth, the coastal hills drop steeply down from heights of between 1200 and 1500 feet to a low, narrow coastal plain, creating a prominent physiographic feature known as the Darling Escarpment, or Darling Range. Along the Darling Range greatest heights are between 1500 and 2000 feet. Along the south coast from Cape Leeuwin to Esperance hill country of moderate relief approaches the sea at intervals, attaining maximum elevations in the Stirling Range about 25 miles inland from Albany, where the highest point is 3640 feet at Bluff Knoll about 50 miles northeast of Albany.

Much of the shoreline within this entire territory is uninhabited because it consists in the main of poorly drained alluvial clays and sand dunes, grassy ridges, and low marshy plains, alternating with many miles of steep, rocky cliffs that stand high above the sea. The south coast in particular is fringed with steep cliffs several hundred feet high, and the shoreline between Perth and Geraldton is chiefly edged either with sand dunes or with coastal bluffs between 300 and 400 feet in height.

The largest drainage system along these shores is that of the Swan River, on whose right bank, near its mouth, stands the city of Perth. From this river the southwestern region of Australia has gained the name *Swanland*. Other rivers of some importance are the Blackwood, flowing into the sea at Cape Leeuwin, and the Frankwood, entering the sea along the south coast west of Albany. Along their lower courses these are persistent streams, but their upper reaches are only intermittent, for they typically dry up during the normal summer drought. Beyond the sources of the coastal rivers where the peneplain maintains an elevation of around

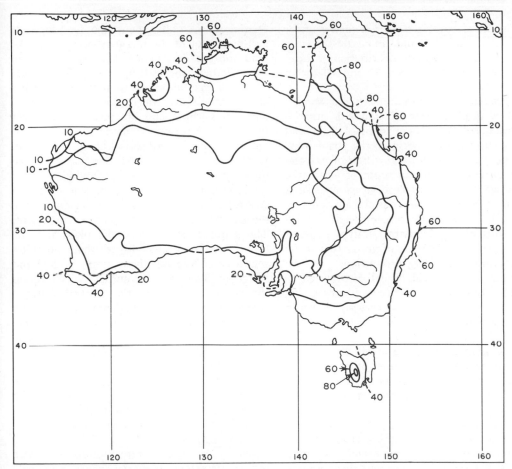

Figure 15.2.   Mean annual precipitation in Australia (inches).

1200 feet is a region of salt flats and playa lakes. Over two hundred of these shallow, intermittent, salt-encrusted depressions extend for over 400 miles into the interior, by their presence indicating a predominantly desert climate of uncertain rainfall north and east of the mediterranean region.

Southwestern Australia, like the Cape region of southern Africa, possesses an unusually rich flora, especially among the smaller herbaceous flowering forms, more than three quarters of which is considered endemic to this region. Outwardly the vegetation is dominated by a half-dozen species of eucalyptus trees that make this one of the major forested areas in the country. Two species alone account for most of the close-crowned forested area and for 90 per cent or more of the timber cut in the region. These are karri (*Eucalyptus diversicolor*) and jarrah (*E. marginata*). Karri is a very tall tree

ranging from around 150 to more than 200 feet and from 7 to 10 feet in diameter, its clean trunk towering to 100 feet before branching into a spreading crown of small, thin, pale green leaves. It is restricted almost entirely to the stretch of country within 50 miles of the south coast between the Blackwood River and Albany at altitudes of less than 1000 feet. It is a fast-growing tree that thrives where mean annual rainfall averages between 40 and 60 inches, and here represents a fragment of coastal evergreen forest related to mediterranean scrub woodland as California redwood is related to the drier, mediterranean portions of California. Jarra is also a tall tree, averaging around 100 feet, occasionally reaching 125 feet, and 4 to 6 feet in diameter. It is frequently free of branches from 50 to 60 feet above the ground. It rules the forest from the middle Swan valley to the south coast and along the south coast as far as Albany at altitudes of under 1000 feet. It thrives under less rainfall than karri and can be considered to indicate the approximate distribution of mean yearly rainfall of between 30 and 40 inches (Fig. 15.2).

Associated with jarrah are scattered wandoo or white gum (*E. redunca*) and red gum (*E. calophylla*), smaller trees of adaptable habit and variable appearance. Between the jarrah zone and the sea, within a narrow belt of lowland some distance north and south of Perth, the very large tree called tuart (*E. gomphocephalla*) is dominant. Preferring the coastal plain at nearly sea level, it commonly reaches heights of 125 feet and is among the many eucalyptus species yielding copious amounts of nectar that is the basis of important honey production.

Where mean annual rainfall is between 30 and 20 inches the wandoo predominates, giving way to York gum (*E. Loxophleba*) as mean amounts of annual rainfall diminish to between 20 and 15 inches. York gum is a medium-sized tree, occasionally reaching about 40 feet, and where it begins to outnumber other eucalypts is usually joined by a good proportion of more drought-tolerant acacias and species of other evergreen broadleaves like the bottle brush (*Melaleuca leucadendron*), together creating an open, parklike woodland of low-crowned trees and brush land. The wandoo and York gum regions of increasingly low rainfall occupy an interior zone roughly between 50 and 100 miles of the coast, extending from about 100 miles north of Perth to the Stirling Range near the south coast. It is in the York gum country that vegetation begins to take on the appearance of maquis where the fragrant plant cover tends to be preponderantly shrubby in nature, most woody plants producing many stems from thick root stocks to form an often impenetrable brush about 10 feet high. In open sandy tracts a very abundant heathlike cover is typical, including bluebush (*Kochia sedifolia*) and saltbush (*Atriplex vesicarum*), the bushy-topped grass tree (*Xanthorrhea spp.*), and species of the yellow-flowering, leathery-leaved Banksia. These are common components of the mallee that extends eastward out of the strictly mediterranean region into the semidesert flatness of the Nullarbor Plain.

The Nullarbor Plain is a low, porous limestone plateau extending to the shores of the Great Australian Bight, where it commonly terminates in cliffs about 200 feet high. It occupies most of the territory between Swanland and the Eyre peninsula. It is remarkable for its flatness, and little open water can be seen on its surface, although subterranean caverns and channels are sources of artesian water. Shrubby saltbush and bluebush are the chief plants of the region. Its name is descriptive—*null arbor* signifies *no trees*—although in shallow, moist depressions, called dongas, low tree forms, particularly acacias, are found.

Beyond, in the section of the state of South Australia called the Adelaide region, is the second area of mediterranean environment. The south coast between the plain and the mouth of the Murray River, about 50 miles southeast of Adelaide, is strikingly broken and irregular. The Eyre peninsula, which forms the eastern side of the Great Australian Bight, is the northwest shore of Spencer Gulf, an arm of the sea more than 50 miles wide that penetrates inland some 200 miles. York peninsula separates Spencer Gulf from the smaller indentation of St. Vincent Gulf, and this in turn is separated from Encounter Bay by the Fleurieu peninsula and Kangaroo Island. The Murray River flows into Encounter Bay and is the only stream of consequence in all of southeastern Australia.

The largest expanse of mediterranean climate in this area extends from the Fleurieu peninsula northward for about 200 miles north of Adelaide. It is seen mainly over the hill country of the Flinders Ranges and is less than 100 miles in breadth. Although the average elevation is only about 1500 feet, at a number of points heights of over 3000 feet are attained, and the barrier presented by these moderate hills to the passage of winter storms is considered primarily responsible for the occurrence of relatively plentiful rainfall. An open scrub woodland originally occupied the land around Adelaide—land that has for some time been cleared for crops, with a notable emphasis on wheat—and from here northward along the hillsides the density of tree growth increased until a close-crowned forest vegetation was almost continuous at higher elevations.[2] Eucalypts dominate, varying in type and size according to variable edaphic situations and local variations

[2] D. W. Meinig, *On the Margins of the Good Earth*, Rand McNally & Co., Chicago, 1962, p. 16.

within the over-all climate. Peppermint (*E. odorata*) represents the shrubby, small tree vegetation of the mallee on drier sites at lower elevation, and sugar gum (*E. cladocalyx*), a small, leafy tree ranging in height from 20 to 40 feet, typifies the middle slope woodland on the hillsides. The stringybarks (*E. obliqua*), which are often tall trees rising to nearly 100 feet, tend to dominate the forested upper slopes of the Flinders Ranges. At lower elevations of the region as a whole an intermixture of the grass tree and she-oak (*Casuarina spp.*) and a variety of acacias is typical. A good deal of treeless grassland alternates with the existing remnants of woodland.

Another very small area of mediterranean climate appears at some distance from Adelaide, near the southern end of the Eyre peninsula, which projects southward enough to intercept winter storms and in the vicinity of Port Lincoln receives an annual rainfall of around 25 inches, creating a small patch of more luxuriant vegetation in a setting otherwise dominated by mallee scrub. Port Lincoln is about 150 miles west of Adelaide.

Southeast of the Flinders Ranges mid-latitude grasslands occupy a vast segment of the eastern lowlands called the Murray basin. Here the Murray River and its leading tributaries, the Darling and Murrumbidgee, form Australia's largest drainage system. Most of the streams in this west-flowing system are intermittent, however, diminishing greatly in volume each year and in many places drying up completely. About 300 miles of grassland separate the Flinders Ranges from the hill country north of Melbourne called the Victoria highlands, southernmost extension of the eastern highlands. It is in the Victoria highlands and the lower hilly country around Melbourne reaching southward to the coast that the transition takes place from a dry summer mediterranean climate to one distinguished by a year-round distribution of rainfall. This temperate mixed forest reaches down into Tasmania and spreads northward for over 1000 miles to the New England Range, remaining near the sea. It has evolved on terrain that is rugged and hilly and elevated enough to augment orographically the precipitation of moisture from invading masses of air from the sea.

For most of its length the mid-latitude mixed forest region rarely reaches more than 200 miles inland from the sea and is modified to a certain extent by the eastern highlands to produce a variety of plant associations and landscapes between the Pacific and the interior basins. It is more generally found, however, only where mean annual rainfall amounts to 30 inches or more. Along its inner margins where the highlands slope westward it degrades into an open woodland, and as rainfall diminishes, into mid-latitude prairie grassland, where it continues down the water courses of the Murray-Darling tributaries in fingerlike projections of riparian forest into the Murray basin. As in eastern North America and eastern Asia, Australia's temperate mixed forest gives way to tropical forests in lower latitudes. Thus, in the New England Range and along the coast south of Brisbane, it blends with tropical elements that dominate the vegetation farther north. A zone in which the vegetation is neither strongly tropical nor temperate in character extends on either side of Brisbane between Great Sandy Island and Port Macquarie. The principal area of luxuriant tropical rainforest of which this is the southern extension is along the northeast coast of Queensland below the Atherton plateau.

Southward the temperate mixed forest grades into a temperate rainforest appearing in particularly well-watered, cool situations of the southeastern hills and Tasmania. No counterpart of the northern hemisphere's boreal forest appears poleward of Australia's mid-latitude forests, for open sea exists in those higher latitudes where such a rigorous climate might otherwise be expected. Because this climatic region is missing, there exists a unique situation in which the temperate rainforest of extreme southeastern Australia is the point of convergence of a dry summer mediterranean climate of west coast exposure and a mid-latitude mixed forest climate of east coast exposure.

The vegetation of the mid-latitude mixed forest in this part of Australia is overwhelmingly dominated by a single genus, *Eucalyptus*, and in this regard the region fails to resemble the temperate mixed forests of the northern hemisphere where a great variety of genera is characteristic. However, the large number of tree-size eucalyptus species and the varieties of morphology and habit among them, plus the presence of a sprinkling of other genera, merit the designation *mixed forest*. Furthermore, the climate under which this unusual vegetation has developed is closely similar to the mid-latitude mixed forest climates discussed earlier.

The main area of mid-latitude mixed forest begins in the New England Range southwest of Brisbane. Here, yellow box (*E. melliodora*), manna gum (*E. viminalis*), white peppermint (*E. cloeziana*), white gum (*E. rubida*), and other tall eucalypts ranging in height from 75 to 150 feet flourish on hilly land up to 4000 feet and wherever the fertile valleys have remained un-cleared for cultivation. Associated with the dominant eucalypts are other tree species, some of which, like the Brisbane box (*Tristania conferta*), are giant trees on the well-watered eastern slopes. In this general area on the western slopes of the divide, where rainfall drops below 30 inches, cypress pine (*Callitris cupressiformis*) and ironbark (*E. paniculata*) are important species.

The forest thins out at higher altitude because of cold and snow and becomes more open and scattered west of the highland summits because of diminishing rainfall, but it reveals the very opposite tendency along the seaward slopes at lower altitude where higher temperatures, a narrower range of temperature variation, and average annual rainfall in excess of 35 inches are characteristic. Thus, one finds a moist and com-paratively mild marine environment as a rule within no more than 50 miles of the sea. It is along the strictly coastal lowlands near the sea and in a few deep, well-sheltered valleys farther inland facing the sea that tropical plant species extend their distribution from the low latitudes of the northeast coast as far south as the hilly region of Victoria called Gippsland, between the Australian Alps and the sea.

Between Brisbane and Port Macquarie a sub-tropical forest, or at least the fragmentary remains of a once luxuriant subtropical forest, includes species of related genera like *Angophora* and *Melaleuca*, as well as the tall hoop pine (*Araucaria cunninghamii*), brown pine (*Podocarpus elata*), turpentine (*Syncarpia laurifolia*), and silk-oak tree (*Grevillea robusta*). Also present in significant proportions are red cedar (*Dedrela australis*), a native teak (*Flindseria australis*), and a good many other trees having affinities with Malayan flora of distinctly tropical nature. Many eucalypts may be numbered among these indigenous tropical forms, including some iron-barks, boxes, and bloodwoods. Intertwined among the branches of this varied vegetation are many lianas and epiphytes, and on the forest floor mosses and ferns take the place of grass as the prevalent ground cover. Most of the tropical species disappear south of Port Mac-quarie, but a few continue on into Victoria, among them the low evergreen shrub *Hakea dactyloides*, the cabbage tree palm (*Livistona australis*), and the tree ferns (*Dicksonia spp.*).

In the hilly Gippsland region of the southeast between Cape Howe and Wilson's Promontory, and also in the Otway Range southwest of Melbourne, unusually large eucalypts, es-pecially gums and peppermints, are joined by the beech (*Nothofagus cunninghamii*) to form a heavy temperate rainforest in which equably cool temperatures and constant moisture pre-vail. This is the coastal evergreen forest of mild, wet mid-latitudes with western exposure. It is more fully developed in Tasmania farther south, and even more so in New Zealand (Fig. 15.1).

Tasmania is almost completely mantled by vegetation from sea level to mountain top, and yet here, as on the mainland, eucalypts domi-nate the forest. But they are generally larger than most species found elsewhere in Australia. In moderately wet circumstances where rainfall averages up to 50 inches they include the blue gum (*E. globulus*), a tree with smooth, blue-gray bark, which towers to more than 150 feet in height, the stringybark (*E. obliqua*), reaching heights of over 200 feet, and various gums achieving a vigorous growth over the eastern two thirds of the island. Wherever rainfall averages above 40 inches, an understory of rain-forest species appears, including a native laurel (really a saxifrage), acacias, and sassafras. In wet places the tree fern also appears, as well as the ti tree (*Melaleuca spp.*). On the uppermost slopes of Mt. Wellington, which is 4166 feet high and lies just west of the capital city of Hobart, the eucalypts become dwarfed, and an alpine heath, with many masses of dense, low-growing forms, prevails. Beyond 4000 feet in altitude a characteristic scrub of rather low-growing vegetation includes a small deciduous beech (*Nothofagus gunnii*), almost the sole deciduous tree in Australia, certain coniferous shrubs belonging to the yews, and species of *Fitzroya*, a genus encountered in southern South America.

CLIMATIC CONDITIONS.   The governing atmos-pheric features in the total weather of all

Australia are the successive anticyclones that move eastward rather rapidly across the continent within the lower middle latitudes throughout the year. They occur with comparative regularity, about one each week, commonly entering the continent along a section of the west or southwest coasts and proceeding at a mean speed of between 15 and 20 miles per hour. They are part of the globe-encircling subtropical high pressure zone of the southern hemisphere. This is not a constant feature, but actually a series of eastward-moving formations that are usually centered poleward of the Tropic of Capricorn. In Australia they are near 28°S. Lat. and in summertime shift to a mean position of 35°S. Lat., the central barometric maxima lying off the southwest coast.

As anticyclonic systems advance across the continent, they become warmer through radiant heating from below, and this, plus the dynamic heating of their characteristic subsidence, makes them drier, producing little or no rain. The rainless condition they engender is thus a primary tendency of the weather over most of the interior throughout the year. With the normal meridional shift of the preferred paths along which they move eastward, dry weather is alternately brought both to the north and the south coasts with the changing seasons. In other words, during the winter season when migrating anticyclones are displaced northward, predominantly clear, dry weather prevails over northern Australia, and transient disturbances bring rain to the south and to the east coast as far north as the New England Range. In summer the situation is reversed; rains occur in the north, and rainfall increases along the east coast and the eastern plateaus north of Port Macquarie, while drought in general prevails in southern sections.

The southeastern mainland and Tasmania are far enough poleward to enjoy a year-round distribution of ample rainfall, although rainfall increases in winter. From Cape Howe northward precipitation is fairly evenly distributed through the year. With decreasing latitude an increasingly larger proportion occurs during the summer. The systematic seasonal north–south displacement of anticyclonic activity primarily accounts for these rhythms, and these regular processes result, in turn, from the earth's orbital relationship with the sun.

Between the migrating highs lower atmospheric pressure always prevails. It nearly always takes the form of a barometric saddle or, to use the geologist's term for a moderate indentation along a mountain crest, a col. A fully developed trough or elongated depression is a rarer occurrence, especially while anticyclones are crossing the continent. When such a trough between a pair of traveling highs appears, however, it allows a meridional flow of air across the continent, bringing unusually copious rains from either north or south to the moisture-deficient interior. In a continent so governed by clear, dry, anticyclonic air, the amount, reliability, and distribution of rainfall is of primary concern.

The principal way in which the mean annual precipitation of the mediterranean regions around Perth and Adelaide differs from that of the temperate rainforest and mixed forest regions from Tasmania to the New England Mountains is in the yearly distribution, the eastern regions receiving adequate rainfall the year round, the mediterranean areas experiencing dry summers. Amounts of rainfall are not regionally distinctive and vary considerably within each of the regions concerned (Fig. 15.2).

In southwest Australia the wettest areas are found along the higher elevations of the Darling scarp and also in parts of the hilly terrain along the south coast between Cape Leeuwin and Albany. Jarrahdale, for example, about 30 miles southeast of Perth and about 25 miles from the sea, is around 1900 feet above sea level, and annual rainfall there averages 48.4 inches. Perth, in contrast, averages only 34.7 inches. Farther south, nearer the axis of migrating winter storms, Karridale averages 47.8 inches, and Denmark, about 25 miles west of Albany, averages 48.4. Amounts vary within short distances, however, largely depending on actual exposure to the onslaught of winter's precipitating disturbances from the southwest. Karridale, for example, is only about 20 miles north of Cape Leeuwin, and the latter station averages only 38.9 inches of annual rain. A better comparison is between Denmark and Albany. Denmark is well-exposed to inflowing air from the sea, and for some 25 miles eastward along the coast from Wilson Inlet on which it is situated are steep cliffs 400 to 600 feet high, rising to nearly 1000 feet a short distance inland.

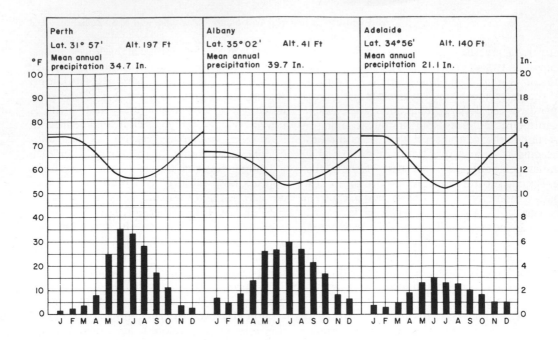

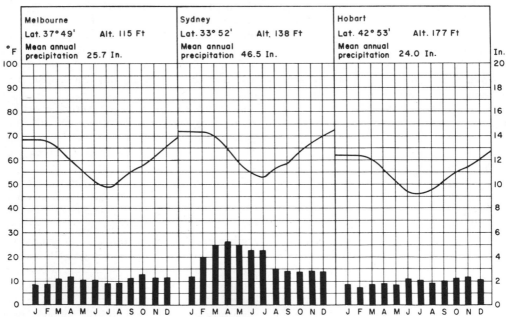

Figure 15.3. Normal temperature and precipitation at mid-latitude forest and mediterranean scrub woodland stations in southern Australia.

Albany is in the lee of these and averages only 39.7 inches of annual rain (Fig. 15.3).

In general, one may observe that areas receiving more than 40 inches of annual rainfall are unevenly scattered from near Perth to near Albany on hilly terrain facing the sea but usually back some distance from the sea. North

of Perth amounts fall off rapidly; at Geraldton, about 250 miles northwest of Perth, mean annual rainfall is 18.7 inches. East of Albany amounts decrease less rapidly. At Esperance, for example, about 250 miles northeast of Albany, the average amount is 26.4 inches. Mean precipitation of more than 15 inches rarely prevails beyond 100 miles from the coast and is commonly confined to between 50 and 75 miles of the coast. Northam, for example, is about 70 miles from the sea almost due east of Perth and averages 15 inches, but Kellerberrin, about 50 miles farther east, averages 13.3 inches. The change from moderate rainfall amounts to semi-aridity, takes place more abruptly along the coast behind Esperance, for rainfall amounting to 20 inches or more is rather narrowly confined to within less than 25 miles of the sea. Balladonia, about 150 miles northeast of Esperance, averages only 9.3 inches (Table 15-1).

Beyond Cape Arid the semi-arid Nullarbor coast of the Great Australian Bight averages between 10 and 12 inches, increasing at Streaky Bay near the western base of the Eyre peninsula to 15 inches. Elsewhere on the peninsula values are less than this but increase toward the southern tip, and the small area of mediterranean environment around Port Lincoln owes its existence to a mean annual rainfall of between 15 and 25 inches, being far enough south to profit more than the rest of the peninsula from passing winter storms (Fig. 15.2).

In that small, elongated expanse of mediterranean climate stretching north for about 200 miles from Adelaide the elevation of the Flinders Ranges plays a primary part in providing rainfall of more than 15 inches, the minimum under which a strictly mediterranean environment develops. Adelaide, at an elevation of only 140 feet, averages 21.1 inches of annual rain, but on the upper slopes of Mt. Lofty, about 15 miles southeast of Adelaide at 2384 feet above sea level, a mean of 47 inches is recorded, the wettest place of record for the Adelaide region. At Clare, about 75 miles north of Adelaide and 1351 feet above sea level, 24.3 inches is normal, and Appila, about 150 miles north of Adelaide at an elevation of 1150 feet, near the northern limits of the region, records an annual average of 14.8 inches. Port Augusta, some 70 miles northwest of Appila at the head of Spencer Gulf, receives only 9.5 inches.

From the southern Flinders Ranges southeastward mean precipitation averages under 20 inches for about 100 miles back from the coast, diminishing from this farther inland. Near Mt. Gambier, however, where the coastal marshes give way to land that rises toward the east, rainfall amounts increase to 25 inches or more,

and in these higher latitudes from this point eastward summers are no longer dry.

In southern Victoria where temperate rainforest and mixed forest are intermingled, relief again plays a major role in determining the geographical distribution of contrasting amounts of annual rain. Even modest elevations are often much wetter than their lower surroundings, and west- to southwest-facing slopes generally receive more copious precipitation than eastern slopes in the lee, resulting in fairly numerous rain shadow situations. Rainforest ordinarily predominates in cooler, wetter, well-exposed places. At Lake Leake near Mt. Gambier's extinct 650 foot crater, an average of 32.7 inches is recorded. Warrambol, at a height of 89 feet about 100 miles farther east, reports 27 inches, as does Hamilton, in the shelter of the Great Victorian Valley farther inland. In the Otway Range southwest of Melbourne, where elevations rise to 1800 feet, mean amounts of over 60 inches are received in places, but Melbourne, about 100 miles northeastward, receives only 25.4 inches. In the Australian Alps between Melbourne and Canberra, annual precipitation also averages over 60 inches at many localities, as at Kiandra (el. 4640), with 63.6 inches. A rain shadow effect is illustrated in a comparison of Kiandra with Canberra, 50 miles northeastward at 1837 feet, which records only 23 inches. A similar comparison may be made between Mt. Kosciusko's weather station at 5020 feet, with Bombala, about 50 miles southeastward at about 3020 feet. On Mt. Kosciusko mean annual precipitation is about 50 inches, but at Bombala it is only 23.6 inches.

In Tasmania the predominantly cool, wet climate of the coastal evergreen forest that dominates the western plateau and the northeast highlands is chiefly the result of latitude and a year-round exposure to migrating mid-latitude storms. Here also, however, variations in relief induce local contrasts in annual precipitation amounts. The entire west coast averages between 50 and 60 inches of annual rainfall, the wettest point being Lake Margaret, about half way down the west coast and 20 miles in from the sea at an altitude of about 2000 feet, where an average of 146 inches of annual precipitation is recorded. In eastern parts of Tasmania values are generally between 25 and 30 inches, but in well-protected, leeward situations even less than this. Launceston, in the

TABLE 15–1

Climatic Data for Mid-Latitude Forest and Woodland Stations in Australia
(Temp., °F; Rainfall, In.)

Station	Lat.	El. in Ft		Jan.	Feb.	Mar.	Apr.	May	Jun.	Jul.	Aug.	Sep.	Oct.	Nov.	Dec.	Year
Geraldton	28°47′	13	T	75	76	74	70	65	62	59	60	62	64	68	72	
			R	0.2	0.3	0.5	0.8	2.8	4.9	3.9	2.9	1.4	0.7	0.3	0.2	18.9
Perth	31°57′	197	T	74	74	71	67	61	57	55	56	58	61	66	71	
			R	0.3	0.5	0.8	1.8	4.9	6.9	6.5	5.7	3.4	2.1	0.8	0.6	33.9
Cape Leeuwin	34°22′	163	T	68	69	67	65	61	58	57	57	58	59	63	66	
			R	0.7	0.9	1.3	2.0	5.7	6.9	6.9	5.2	3.0	2.8	1.3	1.0	37.7
Albany	35°02′	41	T	67	67	65	63	59	55	54	55	56	58	61	65	
			R	1.4	1.0	1.8	2.9	5.3	5.4	6.0	5.4	4.3	3.3	1.7	1.2	39.7
Esperance	33°50′	14	T	69	69	67	61	59	55	54	55	57	59	63	66	
			R	0.7	0.7	1.2	1.8	3.3	4.1	4.0	3.8	2.7	2.2	1.0	0.9	26.4
Eyre	32°14′	15	T	70	70	68	64	60	55	54	55	58	61	65	67	
			R	0.6	0.5	0.9	0.9	1.6	1.6	1.2	1.9	0.9	0.8	0.7	0.6	11.6
Streaky Bay	32°48′	45	T	72	72	70	64	60	55	53	55	58	63	67	70	
			R	0.6	0.5	0.6	0.9	1.9	2.8	2.4	2.0	1.3	1.0	0.7	0.4	14.9
Adelaide	34°56′	140	T	74	74	70	64	58	54	52	54	57	62	67	71	
			R	0.8	0.7	1.0	1.8	2.7	3.0	2.6	2.6	2.1	1.7	1.1	1.0	21.1
Melbourne	37°49′	115	T	68	68	65	60	55	51	49	51	55	58	61	65	
			R	1.9	1.8	2.2	2.3	2.1	2.1	1.9	1.9	2.3	2.6	2.3	2.3	25.7
Canberra	35°20′	1837	T	69	69	62	56	49	44	43	45	50	56	62	67	
			R	1.9	1.7	2.2	1.6	1.8	2.1	1.8	2.2	1.6	2.2	1.9	2.0	23.0
Sydney	33°52′	138	T	72	72	70	65	59	55	53	56	59	64	67	70	
			R	3.5	4.0	5.0	5.3	5.0	4.6	4.6	3.0	2.9	2.8	2.9	2.9	46.5
Port Macquarie	31°38′	64	T	72	72	70	65	60	56	54	56	59	63	67	70	
			R	5.5	7.0	6.4	6.5	5.6	4.7	4.3	3.3	3.8	3.5	3.7	5.0	59.3
Brisbane	27°28′	137	T	77	77	74	70	65	60	59	61	67	70	73	76	
			R	6.4	6.3	5.7	3.7	2.8	2.6	2.2	1.9	1.9	2.5	3.7	5.0	44.7
Launceston, Tasmania	41°27′	253	T	64	65	61	55	50	47	46	47	51	54	58	62	
			R	1.8	1.2	1.7	2.2	2.7	3.2	3.0	3.0	2.9	2.7	1.8	2.0	28.2
Hobart, Tasmania	42°53′	177	T	62	62	60	56	51	47	46	48	51	55	57	60	
			R	1.9	1.5	1.8	1.9	1.8	2.2	2.1	1.9	2.1	2.3	2.4	2.1	24.0

Source: U.S. Naval Oceanographic Office, Sailing Directions for the North and West Coasts of Australia (H.O. 74), 1952, Sailing Directions for the East Coast of Australia (H.O. 75), 1954, Sailing Directions for the Southeast Coast of Australia (H.O. 76), 1952, Sailing Directions for the South Coast of Australia (H.O. 77), 1950; Great Britain, Meteorological Office, Tables of Temperature, Relative Humidity and Precipitation for the World, Part VI, Australasia and the South Pacific Ocean, London, 1962.

sheltered valley of the Macquarie River, averages 28 inches, and toward the south at Ross, about 50 miles farther up the valley, the mean for the year is only 18 inches. Hobart on the south coast annually records an average of 23.8 inches.

In the mid-latitude mixed forest climate that prevails over most of the eastern highlands from the Snowy Mountains to the New England Range and along the coast north of Cape Howe, rainfall is rather heavy within a fairly narrow band near the sea but diminishes rapidly inland. From around Sydney northward mean amounts for localities near the sea are between 40 and 60 inches. Sydney averages 47.4 inches, Newcastle 45.7 inches, Port Macquarie 59.3 inches, and Brisbane 45.4 inches. Within a zone that extends from about 25 to 100 miles from the shoreline mean values range between 30 and 40 inches. At Tenterfield, about 125 miles southwest of Brisbane and about 80 miles from the sea, the average is 32.2 inches; at Armidale, 100 miles farther south and about 80 miles inland, the average is 31.2 inches; at Mudgee, about 125 miles northwest of Sydney and 80 miles from the sea, the average is only 25.4 inches. Beyond the summit areas of the plateaus mean precipitation is between 20 and 30 inches, supporting only the more open woodland of the western slopes.

The principal sources of precipitation for all of southern Australia from southwest to southeast are the migrating depressions that are spawned in the westerly flow of the Roaring Forties over the sea south of the continent. These disturbances affect the mediterranean areas around Perth and Adelaide for the most part only in winter, but in southeastern Australia and Tasmania they are effective throughout the year, simply becoming more productive during winter to make that the season of maximum precipitation. From near Sydney northward a second major source of rain is the summertime occurrence of coastal depressions that usually take the form of troughs moving southward along the western edges of anticyclones centered over the Tasman Sea between Australia and New Zealand. In summertime an additional source of precipitation along this section of the coast is the southeast trade wind flow that, on recurving to sweep from the sea against the northeast coast of the continent, reaches the northern limits of the

mid-latitude mixed forest in the New England Range and along the coast as far south as Port Macquarie (Fig. 4.2).

The importance of the yearly distribution of normal precipitation as a point of distinction between mediterranean and temperate mixed forest–rainforest environments becomes evident from the percentage distribution for representative localities. In the Perth and Adelaide districts during the six-month winter period of April through September the following portions of annual average precipitation are received: Perth 85 per cent, Cape Leeuwin and Karridale 81 per cent, Albany 76 per cent, Esperance 74 per cent, Adelaide and Clare 70 per cent. In the temperate forests of the southeastern mainland and in Tasmania, however, where winter is also the season of maximum precipitation, values are substantially lower, remaining in general below 60 per cent. At Horsham, about 250 miles southeast of Adelaide, and at Hamilton and Warrambool west of Melbourne, the amount of annual precipitation received during winter is 61 per cent. At Bendigo and Albury in the woodlands on the inner slopes of the Victoria highlands values are 59 and 57 per cent respectively, and at Mt. Kosciusko winter precipitation accounts for only 53 per cent, indicating nearly uniform year-round distribution. Yearly distribution is also virtually uniform at Melbourne, where only 49 per cent is received from April through September. Most of Tasmania experiences a winter maximum, Cape Sorel on the west coast receiving 61 per cent and Launceston in the northeast 60 per cent, although the south coastal section around Hobart (51 per cent) has a virtually equable distribution (Fig. 15.3).

From the Australian Alps northeastward the distribution of yearly precipitation is nearly uniform as far north as Mudgee, although from Sydney to Newcastle the rainiest season is actually in autumn, with maximum monthly amounts occurring in April and May respectively. From Port Macquarie northward a change to summer maximum takes place, 52 per cent occurring during October through March at Port Macquarie, 63 per cent at Armidale, 62 per cent at Tenterfield, and 65 per cent at Brisbane, with even more definite summer concentrations in the tropical regions farther north.

The migrating depressions that are the main

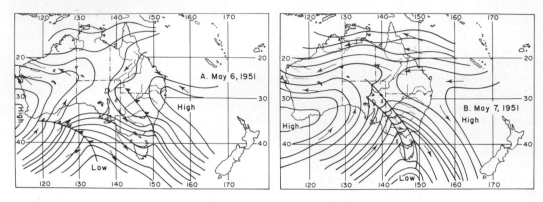

Figure 15.4. Eastward passage of a precipitating depression over southern Australia on May 6 and 7, 1951.

sources of precipitation for all of southern Australia's mid-latitude forest-woodland regions from southwest to southeast are spawned in the procession of anticyclones and storms that are constantly moving eastward in the westerly circulation of higher latitudes over the southern oceanic areas. Such depressions usually appear in the form of deep, V-shaped waves on the weather map, their apexes extending northward across the south coast (Fig. 15.4). Storms of this character on the average endure from about twelve hours to three or four days, depending on their size and intensity. Cyclonic circulations commonly evolve from the V-shaped depressions and tend to bring the most vigorous storms. Cape Leeuwin is notorious for the severity of its northwest gales and the frequency with which they occur during wintertime. High winds driving low, scudding clouds, mist, and drenching rain against the shoreline from Perth to Cape Leeuwin can be expected with increasing frequency beginning in May, and in July and August such periods of dark, gloomy weather have been known to persist for three weeks at a time. During particularly rainy winters the normally wetter, well-exposed points near Cape Leeuwin may experience unbroken rain for a month to six weeks, with only three or four days of fair weather before a similar period commences again. Storms of like intensity and duration are also common during wintertime in Bass Strait between Victoria and Tasmania and are especially effective against Tasmania's western highlands.

Along the east coast north of Cape Howe migrating depressions from the west contribute largely to the year's precipitation. With the onshore flow of moist, maritime air from the Tasman Sea into their converging circulations as they advance eastward, the immediate littoral receives considerably more rain than sections farther inland, as noted earlier. This same segment of east coast and the adjacent highlands also receive an appreciable percentage of the year's precipitation from tropical cyclones that advance southward and occasionally reach as far as Victoria and Bass Strait. Tropical storms from the northwest very occasionally cross the interior in autumn to bring rain to the south coast between Adelaide and Melbourne. To these sources must be added the effects of frontal rains that usually last only a few hours and contribute only a small fraction of the yearly total. Convective showers and thunderstorms are also a source of precipitation and average between fifty and sixty each year along the east coast between Brisbane and Sydney, where they are most frequent from October through March, decreasing in frequency farther south. Along the south coast they are much less common, occurring only about sixteen times yearly (mainly in winter) near both Cape Leeuwin and Adelaide. Along the inner slopes of the eastern highlands summer thunderstorms contribute a large percentage of the year's precipitation through the more intensive heating of those drier surfaces. Hailstones are a well-known product of thunderstorm activity and are often destructively large, increasing in size toward the interior. Hail occurs most often in winter along the south coast and in summer along the east coast. Light snow has been observed infrequently over most of southern Australia as far north as northern Swanland, the northern Flinders Ranges, and in the New England Mountains. It is a fairly frequent wintertime occurrence over only three sections of the continent: the higher parts of Swanland in the southwest, the southern Flinders Ranges, and the southeastern highlands, as well as on the island of Tasmania. Heavy snow appears every winter in the Australian Alps and accumulates to depths of many feet. It often remains in patches on the plateau around Mt. Kosciusko throughout the summer following an unusually severe winter. At times unusually heavy snows come to summit areas of the Great Dividing Range from the New England Mountains to the Victoria coast, and on one occasion snow fell as far north as Toowoomba, west of Brisbane.

The reliability of annual precipitation throughout the temperate forests and woodlands of southern and southeastern Australia increases in almost direct proportion to the amounts normally received. Thus, the temperate rainforest areas of the southwest show the lowest variability (10 per cent) of the entire continent (Fig. 15.5). Reliability in the southeastern rainforests is almost as great, for probable variability is there only 15 per cent. Variability increases northward from Geraldton on the west coast and from Sydney on the east coast to more than 20 per cent. Australia's greatest variability is, of course, in the arid central interior, where in places it is believed to be over 60 per cent. The southwest coast between Perth and Cape Leeuwin seems to be the area of maximum reliability, the probably deviation from normal being something less than 10 per cent.

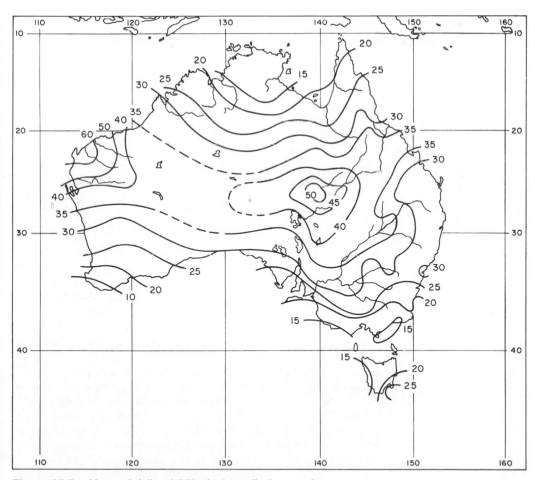

Figure 15.5.   Mean rainfall variability in Australia (per cent).

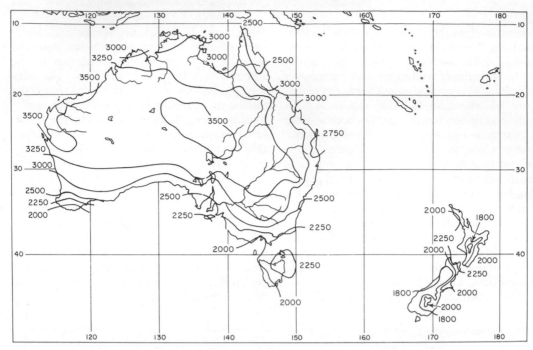

Figure 15.6. Mean annual number of hours of sunshine in Australia and New Zealand.

The number of days during a normal year when some precipitation can be expected varies from over 250 in western Tasmania to around eighty in the Flinders region. In southwestern Australia the yearly number of days with rain is generally between 120 and 160, the maximum being near Cape Leeuwin. Along the east coast the number is about 120 days, diminishing to around eighty days in the summit areas of the eastern highland plateaus.

Relative humidity is generally at a minimum in summer in all the temperate forest regions from southwest to southeast. Mean values recorded for 0900 daily are lowest around Adelaide, where they average about 40 per cent, and at Perth, where they are only slightly higher at 50 per cent. Over both the temperate mixed forest and rainforest areas values for stations near sea level are around 60 per cent. In winter, however, relative humidities vary within a higher range, at Adelaide and Perth up to about 75 per cent, at Melbourne, Hobart, and Canberra over 80 per cent. In the cloud zone about 4000 feet during the winter months many localities are enveloped in mist during the morning hours and experience relative humidities of more than 90 per cent a good share of the time.

It is plain that the mediterranean areas around Perth and Adelaide experience summers that are not only very nearly rainless, in comparison with the well-watered forests of the east and southeast, but are also much drier in terms of sensible atmospheric moisture content. Winters are also less humid in the mediterranean areas, although the comparison is not as great. A further point of distinction is the fact that summer in mediterranean areas is often a period of almost unbroken sunshine, especially some distance back from the coast, and cloud cover is at a minimum for the year. At Perth, for example, only 30 per cent of the sky is cloud covered on the average during January, and at Adelaide the mean is just under 40 per cent. Sydney and Brisbane, on the other hand, experience about 60 per cent cloud cover in the summer. During wintertime the sky is cloud-covered almost equally in all the mid-latitude forest-woodland regions except around Cape Leeuwin and exposed coastal points of the southeastern mainland and western Tasmania, where inclement weather is the rule for the season. At Cape Leeuwin in July about 75 per cent of the sky is obscured by cloud at the recorded times of observation during the day.

Comparing the yearly number of hours of sunshine, Perth and Adelaide average 2791 and 2543 hours respectively, and Sydney and Melbourne average 2129 and 2256 hours respectively. Brisbane, so much nearer the Tropic and a year-round higher sun, averages 2631 hours of sunshine per year (Fig. 15.6).

The normal annual range between summer and winter temperatures is seriously affected by exposure to humid, maritime air from the sea. Marine situations everywhere are favored by cooler summers and milder winters. Thus, the lowest recorded annual temperature ranges in the temperate forest regions are obtained from seaside stations in southwestern and southeastern Australia (Fig. 15.7). Cape Leeuwin reports a value of 12 degrees, and farther east along the coast at places less exposed to the brunt of advancing storms from the west the range becomes larger, as at Albany (13 degrees) and Esperance (15 degrees), and at lower latitude points farther north the same is true, as at

Perth (19 degrees). At Cape Otway and Wilson's Promontory in southeastern Australia the mean annual temperature range is again 12 degrees, for both of these stations project well into the paths of migrating disturbances. Where stations are at all protected from relatively mild, moisture-laden air moving in directly from the sea for appreciable periods, summer temperatures tend to be higher and winter temperatures lower than at shoreline stations. Thus, whereas Cape Borda at the western end of Kangaroo Island reports a mean annual temperature range of 14 degrees, Adelaide reports 22 degrees. Cape Otway and Wilson's Promontory reporting 12 degrees compare with Melbourne (18 degrees), Ballarat (21 degrees), Sydney (19 degrees), and Canberra (26 degrees). In Tasmania the range for Stanley on the northwest coast is 14 degrees, but for Launceston

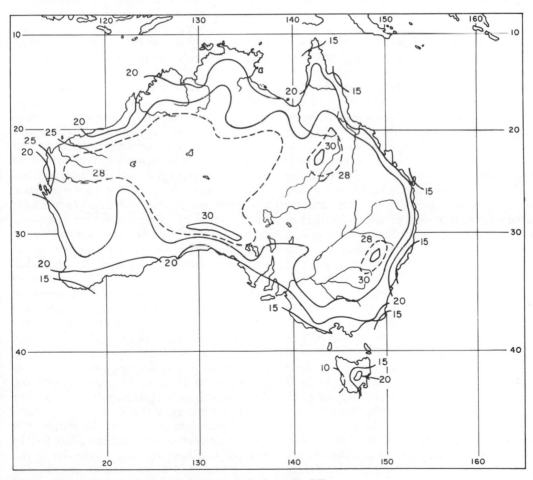

Figure 15.7. Mean annual temperature range in Australia (°F).

in the northeastern interior it is 20 degrees (Table 15-1).

Extreme temperature ranges are also least at well-exposed maritime stations, as we note by the comparison of Cape Leeuwin (69 degrees) with Adelaide (86 degrees) and Port Augusta (88 degrees). Along the east and west coasts a general trend toward lower mean and extreme temperature ranges indicates the influence of decreasing latitude and the generally more equable temperature experience that holds for tropical northern Australia.

Summer. During the summer period of December through February the daily duration of sunshine and solar radiation intensity reach a maximum for the year. The intensity of solar radiation is increased not only by the higher angular elevation of the sun at this time but also by the fact that the earth is at perihelion around January 1 and is thus about 3 million miles nearer the sun's great source of heat. Increased solar warmth brings extremely high temperatures to the interior, inviting a general influx of surface air from the sea (Fig. 15.8). The mean paths of mid-latitude storms are displaced southward, touching for the most part only the southeastern corner of the continent. Meanwhile, a succession of tropical depressions, chiefly evolving near northwestern Australia, marks the southward, onshore advance of the equatorial trough and brings heavy summer rains to the north coast. At the same time, the southeast trades are deflected to blow from the northeast against the northeast coast and are effective, at least to some extent, as far south as Port Macquarie. In the mediterranean areas the air remains for the most part clear, dry, and sunny, but from Tasmania to the New England Ranges this is a season of considerable rain.

In general, the onset of summer takes place gradually in all the forest-woodland areas from Swanland to the New England plateau. Temperatures begin to rise in the latter part of August, and from October onward frosts and winter mists are seldom experienced in inland stations, as the thermometer continues to climb toward the season's maximum following the December solstice. As a rule, January and February register almost equal mean temperatures along the entire south coast and in Tasmania, although February is actually slightly higher at stations near the sea (Fig. 15.3). The lag in the occurrence of the maximum is occasioned

by the slow temperature rise of the adjoining seas over which the dominant oceanic air of the southern littoral originates. At inland stations wherever shelter from the sea exists, such as Katanning and Kellerberrin in the southwest, January tends to be the warmest month, a characteristic of continental climates and particularly notable in Australia's warm, dry interior. At Sydney and Brisbane January also averages slightly higher than February, although the difference is small. Temperatures are about the same during both January and February along most of the east coast, as, indeed, they are at higher elevations near the Great Divide, of which Canberra is an example (Table 15-1).

The mean temperature of the warmest month is characteristically higher under the sunny summer skies of the mediterranean areas than in the more heavily forested southeast, even at stations near the moderating influence of the sea. Perth and Adelaide, for example, both average 74°, but on the southeastern part of the mainland and in Tasmania values remain below 70°: Melbourne and Sale average 67°, Launceston 65°, and Hobart 62°. At higher altitudes summers are cooler, as at Ballarat, west of Melbourne at 1430 feet, where the February average is 65°. Canberra, although nearly 300 miles northeast of Melbourne, remains cool in summer due to its position well within the eastern highlands at an altitude of 1837 feet, averaging 68° in January and February. Only from near Sydney northward are mean temperatures during the warmest month above 70°. Sydney and Port Macquarie both average 72°, and Brisbane reports 77°.

At mediterranean stations, and also in the temperate rainforest areas of the southeast, summer is the season during which the mean daily range of temperature is the greatest for the entire year. Actual values, however, vary considerably depending on proximity to the sea. At Perth, for example, the mean daily range in January and February is 22 degrees. At Kellerberrin it is 32 degrees, and at Katanning 31 degrees in January. At Cape Leeuwin the daily range is only 11 degrees from December through February, reflecting the almost completely maritime position of the station. But oceanic air exerts a less definite effect farther east, for at Albany the daily range during the same period is 15 degrees and at Esperance 18 degrees. At Adelaide it is 25 degrees in January

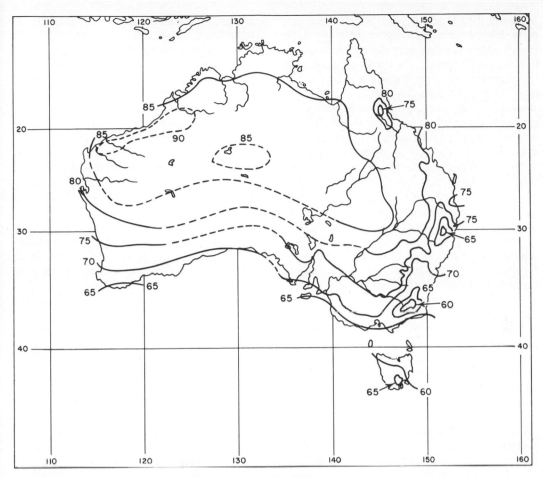

Figure 15.8.   Mean January temperatures in Australia (°F).

and at Melbourne 21 degrees from December through February. In Tasmania the sheltered Macquarie valley around Launceston experiences a larger daily range, 24 degrees in January and February, than the south coast near Hobart, where an average of 18 degrees holds for December through February. From Sydney northward summer is the season of lowest mean daily range, averaging only 14 degrees from December through February at Sydney and 16 degrees at Brisbane.

Extremely high temperatures are a common occurrence every summer throughout all the temperate forest-woodland regions of southern and eastern Australia. The thermometer has registered more than 100° nearly everywhere, the only exception being the very highest section of the Australian Alps. At Perth the extreme maximum on record is 112°. Elsewhere in the southwest it is 109° at Cape Leeuwin, 113° at Albany, and 117° at Esperance. The highest value for the entire south coast is 123° at the semiarid locality of Eucla, over 400 miles northeast of Esperance at the edge of Nullarbor Plain. At Adelaide the maximum has risen to 118°, but elsewhere in the southeast values are lower: Melbourne reports 111°, Hobart 105°, Sydney 109°, and Brisbane in the north 110°. Farther inland, however, higher extremes are known, and at Schofields Airfield, about 20 miles northwest of Sydney, the thermometer reached 115° on a January day in 1946.[3] Occasionally, the atmospheric pressure gradient induces a fairly persistent southward flow of hot, dry, dusty air from the interior toward a

[3] S. R. Eyre, "Between the Tasman Sea and the Blue Mountains," *Geography*, **35**, 155–65, 1950.

section of the south coast. This is a phenomenon related to the trailing edge of an anticyclone that is either moving very slowly eastward or has stalled altogether. In these circumstances the thermometer may register a maximum of more than 100° each day for several days in succession. On one such occasion the daily maximum temperature rose above 100° at Adelaide for nine consecutive days, on another at Canberra for eight days, and at various times at both Melbourne and Perth for six days. Fortunately, these extremely high values are normally attained for only a short interval during early to mid-afternoon, and relief from the excessive heat comes with the setting sun. In partial compensation, very hot air from the interior is usually dry, and its evaporative capacity is a great advantage for the relative comfort of human beings. Relative humidities of as low as 17 per cent have been recorded during a hot spell at Adelaide.

Another fortunate circumstance that appears to mitigate the affects of hot summer weather is the fairly regular sea breeze that brings its cooling influence at least to immediate shoreline areas from Swanland to the east coast. In the southwest from early October to the beginning of April most winds are from southward. A gentle southeast breeze is usually felt at sunrise, normally shifting to eastward by noon, then ceasing altogether for a brief interval, and by early afternoon a moderate to strong south-southwest wind blows in from the sea, drawing to south-southeastward by sunset. At Fremantle, a few miles southwest of Perth, strong southwesterly winds averaging from 25 to 40 miles per hour prevail from around noontime until after midnight for intervals of three to five days during the period December through February. As autumn advances they become more moderate, and winds off the land persist for longer periods. By April the sea breeze tends to bring unsettled weather as the seaborne storms from the west begin to advance farther northward. At Adelaide a very marked sea breeze effect develops during the hot months of January through March and brings its welcome cooling influence from the southwest in the afternoon.

Along the east coast where the summertime pressure gradients commonly tend toward the reheated onshore flow of surface air from the easterly quarter, the sea breeze acts as an accelerator, frequently raising the wind speed to gale force. Around Sydney the sea breeze generally sets in about 10 o'clock in the morning, reaches a maximum in midafternoon, and subsides after sunset. Toward midnight a weaker offshore land breeze commences but usually disappears by about 8 A.M. When maximum velocities are reached around 3 P.M., the direction will normally have shifted to southeasterly, and moist, cool, hazy air will sometimes be driving against the seaside cliffs and beaches at speeds of 40 miles per hour or more. The sea breeze is shallow, however, remaining below about 1000 feet and not often extending farther inland than about 25 miles. Indeed, it often encounters a gentle, opposing flow of air from down the slopes farther west during midafternoon, producing moderately strong convective activity along a weak local front. This phenomenon has been observed at Schofields Airfield, where the relatively cool, damp, maritime air and the hot, dry, dusty continental air are in contest with one another, alternately holding sway as the afternoon wears on. Along this landward limit of the sea breeze whirlwinds, or willy-willies, frequently develop. They vary in size from "slender tubular columns of dust 3 or 4 feet in diameter to destructive circulations over 50 yards across rotating at speeds up to 50 knots."[4]

Another distinctive feature of spring and summer, well known along the coast of New South Wales, is the line squall that precedes an advancing cold front, called a southerly burster. It usually results when the northern arm of a moderate to strong cold front advancing from the west or southwest has been retarded over the continental interior while its southern arm over the sea has crept ahead. The highlands may also act to hold back the continental portion, especially the Blue Mountains behind Sydney. The southern arm advances up the east coast as a damp, cool mass of air, forming a coastal bulge that is augmented to some extent by the sea breeze in some cases. One sees in this an instance of a general cool change advancing from the west but actually reaching points along the eastern seaboard in the form of a southeasterly flow from the sea.

Cool changes of this character occur most frequently from October through February and

---

[4] *Ibid.*, p. 162.

are commonest between Sydney and Port Macquarie, although they are occasionally reported as far north as Brisbane. "The burster is accompanied by a sudden shift of wind from a northerly direction to south or southwest, a sudden drop in temperature and, at times, by gales of considerable intensity. Winds during the squall usually range between 20 and 35 knots, but have on occasion reached 60 to 70 knots or more."[5] The duration of squally weather may be from a few hours to several days, and the mean drop in temperature from 18 to 20 degrees. The suddenness with which the weather is known to change is suggested in the fact that the thermometer has registered a temperature drop of 37 degrees in five minutes. In September 1876 the Dandenong gale (named for the ship that was wrecked by that storm off Jervis Bay) affected an area of several hundred square miles. For nine hours winds of 50 knots or over were maintained at Sydney. During one ten-minute period the average was 97 knots, and gusts reached 133 knots. Gales of this severity are rare, winds over 70 knots being exceptional, but they indicate the extremes that may be reached by the southerly burster. An average of thirty-two bursters occur each year. They may appear at any time of day but develop most frequently between 7 P.M. and midnight.

Tornadolike cyclonic storms of small size but destructive intensity are well known in several areas of Australia, occurring with particular frequency in the southwest, between Adelaide and the Victoria highlands, and also along the Queensland coast. In southern Australia local wind storms have developed during every month of the year, but the season of maximum occurrence is November through January.[6]

It is in summertime that the contrast between Australia's mediterranean regions and the eastern forest regions becomes most apparent (Fig. 15.3). Along the south coast this is a season of almost no rain at all, of repeatedly bright, sunny skies flecked with scattered fair weather cumulus clouds, and of hot, dry days and warm, clear nights. During the season no more than one precipitating storm per month passes from the southern ocean within range of Swanland or the Flinders region. In late spring an occasional tropical depression from the north brings a wet spell lasting from two to four days to southwestern Australia. Very little fog develops, save in interior valleys where nocturnal radiation sometimes induces radiation fog patches. For the most part, the moderately frequent haziness of the atmosphere in seaside situations is due to the influx of moist maritime air on the daily sea breeze. January and February are usually the months of least precipitation for the year, and throughout the mediterranean areas values are less than 1 inch. Perth, for example, normally records 0.3 inch, Cape Leeuwin 0.6, Albany 0.9, Esperance 0.7, and Adelaide 0.7 during either January or February (Table 15-1).

Farther east in the mid-latitude mixed forest and temperate rainforest regions no month averages less than 1 inch of precipitation, and, with few exceptions, summer is a season of fairly frequent rain. The year's minimum mean monthly rain is commonly recorded in February in southern Victoria and Tasmania. In this month Hobart averages 1.5 inches, Launceston 1.1, Melbourne 1.7, and Bendigo 1.2. At Sydney a minimum of 2.8 inches is normal for October, the driest month. In southeastern sections migrating depressions of the oceanic West Wind Drift pass with moderate frequency, releasing about half of the normal summer's rain. In late summer this same area is frequently visited by an extended trough reaching southeastward from the northwest coast. Along the eastern edge of such a tongue of low pressure, moist, warm air sometimes advances in sufficient amounts and for a long enough period to lead to the development of a closed cyclonic system near Adelaide that may persist for two or three days. This, in turn, usually passes southeastward over Tasmania, bringing rain over most of the southeast in its passage. In late summer a tropical depression sometimes unites with a mid-latitude cyclone from over the sea west of Tasmania, and the combined effect can then produce six to eight times the normal monthly rain in parts of Tasmania.

East coast troughs are the principal sources of summer rain along the eastern seaboard north of Cape Howe, and they usually arise when an anticyclone tends to stagnate over the Tasman Sea. This allows a substantial southward flow

[5] U.S. Navy, Hydrographic Office, *Sailing Directions for the East Coast of Australia* (H.O. 169), 1954, p. 41.

[6] R. H. Clarke, *Severe Local Wind Storms in Australia*, Division of Meteorological Physics Technical Paper No. 13, Commonwealth Scientific and Industrial Research Organization, Melbourne, 1962.

of warm, moist air down the eastern edge of the low pressure tongue, resulting in widespread rains from northeastern Australia to Tasmania. From Port Macquarie northward tropical cyclones originating over the South Pacific northeast of Australia become increasingly important sources of summer rainfall, and their frequency increases toward autumn. Very heavy rains are normally produced and near Brisbane as much as 36 inches of rain has fallen in twenty-four hours during such a storm.

Winter. As the sun's path moves equatorward during the autumn months of March through May, the interior of Australia loses a larger and larger percentage of the heat taken up between dawn and sunset during the ensuing hours of the lengthening nights. Anticyclones begin to appear with increasing frequency and intensity over the land, and the mid-latitude belt of migrating storms shifts farther and farther northward. Mean monthly temperatures drop slowly as winter approaches, reaching a minimum at all stations of record in July (Fig. 15.9).

In the mediterranean areas the coolest month remains above 50° and is, of course, higher at coastal than at inland stations. In the southwest, Perth, for example, averages 55° in July, Kellerberrin 52°, Cape Leeuwin 57°, Albany and Esperance 54°, but Katanning only 50°. At Adelaide the July mean is 52°. In southeastern Australia values for the coldest month are below 50°, for Melbourne registers a July mean of 49°, Sale in Victoria and Stanley in northwestern Tasmania 48°, and Hobart on the south coast 46°. Mean values are lower at higher elevations: Ballarat at 1430 feet averages 44° in July, and Canberra at 1837 feet averages 42°.

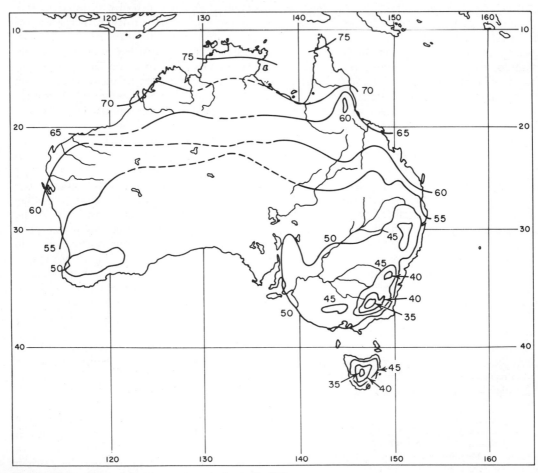

Figure 15.9. Mean July temperatures in Australia (°F).

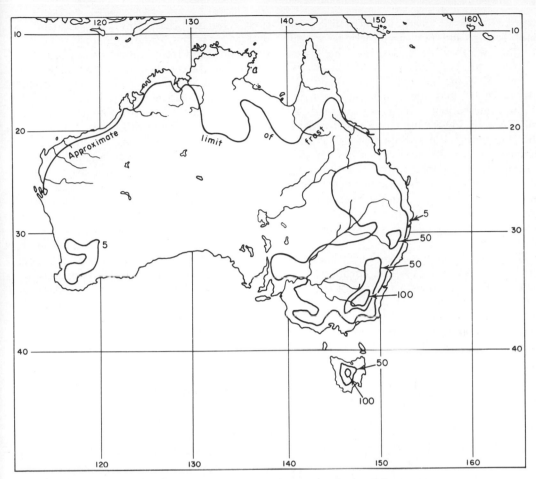

Figure 15.10.   Number of days per year on which frost occurs in Australia.

From Cape Howe northward the coldest month again averages above 50°, Sydney reporting 53°, Port Macquarie 54°, and subtropical Brisbane 59° (Table 15-1).

The mean daily temperature range at most mediterranean stations is a great deal less in winter than in summer, for the repeated inclemency of the season acts as a temperature moderator. At Perth and Adelaide the value for June is 14 degrees, whereas in summer the amplitude at Perth is 20 to 22 degrees and at Adelaide 24 to 25 degrees. At coastal points, however, the seasons do not contrast greatly in this respect. At Cape Leeuwin the mean daily range is 9 degrees, June through August, compared with 11 degrees in summer; at Albany 15 degrees, compared with 14 to 15 degrees in summer; at Esperance 16 to 17 degrees, compared with 17 to 18 degrees in summer. In the

southeast and Tasmania, however, lower daily temperature ranges generally prevail: 13 degrees in June and July, and in June at Launceston 16 degrees and Hobart 12 degrees. From Cape Howe northward very little difference is seen between summer and winter in the mean daily amplitudes, for the June and January averages at Sydney are both 13 degrees, although at subtropical Brisbane the July mean is 19 degrees compared with 16 degrees for January. At Canberra the thermometer in winter varies less widely than in summertime, for the mean daily temperature range in July is 19 degrees but in January 27 degrees.

The threat of frost in wintertime is not really a very serious one anywhere within the mid-latitude forest-woodland regions except, of course, in the higher altitudes (Fig. 15.10). From November through March frost can be expected to occur at any inland stations, but only briefly, and prolonged periods of sub-freezing weather are unknown. The lowest recorded temperature at Geraldton is 39°, Perth 34°, Cape Leeuwin 39°, Albany 33°, Esperance 31°, and Adelaide 32°, all occurring in the coldest month of July. In the southeast and Tasmania lower values have been recorded; the thermometer has dipped to 27° at Melbourne, 28° at Ballarat, 21° at the interior station of Launceston, and 27° at the south coastal station of Hobart. Farther north along the east coast Sydney and Brisbane have reported an extreme minimum of 36°, but at Canberra much higher in elevation a low of 14° has occurred.

The winter's precipitation, which is such a strong characteristic of the mediterranean areas, ordinarily attains a maximum in those sections in either June or July, although actual amounts are by no means large. The largest mean values are found in Swanland in the southwest, as at Perth with 6.9 inches for June and Cape Leeuwin with 7.3 inches for July. Albany and Esperance register 5.7 and 4.1 in July and June respectively. At no great distance from the sea in the southwest, however, means for the months of maximum fall are considerably less. Kellerberrin east of Perth records 2.2 inches for June, and Katanning, northeast of Cape Leeuwin, 3 inches in July. North of Cape Leeuwin most precipitation comes in heavy showers at night. Adelaide averages 3 inches for the maximum rainfall month of June (Table 15-1).

In southwestern Australia the major portion of winter's rains arrives in the onshore flow of the northwest gales that mark the leading edge of an advancing depression. In the southeast, however, most of the winter's rains arrive from the southeast and result in the main from the convergence troughs between two anticyclones. In most cases the rains begin far out at sea before reaching the coast on the persistent southeast flow.

New Zealand

Approximately 1000 miles southeast of the Australian mainland lie the islands of New Zealand, extending from about 34°30' to nearly 47°30'S. Lat. Their middle latitude position and the fact that they are surrounded by a tremendous expanse of ocean profoundly affect

their climatic character. New Zealand is decidedly a remote, insular territory, not only a thousand miles from Australia but about 1800 miles from the continent of Antarctica.

Having an area of about 103,000 square miles, the combined expanse of land surface is only about two thirds of that of California and about four fifths that of the British Isles. The country comprises two main islands, North Island and South Island, and a number of small islets, of which Stewart Island off the extreme south coast is the largest (Fig. 15.1). The irregular outline of North Island reaches from about 34°30' to 41°40', an extreme distance of over 500 miles. It is slightly overlapped in latitude by South Island, which extends from about 40°30' to nearly 47°00', an extreme distance of nearly 600 miles. Cook Strait separates the two, interposing a stretch of open water about 100 miles wide at its western entry and narrowing in the southeast where it assumes a north–south alignment, to about 15 miles wide.

New Zealand is a mountainous island domain. From the towering heights of its interior eminences rugged, stream-dissected terrain, well mantled with vegetation, reaches out boldly toward the never-too-distant sea. At countless points along the shoreline the land plunges steeply down to the water's edge. Coastal plains are small and widely scattered, although moderately extensive lowland tracts on South Island are found in the vicinity of Invercargill at the southernmost end, near Dunedin on the southeast coast, and the Canterbury Plains southwest of Christchurch. On North Island a comparatively large coastal plain borders the curving southwest shore north of Cook Strait for about 150 miles, reappearing northwestward to all but surround the 8260 foot volcanic cone of Mt. Egmont. On the opposite side of the island a smaller lowland lies southwest of Napier on Hawke Bay, and a long, narrow plain borders the Bay of Plenty on the north side, east of the Coromandel peninsula. Moderately low, hilly terrain occupies most of the Auckland peninsula, a narrow, elongated arm outstretched toward the northwest. The city of Auckland is at the southern end of the peninsula.

Over half of North Island lies at an elevation of more than 1000 feet, rising gradually to the highest point in the south central portion at Mt. Ruapehu (9175 feet). A number of peaks rise to more than 5000 feet from the Rauku-mara Range in the northeast to the Tararua Range in the south, not far from Cook Strait and the city of Wellington. Most of South Island is also above 1000 feet in elevation, and high ranges form an unbroken mountain core from end to end. Over seventeen peaks tower above 10,000 feet, and the summit area approaches within less than 20 miles of the west coast in the central section. It is in this section that New Zealand's highest point, Mt. Cook, rises to 12,349 feet within 25 miles of the west coast and about 130 miles almost due west of Christchurch.

New Zealand thus presents a narrow, curving, mountainous barrier to the endless succession of anticyclones, troughs, and fronts that travel a generally eastward course in these latitudes throughout the year. It is these geographical circumstances—latitude, size, oceanic position, surface configuration, and alignment of major surface features—and their combined effect upon the constantly variable atmospheric circulations that are largely responsible for the climatic character of New Zealand as a whole.

The over-all climate of New Zealand is marine in nature, moisture-laden air from the sea the dominant influence, and a pervading uniformity the result. Changes in weather occur frequently and rapidly, inclement conditions giving way to bracing winds and sunny skies. Though the incidence of rain-bearing disturbances is high, so also is the incidence of sunshine and fair weather. Abundant rain and sunshine plus the moderate range of temperature variations typical of marine climates produce in New Zealand a flourishing vegetation that is mainly evergreen. Above all, the dominant plant life of the country is forest, and forest in which only a few deciduous species are known. Thus, through its evergreen character and its climatic significance, it resembles those coastal evergreen or temperate rainforests of Tasmania, southern Africa, southern Chile, northwestern North America, and northwestern Europe.

From north to south the ruling elements of indigenous forest are most closely akin to species found elsewhere in the well-watered mid-latitudes south of the equator and belong to the evergreen podocarp–southern beech associations. On the better-drained inland areas of North Island, under the influence of warm,

wet summers and mild, wet winters, the podocarps predominate, the chief species being the tall totara (*Podocarpus totara*), whose foliage consists of long, straight, stiff, pointed leaves affording little shade. Smaller proportions of kahikatea or white pine (*P. dacrydioides*), matai (*P. spicata*), and rimu or red pine (*Dacrydium cupressinum*) are combined to make up the bulk of the undisturbed stands.

At higher elevations on cold, wet mountainsides the predominant trees are hardwood beech (*Nothogafus spp.*), any one of five principal species, with characteristic small, round, glossy evergreen leaves. An appreciable expanse of scrub and grassland occupies the uppermost levels of the central interior, where recent volcanic deposits are widespread. Over the scattered coastal lowlands, most notably around the shores of Hawke Bay, are extensive prairie grasslands. The peninsular projections of North Island, Auckland and Coromandel peninsulas, are the site of a once flourishing kauri pine forest. The kauri (*Agathis australis*) is a conifer of great size, towering up to more than 180 feet. Fringing the shores of Auckland peninsula are mangrove swamps of tropical character. Slender palms may be seen in the scrub growth of the hilly interior.

The steeply sloping western flanks of the South Island are richly mantled by a luxuriant evergreen forest in which tree ferns and herbaceous ferns abound, and the damp forest floor is carpeted with mosses and liverworts. Lianas and epiphytes as well as mosses and lichens hang from the tall, buttressed trees, and from the northern tip at Cape Farewell to the shores of Foveaux Strait the prevailing scene is aptly suggested in the term *rainforest*. Rimu, or red pine, is the dominant podocarp at lower elevations, although others are present along with a variety of hardwoods, prominent among which is rata (*Metrosideros lucida*). At elevations above 1000 feet evergreen beech predominates, giving way to alpine meadows, glaciers, and snow fields above its upper limits. Forest ceases at elevations ranging from about 5000 feet in the north to around 3000 feet on Steward Island. Beech forest appears on the eastern upper slopes of the main mountain axis and also on the upper levels of scattered ranges east of the mountain rampart. In drier portions of eastern sections of South Island grassland prevails and was notably widespread in colonial times over the Canterbury Plains. In fact, between Christchurch and Dunedin tussock and turf grassland reveal the rain shadow effect of the western ranges on the prevailing eastward movement of rain-bearing storms.

CLIMATIC CONDITIONS. New Zealand's climatic character has been admirably described by B. J. Garnier,[7] whose work is drawn upon for much of the information that follows.

Five fundamental features distinguish New Zealand's climate as a whole: it is windy and sunny; its weather is highly changeable; it is without prolonged hot or cold spells; it experiences extraordinary contrasts in annual rainfall within short distances; and it possesses a great variety of strongly contrasting climatic types within the country's small area. To these should be added the fact that New Zealand is dominated by marine influences and that these are unusually regular in nature, producing amazingly regular weather cycles in which changes occur within a mean period of from six to ten days.

Daily weather conditions are commonly described in terms of wind direction—a northwester, westerly weather, a southerly—each a meaningful expression understandable to residents of town and country alike. Northwesterly winds in the wake of a receding anticyclone and preceding a slowly advancing cold front herald the onset of warm weather for North Island, rain for the west coastal sections of both islands, and clear, hot, dry conditions over the Canterbury Plains. The start of southwesterly winds, on the other hand, augurs fair weather on the western shores but rain and cold in the east. The westerly weather south of Cape Egmont often brings showers with bright, clear intervals. A southerly regularly occurs after the passage of a cold front, an event preceded by winds from a northerly quarter that commonly set in as light to moderate breezes over a period of two or three days, only to end in gales through Cook Strait and over the Canterbury Plains. The southerly itself usually arrives with marked suddenness, its advance visible in the form of a dark line of approaching cloud. Rain and sometimes hail occur during its passing, driven by gusty squalls, resulting in a hard, drenching

downpour. The exact direction of its approach is determined by the directional slope of the barometric gradient and its intensity by the steepness of the gradient, which in turn depends mainly on the size and vigor of the approaching cold air mass. Southerly winds then diminish gradually, and fair anticyclonic weather returns again to the islands.

Very strong winds are usually confined to the well-exposed flanks of higher mountains, especially through the notches and around the ends of prominent ranges. They also occur through the wind gap at Cook Strait and through Foveaux Strait between Stewart Island and the southern end of South Island. Elsewhere New Zealand's winds rarely exceed 25 miles per hour, although due to the ruggedness of the terrain they are singularly gusty. Through gaps, down valleys, and across the interrupted plains they vary in strength, steadiness, and direction within very short distances. These properties are conspicuous features of the normal weather.

A continuous cloud cover rarely prevails for any great length of time. This is mainly due to the characteristic turbulence of the atmosphere engendered by the effect of topography on transient weather systems. In consequence, abundant sunshine is a typical feature of the country's climates. Nearly all the country annually receives over 1800 hours of sunshine and east of the mountains some areas are favored by over 2200 hours (Fig. 15.6). Through a normal year the sun shines down from clear blue skies for a great many days at fairly short intervals of a few days at a time, regularly interrupted by spells of inclement weather. The frequency and relative regularity of weather change are conspicuous qualities of the over-all climate.

The absence of prolonged hot or cold spells is chiefly a consequence of New Zealand's dominantly maritime environment and the regularity of weather sequences. No continental land mass lies near enough to provide persistent periods of any kind of continental weather, and temperatures fluctuate frequently under the overpowering influence of constantly changing migrating weather systems.

Perhaps the most significant quality of New Zealand's annual rainfall is the marked way in which it varies in both time and space. Amounts and intensities vary widely within very short distances from day to day, from season to

[7] B. J. Garnier, *The Climate of New Zealand, A Geographical Survey*, Edward Arnold Publishers Ltd., London, 1958.

season, and then from year to year for the same season. Hence, the subject of annual rainfall is the hardest of all the major climatic qualities to generalize about. One of the more singular characteristics is the extremely large amount that may fall in an hour's time, in twenty-four hours, or during a longer period. At Milford Sound on the southwest coast of South Island 22 inches have fallen in twenty-four hours, at Rissington on North Island over 20 inches fell in ten hours, and at many other points in a variety of geographical settings similar large amounts have fallen. Heavy rains are generally characteristic of the islands as a whole. Yearly totals of rainfall vary appreciably from the statistical mean, the average deviation being above 12 per cent for most of the territory, rising to a maximum of over 20 per cent along the shores of Hawke Bay.

The fifth major climate feature is the very striking variety of climates within small spaces. Garnier identifies eleven kinds of climate and has determined nine clearly defined climatic regions within the country's 103,000 square miles. We shall take advantage of his studies by presently discussing one of the regions in some detail, but first let us consider some climatic qualities of a more general nature.

Unlike Australia, which is fairly well centered within the zone of persistent subtropical anticyclonic systems, New Zealand is just to the south of it and reaches well into the vigorous circulations of the southern hemisphere's oceanic westerlies. It is thus the scene of an endless procession of weather changes. They arise from the constant conflict between air masses of maritime tropical and maritime polar air, taking the form of alternate warm and cold front advances across the islands, with all the attendant types of disturbance (Fig. 15.11).

In winter the predominant westerlies rule the weather of both islands. Most storm centers pass to the south, but the cold fronts along which they typically form become elongated northward, and it is these, and the weather they bring, rather than the central storm areas themselves, that influence New Zealand in winter (Fig. 15.12). During the summer season South Island remains in the grasp of the dominant westerlies and cold front weather, but North Island becomes more closely associated with the milder, relatively drier air of subtropical character.

The typical counterclockwise circulation of an advancing anticyclone brings cold air from the south as it approaches from the west, and after its central area has moved off to the eastward, warm air begins to flow from some northerly quarter. The circulation in the intervening depressions between successive anticyclones is, of course, clockwise, and thus their approach is heralded by winds from a northerly quarter, northeasterly when their paths are north of the islands, and northwesterly when their paths are south of them. Anticyclones tend to travel on a west-southwest to east-northeast

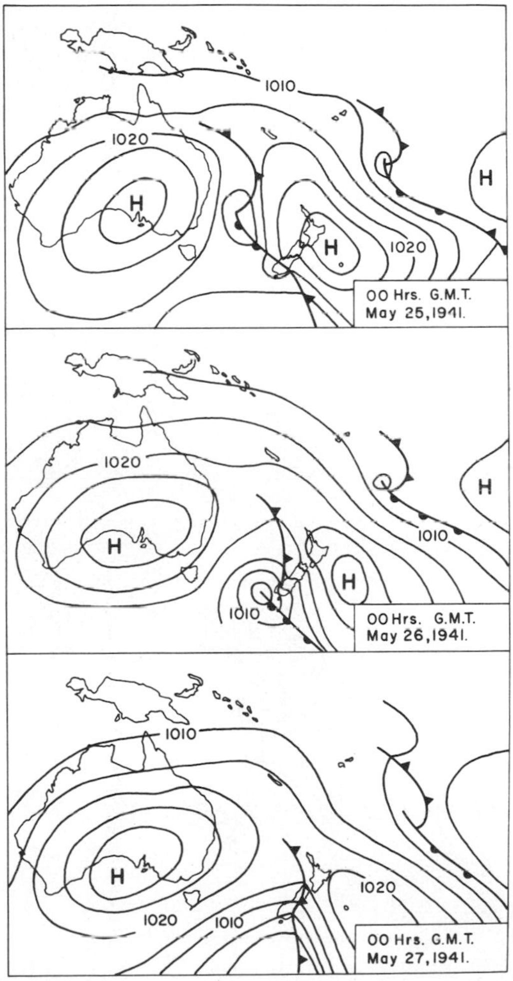

Figure 15.11. Successive warm and cold front passages over New Zealand. [From B. J. Garnier, *The Climate of New Zealand*, London, Edward Arnold Publishers, 1958.]

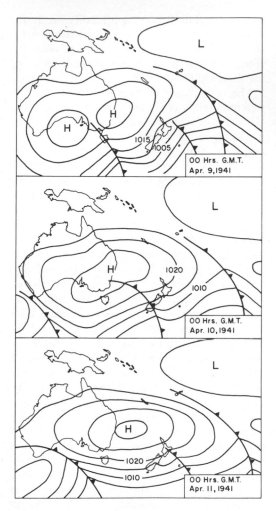

Figure 15.12. Successive cold fronts passing eastward over New Zealand. [From B. J. Garnier, *The Climate of New Zealand*, London, Edward Arnold Publishers, 1958.]

trajectory, and troughs tend to follow, but in an erratic manner. Anticyclones travel faster in spring and early summer than at other times, averaging about 450 miles per day in November and December and about 300 miles per day in May. As a rule, one crosses New Zealand or passes just to the north once every six to ten days, thus providing the key element in the relatively systematic rhythms of the country's normal weather experience.

Mean annual precipitation ranges from over 100 inches along nearly the entire west coast of South Island, and at higher, freely exposed points in North Island to less than 20 inches in

an inland area from 50 to 100 miles northwest of Dunedin (Table 15-2 and Fig. 15.13). On the west coast of South Island during the thirty-year period 1921–50, Milford Sound (el. 20) averaged 245.2 inches, Hermitage near Mt. Cook (el. 2510) 172.4 inches, Hokitika (el. 12) 115.4 inches, and Chateau Tongariro (el. 3670) on the northwest side of Ruapehu in central North Island 108.2 inches. By comparison, Alexandra (el. 520) in the dry part of Otago northwest of Dunedin averaged 13.2 inches, and is one of many localities in the area reporting similar amounts. Of the two main sources of New Zealand's rain and snow, warm fronts and cold fronts, the latter are the chief producers, and most of the year's precipitation arrives from the west with the passage of cold air across the country. Such rainfall is frequently heavy but not often prolonged. It tends to fall in irregular showers of large drops, particularly east of the mountain ranges. Thus, as Garnier says, "The average

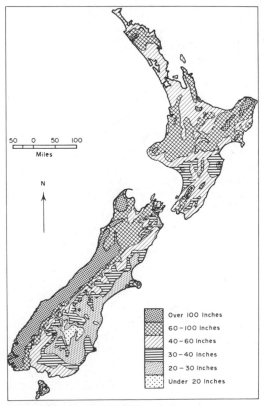

Figure 15.13. Mean annual precipitation in New Zealand. [From B. J. Garnier, *The Climate of New Zealand*, London, Edward Arnold Publishers, 1958.]

TABLE 15–2

Climatic Data for Mid-Latitude Forest Stations in New Zealand
(Temp., °F; Rainfall, In.)

Station	Lat.	El. in Ft		Jan.	Feb.	Mar.	Apr.	May	Jun.	Jul.	Aug.	Sep.	Oct.	Nov.	Dec.	Year
Auckland	36°51'	160	T	66	67	65	61	57	53	51	52	55	57	60	64	
			R	3.2	3.9	3.2	4.4	4.8	5.4	5.5	4.4	3.8	4.1	3.3	2.9	48.8
Chateau Tongariro	39°12'	3670	T	52	53	51	46	41	37	36	37	40	43	46	50	
			R	8.6	8.9	6.7	9.5	8.6	10.4	9.3	8.3	9.1	10.4	8.4	10.1	108.2
Hastings	39°39'	45	T	65	65	62	57	51	47	46	48	51	55	59	63	
			R	2.5	2.6	2.4	2.8	3.5	3.1	3.3	2.8	2.1	2.1	2.0	2.0	31.3
New Plymouth	39°04'	160	T	62	63	61	58	54	50	49	50	52	54	57	60	
			R	4.5	4.0	3.7	4.8	6.1	6.2	5.4	5.8	4.9	5.6	4.7	4.6	60.2
Wellington	41°17'	415	T	61	61	59	56	51	48	46	48	50	53	56	59	
			R	3..	3.3	3.2	3.8	4.9	4.7	5.4	4.7	3.8	4.2	3.4	3.5	47.8
Nelson	41°17'	24	T	63	63	60	56	51	46	45	47	50	54	57	61	
			R	3.0	2.9	2.9	3.0	3.2	3.5	3.4	3.3	3.5	3.5	2.9	3.0	38.2
Milford Sound	44°41'	20	T	57	57	55	51	46	42	41	43	47	50	52	55	
			R	26.4	15.2	22.2	21.8	21.6	14.0	13.9	17.2	19.8	25.8	24.1	23.4	245.2
Alexandra	45°15'	520	T	62	61	58	51	43	38	36	41	47	52	56	60	
			R	1.8	1.5	1.2	1.4	0.9	0.8	0.7	0.6	0.8	1.2	1.1	1.3	13.2
Christchurch	43°32'	22	T	61	61	58	54	48	43	42	44	49	53	56	60	
			R	2.2	1.8	1.9	1.9	2.9	2.6	2.6	2.1	2.1	2.0	1.8	2.5	26.3
Fairlie	44°06'	1004	T	59	59	55	50	44	38	37	40	45	50	54	57	
			R	3.0	2.9	2.4	2.4	2.0	1.8	2.0	1.9	2.7	2.9	2.4	2.9	29.2
Ophir	45°07'	1000	T	60	60	56	49	41	36	35	40	45	51	54	58	
			R	1.8	1.9	1.5	1.5	1.1	1.0	0.8	0.8	1.1	1.7	1.3	1.8	16.3
Dunedin	45°52'	240	T	59	58	56	53	48	44	43	45	49	52	54	57	
			R	3.4	3.3	3.3	3.2	3.5	3.3	3.1	3.0	2.9	3.2	3.4	3.8	39.3

Source: B. J. Garnier, *The Climate of New Zealand, A Geographic Survey*, Edward Arnold Publishers Ltd., London, 1958.

intensity of rainfall is, therefore, high, and the number of days on which it falls is comparatively low."[8] For most of New Zealand rain falls on between 150 and two hundred days, although more than two hundred days are characteristic of some western sections of South Island.

The year's precipitation is rather evenly distributed, no area receiving more than 35 per cent or less than 15 per cent during any three-month season. Climatically meaningful contrasts do exist, however. In north and east sections of North Island over 30 per cent of the annual total occurs during the winter months of June through August. By comparison, in the dry inland area of South Island almost a third of the year's precipitation arrives in the summer quarter December through February. From the standpoint of moisture effectiveness the contrasts are important. Over much of South Island east of the mountain ranges most of the rain comes in summer when it is least effective, and irrigation of crops becomes a necessity in central Otago and the Mackenzie Plains. Warm, drying föhn winds add to the aridity of these rain shadow areas.

Snow is rare in North Island save at high altitudes, and when it falls seldom remains on the ground for more than a day or two below 1000 feet. It occurs more frequently and remains longer above this level. Snow pockets have been observed to remain high in the central mountain area for as much as three weeks. At 9175 feet on the slopes of Mt. Ruapehu is a small snow field feeding a number of minor glaciers. The isolated cone of Mt. Egmont becomes white with snow each winter but seldom retains its accumulation to the end of summer.

On South Island, where so much of the mountainous backbone exceeds 7000 feet in elevation, permanent snow fields are common. The snow line is estimated to be about 6500 feet in the region around Mt. Cook, and in winter snow accumulates down to about 4000 feet in the northern and middle sections of the island and down to about 3500 feet near the southern end. Very extensive glaciers are found in the Southern Alps and include some of the world's more notable examples of alpine ice fields. Tasman Glacier is 18 miles in length, and the Franz Josef and Fox glaciers descend through heavy,

luxuriant temperate rainforest to levels of less than 700 feet. Permanent ice and snow at high altitudes in South Island are a major asset for New Zealand's irrigation farming in the central interior and for hydroelectric power development.

Thermal convection plays a small part in producing the annual precipitation of New Zealand, as one would expect in a temperate marine environment of this kind. Hence, thunderstorms are not very numerous. In inland areas they increase in frequency from south to north, in short toward the warmer latitudes, where they number about twenty-one per year. They occur chiefly with the indraft of warm, maritime tropical air from the northwest in advance of a cold front, and the hail they sometimes release rarely attains damaging size. Fog is rare along the coast except at the south end of South Island. Interior valley fogs are common, on the other hand, during spells of clear weather.

Gales of fairly short duration are relatively common in Cook Strait, blowing chiefly out of the northwest in spring and summer and from southeast during May through July. The stormiest part of New Zealand is Foveaux Strait and the north coast of Steward Island. Heavy northwest to southwest gales occur at all times of the year, sometimes continuing for weeks without interruption, the winds at more than 50 miles per hour furiously lashing the sea and driving heavy, steady rain in drenching squalls.

In this primarily temperate rainforest climate the mean annual range of temperature is less than 20 degrees nearly everywhere. Summer temperatures average less than 70°, and in fact no station in New Zealand has recorded a monthly temperature of more than 67° (Fig. 15.14). The highest values are recorded at northern points on the Auckland peninsula. The city of Auckland reports a February mean of 66.7°, and Te Aroha, about 50 miles southeast of Auckland and farther from the sea, reports a mean for January and February of 66.8°. In most of the country mean temperatures for both January and February differ only very slightly, and even at inland stations they differ less than 1 degree. The mean daily range of temperature is higher in summertime at eastern and inland stations less moderated by weather from the west. Ophir and Fairlie,

[8] Garnier, *op. cit.*, p. 27.

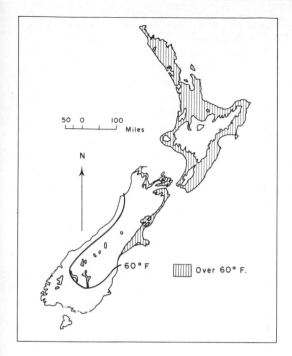
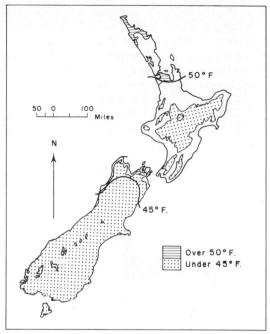

Figure 15.14. Mean January and July temperatures in New Zealand. [From B. J. Garnier, *The Climate of New Zealand*, London, Edward Arnold Publishers, 1958.]

inland localities in the southern part of South Island, report February ranges of about 25 degrees. This is largely on account of frequent clear sky weather in the lee of the mountain ranges, allowing a substantial intake of heat from the sun during the day and rapid re-radiation of terrestrial warmth at night. At seacoast stations values of the lower mean daily range are nearly half those reported above, and we note that Auckland records 12.7° and Wellington 13.2 (Table 15-2).

Though lengthy spells of hot weather are unknown in New Zealand, the thermometer has risen above 90° in summer on almost every part of the island except stations with a good westerly exposure. Christchurch has reported 98° in December and January, but the extreme maximum at Wellington has been 88°, and at Hokitika on South Island's west coast it has been 87°.

July is the coldest month everywhere in the country. Most stations average above 40° at this time (Fig. 15.14). Naturally, with increasing altitude the mean monthly value for the coldest month approaches freezing, and Chateau Tongariro on North Island averages 37.3° in July,

compared with Hastings, about 50 miles southeast and 3625 feet lower, which averages 47.1°. Manorburn Dam in the south central part of South Island is at an altitude of 2448 feet, and there the July mean is 33°, compared with 37.7° at Alexandra, some 2000 feet lower. Below-freezing temperatures are experienced every winter, especially in July, nearly everywhere in the country, even at marine coastal stations, except on the Auckland peninsula. Auckland itself has registered 32° in May, July, and August, and the thermometer has dropped to 27° at Napier, 29° at Wellington, 21° at Christchurch, and 9° at Wallacetown in the extreme south. The mean extreme minima in July at inland stations indicate the lower values reported there from time to time. At Fairlie the mean extreme minimum temperature is 14.1°, at Ophir 13.8°, and Manorburn Dam 7.8°. These are all values obtained from thermometer readings in a conventional weather shelter in which thermometers are positioned about 5 feet above the surface of the ground. Much lower temperatures are known for the ground beneath, and ground frosts are, therefore, not only more severe but occur more frequently than the records indicate. At Napier, for example, about seven "screen"[9] frosts are the average for the year, but ground frosts occur an average of twenty-seven times each year. Wellington records 0.1 screen frosts over an eighty-nine-year period, but 13.9 ground frosts are reported for that period.

Turning our attention now to Middle New Zealand (Fig. 15.15) as one of the nine climatic

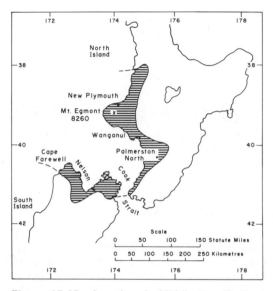

Figure 15.15.   Locations in Middle New Zealand.

regions described by Garnier, let us consider some of the salient features by which this region is identified. Middle New Zealand extends from a point about 100 miles northeast of Mt. Egmont at the base of the Auckland peninsula in a narrow belt about 25 miles wide down the west coast of North Island. It widens inland to include the Mt. Egmont region, turning southeastward to follow the curving north shore of Cook Strait, finally crossing Cook Strait to include the two northern projections of South Island and the small coastal plain around Nelson between them.

Quoting from Garnier,

It is better to begin the analysis of the climatic regions of New Zealand by studying Middle New Zealand, rather than by following the more con-

ventional way of working systematically through the country from north to south. This is because the area's climatic qualities epitomize, to a remarkable degree, those of the country as a whole. Here are sunny, windy conditions, and a plentiful rainfall evenly distributed through the year. Moderate as the mean temperatures undoubtedly are, they represent averages derived from fairly large diurnal and extreme ranges. Finally, the exposure of the region to westerly influences, and its susceptibility to the whole gamut of the weather contrasts associated with the passage of migratory anticyclones, combine with the foregoing factors to make it in effect a miniature of the whole country's climate. In this respect, Middle New Zealand is unique, since no other region conforms so closely to the average conditions associated with New Zealand as a whole.[10]

Mean summer temperatures lie within a few degrees of 60° in all but the most elevated parts, and in winter all but 15 per cent of the region has mean temperatures of 45° or over. Thus, the region is one of mild winters and warm summers, and the mean annual range is small, being less than 20 degrees. Snow is rare, but many thermometers register subfreezing temperatures about fifty times a year, and the mean number of ground frosts varies along the following lines: at Wanganui, about 70 miles southeast of Mt. Egmont the average number is thirteen, a few miles along the curving shoreline it is fifty-seven, at Appleby near Nelson it is seventy-six, but at Nelson itself it is sixty-one.

The mean annual temperature range is low, in keeping with a marine environment, and varies from 13.6 degrees at New Plymouth, 20 miles north of Mt. Egmont, to 17.8 degrees at Taihape, on the southern slopes of the central uplands about 50 miles from the sea at 2157 feet. The average of extreme monthly maxima and minima observed over a period of several decades indicates that although the fundamental temperature program is a conservative one, the region is frequently subjected to rather wide temperature variations. The mean of extreme minima for June or July is 32.3° at New Plymouth, 30.3° at Wanganui about 70 miles southeast of Mt. Egmont near the shore, 28° at Palmerston North 45 miles farther southeastward and about 25 miles from the sea, 27.5° at

[9] Reference is to the Stevenson Screen.

[10] Garnier, *op. cit.*, p. 53.

Taihape, and 29.4° at Nelson. The mean of maxima in January or February is 76.9° at New Plymouth, 80.6° at Wanganui, 80° at Palmerston North, 78° at Taihape, and 79.3° at Nelson. Thus, the mean extreme temperature range is nearly 45 degrees at New Plymouth and over 50 degrees at the remaining stations. From these data it is evident that Middle New Zealand is no exception to the rule that the country is occasionally subjected to very cold and very hot conditions, however briefly they may prevail. The thermometer drops below freezing a dozen or more times each winter, and every summer generally sees at least a day or two when the temperature rises well into the 80s (Table 15-2).

Mean annual rainfall is plentiful and evenly distributed throughout the year, amounting to more than 30 inches everywhere, and in most of the area to over 40 inches (Table 15-2). This and the predominantly conservative temperature experience are typical of coastal evergreen forest regions of the middle latitudes everywhere. The New Zealand variation of normal temperate rainforest climate is expressed in the frequent regularity of its weather changes, its high percentage of sunny weather, and gusty winds.

References

BURBIDGE, N. T.: "The Phytogeography of the Australian Region," *Australian Journal of Botany*, 8(2): 75–211, 1960.

CLARKE, R. H.: *Severe Local Wind Storms in Australia*, Division of Meteorological Physics Technical Paper No. 13, Commonwealth Scientific and Industrial Research Organization, Melbourne, 1962.

GARNIER, B. J.: *The Climate of New Zealand, A Geographic Survey*, Edward Arnold Publishers, Ltd., London, 1958.

KEAST A., CROCKER, R. L., and CHRISTIAN, C. S.: "Biogcography and Ecology in Australia," *Monographiae Biologicae*, Vol. 8, W. Junk, Den Haag, 1959.

PENFOLD, A. R., and WILLIS, J. L., *The Eucalypts*, Leonard Hill, Ltd., London, 1961.

REES, H.: *Australasia: Australia, New Zealand and the Pacific Islands*, London House and Maxwell, New York, 1962.

TAYLOR, T. G.: *Australia*, E. P. Dutton & Co., Inc., New York, 1940.

chapter 16

MID-LATITUDE GRASSLANDS
NORTH OF THE EQUATOR

The grasses are among the world's most varied and most widely distributed flowering plants. They vary greatly in both habit and appearance. They include the close-growing, fine-textured forms of cultivated lawns and gardens, especially the blue grasses, creeping bents, and fescues, so well known for their capacity to produce dense turf or sod. They also include the taller, tree-size bamboos of the tropics. Some of these tower to 100 feet on hollow, hard, woody stems that may be only a foot in diameter near ground level.

Grasses are found in successful adjustment to habitats too wet or too dry for trees. They can be seen densely rooted in luxuriant abundance, along with grasslike reeds and rushes, in the watery muck of bogs and marshes. They can be seen in the sparse vegetation of wind-blown deserts, tenaciously withstanding the inimical dessication of those arid climates. Grasses can even be found along the northernmost limits of flowering plant development among the hardier plant communities of the Arctic tundra. In latitude they extend from more than 80° to the equator. The distribution of grasses in altitude ranges from sea level to more than 17,000 feet in the Andes and more than 18,000 feet in the Himalayas, at such lofty heights reaching the uppermost limits of flowering plant growth.

Over six hundred genera and more than seven thousand species of this large plant family are known. These, the *Gramineae* (alternately, *Poaceae*), provide the world with its greatest number of individual plants. The largest number of grass species are found in the tropics, but the largest number of individual plants, the densest distribution of the world's grasses, is in the cooler climates of the middle latitudes.

In this chapter we will study the grassland climates of the middle latitudes north of the equator. Their distribution and their relationships with adjoining climates can most easily be understood by a consideration of the major grassland associations, principally the tall grass prairie and the short grass steppe. These associations provide the tangible, visible expression of those discrete qualities of atmospheric behavior that identify the mid-latitude grassland climates on every continent.

The mid-latitude grassland climates are generally intolerable for persistent forest growth and yet moist enough to support a complete cover of grass, in contrast to the scattered vegetation or barren wasteland of arid desert. Thus, they are regions of transition between well-watered forest and water-deficient desert. They are most commonly found on terrain that is level to rolling or hilly, and range in altitude from sea level to a mile or more above sea level.

The grassland climates of the middle latitudes are found in five principal areas: the central interior of North America, the central interior of Eurasia, southern South America, southern Africa, and southeastern Australia (Fig. 7.1). Although grassland climate appears in fragmentary distribution in scores of small areas elsewhere within the mid-latitudes, these five areas are the largest, the prototypes of the grassland climate on each continental land mass. Despite the fact that each area has many points of individuality giving each a unique geographical identity, all to a certain degree possess a good many points of similarity. These are the features that establish their common distinction as the mid-latitude grassland climates of the world.

All the mid-latitude grasslands are distributed over a wide range of latitude, and roughly within the same latitudinal range on either side of the equator. North of the equator they reach from about 30° to 55°, and south of the equator from about 23° to about 50°.

All are identified by a nearly complete vegetative cover in which grasses are overwhelmingly the dominant forms. Generously intermingled within the thick-sown cover of slender grasses are other herbaceous forms— sedges, forbs, and legumes—that thrive companionably under the ruling influences of the climate peculiar to these regions. Reference here is to the mesophytic vegetation, the plant associations developing under edaphic conditions that are neither excessively dry nor excessively wet.

Under mesophytic conditions is found one of the more striking features of a region dominated by close-growing grass and other herbaceous plants. This is the unusually dense network of roots and rootlets that occupy the ground from the surface to a depth of 1 or 2 feet, and sometimes to 5 or 6 feet, depending on soil moisture and the types of grasses prevailing. The impenetrable density of the root systems practically precludes the success of tree seedling development in such soils. It is a condition almost entirely dependent on climate and is scarcely at all influenced by the geological origin of the parent soil material. It is chiefly responsible for another typical feature of the grasslands, the distinctive openness of the terrain, often an unbroken view from horizon to horizon without the interruption of a single tree.

Soil moisture conditions are directly responsible for the prevalence of grassy vegetation and are intolerable to the successful intrusion of tree forms. Adequate soil moisture near the surface of the ground during the early part of the growing season when vegetative development is most rapid and an accumulation of calcareous salts toward the lower limits of root penetration are typical.

The climate of the grasslands is decidedly continental in character, that is, with four well-defined seasons, a large annual range of temperature, and a pronounced summer increase in precipitation. The mean annual temperature range for the latitudes in which grassland regions are found is in the order of 30 degrees or more, featuring hot summers and winters that are either very cold or at least experience frequent frosts. The normal daily temperature range is also high, another quality of continental climates.

A concentration of 70 per cent or more of annual precipitation during the summer, with a distinct tendency toward maximum amounts during the early part of the growing season, is common. To this must be added the relatively high variability in both the amount and occurrence of precipitation. The bulk of summer's precipitation is the product of thermal convective showers of relatively short duration, occurring under the dominant influence of maritime tropical air masses. Thunderstorms are a common occurrence, frequently producing hail and heavy rains that result in considerable runoff into the drainage basins.

Summers are periods of frequent but irregular spells of hot, dry weather, and they are occasionally seasons of severe and unpredictable drought. Strong influxes of hot, drying wind also occur with some frequency.

Winter may be very cold, as in the poleward reaches of the grasslands in the northern hemisphere, or at least, in the lower latitudes, have a large number of nights with frost. Relative humidity is low at this season, and precipitation light. Strong, cold winds are also common, and the ground is often bare, even in areas regularly receiving a certain amount of winter snow, allowing the deep penetration of hard frost in the soil.

A high percentage of possible sunshine is also typical. This holds true even in summer when precipitation increases, for as mentioned earlier, most rain falls in relatively heavy showers of short duration.

The difference between tall grass prairie and short grass steppe vegetation is based upon climatic qualities that differ rather widely in actual values from continent to continent and from place to place within each continental grassland region. No single meteorological element can be solely responsible for the presence of either tall or short grass. It is rather a combination of precipitation (amount, kind, time of occurrence, and degree of reliability), temperature, evaporation, solar radiation intensity and duration, length of growing season, and wind. One direct effect of these combined influences that provides a further key to the geographical distribution of prairie and steppe environments is the difference in soil moisture conditions. Under tall grass prairie the soil is moist from just below the surface down to the water table, and a layer of lime accumulation appears toward the lower limit of the root zone, usually between 4 and 6 feet below the surface. Under short grass a dry zone of variable depth exists between the subsurface moisture layer within the limits of root penetration (from 1½ to 4 feet) and the water table. A calcareous layer of accumulated salts in greater concentration than under tall grass appears at shallower depths of from 18 to 48 inches.

The continental characteristics of the mid-latitude grassland climates, their strongly developed seasonal rhythms, are traceable to yearly fluctuations in the general circulation. These, in turn, owe their systematic qualities to the precise geometric nature of the earth's dynamic relationship with the sun, consequent upon its motions around the sun.

North American Grasslands

The great grassland region that occupies the central interior of North America extends from southern Alberta, Saskatchewan, and Manitoba to the southern part of central Texas, and from the eastern flanks of the Rocky Mountains to the northwestern corner of Indiana. Extending over a broad range of latitude, from about 30° in Texas to about 55° in Alberta, it spans a distance of approximately 1800 miles in a roughly north–south direction, and a maximum east–west extent of about 1000 miles. Throughout its entire north–south range the region has evolved on surfaces that maintain a generally downward slope from west to east. Ranging in altitude from about 5000 in the foothills of the

Rockies to less than 500 feet in the Mississippi valley, a maximum height of more than 6000 feet is attained in eastern New Mexico and along the Laramie Range of Wyoming and the Front Range of Colorado (Fig. 16.1).

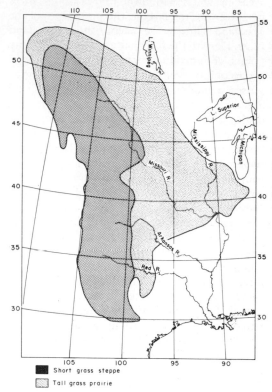

Short grass steppe

Tall grass prairie

Figure 16.1. Mid-latitude grasslands of central North America.

Although the general slope of the terrain is a gradual one, averaging about 10 feet per mile, the change in elevation from west to east is accomplished over a variety of landscapes that repeatedly interrupt the gradual descent toward the Mississippi from the abrupt declivity of the Rocky Mountains. East of the Mississippi a relatively gentle gradient is maintained, rising from less than 500 feet to levels of between 600 and 700 feet in northwestern Indiana. A close inspection of the topographic detail reveals a great many kinds of surface features across the length and breadth of this large central lowland of North America. With only a few exceptions they are geomorphic features of low relief. The partly wooded Sand Hills and Cypress Hills of southern Alberta and Saskatchewan between the Saskatchewan River and the Montana border are examples, as are the Sand Hills that occupy most of central Nebraska, and the rough, loose, sandy surface along the Arkansas River in southern Kansas. Deeply dissected ridges and plateaus alternate with slightly elevated level plains and rather deep deposits of wind-borne loess. The Missouri Coteau is the longest and best known of the ridges, extending from southern Saskatchewan to South Dakota, where in less than 2 miles a sharp rise in elevation of some 300 feet marks the relative steepness of this prominent escarpment. The Edwards Plateau of south central Texas is perhaps the best known of the plateau features, although a great many companion forms, often very small in crown area, called buttes and mesas appear in the southwestern reaches of the region. The Staked Plains (Llanos Estacados) of west Texas and the High Plains of eastern Colorado and west Kansas are well-known tracts of level to gently sloping terrain. The stark, barren Badlands of South Dakota illustrate still another type of land form, presenting a surface of formidable ruggedness that lies southeast of the Black Hills. The Black Hills are perhaps the most striking low mountain system entirely contained within the grassland regions, rising well above the surrounding plains toward a summit height of 7242 feet in Harney Peak.

Continental glaciation has softened the contours of the land approximately north and east of the Missouri and north of the Ohio by the creation of low, rounded terminal moraines and flat till plains. In many areas glaciers have left deep deposits of rock materials to fill the valleys of preglacial streams. In the interfluvial areas they have virtually eliminated the sharpness and angularity of original land forms.

Most of the region is drained by the waters of the Missouri-Mississippi River system. From the Canadian border to the Oklahoma-Texas boundary the Missouri and its tributaries, as well as the southern tributaries of the Mississippi, move generally eastward in their steady downward flow to the big river. In most of the grasslands in Canada and in eastern North Dakota and northwestern Minnesota are streams destined to empty into Hudson Bay. The Saskatchewan River system takes its rise in the Canadian Rockies, flowing eastward into Lake Winnipeg, where its waters mingle with those of the Red River of the North, which flows northward from its source in southeastern North Dakota.

PLANT LIFE. The great grasslands of interior North America possess an impressive degree of uniformity due to the predominantly grassy vegetation. The original qualities of the plant life of the North American grasslands have largely been erased by the settlement of the prairie and steppe lands, but wherever the land has been left untouched, or wherever it is allowed to revert to a natural state, the evidence of its original character emerges. From the accounts of early travelers who first ventured westward out of the forests into the open sweeping prairies and plains the indigenous qualities of the landscapes can also be ascertained.

Prairie and steppe are two distinct plant associations (Fig. 16.1) of the central grassland formation. They owe their separate identities to certain distinguishable contrasts in the over-all climate of the grasslands. Prairie is primarily the product of wetter conditions and more reliable annual rainfall: steppe is the product of drier conditions and less reliable precipitation. They, and the wetter and drier and colder and warmer regions into which they grade, are in dynamic competition. Vegetative change is common along all the margins of the entire grassland formation. Periods of only a few years of drier or wetter, colder or warmer conditions can tip the balance toward the advance or retreat of grass vegetation. So also can interference by the hand of man, through the establishment of continuous land use practices such as burning, draining, grazing, planting, and cultivation. Thus, the exact distribution of both prairie and steppe is neither permanent nor precisely determinable.

Forest yields to grassland little by little from the north and from the east. In Alberta, Saskatchewan, and Manitoba the boreal forest, dominated by coniferous species, becomes a mixed forest in which oaks, poplars, and other deciduous forms are strongly intermingled. The change appears south of Great Slave Lake, the Churchill River, and Lake Winnipegosis. This association in turn yields to an open parkland dominated by tall grass vegetation, yet interrupted again and again by groves of deciduous trees, chiefly poplar, oak, ash, and boxelder. The open parkland, or aspen-grove, forms a narrow, semicircular belt less than 100 miles in width from northwestern Montana northward, then eastward, and finally southeastward into Minnesota.

Figure 16.2. Tall grass prairie in central North America. [U.S. Department of the Interior, Bureau of Land Management]

From the great mid-latitude mixed forest of eastern North America the westward change into grassland is accomplished through an increasing number of forest openings. At times referred to as oak openings, from the fact that the forest in which they appear is composed very largely of oaks, these eastern outliers of grassland were observed by the first explorers of the land between the Ohio and the Great Lakes. Noted as far east as Ohio, they were composed chiefly of tall grass species and had persisted for a great length of time, as evidenced by the fact that their soils were typical grassland soils, deep, dark, and very fertile. The main body of the interior continental grassland has for some time been considered to begin in northwestern Indiana, roughly between the Wabash River and Lake Michigan.

The forest in a sense reluctantly relinquishes its hold on the land, for one continues to see it flourishing profusely not only along the bottom lands of the major rivers but on the stream banks of their tributaries as well. Riparian, galleria forest continues westward in narrow, elongated, winding ribbons of dark green foliage up the incised valleys of the Yellowstone, Cheyenne, Platte, and Kansas, and other tributaries of the Missouri, as well as the Arkansas and Red rivers farther south. Adequate moisture is available here for the greater needs of trees, in addition to protection from the high winds of the open plains.

It is on the rising land between the rivers, the interfluvial watersheds, in mesophytic situations of soil and drainage that grass vegetation firmly takes hold and, with only rare exceptions, cannot be invaded by other formations, so admirably adjusted has it become to the controlling influence of its climate (Fig. 16.2).

Once within the grasslands, the general character of the plant cover changes as one advances westward farther and farther from wooded parkland and forest. This is the change from tall grass prairie to short grass steppe. A great deal of serious study has been given the vegetation of both prairie and steppe, revealing the many complexities of their character and distribution in considerable detail. The reader's attention is commended to certain works on the subject listed in the bibliography for this chapter, especially *The North American Prairie* by J. E. Weaver and *Grasslands of the Great Plains* by Weaver and Albertson. Much of the material on grassland ecology that follows is taken from these two works.

Tall grasses, ecologically defined, are those that naturally grow to heights of from 5 to 8 feet; short grasses range from ½ to 1½ feet. A third height range is that of the mid-grasses, between 2 and 4 feet. Mid-grasses are found both in the eastern part of the steppe region and in the prairie, where they are considered the dominant height class from the fact that there they are the chief mesophytic grasses of slopes and hilltops. It is usually only in low, moist edaphic situations that truly tall grasses of 5 to 8 feet are found.

A traverse from east to west across the central part of the United States beginning in north-western Indiana would reveal a change in height classes among the mesophytes from dominantly mid-grass to a two-layered mixed grass association consisting of taller mid-grasses and beneath them short grass species, and finally, in the western reaches of the steppe, a vegetation of mainly short grass. Where mid-grass dominance ends and mixed-grass begins, the change from prairie to steppe takes place.[1] It occurs in a transition zone that averages (Fig. 16.1) about 50 miles wide in the central part of the country but is considerably less than this toward both the northern and southern limits of grassland. Examples of the chief grasses encountered by early settlers along this traverse are: (1) tall grasses of the lowlands and wetter uplands in the prairie, including big bluestem (*Andropogon gerardi*), Indian grass (*Sorghastrum nutans*), sloughgrass (*Spartina pectinata*), also called cordgrass, switchgrass (*Panicum virgatum*), and Canada wild-rye (*Elymus canadensis*); (2) mid-grasses of the well-drained upland prairie, such as little bluestem (*Andropogon scoparius*), side-oats grama (*Bouteloua curtipendula*), June-grass (*Koeleria cristata*), needlegrass (*Stipa spartea*), and prairie dropseed (*Sporobolus hetero-lepis*), and mid-grasses of the wetter, eastern section of steppe, such as needle-and-thread (*Stipa comata*), sand dropseed (*Sporobolus cryp-tandrus*), western wheatgrass (*Agropyron smithii*), and red three-awn (*Aristida longiseta*); (3) short

grasses of the drier steppe, including blue grama (*Bouteloua gracilis*) and buffalo grass (*Buchloe dactyloides*) (Fig. 16.3).

Vegetation of the grasslands is by no means all grass. Sedges like threadleaf (*Carex filifolia*), and needleleaf (*C. eleocharis*), short species of boreal origin, and countless forbs such as sunflower, goldenrod, fleabane, aster, loosestrife, and spurge, besides a flourishing population of legumes, including clover, lupine, and indigo, are common components of the vegetation.

The species that actually dominate the composition of the grasslands change from north to south according to whether they are of boreal or of subtropical origin. Important species with a northern affinity are Junegrass, Canada wild-rye, needlegrass, and western wheatgrass. They are also referred to as cool season species. They renew their growth above the ground early in spring, with maximum development from late March to early June, remain dormant during the hot weather of summer, and resume vegetative growth in autumn. Contrasted with them are grasses of southern origin, little bluestem, big bluestem, Indian grass, prairie dropseed, and switchgrass. Their vegetative growth is renewed much later in spring and continues through the heat of summer. Side oats grama, blue grama, and buffalo grass trace their origins to the subtropical mountainous plateau of Mexico and the highlands of Central America, although they now are among the major dominants of steppe lands northward to Canada.

It is important to emphasize again the fluctuating nature of the boundaries indicated for prairie and steppe. A series of wetter summers tends to support the westward advance of dominant forest elements into prairie, of prairie flora into the steppe of the Great Plains, and of steppe vegetation into the arid margins, especially toward the southwest (Fig. 16.4). A series of cooler summers encourages a southward displacement and of warmer summers a northward displacement of the grasslands.

CLIMATIC CONDITIONS. The length of the meteorological record at most weather observation stations in the grasslands is only a few decades. A thin scattering of stations provide data for from seventy to ninety years to 1961: Edmonton,[2] Alta., seventy; Regina, Sask.,

---

[1] Weaver designates the tall grass prairie as True Prairie, dominated by mid-grasses, and steppe as Mixed Prairie, considering short grass to be an induced association brought about by overgrazing.

[2] Edmonton, a boreal forest station, is included here to indicate its transitional position.

Figure 16.3. Short grass steppe in eastern Wyoming. [U.S. Department of the Interior, Bureau of Land Management]

Figure 16.4. Bunch grass west of the short grass steppe in eastern New Mexico. [U.S. Department of the Interior, Bureau of Land Management]

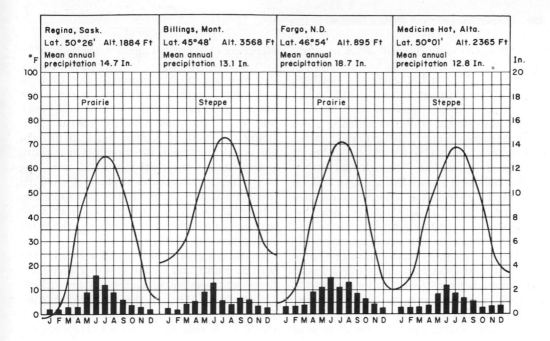

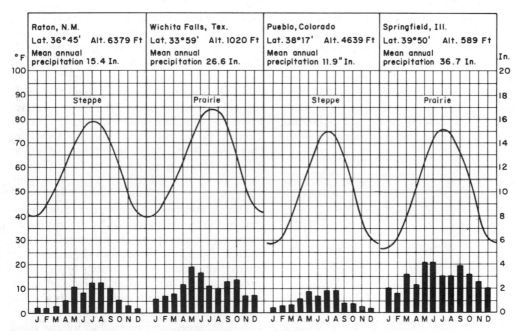

Figure 16.5. Temperature and precipitation at mid-latitude grassland stations in North America.

sixty-nine; Winnipeg, Man., eighty; Havre, Mont., eighty; Lawton, Okla., eighty-eight. At some points the record is a good deal longer, as at St. Louis, Mo., where it is 124 years; at Leavenworth, Kan., and Marengo, Ill., 106; at Independence, Iowa, ninety-eight.

Mean annual precipitation amounts vary, from about 40 inches along the southeastern borders of the grasslands from Texas to Illinois, decreasing westward to about 10 inches and northwestward to about 12 inches along the drier margins of the steppe (Fig. 16.5). Along the eastern limits of grassland where forest yields to prairie, the values decrease northward from about 40 inches in Texas to 30 inches in south-eastern Minnesota to 20 inches in southern Manitoba and 15 inches along the northern border in Saskatchewan and Alberta. At points near the undulating transition zone between prairie and steppe, amounts decrease from about 24 inches in northern Texas to 18 inches in northern South Dakota and 14 inches in southern Saskatchewan. Through Kansas, Nebraska, and eastern South Dakota this transition takes place very near the 20-inch mean annual precipitation line. The fact should be noted that differences in precipitation between prairie and steppe from east to west become increasingly smaller from south to north. Also to be noted is that normal annual amounts drop off with increasing distance northward, more substantially in prairie than in steppe. Values in the northern prairies sections are only about 37 per cent of those farther south; in the short grass region northern amounts are about 50 per cent of those in the south.

The warmer half of the year, from April through September, is the time when the grasslands normally receive the great bulk of the year's precipitation, 70 per cent or more occurring in this period throughout most of the area, and 80 per cent in much of North and South Dakota (Fig. 16.6). In wetter areas of the southeastern prairie, central Texas, and Oklahoma, Missouri, and Illinois values are between 60 and 70 per cent but are still significantly large. With only a few exceptions, late spring and early summer are most commonly the time of maximum rainfall. Maximum amounts are about equal in April and May in central Texas, and May is the peak month in central Oklahoma and southern Kansas, but over most of the grasslands June is the month of maximum precipitation. Exceptions are noted along the western margins of the short grass region in the Texas Panhandle, New Mexico, and Colorado, where July and August are the rainiest months, summer convective showers bringing the year's maximum. (See Fig. 16.5.)

In the tall grass prairie mean values for the wettest month and for the year as a whole are, from south to north, as follows (in inches): Dallas, Tex., May, 4 (34.4); Oklahoma City, Okla., May, 4.3 (30.2); Wichita, Kan., June, 5 (30.7); St. Joseph, Mo., June, 6.5 (35.3); Springfield, Ill., May and June, 4.2 (36.7); Logansport, Ind., June, 4.5 (39.2); Burlington, Iowa, June, 5.6 (36.6); Lincoln, Neb., June, 4.1 (25.7); Huron, S.D., June, 3.1 (17.5); Rochester, Minn., June, 4.3 (28.5); Bismarck, N.D., June, 3.3 (15.4); Winnipeg, Man., June, 3.2 (21.2); Regina, Sask., June, 3.3 (14.7); Calgary, Alta., June, 3.1 (16.7).

For the short grass steppe region the values are as follows: Lubbock, Tex., May, 3.4 (18.9); Raton, N.M., July and August, 2.5 (15.4); Pueblo, Colo., July and August, 1.8 (11.9); Sheriden, Wyo., May and June, 2.6 (16.8); Billings, Mont., June, 2.6 (13.1); Swift Current, Sask., June, 3 (15); Medicine Hat, Alta., June, 2.4 (12.8).

The effectiveness of the warm season rains, that is, the amount retained by the ground for plant use after evaporation and runoff are subtracted from the precipitation received, is greatly influenced by a number of significant circumstances: the kind and condition of the vegetative cover, depth and porosity of the soil, temperature of the soil, temperature of the rain as it falls, speed and persistence of the wind, duration and intensity of solar radiation, saturation deficit of the atmosphere, and air temperature, before, during, and after precipitation.

Air temperature alone is highly significant, especially during the months of maximum rainfall. For each month of the growing season mean temperatures decrease appreciably from south to north (Table 16-1). Temperatures

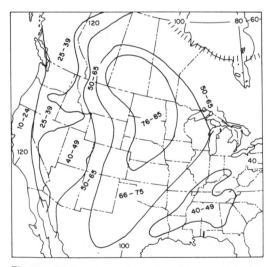

Figure 16.6. Proportion of yearly precipitation normally received during April through September in western North America (per cent).

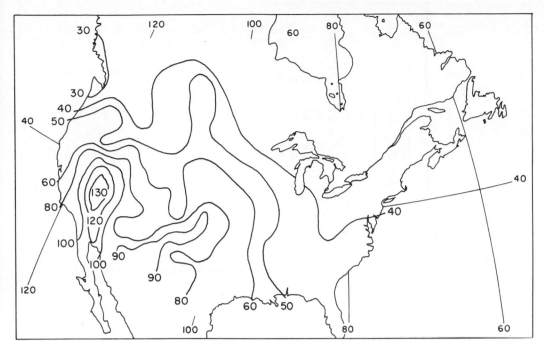

Figure 16.7.   Mean annual evaporation from 5-foot pans in North America (inches).

during May, June, and July are considerably higher in the southern, rainer areas of both prairie and steppe than they are toward their northern limits. In May, when peak rains come in the south, temperatures average around 70° or higher but are only between 50° and 55° in the northern states and the grasslands of the prairie provinces. In June, the month of maximum rainfall for most of the grasslands, temperatures are above 80° in central Texas, above 70° as far north as central Iowa, but only around 60° in Montana, Alberta, Saskatchewan, and Manitoba. In the warmest month, July, mean temperatures are above 80° in central Oklahoma and Texas, about 70° in the northern states, and around 65° in the southern prairie provinces.

Evaporation values provide another key to the differences in precipitation effectiveness from south to north. By the system of measuring water evaporation from large, open pans 5 feet in diameter, water losses to the atmosphere from May through October average more than 60 inches in northeastern New Mexico, the Texas Panhandle, western Oklahoma, and southwestern Kansas and diminish sharply northward, averaging from 40 to 50 inches in most of the Canadian grasslands and less than

30 inches in northern Minnesota and southern Manitoba (Fig. 16.7). It is thus apparent that the decrease in normal precipitation from south to north is largely offset by a concomitant decrease in evaporation, precipitation effectiveness generally increasing from south to north. Thus, the primary requirement of soil moisture conditions necessary for either tall grass or short grass vegetational development is met in spite of the marked northward decrease in normal precipitation.

The variability of annual precipitation over a period of many years is a strong characteristic of mid-latitude grassland climates. It varies from amounts that are as much as 50 per cent greater than the mean to those that are 50 per cent less. However, as summer is the important season of vegetative growth, the time when the great bulk of the year's precipitation occurs, rainfall variability at this time of year is most critical.

The mean annual range of temperature, as expected in a region spread over 25 degrees of latitude, differs considerably from south to north (Fig. 11.3). The change is a gradual one, however, increasing from about 40 degrees in central Texas to about 50 in central Nebraska and 65 or more in the grasslands of the prairie

TABLE 16-1
Climatic Data for Mid-Latitude Grassland Stations in Central North America
(Temp., °F; Rainfall, In.)

Station	Lat.	El. in Ft		Jan.	Feb.	Mar.	Apr.	May	Jun.	Jul.	Aug.	Sep.	Oct.	Nov.	Dec.	Year
Prairie Grasslands																
Lethbridge, Alta.	49°42'	2983	T	16	20	29	42	51	59	64	62	53	44	31	21	
			R	0.6	0.7	0.9	1.2	1.9	2.7	1.6	1.5	1.5	1.0	0.8	0.8	15.0
Edmonton, Alta.	53°33'	2158	T	6	11	23	40	51	58	62	59	50	41	25	13	
			R	0.9	0.6	0.8	0.9	1.9	3.1	3.3	2.4	1.3	0.8	0.8	0.8	17.4
Regina, Sask.	50°27'	1880	T	−1	2	16	38	51	60	65	52	51	39	21	8	
			R	0.5	0.4	0.7	0.7	1.8	3.3	2.4	1.8	1.3	0.9	0.6	0.4	14.7
Winnipeg, Man.	49°51'	770	T	−3	2	16	38	52	62	67	64	54	41	22	6	
			R	0.9	0.9	1.2	1.4	2.3	3.2	3.1	2.5	2.4	1.5	1.1	1.0	21.2
Bismarck, N.D.	46°46'	1650	T	9	13	27	43	55	64	72	69	59	46	28	16	
			R	0.4	0.4	0.8	1.4	1.9	3.3	2.3	1.5	1.4	1.0	0.5	0.4	15.4
Huron, S.D.	44°23'	1282	T	14	18	32	46	58	68	75	73	63	50	33	20	
			R	0.6	0.5	1.1	1.9	2.3	3.1	2.1	2.0	1.7	1.3	0.7	0.5	17.5
Rochester, Minn.	44°00'	1017	T	14	18	30	45	57	67	72	69	61	49	33	19	
			R	0.9	0.8	1.6	2.3	3.4	4.3	3.5	3.5	4.1	1.7	1.5	1.0	28.5
Lincoln, Neb.	40°49'	1166	T	25	29	39	53	63	73	79	77	68	56	40	29	
			R	0.8	0.9	1.5	2.3	3.1	4.1	3.1	3.1	2.9	1.7	1.4	0.9	25.7
Springfield, Ill.	39°50'	589	T	27	31	40	52	62	72	76	74	67	56	41	31	
			R	2.0	1.6	3.3	3.4	4.2	4.2	3.1	3.0	3.9	3.2	2.6	2.0	36.7
Wichita, Kan.	37°39'	1321	T	32	37	45	56	65	75	81	80	72	60	45	36	
			R	1.1	1.0	1.7	3.5	3.8	5.0	3.4	3.0	3.2	2.2	1.7	1.1	30.7
Oklahoma City, Okla.	35°24'	1280	T	37	42	50	60	68	78	82	82	74	63	49	40	
			R	1.5	1.2	2.1	3.2	4.3	3.9	2.2	2.5	3.4	2.7	1.8	1.5	30.2
Fort Worth, Tex.	32°50'	544	T	45	50	56	66	73	81	85	85	78	69	56	48	
			R	2.4	2.6	2.7	3.9	4.9	3.4	1.9	1.9	2.7	2.7	2.2	2.5	33.7

Steppe Grasslands

				1	2	3	4	5	6	7	8	9	10	11	12	Year
Medicine Hat, Alta.	50°01′	2144	T	12	15	28	45	55	63	69	67	56	46	28	19	
			R	0.6	0.6	0.6	0.8	1.6	2.4	1.7	1.4	1.1	0.6	0.7	0.7	12.8
Swift Current, Sask.	50°18′	2440	T	8	11	23	41	52	61	66	64	53	42	26	16	
			R	0.7	0.6	0.7	0.8	1.8	3.0	2.3	1.8	1.3	0.8	0.6	0.7	15.0
Havre, Mont.	48°34′	2488	T	16	19	30	45	56	63	71	68	57	47	31	20	
			R	0.5	0.4	0.7	0.9	1.5	3.0	1.5	1.1	1.2	0.7	0.5	0.6	12.3
Billings, Mont.	45°48′	3568	T	23	26	34	46	56	64	73	71	60	49	36	27	
			R	0.5	0.4	0.9	1.1	1.8	2.6	1.1	0.9	1.3	1.1	0.7	0.6	13.1
Sheridan, Wyo.	44°46′	3942	T	20	23	32	44	53	61	71	69	58	47	33	24	
			R	0.8	0.6	1.4	2.3	2.6	2.6	1.4	0.8	1.5	1.3	0.9	0.7	16.8
Cheyenne, Wyo.	41°09′	6131	T	26	28	32	41	50	60	68	67	57	46	35	29	
			R	0.6	0.7	1.2	2.1	2.5	2.1	2.0	1.6	1.2	1.1	0.7	0.5	16.3
Pueblo, Colo.	38°17′	4639	T	29	34	40	50	59	69	75	73	65	53	39	31	
			R	0.4	0.5	0.7	1.2	1.7	1.4	1.8	1.8	0.8	0.7	0.5	0.4	11.9
Raton, N.M.	36°45′	6379	T	26	32	38	47	56	64	69	67	61	51	38	29	
			R	0.4	0.4	0.6	1.1	2.2	1.7	2.5	2.5	2.0	1.1	0.6	0.4	15.4
Lubbock, Tex.	33°39′	3243	T	39	43	50	60	68	76	79	78	71	61	49	41	
			R	0.7	0.5	0.8	1.1	3.4	2.5	1.9	1.8	2.9	2.1	0.6	0.7	18.9

Source: U.S. Weather Bureau, *Climatography of the United States, Climates of the States*, 1959–60; Canada, Department of Transport, Meteorological Division, *Climatic Summaries*, Vol. 1, Toronto, 1954.

TABLE 16–2

Mean and Extreme Maxima and Minima at Selected Central Grasslands Stations (°F)

Station		Jan.	Feb.	Mar.	Apr.	May	Jun.	Jul.	Aug.	Sep.	Oct.	Nov.	Dec.	Extreme Range
Edmonton, Alta.	Ext. max.	57	62	72	88	94	99	98	96	90	83	74	61	156
	Mean max.	15	22	34	52	64	70	74	72	62	52	34	21	
	Mean min.	-4	1	12	28	38	45	49	47	38	30	16	5	
	Ext. min.	-57	-57	-40	-15	10	25	29	26	12	-15	-44	-46	
Winnipeg, Man.	Ext. max.	46	47	74	90	100	101	108	103	99	86	71	53	162
	Mean max.	7	12	27	48	65	74	79	76	65	51	30	15	
	Mean min.	-13	-9	5	27	40	50	55	52	43	21	14	-3	
	Ext. min.	-48	-47	-38	-18	11	21	35	30	17	-5	-34	-54	
Havre, Mont.	Ext. max.	65	71	77	95	98	107	107	106	98	91	74	71	164
	Mean max.	26	30	41	58	69	75	86	83	71	60	42	30	
	Mean min.	6	8	20	33	43	51	57	53	43	34	20	10	
	Ext. min.	-57	-48	-32	-8	14	29	37	27	18	7	-28	-36	
Huron, S.D.	Ext. max.	63	61	89	89	98	106	110	109	102	97	75	71	144
	Mean max.	25	28	43	60	72	81	90	87	77	64	44	30	
	Mean min.	2	7	20	33	44	55	61	59	48	36	21	9	
	Ext. min.	-34	-29	-18	10	20	32	40	36	20	13	-14	-24	
Pueblo, Colo.	Ext. max.	75	78	86	88	97	105	103	101	98	91	80	76	134
	Mean max.	45	49	55	65	73	84	90	88	81	69	55	47	
	Mean min.	14	19	25	35	45	54	60	59	49	37	23	16	
	Ext. min.	-29	-21	-20	2	25	38	44	43	30	20	-11	-19	
Springfield, Ill.	Ext. max.	71	71	83	88	93	103	112	98	100	93	83	72	127
	Mean max.	35	39	50	62	73	83	87	85	78	67	50	38	
	Mean min.	19	23	31	41	51	61	65	63	56	45	32	23	
	Ext. min.	-14	-15	-8	22	30	43	50	44	35	17	-2	-12	
Lubbock, Tex.	Ext. max.	81	83	88	95	104	107	108	102	103	92	85	80	117
	Mean max.	52	57	64	74	81	90	92	91	83	74	63	53	
	Mean min.	26	30	35	45	54	63	67	66	60	48	35	28	
	Ext. min.	-9	-7	2	22	33	44	51	52	40	25	-1	1	
Fort Worth, Tex.	Ext. max.	82	88	96	95	96	103	109	107	102	96	89	88	96
	Mean max.	55	60	66	76	83	91	95	96	89	79	66	58	
	Mean min.	36	40	46	55	63	72	75	75	68	58	45	38	
	Ext. min.	13	17	23	30	41	54	71	61	53	29	23	18	

provinces. Although summers are increasingly cooler farther north, it is the fact that winters are increasingly colder from south to north that accounts for most of this difference. In central Texas mean July temperatures are 85°, mean January temperatures 45°; in central Nebraska July averages 76°, January 25°; in the prairie provinces, July averages 65°, January 0° or less.

The mean extreme range of yearly temperature variation also increases northward, from 62 degrees in central Texas, where the mean maximum in July is 96°, the mean minimum in January 34°, to 78 degrees in central Nebraska, where the mean July maximum is 90°, the mean minimum in January is 12°, to 90 degrees in the prairie provinces, where the July mean maximum is about 80° and the mean minimum of January − 10° (Table 16-2).

January is everywhere the coldest month, July the warmest. The extreme limits of recorded thermal variation are very large, ranging from over 140 degrees in the south to more than 180 degrees in North Dakota. It is once again the greater severity of winter's cold that explains the wider extreme fluctuations of the thermometer farther north, for the lowest recorded temperature reading in North Dakota is − 60°, in central Nebraska − 47°, and in central Texas − 23°, whereas the highest July temperatures of record are nearly the same from North Dakota to Texas, being 121° in the former and 120° in the latter, and at most points between the values range from 118° to 121° (Figs. 11.9 and 11.15).

Temperature experience expressed in both mean and extreme values, as suggested above, changes gradually from south to north and is primarily due to change in latitude. Very little change is observed from east to west. So it is with the length of the growing season. The frost-free season is about twice as long toward the southern limits of the grasslands as it is near their northern limits, ranging from about 230 days in central Texas to about 160 days in Nebraska and between a hundred and 110 days in the grasslands of the prairie provinces. Very little change is seen from east to west, although at a number of localities in the western margins of the short grass region along the foothills of the Rockies the growing season averages about twenty days shorter than in eastern sections of the tall grass prairie (Fig. 11.6).

The well-defined rhythmic changes in the season-to-season weather of the grasslands are primarily due to north-south shifts and variations in strength of the mean eastward flow of the mid-latitude westerlies in the general circulation (compare Figs. 4.2 and 4.3). In winter, as the interior of the continent becomes steadily colder, maritime tropical air retreats southeastward, and continental polar air extends its influence farther and farther southward. Continental polar air dominates the winter weather of the grasslands and at the same time strengthens the flow of the westerlies. With the onset of spring, these cold, dry air masses become weaker and begin their annual retreat poleward. As summer advances, the strength of the normal eastward flow is greatly diminished. Summer heating of the continental interior allows a northward expansion of maritime tropical air over most of the prairies as far north as South Dakota and southern Minnesota. Over the short grass region of the High Plains west of the prairies the weakened flow of the westerlies is the dominant weather influence of the summer season.

Three air mass source regions must be considered in explaining the normal weather experience of the grasslands (Fig. 5.1): the northern interior of the continent, a source of continental polar air and continental arctic air in winter and of continental polar air in summer; the South Atlantic and Gulf of Mexico, sources of maritime tropical air throughout the year; and the mountainous highlands of western North America, a source of air of continental polar characteristics in winter and of continental tropical characteristics in summer.

Winter. The change from summer to winter occurs with characteristic rapidity following the autumnal equinox around September 21, when nights begin to lengthen and days to shorten and a period of net heat loss sets in. The change takes place more rapidly in northern than in southern sections. The maximum drop in mean monthly temperature reflects this change and usually occurs from October to November. At Regina, Sask., October averages 39° and November 21°, a drop of 18 degrees; at Lincoln, Neb., October averages 56° and November 40°, a drop of 16 degrees; at Fort Worth, Tex., the change is from 69° in October to 56°, a drop of 13 degrees (Table 16-1).

By December the ruling influences of winter's weather have normally been established. These are, first of all, a moderate to strong eastward flow of air from the Rockies that almost exactly coincides with the distribution of grassland. This air is continental polar in type, that is, subsiding air that is dominantly clear, cold, and dry. It most commonly originates over the North Pacific as moist maritime polar air that has released most of its moisture in the mountains and valleys farther west. It often stagnates and subsides over the Great Basin and the Rockies, becoming colder in the process before spilling down the eastern flanks of the mountains. In descending the mountain slopes, it becomes warmer adiabatically, and consequently drier. A second source of cold, dry air is the continental polar air from the northern interior of the continent. This is originally colder than the air from the west, but it warms slightly as it moves southward. At the same time, it becomes drier. It often originates as continental Arctic air in the north Canadian archipelago and the Arctic basin. A third significant source is the warm, moist maritime tropical air of the Gulf of Mexico and the South Atlantic.

As winter progresses, the competition among these contrasting types of air from time to time gives rise to cyclogenesis at points along the eastern front of the Rockies. Although cyclonic storms may form anywhere, most of them develop either in Texas or Alberta, and of these the chief center of origin is Alberta, where twice as many winter disturbances originate or at least intensify as in Texas. The preferred paths followed by migrating cyclones in wintertime bracket the grasslands as they converge toward a common focal point in the upper Great Lakes. Thus, in winter the grasslands normally lie between the main storm tracks, the main loci of maximum cyclonic occurrence (Fig. 5.12). This explains the typical dryness of winter in the central grassland area. Coupled with the overriding dominance of continental polar air over most of the region at this season, it also explains the prevalence of clear, dry, sparkling weather, with plenty of sunshine, crisp, bracing air, and a tendency toward strong west to northwest winds.

But these qualities of general uniformity obscure a great many points of difference among various sections of this very extensive region. The greatest contrasts are, as expected, between southern and northern sections of the grasslands, chiefly with regard to winter temperatures. In general, mean January temperatures are above freezing south of the Missouri and upper Mississippi drainage basins, that is, from southern Kansas and central Missouri southward. Elsewhere in the grasslands average January temperatures are below freezing (Fig. 11.12). Mean temperatures on the Edwards Plateau of Texas are near 50° in January, in central Oklahoma between 35° and 40°, in central Nebraska about 25°, in central South Dakota about 15°, and in the eastern part of the prairie provinces 0° or less. Thus, the span of normal January temperatures from south to north in the grasslands is more than 50 degrees.

The mean daily range of temperature in January is just about the same from south to north in spite of the great differences between the temperatures actually experienced (Table 16-2). As a general rule, however, the mean daily range of temperature is considerably less in prairie than in steppe (Fig. 11.14). In northeastern Illinois, for example, it is about 15 degrees, compared with values of more than 30 degrees in eastern Colorado and New Mexico and west Texas. The difference arises mainly from the greater prevalence of clear weather over short grass areas in the southwest than in the eastern tall grass prairie. Clear skies allow a maximum input of radiant heat from the sun each day and a maximum radiational heat loss to outer space by night. The eastern prairies receive only about four hours of sunshine on an average winter day, whereas the southwestern steppe receives about seven.

South of the Missouri drainage the prairie region tends to be slightly warmer in winter than the steppe farther west, a consequence mainly of the fact that the Great Plains rise to altitudes of 3000 to 4000 feet higher than the eastern prairie. On the other hand, from Nebraska northward the opposite is true, with the Great Plains, still several thousand feet higher in elevation, remaining as much as 10 degrees warmer than the eastern prairies at the same latitude. This condition arises in part from the fact that northern sections of short grass are several hundred miles nearer the Pacific Ocean, but mainly on account of the high frequency in winter of warm, downslope winds from the Rockies in these northern sections.

Another major difference in mean winter weather from south to north is in the kind of

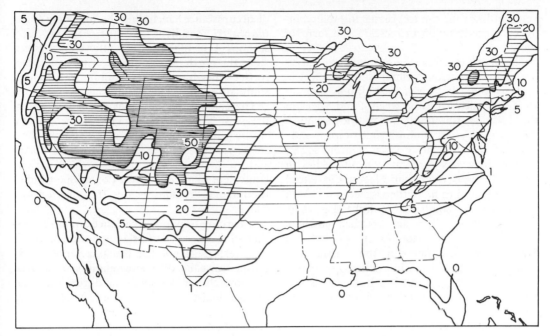

Figure 16.8. Proportion of annual precipitation falling as snow in the United States (per cent). [By permission of the publishers from Stephen S. Visher, *Climatic Atlas of the United States*, Cambridge, Mass.: Harvard University Press, Copyright, 1954, by the President and Fellows of Harvard College.]

precipitation. In the south, although some snow can be expected every winter, precipitation chiefly falls as rain. In northern areas it is virtually all in the form of snow (Fig. 16.8).

The moisture for winter's precipitation is mainly supplied by air from the Pacific, except along the southeastern margins of the prairie region where maritime tropical air from the Gulf contributes an almost equal amount. The average snowfall on the grasslands is very much less than that in the mountains to the west and in the forested regions northeast of the region. Amounts in excess of 50 inches are normal only along the western fringes of the short grass country in the foothills of the Rockies from Wyoming to Alberta. At Cheyenne in southeastern Wyoming, altitude 6131 feet, the average is 58 inches; at Sheridan in northern Wyoming, altitude 3942 feet, it is 70 inches; at Billings in southern Montana, altitude 3568 feet, it is 53 inches; and at Lethbridge, Alta., altitude 2961 feet, it is 51 inches. From southern Nebraska and Iowa normal winter snowfall increases from about 25 inches to about 50 inches in the curving belt of tall grass country in the prairie provinces, and decreases to less than 5

inches in central Texas. The number of days during an average winter when snow may be expected to fall is fewer than five in central Texas, about twenty-five in central Nebraska and Iowa, but more than sixty in northeastern North Dakota, northern Minnesota, and Manitoba. The length of time that snow may be expected to lie on the ground during a normal winter is less than five days in central Texas, about sixty days in central Nebraska and Iowa, but over 120 days, more than four months, in North Dakota and Minnesota and the grasslands of southeastern Saskatchewan and Manitoba. March is usually the month of maximum snowfall throughout most of the grasslands, although in northern sections little difference can be seen from November through March, and in the southern areas of light winter snow January is the month of maximum snowfall. Maximum snowfall in March is related to a general weakening of continental polar, anticyclonic air over the Great Basin and the Rockies, resulting in a weakened eastward flow over the grasslands. These conditions, accompanied by an increase in the heating of the surface layers below upper levels of air that is still very cold, giving rise to greater instability, induces a precipitation increase in the form of snow.

The depth to which the ground is frozen by the end of an average winter is about 2 feet in central Nebraska, Iowa, and Illinois and increases northward to between 4 and 5 feet in the northern states and the prairie provinces (Fig. 11.13). Values diminish southward to only 2 or 3 inches in central Texas. During severe winters frost has penetrated to 10 inches in central Texas, to more than 5 feet in the central grasslands, and to more than 8 feet in northern Minnesota and southern Manitoba (Fig. 16.9). These extreme values are matched nowhere else in the United States except in northern Maine. Frost penetration in the grasslands is aided by the fact that winter's precipitation is comparatively light, and much ground is laid bare by the normally high winds of this season, especially in northern sections. Extremely deep frost usually occurs when temperatures are persistently lower than usual and are accompanied by winds of higher than normal velocity.

But very deep frost is only one of the possible extremes of winter weather. The cold wave, blizzard, and chinook are also characteristic. A cold wave, a phenomenon described in Chapter 11, occurs when a large, intensified mass of continental polar air, often originating as continental Arctic air far to the north, expands rapidly southward over the continental interior, frequently reaching as far south as the Gulf of Mexico. Temperatures drop at least 20 degrees in twenty-four hours, to below zero as far south as Nebraska and Iowa, to 10° in Colorado, Kansas, and the eastern prairies, and to 20° farther south (Fig. 11.16). On such occasions very low minima have been reached. The thermometer has dropped to −23° in Texas, −27° in Oklahoma, −40° in Kansas and Missouri, −47° in Nebraska and Iowa, −60° in North Dakota, −54° at Winnipeg, −56° at Regina, and −57° in Edmonton (Fig. 11.15). High northerly winds usually attend the advance of a cold wave, and when they move into a center of low pressure producing snow, a blizzard results. Blizzards occur several times each winter in the central grasslands, often resulting in severe hardship from very low temperatures, high winds, and deep drifts of fine, closely packed snow. The intensity and duration of such storms depends upon a variety

of circumstances, including the steepness of the barometric gradient and the size and persistence of the high pressure anticyclonic system from the north. Most of these disturbances last from twenty-four to forty-eight hours, although some are of longer duration.

The chinook of the Great Plains is a warm, dry west wind off the Rockies. Named after a western Indian tribe, it is an extremely common weather feature from Alberta to northeastern New Mexico, the North American equivalent of a well-known downslope wind of mountainous regions bearing the generic name *föhn*.

According to popular parlance among plainsmen of the western grasslands, a chinook is any dry westerly wind that brings a rapid rise in temperature. By this loose definition a hundred or more chinooks may occur during the year. Meteorologists consider a true chinook to have special characteristics, to arise from special atmospheric circumstances, and by their more rigorous definition, to occur much less frequently than is popularly believed. True chinooks occur on the average of only about forty days per year.

The meteorologist's chinook[2] typically occurs in the wake of a cold spell that has dominated the grasslands for several days. As the mass of clear, cold, high pressure continental polar air of a well-developed anticyclone retreats eastward from the Rocky Mountains, a barometric depression may form over the western plains. A mass of relatively moist air from the Pacific, having previously stabilized over the high mountain country from the Rockies westward, now begins to flow down the eastern foothills onto the plains. It will often, though not always, have released much of its moisture through cloud formation and precipitation in the form of snow or freezing rain on the windward, western sides of the ranges. In doing so, it will have become warmer through the latent heat of condensation. It will also have increased in temperature adiabatically through compression on its descent down the leeward sides of the Rockies. Adiabatic temperature increase may

[2] The reader may wish to look further into this interesting subject in R. L. Ives, "Frequency and Physical Effects of Chinook Winds in the Colorado High Plains Region," *Annals of the Association of American Geographers*, **40** (4): 293–327, 1950, and Chester L. Glenn, "The Chinook," *Weatherwise*, **14** (5): 175–182, 1961.

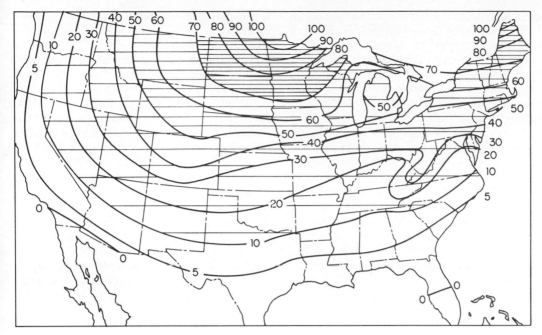

Figure 16.9.   Extreme frost depth in the United States (inches). [By permission of the publishers from Stephen S. Visher, *Climatic Atlas of the United States*, Cambridge, Mass.: Harvard University Press, Copyright, 1954, by the President and Fellows of Harvard College.]

be in amounts approaching the dry adiabatic rate of 5.5 degrees per 1000 feet of decreasing altitude. Warming as it descends, its moisture capacity is greatly increased, and as it flows out over the plains, it typically exerts a rapid and pronounced drying effect along its path.

Chinook weather is characteristically unstable, with the result that the warm winds do not generally blow uniformly from some westerly quadrant but are commonly gusty and variable in direction, producing a good deal of turbulent mixing. Hence, the effectiveness of the chinook very often varies considerably from place to place over very short distances.

The chinook provides one of the more striking variations in winter's weather in western sections of the short grass region, principally through the abrupt rise in temperature that takes place very soon after it begins. The thermometer may rise as much as 40 degrees in three hours and remain unseasonably high for a day or so after the onset of chinook weather. Meanwhile, relative humidity drops, and the air is typically clear and dry. Snow on the ground may be removed by sublimation at rates approaching 1 inch per hour. In eastern

Colorado this unusual drying effect diminishes eastward and seldom reaches more than 30 miles from the foothills, but in Canada it is known to extend with decreasing intensity for some 300 miles into western Saskatchewan. When the ground is bare to begin with, the warm air picks up little moisture, hence remains dry and warm for a much greater distance, and in Colorado may reach as far as the Kansas border.[3] Dust storms occasionally develop in chinook weather when the ground is bare. Although the chinook may occur at any hour of the day or night throughout the year, it most frequently develops in winter, especially in January and March, and is, of course, a much more impressive phenomenon at this season.

Winter begins to relinquish its hold on the grasslands as lengthening days and increasing intensities of solar radiation bring higher temperatures in February, March, and April. Subfreezing temperatures become rare toward the end of February in the southernmost sections, toward the end of March in Kansas, Missouri, and Illinois, but they continue as a common

[3] Ives, *op. cit.*, p. 304.

occurrence until the end of April and early May in the northern states and the prairie provinces. Precipitation begins to increase noticeably in April with the start of the spring rains. Except in the northern and northwestern fringes of the grasslands, snow contributes only a small fraction of April's mean monthly precipitation throughout the region.

Summer. The interior of the continent gradually becomes warmer as spring advances. By May and June cold continental polar air masses have retreated far to the north, and the westerlies that have dominated the weather throughout most of the winter are greatly weakened. Outbursts of chill boreal air become rare. Instead, maritime tropical air spreads northward and westward from its contracted winter position and begins to play a major role in the summer weather of the grasslands as far north as North Dakota and Minnesota. It is the chief source of precipitable moisture in the grasslands during summertime, except in the far north and northwest, where maritime polar air from the North Pacific is the leading source. a delayed outburst of cold subfreezing air from the north, driving deeply southward after the year's vegetative growth has resumed, has on occasion brought late frost to the central and southern grasslands, with great damage to crops. In central Texas killing frost has occurred as late as May 1; in central Kansas, northern Missouri, and Illinois as late as May 15; in eastern Colorado, central South Dakota, and southern Minnesota as late as June 1; and in Montana, Alberta, and Saskatchewan after June 15.

July is the warmest month of summer everywhere in the grasslands, a typical feature of their continental climate. Mean July temperatures, of course, differ from south to north, but the difference is considerably less than in winter (Fig. 11.8). Mean values for the prairie area of north central Texas are slightly above 85°, between 80° and 85° northward through central Kansas, between 75° and 80° as far northward as South Dakota and eastward into Illinois, and generally between 65° and 70° on either side of the Canadian border, but less than 65° along the northern edges of the grasslands in Canada. The difference from south to north of only about 20 degrees is less than half the difference observed in January (Table 16-1).

Throughout the grasslands the mean daily range of temperature tends to be slightly higher in the short grass region than in the prairies (Fig. 11.11). A higher percentage of clear skies in both daylight and darkness allows the thermometer to average a daily fluctuation of 30 degrees or more in western sections and generally 25 degrees or less in the eastern prairies. Mean maximum values range over 95° in central Texas, well over 90° northward as far as central South Dakota, and between 80° and 85° in northernmost areas. The thermometer has risen above 100° in all parts of the grasslands, having exceeded 120° in central Kansas and central North and South Dakota. Mean minimum temperatures are high in most areas south of the Canadian border, averaging over 60° from South Dakota and southern Minnesota southward. The warm, humid summer nights of the corn belt, from eastern South Dakota, Nebraska, and Kansas to Indiana, are especially important to the flourishing success of grain and livestock production in that rich farming country. Northward, however, mean minima are lower, averaging between 50° and 55° over most of the Canadian grasslands and less than 50° in Alberta near the Rockies.

In spite of the fact that the great bulk of the year's precipitation comes during the growing season, summer in the grasslands is typically very sunny. The average number of hours of sunshine per day is more than ten in the prairie, increasing to more than eleven in the western margins of the steppe. This is a corollary of the fact that daytime cloud cover averages only a little above five tenths in the eastern sections of the prairie and decreases to less than four tenths along the western edges of the short grass region. An important distinction between the grasslands and the eastern forests is the more abundant sunshine and the smaller amount of cloud cover over the former.

Over most of the grasslands relative humidities at noon average less than 50 per cent. Generally speaking, tall grass prairie lands average between 45 and 50 per cent, except in the Canadian areas bordering the boreal forest, where values are between 50 and 55 per cent, and the short grass region averages between 35 and 45 per cent, with lower values prevailing along the western fringes near the Rockies. Within the arid regions still farther west, of course, values are much lower, but in the eastern forests and along the west coast relative

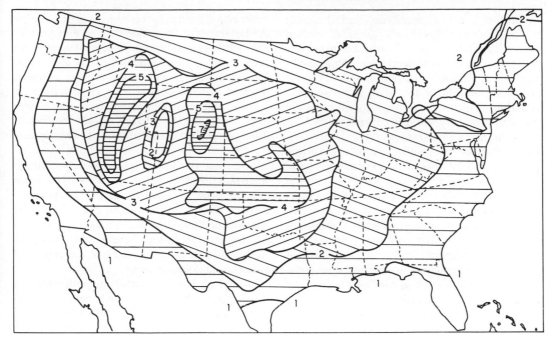

Figure 16.10. Average number of days with hail per year in the United States. [By permission of the publishers from Stephen S. Visher, *Climatic Atlas of the United States*, Cambridge, Mass.: Harvard University Press, Copyright, 1954, by the President and Fellows of Harvard College.]

humidities are considerably higher, between 65 and 75 per cent at noon.

It is typical of the grasslands in general, except in northern and northwestern sections, that at least half the rains of summertime, from June through August, fall after 6 P.M. local time. Thus, an early impression of the first time visitor to the grasslands is the frequency of rains during the early evening and after sundown. In the central grasslands from eastern Wyoming and Colorado to Iowa rains occur after 6 P.M. more frequently than elsewhere, averaging between 60 and 65 per cent of all rains during the summer months. They are usually short showers of varying intensity and are largely the result of a late afternoon build-up of cumulus clouds by intensified thermal convection brought about by an excessive accumulation of heat from the high summer sun on the open plains. Heavy evening thunderstorms are common; between twenty and twenty-five can be expected during a normal summer season. Little of this rain is lost through evaporation because these are evening storms and relatively little is lost through runoff. Less than 25 per cent of the mean annual precipita-

tion is lost through runoff in the prairie, and less than 5 per cent is lost over most of the steppe south of the Canadian border. However, the showery nature of most of the summer rain produces a spotty distribution, with recorded amounts and intensities differing widely within short distances.

Hailstorms with gusty, destructive winds occur fairly frequently, much more so over the grasslands than anywhere else in North America, generally averaging ten or more during the growing season, and occurring with peak frequency in Kansas and Iowa, where an average of more than twenty is recorded. May and June are the months of highest hailstorm probability. Figure 16.10 indicates the normal number of days per year on which hail is reported. This is also the period of maximum tornado frequency, and the reader will recall from the earlier discussion of tornados in Chapter 5 that the grasslands east of the Rocky Mountains in the United States experience far more tornados than any other part of the world.

Although showery rains of the late afternoon, originating from well-developed thermal convection in mainly maritime tropical air, are the chief source of summer's rain as far north as North Dakota, they are of only secondary importance from northeastern Wyoming northward into Montana, Alberta, Saskatchewan, and Manitoba. Here the main source of precipitable moisture is the Pacific, and rains are induced primarily when excursions of cold air from the Arctic penetrate southward, mechanically uplifting the moist, warmer maritime polar air into cold upper air to produce frontal showers. When, on occasion, maritime tropical air from the Mississippi valley reaches these districts and is upthrust by an advance of continental polar air, a more general frontal rain results, although this is comparatively rare. The main agent responsible for inducing rain in these northern and northwestern sections is the leading edge of a mass of continental polar air displaced southward. Failure on the part of this cold northern air to appear frequently during the summer results in drought. Drought is especially likely in the short grass areas of southeastern Alberta and southwestern Saskatchewan. The increase in summer rainfall from this area and from eastern Montana westward and northward is the chief reason for the change observable there from short grass steppe to tall grass prairie.

To the summertime hazards of hail, tornados, and high winds in the grasslands must be added the threat of drought. Late summer and early fall are normally dry and hot, especially in the short grass region of the Great Plains, but the menace of less than average rainfall is a constant source of concern among plainsmen and prairie dwellers alike. A drought begins when in May and June an ominously smaller than usual amount of rain falls, just when growing plants are most in need of water. As summer wears on with a continued rainfall shortage, less than half the normal moisture may be detected in the soil. It is just at this time that normal cloud cover diminishes and sunshine prevails at near the yearly maximum. In consequence, temperatures soar higher than usual, and hot, dry winds often blow for days in succession, resulting in severe dust storms, especially in the western short grass region. Weaver[4] describes conditions in the mixed prairie during the worst drought of record in that area, in 1934.

[4] Weaver, *op. cit.*, p.226.

No rain fell; clouds were rare—in fact, during the latter half of the period they seldom formed. The light was intense; dust-filled, yellow, western sky in evening portended another day of drought. The hot southerly winds blew as from a desert; drought that had bleached the green hilltops to patches of brown alternating with white, now crept down the slopes. Late in July the area of dried grasses had extended to the lower slopes.

When these conditions spread widely through the mid-latitude grasslands, the visual evidence of acute drought is present on every side in the brown, waving stems of the grasses and the haze of the dust-filled air. It is also apparent in the dry, rustling sound of the wind-blown grass stems and the monotonous, staccato clatter of crickets and grasshoppers.

Drought is less frequent in the prairie than in the steppe farther west, but whenever it occurs in either region, less hardy plants tend to yield their place to drought-tolerant species, and the composition of both prairie and steppe changes toward that of more arid vegetation. Droughts have occurred on an average of nearly one every five years over a substantial part of the grasslands since 1889.

Mid-Latitude Grasslands of Eurasia

It is at once apparent from a glance at Figure 7.1 that the mid-latitude grasslands of Eurasia are the largest in the world. They can be seen in countless valleys and hillsides of the Atlas Mountains of north Africa, in the drier basins of eastern Spain, the middle Danube, central Turkey, and eastward across Asia to the Manchurian plain. Isolated, scattered, and interrupted by other environments though they are, they represent less humid conditions within those environments, as in Spain, Hungary, and Turkey, and elsewhere a transition into arid desert, as they do from the Atlas Mountains into the Sahara, from the highlands of Turkey and Iran into Arabia, from the forests of western Eurasia into the desert of central Asia, and from the forests of east Asia into the deserts of northwest China. Some allusion has been made in previous chapters on the mid-latitude forests to their marginal relationships with forest and woodland, and further reference will be made in the chapters on desert and mountain climates that follow. Our discussion in this chapter will be confined to the great expanse of tall grass prairie and short grass steppe that extends from the middle Danube to the upper Ob valley and the Altai Mountains of central Asia (Fig. 16.11).

The change from mid-latitude mixed forest to grassland is first encountered in the enclosed, low-lying basins of the middle Danube, the Little Alföld about 100 miles broad, east of Vienna, and the much larger Great Alföld spanning about 250 miles from north to south, east and south of Budapest. These rolling to level plains, separated by the once wooded slopes of the low hill range called the Bakony Forest that cuts diagonally across the Danube and there makes an abrupt turn southward north of Budapest, are generally below 500 feet in elevation and are surrounded by mountainous country of much higher elevation. The encircling mountains rise to 10,000 feet and more in the Alps on the west, to 5000 feet in the Transylvanian mountains on the east, and to over 5000 feet in the mountains of Yugoslavia toward the south. Isolated from the main body of Eurasian grassland by the Carpathians and the Transylvanian Alps, the Hungarian plains possess a tall grass prairie climate that is encircled by more humid mixed forest and mountain environments.

The main body of Eurasian grassland begins in the Wallachian plain of southern Rumania and the Danubian plateau of northern Bulgaria, east of that deep, narrow gorge in the Danube known as the Iron Gate. Continuing eastward to the Black Sea coast and northeastward between the sea and the eastern Carpathians, the region widens, recurving northwestward into the upper Dnestr valley in former Polish Galicia, which marks the western extremity of the great agricultural region of the Ukraine. From here the grasslands widen eastward to a maximum north-south extent of about 800 miles, between the Caucasus at about 43° and the middle Volga as far north as Kazan at about 55°, occupying nearly all the watershed areas between the Siret, Pruth, Dnestr, and Bug and Dnepr rivers.

Between the eastern bend of the Don and the lower Volga the more scattered vegetation of a semidesert environment begins, reaching eastward to the Caspian and spreading over the land (largely below sea level) between the lower Volga and the Ural rivers to the northeastern shores of the Caspian. From here southward grassland gives way to desert in Tur-

kestan. The change from continuous grass cover to more scattered semidesert vegetation takes place along an irregular boundary beginning on the west coast of the Caspian near the mouth of the Terek River, from here bending northwestward to the Ergheni hills, northward to the vicinity of Stalingrad, up the Volga to near Saratov, thence turning eastward to the middle Ural valley near Ural'sk.

After narrowing south of the Urals to a belt about 200 miles wide, the grassland continues eastward in an expanded breadth averaging nearly 500 miles between the taiga and the desert, rising over the Kazakh uplands and into the foothills of the Altai Mountains between the upper valleys of the north flowing Irtysh and Ob rivers. Here the unbroken distribution of mid-latitude grassland reaches its eastern limits. Still farther eastward both prairie and steppe appear as scattered, isolated tracts in the upper tributary valleys of the Yenesei, notably between Krasnoyarsk and Irkutsk, and east of Lake Baikal in the Selenga and upper Amur valleys.

Southwestward from the Altai Mountains steppe grassland is abundantly present as a transition between the great mountain ranges of central Asia and the desert of Turkestan. This area, which has a meteorological orientation toward southwest Asia, will be discussed in the later chapters on desert and mountain climates. The grasslands of Manchuria have been dealt with as part of the mid-latitude mixed forests of east Asia (Chapter 12), where they are related to the east Asiatic atmospheric circulation and are a drier aspect of the predominantly forest environment.

PLANT LIFE. The main body of Eurasian grassland, extending for some 2700 miles from the middle Danube to the upper Ob in the Altai Mountains, is the largest continuous expanse of mid-latitude grassland in the world. The climate in which forest develops to the general exclusion of other formations begins to yield to the less humid grassland climate along a line approximately as follows: from the foothills of the Transylvanian Alps and the Carpathians it continues northwestward into the upper Dnestr near Lwow, eastward across the Dnepr just south of Kiev, northeastward between Kursk and Tula toward the junction of the Volga with the Kama River from the Urals just south of Kazan, thence eastward to the

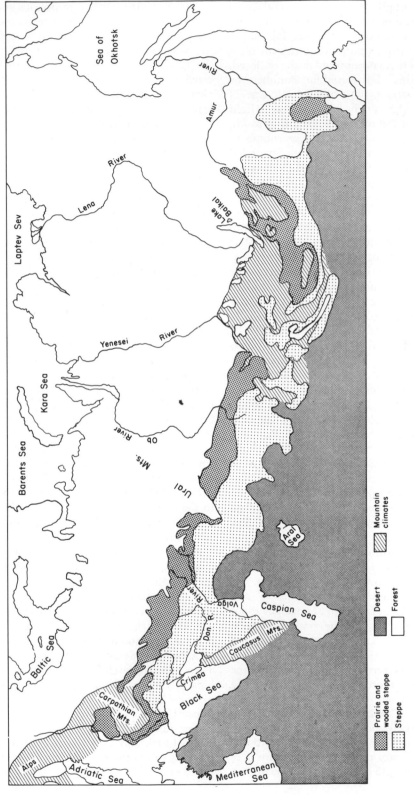

Figure 16.11. Mid-latitude grasslands in central Eurasia.

Sea of Okhotsk

Amur River

Lena River

Laptev Sev

Lake Baikal

Barents Sea

Kara Sea

Yenesei River

Ob River

Ural Mts.

Aral Sea

Baltic Sea

Volga River

Caspian Sea

Don R.

Caucasus Mts.

Crimea

Carpathian Mts.

Black Sea

Alps

Adriatic Sea

Mediterranean Sea

Prairie and wooded steppe

Steppe

Desert

Forest

Mountain climates

Urals foothills around Ufa, southward to the upper Ural River near Orsk, northward beyond Cheliabinsk, and thence eastward to points a hundred miles or so beyond both Novosibirsk and Barnaul on the Ob River. Most of the boundary is an undulating line, a result of the deep interpenetration of forest and grassland. Indeed, the tall or mid-grass association of the grassland formation consisted originally of alternate grassy clearings and deciduous groves, to the extent that the Eurasian counterpart of North American prairie has long been known as wooded steppe, in contrast to the nearly treeless, drier association of short or mixed grass steppe. Progressing southward, one tends to find forest groves persisting along the inter-fluvial ridgetops as well as in the valleys, yielding to meadows on the well-drained slopes. This is an especially conspicuous feature east of the Urals. West of the Urals the forest elements of the wooded steppe are mainly oaks, especially English oak (*Quercus robur*), ash, linden, elm, and maple. Norway maple (*Acer platanoides*) and Tatarian maple are common, and Tatarian maple and European filbert (*Corylus avellana*) form thickets of undergrowth along the forest borders.[5] But the composition of the forest groves varies from place to place and includes a selection of most of the common deciduous trees of eastern Europe. In sandy situations, occasionally in bog and on limestone as well, pine may be seen to flourish. East of the Urals aspen groves are the principal features of the forest steppe and are composed largely of aspen (*Populus spp.*), birches, including pubescent birch (*Betula pubescens*) and European white birch (*B. verrucosa*), and an undergrowth of willows.

The close cover of sod-forming taller grasses, often spoken of as meadow, is composed chiefly of broadleaved species, of which hairy oat (*Avena pubescens*), meadow brome (*Bromus erectus*), and velvet bent grass (*Agrostis canina*) are examples. A protective carpet of moss (*Thuidium abietinum*) is very characteristic of the wooded steppe, and a great many tall, flowering herbs often submerge the slender grass plants.

The drier environment of the short grass steppe extends in a narrow tongue up both

sides of the Danube for about 250 miles from the Black Sea coast. From here the change from forest steppe to nearly treeless short grass occurs along an irregular line beginning about where the Siret and Pruth rivers join the Danube near its sharp bend eastward before it enters the Black Sea. Thence the transition continues northeastward, passing south of Kishinev, north of Kharkov, and north of Saratov and Kuibyshev on the Volga. It continues eastward between the Urals and Chkalov, northward a little beyond Magnitogorsk, and from there eastward south of Omsk to the Baraba steppe and Kulunda steppe regions southwest of Novosibirsk and Barnaul. Outliers of forest steppe appear in narrow bands at the edge of the steppe on the north slopes of the Yaila Mountains in the Crimea and along the north slopes of the Caucasus.

Components of the steppe vegetation are dominantly narrowleaved species, among which feather grass (*Stipa stenophylla*), capillary feather grass (*S. capillata*), fescue (*Festuca sulcata*), and koeleria (*Koeleria gracilis*) are prominent members. A large number of flowering herbs are seen, including anemone, pasque flower, and sage, plus perennial bulb plants such as crocus, grape hyacinth, iris, and tulip. Unlike the meadows of forest steppe, a complete sod cover is rare, bare spaces being typically present among the plant stems at ground level.

CLIMATIC CONDITIONS. The fundamental atmospheric processes and the resultant year-to-year weather patterns primarily responsible for grassland distribution in the Eurasian mid-latitudes resemble very closely those of North America. It is a climate, above all, of increasing moisture deprivation from its forest to its desert margins, exposed in winter to subfreezing temperatures, a thin blanket of snow, and strong, icy winds from north and east. In summer it receives increased precipitation, a great deal of sunshine, frequent high temperatures, and the constant threat of drought. As in North America, major storm tracks, the mean paths of migrating cyclones, pass to the north or south of it (Fig. 5.13). The increased precipitation of summer is largely a product of thermal convection, and the much lighter precipitation of winter a result of infrequent and usually weakened cyclonic and frontal activity (Fig. 5.12).

But the geographical circumstances under

[5] Leo S. Berg, *Natural Regions of the U.S.S.R.*, The Macmillan Company, New York, 1950, p. 80.

TABLE 16–3

Climatic Data for Mid-Latitude Grassland Stations in Central Eurasia
(Temp., °F; Rainfall, In.)

Station	Lat.	El. in Ft		Jan.	Feb.	Mar.	Apr.	May	Jun.	Jul.	Aug.	Sep.	Oct.	Nov.	Dec.	Year
Prairie/Wooded Steppe																
Budapest, Hungary	47°31'	426	T	31	34	43	52	62	68	71	69	61	52	41	35	
			R	1.5	1.2	1.8	2.3	2.9	2.9	2.1	2.0	2.0	2.6	2.1	1.9	25.2
Bucarest, Romania	44°25'	269	T	26	31	42	52	62	69	73	73	64	54	42	31	
			R	1.5	1.1	1.7	1.6	2.5	3.8	2.3	1.8	1.5	1.6	1.9	1.5	22.8
Lwow, Poland	49°50'	983	T	25	30	34	46	56	63	66	64	57	48	36	28	
			R	1.2	1.2	1.4	1.8	2.5	4.2	4.1	2.8	2.1	2.0	1.7	1.5	27.1
Kharkov, U.S.S.R.	50°00'	472	T	19	22	30	41	58	64	69	67	57	45	32	23	
			R	1.1	1.1	1.1	1.5	1.9	2.7	2.4	2.0	1.2	2.0	1.4	1.3	19.7
Saratov, U.S.S.R.	51°32'	197	T	11	13	21	43	60	69	73	69	56	42	28	17	
			R	1.0	1.0	0.8	1.0	1.3	1.8	1.2	1.3	1.1	1.4	1.4	1.2	14.5
Ufa, U.S.S.R.	54°43'	571	T	2	8	19	37	54	63	67	62	51	36	19	8	
			R	1.6	1.3	1.2	0.9	1.6	2.4	2.6	2.2	1.8	2.3	2.2	2.3	22.5
Chelyabinsk, U.S.S.R.	55°10'	751	T	3	7	17	36	53	62	66	61	51	46	20	9	
			R	0.6	0.4	0.5	0.8	1.4	2.0	3.0	2.2	1.3	1.3	0.9	0.7	15.1
Omsk, U.S.S.R.	54°58'	289	T	-3	0	11	32	51	62	66	61	51	34	15	3	
			R	0.6	0.3	0.3	0.5	1.1	2.0	2.0	1.7	1.1	0.9	0.7	0.9	12.1
Novosibirsk, U.S.S.R.	54°58'	436	T	-3	0	11	31	49	61	66	61	50	33	15	3	
			R	0.8	0.6	0.6	0.5	1.3	2.1	2.3	2.1	1.3	1.2	1.1	0.9	14.8
Barnaul, U.S.S.R.	53°20'	535	T	-1	2	15	34	52	64	68	63	52	36	17	5	
			R	0.8	0.5	0.6	0.6	1.3	1.7	2.1	1.8	1.1	1.3	1.1	1.0	13.8
Steppe																
Odessa, U.S.S.R.	46°29'	214	T	26	27	36	47	60	68	72	71	62	51	40	31	
			R	0.9	0.8	1.1	1.0	1.3	2.1	1.7	1.2	1.1	1.1	1.3	1.3	15.1
Dnepropetrovsk, U.S.S.R.	48°27'	259	T	20	24	33	46	60	66	71	69	59	48	33	25	
			R	1.4	1.1	1.2	1.4	1.8	3.0	1.9	1.6	1.0	1.8	1.6	1.6	19.4
Rostov, U.S.S.R.	47°13'	157	T	21	25	34	48	62	69	75	73	62	50	36	28	
			R	1.4	1.4	1.3	1.3	1.7	2.4	2.2	1.2	1.2	1.3	1.5	1.5	18.6
Saratov, U.S.S.R.	51°32'	197	T	11	13	21	43	60	69	71	69	56	42	28	17	
			R	1.0	1.0	0.8	1.0	1.3	1.8	1.2	1.3	1.1	1.4	1.4	1.2	14.5
Chkalov, U.S.S.R.	51°50'	374	T	5	7	18	39	59	67	72	67	55	39	24	12	
			R	1.3	0.9	0.7	0.9	1.5	1.8	1.2	1.3	1.0	1.1	1.7	1.5	15.2
Akmolinsk, U.S.S.R.	51°10'	1148	T	0	3	12	33	56	66	70	65	53	36	19	8	
			R	0.6	0.5	0.5	0.5	1.0	1.8	1.4	1.5	1.1	1.1	0.7	0.6	18.3
Semipalatinsk, U.S.S.R.	50°24'	663	T	3	4	14	37	58	68	71	67	56	38	21	9	
			R	0.8	0.5	0.5	0.6	1.0	1.7	1.2	1.0	0.6	1.1	1.1	0.9	11.0

Source: M. Y. Nuttonson, *Agricultural Climatology of Siberia*, International Agro-Climatological Series, Study No. 13, Washington, D.C., 1950, and

which the climate has evolved, and its consequent distribution, are strikingly different from those in North America: the great east-west expanse of the continent in these latitudes, the deep interpenetration of land and sea in western Eurasia, the absence of large mountain barriers (with the exception of the Alps) to zonal (west to east) atmospheric movements near the surface, and the North Atlantic, the main source of precipitable moisture. To these should be added the fact that the grassland climates have developed on land that lies very largely below 500 feet above sea level (below sea level north of the Caspian Sea), except in the bordering foothills of the Carpathian, the Ural, and the Altai mountains, as well as the Kazakh hills north of Lake Balkash. Also worth consideration is the fact that the region's western extremities approach within 300 miles of the Mediterranean's shores and border the north coast of the Black Sea, whereas its eastern portions, deep within the heart of the continent, are remote from maritime influences and are fully exposed to the sharply contrasting atmospheric qualities of winter and summer in the continental interior. Finally, the main body of mid-latitude grassland in Eurasia appears within a relatively narrow latitudinal range of from about 43° to 55° and consequently lacks any important tropical components in the natural vegetation.

The main air masses that strongly influence the day-to-day weather of the grasslands include, in summertime, continental polar air from the north and east, continental tropical air indigenous over the Ukraine, and maritime polar air from the North Atlantic. In winter continental tropical air disappears and is replaced by intensified continental polar air spreading westward; maritime polar air continues important, although considerably modified by the colder surfaces of the land. Maritime polar air brings the bulk of precipitable moisture from the North Atlantic for all of western Eurasia throughout the year, projecting its influence eastward beyond Lake Baikal in summertime.

The general east-west alignment of the main grassland area between humid forest generally northward and arid desert southward indicates a decrease in precipitation effectiveness from north to south. Whatever precipitation occurs is capable of supporting less and less vegetation as

one proceeds southward. This, as we have noted earlier, is not by any means due to less precipitation alone, but results from a combination of many qualities both atmospheric and terrestrial, including air temperature and humidity, wind, soil moisture and porosity, and topography. Still, there is less precipitation from north to south and this must be acknowledged as a major factor in the observable change from forest to desert (Table 16-3).

From west to east precipitation also decreases, and the fact that both prairie and steppe vegetation persist for more than 2000 miles in spite of the decrease indicates an increased efficiency in the moisture budget available in the soil for the support of plant life. This is partly the result of longer, colder winters farther east, moisture being preserved in the soil by frost (Fig. 16.12).

Mean annual precipitation in the forest steppe is slightly greater than 25 inches in the northern and western part of the Hungarian plain and around Lwow in the Polish Ukraine. Budapest with 25.2 inches, Pecs with 27.2, and Lwow with 27.3 are examples. Elsewhere in the western reaches of the forest steppe values range between 20 and 25 inches, diminishing eastward, and from the upper Donetz valley near Kharkov to the Urals are between 15 and 20 inches; from the Urals to the upper Ob valley mean precipitation is everywhere near 15 inches. In the less humid short grass steppe mean annual precipitation ranges from nearly 20 inches along the wetter fringes to about 12 inches on its drier edges in western sections and between 10 and 14 inches east of the southern Urals and the Caspian Sea.

Orographic influences are evident at widely distant points, in the Moldavian foreland east of the Carpathians creating a slight rain shadow effect, as at Iasi with 19.7 inches and Braila with 16.2, in comparison with mountain stations reporting over 40 inches, and through orographic uplift bringing higher precipitation to stations in the foothills of the southern Urals (Ufa 23.1 inches), to the Yaila Mountains of the Crimea (Simferopal 17.2 inches), and to several stations along the northern slopes of the Caucasus. In the last example a combination of marine exposure to moist air from the Black Sea and orographic uplift leads to the greatly increased precipitation of the north Caucasus. This produces a narrow, uneven band of forest

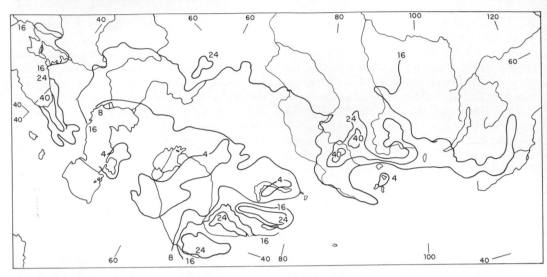

Figure 16.12. Mean annual precipitation in central Eurasia (inches).

steppe between the lower grassy plains and the forested zone above.

Most precipitation occurs throughout the grasslands from April through September, although proportions differ rather widely. In the steppe region between 50 and 60 per cent occurs during this season (Odessa 51 per cent, Rostov and Saratov 53 per cent), in the forest steppe generally between 60 and 65 per cent (Bucharest 61 per cent, Kazan 62 per cent, Barnaul 63 per cent), and in the section of forest steppe east of the Urals as far as Omsk the proportion is greater than 70 per cent (Cheliabinsk 71 per cent, Petropavlovsk 73 per cent, Omsk 70 per cent). Departures from normal anticipated precipitation vary from 15 to 20 per cent in both forest steppe and treeless steppe and between 20 and 25 per cent in western sections of the steppe region. Extreme variations from normal may be as high as 50 per cent more or less than mean yearly precipitation. These variations are not surprising in view of the fact that summer rains occur mainly as thermal convective showers and thunderstorms, with their typical random geographical distribution. The rapid heating of the ground in early summer while cold air continues to surge into the grasslands from farther north and east makes the early summer months the normal time of maximum precipitation and June most commonly the peak month (Fig. 16.13).

The mean annual range of temperature

increases very considerably from west to east in the grasslands, from 40 degrees or more in western sections to around 70 degrees in eastern areas (Table 16-3). The increasing amplitude results, as expected, almost entirely from the very much lower winter temperatures that are experienced as one moves from west to east. Budapest, for example, records a mean annual temperature range of 41 degrees, between a mean July level of 71° to a mean January level of 30°, Odessa on the Black Sea coast a range of 47 degrees (73° to 26°), Lwow a range of 41 degrees (66° to 25°). Far to the east Omsk and Novosibirsk both record a mean range of 69 degrees (66° to −3°), Barnaul a range of 67 degrees (67° to 0°), Akmolinsk 70 degrees (70° to 0°). The extreme variations are also much greater in eastern than in western sections: Budapest reports an extreme range of 102 degrees, from 92° to −10°, Odessa 110 degrees (95° to −15°), and Kwow 84 degrees (89° to 5°), compared with 158 degrees at Omsk (102° to −56°) and 157 degrees at Barnaul (96° to −61°).

The length of the normal frost-free season diminishes from west to east, averaging 180 days or more in the western Ukraine to about 150 days along the lower Volga, about 130 days along the middle Ural valley, and about 120 days in the upper Ob valley. In the western grassland areas, Lwow in the upper Dnestr valley averages 190 days, Nikolaev northeast of Odessa 189 days, and Odessa, gaining the

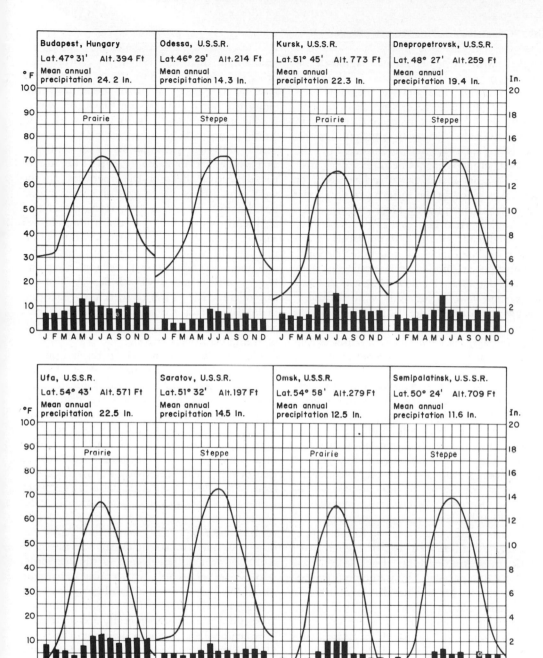

Figure 16.13. Temperature and precipitation at mid-latitude grassland stations in central Eurasia.

advantage of a shoreline situation, 208 days. Farther east Kkarkov in the upper Donetz valley averages 151 days, Novosibirsk 122 days, and Barnaul 116 days. Localities differ widely within a short distance according to whether or not the setting favors the occurrence of frost. The oak and aspen groves of the forest steppe, for example, prolong the frost-free period beyond that of the neighboring meadows and grassy slopes of treeless hilltops for two to three weeks.

The fact that the growing season is more than two months shorter in eastern than in western sections of the Eurasian grasslands, coupled with the increasing magnitude of annual temperature fluctuations and diminishing precipitation, indicates the increased continentality of the climate from west to east. The interior of the continent cools rapidly in autumn with the decreasing length of day and diminishing solar radiation intensities. After the autumnal equinox nights become longer than days, and a net loss of radiative heat to outer space takes place. In the eastern grasslands the change from summer to winter occurs much more rapidly than in areas farther west. The drop in mean monthly temperature from October to November is 21 degrees at Semipalitansk, 19 at Omsk and Novosibirsk, 18 at Barnaul, but 15 at Chkalov, 14 at Kazan, 11 at Odessa and Lwow, and only 9 at Budapest. Everywhere east of the Urals temperatures average near freezing in October and are well below freezing by November, but subfreezing means are delayed until December in western areas (Table 16-3).

Winter. As winter advances and temperatures become steadily lower over the interior of Eurasia, the clear, dry, cold air subsides, inviting replacement aloft, and atmospheric pressures increase. Intensifying and expanding toward the continental perimeter, higher atmospheric pressures prevail over most of the land mass westward to the mountains of southern Europe. Anticyclonic circulation brings chiefly easterly winds to the steppe and the deserts south of it. Over the forest steppe, however, a well-defined axis of higher barometric pressure develops, roughly centered along the 50th parallel. This is known meteorologically as a major pressure divide. South of it winds tend to be easterly, along it they are southerly, and north of it southwest and westerly. Thus, to the north of this divide predominantly westerly winds repeatedly bring maritime polar air from the North Atlantic, but south of it this influence is usually absent. The forest steppe, transitional between mixed forest on the north and treeless steppe on the south, is the result of an interplay between the largely milder, more humid westerly weather of the forest and the drier, colder, easterly weather of the steppe.

The unfrozen Mediterranean is a region of lower atmospheric pressure in winter, as are the largely unfrozen Black and Caspian seas. There is, thus, a thermal and barometric gradient in their direction from central Asia, bringing east winds into the north Caspian lowland (Fig. 4.2). West of here, however, along the north coast of the Black Sea winter winds are dominantly from northward. This would seem to be a contradiction of the prevailing anticyclonic circulation for the continent as a whole. It is explainable in part because of the deflective effect of the open sea on the westward airflow from central Asia and in part because a separate anticyclonic circulation frequently develops over the mountains of eastern Europe. Thus, a southward flow of air prevails the western Ukraine, bringing north and northwest winds down over the Dnepr and Dnestr valleys and the Black Sea. An illustration of these effects can be seen in the fact that in January winds are mainly east to southeast at Chkalov, south to southwest at Kazan, but west and northwest at Kiev.

The much diminished precipitation of winter results in part from weak cyclonic storms that pass from the Mediterranean northeastward across the Black Sea and dissipate in central Asia, and in part from similar disturbances that originate from time to time as lee depressions east of the Carpathians. Also important are linearly extended frontal storms that develop when relatively warm, humid air from the North Atlantic moves eastward across the north European plain and overrides resident continental polar air or still colder continental Arctic air. Continental Arctic air originates over the Arctic Ocean and northern Asia, and when the ground is snow-covered, retains its very cold, dry qualities virtually unmodified well into the grassland areas.

Although January is the coldest month in all sections, values are generally above freezing in much of the Hungarian plain and the lower Danube valley but are less than 20° east of the Dnepr, less than 10° east of the Volga, and between 0° and −10° east of the Urals (Table 16-3). The number of months during which the thermometer averages below-freezing temperatures increases from three at Lwow, Bucharest, and Dnepropetrovsk to five at Kazan, Chkalov, and Chelyabinsk and six at Omsk and Novosibirsk. The mean daily range of temperature in January is greater toward both western and eastern reaches of the grasslands than in the central portions, with Debrecen in the Hungarian plain and Iasi in Moldavia reporting

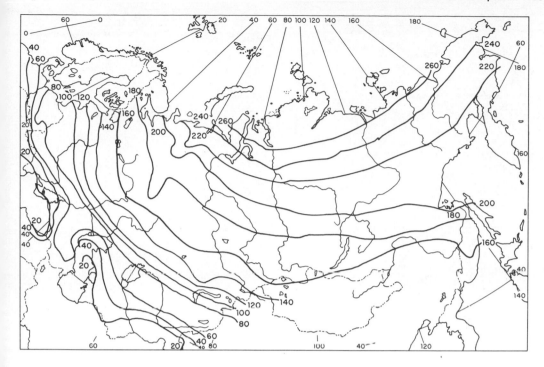

Figure 16.14. Mean duration of snow cover in central Eurasia (days).

26 degrees, Omsk and Barnaul reporting 22 degrees, compared with Dnepropetrovsk reporting 12 degrees, Kazan 16, and Chkalov 14. A higher percentage of cloud cover in the central portions is related to the lower daily range, for mean values there are on the order of eight tenths in comparison with values between six tenths and seven tenths elsewhere. Cold thrusts of continental Arctic air have brought the thermometer to subzero readings in all parts of the grasslands: Budapest has recorded −10°, Dnepropetrovsk −25°, Kazan −44°, Omsk −56°, and Barnaul −61°. Again the west to east increase in severity can be noted.

Still another expected gradation is seen from west to east in the increased amount and duration of snow cover (Fig. 16.14). At least some snow falls each winter in the Danube valley, but yearly amounts rarely exceed 8 inches. Although snow may fall on as many as thirty days during the season, such occurrences are usually widely spaced, with rain providing the principal form of winter's precipitation. Along the Black Sea coast snow may cover the ground for a period of about one month in winter, but the accumulated amounts vary from 1 inch or

less to around 8 inches. Eastward and northward the duration of snow cover increases rapidly to more than two months at Dnepropetrovsk, more than three months at Stalingrad, more than five months at Kuibyshev and Chkalov, and between five and six months in eastern sections. The mean depth of yearly snow cover also increases eastward, averaging up to 2 feet in the easternmost area. The character of the snow also changes progressively eastward, becoming finer, lighter, and drier toward the interior of the continent and thus more susceptible to drifting. And it is in eastern areas that the dreaded buran or purga, Asiatic equivalent of the North American blizzard, becomes more frequent and more violent. Accompanied by very low temperatures, very strong winds out of the northeast commonly filling in behind a traveling cyclone often sweep large tracts of land free of the fine light snow, here and there piling it high into hard-packed, impassable drifts. Loss of a protective snow cover is especially damaging in the treeless steppe because frost is thus allowed to penetrate deeply into the ground, reaching depths of 5 or 6 feet east of the Urals. As winter

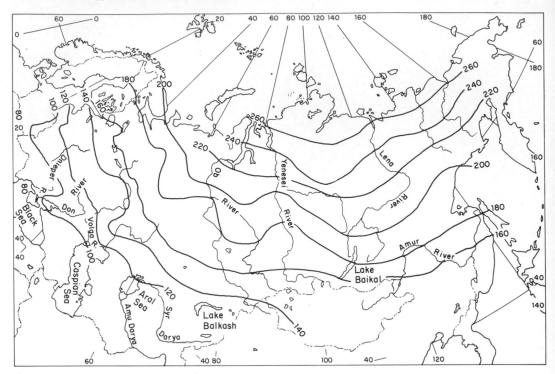

Figure 16.15. Mean number of days rivers are frozen over per year in northern Asia.

advances, diminishing amounts of precipitation augment the problem of an insufficient snow cover against frost penetration. February is normally the month of minimum precipitation for the year west of the Urals, and March the minimum month east of the Urals.

The cold of winter may be gauged by the length of time that rivers remain frozen over. In the middle Danube, which has rarely been entirely frozen over, ice floes commonly form at this season without impeding navigation. But the Dnestr becomes ice-bound for an average of seventy days, the middle Volga for 140 days, the upper Irtysh for 180 days, and the upper Ob for more than 180 days (Fig. 16.15). The Black Sea and the Caspian remain largely unfrozen, though the northern shores of both are usually ice-bound for part of the winter, the port of Odessa normally being closed for two or three weeks in February, and shipping in the north Caspian at a standstill for about three months in an average winter. The Sea of Azov is normally ice-covered for about the same length of time.

Summer. Around the middle of June the steppe changes color from silver to gray to yellow as the steppe fescue matures, and by the end of July the capillary feather grass forms a deep and continuous carpet that may, when conditions are favorable, reach a height of nearly 6 feet.

July is the hottest month throughout the grasslands. Reported mean temperatures for that month are remarkably uniform in both steppe and forest steppe. In general, values in the latter range between 65° and 69°, in the steppe region between 70° and 75°, the higher temperatures in each case appearing along the drier side of the region. And the mean daily range is generally greater on the treeless steppe. Budapest, with a mean July temperature of 71°, has a mean daily range of 22 degrees, Kiev 67° and 16, and Kazan 68° and 20; stations in the steppe at Dnepropetrovsk report 73° and a range of 24 degrees, Chikalov 71° and 24. Stations east of the Urals have recorded wider daily fluctuations, as reported at Barnaul, mean July temperature 66° and a mean daily range of 30 degrees, and Akmolinsk 70° and 30°. Extreme maxima have not exceeded 100° in many places, but temperatures above 90° are common every summer in most localities. Lwow has reported 89°, Kiev 97°, Nikolaev 102°, Kursk 95°, Saratov 104°, Poltava 101°, and Novosibirsk 99°. Prolonged periods of hot weather, especially in late summer, are very common. The greatly diminished cloud cover of July and high summer sun are chiefly responsible for the concentration of heat in this season. Mean cloud cover amounts to less than five tenths over nearly all the steppe and only slightly above five tenths in the forest steppe.

Heat and drought combine late in July to usher in the drier phase of summer. Although precipitation continues in moderate amounts not very much less than for the peak precipitation month of June, most of the rain falls in short, hard showers, followed by a rapid return of clear, hot, dry weather. Throughout the grasslands, especially in the treeless steppe,

the sun-baked hills, brownish-green in the foreground, fade away among lavender shadows in the misty distance of the horizon. Above them the deep, transparent blue of the sky can seem perpetually dreary; the air after the sun has evaporated the dew at dawn grows stagnant, dry, and is filled with the sound of locusts, crickets, and grasshoppers and the occasional cry of a crow, a hawk, or a partridge.

The combination of heat and drought is often augmented by hot winds importing air with higher temperature and lower relative humidity. These winds, called sukhovei, like the hot, dry winds of the North American plains, disturb the well-defined rhythms of daily temperature fluctuation that occur through the primary influence of the systematic diurnal insolation pattern. The sukhovei is chiefly a

Figure 16.16. Mean frequency of Sukhovei in late spring and summer in central Eurasia (days). [After Lydolph]

product of adiabatic warming through the subsidence of anticyclonic air that sometimes originates as rather cool air in the far north. When the easterly winds of such a circulation advance westward over the hot deserts east of the Caspian, additional heat of radiation is entrained, and temperatures rise rapidly, while relative humidity falls. Temperatures have exceeded 104° and relative humidity has dropped below 15 per cent on such occasions. Wind speeds are usually between 5 and 10 miles per hour but may rise to more than 70 miles per hour. When high winds occur and the ground is dry for lack of rain, dust is whirled high in the air in great clouds, creating one of the more disagreeable aspects of summer weather called the black blizzard. Thus, to the discomfort of excessive heat, parching drought, and punishing winds must be added the dread effects of choking dust that can be piled into wind drifts like the snow of winter's white blizzard, to the point of halting highway traffic and all movement on the railroads of an afflicted area.

The sukhovei occurs with greatest frequency over the desert east of the Caspian, becoming less frequent northward and westward (Fig. 16.16). From the lower Volga to the upper Ob valley between six and ten of these hot, dry, windy periods can normally be expected in July, but in the forest steppe to the northward and in both steppe and forest steppe to the westward only one or two are apt to occur.

Relief from drought and heat in the grasslands is often brought quite suddenly at the end of the day by thunderstorms of unusual intensity. Repeated flashes of brilliant lightning, the crackle and crash of thunder, strong, gusty winds, and a heavy deluge of rain are typical of these storms of the open plains. These phenomena are most commonly observed from a little before sunset to around midnight. Midsummer drought continues into early autumn as monthly rainfall amounts progressively diminish, and plant life becomes dusty, brown and gray. The first frosts are felt in late September in eastern sections and progressively later farther west, soon to be followed by the first snows of winter.

References

BORCHERT, J. R.: "The Climate of the Central North American Grassland," *Annals of the Association of American Geographers*, **40**(1): 1–39 (1950.

CALEF, W.: "The Winter of 1948–49 in the Great Plains," *Annals of the Association of American Geographers*, **40**(4): 267–93, 1950.

HARLAN, J. R.: *Theory and Dynamics of Grassland Agriculture*, D. Van Nostrand Co., Inc., New York, 1956.

JACKSON, W. A. D.: "The Virgin and Idle Lands of Western Siberia and Northern Kazakhstan, a Geographical Appraisal," *Geographical Reviews*, **46**(1): 1–19, 1956.

KINCER, J. B.: "The Climate of the Great Plains as a Factor in their Utilization," *Annals of the Association of American Geographers*, **13**(2): 67–80, 1923.

KÖPPEN, W.: "Klimakunde von Ruszland," *Handbuch der Klimatologie*, **3** (Part N), Berlin, 1939.

LYDOLPH, P. E.: "The Russian Sukhovey," *Annals of the Association of American Geographers*, **54**(3): 291–309, 1964.

NUTTONSON, M. Y.: *Ecological Crop Geography of the Ukraine and the Ukrainian Agro-Climatic Analogues in North America*, International Agro-Climatological Series, Study No. 1, Washington, D.C., 1947.

WEAVER, J. E.: *North American Prairie*, The Johnson Publishing Co., Lincoln, Nebr., 1954.

WEAVER, J. E., and ALBERTSON, F. W.: *Grasslands of the Great Plains*, The Johnson Publishing Co., Lincoln, Neb., 1956.

chapter 17

MID-LATITUDE GRASSLANDS
SOUTH OF THE EQUATOR

South of the equator mid-latitude grassland climates are found in three major areas: the pampas of southeastern South America, the highlands of eastern South Africa, and the interior of southeastern Australia (Fig. 7.1). They are confined to lower latitudes than are similar grassland regions of the northern hemisphere, are in all cases not far from the sea, and are smaller in area. Furthermore, they are deeply interpenetrated by tropical plant species. In short, they are milder variations of the mid-latitude grassland climates.

South America

Grassland is found in several widely spaced areas of the middle latitudes in South America, transitional between humid and arid situations. Reference has been made in an earlier chapter to the grassland transition equatorward from mediterranean scrub woodland in middle Chile to the aridity of the Atacama desert and to the presence of many mist-supported meadows along the Pacific coast ranges. Grassland also appears along the lower eastern slopes of the Andes in the higher latitudes of southern Argentina in the lee of the westerly circulation. Here, a very narrow elongated ribbon of short grass steppe vegetation occupies a series of interrupted basins for some 1200 miles north-ward from the Straits of Magellan (Fig. 17.1). This is a feature of the rain shadow effect.

But the chief grassland region in the mid-latitudes of South America is the great pampas of Argentina, Uruguay, and southern Brazil (Fig. 14.2). It is transitional between the mid-latitude forests of southern Brazil and the rocky, wind-buffeted desert plateau of Patagonia. Prairie grassland is first encountered in the form of grassy, forest openings in the Parana Pine region between 1800 and 4000 feet. They thus appear in the southern part of the Brazilian highlands, and begin to dominate the landscapes where those upland surfaces descend to lower altitudes. From the southern escarpment of the Brazilian highlands west of Porto Alegre a tall grass prairie is the prevailing vegetation, reaching southward over most of Uruguay and across the Rio de la Plata into eastern Argentina. It continues southward to the shores of Bahia Blanca, a total distance of some 1000 miles, and spans a latitude of about 10 degrees, from 30° to 40°S. It spreads west-ward for nearly 500 miles from the Atlantic in the Argentine pampa, throughout its length and breadth one of the great grazing regions of the world. It provides the basis of a major livestock industry that is important in Brazil and is the leading economic activity in Uruguay and Argentina.

Fringing its inland margins is a belt between

Figure 17.1. Short grass steppe along the eastern base of the Andes in southwestern Argentina. [Pan American photo]

100 and 300 miles wide of wooded steppe, a short grass region heavily interspersed with shrubs and low trees. This drier scrub land, in which woody plants of tough-barked, spiny, drought-resistent character predominate, is called monte. It borders the more humid pampa from northwestern Uruguay to the coast between the Rio Colorado and Rio Negro south of Bahia Blanca.

In southern Brazil and Uruguay the terrain over which the luxuriant, indigenous prairie existed before man's intervention is moderately hilly, rising between the stream valleys into many linear ranges of low hills called cuchillas. In Uruguay the highest of these is the Cuchilla Grande, cresting to heights of between 1500 and 2000 feet and extending parallel to the east coast about 100 miles from the Atlantic from the north border to Montevideo. Though the predominant vegetation is open grassland on the interfluvial watersheds, a good deal of forest, composed chiefly of deciduous trees, occupies the valley floors. This is especially true in southwestern Uruguay. West of the Uruguay

River, in the southern part of a section between that river and the lower Parana known as Mesopotamian Argentina, a high proportion of scrub woodland appears. It is an area drained by many short streams flowing into the larger rivers, as well as large tracts of marshland, particularly along the Parana.

West and south of the lower Parana the main body of the Argentine pampa occupies land that is remarkable for its unrelieved flatness. Except in the southern section, it rises only very gradually westward from near sea level along the coast to more than 1000 feet where its western margins yield to the desert interior. The soil material is typically fine, porous, and almost entirely lacking in loose stones and gravel. It is an unusually deep accumulation of fine alluvial sands, silts, and clays and the very fine yellowish material of wind-laid loess. The coarser, rank vegetation of marshland appears in broad, very shallow depressions, the most notable of which is the Salado slough, beginning along the coast between Buenos Aires and Mar del Plata and extending from here northwestward for more than 300 miles. In the southern part of the pampa are two conspicuous ranges of hills standing well above the surrounding plain, the Sierra del Tandil, rising to 1600 feet, and the Sierra de la Ventana, rising to 4200 feet.

The grasses composing this prolific vegetation change from species with a strong tropical affinity in northern sections to those of more temperate character in the southern part of the Argentine pampa. The milder winters of the lower latitudes support such species as the rescue grass (*Bromus catharticus*), bearded species of *Andropogon*, feathery species of *Panicum*, species of *Paspalum*, and many others. The colder winters of southern sectors are mainly responsible for a change to the higher latitude forms like the blue grasses (*Poa spp.*), the bent grasses (*Agrostis spp.*), oat grasses (*Danthonia spp.*), Festuca species, and the silky pampas-grass (*Cortaderia selloana*).

The presence of a dominantly grass vegetation in the extratropical latitudes of southern Brazil, Uruguay, and northeastern Argentina is not climatically explainable. The features typical of a continental climate are lacking, for the growing season is long, mean and extreme ranges of annual temperature variation are very moderate, and winters are especially mild. Furthermore, there is more than enough precipitation, well distributed throughout the year, to support forest growth (Fig. 14.3). The existence of grassland here must be explained in terms of the edaphic conditions of soil depth and porosity, the slope and drainage of the land, and the depth and variability of the water table. A satisfactory explanation, as pointed out in Chapter 14, must await more detailed studies of plant and soil ecology and hydrology. Grassland vegetation, having once gained the upper hand in whatever way this was originally managed, produced a dense sod and a deep mass of thickly intertwined rootlets, and thus created a soil environment hostile to the invasion of tree seedlings. To what extent man's intervention through burning and other land use practices may have virtually eliminated original tree growth is not known, although the possible importance of this cannot be ignored.

Only west of the Uruguay River do those qualities of the continental climate typical of mid-latitude grasslands everywhere begin to appear, and here they are much more mod- erately developed than in the grasslands of the northern hemisphere. Geographical circumstances prevent the development of the more extreme atmospheric variations typical of grassland climates over the broad expanses of North America and Eurasia. The tapering shape of South America, narrowing rapidly southward, ends a little beyond the latitude of 55°; and very little land surface lies within those latitudes where grassland might otherwise be expected to appear. As one proceeds eastward with increasing proximity to the sea, the South Atlantic becomes the major source of moisture for the support of grassland regions. From west to east the main body of the grasslands in mid-latitude South America form a transition from the desert interior to the water's edge, and the atmospheric qualities that give rise to them undergo a change from moderately continental to marine in character.

The ruling atmospheric influences over southern South America have been discussed in Chapter 14. It will be recalled that variations in weather over this part of the continent are mainly the product of the ceaseless competition between air of maritime tropical character originating over the South Atlantic and flowing poleward over the land from the northeast, and air of maritime polar character moving northeastward from the South Pacific over the southern Andes and from the general area of Tierra del Fuego (Figs. 5.2 and 5.3). Organized storms of either a cyclonic or a linear frontal nature are the main source of precipitation over the grasslands, occurring with greater frequency during summer time than in winter. Systematic disturbances occur along a frontal zone of contact whose mean position extends from the central Argentine pampa east-southeastward over the Atlantic and shifts only very slightly with the changing seasons. Although migrating depressions cross the decreasing elevations of the southern Andes into Patagonia, few make the transit into the latitudes of the temperate grasslands.

However, a great many lee depressions form east of the Andes in these latitudes and proceed along preferred paths that cross the grasslands on a generally east-southeastward course, intensifying as they approach the sea. Many violent, blustery storms arise along the frontal zone, and in summer convective uplift is frequently generated when cold air from the

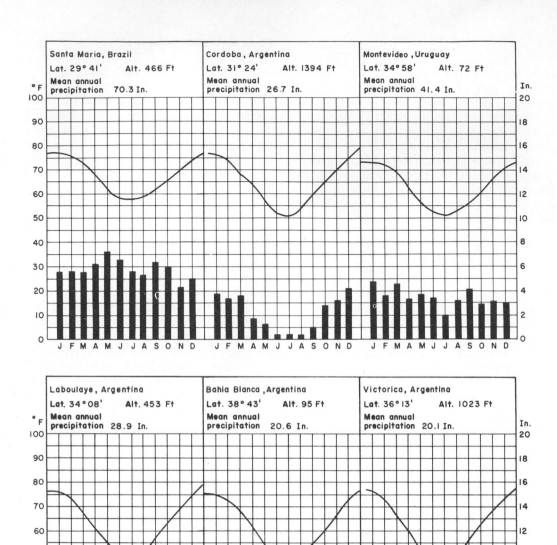

Figure 17.2. Temperature and precipitation at mid-latitude grassland stations in South America.

south moves vigorously under a resident mass of warm, humid maritime tropical air, often producing thunderstorms of unusual intensity, accompanied by brilliant displays of lightning, crashing thunder, and drenching rainfall. Most of the grassland precipitation is thus the outcome of systematic, organized weather patterns, and only a small percentage results from the more random occurrence of thermal convective showers. These are almost exclusively a feature of summer weather and contribute a higher proportion of the rainfall of that season with increasing distance westward toward the drier grassland margins. The number of organized

precipitating disturbances decreases from more·
than 40 per year in northeastern sections, in
southern Brazil and Uruguay, to around twenty
per year in the drier southwest. And the number of days with such rainstorms also decreases
from northeast to southwest, from more than
one hundred in southern Brazil and Uruguay to
fewer than fifty in the southwest.[1]

Mean annual precipitation over the tall grass
prairie ranges from well over 60 inches in
southern Brazil to around 25 inches along the
western margins of the central Argentine
pampa (Fig. 14.3). Amounts diminish southwestward: Santa Maria, about 50 miles south
of the Brazilian escarpment and about 200
miles inland from the sea, records a normal
yearly amount of 70 inches, and Alegrete some
100 miles farther west records 61 inches, but
Artigas in northwestern Uruguay reports a
mean of 49 inches, and Bages, Brazil, about 150
miles east, a mean of 54 inches. Villaguay, between the Uruguay and Parana rivers, averages
42 inches, Santa Isabel, in central Uruguay, 40,
Montevideo 41, Rosario, on the lower Parana,
38, Buenos Aires 39, Laboulaye, about 300 miles
west of Buenos Aires, 29, Trenque Lauquen,
about 100 miles south, 27, Pigue, 100 miles
farther south, 27, and Bahia Blanca 22 (Fig. 17.2).

The variable breadth of the bordering shrub
and short grass monte reveals a rapid decrease
in mean amounts from its wetter margins
adjoining the prairie to the deserts farther inland. Actual values are much less in southern
sections than in northern parts of this borderland, for we note that the station of Rio
Colorado on the river of that name about 75
miles southwest of Bahia Blanca averages 14
inches and Choele Choel about 100 miles farther
west at the edge of the Patagonian desert on
the Rio Negro averages about 10 inches. Stations
along the western edges of this more arid grassland report increasingly larger amounts as one
advances northward. The station at General
Acha, for example, about 200 miles northwest
of Bahia Blanca, reports an annual average of 18
inches, Victorica, about 100 miles farther northwest, about 20, Mercedes, some 200 miles north,
22, and Cordoba, another 200 miles northward, 27.

[1] M. J. Olascoaga, "Some Aspects of Argentine
Rainfall," *Tellus*, 2: 312–18, 1950.

Mean precipitation is quite uniformly distributed through the year in southern Brazil,
all of Uruguay, and the coastal fringes of
Argentina. Normal amounts are about equally
shared by both the cooler and the warmer
seasons of the year. In fact, in southern Brazil
the winter season receives more than half the
mean yearly amounts, as illustrated by Santa
Maria with 54 per cent from April through
September, Alegrete with 53 per cent, Bages 57
per cent, and Punta del Este, on the southeast

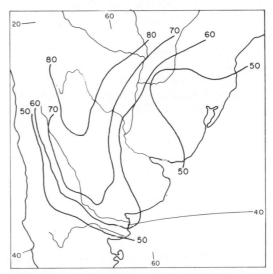

Figure 17.3. Proportion of annual precipitation
normally received during the warm season, October
through March, in southern South America (per
cent).

coast of Uruguay, 51 per cent. Elsewhere in
Uruguay slightly more than half the year's
precipitation occurs in summer, with percentages of 53 at Artigas, 55 at Santa Isabel, 56
at Concordia, on the Rio Uruguay, and 51 at
Montevideo. This is, of course, one of the
puzzling features of the mid-latitude grasslands in these northeastern areas. It is not until
one passes west of the Rio Uruguay and inland
from coastal stations in Argentina that the
warm season precipitation accounts for more
than 60 per cent of the yearly amounts received,
a condition more typical of continental grassland climates (Fig. 17.3).

The proportion of mean yearly precipitation
occurring in the warm season from October
through March increases from about 60 per
cent between the Rio Uruguay and the Parana

and about 50 miles from the coast in the central Argentine pampa to about 70 per cent where the tall grass prairie gives way to monte along its western edges. At Villaguay, for example, and at Rosario, Azul, and Tres Arroyos the percentage is 60, at Pigue it is 66, at Trenque Lauquen 69, at Laboulaye 72. The summer increase is much more definitely established in the drier monte where warm season values range between 70 and 80 per cent, as indicated by the reported 69 per cent at General Acha, 75 per cent at Victorica, 76 per cent at Mercedes, and 79 per cent at Cordoba.

The change from an equable distribution in northeastern sections to a very pronounced summertime intensity in the southwest is, of course, an indication of a gradual change from a well-developed marine climatic situation to a distinctly continental one. The main flow of moisture-laden air available for entrainment in precipitating disturbances is southwestward from the Atlantic, a flow that persists throughout the year. In wintertime, when cyclogenesis is less frequent east of the Andes in these latitudes, the coastal disturbances remain active and continue to supply precipitation in northeastern areas. Neither the influence of summer's more frequent storm development over the grasslands nor the slight augmentation by thermal convective showers in the more arid western grasslands is felt as often in north-eastern areas as in sections farther south and west.

Rainfall reliability is high from around Rosario on the Rio Parana eastward over Uruguay and northward into southern Brazil; serious drought is virtually unknown in these areas. Drought is a threat over most of the Argentine pampa and increases in likelihood and severity toward the drier western edges of the grassland. Cordoba, for example, has experienced a rainless period of 103 days, according to Kendrew,[2] and elsewhere damaging drought is equally hazardous to the crop and livestock industries, especially because of the strength and persistence of blazing heat from the sun. At times a succession of unusually dry years has produced accumulative aridity in the grasslands causing an eastward shift of the monte into the humid pampa and of desert into monte.

[2] W. G. Kendrew, *Climates of the Continents*, The Clarendon Press, Oxford, 1961, p. 509.

The mean annual range of temperature is very nearly the same throughout most of the prairie lands, averaging between 20 and 25 degrees but increasing to 30 degrees in the drier monte margins farther inland. The wider fluctuations in the monte result mainly from lower mean temperatures for the coldest month of winter, for summers are almost uniformly hot in all sections, temperatures for the warmest month usually averaging in the higher 70s. In the southern pampa, however, ranges near 70 degrees are common, as at Azul and Tres Arroyos, both reporting 70 degrees for January, and Pigue 71.

The extreme range of temperatures reported over a period of several decades also increases from the northeast to the western margins, ranging from about 100 degrees along the drier rim of the pampa. Marine stations are more favored in this regard, but the stabilizing influence of the sea is effective chiefly in winter, for even along the coast the thermometer in summertime has risen well above 100° at most reporting weather stations.

The growing season is long throughout most of the pampa lands, lasting for three hundred days or more from the lower Parana valley northward and only slightly less than this in the remainder of the region. Winters are short and mild, and although frost occurs frequently, killing frost has rarely interfered with the continuous year-round grazing of livestock, a special advantage to the pastoral economy. The chance of killing frost on cold winter nights increases westward where cloud cover and relative humidities diminish with increasing distance from the sea.

Winter. The mildness of the winter months, from June through August, is one of the striking features of the mid-latitude grasslands in southeastern South America (Fig. 17.2). July is normally the coldest month, but it is actually just a little colder than either June or August, its mean temperature more often than not differing by only 1 or 2 degrees (Table 17-1). From the latitude of Rosario northward in Argentina and in all of Uruguay and southern Brazil mean July temperatures are above 50°, ranging above 55° in the northernmost areas. South of Rosario July averages are between 45° and 49°, lowering to less than 45° along the drier inland borders.

With the lower temperatures of winter

TABLE 17-1

Climatic Data for Mid-Latitude Grassland Stations in South America
(Temp., °F; Rainfall, In.)

Station	Lat.	El. in Ft		Jan.	Feb.	Mar.	Apr.	May	Jun.	Jul.	Aug.	Sep.	Oct.	Nov.	Dec.	Year
Prairie Grasslands (Pampa)																
Santa Maria,	29°41′	466	T	77	76	73	67	62	58	58	59	62	65	70	74	
Brazil			R	5.6	5.6	5.6	6.3	7.3	6.6	5.7	5.4	6.5	6.1	4.3	5.1	70.3
Artigas,	30°24′	384	T	80	79	75	66	61	57	56	60	63	66	73	76	
Uruguay			R	4.8	3.8	5.3	4.8	4.1	4.5	3.0	1.9	4.8	5.2	2.9	4.1	49.3
Bages,	31°20′	559	T	75	74	71	65	59	54	54	56	59	62	68	72	
Brazil			R	4.2	4.2	4.0	4.5	5.4	5.5	4.5	5.0	4.8	4.2	3.5	4.0	53.8
Santa Isabel,	32°46′	259	T	77	76	71	64	58	54	51	57	59	63	69	75	
Uruguay			R	5.5	2.8	4.4	3.5	3.9	3.4	1.5	1.2	4.6	3.9	3.5	2.2	40.4
Montevideo,	34°58′	72	T	73	72	69	63	57	53	51	53	56	60	66	70	
Uruguay			R	4.8	3.6	4.7	3.3	3.7	3.4	2.0	3.2	4.2	2.9	3.4	2.1	41.4
Rosario,	32°55′	72	T	75	74	68	62	56	51	50	53	57	62	68	73	
Argentina			R	4.5	3.5	5.3	3.3	2.2	1.5	1.3	1.8	3.1	3.6	4.1	3.9	38.1
Buenos Aires,	34°35′	82	T	74	74	68	63	57	52	51	53	57	62	68	72	
Argentina			R	3.4	3.4	4.6	3.6	3.1	2.2	2.2	2.7	3.5	3.5	3.3	3.7	39.1
Laboulaye,	34°08′	453	T	76	74	67	62	55	49	48	51	56	63	69	75	
Argentina			R	3.3	3.6	3.9	2.4	1.2	0.6	0.8	0.7	2.0	3.3	3.1	3.9	28.9
Trenque Lauquen,	35°58′	315	T	75	73	66	60	53	48	47	50	55	61	69	74	
Argentina			R	2.4	3.1	3.8	1.9	1.4	1.0	1.0	1.0	1.9	3.2	3.0	3.3	27.1
Bahia Blanca,	39°00′	30	T	69	69	64	59	52	47	46	46	52	57	63	67	
Argentina			R	1.6	2.7	3.3	2.6	2.1	1.0	1.2	1.2	3.1	1.9	2.7	1.7	24.9
Shrub Steppe (Monte)																
Choele Choel,	39°17′	436	T	76	74	67	60	52	47	45	49	54	62	69	75	
Argentina			R	0.7	0.9	1.0	0.6	1.2	0.6	0.7	0.8	1.0	1.4	0.8	0.7	10.3
Santa Rosa,	36°37′	600	T	76	73	66	60	52	47	46	50	54	62	68	74	
Argentina			R	2.1	2.8	2.9	1.5	1.2	0.8	0.7	0.8	1.3	2.8	2.5	2.5	21.8
Victorica,	36°13′	1023	T	76	73	66	60	52	47	46	49	55	62	68	74	
Argentina			R	2.3	2.4	2.7	1.4	1.0	0.7	0.4	0.6	1.0	2.7	2.3	2.7	20.1
Mercedes,	33°41′	1689	T	75	73	67	61	54	48	47	50	58	64	70	75	
Argentina			R	3.7	2.3	2.5	1.5	1.0	0.4	0.6	0.5	1.1	2.7	2.5	2.8	21.6
Cordoba,	31°24′	1394	T	76	74	68	64	57	52	51	54	60	65	70	75	
Argentina			R	3.8	3.4	3.6	1.8	1.3	0.4	0.4	0.4	1.1	2.9	3.2	4.2	26.7

Source: F. L. Wernstedt, *World Climate Data, Latin America and the Caribbean,* Pennsylvania State University, 1959.

relative humidities increase, augmenting the general discomfort of the season, even though extreme cold is rare in most sections. During the early afternoon in July relative humidity at Buenos Aires may be expected to average around 79 per cent, compared with 61 per cent in January, at Trenque Lauquen and Bahia Blanca 56 per cent in July but 40 and 41 per cent respectively in January. Toward the northeast winter and summer humidity differences are less.

Also typical of winter is a higher percentage of cloud cover and a lower percentage of possible sunshine than in summer, with Buenos Aires reporting a mean daily cloud cover of 50 per cent in July against 40 per cent in January; Cordoba 64 per cent in June, 51 in January; Trenque Lauquen 64 per cent in June, 42 in January; Bahia Blanca 53 per cent in July and 39 in January. The combined effect of these conditions on temperature is to lower the mean daily range as compared with summer. Amplitudes of 15 degrees are reported for Montevideo and Buenos Aires in July against 21 and 22 respectively for January, 18 at Bahia Blanca in July and 26 in January, 22 in July at Trenque Lauquen and 31 in January, and at Victorica 29 for July and 35 for January.

Under the influence of the semipermanent oceanic high over the South Atlantic, the dominant flow of air over the grasslands is from the north and northeast. Beginning at Bahia Blanca, however, entrainment in the prevailing flow of the strong westerlies over Patagonia results in northwest winds during most of the year at that station. Naturally, the passage of cyclonic disturbances with their clockwise circulations brings winds that blow from all points of the compass.

Notable among the regional climatic features of this part of South America are the winds related to dramatic changes in weather. The pampero is especially identified with the winter season, occurring principally from July to September, although it may occur infrequently throughout the year. It most commonly appears as a very strong, cold, dry wind from the southwest, originating when higher pressure advances eastward in response to a steep barometric gradient in the direction of a depression over southern Brazil. It may last for a few hours or continue for several days, and in many cases it lowers the temperature some 30

degrees. Wind speeds occasionally attain hurricane force, and highly unstable air is often vigorously thrust upward to produce very severe thunderstorms and heavy rains, for which the pampa is notorious. From time to time southeasterly gales set in, lasting for a day or two, and have on occasion held back the outpouring waters of the Parana and Uruguay rivers, causing serious flooding of the lowlands.

Below-freezing temperatures have been experienced from southern Brazil to the coast of Uruguay, but much less frequently in those eastern reaches than over the Argentine pampa. Here the thermometer has reached 22° at Buenos Aires and Mar de la Plata, 18° at Rosario and Bahia Blanca, 16° at Azul, and 13° at Trenque Lauquen. Nor is snow unknown in these very temperate regions, having been reported east of the Rio Uruguay and with increasing frequency farther southward. Amounts are rarely more than an inch or two, however, and snow does not remain on the ground for more than two or three days in succession.

Summer. During this season of the year mean temperatures are not widely different throughout the grassland regions, averaging between 70° and 80° during January, the warmest month (Fig. 17.2). Once again it should be noted (Table 17-1) that normal temperatures differ only slightly from month to month, suggesting the moderate nature of this particular grassland climate. Along the coast values tend to be lower, and February commonly averages about the same temperature as January, reflecting the direct influence of the sea, whereas for Mar de la Plata, February is actually the warmest month, with a value of 68°.

Summer is the season of maximum precipitation west of the Rio Uruguay and normally experiences a double maximum, one early in the season, usually during October, and the other at the end of the season in March (Fig. 17.2). For most of the grasslands March is the peak precipitation month of the year, although in the monte along the southwestern rim of the more humid pampa, October receives the yearly maximum. As noted above, warm season rains mainly result from the passage of organized weather systems, and only along the drier inland margins are the thermal convective showers an important source.

At this season of the year the interior of

northwestern Argentina becomes warm and very dry, taking on the qualities of continental tropical air and thus becoming a source region for warm, dry air that occasionally moves southeastward over the grasslands. At times it does so in the form of a vigorous wind called a zonda (sondo), which brings a strong blast of hot, dry, oppressive air over the pampa from the northwest. It is this condition, very similar to the sirocco of the Mediterranean basin, that invites a special appreciation of the summer winds from the southwest, which bring cool, dry air to the region and are usually preceded by heavy thunderstorms. When strong enough, these southwest winds are also called pamperos, like those of wintertime.

Southern Africa

A mid-latitude grassland climate prevails over the southeastern part of southern Africa's high plateau at elevations for the most part between 4000 and 6000 feet. High altitude is one of the main reasons for the presence of a temperate grassland in this part of the continent, within the lower middle latitudes roughly between 23 and 33°. The region constitutes a transition between that narrow fringe of temperate, humid forest along the southeast coast and the arid desert that spreads westward over the interior to the southwest coast. It can also be regarded as a transition from the mid-latitude forests of the south coast northward into the tropical savanna woodlands.

It will be remembered from Chapter 14 that the continent's massive upland here reaches very nearly from coast to coast before dropping rather abruptly downward to the sea, and that a gradual eastward rise in elevation is seen, culminating in a disrupted series of deeply eroded tablelands. The highest of these is found among the Drakensberg, reaching heights of more than 10,000 feet. The change from the relative evenness of the interior plateau to the broken, deeply dissected slopes that descend to the narrow coastal plain is marked by the steep-sided bluffs of the Great Escarpment. This very pronounced divide winds sinuously northward in southeast Africa, remaining well back from the sea, occasionally approaching to within 100 miles of the coast (Fig. 14.7).

The well-watered seaward slopes are drained by many short, swift-flowing streams that rise between 100 and 150 miles from the sea and have cut effectively into the surface, creating a succession of alternately deep, often steep-sided valleys and tapering mountain spurs. Inland, however, the principal drainage is provided by the upper tributaries of the slow-moving Orange River that winds easily westward down the gentle decline of the interior plateau for more than 1000 miles to the Atlantic. Farther north the broad valley of the Limpopo River, flowing eastward into the Indian Ocean, provides a large entrenchment into the eastern edge of the interior upland. The valleys of its many southern tributaries sloping northward down the watershed and those of numerous lesser streams entering the Indian Ocean allow the inland penetration of tropical atmospheric influences toward the more severe environments of the uplands.

It is on the interfluves between those many stream courses of the southeast coast that one first encounters the mid-latitude grasslands. The uneven distribution is largely governed by altitude and the effect this has on climate, plus the edaphic influences of soil porosity and subsurface drainage. Temperate grassland generally dominates the terrain between 3500 and 6000 feet in elevation. Now advancing seaward down the descending slopes of the highland foothills to within 30 miles of the shore, now receding inland for 100 miles or more where the stream valleys permit the intrusion of moderating maritime atmospheric influences, the grassland presents an escalloped pattern of distribution. Above 6000 feet it yields to alpine vegetation of grass and scrub brushland that responds to the lower temperatures and more abundant, more equable precipitation of those greater heights. Inland of the Great Escarpment temperate grassland is again dominant below 6000 feet, generally giving way to more arid environments of scattered shrub and xerophytic trees below 4000 feet. The gentle westward gradient of the land it occupies in the upper Orange River valley west of the Drakensberg possesses an apparent levelness that is only moderately relieved by a great many low, steep-faced mesa and butte formations.

All in all, grassland occupies a tract extending nearly 700 miles northward from the Great Winterberg and Katberg ranges southwest of the Drakensberg to the Soutpansberge about 50 miles south of the middle course of the Limpopo. It attains a maximum breadth of somewhat less than 400 miles between the lower Vaal River and the foothills of the southeast coast.

This is a dominantly tall grass vegetation very closely resembling the pampas of South America and the prairies of the northern hemisphere. Trees are rarely seen except in the valleys and occasionally on the sheltered slopes of the intervening ridges. The plateau grassland of the high veld is largely a climax vegetation in which red grass, or Themedaveld (*Themeda trinadra*), is the principal species, occupying over 60 per cent of the area.[3] Toward the margins of the central body of the plateau grassland other species become important. Above 6000 feet, for example, cold-tolerant species such as the fescues (*Festuca spp.*), wild oats grass (*Danthonia disticha*), and a high proportion of alpine shrub appear. Along the western limits of the region, below 4000 feet, more drought-tolerant species are encountered, such as the wire grass (*Aristida spp.*) and species of *Eragrostis* and *Sporobolus*. Two rather distinct forms of Themedagrass are found, a tall form called sour veld, attaining a height of 2 to 3 feet, which appears in wetter areas with loose, deep soils, and a shorter form known as sweetveld, often of a height of 18 inches to 2 feet, that generally grows in better drained, more fertile soils.

The presence of a temperate grassland here, in a position transitional between humid coastal forest and interior desert, reflects the prevailing influence at altitudes of 4000 to 6000 feet of those atmospheric qualities typical of the mid-latitude grassland climate. Like such climates elsewhere in the world, a mean annual precipitation of between 15 and 40 inches or more with a marked summer increase, comparatively dry winters with frequent frosts, a moderately strong mean annual temperature range, and plentiful sunshine are characteristic. These are qualities arising from the seasonal swing of solar relationships, changing air mass distribution, and shifting patterns of the general

[3] This and other material on vegetation is derived from J. H. Wellington, *Southern Africa*, Vol. 1, Cambridge University Press, Cambridge, 1955, pp. 273–304, and R. S. Adamson, *The Vegetation of South Africa*, British Empire Vegetation Committee, London, 1938, *passim*.

circulation, as they are modified by the vast bulk of southern Africa's high tableland.

It is important to recognize that the marked seasonal fluctuations in mean weather over this southern extremity of the continent are traceable to the fundamental yearly increase and decrease in the intensity of radiant energy received from the sun. The systematic rise and fall of thermal intensities over the interior plateau produces a period of predominantly clear, dry anticyclonic weather in winter and persistently lower atmospheric pressure with more humid air, increased cloudiness, and abundant rainfall in summer. The principal source of surface air flowing over the grasslands is the semipermanent oceanic high over the southwestern Indian Ocean (Figs. 4.2 and 4.3). This holds true throughout the year, with the result that the prevailing winds of the anticyclonic circulation approach the southeast coast from eastward and recurve southward over the eastern grassland part of the plateau. It will be remembered, incidentally, that the ruling circulation over the Cape region of the southwest and the Namib desert of the west coast is controlled by the action of the oceanic high over the South Atlantic.

Mean annual precipitation over the main body of Themedaveld attains a maximum of over 40 inches along the Great Escarpment. It diminishes to 30 inches, and in places to less than 25 inches, down the eastern slopes before increasing again near the coast (Fig. 14.8). Westward from the eastern rim of the plateau values lessen to between 15 and 20 inches where the plateau declines below 4000 feet. At elevations above the temperate grasslands precipitation increases to between 40 and 60 inches. Few weather stations exist in the high rainfall areas, but the values reported from points along the eastern slopes are suggestive. At Pilgrim's Rest in eastern Transvaal north of Swaziland, at an altitude of 4198 feet, normal precipitation averages 38.3 inches; at Piet Retief near the southwestern border of Swaziland, at 4133 feet, it is 36.2 inches; at Dundee about 100 miles southward, at 4090 feet, it is 33.2 inches. The precipitation change with elevation down the eastern slopes is suggested by the following mean amounts: Matatiele (el. 4789), 27.9 inches; Cala (el. 3929), 23.1 inches; Queenstown (el. 3533), 22.1 inches; Umtata (el. 2283), 25.8 inches; Durban (el. 16), 39.7 inches.

The gradual westward decrease in mean yearly precipitation is indicated by the amounts reported from the following: Piet Retief (el. 4133), 36.2 inches; Bethal, less than 100 miles west-northwest (5379), 29.7 inches; Potchefstroom, about 150 miles farther west (el. 4435), 23.9 inches; Bloemhof, in the Vaal River valley about 100 miles southwestward (el. 4048), 19.1 inches; Christiana, about 30 miles farther down the valley (el. 3959), 17.8 inches. Bloemhof is a representative station along the drier western limits of the grassveld, although its boundary is very irregular, reaching farther westward south of the Vaal almost to Kimberley (el. 3926), which has a mean precipitation of 16.3 inches. Continuous grassland of the mid-latitudes comes to an end not far north of Pilgrim's Rest, which lies north of the Mauch Berg. Beyond this area, with decreasing latitude temperate grassland is found only in discontinuous distribution on the higher eminences near the Great Escarpment as far as the Soutpansberge. This is chiefly the result of milder winters and longer summers during which temperatures remain above 70° for four or five months. Despite ample rains for the support of mid-latitude grasses, the long period of high temperatures and the very considerable moisture loss through evaporation allow tropical types of vegetation to gain proportional superiority. Louis Trichardt (el. 3152) southwest of the Soutpansberge is an example of a marginal station in northern Transvaal, with a normal precipitation of 28.8 inches. Similarly, Pietersberg (el. 4208), about 65 miles farther southwest, averages 20.5 inches (Fig. 17.4).

The mean annual temperature range understandably increases with increased aridity from east to west. It is only 16 degrees at Pilgrim's Rest, but at Bethal it is 20 degrees, at Potchefstroom 23, and at Bloemhof 27. East of the escarpment it is generally less than 20, as at Piet Retief (15), Matatiele (16), and Cala (18). Both greater precipitation and closer proximity to the direct influence of maritime air work to compress the variation of temperature. Absolute maxima in January and absolute minima in July produce an extreme range of temperature amounting to about 60 degrees in wetter, eastern sections, between 90° and 30°, and about 75 degrees along the inland margins, where the thermometer in summer may soar to 95° and in winter drop to about 20°.

The frequent occurrence of frost in winter is a marked feature of that season, but the average length of the frost-free period is nearly 240 days over most of the region, increasing to more than 270 days in western Transvaal and to more than three hundred along the limits of the region down the eastern slopes. Along the southeast coast a year-long growing season normally prevails. At elevations between 5000 and 6000 feet the frost-free period is approximately two hundred days, and in alpine situations at still higher altitudes frost may occur in any month of the year.

Winter. The occurrence of frost during a period of from four to six months, depending on altitude, is anticipated in the grassveld during a normal winter, but the actual number of days when the thermometer may be expected to register subfreezing temperatures ranges from about twenty east of the escarpment to between forty and sixty on the interior plateau. Early morning frosts are invariably followed by a rapid warming of the land surfaces and the lower layers of the atmosphere after sunrise. The clear, dry, rarified air at these higher altitudes allows both a rapid intake of radiant heat from the sun during the day and a rapid reradiation heat loss at night.

The ruling weather of winter is anticyclonic in character, when a succession of migrating anticyclones detached from the semipermanent high over the South Atlantic moves eastward over southern Africa to the Indian Ocean, resulting in the appearance on the July weather map of an almost unbroken high pressure ridge centered approximately along the 30th parallel. This is the season of minimum precipitation for the year, and June in the grassveld is commonly the driest month, averaging less than half an inch on the plateau. Most winter precipitation is derived from migrating cyclones and elongated depressions that pass along the south and southeast coasts and consists chiefly of rain, with occasional snow in the eastern tableland. Snow falls much more frequently in the high mountains, but widespread snowfalls over the plateau grassland are experienced much more rarely, usually at intervals of several years, and snow does not usually remain on the ground for more than a day or two.

June and July together are commonly the colder months of the year (Fig. 17.4), and the mean temperatures then are close to 45° over

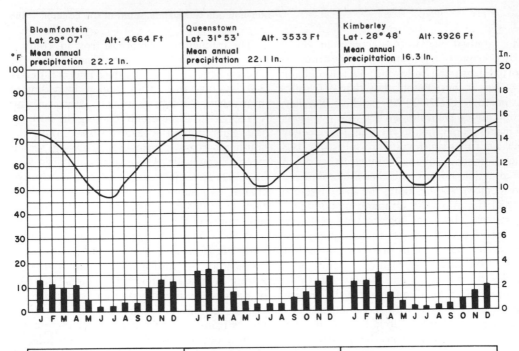

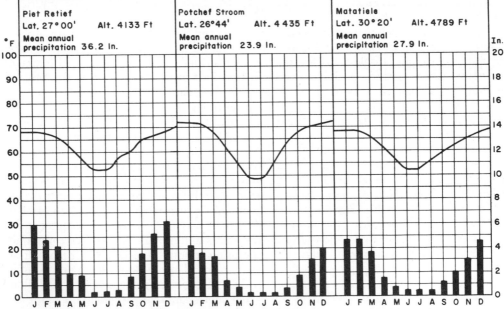

Figure 17.4. Temperature and precipitation at mid-latitude grassland stations in the Republic of South Africa.

most of the plateau grassland west of the Great Escarpment (Table 17-2). Northward, however, at lower latitude, midwinter temperatures range between 50° and 55°, and also down the eastern slopes below the escarpment where the moderating influence of oceanic air is effective (Fig. 14.15). Pretoria reports an average

fluctuation of 30 degrees, between 38° and 68°; Bloemfontein 28 degrees, between 32° and 60°; Potchefstroom 33 degrees, between 32° and 65°. East of the escarpment values are usually less than 20 degrees: Queenstown, for instance, averages 19 degrees, between 41° and 60°. Winter nights are moderately cold, but

TABLE 17-2

Climatic Data for Mid-Latitude Grassland Stations in Southern Africa (Republic of South Africa)
(Temp., °F; Rainfall, In.)

Station	Lat.	El. in Ft		Jan.	Feb.	Mar.	Apr.	May	Jun.	Jul.	Aug.	Sep.	Oct.	Nov.	Dec.	Year
Louis Trichardt	23°03'	3152	T	72	71	70	67	62	57	57	60	65	69	71	72	
			R	6.0	5.0	4.1	1.5	0.8	0.5	0.7	0.3	0.5	1.9	3.5	4.2	28.8
Pilgrim's Rest	24°54'	4198	T	68	68	66	63	57	52	52	56	61	65	66	68	
			R	7.5	6.9	5.8	2.3	0.9	0.4	0.6	0.5	1.2	2.1	4.6	5.6	38.3
Bethal	26°27'	5379	T	67	66	64	59	53	47	47	52	58	63	64	66	
			R	5.3	3.9	3.4	1.5	0.8	0.3	0.3	0.4	0.9	3.0	5.0	4.9	29.7
Piet Retief	27°00'	4133	T	68	68	66	63	58	53	53	57	60	65	66	68	
			R	6.0	4.8	4.2	2.0	0.9	0.4	0.5	0.6	1.7	3.7	5.2	6.2	36.2
Potchefstroom	26°44'	4435	T	72	71	68	62	55	49	49	55	62	68	70	71	
			R	4.2	3.7	3.3	1.3	0.8	0.3	0.3	0.4	0.7	1.8	3.1	4.0	23.9
Bloemhof	27°39'	4048	T	76	74	71	65	57	50	49	55	62	69	71	74	
			R	3.0	2.9	3.6	1.4	0.6	0.2	0.3	0.3	0.5	1.3	2.4	2.7	19.1
Christiana	27°55'	3959	T	76	74	71	64	55	49	48	53	60	67	71	74	
			R	2.9	2.4	3.1	1.6	0.7	0.2	0.2	0.4	0.4	1.2	2.1	2.6	17.8
Kimberley	28°48'	3926	T	77	75	71	65	57	51	51	56	62	68	72	75	
			R	2.4	2.5	3.1	1.5	0.8	0.2	0.2	0.4	0.6	1.0	1.6	2.1	16.3
Bloemfontein	29°07'	4664	T	73	71	67	60	53	48	47	53	58	64	68	71	
			R	3.6	3.2	3.0	2.2	1.0	0.3	0.4	0.8	0.8	2.0	2.6	2.4	22.2
Queenstown	31°53'	3533	T	72	71	69	63	57	51	51	55	60	64	66	71	
			R	3.2	3.5	3.4	1.6	0.9	0.5	0.6	0.6	1.1	1.5	2.4	2.8	22.1
Matatiele	30°20'	4789	T	68	68	65	61	56	52	52	56	59	62	65	67	
			R	4.7	4.6	3.7	1.5	0.9	0.5	0.6	0.6	1.1	2.0	3.1	4.7	27.9
Cala	31°31'	3929	T	69	69	67	62	57	52	51	56	59	62	65	68	
			R	3.6	3.1	3.5	1.4	0.9	0.4	0.7	0.7	1.2	1.5	3.0	3.1	23.1

Source: F. L. Wernstedt, *World Climatic Data, Africa*, Pennsylvania State University, 1959.

daytime brings cool to warm temperatures with clear, dry, bracing air and blue, sunny skies. The per cent of possible sunshine in midwinter is high over most of the region, amounting to between 75 and 85 per cent during July west of the upland escarpment and between 65 and 70 per cent down the seaward declivity.

As the cool, dry, almost rainless weather of winter continues, the month of August frequently sees a large number of local dust storms over the dessicated grasslands, especially in areas laid bare by cultivation, overgrazing, and other land use practices. In September, as winter begins to wane, the clear, dry air of the high plateau freely admits the sun's rays to the parched earth, warming it with increasing intensity, and hence the air above, with such effect that convective turbulence with strong, gusty winds at the surface and towering cumulus clouds above announce the approach of summer's shower season. Lower atmospheric pressures over the continental interior, largely of thermal origin, lead to a steepening of the pressure gradient from the Indian Ocean, and easterly winds begin to advance progressively farther westward over the land.

Summer. The increasing height of the sun, rising air temperatures, more frequent cloudiness, and the beginning of summer's rains all mark the change into the long warm season of the year. Precipitation begins to increase at first over the eastern slopes seaward of the Great Escarpment. Here, at stations like Pilgrim's Rest, Paulpietersburg, Dundee, and Matatiele, September rains amount to twice the amounts of those in August, averaging $1\frac{1}{2}$ inches or more. At the same time, rainfall increases only slightly west of the plateau rim, and the seasonal change there is chiefly evident through a noticeable increase in daytime cloudiness. By October, however, summer's rainfall has spread over most of the temperate grassland and continues until March. The period from November through March is the time of heaviest rainfall, when amounts between 3 and 5 inches occur per month over most of the grassveld. Along the eastern slopes December is commonly the wettest month, although January is the peak precipitation month elsewhere. Orographic uplift over the rising terrain of the southeast coast toward the Great Escarpment accounts for the large rainfall amounts that come to mountain country from the Drakensberg northward. The start of the season's rains in early summer that takes place at first on these seaward exposures is brought about by rains of orographic nature. West of the escarpment, however, the rains that start a little later in October are almost entirely of convective origin, arising from the powerful heating effect of the high summer sun upon the elevated surface in the presence of warm, moist air from the Indian Ocean. The flow of most of the precipitable moisture is believed to be up the relatively easy gradient over Swaziland and into the upper Vaal River valley during the early part of summer. As the season progresses, a supplementary flow of warm, humid air advances from farther north, moving up the broad Limpopo valley and curving southwestward over the grassveld, to release its moisture in thermal convective showers.

Thunderstorms are the most common form of precipitating disturbance in the summer and account for the fact that most rains are of substantial intensity, typically producing more than $\frac{1}{2}$ inch of rain at each occurrence. At rather frequent intervals hail is released from more violently turbulent convective storms, and hailstones of considerable size and weight have fallen. One left a 3-inch hole in an iron roof, another weighed 4 pounds, and during one severe storm a cow and thirty sheep were killed by hailstones.[4]

Another hazard of the summer season is the spectre of drought, which haunts the residents of southern Africa's temperate grassland as much as any other. It is difficult to settle on the exact meaning of the term *drought* and the precise conditions under which it may be said to occur. A conservative estimate for the grassveld of southern Africa indicates that about 50 per cent of the area may suffer damaging drought once every three years.

In spite of the higher position of the summer sun and the greater length of day, the actual percentage of possible sunshine is considerably less than that of wintertime. In January it amounts to between 60 and 70 per cent over most of the eastern plateau but only between 50 and 60 per cent east of the escarpment. The effect of summer's cloudier conditions, higher atmospheric humidity, and frequent rains upon

[4] Wellington, *op. cit.*, p.250.

the mean daily range of temperature is revealing, for most of the region experiences a mean daily fluctuation of about 20 degrees, from the low 60s to the low 80s. At Pretoria, for example, the range is 19 degrees (63° to 82°), at Potchefstroom 20 degrees (60° to 80°), at Kimberley 22 degrees (64° to 86°), and at Queenstown 20 degrees (60° to 80°). Less cloudy, less humid, and less rainy areas near the drier margins experience wider daily temperature ranges, as illustrated by the mean for Bloemfontein of 24 degrees (59° to 83°).

An interesting feature of the summer season in this elevated region of mid-latitude grassland is the fact that over more than half the region, in the eastern areas that generally lie above 5000 feet, maximum mean monthly temperatures hold for two months instead of a single, pivotal month of maximum temperatures as in the northern hemisphere. In these sections mean summer temperatures average between 65° and 70°, and from Basutoland north to the Soutpansberge, December and January average about equal temperatures (Fig. 14.14). At Louis Trichardt (el. 3152) in the shadow of the Soutpansberge to the north the mean for these two months is 72°, and for the same two months at Pretoria (el. 4490) it is 71°. These stations represent the warmer, borderland transition into more tropical savanna environments. At Belfast (el. 6134), over 100 miles east of Pretoria, December and January average 62°. Along the seaward decline from north of Swaziland southward the uniformity of summer temperatures is prolonged even further; mean temperatures for December through February are often the same or nearly the same, as at Pilgrim's Rest and Piet Retief, 68°, Paulpietersberg 69°, and Dundee 64°. In the western half of the grassveld highest mean monthly temperatures are attained in a single month, in January, and tend to range between 70° and 75°. At Lichtenburg, for example, January's mean temperature is 71°, at Potchefstroom it is 72°, at Bloemhof 76°, and Bloemfontein 73°. Still, one may observe from Table 17-2 that the difference between December and January or February and January is more often than not only 1 degree. It should also be noted that along the southeastern slopes, the two months of equal temperature are January and February rather than December and January.

Australia

Over that large part of southern Australia lying outside the tropics major areas of mid-latitude grassland environment are found in interior situations of both the southwest and southeast. As the drier, transitional aspect of mediterranean scrub woodland, grading into arid desert, they appear along the inland margins of the Perth and Adelaide regions, where they take the form of short grass steppe almost uniformly dotted with low, many-branched, shrubby forms of eucalypts forming a vegetation called mallee. In many local wet depressions along the perimeter of the great central desert in the same latitudes grassland can be found in a scattering of minor localities. The main body of temperate grassland environments extends from the highlands of Victoria at a latitude of about 37°S. northward to about 30°, a distance of nearly 500 miles, occupying a moderately uneven surface that for the most part maintains a gently downward slope westward from the Great Divide (Fig. 15.1).

Certain significant circumstances bearing upon the character and distribution of the grasslands should be borne in mind. They occupy terrain within the eastern lowlands of the country that lies mainly below 1000 feet in elevation and in its western and southwestern sectors is substantially less than 500 feet. In the open country between Adelaide and the Victorian highlands the southwestern part of the region is freely exposed to influxes of maritime polar air from the west. Northern sections are scarcely less freely exposed to invasions of maritime tropical air from the northeast because the broad upland of the Great Divide is nowhere sufficiently high (generally below 2000 feet) to interpose a significant barrier. Furthermore, the region lies within the lower middle latitudes, and this fact, coupled with low elevation and exposure to the influx of air from the sea, creates a milder form of the mid-latitude grasslands. Evidence of this is seen in the rather long period of high summer temperatures, mild winters, and the strong interpenetration of tropical flora in northern sections.

It should also be remembered that grass vegetation appears in a number of areas throughout the temperate forest on the south and southeast coasts, where edaphic conditions of soil and drainage are favorable. An example of this is the meadow land of southern Victoria both east and west of Port Phillip Bay and Melbourne. In addition, most of the grasslands are occupied by a fairly uniform scattering of low tree and shrub vegetation, creating an open, parklike woodland condition commonly described by the term *savanna*, and indeed, resembling in outward appearance the savanna grasslands of the tropics. In the wetter, eastern sections nearer the Great Divide low eucalypt trees and shrubs provide the principal components of the woody vegetation, but in the drier areas farther west various species of acacia prevail.

The southern section of grassland is dominated by a rainfall regime in which maximum amounts are received during the winter season. This area extends northward from the Victoria highlands for about 400 miles into the central part of New South Wales. Here the grass vegetation is a short grass association consisting chiefly of species of the slender, sparsely flowered wild oat grass (*Danthonia spp.*), found in its best development where rainfall averages between 15 and 25 inches. Although it appears as a nearly treeless grassland in the open plains of west Victoria, it is most commonly seen as a savanna woodland. A variety of other herbaceous plants is included in the association, as well as a number of other important grasses, particularly spear grass (*Stipa spp.*), and fields of waving kangaroo grass (*Themeda australis*), which closely resembles Themedagrass of southern Africa. Colorful flowering plants of springtime brighten the luxuriant pasture and include a large number of composites like the strawflower (*Helichrysum bracteatum*) and species of *Senecio* and *Helipterum*. Immediately north of the winter rain region is a mixture of grass species, some of which grow most successfully in winter and some that flourish in summer. They include such species as red grass (*Bothriochloa ambigua*), wire grasses (*Aristida spp.*), tussock grasses (*Poa spp.*), and in the drier western areas kangaroo grass, Australian millet (*Panicum decompositum*), and the love grasses (*Eragrostis spp.*). In the Darling Downs, an undulating region west of the Great Divide in southeastern Queensland, such a mixture of summer-growing and winter-growing grasses develops under a rainfall of between 25 and 30 inches, and the dominant plant species are the blue grasses (*Dicantheum sericeum*) and others of this genus.

Along the western edges of the temperate grasslands where normal yearly precipitation drops below 10 inches is a change into a series of arid landscapes rather like the sagebrush country of southwestern United States, called the saltbush-bluebush steppe lands. The low, fleshy-leaved species of saltbush (*Atriplex spp.*), along with many-branched shrub forms of acacia are especially common in northwestern New South Wales, and bluebush (*Kochia spp.*) species farther south provide the chief components of a desert vegetation where no grass will grow, and at the same time, successfully penetrate into the less arid grasslands.

The northern part of the main body of temperate grassland is dominated by a number of species of Mitchell grasses (*Astrebla spp.*), Queensland blue grasses, and species of *Agrostis*, mainly tussock-forming species with a liberal development of other herbaceous plants between, and surmounted by an almost universal scattering of small trees and shrubs that create a typically open, parkland aspect.

Throughout the winter rainfall area of the southern grasslands in Victoria and New South Wales precipitation is mainly supplied by systematic cyclonic and linear frontal storms deriving most of their moisture from maritime polar air of the West Wind Drift off the south coast of Australia. In northern New South Wales and southern Queensland where summer is the season of maximum rainfall, precipitation is again the primary result of systematic disturbances, although here related to the poleward extension of tropical troughs toward which air of maritime tropical character is drawn from the sea off the east and northeast coasts of the continent (Figs. 4.2 and 4.3). Within the northern part of the grasslands thermal convective showers play an increasing role in the rainfall supply, often taking the form of severe thunderstorms. The Darling Downs experience the highest frequency of thunderstorms in the region, annually averaging up to twenty-five, and associated with them are frequent occurrences of hail (Fig. 23.15).

The more humid section of grassland where annual precipitation is normally between 20 and 30 inches is confined to a narrow belt less than 100 miles wide along the gently descending western slopes of the Great Divide at elevations between 1000 and 2000 feet (Fig. 15.2). The remainder of the region, receiving less than 20

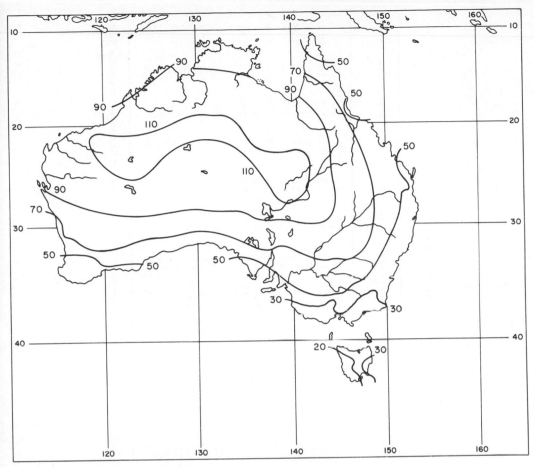

Figure 17.5. Normal evaporation per year in Australia (inches).

inches of normal precipitation, extends for nearly 300 miles farther west where the regional limits approximately coincide with the 10 inch isohyet. Of the few reporting stations supplying data, Goondiwindi in the south Darling Downs (el. 718) affords an example of the more humid eastern section with a mean precipitation of 24.9 inches. Charleville, about 300 miles northwest (el. 965), with 19.2 inches, and Thargomindah (el. 400), with 10.8 inches, represent the drier aspect in the northern part of the region. A similar transition can be observed from coastal forest to interior desert throughout the region. Bendigo, on the north slopes of the Victoria highlands (el. 814), reports 21.1 inches; Swan Hill, about 100 miles northwest on the banks of the Murray River (el. 230), reports 13.2 inches; Wentworth about 150 miles farther down the Murray where it is joined by the Darling River (el. 125) averages 11.8 inches.

Rainfall reliability is greatest in the southern section where most of the year's rain comes in the winter season. Here the variation from normal amounts to about 20 per cent, increasing to 40 per cent in northern areas where the more random convective showers contribute substantially to the year's precipitation. The risk of drought, a constant threat to grassland regions everywhere in the mid-latitudes, is especially typical of the region, increasing in seriousness from south to north and also westward toward the central desert.

The growing season in the grasslands is scarcely affected by occurrences of frost. True, the thermometer may drop to the subfreezing point as many as fifty days during an average winter in southern sections, but persistent subfreezing weather is rare. In northern areas the mean frequency of frost is less than five days per year (Fig. 15.10). June and July are the

TABLE 17–3
Climatic Data for Mid-Latitude Grassland Stations in Australia
(Temp., °F; Rainfall, In.)

Station	Lat.	El. in Ft		Jan.	Feb.	Mar.	Apr.	May	Jun.	Jul.	Aug.	Sep.	Oct.	Nov.	Dec.	Year
Prairie Grassland																
Charleville, Queensland	26°25'	965	T	84	83	78	70	62	56	54	58	64	73	79	82	
			R	2.5	2.6	2.3	1.3	1.2	1.3	1.2	0.7	0.8	1.2	1.7	2.4	19.2
Walgett, New South Wales	30°02'	436	T	83	81	76	68	59	53	52	55	62	69	77	81	
			R	2.2	1.9	1.6	1.2	1.5	1.6	1.3	1.1	1.0	1.2	1.5	1.7	17.8
Dubbo, New South Wales	32°15'	870	T	79	78	73	64	56	50	48	50	57	64	71	76	
			R	2.1	1.7	1.9	1.8	1.7	2.0	1.7	1.7	1.6	1.6	2.0	2.0	21.8
Hay, New South Wales	34°30'	310	T	76	76	71	62	55	50	49	52	56	63	69	74	
			R	0.9	0.9	1.0	1.2	1.4	1.6	1.2	1.3	1.2	1.2	0.9	1.0	13.7
Shrub Steppe																
Windorah, Queensland	25°26'	390	T	88	87	82	73	64	58	57	61	68	76	82	86	
			R	1.4	1.6	1.6	0.9	0.8	0.8	0.5	0.4	0.5	0.6	0.9	1.4	11.4
Bourke, New South Wales	30°05'	361	T	85	83	78	69	60	54	53	57	64	71	78	82	
			R	1.4	1.5	1.1	1.1	1.0	1.1	0.9	0.8	0.8	0.9	1.2	1.4	13.2
Wilcannia, New South Wales	31°33'	267	T	81	81	75	65	58	52	51	55	61	68	75	80	
			R	0.9	0.9	0.8	0.7	1.0	0.9	0.6	0.7	0.6	0.9	0.7	1.0	9.7

Source: Great Britain, Meteorological Office, *Tables of Temperature, Relative Humidity and Precipitation for the World*, Part 6, *Australasia and the South Pacific Ocean*, London, 1962.

months when temperatures of 32° or a little lower are apt to occur within the region, and July is normally the coldest month. Mean July temperatures remain above 50° in almost all the grasslands, except the area immediately north of the Victoria highlands, where the average is about 45°. Charleville and Thargomindah in Queensland both average 54° in July, but in eastern New South Wales, Dubbo (el. 869) averages 47°, Albury (el. 541) averages 46°, and Mildura (el. 125) on the lower Murray River averages 49° (Fig. 15.9).

The governing condition of the length of the growing season in Australia is the length of time that moisture remaining in the soil is sufficient for the continuous support of pasture and crop plants, and not the amount or the season of normal precipitation. In this the ratio between precipitation and evaporation has been determined by Australian investigators to be the best indicator of growing season length.[5] The formula $Mo_nP/E > \frac{1}{3}$ signifies that common economic plants will grow only when rainfall is greater than one third of the calculated evaporation from a free water surface. According to this formula only the east and south coasts and a small section of the southwest coast are favored with a growing season of nine to twelve months. In the grasslands of the mid-latitudes only the southern areas for about 200 miles north of the Victoria highlands experience a growing season of from five to eight months. In most of the region the season is between one and four months, and in the drier western

sections just south of the Tropic of Capricorn it is less than one month. The combination of high summer sun, resulting in high intensities of radiant heat from the sun, a long, hot summer, and wind are important in raising the evaporative rate to excessive heights in northwestern areas of the temperate grasslands (Fig. 17.5).

Mean monthly temperatures in summertime are persistently high in northern areas, averaging above 80° for three months at Charleville, for five months at Windorah about 200 miles west-northwest, and for four months at Thargomindah about 200 miles southwest of Charleville (Table 17-3). January is the hottest month during a normal summer, and at Charleville it averages 84°, at Windorah 87°, and Thargomindah 86° (Fig. 15.8). Mean values for the warmest month are above 80° well into New South Wales, and only in southernmost sections and at slightly higher elevations along the southeastern rim of grassland are they below 80°. Here the mean annual temperature range is about 25 degrees, and in the north about 30 degrees.

One of the more notorious features of Australia's summer weather, occurring during the period December through February, is the hot spell referred to in Chapter 15. The hot spell is said to occur when the thermometer readings exceed 90° on several successive days. In the temperate grasslands hot spells normally last for about twenty days in southern areas but up to eighty days in the more arid parts of the north. The region of maximum hot spell duration, of more than 120 days, is the north central desert farther west.

---

[5] G. L. Wood, *Australia*, The Macmillan Company, New York, 1951, pp. 25–27.

References

Burgos, J. J., and Vidal, A. L.: "The Climates of the Argentine Republic According to the New Thornthwaite Classification," *Annals of the Association of American Geographers*, **41**(3): 237–63, 1951.

Malin, J. C.: "Grassland, Treeless and Subhumid," *Geographical Review*, **37**(2): 241–50, 1947.

Prescott, J. A.: "The Comparative Climatology of Australia and Argentina," *Geographical Review*, **42**(1): 118–134, 1952.

Roseveare, G. M.: *The Grasslands of Latin America*, Imperial Bureau of Pastures and Field Crops, Bulletin 36, Aberystwyth, Wales, 1948.

Russell, A.: *Murray Walkabout*, Melbourne University Press, Melbourne, 1953.

Wellington, J. H.: "Land Utilization in South Africa," *Geographical Review*, **22**(2): 205–24, 1932.

Wood, G. L.: *Australia, Its Resources and Development*, The Macmillan Company, New York, 1947.

chapter 18

DESERTS IN NORTH AMERICA, SOUTH AMERICA, AND SOUTHERN AFRICA

The term *desert* has traditionally been applied to a tract of land afflicted by permanent drought. In the desert the atmosphere's capacity to take up and retain moisture is overwhelmingly greater than its capacity to release it; in short, evaporation is far in excess of precipitation. A desert area preserves an aspect of unrelieved aridity despite the occurrence of random rain or snow or even regular rains in small amounts. These may for a spell enliven its dominantly dessicated appearance by the temporary flowering of long-dormant plants or the ephemeral presence of flowing streams or shallow sheets of quickly evaporated water. Desert occupies areas where the atmosphere is almost constantly incapable of delivering precipitated water to the ground, where for a variety of reasons the atmosphere fails to attain dew point temperatures often enough or for sufficiently long intervals of time to produce reliable rain. But a rigid, precise definition of a desert, as compared with near-desert or semi-desert, of arid in contrast to semi-arid, is wanting. For example, many parts of the world receive only a few inches of rain during a normal year, in some years none at all, and are dusty and dessicated in aspect. Other areas receiving up to 10 inches or more of annual precipitation may possess equally arid landscapes. The latter are often due to special qualities of soil porosity, geological structure, slope, drainage, transpiration of plants, and atmospheric properties of evaporative capacity, temperature, moisture content, sunshine intensity and duration, and wind.

To stand at midday in June in the central Sahara when the glaring sun, blazing down from high overhead through cloudless blue skies, has heated the dry, hard rock beneath one's feet to 150° or more, and to scan the surrounding terrain to the horizon's edge seeking in vain a single sign of life, is to sense the parched, barren desolation that only the desert can impart. The only evident motions within the circumference of visibility are the drifting eddies of whirling sand and dust borne along by the hot, dry wind. Neither plant nor animal nor lake nor stream may be present to offset the feeling of a completely hostile, uninhabitable realm.

But by no means all deserts are lacking in life or water. Most desert areas are not entirely barren, not altogether deprived of drought-resistant plant and animal life, of underground reserves of water, or, in fact, of flowing streams and large, shallow lakes, however brackish they may be. Desert landscapes are infinitely varied in land forms, flora, fauna, and hydrological features. But there are certain types of terrestrial features common to nearly all deserts and distinctive atmospheric qualities that are, within broad limits, typical of all deserts.

Strangely enough, running water is held chiefly responsible for the basic morphology of desert land forms. This is the view of geographers who have systematically described and explained the topography of the world's deserts. Temperature change, frost action, and wind are secondary agents, coupled, of course, with gravity, in the production of the principal formations in desert terrain. But the process of stream erosion, of transport and deposition, in arid regions is very, very slow and characteristically intermittent, taking place as a rule during short, unpredictable intervals of sporadic rains, separated by long, dry periods of little or no erosive activity. Rainfall variability is extremely high in all desert regions (Fig. 18.1).

It is usually in mountainous areas, either within the desert or along its wetter margins, that stream flow originates, drawing its energy there from rainfall or snowmelt produced by the fairly frequent precipitation on such elevated formations. It accomplishes the bulk of its erosive work within the wetter borderlands and only rarely affects the desert. But it is those rare and unpredictable flushes of water that very slowly but effectively modify the desert surface, transporting gravel, sand, and finer particles of silt and clay into the lower catchment areas. Seldom is the process impeded by the restraining rootlets of plants, for vegeta-

tion is typically scattered and is often entirely absent.

The gradual wearing away of uplifted rock masses and the accumulation of mineralogical materials in the depressions is a dynamic process leading toward eventual stability, a stage that has been reached in only a few areas. Hence desert land forms, like the geomorphic features of humid regions, are in a constant state of change, eternally subjected to a leveling process that extends over eons of time. Stages in the process are revealed by the kind and distribution of the major relief features.

Where streams flow down out of mountainous country into the unwatered desert, their volume and velocity are reduced when they leave the steeper slopes of their source regions and enter the easier gradients and eventually the level surfaces of the desert floor. Relinquishing first the larger, coarser components of their burden of rock particles at the base of the mountainside and finally the finer materials, they produce a geomorphic formation called an alluvial fan. Where the erosive process has continued for a sufficiently long period of time, many alluvial fans may have coalesced to form an almost continuous, uniform slope called a pediment, an alluvial formation intermediate between the deeply dissected flanks of the mountain and the smooth, nearly level surface of the desert floor. From time to time the

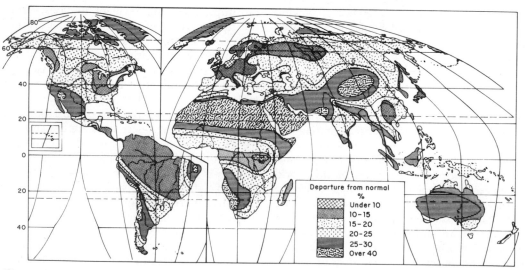

Figure 18.1. Average variability of annual rainfall.

Figure 18.2. Mountain and bolson terrain in central Arizona. [U.S. Bureau of Land Management]

waters of a mountain stream may be of sufficient volume and velocity to course their way down over the alluvial fan and out over the open plain beyond, providing the unusual spectacle of a lake in the desert. But this is a shallow, temporary body of water, sinking rapidly into the porous ground and evaporating quickly in the dry air, leaving a thin crust of salts to whiten the surface of the basin, or bolson, and known as a playa lake. The combination of landforms just described is called mountain and bolson topography and is especially prevalent in the arid regions of North America, although in one or more of its many variations it appears in other desert areas throughout the world as well (Fig. 18.2). During the later stages in the gradual wearing away of mountain features within the desert only isolated peaks remain of once massive formations, and these are commonly spoken of as inselbergs. The gradients of alluvial fans and pediments may now be much lower, often nearly level, forming a broad expanse of gravel plain called hammada, alternating with areas of sand and silt mixed with residual salts that are often drifted by the wind into ridges and dunes in a type of topography called erg (Fig. 18.3).

Another set of surface features associated with the gradual erosion of uplifted tablelands are the plateaus composed of many horizontal or slightly tilted layers of sedimentary rock formations, capped by a stratum of resistant sandstone or basalt. Where such an upland has been subjected to long-continued erosion, and where, in part at least, only isolated remnants remain, those persistent portions often appear as towering, steep-sided features that may stand several hundred feet above their surroundings as flat-topped mesas or, when they possess only small crown areas, buttes (Fig. 18.4). Another feature commonly found in the desert is a cuesta, a sharp-edged, steeply sloping bluff abruptly terminating the upper margin of a gently rising rocky plain.

Streams that do occasionally enter a tract of desert are, by the uncertainty of their flow, termed intermittent streams. In many desert regions perennial rivers of larger size maintain a constant flow to the sea. Enduring rivers of this kind are called exotic streams. They rise in well-watered regions outside the desert but, lacking tributaries on their long journey across arid country, diminish in volume downstream and in many cases all but disappear before reaching the sea. The Nile, the Indus, the Orange, and the Colorado are examples of exotic streams.

Where plant life appears in the desert its unusual hardiness in the face of protracted drought and uncertain precipitation is made possible by special properties of form and physiology. Dry periods often last for several years, and yet desert plants are able to revive quickly and in a remarkably short space of time to grow, to develop foliage, and to break into flower. Such plants are normally dwarf forms of genera that flourish more fully in wetter circumstances, possessing drought-resistant features like thick, waxy, or shiny leaves, often hairy or armed with spines or thorns to dissipate internal heat, with many small stomata often confined to the shaded underside. Plants with such properties are called xerophytes. Some desert plants, described as heliophytes, turn the edges of their leaves to the sun as it moves across the cloudless sky, curling or rolling into semicylindrical form to reduce exposure to the sun and place at least some part of the plant in shade.

Most desert plants are low-growing forms, thick-crowned to shade the site of their attachment to the ground. Beneath the surface they often send out extensive, shallow networks of rootlets to catch whatever rain does fall, or unusually long tap roots to reach the water table that lies deep in the earth. Some plants, like the date palm, draw essential water through a dense, close-packed, shallow cluster of pencil-size roots at the base of their trunks. Still other forms, like the organpipe cactus, are entirely without leaves, possessing instead a tough cuticle within which water is stored at times when the soil is moist; these plants are bloated during a wet period and shrink when drought returns.

The vegetation in desert areas, where it is not altogether absent, is typically scattered in a very open distribution, leaving most of the ground without plant cover. This condition, plus the low heights of most desert xerophytes, allows a long view to the horizon's edge in nearly every desert region. In some instances, however, the view may be interrupted by the presence of tree-size plants like the baobab (*Adansonia digitata*), which may reach a height of 60 feet or more on a heavy, compound trunk that can be more than 30 feet in diameter, specimens of which are found in southern Africa and Australia. In southwestern United States there are the Joshua tree (*Yucca brevifolia*), rising to 40 feet or more, the giant cactus (*Cereus giganteus*), which may reach 75 feet in height, and the cardon (*Pachycereus pringlei*), which

Figure 18.3.   The shifting sands of erg desert in Saudi Arabia. [ARAMCO photo]

Figure 18.4. Buttes and mesas of hammada desert terrain in Monument Valley, Ariz.
[American Airlines photo]

occasionally stands as high as 60 feet above the ground.

The qualities of the atmosphere giving rise to terrestrial qualities like those described in the preceding paragraphs cannot be summarized for all the world's desert regions save in the one particular mentioned at the beginning of the chapter: unrelieved drought, arising from the lightness and uncertainty of precipitation. In most mid-latitude desert regions mean precipitation is less than 10 inches. In lower latitudes desert may prevail where values exceed 10 inches, and at higher latitudes desert may only appear where values are nearer 5 inches. Persistent drought results from a failure of atmospheric moisture to condense and precipitate often enough and in large enough quantities to support more than a scattering of living forms. Desert plants must be capable of withstanding dormant periods of many months or several years. Desert animals sleep during the day and are active at night. Atmospheric properties such as relative humidity, annual range and daily fluctuation of temperature, cloud cover, and sunshine vary from region to region and render invalid a detailed climatic generalization for the world's deserts as a whole.

The map of the world's climatic regions (Fig. 7.1) reveals the unequal size and uneven distribution of the arid regions. In North America desert is found along the southwest coast and in the southwestern interior. In South America it is also found along the west coast and in the southern interior, but it appears as well along the southeast coast in the rain shadow of the Andes. In southern Africa it is again found along the west coast and in the interior, but it occupies the east coast northward from the equator and spans the entire breadth of the continent in northern Africa, continuing northeastward over most of southwestern Asia and well into central Asia. It occupies perhaps half of Australia's 3 million square miles.

But a closer examination of the map does reveal a certain degree of symmetry in the global arrangement of deserts, a tendency toward balanced distribution on either side of the equator and at some distance from it. On every major land mass the larger proportion of arid country lies poleward of the Tropic. Arid conditions are found on the west coasts of all the major land masses, extending equatorward from about 30° latitude for several hundred miles, the actual distance varying according to the alignment of the coast. But here the tendency toward symmetry ends, for the size and shape of each continent and the latitudes between which they lie differ greatly, and hence their relationships with prevailing characteristics of the general circulation also vary.

Deserts can be found from the equator to about 50° latitude both north and south of the equator and occupy about one fifth of the world's land surface. They range in altitude from below sea level, as in Death Valley, Calif., and the Caspian Sea basin, to about 6000 feet above sea level. Desert tracts beyond 6000 feet tend to share certain qualities with other mountainous environments in whose development altitude plays a leading role, and are discussed in Chapter 24 on mountain climates.

Let us study first those desert regions of the lower middle latitudes that are arranged in a roughly balanced distribution in North America and South America, northern Africa and southern Africa, and Australia. It is permissible to designate these five areas loosely as the subtropical deserts, for they lie in part along the Tropics, and their presence is primarily related to the systematic anticyclonic circulations of the semipermanent subtropical oceanic highs. In certain areas they merge with west coast deserts toward the equator and mid-latitude deserts in a poleward direction.

An eastward flow of air around the oceanic highs brings reliable, year-round precipitation to the poleward reaches of continents that extend into sufficiently high latitudes, giving rise to coastal evergreen forest regions (Figs. 4.2, 4.3, and 7.1). In the somewhat lower latitudes of the mediterranean regions reliable precipitation occurs only in winter when the oceanic highs shift equatorward, and in those regions summers are nearly rainless when the highs are displaced poleward and expand eastward over the continental margins. The flow of air in eastern sectors of all the oceanic highs is equatorward, bringing winds that are approximately parallel to the west coasts of the continents in the lower middle latitudes but deflect westward as they approach the equator. This circulation is responsible for the equator-ward transport and upwelling of cold coastal currents, producing sea surface temperatures that are abnormally low for the latitudes in which they flow. They thus play a leading part in the establishment of coastal desert along the western shores of the continents equatorward of about 30°, extending them well into lower latitudes, especially in South America and southern Africa.

It is also important to bear in mind that air moving into lower latitudes becomes warmer and hence increases its moisture-retaining capacity, reducing the possibilities of precipitation. In addition, anticyclonic air is subsiding air, warming adiabatically as it descends, however slightly, but in any case tending to become warmer and thus to retain rather than to release its contained water vapor. All these characteristics of atmospheric circulation in the eastern subtropical segments of the semipermanent oceanic highs contribute to the presence of subtropical deserts on either side of the equator.

Another contributing circumstance arises from the prevailing movement of air streams in the western sectors of the persistent oceanic highs. This movement is normally poleward in the middle latitudes, recurving gradually eastward on entering increasingly higher latitudes. Moist air from the sea is thus deflected away from the southwestern section of North America, southern South America, southern Africa, and the central interior of Australia, depriving those areas of reliable precipitation. Still another factor is the influence of major mountain ranges on the prevailing atmospheric circulation. This produces a rain shadow effect in countless areas of diverse size and configuration.

Subtropical deserts occupy positions along whose equatorward borders are tropical savanna grasslands with rainy summers and dry winters. Along their poleward coastal margins are mediterranean regions of wet winters and dry summers. East of them are mid-latitude grasslands with a summer increase in precipitation, into which they gradually merge through semiarid borderlands of mixed desert shrub, bunch grass, and steppe. (In the last regional relationship the Sahara is an exception, which will be explained in Chapter 19.)

Geographical circumstances, leading to great variety in the size, shape, and distribution of subtropical deserts, also produce a great many variations in climatic characteristics. Coastal alignment, land elevation, and surface configuration are among the significant features leading to climatic contrasts. But subtropical deserts tend to share a number of climatic qualities in common. If we ignore for a moment the coastal deserts, the following similarities generally hold true among the interior subtropical deserts: a high percentage of possible sunshine, clear nights and clear, sunny days, low relative humidity, large annual temperature range and large daily temperature fluctuations, considerable windiness and a high frequency of dust storms, unreliable precipitation and yet catastrophic flooding when rare and unpredictable rains do occur.

West coast deserts, although sharing the same generic origins traceable to the primary influence of the subtropical highs and experiencing the same uncertainties of precipitation, the same pervading aridity, and occasionally many other qualities of interior deserts, normally experience higher relative humidities and a much higher percentage of cloud cover. In many cases they are typically visited by a great deal of foggy weather, their seaward margins exposed to drenching mist or very light drizzle. Maritime exposure also delays and prolongs both the warmest and coldest seasons of the year, producing the expected temperature lag of marine situations in contrast to interior locations in the mid-latitudes.

North American Deserts

Ascending the eastern slopes of the Rocky Mountains from the western margins of the Great Plains in the United States, one leaves the broad central lowland of North America and enters a region of elevated basins and plateaus that extends from British Columbia southward into central Mexico. It is partly enclosed by the high rim of the Rocky Mountain ranges to the east and the Sierra Nevada and Cascade ranges to the west, and is commonly referred to as the intermontane plateau. Most of this extensive territory stands more than 5000 feet above sea level. The surface is generously varied by the presence of countless lesser mountain ranges, elevated plateaus, a scattering of buttes, mesas, and pinnacles, and a number of steep-sided deep canyons, and shallower arroyos. The distinctive character of the intermontane

plateau is preserved southward into central Mexico between the higher converging ramparts of the Sierra Madre Oriental and the Sierra Madre Occidental, rising toward its southern limits in the belt of volcanic mountains lying transversely across the narrowing span of the middle part of the country.

A sizeable number of shallow stream courses empty into enclosed, elevated basins, and the intermittent flow of their waters, failing to reach the sea, is described as interior drainage. Three rivers, however, maintain a constant flow of sufficient volume to gain the coast and enter the sea. These are the Snake River and its tributaries, flowing northwestward into the lower Columbia, the Colorado, flowing southwestward into the Gulf of California, and the Rio Grande, draining southeastward into the Gulf of Mexico. Where these rivers and their tributaries have been eroding the broad intermontane upland, the ruggedly dissected surface has been unevenly eaten away, and elevations fall off toward sea level. Southwestward elevations drop down toward an elongated structural depression called the California Rift, which includes Death Valley, east of the southern end of the Sierra Nevada at 282 feet below sea level, Salton Sink, near the Mexican border at 235 feet below sea level, and the Gulf of California. Beyond the Sierra Nevada is the structural depression of California's Central Valley.

It is within the compass of this great western upland and certain of the Pacific lowlands in the United States and northern Mexico that the North American deserts are found. From the middle Columbia valley southeastward for about 2000 miles to the arid basins northeast of Aguascalientes in central Mexico, arid regions extend over a span of 26 degrees of latitude, from 48° to 22° (Fig. 18.5). From their eastern limits to the southwest coast they extend in scattered distribution for some 800 miles, and they range in altitude from more than 7000 feet above sea level to less than 200 feet below sea level.

The details of desert distribution are enormously complicated by the tumbled complexities of land form variety and distribution. Although arid conditions extend over vast expanses of the intermontane plateau and adjoining lowlands, they are again and again interrupted by forested mountain ranges,

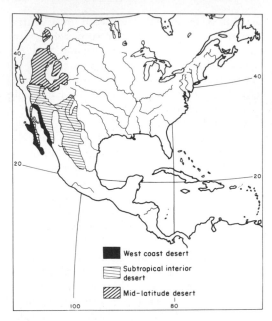

Figure 18.5. Distribution of desert in North America.

extensive, grass-covered plains, and the grassy slopes of mountain foothills. Many a small, arid basin receiving less than 10 inches of annual precipitation lies in the eastern lee of a humid, well-wooded mountain range where yearly amounts may exceed 40 inches. Rising up into the forested mountain from the desert plain there is often a semi-arid transitional belt of grassland where precipitation increases with altitude to much more than 10 inches. Throughout the west arid conditions are invariably bordered by conditions of semi-aridity. But the distinction is seldom plain, for the boundaries between aridity and semi-aridity are in a constant state of dynamic change. Indeed, the inclusion of many areas in the category of the arid lands is seriously open to question, for surface aridity—enduring soil moisture deficiency—is a consequence not only of low and variable precipitation but, as noted above, of soil porosity, geological structure, slope, and exposure as well.

The distribution of specific desert regions, proceeding from north to south, begins in the great bend of the Columbia River in southeastern Washington at the northern end of the geomorphic region called the Columbian plateau. This is a rain shadow desert, occupying a deeply channeled rocky plateau averaging

about 2000 feet above sea level, extending about 100 miles in east-west breadth and about 150 miles from north to south into the northern fringe of Oregon. In central Oregon is an area of about equal size called the Great Sandy desert, an elevated basin averaging about 5000 feet above sea level, with intermittent streams, playa lakes, and other features of internal drainage. It is almost continuous with the somewhat lower rocky plains of the middle Snake River valley in southern Idaho. In north central Wyoming the Bighorn basin, nearly 5000 feet in altitude, and in the southwestern part of the state Bridger basin, about 7000 feet, are slightly smaller desert tracts almost entirely hemmed in by the lofty ranges of the Rockies.

Beginning in southeastern Oregon and southwestern Idaho is the Great Basin, a region of mountain and bolson desert that extends southward to occupy nearly all of Nevada and eastward into the Great Salt Lake desert of western Utah, including Great Salt Lake. The mean elevation of the Great Basin exceeds 5000 feet save in the lower interior drainage areas of western Nevada, occupied by the Humboldt River and Pyramid Lake, and western Utah, where elevations are between 4000 and 5000 feet. The Wasatch Range of the Rocky Mountain system, extending from north to south through central Utah, separates the Great Basin from the Colorado plateau, where the upper Colorado River and its tributaries, fed by the rains and meltwater of the southern Rockies, have cut deeply into the horizontal sedimentary and volcanic rock formations of eastern Utah, western Colorado, northwestern New Mexico, and the Painted Desert of northeastern Arizona. Elevations in southern Nevada drop rapidly down toward the sub-sea level depressions of the California Rift and rise again into the Mojave desert between the southern end of the Sierra Nevada and the Transverse Ranges north of the Los Angeles lowland, where the mean surface altitude is about 2000 feet. The designation *Mojave desert* is applied to the entire area between the Colorado River and the southern end of the Sierra Nevada, including the Owens valley in the shadow of the mountains and from the 34th parallel into southern Nevada, south of the Great Basin.[1] Along the southwestern side

[1] Carle Hodge and P. C. Duisberg, eds., *Aridity and Man*, American Association for the Advancement of Science, Washington D.C., 1963, p. 40.

of the San Joaquin valley a desert plain extends for more than 100 miles from the foothills of the Diablo Range to the Transverse Ranges.

South of the Mojave desert region between the coastal ranges west of the Salton Sea and the Mogollan plateau of central Arizona the Sonoran desert begins, extending southward over most of the mountainous peninsula of Lower California (except the northwestern part sloping toward the Pacific which is the southernmost extension of mediterranean California) and along the mainland shores as far south as the Rio Yaqui valley in Mexico, near the port of Guaymas.

From southern New Mexico southward over the interior highlands of central Mexico as far as the 22nd parallel, a distance of about 1000 miles, is the great Chihuahuan desert, reaching up the Rio Grande valley onto the eastern slopes of the Gallina and Zuni mountains southwest of Albuquerque and up the Pecos valley east of the Sacramento Mountains spreading to the western edges of the Edwards Plateau in southern Texas. Just north of the uppermost drainage of the Rio Grande in south central Colorado is the arid basin of the San Luis valley, between the San Juan and the Sangre de Cristo ranges of the southern Rockies, one of the higher desert areas in the west, averaging between 7000 and 8000 feet in elevation and occupied by extensive sand dunes.

The typically scattered vegetation of the North American deserts includes an impressive variety of low-growing plants. The dominant desert shrub formations fall into two major classes. From the Columbia and Wyoming basins to the southern limits of the Great Basin and the Colorado plateau, silvery brown species of fragrant sagebrush (*Artemisia spp.*) carpet the desert floor in those cooler and frequently higher sections of arid land. In the more southerly deserts where temperatures are higher creosotebush (*Larrea divaricata*) is the dominant shrub, often intermingled with a high proportion of mesquite (*Prosopis spp.*). Creosotebush imparts a pale, olive-green cast to the landscape against the darker brownish-green of mesquite and emits a pungent smell of tar after the moistening of a desert rain.

The atmospheric qualities that prevail over the great variety of arid areas comprising the North American deserts are, in their turn, also considerably diverse. Those characteristics that we have considered for each climatic region, including mean annual precipitation, mean and extreme yearly temperature ranges, length of growing season, and related qualities, cannot satisfactorily be generalized. Differences arise in consequence of many contrasts among specific desert localities in size, elevation, distance from the sea, and relation to major relief features.

In general, mean annual precipitation is less than 10 inches throughout all the desert areas except in central Mexico, where, toward the southern limits of regional aridity, values rise to 15 inches or more (Fig. 6.10). In those lower latitudes the radiant heat from the higher sun is especially effective as an evaporative agent, compensating for the larger amounts of rain. But of greater importance than amount of precipitation, consistent with the concept of a desert as a region of pervading moisture-deficiency, are the kinds of precipitation, the seasons of their expected occurrence, and their relative reliability, or rather, the degree of their unreliability.

Over most of the northern sagebrush section west of the Rockies and southward into Death Valley, the Mojave desert, the upper San Joaquin valley, and on into northern Baja California, the cooler season of the year sees the maximum precipitation. Those small amounts of rain or snow that fall over this segment of arid land are chiefly produced by the cyclonic storms from the Pacific that are typical of the winter half-year. Over much of the northern Great Basin and in the higher desert areas of Wyoming and Colorado more than 30 per cent of the year's precipitation falls in the form of snow. In the southern creosotebush deserts snowfalls are much less frequent, the amount and duration are negligible, and along the water's edge in the Gulf of California and the Pacific side of Baja California they are scarcely known at all. The bulk of the precipitation between October and April occurs in the form of light, prolonged, soaking rain.

Over the eastern desert tracts near the Rockies from the upper valley of the Snake and the Bighorn basin in Wyoming southward to central Mexico the season of maximum precipitation is summer. The main source of moisture is north-flowing air from the Gulf of Mexico, precipitated in the form of thermal convective showers. Summer rainfall maxima hold true as well for the southern part of Baja

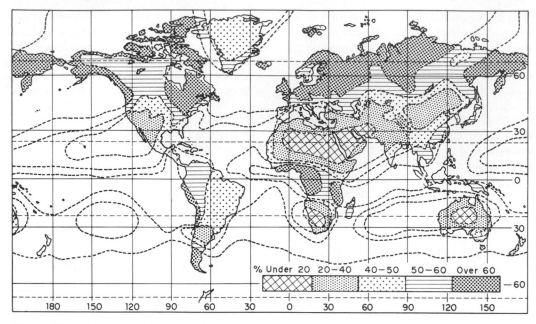

Figure 18.6. Mean annual cloud cover for the world in per cent of sky covered.

California and the mainland coast of the Gulf of California, where moist air from over the warm waters of the tropical Pacific flows onshore, augmented by occasional tropical cyclones originating far to the southward late in the season.

The change in regime from a winter maximum to a summer maximum takes place rapidly in eastern sections of desert country (Fig. 13.14). For example, Redmond, Ore., averaging 8.5 inches, receives a peak monthly precipitation of 1.1 inch in December. Twin Falls, Idaho, averaging 8.7 inches, receives 1 inch in January, whereas Idaho Falls about 150 miles northeast, averaging 7.4 inches, receives 1.1 inch in June, and Deaver in the Bighorn basin, averaging 5.3 inches, receives 1.2 inch also in June. Reno, Nev., averaging 7 inches, receives a peak precipitation of about 1 inch in both January and February, compared with Milford, Utah, about 400 miles east, averaging 8.4 inches, which receives its largest monthly amount of 1.1 inch in March. Grand Junction, Colo., about 240 miles farther eastward, averages 9.1 inches, receiving a peak amount of 1.2 inch in August, and Alamosa, about 180 miles southeastward, averaging 6.2 inches, receives 1.1 inch again in August. Very low mean annual amounts are reported from stations in the depressions of the

California Rift, where, at Greenland Ranch in Death Valley, the value is 1.8 inch, at Brawley, Imperial Valley, near the Mexican border, it is 2.5 inches, at Yuma, Ariz., 3.4 inches, and at Guaymas, Sonora, on the Mexican mainland coast, it is 4.9 inches.

Relative reliability of precipitation is an important key to the existence of desert areas (Fig. 18.1). Variability is least in the northern deserts where winter is the season of maximum precipitation, and a certain amount of rain and snow can be counted on each year. But the relative reliability of winter's precipitation is offset by the fact that summers are normally dry, and drought-ridden landscapes prevail. Departures from normal annual amounts ordinarily exceed 20 per cent. Thus, where 10 inches is the expected value, the actual amount that can be anticipated during any given year is between 8 and 12 inches and is often widely different from these deviations.

The dependability of yearly precipitation is least in the areas of summer maximum. Any year may produce a rainfall total that deviates from the statistical average by one fourth to one third. A single heavy rain may compensate for a prolonged period of subnormal precipitation lasting for several years. Bagdad in the Mojave desert, averaging 2.3 inches, received during the period from February 1917 to January 1920 only 0.01 inch, in March 1919. During a subsequent year it reported 9.9 inches. Yuma, Ariz., having a mean rainfall of 3.4 inches, received 11.4 inches in 1905 and 0.3 inch in 1953.[2]

In the summer maximum deserts thermal convection frequently produces towering cumulus clouds that actually release considerable quantities of rain. But the downward drifting veils of shadowy showers are evaporated in the hot dry air before reaching the ground. By contrast with this discouragingly unrewarding phenomenon, heavy thunderheads occasionally grow to the point of producing torrential thunderstorms. They occur with special intensity over mountainous terrain, aided by orographic uplift, then drift out over the adjoining desert, delivering unusually large amounts of water to the thirsty land. The resulting cascade of water rushing down the dry or nearly dry stream courses sets off the much dreaded flash flood in canyon or arroyo. As

much as 2.9 inches of rain have fallen at El Paso in twenty-four hours, 2.6 inches at Las Vegas, 2.4 inches at Reno, and 2.1 inches at Yuma.

As many as twelve separate thunderstorm centers may appear over an area measuring about 10 by 10 (100 square) miles, but 80 per cent of them together may cover less than 4.5 square miles.[3] Thus, the scattered distribution of potentially rain-bearing convective showers, which in itself is important in the random distribution of desert rains, is augmented by the fact that such disturbances are small and typically affect only very small areas.

Clear, cloudless skies are the overriding atmospheric condition of the desert environment from dawn until dusk (Fig. 18.6). In summer most of the western deserts receive more than 80 per cent of possible sunshine from day to day, and from the San Joaquin valley southward over the Gulf of California more than 90 per cent is the rule (Fig. 18.7). During the winter months clear skies are less frequent, although even then the southern deserts experience more than 70 per cent of possible

[2] E. C. Jaeger, *The North American Deserts*, Stanford University Press, Stanford, Calif., 1957, p. 13.

[3] Hodge and Duisberg, *op. cit.*, pp. 124–25.

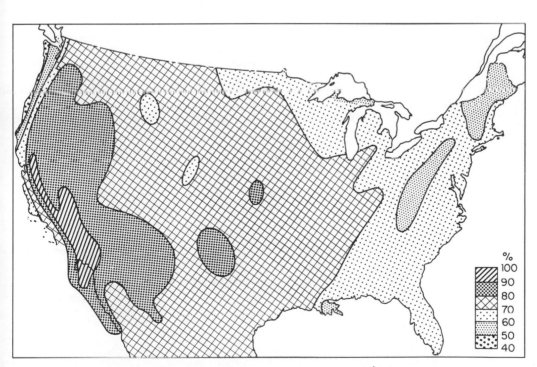

Figure 18.7. Percentage of possible sunshine received in the United States and adjacent Mexico from June through August.

sunshine. In the northern deserts, however, an abundance of cloudy weather brought in by the passage of numerous storm systems from the Pacific reduces the percentage of possible sunshine to between 40 and 50 per cent in general and between 30 and 40 per cent in the Columbia basin.

Under clear skies the sun's rays at dawn rapidly heat the bare ground, and the air adjacent to it begins to warm at once. Air temperatures rise swiftly to a maximum in midafternoon, dropping somewhat less quickly as the sun begins to lower in the west. At Yuma, Ariz., on August 6, 1951, a representative summer day, air temperature reached a minimum of 78° during the calm hours at dawn, but by 10 A.M. had reached 90°, by noon 103°, and by 3 P.M. the thermometer stood at 112°. Meanwhile, the dry soil, absorbing most of the sun's radiant heat in the top few centimeters, had attained a temperature of 147° at 3 P.M. Relative humidity was 8 per cent at noon and remained below 10 per cent during the early hours of the afternoon. The range of temperature fluctuation of 34 degrees from dawn to

midafternoon on that August 6 is representative for interior desert situations in summer but is not distinctive of arid regions alone. In a cleared valley near Storrs, Conn., for example, during July or August a daily temperature range of between 35 and 40 degrees is not at all uncommon under the clear, relatively dry air of a continental polar air mass. But the high levels within which the thermometer fluctuates at Yuma, as well as the very low relative humidity (Fig. 18.8), are distinctive of summer desert conditions and represent the common experience of interior arid regions the world over. In the North American deserts the mean daily temperature range averages more than 40 degrees in most areas at this season except at the higher altitudes and along the coast (Fig. 11.11). At coastal stations both the mean daily range and mean annual range of temperatures are inhibited by the frequent occurrence of advective fogs from the sea. But these effects seldom reach very far inland and remain largely confined to the seaward slopes of coastal mountain ranges.

The extremes of summer heat are well

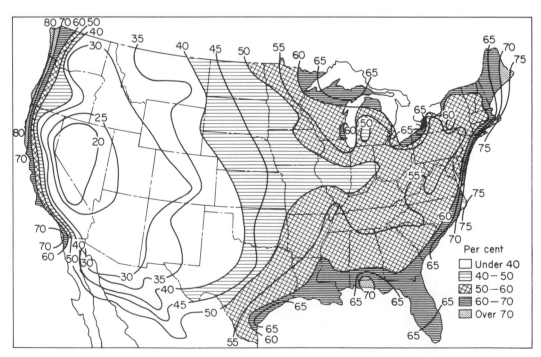

Figure 18.8. Mean relative humidity at noon in July in the United States (per cent). [By permission of the publishers from Stephen S. Visher, *Climatic Atlas of the United States*, Cambridge, Mass.: Harvard University Press, Copyright, 1954, by the President and Fellows of Harvard College.]

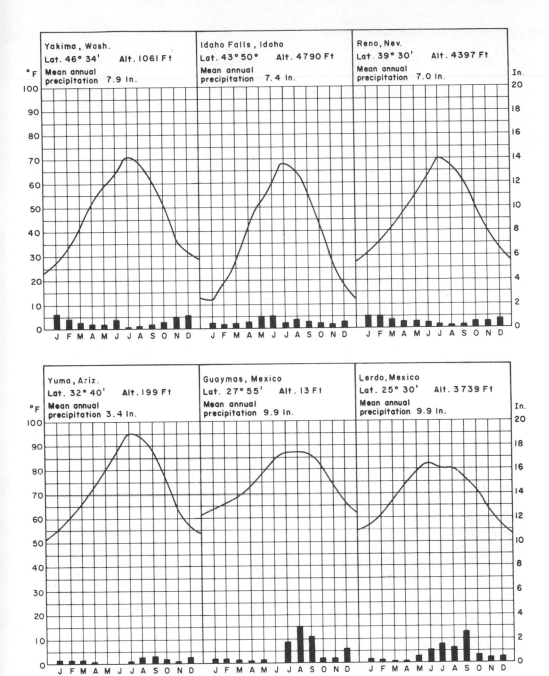

Figure 18.9. Temperature and precipitation at desert stations in North America.

known in certain desert situations (Fig. 11.9). In those below-sea level depressions of southern California, for example, mean July temperatures are unusually high, averaging 101° at Greenland Ranch (el. −178) in Death Valley, 95° at Yuma (el. 199) on the lower Colorado, and 93° at Brawley (el. −100), in the Imperial Valley. At these very low altitudes the denser

atmosphere is capable of taking up a high proportion of the heat transmitted from the desert floor. But at higher altitudes normal July temperatures are as a rule considerably lower. At Bakersfield in the southern end of the San Joaquin valley at an elevation of 489, the mean July temperature is 84°, but at Reno (el. 4397) and Elko (el. 5075) it is 70°, at Rock

Springs (el. 6741), in the upper Green River valley of southern Wyoming, it is 69°, and at Alamosa (el. 7536), in the upper Rio Grande valley of southern Colorado, it is 64° (Fig. 18.9).

The character of a site also influences thermal experience. Thus, Las Vegas (el. 2162) reports a July mean temperature of 91°, compared with that from the low altitude station of Bakersfield of 84°. Grand Junction, Colo., (el. 4849) averages 78° in July compared with 70° at Reno, which has a lower elevation of 4397 feet. July temperatures along the arid coast of northwestern Mexico are generally above 80° and at Guaymas are 87°.

But mean values, as usual, mask the details of actual thermal experience in desert situations, and one finds that even in the northern desert areas the thermometer commonly climbs to over 90° in midafternoon during most of July. From the Mojave desert southeastward the thermometer normally reads above 100° by midafternoon, and in Death Valley above 110°. Nocturnal cooling compensates for these mean daily maxima, and the mean temperature at dawn is between 70° and 80° in southwestern areas, between 50° and 60° in northern areas, and between 60° and 70° over the Mexican highlands, producing a mean daily range approaching 40 degrees in most interior situations.

The extreme maximum temperatures recorded in nearly all desert areas are well above 100° except in unusually high altitude basins, illustrated by the value of 91° for Alamosa at an altitude of 7536 feet. Greenland Ranch has recorded an extreme maximum of 134°, Yuma 120°, and Las Vegas 117°.

Winter temperatures in the southern creosotebush areas of desert country tend to remain above freezing (Fig. 11.12). In the somewhat lower altitude situations in parts of the Columbia basin and the Great Sandy desert of Oregon above-freezing means are also maintained, as at Yakima, with 36° in January, and Redmond, with 32°. With increasing altitude and increasing distance eastward from the coast, mean January temperatures become lower. The January average of 32° at Redmond (el. 2994) may be compared with those at Twin Falls, Idaho (el. 3770) of 27°, and at Idaho Falls (el. 4790) of 12°. (See Table 18-1.)

Throughout the sagebrush desert areas of the Great Basin and plateau regions midwinter temperatures frequently drop to well below zero. Alamosa has recorded an extreme minimum of −50°, which, with an extreme maximum in summer, gives it an extreme temperature range of 141 degrees; Elko has recorded −43° in winter, 107° in summer, producing a range of 150 degrees; and Deaver in the Bighorn basin has recorded −42° in winter and 106° in summer, producing an extreme range of 148 degrees. Extreme variations become lower in the southern creosotebush deserts: Greenland Ranch, where the thermometer has dropped to 15° in winter, has an extreme variation of 119 degrees, Yuma 92 (between the extremes of 120° in summer and 28° in winter). Along the coast winters are much milder and extremes not nearly as low as in interior areas. The mean January temperature at Guaymas is 64° and the lowest recorded value 47°, and at La Paz near the southern end of the peninsula January averages 57°, and the lowest reported value has been 45°. The extreme thermal variation at Guaymas is only 60 degrees (between 107° in summer and 47° in winter), and at La Paz 58 (103° to 45°).

The mean annual temperature range averages more than 50 degrees in the eastern part of the Great Basin and the Colorado plateau (Fig. 11.3), but with decreasing altitude the range becomes lower. It also lessens with decreasing latitude, and we note from Table 18-1 that in central Mexico at Lerdo it is 25 degrees, and at San Luis Potosi 16. Coastal localities also experience lower percentages of possible sunshine due to the higher frequency of cloud cover, fog, and more humid air in general. This can be attributed in large part to the sea surface temperature of the adjoining waters. In the Gulf of California the sea water temperature rises to more than 80° in August but is between 65° and 70° in February. Thus Guaymas experiences only about 57 per cent of possible sunshine in August and 65 per cent in February. The sunniest months are April, June, and October, when values are 70 per cent or more. Here relative humidities are much higher than in interior deserts, averaging 59 per cent for the year and ranging from a minimum of 48 per cent for afternoon readings in April, when clear weather prevails most of the time, to a maximum of 72 per cent for afternoon readings in December. It happens that April and May see a larger number of days with fog than other

TABLE 18–1
Climatic Data for Desert Stations in North America
(Temp., °F; Rainfall, In.)

Station	Lat.	El. in Ft		Jan.	Feb.	Mar.	Apr.	May	Jun.	Jul.	Aug.	Sep.	Oct.	Nov.	Dec.	Year
Redmond, Ore.	44°17'	2904	T	32	36	41	47	53	58	66	64	58	50	40	35	
			R	1.0	0.7	0.6	0.6	0.8	1.1	0.3	0.3	0.5	0.7	0.9	1.1	8.5
Idaho Falls, Idaho	43°50'	4790	T	12	19	29	42	52	60	68	65	55	44	29	18	
			R	0.5	0.4	0.5	0.6	1.0	1.1	0.5	0.8	0.6	0.5	0.3	0.6	7.4
Deaver, Wyo.	44°53'	4105	T	17	23	32	45	55	63	72	69	58	46	31	22	
			R	0.2	0.1	0.2	0.5	0.9	1.2	0.6	0.3	0.5	0.4	0.2	0.2	5.3
Reno, Nev.	39°30'	4397	T	31	36	41	48	55	62	70	67	61	51	40	33	
			R	1.0	1.1	0.7	0.5	0.5	0.4	0.2	0.2	0.2	0.6	0.6	0.9	7.0
Milford, Utah	38°26'	5028	T	24	31	39	48	57	66	74	72	63	50	37	28	
			R	0.6	0.7	1.1	0.8	0.7	0.5	0.8	0.8	0.4	0.9	0.5	0.8	8.4
Grand Junction, Colo.	39°07'	4849	T	24	32	41	52	62	71	78	76	67	54	39	29	
			R	0.6	0.6	0.9	0.8	0.7	0.5	0.8	1.2	1.0	0.8	0.6	0.7	9.1
Alamosa, Colo.	37°27'	7536	T	17	23	32	42	51	59	64	62	55	44	30	19	
			R	0.2	0.2	0.4	0.5	0.6	0.5	0.9	1.1	0.7	0.6	0.4	0.2	6.2
Bakersfield, Calif.	35°25'	489	T	47	53	57	63	70	77	84	82	76	67	56	49	
			R	1.0	1.1	1.1	0.8	0.4	0.1	0.0	0.0	0.1	0.4	0.4	1.0	6.4
Greenland Ranch, Calif.	36°28'	-178	T	52	58	67	77	85	93	101	99	91	77	62	53	
			R	0.2	0.3	0.2	0.2	0.1	0.0	0.1	0.2	0.1	0.1	0.2	0.3	1.8
Brawley, Calif.	32°59'	-119	T	54	58	64	72	79	86	93	93	88	76	63	56	
			R	0.3	0.4	0.1	0.1	0.0	0.0	0.0	0.4	0.3	0.3	0.1	0.4	2.5
Yuma, Ariz.	32°40'	199	T	55	60	66	73	80	88	95	94	88	76	64	57	
			R	0.3	0.3	0.3	0.1	0.0	0.0	0.2	0.5	0.6	0.3	0.1	0.6	3.4
Guaymas, Mexico	27°55'	13	T	64	66	69	73	78	84	87	87	86	81	73	66	
			R	0.3	0.3	0.2	0.1	0.1	0.0	1.8	3.0	2.2	0.4	0.4	1.1	9.9
El Paso, Tex.	31°48'	3920	T	43	49	55	63	72	80	81	80	75	65	52	45	
			R	0.4	0.4	0.3	0.3	0.4	0.6	1.3	1.3	1.1	0.8	0.4	0.5	7.8
Lerdo, Mexico	25°30'	3739	T	57	61	67	73	79	82	80	80	76	71	63	57	
			R	0.2	0.2	0.1	0.1	0.6	1.1	1.7	1.2	2.7	0.7	0.4	0.5	9.9
San Luis Potosi, Mexico	22°09'	6157	T	55	59	63	69	71	70	67	67	65	63	59	57	
			R	0.5	0.2	0.4	0.2	1.2	2.8	2.2	1.7	3.4	0.7	0.4	0.6	14.2

Source: U.S. Weather Bureau, *Climatography of the United States, Climates of the States,* Washington, 1959–60; F. L. Wernstedt, *World Climatic Data, Latin America and the Caribbean,* Pennsylvania State University, 1959.

months, but this is advected fog from the sea, which is normally dissipated by late morning or early afternoon.

The sea water temperatures in the Gulf of California do not represent the mean values experienced along the Pacific coast of the peninsula. Here, mean sea surface temperatures are between 60° and 68°, from north to south in February, and between 68° and 80° in August. Reliable station records of atmospheric parameters are lacking for the Pacific desert coast of Baja California, however.

South American Deserts

The deserts of South America are found in two major regions on opposite sides of the Andes: along the west coast between Ecuador and middle Chile (Fig. 18.10), and east of the Andes from northwestern Argentina to southern Patagonia (Fig. 14.2). On the inter-

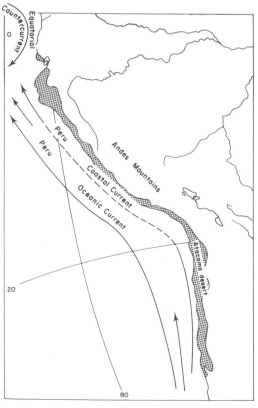

Figure 18.10. West coast desert in South America.

vening high plateaus of the lofty Andes in southern Peru, western Bolivia, northern Chile, and northwestern Argentina desert landscapes also appear, linking those at lower elevations in a single, unbroken sweep of aridity extending for more than 3500 miles from near the Gulf of Guayaquil almost to the Straits of Magellan. But the chill, bleak, barren lands of the high Andes trace their origin and climatic characteristics primarily to the influence of altitude (see Chapter 24). Two lesser areas should be mentioned: a persistent semidesert belt along the Caribbean coast of Venezuela, and a larger segment in northeastern Brazil where serious drought is a constant threat and the thorn scrub woodland is repeatedly reduced to a condition of stark aridity by the failure of the seasonal rains. Our present concern is with the west coast deserts of Peru and northern Chile, and with the deserts of Argentina.

THE WEST COAST DESERT. Along the Pacific coast of South America stretches a narrow, unbroken band of desert reaching for nearly 2000 miles from northern Peru to the Rio Elqui in Chile (Fig. 18.10). Thus, desert approaches La Serena and Coquimbo, some 200 miles north of Valparaiso, at 30°S. Lat. This unusually long, thin band of coastal desert, where in many places measurable rain occurs only at intervals of several years and where at some points it has never occurred at all, must be ranked among the world's most arid regions. Although west coast deserts are systematically distributed, nowhere else in the world are they found so near the equator.

The governing condition primarily responsible for the existence of this long desert strand between 4° and 30°S. Lat. is the counterclockwise circulation of the East Pacific High south of the equator (Figs. 4.2 and 4.3). Also important is the alignment of the coastline approximately parallel to the prevailing flow of air around the oceanic high, lying in a roughly north-south position as far north as about 18° and there turning northwestward to about 4° latitude. Still another important condition is the northward flow of relatively cold water in the Peru Current, bringing to each latitude it crosses sea surface water that is considerably colder than normal and causing the upwelling of still colder water close to the shore (Fig. 6.11). A final determining factor is the proximity of the Andean ranges, averaging between 2 and 3 miles in height throughout the length of the region, which effectively shield the Pacific shores from thrusts of air from the east. Acting upon these major conditions is the influence of altitude and surface configuration to produce the countless local variations of the over-all desert environment from end to end.

The long, narrow band of coastal desert separates environments of distinctly different kind. Along the coast in northern Peru there is a change to less arid conditions distinguished by xerophytic shrub from Punta Aguja northward across the Gulf of Guayaquil in westernmost Ecuador, then into tropical savanna, scrub forest, semideciduous forest, and finally tropical rainforest on the northwest coast of Ecuador (Fig. 18.11). Along the southern shores of the Gulf of Guayaquil in northernmost Peru mean annual rainfall amounts drop from about 10 inches at Zorritos to about 2 inches at Lobitos only 60 miles to the southwest. Inland, higher altitudes and more complex topography induce precipitation in amounts between these extremes, and xerophytic shrub desert continues somewhat farther southward of Punta Aguja. This is a region of warm season rainfall increase. Toward the southern limits of the great coastal desert, however, aridity yields to a steppe grassland transitional into mediterranean middle Chile, where annual rains occur chiefly in wintertime.

The slender arid zone extends inland from the Pacific an average distance of between 30 and 50 miles. It widens in a few places to a breadth of about 100 miles east of Punta Aguja in northern Peru, farther south about 70 miles east of Pisco, and again about 100 miles east of Antofagasta, Chile.

The seasonal shifts in position and changes in intensity of the dominant counterclockwise circulation of the semipermanent oceanic high in the eastern Pacific have been discussed in Chapter 14 (see Figs. 4.2 and 4.3). It is sufficient to recall that the persistent subtropical anticyclone reaches a maximum intensity and expands both poleward and equatorward to maximum size in November, at the beginning of summer, and contracts to its smallest size and weakens to minimum intensity in May, at the start of winter. Throughout the year the prevailing flow of air around this system along the coast of Peru and northern Chile is northward and northwestward, basically parallel to the shore-

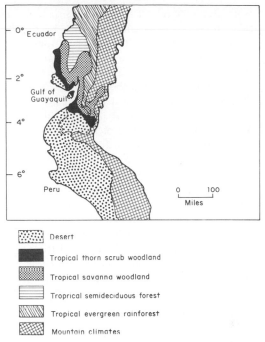

Desert

Tropical thorn scrub woodland

Tropical savanna woodland

Tropical semideciduous forest

Tropical evergreen rainforest

Mountain climates

Figure 18.11. Transition from tropical rainforest to desert in southern Ecuador and northern Peru.

line. Along the Peruvian coast it is commonly deflected inland, and in northern sections during the southern hemisphere summer is often augmented by a daily sea breeze. The reliability and strength of these onshore winds is locally sufficient to carry large quantities of sand and dust far inland, giving rise to long, low sand ridges and symmetrical crescent-shaped dunes attesting to the direction, the strength, and the frequency of such winds. Elsewhere, where the wind has removed the finer materials, are broad sheets of pebble pavement (the *reg* desert surface), gravel plains, and exposed bedrock.

The Peru Current, largely a product of the atmospheric circulation, maintains a fairly constant flow in the same north to northwesterly direction. It consists of two essentially distinct parts: the blue-green coastal current, between 100 and 250 miles wide, that hugs the shoreline at a speed of 0.3 to 1 knot, and the somewhat slower oceanic current, extending from 500 to 600 miles offshore, that is a deep, transparent indigo blue in color. The winter temperatures of the coastal current range from about 55°F (August) at 32°S. Lat. to 70°F near the Gulf of Guayaquil (Fig. 6.12) and in summer (February) from about 60° to 75°F within the same latitudes (Fig. 6.13). The oceanic current is slightly warmer at all seasons. The lower temperatures of the coastal current immediately adjacent to the shoreline are caused by the upwelling of deeper water brought about by a seaward deflection of surface water at many points. These temperatures in general average about 10 degrees lower than those of the sea surface far to the west in the open Pacific.

The fundamental process by which persistent aridity is maintained for some 2000 miles of South America's Pacific coast is thus seen to begin with the chilling of oceanic air in its passage over the Peru Current. As the air warms gradually on its northward journey into lower latitudes and even more so upon drifting over the highly heated land surfaces with these low latitudes, its moisture-retaining capacity is increased, and precipitation does not occur. This process is modified in several localities to produce certain distinctive features of climate.

The situation along the seaward flanks of the boldly rising coastal ranges in Chile and the piedmont margins in Peru is strikingly different from the interior. Along the high-rising seashore from the southern limits of desert northward beyond Lima, Peru, the winter season, roughly between May and October, is a time of cloudiness, fog, and high relative humidity. Rain, if it comes at all, occurs during this season along the coast. In the southernmost sections a blanket of cloud settles over the sea and the adjoining strand, sometimes enduring for several weeks, rising from time to time during daylight hours to produce a low overcast at sea level and drenching mist on the hillsides above. But the cloud deck is not a deep one, for the air is stable, and its upper surface is often not more than 200 feet above the sea. From the clear skies beyond the sun shines brightly and the air is dry. Northward the typical stratus cloud cover becomes increasingly thicker and develops at higher elevations. At Lima, for example, its lower surface averages about 2600 feet in altitude, and it is about 2000 feet thick. The yearly appearance of cloud and fog in winter takes place only about as far north as a point some 200 miles northwest of Lima. It is a coastal phenomenon, and only where deeply entrenched stream valleys along the Peruvian coast allow does it ordinarily penetrate inland. However, in the Atacama from time to time it advances down the inner slopes of the coastal ranges to blanket the interior bolsons, rising, retreating westward, and dissipating soon after dawn. The mists that occur when the stratus blanket touches the higher slopes of the coastal ranges and forelands are known as garuas and give rise to a grassy vegetation called loma.

From the Gulf of Guayaquil southward into Chile a summer regime of unstable air, scattered convective clouds, and perennial showers prevails along the high interior margins of the desert region. This zone of relatively reliable rainfall forms a transition between the alpine environments at higher altitudes and the desert below. Its lower limit rises with increasing distance southward. At about latitude 7° opposite the coastal station of Guadalupe it is around 3000 feet; at 12° inland from Lima it is around 5000 feet; at 14° opposite Pisco it is more than 7000 feet; at Arequipa in latitude 17° it is above 8000 feet. The lower limit of perennial rains continues at this high altitude as far south as the Tropic of Capricorn opposite Antofagasta, where it occasionally rises to over 10,000 feet. Thus, the altitudinal range of the west coast desert as a whole increases from between sea level and 3000 feet in the north to between sea level and about 10,000 feet in the central part of the Atacama. It is here, near where the Tropic intersects the Andes, that the summer rainfall regime of the interior mountain slopes comes to an end.

Along the coast southward from Punta Aguja for about 350 miles summer is also the period when rains, if they occur at all, are most apt to fall. Thus, the change from a summer to a winter season of possible rain takes place at about latitude 10°.

One further climatic characteristic is the rare occurrence of heavy rains along the northern portions of the Peruvian coast. They take place when a branch of the Equatorial Countercurrent brings unusually warm water southeastward along the shore beyond Lima, sometimes extending as far as Pisco. The southward displacement of warm equatorial water is a systematic phenomenon that occurs during the latter part of summer from about January through March. But the warm layer is normally shallow, persists for but a few days, seldom advances farther than Guadalupe, and normally does not appreciably raise the temperature of the air above it. Because it appears soon after Christmas, it is known locally as El Nino, the Christ Child.

At intervals that average about once every seven years, El Nino is deeper (about 75 feet), much warmer, and remains a good deal longer than usual, pushing a narrow tongue of equatorial water about 20 miles wide steadily southeastward to raise the air temperature above it to abnormally high levels. The higher than usual temperature of the air and the consequent increase in its capacity to take up moisture produce a condition of instability resulting in exceptionally heavy rains at points along the north coast. "At Trujillo, between 1918 and 1925, the total rainfall was only 1.4 inches; but during the month of March, 1925, a total of 15.5 inches fell, and on the three days from the 7th to the 9th rainfall was 8.9 inches."[4]

It is certainly as true of most of South America's west coast desert as it is of any of the world's more arid regions that there is no such thing as a normal rainfall.[5] But even at places

[4] Preston E. James, *Latin America*, The Odyssey Press, New York, 1959, p.193

[5] This and other comments on details of rainfall in Peru and the Atacama are derived from Isaiah Bowman, *The Andes of Southern Peru*, New York, 1916, pp. 121–81, and Bowman, *Desert Trails of Atacama*, American Geographical Society Special Publication No. 5, New York, 1924, pp. 40–59.

where no rain has ever been known to fall, the record may some day be broken. At Calama (el. 7438) about 125 miles northeast of Antofagasta, where no rainfall had ever been recorded, a thick blanket of snow fell in June 1911. At Iquique on the coast, after fourteen years without precipitation, a hard rain fell during a single night, and in 1906 a series of showers alternating with spells of mist continued for three days.

Elsewhere in the Atacama meltwater from heavy snows in the Andes has sent torrents of water raging down the valleys of the foothills out over the floors of the salars, or playa basins, scouring the stream courses and spreading sand and gravel into the bolsons. Nearly all the work of erosion here, as in other arid regions, is accomplished by running water, although its arrival is sporadic and unpredictable. Most of the anomalous rains of the interior, as far south as the Tropic of Capricorn, take place in the warmer season when an unusual expansion of warm, unstable air moves down off the high Andes, spreading its effects progressively southward. From the Tropic southward sporadic rains can be expected chiefly in the winter months (Fig. 18.12). The change from drought-ridden desert to the more certain but still minute amounts of rain producing steppe

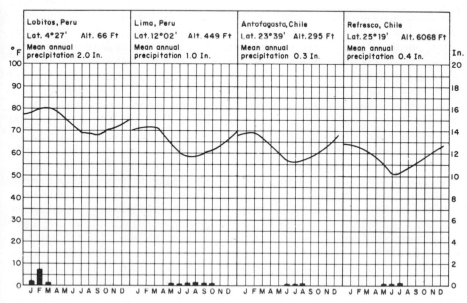

Figure 18.12. Temperature and precipitation at west coast desert stations in South America.

grasslands takes place within the relatively short distance of about 100 miles between Copiapo and Vallenar. At Copiapo (el. 1214), where 1.1 inch is the statistical average rainfall, one wet year of a few showers is expected every twelve years, but at Vallenar (el. 1542), where 2.5 inches is the calculated average, one dry year in twelve is anticipated.

Summer, when the sun is high overhead throughout the length of the coastal desert region, is well established by November. By this time the oceanic high pressure system over the eastern Pacific has attained its maximum mean intensity of 1022.5 millibars and by expanding both northward and southward has gained its greatest extent. From November onward the north coastal and interior desert borders high up on the Andean slopes experience an increase in the percentage of the sky occupied by scattered clouds, the long, thin lines of cumulus reaching increasingly farther southward as the season advances. Meanwhile, coastal cloud and fog retreat southward, progressively lessening the amount as summer continues, diminishing at Lima from 66 per cent in November to a yearly minimum of 44 per cent in April; at Arica from 54 per cent in November to a minimum of 33 per cent in March; at Antofagasta from 41 per cent in November to a minimum of 27 per cent in February and March.

Fog as well as cloud cover decreases, along with the likelihood of rain along the coast, but relative humidity remains high. Afternoon mean values at Lima reach a yearly minimum in March of 64 per cent, at Arica in February of 72 per cent, and at Antofagasta in January of 62 per cent. Inside the coastal ranges and forelands, however, percentages are commonly less than half the above amounts where cloudless skies and warm, dry sunny weather prevails.

Highest mean monthly air temperatures are delayed until well past midsummer, as might be expected in this conspicuously marine climate. January and February are the warmest months from Caldera to Iquique, February the maximum month northward to Mollendo, February and March from Lima to Lobitos, and March at Zorritos, near the border of Ecuador. Also, as expected, mean values for the warmest month, responding to the primary influence of sea surface temperatures along the coast, increase northward, with 68° at Caldera, 71° at

Taltal, 70° at Iquique, 71° at Arica, Mollendo, and Paramonga, 78° at Guadalupe, and 80° at Lobitos and Zorritos (Table 18-2). In the interior values for the warmest months are usually higher where stations stand less than about 2000 feet above sea level. At Copiapo (el. 1214) February averages 69° compared with the coastal station of Caldera, which averages 68°, and Piura (el. 174), averages 82° in February compared with 80° at Lobitos on the coast. But at higher elevations in the interior temperatures of the warmest month are usually considerably lower. At Potrerillos (el. 9368), about 100 miles northeast of Caldera, the mean February temperature is 58°, 10 degrees lower than Caldera; Refresco (el. 6068) reports 64° in January compared with 71° at Taltal, about 40 miles distant on the coast; Arequipa (el. 8041) reports 58° for February compared with 71° at Mollendo, about 50 miles away on the coast (Fig. 18.12).

May marks the onset of winter, when the semipermanent oceanic high contracts to its minimum extent and attains its minimum intensity of 1017.5 millibars. The incidence of convective clouds diminishes along the northwest coast and the high interior desert margins, but cloud cover and fog set in rapidly along most of the shoreline. At Antofagasta cloud cover increases from 31 per cent in April to 39 per cent in May, rising to a maximum of 47 per cent in September; at Arica it increases from 39 per cent in April to 60 per cent in May, reaching a maximum of 72 per cent in August; at Lima, from 44 per cent in April to 66 per cent in May, reaching a maximum of 91 per cent in August. Temperatures lower to the season's minimum in July from Punta Tortuga to Taltal, July and August from Antofagasta to Arica, August from Mollendo to Lima, and September from Paramonga to Lobitos. The temperature of the coldest month increases gradually northward along the coast, from 54° at Punta Tortuga to 71° at Zorritos (Table 18-2). Inland stations at higher altitudes report values appreciably lower than those for sea level stations. The difference is slight between Copiapo (el. 1214), averaging 54°, and Caldera 55°. Potrerillos (el. 9368), on the other hand, averages 46° and Refresco (el. 6068) 51° compared with 56° at Taltal, and Arequipa (el. 8041) averages 56° compared with 59° for Mollendo.

Mean annual temperature ranges are between 10 and 15 degrees, a further consequence

TABLE 18-2

Climatic Data for West Coast Desert Stations of South America
(Temp., °F; Rainfall, In.)

Station	Lat.	El. in Ft		Jan.	Feb.	Mar.	Apr.	May	Jun.	Jul.	Aug.	Sep.	Oct.	Nov.	Dec.	Year
Lobitos, Peru	4°27'	66	T	78	80	80	79	75	72	69	69	68	70	71	73	
			R	0.4	1.5	0.1	0.0	0.0	0.0	0.0	0.0	0.0	0.0	0.0	0.0	2.0
Guadalupe, Peru	7°15'	328	T	77	78	78	75	74	68	66	66	65	67	69	72	
			R	0.1	0.2	0.2	0.1	0.0	0.0	0.0	0.0	0.0	0.1	0.1	0.1	0.9
Trujillo, Peru	8°08'	197	T	77	77	74	72	68	63	64	64	64	68	69	72	
			R	0.2	0.5	0.3	0.0	0.0	0.0	0.1	0.0	0.0	0.0	0.1	0.0	1.2
Lima, Peru	12°02'	449	T	71	72	72	68	64	60	59	59	60	61	63	66	
			R	0.0	0.0	0.0	0.0	0.1	0.1	0.2	0.3	0.2	0.1	0.0	0.0	1.0
Mollendo, Peru	17°02'	79	T	70	71	70	67	65	62	60	59	60	62	66	68	
			R	0.0	0.1	0.0	0.0	0.1	0.0	0.0	0.2	0.2	0.1	0.1	0.0	0.8
Arequipa, Peru	16°27'	8041	T	57	57	56	57	57	56	56	57	58	57	57	57	
			R	1.2	1.8	0.6	0.2	0.0	0.0	0.0	0.0	0.0	0.0	0.0	0.4	4.2
Iquique, Chile	20°12'	98	T	70	69	68	65	63	61	60	60	61	63	65	68	
			R	0.0	0.0	0.0	0.0	0.0	0.0	0.0	0.0	0.0	0.0	0.0	0.0	0.1
Potrerillos, Chile	26°30'	9348	T	57	58	56	54	50	46	47	47	50	53	56	57	
			R	0.1	0.1	0.1	0.1	0.6	0.4	0.4	0.6	0.1	0.1	0.0	0.0	2.4
Refresco, Chile	25°19'	6068	T	64	63	61	59	55	51	52	54	56	58	61	61	
			R	0.0	0.0	0.0	0.0	0.1	0.1	0.2	0.0	0.0	0.0	0.0	0.0	0.4
Antofagasta, Chile	23°39'	295	T	69	69	66	63	60	57	56	57	58	60	63	66	
			R	0.0	0.0	0.0	0.0	0.0	0.1	0.1	0.1	0.0	0.0	0.0	0.0	0.3
Copiapo, Chile	27°21'	1214	T	68	69	66	62	57	54	54	56	58	61	64	67	
			R	0.0	0.0	0.0	0.0	0.2	0.5	0.2	0.1	0.0	0.1	0.0	0.0	1.1
Vallenar, Chile	28°34'	1542	T	67	67	66	61	57	52	53	54	55	57	61	65	
			R	0.0	0.0	0.0	0.1	0.4	1.0	0.4	0.5	0.1	0.1	0.0	0.0	2.5
Caldera, Chile	37°03'	46	T	68	68	65	62	59	56	55	56	57	59	62	65	
			R	0.0	0.0	0.0	0.1	0.1	0.4	0.2	0.2	0.0	0.1	0.0	0.0	1.1

Source: F. L. Wernstedt, *World Climatic Data, Latin America and the Caribbean*, Pennsylvania State University, 1959; W. Köppen and R. Geiger, *Handbuch der Klimatologie*, 2 (Part G), 1930.

of the prevailing influence of air from the sea. Extremes of temperature are not great, even in the interior. Except at very high altitudes, frost is rare, but the thermometer has registered above 100° at many inland stations. Along the coast values above 90° have been attained, 92° at Antofagasta, 90° at Arica, and 93° at Lima, but subfreezing temperatures have not been reached.

DESERTS OF ARGENTINA.   East of the Andes a second major desert region in South America extends southward for about 1600 miles from the uneven margins of the high, wide plateau called the Puna de Atacama in northwestern Argentina to the Straits of Magellan (Fig. 14.2). Its latitudinal span is about 25 degrees, from 27° to 52°S. The Puna de Atacama is a bleak, barren, arid region of xerophytic shrubs and grasses, but as it is a high plateau of between 11,000 and 13,000 feet in altitude, its climate belongs to those of the mountain regions of the world and will not be discussed here. The alpine plateau comes to an end where its massive bulk breaks off into attenuated ranges that extend southward at decreasing elevations, approximately between the latitudes of Tucuman and Mendoza. Tucuman, center of a flourishing, well-watered agricultural region, and Santiago del Estero, about 100 miles to the southeast, lie within the Gran Chaco of northern Argentina, where tropical savanna begins to merge with the mid-latitude grasslands discussed in Chapter 17.

The northern limits of arid land at lower elevations in Argentina are marked by the isolated bolson of Fiambala, which lies about 150 miles west-southwest of Tucuman. It is about the same distance east of Copiapo in the southern Atacama, from which it is separated by the high rampart of the Andes, here rising at many points to more than 19,000 feet. The basin averages about 5000 feet above sea level, is open to the southeast, but otherwise is hemmed in, not only by the Andean heights toward the west but also by very lofty spurs of the Puna de Atacama, which reach well over 13,000 feet. Mountain and bolson topography provides the physical setting of Argentina's northern arid country southward from the Fiambala basin for about 400 miles. Isolated ranges, alluvial pediments, intermittent streams, interior drainage systems in which extensive saline playa flats called salinas have accumulated—these are the principal features. This topography comes abruptly to an end at the Rio Mendoza, which is approximately opposite Valparaiso on the Pacific coast. From here to the Straits of Magellan are the dreary, barren rock plains of the Patagonian plateau. This inhospitably arid region consists chiefly of interrupted rock terraces, arid, gravel-covered plains supporting scattered bunch grass and dwarf thorn shrubs that descend gradually seaward, dropping off abruptly in steep cliffs a few hundred feet above the waters of the Atlantic. The region is drained by many small streams that never reach the sea but empty instead into shallow, occasionally marshy, elevated depressions that in winter may contain water but in summer are dry and white with heavy accumulations of salts. A few flow from the Andes across the arid upland to the Atlantic, often deeply entrenched in steep-sided arroyos.

The northern half of the Argentine desert environment is interposed between the Andes and the grasslands of the north and east, the southern half between the Andes and the Atlantic. In the section around the Fiambala basin its western limits are far up the Andean slopes at about 12,000 feet in altitude, lowering to about 5000 feet near Mendoza and to about 3000 feet in the headwaters region of the Rio Colorado. From here southward the western inland margins of desert country remain at between 2000 and 3000 feet, descending to only a few hundred feet above sea level near the Straits of Magellan.

The existence of Argentina's elongated desert environment is primarily due to the influence of the Andes on the predominantly eastward flow of the zonal circulation in the middle latitudes. In the southern half of the arid region the Andes produce an effective rain shadow, wherein maritime polar air from the Pacific loses most of its precipitable moisture on the western mountain slopes and, flowing down over Patagonia, fails to produce rain until well out over the South Atlantic. The surface circulation here is mainly from the west and southwest. In the northern half of the desert regions the dominant flow of air is northward, which results from the fact that the Andes deflect a portion of the westerlies air stream in that direction. This air, warming on its journey into lower latitudes, tends to retain its moisture, and little precipitation occurs. From time to

TABLE 18-3

Climatic Data for Desert Stations in Argentina

(Temp., °F; Rainfall, In.)

Station	Lat.	El. in Ft		Jan.	Feb.	Mar.	Apr.	May	Jun.	Jul.	Aug.	Sep.	Oct.	Nov.	Dec.	Year
Andalgala	27°33'	3486	T	77	75	70	64	57	50	50	55	62	66	73	78	
			R	2.8	2.9	1.8	0.8	0.5	0.2	0.2	0.2	0.3	1.0	1.5	2.1	14.2
Tinogasta	28°04'	3949	T	77	75	70	64	55	48	48	55	61	68	73	78	
			R	2.2	1.6	0.8	0.3	0.0	0.0	0.1	0.1	0.1	0.2	0.3	0.9	6.5
Chilecito	29°10'	3611	T	76	75	69	62	55	47	48	53	60	66	71	77	
			R	1.9	1.4	1.1	0.3	0.2	0.0	0.1	0.1	0.2	0.3	0.5	0.9	7.1
San Juan	31°37'	2066	T	79	75	69	62	53	47	46	51	58	66	72	78	
			R	1.0	0.6	0.5	0.2	0.1	0.1	0.1	0.1	0.2	0.2	0.4	0.3	3.8
Mendoza	32°53'	2713	T	75	73	68	61	53	48	46	51	57	63	69	74	
			R	1.1	1.1	0.9	0.4	0.4	0.3	0.3	0.3	0.6	0.8	0.6	0.8	7.6
Malargue	35°29'	4651	T	67	65	58	52	44	39	37	40	48	56	60	65	
			R	0.4	0.9	0.8	0.5	0.6	0.8	1.3	1.4	0.4	0.3	0.3	0.2	7.8
Chos Malal	37°23'	2788	T	71	68	62	55	50	45	43	46	50	58	64	68	
			R	0.4	0.4	0.5	0.5	1.6	2.1	1.3	1.1	0.5	0.4	0.3	0.3	9.3
Cipolletti	38°56'	869	T	71	69	62	55	48	43	42	46	52	60	66	70	
			R	0.6	0.4	0.5	0.3	0.9	0.5	0.5	0.6	0.5	0.9	0.4	0.3	6.4
Colonia Sarmiento	45°35'	863	T	64	62	58	52	45	41	39	41	47	54	57	62	
			R	0.3	0.4	0.5	0.5	0.8	0.8	0.7	0.7	0.4	0.3	0.4	0.3	6.1
Commodoro Rivadavia	45°47'	200	T	66	65	60	56	49	46	44	45	50	56	60	64	
			R	0.4	0.6	0.7	0.7	1.2	1.0	0.9	0.7	0.6	0.4	0.6	0.5	8.3
Santa Cruz	50°01'	36	T	58	58	53	48	41	37	37	38	43	50	53	57	
			R	0.7	0.5	0.8	0.7	0.8	0.6	0.6	0.6	0.4	0.3	0.6	0.8	7.4

Source: F. L. Wernstedt, *World Climatic Data, Latin America and the Caribbean*, Pennsylvania State University, 1959.

time during the warm season the northern deserts are invaded by surges of warm, moist maritime tropical or equatorial air that is then acted upon by the powerful heating effect of the high sun in those lower latitudes, producing thermal convective showers of sporadic character that supplement the precipitation of occasional systematic storms. The South Atlantic exerts little or no direct effect on the deserts of Argentina, save in moderating the temperature of stations immediately adjacent to the sea.

Compared with the west coast deserts, the region east of the Andes is, on the whole, less arid. Mean annual precipitation amounts average less than 10 inches, vary widely from year to year, and are typically uncertain in actual amount and time of occurrence (Fig. 14.3). But prolonged periods without measurable rain are not known. San Juan, about 100 miles north of Mendoza, affords an extreme example, having experienced a rainless period of 671 days.[6] In the northern section from the Fiambala basin to about 150 miles south of Mendoza rains, when they occur, are chiefly a warm season phenomenon. South of here, in Patagonia, winter is the season of maximum probable precipitation.

In summertime, from October through March, when days are long and the sun is high in the sky, January is most commonly the month when mean temperatures are the highest for the year (Table 18-3). Along the coast, where the moderating influence of the sea prolongs the warm period, mean values are about equal in January and February. In the northernmost part of the mountain and bolson country, where the thermal experience of certain of those well-sheltered depressions is in close accord with the maximum height of the sun around the time of the solstice, December is the warmest month. Tinogasta, at the southeastern entrance to the basin of Fiambala, affords an illustration of this with a December mean temperature of 78°. Andalgala, about 100 miles northeastward, and Chilecito, about 100 miles south, both record 77° in December (Fig. 18.13).

From the Gulf of San Matias northwestward at altitudes of about 3000 feet or less the

warmest summer month averages above 70°. Mean values are below this from the Rio Negro southward to within about 200 miles of the Straits of Magellan, and from here to the Straits they are less than 60°. The mean daily range of temperature is between 30 and 35 degrees from the Rio Negro northward and between 25 and 30 degrees from here southward. Extreme summer temperatures have exceeded 100° throughout the region as far south as Puerto Deseado on the coast, about 350 miles north of the straits, where the thermometer has reached 102°. It has climbed to 110° at Tinogasta, 115° at San Juan, and 111° at Choele Choel on the Rio Negro.

During the summer most of the arid region enjoys more than 60 per cent of possible sunshine, although considerably less than this is the case in the area from the Rio Chubut to the Straits of Magellan. Expressed in terms of relative cloud cover, interior Patagonia south of Rio Chubut averages a summertime cover of more than 60 per cent (Colonia Sarmiento 66 per cent), compared with 38 per cent at Cipolletti, 36 per cent at Chos Malal, about 300 miles south of Mendoza, and 33 per cent at Mendoza. Fog is also more prevalent in the southernmost part of Patagonia. Sarmiento, about 90 miles inland from Commodoro Rivadavia on the shores of the Gulf of San Jorge, averages about ten days with fog in summer, whereas inland stations farther north rarely record more than two or three days. Relative humidity in most desert localities is lower at this season, averaging 31 per cent at Cipolletti and 41 per cent at Mendoza, with almost equally low values along the coast, Bahia Blanca reporting 40 per cent and Santa Cruz, about 150 miles north of the straits, 41 per cent.

The intensity of uncertain desert rains has brought amounts in excess of the statistical monthly average on a single day. Mendoza, for example, has recorded 1.9 inch in twenty-four hours during January (1.1 inch is normal for the entire month), and San Juan has recorded 1.5 inch in twenty-four hours in January (1 inch is the computed normal for the month). The number of days on which any measurable rain can be expected in Patagonia is generally greater than in the desert basins of the north.

Winter is not a particularly cold season, considering the relatively high latitudes into which the arid environment extends, although very

[6] W. G. Kendrew, *The Climates of the Continents*, Oxford, 1961, p. 509.

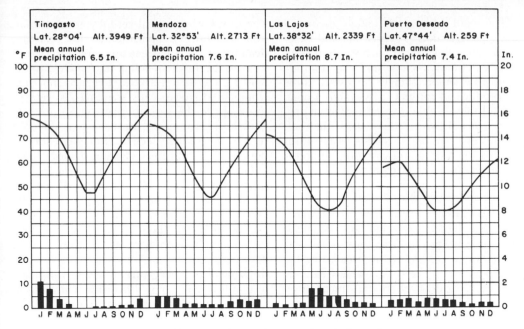

| Tinogasta Lat. 28°04' Alt. 3949 Ft Mean annual precipitation 6.5 In. | Mendoza Lat. 32°53' Alt. 2713 Ft Mean annual precipitation 7.6 In. | Las Lajas Lat. 38°32' Alt. 2339 Ft Mean annual precipitation 8.7 In. | Puerto Deseado Lat. 47°44' Alt. 259 Ft Mean annual precipitation 7.4 In. |

Figure 18.13. Temperature and precipitation at desert stations in Argentina.

low temperatures have been recorded. The coldest month is usually July (June and July in southernmost Patagonia), and mean temperatures for this month are 40° or above as far south as Sarmiento in the interior at nearly 46°S. Lat., and Puerto Deseado, about 200 miles southeastward on the coast. South of these points the coldest months average between 35° and 39°. The mean daily range of temperature during the cold season is less than in summertime, averaging 23 degrees at Mendoza in June (30 in December and January), 25 degrees in June at Cipolletti (33 in February and March), and 16 degrees at Sarmiento (27 in December). An exception should be noted for Tinogasta, where the mean daily temperature range at the end of winter in September is 43 degrees, compared with 34 degrees in January and February. Tinogasta may be taken to illustrate the fact that winters in those northernmost bolsons are very often completely rainless, and the dry, cloudless air allows an input of more intensive radiant heat from the sun and an alternate nocturnal radiant heat loss than southern localities under winter's cloudy skies.

The mean daily temperature ranges cited above suggest that for two or three months in winter subfreezing readings may be expected in southern areas. Throughout the arid region

the thermometer has registered values well below freezing from time to time. Tinogasta, for example, has recorded 14° in July, San Juan 17°, San Luis 14°, and Mendoza 15° in June. South of here much lower readings have been reported, Malargue registering − 10°, Puerto Deseado 1°, and Santa Cruz 5°. At Colonia Sarmiento in June 1907, − 27° was reported.

The northern desert areas in winter experience a high percentage of possible sunshine, a great many days passing in succession without a single cloud, but the areas south of Mendoza tend to average a cloud cover of between 50 and 60 per cent from April through September. Relative humidity rises as temperatures drop, and the frequency of days with cold, misty weather increases. Over most of Patagonia more than half the year's uncertain precipitation occurs during the colder season, and May is most commonly the month of maximum amounts.

Snow can be expected every winter as far north as Mendoza, especially in July and August, although in northern areas it does not usually remain on the ground for more than two or three days and rarely falls on more than six or seven days during the season.

As winter begins to wane and warm air is felt more frequently from the north, a singularly hot, dry wind, the zonda, often occurs in spring, especially during September and October. Beginning about noon, such winds are said to blow with hurricane force and may continue until after sunset, occasionally for two or three days, producing unusual dessication among plants and animals alike. Sometimes, when they have blown for two or three days, they are abruptly replaced by a cooling wind from southward that may cause a drop in temperature of as much as 45 degrees.[7]

Deserts of Southern Africa

Desert in southern Africa, largely confined to southwestern sections, is found both along the Atlantic coast below the Great Escarpment and on the elevated surface of the broad, interior plateau (Fig. 14.7). The coastal desert extends from about 200 miles north of the Cunene River in Angola to the Olifants River about 200 miles south of the Orange River, a linear distance of some 1300 miles. This, the Namib desert, is a region of shifting sand and bare rock plains and terraces that lies generally between sea level and altitudes of about 2000 feet. These are the dominant landscapes from Walvis Bay near the Tropic northward along the coast, from here southward spreading up to and across the Great Escarpment onto the inner upland. The Namib varies in width but usually reaches inland from the surf line for between 20 and 50 miles. Except for a very few small seaports it is an inhospitable, virtually uninhabited region where precipitation along the shoreline is estimated to average less than $\frac{1}{2}$ inch per year.

From the Olifants River northward for about 300 miles the coastal zone is an unusually even, sand-covered rock platform, called sandveld, that terminates in low cliffs between 25 and 60 feet high at the water's edge. Although rainfall-deficient, this section is covered with a vegetation composed of closely spaced dwarf shrubs and fleshy succulents having good water storage capacities. Prominent among the latter are species of *Mesembryanthemum*, a low-growing form with thick, three-sided leaves, sometimes rounded or flattened, some of which are known by the name *ice plant* from their habit of accumulating heavy drops of crystal clear dew.

These and other coastal xerophytes are climatically adapted to persistently low rainfall, thriving on the prevalent mists from the sea.

From the northern end of the sandveld to the bay at Luderitz is a stretch of rugged shoreline where bold, rocky cliffs standing 200 feet or more above the surf alternate with towering sand hills. From Luderitz to Walvis Bay is a region of strikingly active sand dune formations where individual crescent-shaped dunes called barchans are numerous, some of the crests rising to 500 feet or more above the adjacent troughs. Scarcely a living plant can be found among them. Near Walvis Bay the Namib widens to about 100 miles inland from the sea, and between here and the Cunene sand dunes are confined to a narrow belt adjoining the zone of pounding surf, inland of which the terrain is chiefly exposed bedrock. This barren, hostile strand is known among mariners as the Skeleton Coast.

From the Cunene northward the surface is alternately sand and clay hardpan, pebble pavement of weathered stones, and bare expanse of sandstone and limestone bedrock. The Namib is commonly considered to terminate about 50 miles north of Mossamedes, although the arid aspect of sand and rock plains and terraces continues beyond Lobito. North of Lobito coastal surfaces are sparsely mantled with desert grasses, succulent plants, and thorn shrubs, semi-arid thorn scrub woodland transitional into more humid tropical savanna woodland.

The Great Escarpment along most of its length marks a rather well-defined drop-off, at an approximate altitude of 4000 feet, toward the lower coastal plains and terraces. Dissected by a number of entrenched stream valleys like those of the Coroca, Cunene, Swakop, Kuiseb, and Orange rivers, it is broken and discontinuous and at many places between Walvis Bay and the Orange River is surmounted farther inland by the western highlands, which rise to more than 7000 feet in altitude. Together, the escarpment and the highlands form the higher western rim of the interior plateau whose mean surface elevation is close to 3000 feet.

South of Walvis Bay the arid environment expands upward and eastward across the western highlands onto the plateau, widening toward its eastern limits to an extreme breadth of 400 miles from the Atlantic, near where the

[7] W. W. Reed, "Climatological Data for Southern South America," *Monthly Weather Review*, Supp. No. 32, 1929, p. 21.

Vaal River joins the upper Orange. Desert continues southward, approaching the rising highlands along the southern rim of the plateau. Skirting their more humid slopes, it continues into the elevated basins of the Great Karroo, below the escarpment and the western end of the lower Little Karroo (see Chapter 14).

Southwestern Africa's desert lands span about 20 degrees of latitude, from 14° to about 34°S., interposing an arid realm between the dry summer mediterranean environment of the Cape region and the dry winter environment of the tropical savanna woodlands toward the north, and grading through semi-arid grassland into the mid-latitude prairies toward the east.

The desert land of the interior plateau is essentially a hammada region of extensive rock surfaces mantled by gravel and reg pavements, rising here and there to form steep-faced buttes, broad-crowned mesas, and occasional pinnacles, with scattered, sand-filled basins. At a point about midway between the junction of the Vaal with the Orange and the Atlantic is the Aughrabies Falls, where the Orange drops some 400 feet into a deep, steep-sided canyon that widens in its downstream course as the river cuts through the highland rim of the plateau. North of the falls the interior desert extends into the southwestern corner of the Kalahari. The term *Kalahari* is sometimes mistakenly assigned to the entire interior desert region of southwestern Africa. It is actually a semi-arid region of grass and thorn shrub savanna where mean annual precipitation exceeds 10 inches, increasing northward to 40 inches or more, and thus belongs to the less arid tropical and subtropical regions. The Kalahari is a most remarkably flat region, and it is the southwestern part of this strikingly level sand and rock plain that is afflicted by persistent drought, where the intermittent flow of the Nossob River from the highlands toward the northwest and the Molopo River from the east disappear into the porous surface about 100 miles or more north of the Aughrabies Falls. The term *Orange River desert* might more accurately designate the location of the interior upland arid region of southwestern Africa.

The presence of arid land in southwestern Africa is partly attributable to the cooling effect of the north-flowing Benguela Current upon air from the South Atlantic, and partly to the failure of sufficient precipitable moisture from air over the Indian Ocean to reach far enough inland. Recall (see Chapter 14 and Figs. 4.2 and 4.3) that in wintertime, from April through September, the sun has withdrawn the directness of its rays far to the northward. Clear, dry, subsiding anticyclonic air at this time extends almost continuously from the South Atlantic across southern Africa to the Indian Ocean within the lower middle latitudes. Most of interior southern Africa at this season receives little if any precipitation. But in the mediterranean Cape region and the south coast it is otherwise, and it is also in this period that very light rains, averaging no more than 5 inches near the Olifants River and less than $\frac{1}{2}$ inch northward, may be expected along the Namib coast as far north as Luderitz.

In the interior during the summer from October through March, however, when the land is warmed and the shallow Kalahari Low appears, abundant moist, maritime air from the Indian Ocean flows into southern Africa to bring the bulk of the year's normal precipitation to eastern areas. At the same time, the northward flow of air along the eastern arc of the South Atlantic semipermanent oceanic high sends offshoots eastward up the Great Escarpment and into the interior plateau. There it converges with the dominant air streams from the east and southeast in the persistent low pressure field of the equatorial trough (intertropical convergence), which, in summer, loops southward as far as the Tropic of Capricorn. During this period whatever sporadic rains may be expected in the arid interior tend to occur in the form of thermal convective showers, a condition that also holds true for the northern Namib coast southward beyond Walvis Bay. The southernmost Namib is, at this season, without rain.

Winter is a period of unusually persistent clear, sunny weather over most of southern Africa's interior plateau. Indeed, most of the continent within the bounds of the peripheral highlands experiences more than 80 per cent of possible sunshine during this season, and in arid areas north of the Orange River the amount rises to more than 90 per cent (Fig. 18.14). Windhoek (el. 5668) lies inland of the western highlands, about 150 miles east of Walvis Bay and about 400 miles north of the Orange River, and averages 97 per cent of possible sunshine in

August, a value that is probably the highest reported from any station in Africa.

Clear, dry, calm air prevails during the hours of darkness and early morning but often becomes hazy as the almost daily winds rise in the late forenoon, usually reaching a maximum velocity in midafternoon. Small whirling dust devils are common, and at times severe dust storms sweep across the dessicated surface.

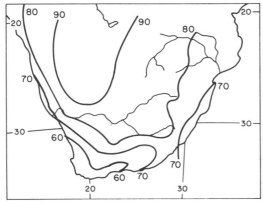

Figure 18.14. Percentage of possible sunshine received in July in southern Africa.

Because most winds are west to northwest, dust is frequently carried eastward into the grasslands. The prevalence of northwest winds in the Nossob River area is attested to by the presence there of stabilized sand ridges, aligned in a northwest-southeast direction.

The coldest month of the year nearly everywhere in the interior upland is July, although mean temperatures in June are nearly as low at most stations (Table 18-4). Actual values at inland stations are determined primarily by latitude and secondarily by altitude. Thus, one finds July temperatures average 55° or more from the Orange River northward at a small number of widely scattered observation points, between 50° and 55° over most of the area south of the middle Orange valley, and between 45° and 50° near the southern highland rim. The influence of altitude may be observed by comparing the July temperature of 58° at Goodhouse (el. 666) on the lower Orange River with 52° at Okiep (el. 3041), about 50 miles toward the southwest, and 51° at Pofadder (el. 3260), about 60 miles eastward. The mean daily range of temperature at inland stations in winter is between 25 and 30 degrees, with stations in the

bordering highlands experiencing nightly frosts for a period of several weeks. Above 4000 feet nocturnal minimum temperatures commonly reach below 20°, and 14° has been observed at standard instrument shelter height.

Along the Atlantic coast temperatures in the Namib desert respond to the presence of the Benguela Current. In August sea water surface temperatures average about 55° between the Orange River mouth and Walvis Bay, rising to about 58° southward beyond the Olifants River mouth and to about 65° northward beyond Mossamedes (Fig. 6.12). August is normally the coldest month of the year, revealing the expected lag in a marine climate, and air temperature averages 54° at both Port Nolloth and Swakopmund (Fig. 18.15).

In August cloud cover averages between 25 and 35 per cent, allowing a mean daily temperature range of 18 degrees at Port Nolloth (45° to 63°) and 16 degrees at Swakopmund (47° to 63°). This is a wider range of thermal fluctuation than might be expected in a strictly marine situation. It is partly explained in terms of the high frequency of clear skies, and partly in terms of the Berg winds that blow down off the highlands from time to time in the winter season, advecting a föhn effect to the desert coast. These occur as a rule when the oceanic high is displaced somewhat west of its usual position, allowing a warm, shallow anticyclone to develop over the interior upland, air from which spills down the western slopes toward the sea. Such winds have been known to raise coastal temperatures north of the Orange River as much as 20 degrees in about five minutes. They are responsible for the fact that the highest temperatures of record at Walvis Bay and Swakopmund have been observed in winter rather than in summer. At Walvis Bay, for example, the thermometer climed to 107° in April, 103° in May, and 102° in July during a period of ten years. In the same period summer values did not exceed 90° from November through February.

Winter temperatures have occasionally reached the freezing point on the coast, for Port Nolloth has reported a shelter height value of 32°, and Swakopmund 34°. Relative humidities are high throughout the season as a result of persistent dew, fog, and misty weather as far north as Luderitz. At Port Nolloth mean relative humidity for July is 78 per cent, and at

TABLE 18–4

Climatic Data for Desert Stations in Southwestern Africa
(Temp., °F; Rainfall, In.)

Station	Lat.	El. in Ft		Jan.	Feb.	Mar.	Apr.	May	Jun.	Jul.	Aug.	Sep.	Oct.	Nov.	Dec.	Year
Mossamedes, Angola	15°12'	10	T	73	75	76	74	68	64	62	63	65	68	71	72	
			R	0.4	0.5	0.6	0.3	0.0	0.0	0.0	0.0	0.0	0.0	0.1	0.1	2.0
Walvis Bay, Southwest Africa	22°50'	24	T	66	67	66	65	63	61	58	57	57	59	62	64	
			R	0.1	0.2	0.3	0.1	0.1	0.0	0.0	0.1	0.0	0.0	0.0	0.0	0.9
Windhoek, Southwest Africa	22°34'	5668	T	74	73	70	66	60	56	55	60	66	69	72	74	
			R	2.7	2.7	3.2	1.7	0.4	0.0	0.0	0.0	0.1	0.4	1.0	1.8	10.1
Port Nolloth, Republic of South Africa	29°14'	23	T	60	61	60	58	57	56	53	54	55	56	59	59	
			R	0.1	0.1	0.2	0.2	0.4	0.3	0.4	0.3	0.2	0.1	0.1	0.1	2.4
Garies, Republic of South Africa	30°34'	745	T	75	75	73	68	63	58	56	58	61	66	69	72	
			R	0.1	0.1	0.2	0.5	0.7	0.9	0.8	0.8	0.5	0.4	0.2	0.1	5.4
Klaver, Republic of South Africa	31°47'	138	T	75	75	73	69	63	59	57	60	62	66	70	73	
			R	0.1	0.2	0.3	0.6	1.0	1.2	1.1	1.0	0.6	0.4	0.4	0.1	6.9

Source: F. L. Wernstedt, *World Climatic Data, Africa*, Pennsylvania State University, 1959.

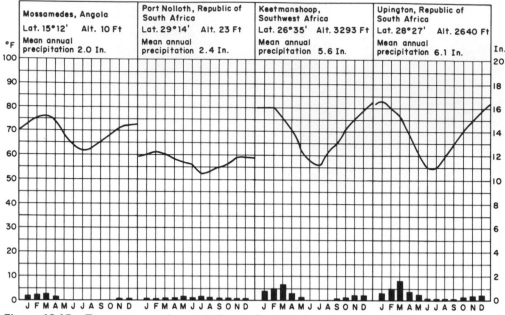

Mossamedes, Angola	Port Nolloth, Republic of South Africa	Keetmanshoop, Southwest Africa	Upington, Republic of South Africa
Lat. 15°12' Alt. 10 Ft	Lat. 29°14' Alt. 23 Ft	Lat. 26°35' Alt. 3293 Ft	Lat. 28°27' Alt. 2640 Ft
Mean annual precipitation 2.0 In.	Mean annual precipitation 2.4 In.	Mean annual precipitation 5.6 In.	Mean annual precipitation 6.1 In.

Figure 18.15. Temperature and precipitation at desert stations in southern Africa.

Swakopmund in June 67 per cent, those months averaging the yearly minimum at both stations. Although precipitation is very light and sufficient to support only xerophytic vegetation south of Luderitz, it is comparatively reliable, and June is usually the month when the peak amounts are expected (Table 18-4). North of Luderitz the season is normally without measurable rain.

In summer, when the influx of moist air from the Indian Ocean spreads upward and westward onto the interior plateau, the cumulus cloud cover and convective showers that produce the bulk of the season's rainfall are concentrated for the most part in the eastern highlands and mid-latitude grasslands. The arid southwestern portions of the upland receive only small amounts of rain at sporadic intervals. Here, cloud distribution is much more scattered, and generally sunny weather prevails. Even in January and February over 80 per cent of possible sunshine is normally received in most of the arid upland. Although less than 10 inches of rainfall may normally be expected, the evaporation rate is extremely high. Open pan water losses through evaporation are more than 70 inches, increasing to 110 inches in the Nossob River area of the southwestern Kalahari (Fig. 18.16). Along the coast, however, fog and low stratus mists reduce the amount of sunshine, and an average of between 50 and 60 per cent of possible amount is characteristic.

The warmest month at inland stations is usually January, although both January and February are about equally warm, indicating the characteristic tendency toward long, warm summers in the elevated, subtropical parts of southern Africa (Fig. 18.16). Except in the southern highlands, most interior stations average 80° or higher during the warmest month. A growing season free of frost endures for between 240 and three hundred days in most of the interior deserts and normally for

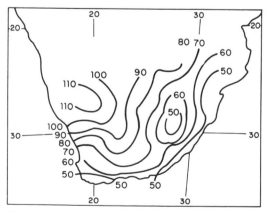

Figure 18.16. Annual evaporation from free water surfaces in southern Africa (inches).

the entire year in the coastal Namib desert. In the peripheral highlands, however, the frost-free period is a good deal shorter, and in higher valleys and basins near the southern edge of the Great Escarpment it may last for only 180 days or less.

Along the coast the warm season is unusually protracted, and this, plus the fact that the warmest months average about 20 degrees cooler than those at inland points of observation, attests to the pervading influence of the Benguela Current. Warm air over its cool waters results in a high percentage of fog and mist. Port Nolloth mean temperatures are 60° from December through February and 63° at Swakopmund from January through March. The more sheltered situation at Walvis Bay produces a mean value of 66° during February and March. Mean daily temperature ranges are lower in summer than during the cooler season, averaging 13 degrees (53° to 66°) at Port Nolloth and 10 degrees (59° to 69°) at Swakopmund in January.

The mean annual range of temperature between the warmest and coldest months is approximately 25 to 30 degrees over most of the interior arid land, dropping to between 20 and 25 degrees at higher points near the highland rim. Along the Atlantic coast, however, values are much lower. The mean range at Port Nolloth is 6 degrees (54° to 60°), and at Swakopmund (54° to 63°) and Walvis Bay (57° to 66°) 9 degrees. The marine influence extends toward the escarpment to reduce the ranges of stations somewhat removed from the water's edge; Garies, about 30 miles from the sea, records a mean range of 19 degrees (56° to 75°), and Klaver (el. 138), about 25 miles from the Atlantic on the lower Olifants River, records 18 degrees (57° to 75°).

In southwestern Africa we thus find two rather well-defined desert environments in continuity. A narrow, cool, coastal desert, where much cloud, fog, dew, and misty weather prevail during the summer months, experiences unusual thermal fluctuations during the less cloudy winter season, when the highest recorded temperatures have been reached. Merging with it is an elevated, interior desert of only moderate continental characteristics resulting from its mean altitude of over a half-mile above sea level.

References

CHAPMAN, V. J.: *Salt Marshes and Salt Deserts of the World*, Plant Science Monographs, Interscience Publications, Inc., New York, 1960.

HODGE, C., ed.: *Aridity and Man, The Challenge of the Arid Lands in the United States*, American Association for the Advancement of Science, Washington, D.C., 1963.

JAEGER, E. C.: *The North American Deserts*, Stanford University Press, Stanford, Calif., 1957.

RUDOLPH, W. E.: *Vanishing Trails of Atacama*, The American Geographical Society, New York, 1963.

TALJAARD, J. J., and SCHUMAN, T. E.: "Upper-Air Temperatures and Humidities at Walvis Bay," *Bulletin of the American Meteorological Society*, **21**(7): 370–81, 1940.

U.S. NAVAL OCEANOGRAPHIC OFFICE: *Sailing Directions for the Southwest Coast of Africa* (H.O. 50), 1951.

————: *Sailing Directions for South America*, Vol. 3 (H.O. 25), 1960.

WARD, R. DEC., and BROOKS, C. F.: "The Climates of North America," *Handbuch der Klimatologie*, 2 (Part J), Berlin, 1936.

chapter 19

DESERTS OF AUSTRALIA, NORTHERN AFRICA, AND ASIA

Australia

The arid regions of Australia occupy the greater part of the central and western sections of the country. Extending westward from the Simpson desert north of Lake Eyre for some 1600 miles to the west coast north of the Hammersley Range and northward about 750 miles from the south coast at the head of the Great Australian Bight, they cover an area of about 1,200,000 square miles, or about 40 per cent of the country's 2,974,581 square miles. But this is only a first approximation, for the actual extent of desert is not known. This is partly for want of sufficient climatological data and partly for want of a universally satisfactory definition of *desert*.

Very few weather observation stations are maintained within Australia's interior, and thus little detailed information on atmospheric parameters is available, a condition arising from the fact that most sections are very sparsely inhabited, and a high proportion of the central part is entirely unpopulated. From the scanty data obtainable efforts have been made to delineate the limits of arid and semi-arid territory, but the problem is further complicated by the fact that Australia is a continent of low relief. No conspicuous mountain systems are present to act as significant rain shadow barriers or otherwise plainly to set off the desert from the less arid areas. The aridity of interior

Australia is primarily due to the latitudes within which the compact land mass lies and the relation of the land mass with the dominant features of the general circulation in those latitudes. Aridity increases, in a general way, toward the interior from the more humid coasts, reaching a maximum in the interior drainage basin centered around Lake Eyre, which is about 300 miles north of Spencer Gulf. The gradual environmental change is approximately as follows: from tropical semideciduous forest along parts of the north coast, southward through savanna woodland and thorn scrub woodland into desert; from mid-latitude mixed forest along the east and southeast coasts westward through mid-latitude grasslands into desert; and from mediterranean scrub woodland around Perth and Adelaide northward through fringing grassland into desert.

But the decision as to what constitutes desert in Australia has not been reached with any finality. Several methods of delineating arid and semi-arid lands have been proposed. One of them is that areas receiving less than 10 inches of annual rainfall can be classed as desert, but this is much too simple a relationship in a desert region that straddles the Tropic of Capricorn, thus extending from the tropics to the mid-latitudes. As we have noted before, climatic regions cannot be distinguished by precipitation amounts alone. Effective precipitation, the amount retained by the soil for the use of plants, ground water recharge, and stream flow must be considered. This requires the assessment of evaporative influences—wind speed and duration, air temperature and humidity, cloud cover and sunshine, as well as edaphic conditions of the earth itself. In southern Australia, where winter is the rainy season, effective precipitation sufficient for the support of semi-arid grasslands begins in many places where annual amounts are above 8.5 inches, approximately marking the wetter margins of desert. This is especially true of the mediterranean sections around Perth and Adelaide. Here the transitional grassland dominates where mean yearly rainfall is generally between 8.5 and 15 inches. The vegetation changes toward the more humid wooded regions where more than 15 inches of rainfall are normal. In northern Australia desert margins can be detected where mean annual precipitation drops below 15 inches. Above this amount tropical thorn scrub woodland spreads northward toward the savanna woodland and semideciduous forests near the coast. Precipitation values in eastern districts bordered by temperate grasslands, are something between 8.5 and 15 inches, higher toward the north.

Because evaporation is unusually high over the greater part of interior Australia, exceeding 100 inches per annum from a free water surface throughout most of the desert, a means of delimiting potentially usable territory has been introduced, expressed as follows: $Mo_n P/E > \frac{1}{3}$, meaning the number of months during which the ratio of precipitation to evaporation is greater than one third.[1] A minimum of five months having a ratio exceeding one third is considered necessary for growing crops.

Although no exact boundaries can be applied to mark the limits of desert on the map of climatic regions, a generalized view of arid distribution is presented in Figure 15.1. Desert is here seen to extend from northwestern New South Wales and southwestern Queensland westward to the coast between Shark Bay and 80-Mile Beach. By far the greater part of this region occupies the Western Shield, consisting of a low, undulating plateau composed of

ancient crystalline rocks, that stands roughly between 1000 and 2000 feet above sea level. In western sections the Shield rises to heights in excess of 4000 feet in the Hammersley Range, which begins about 150 miles east of Northwest Cape, and in slightly lower hilly eminences farther south. In central Australia the Macdonnel Ranges, just south of the Tropic, and the Musgrave Ranges nearly 200 miles farther south again rise above the mean level of the shield to heights above 4000 feet (see also Chapter 15). The eastern section of desert northeast of Lake Eyre lies at much lower elevations, however, substantially less than 500 feet above sea level, decreasing to about 35 feet below sea level at the mean surface elevation of Lake Eyre itself.

Segments of arid country in Australia have long been designated by distinctive names which, for reference purposes, are used here. Northeast of the Hammersley Range and between 80-Mile Beach and the Macdonnel Ranges, is the Great Sandy desert, south of which is the Gibson desert. Between the Musgrave Ranges and Nullarbor Plain, which skirts the south coast, is the Great Victoria desert. The low-lying arid tract north of Lake Eyre, as mentioned earlier, is called the Simpson desert.

Within the arid reaches of the Great Sandy desert surface land forms include a high proportion of fixed sand dunes, arranged in a roughly east-west alignment, built up by the westward movements of the dominant trade wind sweep. From the Gibson desert southward is a broad expanse of rocky plain or hammada, giving way in the eastern part of the Great Victorian desert once again to fixed dunes. The latter belt of dunes is arranged in a confused pattern, in consequence, no doubt, of the variable wind directions prevailing in those higher latitudes. The Simpson desert surface exhibits a hammada character in the northern section, yielding to shifting erg or sand dunes in the central part, and finally to a stony reg surface just northeast of Lake Eyre.

The xerophytic vegetation of the arid regions is dominated by species of acacia throughout, with mulga (*Acacia aneura*) the chief species in the Victoria, Gibson, and Great Sandy deserts, brigalow (*A. harpophylla*) in the Simpson desert. Species of eucalypts are also scattered throughout the desert country, as well as smaller shrubby plants like needlewood (*Hakea leucoptera*), species of *Grevillea*, and the wide circular

---

[1] This is a restatement of the formula cited in Chapter 17 in the discussion of Australia's mid-latitude grassland climates.

tussocks of spiny grass called spinifex (*Triodia spp.*). Taller tree forms often form a linear distribution along the dry stream courses, where flowing water appears only intermittently.

Ordinary maps of Australia indicate the presence of a large number of lakes, especially southeast of the Simpson desert, near Lake Eyre, and in the southwestern part of the country. These, however, are salt or brackish in character and are extremely shallow. They, like the many intermittent streams also shown on many maps of the country, simply reflect the pervading aridity of most of the interior.

Mention should be made of the fact that the waters of the Indian Ocean adjacent to Australia's west coast are substantially warmer than those off the west coasts of South America and southern Africa. Thus, the desert conditions along the western Australian shores cannot be related to the influence of a cold coastal current as in South America and southern Africa but are, instead, attributable almost entirely to the combination of atmospheric conditions inherent in the dominant anticyclonic weather described in earlier paragraphs.

Spanning a breadth in latitude of about 13 degrees (from about 19° to 32°) roughly astride the Tropic of Capricorn, the large arid portion of Australia owes its existence primarily to its position beneath the persistent subtropical high pressure systems that repeatedly form approximately along the 30th parallel and bring protracted periods of clear, dry, sunny weather with light, variable winds to most of the interior (see Chapter 15, Chapter 17, and Figs. 4.2 and 4.3). It is important to bear in mind that migrating anticyclones move eastward regularly over the continent from the Indian Ocean. Individual high pressure systems persist on an average of about four days before passing off over the Pacific. Possessing a roughly elliptical form (elongated east and west), they commonly attain a mean diameter of about 1500 miles but sometimes expand to cover almost the entire continent.

The circulation around Australia's anticyclones is counterclockwise, and thus easterly winds prevail in their northern sectors and westerly winds in their southern portions, with light, variable winds and calms in their central areas of maximum barometric pressure. In winter all of Australia but the southwestern, the southern, and the southeastern coastal regions is subjected to their overwhelming domination. At this time of year, when solar energy is at a minimum over the continent, interior temperatures decrease, and migrating anticyclones intensify as they pass over the land to a maximum intensity for the year. Mean barometric pressures average about 1020 millibars (30.1 inches) over the central desert regions, compared with 1010 millibars (29.82 inches) during the summer.

The desert interior, lying remote from the principal sources of precipitation throughout the year, shares its aridity with northern Australia's tropical regions in winter and with southern Australia's mediterranean regions in summer. Anticyclonic weather, prevailing throughout most of the year, is mainly responsible for the large proportion of annual sunshine, high evaporation rates, uncertainty of precipitation, and large annual and daily fluctuations of temperature that typify the predominant weather of the desert areas.

Quantitative information on the amounts of sunshine experienced in central and western Australia is unfortunately not sufficient to permit meaningful generalization. From the records of scientific observers and travelers in these largely uninhabited regions, it is commonly felt that the country's desert areas on the whole receive more than 70 per cent of possible sunshine during a normal year, and that the Simpson desert and a stretch of country extending for about 800 miles northwest of it annually receive more than 80 per cent. Similarly, along the west coast values are considered to average above 80 per cent for a distance of about 600 miles between Shark Bay and 80-Mile Beach (Fig. 15.6).

The predominantly clear, sunny skies over central and western Australia account for much of the high rate of evaporation that is attributed to those desert tracts. Again, in spite of inadequate data, the rate of annual evaporation over the Great Sandy, Gibson, and Simpson deserts is believed to exceed 110 inches. The long-term average of rainfall amounts received at scattered points in those areas is less than 10 inches, indicating the extreme persistent water deficit that exists (Fig. 17.5). Throughout the desert areas elsewhere mean annual evaporation rates are believed to exceed 90 inches, a value far beyond even the most extraordinary rains.

The relative unreliability of yearly precipitation is evident, again on the strength of a relatively small number of data, from the fact that yearly amounts can be expected to vary more than 30 per cent from the long-term average over most desert areas (Fig. 15.5). The greatest variability is seen in the vicinity of Northwest Cape and over the Hammersley Range, extending inland for about 400 miles, where yearly variability rises to more than 60 per cent from the long-term mean. Roebourne, about 200 miles northeast of Northwest Cape, received 0.13 inch in 1891 but 42 inches in 1900. Onslow, about 60 miles east of Northwest Cape, received the following amounts during the successive years indicated: 1908, 9.8 inches; 1909, 27 inches; 1910, 7.1 inches; 1911, 5 inches; 1912, 1 inch; 1913, 7.1 inches. Wiluna, about 400 miles east of Shark Bay, averaged 2 inches in April over a seventeen-year period, but in April 1900 it received 27 inches. A small area in the Simpson desert also experiences a high degree of variability, averaging a departure of more than 50 per cent from the over-all mean (Table 19-1).

The mean annual range of temperature is 30 degrees or more in most interior desert areas, but along the west coast from Shark Bay to 80-Mile Beach values are nearer 20 degrees (Fig. 15.7). The extreme range of temperature is generally between 70 and 80 degrees, although at Alice Springs it is 88 degrees (115° in January to 27° in July). West coastal stations, subjected to the advection of hot, dry air from the interior by the trades, are not spared extremes of temperature: Onslow has recorded an absolute range of 74 degrees (115° in January to 41° in July), and Carnarvon 79 degrees (116° in January to 37° in July). Subfreezing temperatures are unknown along a narrow belt of the west coast north of Shark Bay and in tropical areas of the north, but everywhere throughout the desert regions frost can be expected to occur on a few days each winter, usually averaging less than five days per annum.

During the winter, from June through August, dry east winds prevail over most of the desert areas except along the southern margins, where west to northwest winds are more common. The season is typically mild, and the coldest month of July averages well above 50° in most interior sections. Along the west coast winter temperatures are considerably milder,

Carnarvon averaging 61° in July, Onslow 64° (Fig. 15.9). Sea water temperatures exert a moderating influence at this season, and in Shark Bay sea surface temperatures are about 64°, at Northwest Cape 68°, and at 80-Mile Beach 75°. The expected delay of the coldest month until August or later along the coast does not occur here, as the predominant east winds during winter offset the effect of the sea. The mean daily range of temperature is about 20 degrees (55° to 75°) at most localities in the Great Sandy, Gibson, and Simpson deserts and about 25 degrees (40° to 65°) in the Great Victoria desert.

In the summer period of December through February the desert regions are normally hot and dry. Relative humidities average 31 per cent at Peak Hill in January and 48 per cent even at the coastal station of Onslow. At most interior stations the driest period is usually the early part of summer. At Wiluna, for example, relative humidity averages 30 per cent in November, 31 per cent in December, 35 per cent in January, and 36 per cent in February. This seasonal increase is traceable to the increasingly southward advance of moist air from the Indian Ocean and the Arafura Sea as summer progresses. A similar rise in values can be observed at Alice Springs, where relative humidities average 26 per cent in October and November, the yearly minimum, increasing to 30 per cent in January and 34 per cent in February. At Farina, December is the month of lowest relative humidity, averaging 32 per cent, increasing as summer progresses.

An impressive feature of the hot, arid interior is the tendency for excessively high temperatures to persist for long periods of time. The hot spells referred to in Chapter 15 are periods during which the thermometer rises to a daily maximum of 100°F or more on several successive days. Such periods are of relatively short duration in the southern, cooler, more humid regions. There they rarely last for more than one week. But hot spells increase in duration with increasing distance northward and westward (Fig. 19.1). Most of the desert areas record at least forty days (although not necessarily successive days) on which the thermometer rises to 100°F or more. Northwestward the number of these blistering days per year increases toward the Great Sandy desert, where at least one hundred such days may be counted

TABLE 19–1

Climatic Data for Desert Stations in Australia

(Temp., °F; Rainfall, In.)

Station	Lat.	El. in Ft		Jan.	Feb.	Mar.	Apr.	May	Jun.	Jul.	Aug.	Sep.	Oct.	Nov.	Dec.	Year
Condon, Western Australia	20°00′	35	T	86	86	84	79	72	66	64	67	72	77	82	85	
			R	2.2	2.5	3.0	1.1	0.7	1.1	0.3	0.2	0.1	0.1	0.1	0.7	11.9
Onslow, Western Australia	21°43′	14	T	86	86	85	80	72	66	65	67	71	75	80	83	
			R	0.9	1.1	1.8	1.0	1.5	1.6	0.8	0.4	0.0	0.0	0.0	0.2	9.3
Nullagine, Western Australia	21°53′	1265	T	89	88	85	77	68	62	60	64	71	79	86	89	
			R	3.0	2.4	2.2	0.8	0.7	0.9	0.5	0.3	0.0	0.2	0.5	1.7	13.2
Mundiwindi, Western Australia	23°52′	1840	T	83	86	82	74	64	58	56	60	67	79	86	89	
			R	1.0	1.9	2.0	0.8	0.6	0.9	0.1	0.3	0.3	0.5	0.5	1.2	10.1
Peak Hill, Western Australia	25°38′	1930	T	87	86	82	74	65	58	56	59	66	72	81	86	
			R	1.3	1.3	1.5	1.0	1.1	1.3	0.6	0.5	0.2	0.2	0.4	0.7	10.1
Laverton, Western Australia	28°40′	1510	T	83	82	77	69	61	54	53	56	63	69	77	79	
			R	0.8	0.8	1.6	0.8	0.9	0.7	0.6	0.5	0.2	0.3	0.8	0.8	8.8
Eucla, Western Australia	31°45′	15	T	70	71	70	66	61	56	55	56	59	63	66	69	
			R	0.6	0.7	0.9	1.0	1.2	1.1	0.9	0.9	0.7	0.7	0.7	0.5	9.9
Alice Springs, Northern Territory	23°38′	1901	T	84	82	77	68	60	54	53	58	65	73	79	82	
			R	1.7	1.3	1.1	0.4	0.6	0.5	0.3	0.3	0.3	0.7	1.2	1.5	9.9
Farina, South Australia	30°05′	303	T	82	82	76	67	59	53	51	55	61	69	76	80	
			R	0.5	0.6	0.5	0.4	0.6	0.6	0.3	0.3	0.3	0.5	0.5	0.5	5.6
Windorah, Queensland	25°26′	390	T	88	87	82	73	64	58	55	61	68	76	82	86	
			R	1.4	1.6	1.6	0.9	0.8	0.8	0.5	0.4	0.5	0.6	0.9	1.4	11.4

Source: Great Britain, Meteorological Office, *Tables of Temperature, Relative Humidity and Precipitation for the World, Part 6, Australasia and the South Pacific Ocean*, London, 1962.

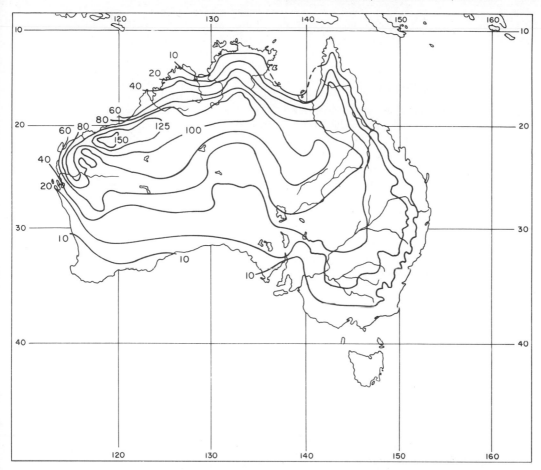

Figure 19.1. Average number of days per year when the thermometer registers 100°F or more in Australia.

on during the year. At Marble Bar (el. 594), about 100 miles south of the west end of 80-Mile Beach, and Nullagine (el. 1267), about 60 miles farther south, temperatures of 100° or more are expected on at least 150 days each year. In the summer of 1921–22 Marble Bay recorded a mean maximum of 110° for a period of 106 consecutive days, during which time the thermometer climbed to 120° in the shade on January 3.[2] In the same general area along the coast the number of days is considerably smaller, but even there the ruling influence of the westward transport of hot, dry air from the interior is felt, as is evident from the fact that Onslow experiences about forty days each year when temperatures reach 100° or more.

[2] W. Köppen and R. Geiger, *Handbuch der Klimatologie,* **4** (Part S), p. S67.

The west coast of Australia is occasionally visited during the latter part of summer by tropical cyclones of destructive intensity. These, usually originating in the generally westward flow of the southeast trades, move along the north coast of the continent, recurving southward in the Indian Ocean, and thus often approach the west coast from the northwest. They have crossed the coast at many different points between Broome and Geraldton. They are commonly small in size, ranging from 20 or 30 up to 100 miles in diameter, and though they may appear almost any time during the summer, they chiefly reach the coastal desert tracts from 80-Mile Beach southward in March. Locally known as willy-willies, they are capable of destroying shipping, causing serious loss of life, usually producing torrential rain. On March 20–21, 1912, such a storm sank the steamer *Koombana* with all hands and delivered over 13 inches of rain to Port Hedland at the west end of 80-Mile Beach.

Northern Africa and Southwest Asia

A virtually unbroken desert environment extends for some 5800 miles from the Atlantic coast of north Africa to the Thar desert of northwest India (Fig. 19.2). The existence and distribution of most of this unusually large arid territory is primarily, although not entirely, a consequence of the prevailing circulation of the same subtropical anticyclonic system. Thus it is reasonable to deal with its climatic character as a single unit. The southward flow of air that has lost much of its original moisture content, warming on its travels into lower latitudes, rules the prevailing weather of nearly all this region throughout the year. But other features also play important roles, and we shall see the influence of ocean currents and the rain shadow effect of prominent highlands, as well as the influence of the summer monsoon circulations of central Africa and the north Indian Ocean

upon east African deserts, southern Arabia, northwest India, and West Pakistan.

The largest single arid region on the earth is the Sahara, the world's great desert. Occupying nearly all of north Africa, it extends in length for nearly 3500 miles from the Atlantic coast to the shores of the Red Sea (Fig. 19.3). From the Mediterranean coast of Libya on the Gulf of Sidra to the basin of Lake Chad its breadth is about 1000 miles, and scarcely less than this throughout its length. It spans some 20 degrees of latitude in the western Sahara, from about 35° in the Atlas region of Algeria to about 15° in the thorn shrub and grassland region of the Sudan.

The general level of the Sahara rises eastward from the Atlantic to well over 1000 feet in the central section and 2000 feet farther east, subsiding to about 1000 feet in the Nile basin, only to rise again rather sharply in the hill ranges along the African shores of the Red Sea to elevations of between 2000 and 5000 feet above the sea. In the central Sahara three separate mountain areas rise to relieve the general monotony of the over-all terrain. These are the

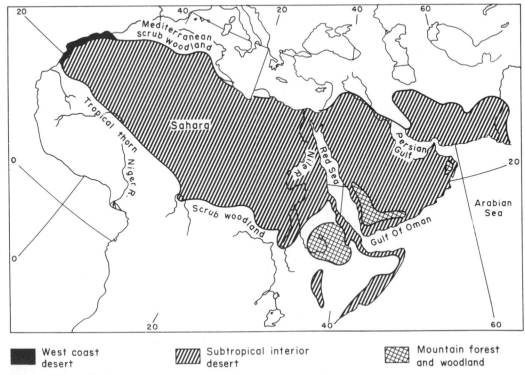

Figure 19.2. Distribution of desert in northern Africa and southwest Asia.

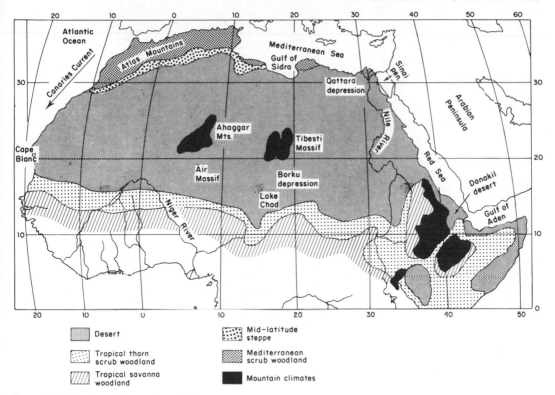

Figure 19.3. Desert in northern Africa.

Ahaggar Mountains in southern Algeria, a dissected mass of granitic and volcanic rock that reaches a summit of 9852 feet in Mt. Tahat; the Tibesti Massif in northern Chad, largely of volcanic origin, surmounted by Pic Tousside at 10,712 feet and Emi Koussi at 11,204 feet; and the less imposing Aïr massif of northern Niger reaching elevations of 5906 feet in Monts Tamgak and 4593 feet in Monts Baguezane.

Elsewhere surface elevations subside to lower than average levels. Lake Chad, at a mean altitude of about 800 feet, lies in a broad basin inclined northeastward to the Borku depression of less than 600 feet above sea level. Lake Chad ranges in area from about 4000 square miles at low water to 8000 square miles at high water. In northeastern Algeria a former arm of the sea called the Chott Melrhir stands about 60 feet below sea level and is continuous with the Chott el Rharsa in western Tunisia (el. −13 to −55 feet), with which it forms a depression about 80 miles in length. The Qattara depression in northwestern Egypt, about 7500 square miles in area, is a completely arid region of soft, impassable sand lying about 440 feet below sea

level. Several smaller basins west of the lower Nile are also below mean sea level.

Save for the isolated mountain formations referred to above, the salt-sprinkled surface of the Sahara is chiefly composed of level, rock plains, and enormous tracts of shifting sand. Wind-swept exposures of solid bedrock hammadas are the commonest features, often mantled with an overburden of loose gravel or a pebble pavement of rock fragments nearly uniform in size. Wind-rippled dunes appear as titanic seas of restless sand in the great erg regions south of the Atlas Mountains and in extensive deposits in Libya and Egypt. Only a single persistent river, the Nile, traverses this mighty arid realm, taking its rise in the Ethiopian highlands and the lake district of east Africa, where it is supplied with nearly all the water it requires to maintain its steady northward flow for 4000 miles. For well over 1000 miles of its lower course it moves slowly across the desert of northern Sudan and Egypt as an exotic stream, receiving little if any additional water from the skies before emptying into the Mediterranean Sea. Nearly all other, much smaller desert streams are intermittent in character, occupying broad, steep-sided wadis near mountain regions, only rarely rising between their banks in flood, and thus at infrequent intervals performing the main work of erosion and deposition, the chief agents by which the desert surfaces are modified.

Vast tracts of the western Sahara are considered lifeless by Tuareg tribesmen and are known by the name *tanezroufts*. Such regions, entirely without accessible water resources, may be regarded as maximum or absolute deserts.[3] The tanezrouft in its worst form is an endless level plain strewn with gravel, and on every side from horizon to horizon without so much as a single tuft of grass. Such extreme aridity notably appears west of the Ahaggar in southern Algeria and in Libya east of the Great Erg.

In southwestern Asia aridity is scarcely less severe than in north Africa, but there the desert expanses are smaller and are interrupted by narrow, elongated arms of the sea and the moderate heights of several mountain systems. Separated from northeast Africa by the long, deep structural trough of the Red Sea, the peninsula of Arabia is the largest single desert tract in southwest Asia. Its roughly rectangular outlines are mainly the result of large-scale blockfaulting in which portions of the earth's crust have subsided in relation to adjoining masses to create a series of connected trough or rifts in the surface exposures of solid bed rock. A system of rift valleys can be traced from the lower Orontes in southern Turkey and Syria down the southward course of the Jordan to the Dead Sea basin. The rift valleys continue to the Gulf of Aqaba, which, with the Gulf of Suez, embraces the Sinai peninsula and enters the Red Sea trough. Continuing southward, the Red Sea trough is lined with the crustal depressions extending across the Ethiopian highlands into the deep rift valleys of east Africa. A large triangular section of northeastern Ethiopia is a down-faulted structural depression that includes the Danakil desert of northern Ethiopia and Eritrea, where a portion of the subsided surface lies at 381 feet below sea level. Branching off at right angles to the axis of the Red Sea trough is another broad structural depression

[3] E. F. Gautier, *Sahara—The Great Desert*, Columbia University Press, New York, 1935, p. 111.

between the bold, opposing shores of Somalia and Aden, occupied by the Gulf of Aden.

The peninsula of Arabia is a tilted tableland that slopes eastward from its high, steep-sided rampart facing the Red Sea in a series of descending plateaus toward the valley of the Tigris and Euphrates in Iraq and the Persian Gulf. Its mountainous western rim attains altitudes at many points of more than a mile, rising southward gradually to heights of over 10,000 feet toward its southern limits in Yemen. Its easternmost reaches south of the Persian Gulf again rise to elevations of more than a mile above sea level, in the coastal mountains overlooking the Gulf of Oman. Except in the mountainous borders the surface is largely a barren wasteland, alternating between gravel-strewn hammada and wind-drifted sandy erg. It measures from the Syrian desert to the Red Sea outlet of Bab el Mandeb a distance of some 1600 miles. From Bab el Mandeb to the Strait of Hormuz, where the Persian Gulf empties into the Gulf of Oman, the great peninsula is about 1200 miles in breadth.

A persistently arid environment continues across the level alluvial plains of the lower Tigris and Euphrates in Iraq and the narrow coastal plains of southern Iran and Baluchistan into the middle Indus valley in West Pakistan and the Thar desert of northwestern India. It rises into the mountains of Baluchistan, spreading northward over western Afghanistan into north central and eastern Iran, where it merges with the deserts of central Asia. Desert distribution in the highland plateau of Iran and Afghanistan ranges in altitude from about 2000 to more than 5000 feet, surmounted at intervals by many low mountain ranges that intercept enough precipitation from passing disturbances to create more humid environments that locally contrast with the characteristic aridity of their surroundings. Aridity continues into the great deserts of central Asia that begin in the basin of the Caspian Sea.

CLIMATIC CONDITIONS. It was stated earlier that the ruling atmospheric circulation giving rise to the enormous arid realm across north Africa and southwest Asia is the mainly southward flow of air in the persistent subtropical anticyclones in this part of the northern hemisphere. In the summer the expanded high pressure systems of subsiding, diverging air over the North Atlantic spread eastward over northern

Africa and the Middle East (Fig. 4.3). At the same time shifting northward, they are mainly responsible for the onshore transport of moist air over northern and western Europe. The principal air streams, after releasing the bulk of their precipitable moisture farther north, recurve southward, warming as they enter lower latitudes, become even drier, and thus bring dry, nearly cloudless air to the deserts. Here abundant sunshine by day and clear, starlit skies by night are the dominant weather features of summertime.

Thus, the rainless summers of the Sahara and most of southwest Asia's arid regions are explainable by the south-flowing return circulation of the anticyclonic systems centered over the North Atlantic. But other circulations play a significant role in producing desert conditions in east Africa, the southern margins of the

Arabian peninsula, West Pakistan, and northwest India. The governing flows of air in these cases are traceable to the onshore movements of maritime air from the sea during the season of the summer monsoon.

In summertime the increasing duration of daily sunshine and the greatly intensified heat of solar radiation warm the land surfaces of the northern hemisphere and, in the lower latitudes of northern Africa and southern Asia, invite the landward invasion of moist oceanic air. Over central Africa north of the equator summer sees the repeated surge of warm, humid air from the sun-bright equatorial waters of the Gulf of Guinea. Over West Pakistan and northwestern India a similar transport of warm, humid air sets in from the Indian Ocean, bringing the great bulk of the year's scanty precipitation to those areas in the summer (Table 19-2). Along

TABLE 19–2

Contrasting Temperature and Rainfall on Opposite Sides of the Intertropical Convergence
(Temp., °F; Rainfall, In.)
Stations North of Intertropical Convergence

	Apr.	May	Jun.	Jul.	Aug.	Sep.	Month of Max. Rainfall	Mean Annual Precipitation
Atar	81	87	*94*	*94*	93	91	Sep.	4.4
Fort Gouraud	76	81	88	*93*	92	89	Sep.	2.3
Gat	79	86	92	*93*	92	88	Jan.	0.5
Aswan	79	87	91	*92*	91	88	May	0.1
Dongala	83	91	92	93	*94*	91	Aug.	1.0
Wadi Halfa	80	88	90	90	*91*	87	Jul.	0.2
Tokar	82	91	93	96	*97*	94	Nov.	3.5
Abu Hamed	84	92	92	94	*94*	94	Aug.	0.8
Port Sudan	80	86	90	94	*95*	91	Nov.	4.2
Jidda	80	83	85	87	*88*	86	Nov.	2.5
Sharja	76	83	87	91	*93*	88	Dec.	4.2
Jask	80	86	90	*91*	89	87	Jan.	4.6

Stations South of Intertropical Convergence

	Apr.	May	Jun.	Jul.	Aug.	Sep.	Month of Max. Rainfall	Mean Annual Precipitation
Akjoujt	83	89	*94*	91	90	91	Aug.	4.1
Araouan	88	94	*99*	95	92	93	Sep.	1.7
Menaka	90	*94*	93	88	84	87	Aug.	9.8
Agades	87	*93*	92	89	87	88	Aug.	6.5
Bilma	84	90	*92*	91	91	88	Aug.	0.9
Largeau	86	93	*94*	92	92	91	Aug.	0.9
Atbara	87	93	*95*	93	91	93	Aug.	2.9
Kareina	86	93	*95*	94	94	94	Aug.	1.3
Kassala	89	*92*	91	85	83	84	Aug.	12.9
Masqat	84	91	*93*	91	87	87	Jan.	3.8
Chah Bahar	80	85	*88*	87	84	83	Jan.	4.0
Jacobabad	86	94	*99*	97	93	89	Jul.	3.5

the southern margins of the Sahara and the deserts of southwest Asia this generally north-eastward flow of moist, maritime tropical air advances to meet the leading edges of warm, dry, south-flowing continental tropical air. The meeting ground is that narrow zone of confluence referred to before as the intertropical convergence, or preferably, equatorial trough.

The fluctuating contact zone of the convergence occupies a general position at the earth's surface about 100 miles north of the northern limit of summer precipitation (Fig. 20.1). At higher altitudes, around 10,000 feet, dry air extends for as much as 500 miles farther south of the surface position. Ordinarily, dry air from the north overrides the more humid air from the south, inhibiting by its very dryness aloft the formation of precipitating convective systems toward the southern limits of its advance in the upper air. Cumulus clouds are often formed, and indeed showers are occasionally seen descending from them. But time and again such rains fail to reach the earth, evaporating in the dry, hot air before reaching the ground.

The rain-inhibiting influence of converging dry air aloft from northward and moist surface air from southward within the equatorial trough extends across the southern Sahara, southern Arabia and Iran, and as far east as northwestern India. Thus, the southern extent of aridity in the Sahara and southwest Asia is largely established through the effectiveness of dry air of anticyclonic character moving equatorward over north Africa.

Warm, dry air aloft is perhaps the chief reason for the presence of desert in the lower Indus valley of West Pakistan and the Thar desert of India. Although the summer monsoon brings a large amount of moist, oceanic air ashore in those areas in response to the summer development of the major low pressure systems centered over northwestern India, little precipitation results. This air is uplifted by normal thermal convective processes, and clouds frequently appear, but only infrequently is there any appreciable rain. Moist air also approaches the northwestern arid region from the Bay of Bengal. Moving up the Ganges valley, it releases copious rains over the Ganges delta region but brings diminishing amounts as it advances westward toward the Indus, failing for the most part in normal years over the Thar desert and the middle Indus valley.

To the surface circulation of the summer monsoon over the northern Indian Ocean may also be attributed the presence of desert in Somali and northern Kenya in east Africa. Here the dominant flow of air is again northeastward, roughly parallel to the east African coast, and precipitable moisture normally fails to reach the condensation point sufficiently often or in sufficient quantity to produce reliable rain except over the higher terrain of interior Somali and the mountains of southern Kenya. Along the desert shores of Somali an upwelling of colder water from the depths produces surface temperatures that average some 10 degrees cooler than those of the open sea to the east. Thus, a rain-inhibiting effect similar to that along the west coasts of South America and southern Africa contributes to the failure of rains along the desert shores of Somali.

A rain shadow effect is created by the lofty mountains of Kenya. Rising to well over 10,000 feet in their general mass and reaching an apex of 17,040 feet in Mt. Kenya, they intercept moisture-laden air moving northward, depriving northern Kenya, where elevations subside to between 1500 and 3000 feet, of any appreciable precipitation. Annual increments are uncertain and tend to average substantially less than 10 inches.

The Ethiopian highlands also interpose a rain shadow effect over the Danakil desert of northeastern Ethiopia. These lofty heights, rising to well over 12,000 feet at many points, receive most of the year's precipitation from the condensation of moisture transported northeastward for more than 2000 miles from the Gulf of Guinea during the summer monsoon of central Africa. Indeed, this eastward flow of air continues across the Red Sea at higher altitudes to bring substantial amounts of rain to the upper levels of mountainous Yemen, where in places the yearly total averages over 40 inches.

During the cooler half of the year, from October through March, the predominant flow of air is southward over northern Africa and southwest Asia (Fig. 4.2). The persistent subtropical anticyclonic circulations retreat southward, and over southwest Asia the equatorward pulsations of clear, dry air are augmented by the outflow of cold, dry air from the expanded and intensified Asiatic high pressure systems, centered over the east central part of Eurasia. The onshore movement of oceanic air from the

Gulf of Guinea is much reduced and brings rain only to a relatively narrow belt along the Guinea coast of central Africa, increased amounts occurring in the Congo basin, over which passes the main onshore flow from the Atlantic. The southern Sahara and the savanna lands along its southern margins are at this season almost completely without rain. The intertropical convergence shifts well to the south of the equator over southern Africa and the central Indian Ocean, allowing predominantly dry air and cloudless skies to prevail not only over the Sahara but also over the Danakil, Somaliland, southern Arabia, and northwestern India (Fig. 20.1).

But the polar frontal zone of precipitating disturbances is also displaced southward at this time of year, resulting in frequent rains in the Mediterranean basin, the Atlas Mountains, and at other elevated points along north Africa's Mediterranean shores (Fig. 5.2). This is the season when light rains may be expected along the Atlantic shores of Morocco and Spanish Sahara and on the upper slopes of the Ahaggar and Tibesti mountains of the central Sahara. Winter rains occur also in the mountainous portions of Iran and Baluchistan and at lower elevations approaching sea level along the Red Sea coasts, in the valley of the Tigris and Euphrates, and on the shores of the Persian Gulf and Gulf of Oman. The latter areas lie along the preferred tracks of migrating disturbances from the Mediterranean basin.

The number and distribution of weather observation stations in arid north Africa and southwest Asia are far from adequate for the analysis of regional climatic qualities (Fig. 19.3). Climatic generalizations, therefore, must be viewed with the unequal distribution of observation points in mind, noting their absence over most of the interior in contrast to their comparative abundance in particular areas such as the Nile valley, the southern Atlas region, and certain coastal sections.

Considering the enormous size of the nearly continuous desert expanse that reaches some 5800 miles from the Atlantic across north Africa to northwest India, it is a region appearing to possess remarkable uniformity. True, the influence of the sea is evident in coastal sections, whose temperature and humidity values contrast with those of the interior. Elsewhere, areas of strong relief and higher elevation intro-

duce a further variety of local climatic characteristics. Still, the interior portions of desert country, even those within a very few miles of the sea at moderate elevations, usually of less than 3000 feet, reveal a notable climatic similarity over the entire territory. The degree of similarity is disclosed in a number of ways, most particularly in the large annual range and strong daily fluctuations of temperature, rainfall variability, high percentage of possible sunshine, minimal cloudiness, the low frequency of fog, low relative humidities, noteworthy winds and dust storms, and the curious optical effect of the mirage.

The mean annual range of normal temperatures between the warmest and coldest months is well above 30 degrees in most interior locations. It rises to more than 40 degrees in the Algerian Sahara, the Syrian desert, the plains of Iraq, the upland of Iran, and the Indus valley. Values are less than 20 degrees in the southern Sahara and along the shores of the Arabian Sea, where winter temperatures are relatively high. They are less than 10 degrees at points along the Atlantic coast, where the relatively cool waters of the Canaries Current is a limiting factor. They are also less than 10 degrees in Somali and northern Kenya, where year-round temperatures are constantly high (Table 19-3).

The great variability of rainfall is a striking feature everywhere throughout these arid regions, despite the fact that small amounts can safely be counted on every year along the wetter margins and the adjacent mountains. In places mean variability exceeds 50 per cent, and extreme variations are common. At Siwa (el. −49) in northwestern Egypt, for example, the statistical rainfall average is 0.4 inch. But from 1900 to 1921 no rain at all was recorded, and yet in 1944–45, 1.7 inch fell. At Port Sudan, where the average is 4.1 inches, only 0.8 inch fell in 1910, but 16.6 inches were recorded in 1925, and 2.8 inches have fallen in twenty-four hours. At Khartoum 6.5 inches is the average, but in 1901, 2.5 inches, and in 1938, 15 inches were recorded. Basra averages 6.4 inches through the years, but as much as 13.9 inches and as little as 2.1 inches have fallen in a given year, and 3.5 inches have been recorded in twenty-four hours. Karachi has averaged 7.5 inches over one hundred years, but 28 inches fell in 1869 and only 4.6 inches in 1870. Summer is the normal wet season at Karachi, but in 1894

TABLE 19–3

Climatic Data for Desert Stations in Northern Africa
(Temp., °F; Rainfall, In.)

Station	Lat.	El. in Ft		Jan.	Feb.	Mar.	Apr.	May	Jun.	Jul.	Aug.	Sep.	Oct.	Nov.	Dec.	Year
Cape Juby, Spanish Sahara	27°56'	20	T	62	62	63	65	66	68	69	70	70	69	67	63	
			R	0.3	0.2	0.2	0.0	0.0	0.0	0.0	0.3	0.3	0.0	0.6	0.3	1.9
Port Etienne, Mauritania	20°56'	26	T	66	66	68	68	70	73	73	75	78	76	72	67	
			R	0.1	0.0	0.0	0.0	0.0	0.0	0.0	0.1	0.3	0.2	0.2	0.0	1.1
Taroudant, Morocco	30°28'	840	T	56	60	64	68	69	74	79	80	76	71	67	59	
			R	1.1	1.1	1.1	0.8	0.2	0.0	0.0	0.0	0.3	0.9	1.5	1.2	8.4
Araouan, Mali	18°54'	935	T	65	70	79	88	94	99	95	92	93	87	75	66	
			R	0.0	0.0	0.0	0.0	0.0	0.2	0.2	0.5	0.6	0.0	0.0	0.0	1.7
Timbuktu, Mali	16°46'	882	T	72	77	83	89	94	93	88	85	88	89	83	74	
			R	0.0	0.0	0.0	0.0	0.1	0.8	2.3	3.2	1.4	0.1	0.0	0.0	7.9
Touggourt, Algeria	33°07'	226	T	51	55	61	69	77	87	92	90	84	72	60	52	
			R	0.2	0.2	0.4	0.1	0.2	0.2	0.0	0.0	0.1	0.2	0.4	0.2	2.3
Tamanrasset, Algeria	22°42'	4593	T	53	57	63	71	78	83	83	82	79	72	64	57	
			R	0.2	0.0	0.0	0.2	0.4	0.1	0.1	0.4	0.1	0.0	0.0	0.0	1.5
Agades, Niger	16°59'	1633	T	68	73	81	87	93	92	89	87	88	85	77	69	
			R	0.0	0.0	0.0	0.0	0.2	0.4	1.7	3.5	0.6	0.0	0.0	0.0	6.5
Azizia, Libya	32°32'	380	T	53	56	60	67	74	81	84	84	82	75	64	55	
			R	1.8	1.3	0.8	0.4	0.2	0.1	0.0	0.0	0.3	0.5	1.1	1.9	8.5
Bilma, Niger	18°41'	1178	T	63	68	76	84	90	92	91	91	88	82	73	64	
			R	0.0	0.0	0.0	0.0	0.0	0.0	0.1	0.5	0.2	0.1	0.0	0.0	0.9

Location	Lat.	Elev.		1	2	3	4	5	6	7	8	9	10	11	12	Ann.
Aswan, Egypt	24°02′	364	T	60	63	70	79	87	91	92	91	88	83	73	63	
			R	0.0	0.0	0.0	0.0	0.1	0.0	0.0	0.0	0.0	0.0	0.0	0.0	0.1
Wadi Halfa, Sudan	21°50′	508	T	61	63	71	80	88	90	90	91	87	84	73	64	
			R	0.0	0.0	0.0	0.0	0.0	0.0	0.1	0.0	0.0	0.0	0.0	0.0	0.2
Khartoum, Sudan	15°36′	1246	T	75	77	82	89	93	93	89	87	90	90	83	77	
			R	0.0	0.0	0.0	0.0	0.3	0.2	2.1	1.4	0.6	0.1	0.0	0.0	4.7
Suez, Egypt	29°56′	10	T	58	60	65	71	77	82	85	85	81	76	69	60	
			R	0.2	0.1	0.2	0.1	0.1	0.0	0.0	0.0	0.0	0.0	0.1	0.2	1.1
Port Sudan, Sudan	19°37′	16	T	75	74	76	80	86	90	94	95	91	86	82	78	
			R	0.1	0.0	0.0	0.0	0.1	0.0	0.2	0.2	0.0	0.6	1.6	1.3	4.2
Djibouti, French Somaliland	11°36′	10	T	78	79	81	84	88	93	95	94	92	86	82	79	
			R	0.4	0.5	0.9	0.5	0.2	0.0	0.2	0.3	0.2	0.4	1.0	0.5	5.2
Berbera, Somali	10°26′	45	T	76	78	80	83	88	97	98	97	94	84	80	77	
			R	0.3	0.1	0.2	0.5	0.3	0.0	0.0	0.1	0.0	0.1	0.2	0.2	2.0
Belet Uen, Somali	4°44′	564	T	84	84	87	87	85	84	82	82	84	84	83	84	
			R	0.0	0.0	0.2	1.6	2.5	0.3	0.1	0.2	0.3	1.4	0.3	0.2	7.1
Mandera, Kenya	3°57′	1085	T	85	87	88	86	85	83	82	82	84	83	83	84	
			R	0.0	0.1	0.8	3.0	1.2	0.0	0.0	0.0	0.1	2.0	0.9	0.1	8.2
Mogadiscio, Somali	2°02′	39	T	80	80	82	84	83	80	78	78	79	81	81	81	
			R	0.0	0.0	0.0	2.3	2.3	3.8	2.5	1.9	1.0	0.9	1.6	0.5	16.9

Source: F. L. Wernstedt, *World Climatic Data, Africa*, Pennsylvania State University, 1959; U.S. Army, Quartermaster Research and Engineering Command, *Analogs of Canal Zone Climate in East Central Africa*, (Tech. Report EP-90), Natick, Mass., 1958.

TABLE 19–4
Climatic Data for Desert Stations in Southwest Asia
(Temp., °F; Rainfall, In.)

Station	Lat.	El. in Ft		Jan.	Feb.	Mar.	Apr.	May	Jun.	Jul.	Aug.	Sep.	Oct.	Nov.	Dec.	Year
Amman, Jordan	31°57'	2548	T	46	48	51	61	70	74	77	77	75	69	60	50	
			R	2.7	2.9	1.2	0.6	0.2	0.0	0.0	0.0	0.0	0.2	1.3	1.8	10.9
Eilat, Israel	29°33'	6	T	60	61	67	76	84	87	90	91	88	80	72	63	
			R	0.1	0.1	0.2	0.0	0.1	0.0	0.0	0.0	0.0	0.0	0.1	0.3	0.9
Jidda, Saudi Arabia	21°30'	20	T	73	72	77	80	83	85	87	88	86	84	80	77	
			R	0.9	0.0	0.0	0.0	0.0	0.0	0.0	0.0	0.0	0.0	1.6	0.6	3.1
Aden, Aden Protectorate	12°45'	94	T	76	77	79	83	87	90	88	86	88	84	80	77	
			R	0.3	0.2	0.4	0.2	0.1	0.1	0.0	0.1	0.1	0.1	0.1	0.1	1.8
Baghdad, Iraq	33°21'	120	T	49	54	61	70	81	90	94	94	88	78	63	52	
			R	1.2	1.3	1.3	0.9	0.2	0.0	0.0	0.0	0.0	0.1	0.7	1.2	7.1
Rutba, Iraq	33°02'	2019	T	44	48	52	64	74	81	85	86	80	70	58	47	
			R	0.6	0.6	0.6	0.7	0.3	0.0	0.0	0.0	0.0	0.2	0.4	0.9	4.3
Riyadh, Saudi Arabia	24°39'	1938	T	58	61	69	77	86	92	93	91	87	78	70	60	
			R	0.1	0.8	0.9	1.0	0.4	0.0	0.0	0.0	0.0	0.0	0.0	0.0	3.2
Abadan, Iran	30°21'	7	T	53	58	65	76	87	93	97	97	90	81	69	58	
			R	1.5	1.7	0.6	0.8	0.1	0.0	0.0	0.0	0.0	0.0	1.0	1.8	7.6
Bahrein, Bahrein Island	26°12'	18	T	61	62	68	76	84	88	91	92	88	82	74	65	
			R	0.4	0.7	0.5	0.2	0.1	0.0	0.0	0.0	0.0	0.2	0.2	0.8	2.9
Musqat, Oman	23°37'	20	T	71	71	77	84	91	93	91	87	87	85	79	72	
			R	1.1	0.7	0.4	0.4	0.0	0.1	0.0	0.0	0.0	0.1	0.4	0.7	4.0
Bandar Abbas, Iran	27°11'	29	T	65	67	73	80	87	91	93	92	90	85	77	68	
			R	2.4	1.2	0.3	0.2	0.1	0.0	0.0	0.0	0.0	0.0	0.0	1.6	5.8
Chah Bahar, Iran	25°17'	26	T	67	69	74	80	85	88	87	84	83	81	76	70	
			R	1.7	0.8	0.2	0.1	0.1	0.0	0.0	0.0	0.0	0.1	0.1	1.0	4.0
Karachi, Pakistan	24°48'	13	T	66	68	76	81	86	87	86	83	82	81	75	68	
			R	0.5	0.4	0.3	0.1	0.1	0.7	3.2	1.6	0.5	0.1	0.1	0.2	7.7
Tehran, Iran	35°41'	4002	T	36	41	49	60	70	79	85	84	77	64	53	42	
			R	1.8	1.5	1.8	1.4	0.5	0.1	0.1	0.1	0.3	0.3	0.8	1.2	9.7
Meshed, Iran	36°17'	3104	T	33	38	46	57	68	75	78	75	67	57	48	39	
			R	0.8	1.0	2.2	1.8	1.2	0.3	0.1	0.0	0.4	0.4	0.6	0.7	9.1
Seistan, Iran	31°00'	2000	T	46	52	60	72	81	88	92	89	81	70	58	48	
			R	0.4	0.4	0.6	0.1	0.0	0.0	0.0	0.0	0.0	0.6	0.5	0.3	2.9
Quetta, Pakistan	30°10'	5490	T	38	42	51	59	68	76	80	77	68	58	48	41	
			R	1.9	2.0	1.7	1.0	0.4	0.2	0.5	0.3	0.0	0.1	0.3	1.0	9.4
Jacobabad, Pakistan	28°17'	186	T	58	63	76	86	94	99	97	93	89	82	70	60	
			R	0.2	0.3	0.2	0.2	0.1	0.3	0.9	0.9	0.2	0.0	0.0	0.2	3.5

no rain fell from April through June, to be followed by 18.6 inches in July, after which no further rain was recorded until December. The total for that year was 22.7 inches. The following year a total of 4.9 inches was recorded, and only 0.13 inch in July, and the year preceding had seen only 0.8 inch in July. An amount equal to the entire yearly average has fallen in twenty-four hours at many stations. At Pasni on the coast of Baluchistan the yearly total is 6.2 inches, but 6 inches have fallen in twenty-four hours; at Khawr Sharja on the Trucial coast of the Persian Gulf, where 4.2 inches is normal, 4.3 inches have been recorded in twenty-four hours; at Bahrein, where 2.9 inches is the average, 2.8 inches have fallen in twenty-four hours.

Most of the precipitation reaching the northern Sahara and the wetter desert margins of southwest Asia is of frontal origin, in which cyclonic storms are the commonest form. They occur chiefly with the advancing cold front associated with an expanding surge of continental polar air from western Eurasia.

Summer. Air masses in summer are chiefly maritime tropical (sometimes spoken of as maritime equatorial) south of the equatorial trough and continental tropical north of it. The latter possess varying thermal properties and degrees of dryness, depending on whether they originate over the Sahara, southeastern Europe, southwestern Asia, or central Asia. Moist maritime tropical air affects the Atlantic coastal areas from the western Atlas southward, occasionally reaching inland for as much as 200 miles.

When the blazing heat of the high summer sun radiates down through cloudless skies, the temperatures of rock and sandy surfaces rise to the point of scorching intensity. Most interior sections north of the intertropical convergence receive between 90 and 95 per cent of possible sunshine from June through September (Fig. 19.4). A very narrow belt along the Atlantic coast is considerably more cloudy during the summer months, however, allowing only 40 to 45 per cent of possible sunshine from June through August at Cape Juby and about 65 per cent during July and August at Port Etienne. The southern portions of the arid regions south of the intertropical convergence both in north Africa and southwest Asia reveal a widespread contrast with the main desert areas north of that undulating zone. In these areas subjected

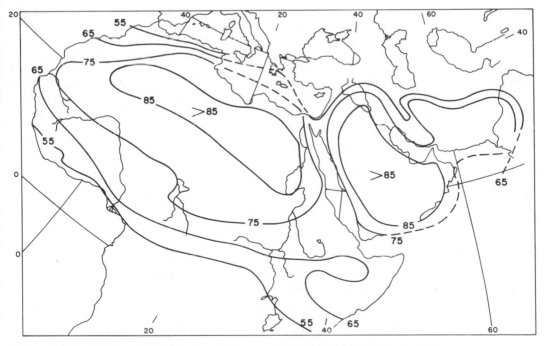

Figure 19.4. Annual percentage of possible sunshine recorded in northern Africa and southwestern Asia.

to the influence of the summer monsoon, a certain amount of cloud cover appears each summer in spite of the fact that rains are very sporadic and often fail altogether. Thus, the amount of possible sunshine along the southern margins of the Sahara is reduced to between 60 and 65 per cent, and in some areas amounts are substantially lower. At the head of the Arabian Sea the change from abundant sunshine in western sections to very cloudy summer weather along the shores of Pakistan appears in the records for July and August at the following stations: Jask, Iran, near the Strait of Hormuz, reports 80 per cent of possible sunshine in July and August, and on the sunny Arabian coast opposite, Muskat averages 85 to 90 per cent; Chah Bahar, about 170 miles eastward on the coast of Iran, reports values of 65 to 70 per cent; Pasni, another 170 miles farther east, in Baluchistan, reports about 50 per cent; Karachi, about 220 miles beyond, 25 to 30 per cent during the same months.

An interesting result of the summertime build-up of cloud cover in July and August south of the intertropical convergence is that the year's warmest weather comes in very early summer or late spring. The warmest month is usually June and quite often May (Table 19-4). But the really significant feature of summer weather everywhere in these extensive desert regions is the persistence of very high temperatures.

It is commonly believed that the erg regions of dry, loosely-shifting sand hills are the hottest desert areas. Data are not available to support a general statement on this point for the entire extent of arid north Africa and southwest Asia, but a number of observations indicate that sand surface temperatures attain values between 170° and 180°. With such extraordinary heat absorption at the land surface it is not surprising that very high air temperatures in the lower atmospheric levels are reached and continue as long as the sun is high in the sky. Mean monthly temperatures average 90° or above for two to five months in widely separated areas (Fig. 19.5). Araouan in the western Sahara is an example, where the warmest month, June, averages 99°. Other examples are Tokar in eastern Sudan, where the warmest month is August, averaging 97°, and Jacobabad, Pakistan, where the warmest month is June, averaging 99°. At these and many other stations the thermometer

reaches well over 100° day after day from April through September. At Araouan the mean maximum temperature is 110° or more from April through August (Fig. 19.6). The mercury has climbed to 121° at Baghdad and Biskra, 122° at Touggourt, 123° at Abadan and Basra, 124° at Mosul, and 136° at Azizia in northwest Libya. Azizia is considered to hold the world record of observed maximum temperatures at normal instrument shelter height.

Nocturnal cooling, which goes forward rapidly after sundown, fails to lower temperatures much below 80° at many stations, and rarely below 70° at most interior localities. The result is a mean daily temperature range of about 30 degrees over wide areas within these arid regions. At Araouan, for example, the mean daily range in April is 42 degrees, in May 38 degrees, in June and July 36 degrees, in August 33 degrees, and in September 34 degrees (Fig. 19.7).

The large daily range of temperatures in desert localities holds true for winter as well as summer, reflecting the relatively cloud-free state of the skies over most sections throughout the year. The rapid approach of darkness after sundown is another feature of daily weather in the desert, for twilight is not prolonged, and the splendor of brilliant starlight and bright moonlight comes on quickly in the desert air soon after the sun has set.

The thermal experience of stations near the sea along the Atlantic coast is considerably modified by the cooling effect of the Canaries Current. In August the sea surface temperature off the Atlantic coast of the Sahara ranges between 68° and 71°, from north to south, and in February from 61° to 65°. The lower monthly temperatures of coastal stations reflect the influence of the sea (Fig. 19.8). At Sidi Ifni and Cabo Yubi in Spanish Sahara the warmest month averages only 70°, and this value is not reached until September, indicating the expected lag under marine conditions.

Stations along the coast of the Red Sea are not helped by their proximity to a major body of water, for the surface temperatures of the Red Sea in August attain a mean value of 94°. Hence, at Port Sudan on the western shores July's mean temperature is 92° and August's 93°, and at Jidda on the Arabian shores July averages 87°, August 88°. In both cases August is the warmest month, and the nocturnal values remain high,

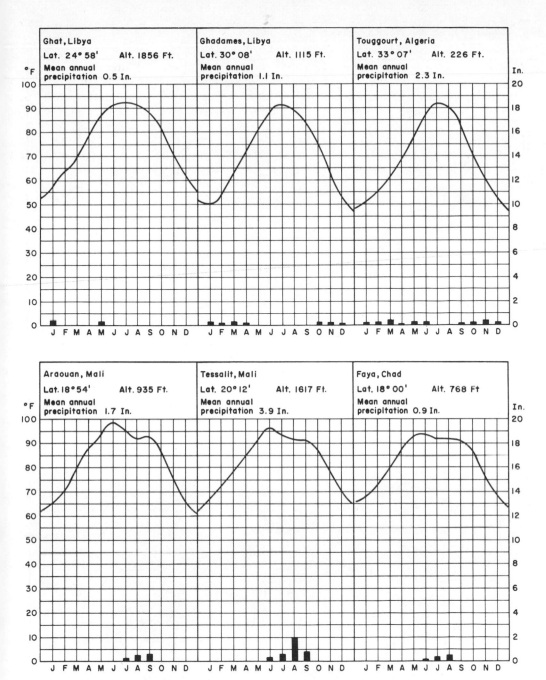

Figure 19.5. Temperature and precipitation at desert stations in the central Sahara.

mainly through the constantly high temperatures of the sea itself, averaging 83° at both stations.

Relative humidity in the desert reaches a minimum during the heat of summertime, and values in interior locations in midafternoon drop to extraordinarily low levels. Mean relative humidity at Araouan, for example, is 29 per cent, lowest value for the year, in May, just before the onset of the summer monsoon and the accompanying rise in partial cloud cover (Fig. 19.9). At Timbuktu about 150 miles farther south the yearly minimum of 17 per cent is reached in April, although by August, when the summer monsoon is in full swing, the value has risen to 58 per cent. At the Nasra

443

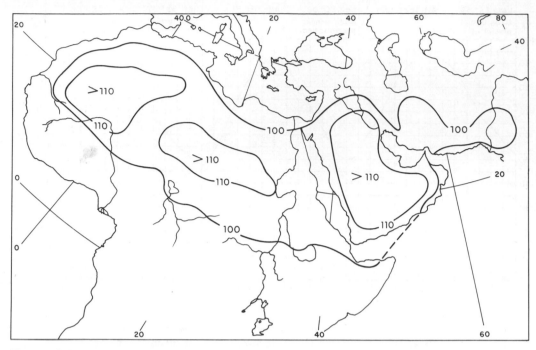

Figure 19.6.   Mean maximum temperatures in northern Africa and southwestern Asia in July (°F).

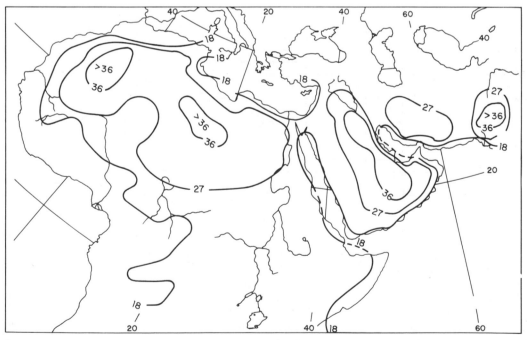

Figure 19.7.   Mean daily temperature range in northern Africa and southwestern Asia in July (°F).

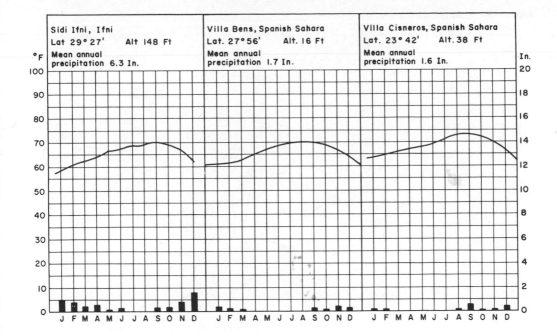

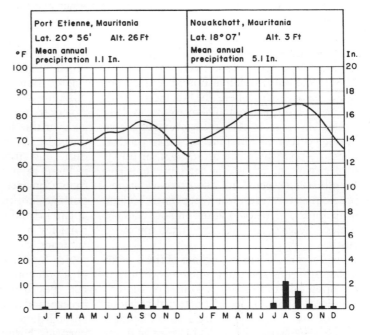

Figure 19.8. Temperature and precipitation at desert stations along the Atlantic coast of the Sahara.

airport during the period 1923–47 afternoon relative humidities at 4 P.M. averaged 18 per cent in July and August, and in the Aïr Mountains values as low as 2 per cent have been observed. Extremely dry, hot air induces among human beings a condition of nervous irritability, called by the French *cafard*, that arises during prolonged periods of high temperature and low atmospheric moisture.

Another unusual condition arising from extreme drought is the high intensity of static electricity. Telephone systems require special devices to reduce the intensity of electrical exchanges in unusually dry weather.

But the humidities along the coastal reaches are higher, adding greatly to the discomfort of summer's heat. At Cape Juby and Port Etienne on the Atlantic coast, for example, in the

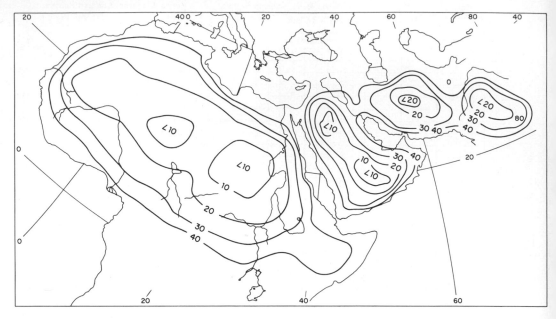

Figure 19.9. Midday relative humidities in northern Africa and southwestern Asia in April (per cent).

warmest month, September, the values are 91 and 77 per cent respectively. At Jidda in August the mean relative humidity is 70 per cent, and at Aden, where the warmest month is June, it is 72 per cent. These are mean daily values. However, at Masqat the average relative humidity at 4 P.M. in June is 72 per cent, at Bandar Abbas the mean at 3:30 P.M. in July is 63 per cent, and at Jask for the same hour and month it is 68 per cent. The excessive atmospheric moisture causes newspapers to become limp as rags, matches to soften and be rendered useless, leather to mildew, and metal to rust.

Fogs occur in northern sections of the interior in late summer and early autumn, when they are often said to precede the onset of winter's occasional rains. These are nocturnal radiation fogs of low density and are not widespread. Along the coasts fogs are also rare and are usually light, occurring for a few hours in the early morning and generally dissipating before noon. But the coasts of the Red Sea and the Persian Gulf commonly experience heavy dews. This nocturnal condensation of invisible water vapor is often heavy enough to drench the land within a few miles of open water to the extent that in coastal towns and villages it often appears as though a moderate fall of rain had occurred. Roofs steam with water in early morning after a heavy condensation of dew.

Reduction of visibility arises from an entirely different cause in these arid regions, however. A very frequent condition is a heavy haze in the air over the Red Sea and the Persian Gulf, produced by a combination of minute salt particles, dust, and moisture. Visibility is sometimes reduced in summertime to a distance of less than a quarter of a mile. Of even greater importance are the dust storms. The desert air is apparently always burdened with suspended particles of fine dust and tiny salt crystals. Whirling dust devils of small size and fairly rapid forward motion are a nearly daily phenomenon. Occurring a few hours after sunrise, they form at the instigation of the slightest breeze and are a strong point of distinction among these extensive arid regions. Many fine particles borne aloft by day remain in suspension at night.

Dust devils are chiefly a daytime phenomenon, pass quickly, and seldom rise more than 600–700 feet above the surface. Large dust storms, the black winds of the desert, are much less often seen but are known to sweep across the barren landscapes in certain areas as often as ten or twelve times each year. Like the smaller dust devils, they are chiefly a daytime occurrence, but occasionally they continue on through the night. The larger dust storms originating in the desert frequently extend their influence far beyond the desert margins. The yellowish dust of the harmattan from time to time blows westward out over the Atlantic, sometimes extending for several hundred miles to seaward. In May 1922 Saharan dust reached the outer rim of the West Indies, where visibility was reduced to 1 or 2 miles at sea. The sirocco is the dry, dusty wind from south and southeast that often spreads northward into the Mediterranean Sea from the Sahara, raising dust clouds to heights of up to 10,000 feet in the gusty, turbulent convective motions of hot desert wind. In such instances visibility has been reduced to less than 10 yards. Over southwest Asia it is not uncommon to observe dense dust clouds reaching upward to a sometimes sharply defined limit of about 5000 feet.

Severe sand and dust storms develop in the Gulf of Aden from June through August when hot, dry winds sweep down from the high tableland of Somali, crossing the coastal plain and spreading out over the sea. Dust storms occur in Iraq and over the Persian Gulf, largely in consequence of the vigorous northwest wind called the shamal. They occur most frequently around the head of the Persian Gulf in summer. They are much more frequent and more severe in eastern and southern Iraq, interior Persia, and western Afghanistan than elsewhere in southwest Asia.

In northwest India and West Pakistan the traveling depressions of summertime are the chief agents of dust storm development. They occur, as a rule, in association with the advance of a cold front. Here and over southwestern Asia in general warm, sometimes moderately humid air blows northward, usually from the southeast, raising surface temperatures to 100° or more. A mass of much cooler air, normally advancing from the northwest, undercuts the resident warm air, setting up a vigorous turbulence along the zone of contact, and towering masses of duct clouds rise upward along the approaching front. Gale velocities are often attained, when winds over the desert floor may drive heavy clouds of dust at speeds of up to 50 miles per hour. The drop in temperature, although usually of short duration, often lowers thermometer readings by as much as 30 degrees in a few minutes, from around 100° to 70°, as

the wind shifts to the northwest following the passage of the leading edge of the advancing cool air mass. The cool change is welcome, but fine dust particles penetrate every structure, sift through every crevice, and visibility may be reduced to zero in the open desert.

The warm, southerly wind that goes by the common name *sirocco* is called in Iran *simoom* (poison wind), in Egypt *Khamsin*, in Syria and Lebanon *Shlour*, in Iraq *sharqi*, and along the Persian Gulf *Kaus*. In the Persian Gulf, as the frontal change approaches from northwest, a shift to southwesterly gales often occurs, and such gales are known as *swahili*. The sirocco type of wind normally lasts for about one day, both at the beginning and the end of the summer season, but it may endure for three or four days in midsummer.

Dust storms are also associated with northwest winds in the Seistan basin of southeastern Iran and western Afghanistan, where a northwest wind called in Iran the *bad-i-sad-o-bist* (wind of 120 days) may blow steadily from June through September, bringing gales that sometimes reach speeds up to 70 miles per hour. Hot, dry air laden with dust and salt particles engulfs the region when these winds of the summer season are in play. A similar wind called *Bakharz* is known in northwestern Iran.[4]

The extraordinary daily heating of the desert floor throughout northern Africa and southwest Asia produces still another atmospheric phenomenon that creates a special problem to the traveler. This is the mirage. The air in contact with the desert floor is rapidly and excessively heated soon after sunup, and the lower atmosphere speedily changes in density, forming a surface atmospheric layer quite distinct in this respect from the air layers adjacent to and immediately above it. The contrast in atmospheric density bends and distorts the line of sight, producing at times the illusion of water in the arid desert, caused by the apparent lowering of the sky below the horizon, the distortion and rapid motions of the lower air layer suggesting the movement of ripples on water. Objects above the horizon appear to be below it and nearer than they actually are. The actual outlines of the horizon are also distorted and are seen constantly to change as the day

---

[4] George B. Cressey, *Crossroads*, J. B. Lippincott Co., New York, 1960, p. 100.

advances, some features being magnified for a time, changing, then disappearing altogether. The mirage usually develops about three hours after sunrise, and accurate visibility may be reduced to a few hundred yards. The mirage layer is shallow, however, and is seldom evident more than 20 feet above the ground.

Winter. The change from summer to winter throughout the desert regions of northern Africa and southwestern Asia takes place very rapidly, usually in less than one month, and thus the inhabitants normally think of the year's weather in terms of just two seasons, the hot season and the cold season. The rapid change from one season to the next occurs between dates that vary sufficiently from year to year to eliminate any clearly definable stages that in other climates might be described as autumn or spring. Exceptions are the highland borders of arid country, favored by adequate moisture for the support of more luxuriant vegetation and thus the setting for a colorful display of flowering plants that burst into life for a week or so to enliven the desert scene.

Air masses in winter are dominantly warm, dry continental tropical in character, originating chiefly over the Sahara or interior sections of southwest Asia. Next in importance are masses of cold, dry continental polar air from source regions either in eastern Europe or central Asia. The Asiatic air is largely responsible for occasional spells of unusually cold winter weather. Maritime tropical air from the Mediterranean basin or the Atlantic is also effective, bringing the principal influxes of precipitable moisture to those northern desert margins that can ordinarily expect to receive small but uncertain amounts of rain in winter. Maritime tropical air from the Arabian Sea is also carried into southwest Asia through the northward flow from the sea into the leading sectors of migrating depressions from the Mediterranean.

Winter sets in toward the end of October, lasts until April, and in most localities can be regarded as a season that is comfortably cool. During this period temperatures vary more widely from place to place than in summertime. January is normally the coldest month, although February is often almost as cold. At coastal stations very little difference is seen in mean monthly temperatures from December through February. Mean values for the coldest month are, on the whole, between 50° and 70°

(Table 19-3), although the influences of latitude, altitude, and proximity to the sea are plainly evident.

The influence of altitude on mean January temperatures is suggested by noting the comparative elevations of stations listed in Table 19-3. The effect of altitude may be more definitely observed by comparing four particular stations in Morocco. Taroudannt (el. 840), reports 56° in January, whereas Ouarzazate (el. 3721), about 120 miles east-northeast, reports 49° Midelt (el. 4986), about 150 miles northeast of the latter, 43°, and Guercif (el. 1214), about 130 miles northeast of Midelt and considerably lower in elevation, 50°.

As expected, nearness to the sea preserves the temperatures of the coldest months at higher levels. At Cabo Yubi, for example, mean values for both January and February are 61°, and at Port Etienne, 67° is the mean for December and January. At both of these points the monthly means vary little more than 1 degree from the four months from November through March.

Interior stations in the southern Sahara appear to undergo a maximum daily range for the year toward the end of winter in April, when relative atmospheric humidities are lowest and cloud cover is at or near the yearly minimum. This is the case at Araouan in Mali, where the mean daily temperature range in April is 42 degrees, mean cloud cover is less than 10 per cent, and relative humidity averages 31 per cent, and at Timbuktu, Mali, which reports a mean daily range of 34 degrees from February through April, mean cloud cover of 24 per cent, and relative humidity of 17 per cent in April. Khartoum, Sudan, also experiences its maximum daily range for the year in April, when mean cloudiness is less than 10 per cent and mean relative humidity reaches a yearly minimum of 32 per cent.

In northern sections, however, the mean daily temperature fluctuations are smaller in winter than in summer, resulting chiefly from lower mean daily maximum temperatures, which in turn are the consequence of diminished heat from the sun during the winter. Also inhibiting the development of wide daily thermal variations is the higher frequency of cloudy weather, fairly frequent though light sporadic rains, and higher relative humidities. The preferred trajectories of migrating winter storm centers tend to lie along the Tigris-Euphrates plains and the northern Persian Gulf, and to a lesser extent down the Red Sea trough. Hence, along these corridors one may observe the influence of winter's occasional rains, greater cloudiness, and higher relative humidities in the reported mean daily temperatures at representative stations. At Suez in January mean cloud cover is 36 per cent, relative humidity 71 per cent, and the mean daily temperature range is 18 degrees, compared with July, when mean cloud cover is 4 per cent, relative humidity 64 per cent, and the mean daily range 24 degrees. At Port Sudan in January mean cloud cover is 35 per cent, relative humidity 68 per cent, and mean daily range 13 degrees, whereas in July the mean cloud cover is 23 per cent, relative humidity 47 per cent, and the mean daily temperature range 24 degrees.

In the Persian Gulf the influence of winter weather comes to an end around the Strait of Hormuz, for at Jask, less than 150 miles southeast of Bandar Abbas, in January the mean cloud cover is 33 per cent, not appreciably greater than the 20 per cent in July, and mean relative humidities average 60 per cent in January compared with 68 per cent in July. The mean temperature range in January is 14 degrees, not substantially larger than the value of 11 degrees for July. Conditions east of this point, in Baluchistan, West Pakistan, and northwest India, are similar, reflecting a diminishing influence eastward of winter's disturbances, and a moderately large mean daily temperature range in January compared with values in summertime during the season of the southwest monsoon. In these eastern reaches of the deserts of southwest Asia winter is a season of clear, cool, dry weather when the shallow, dissipating disturbances from the Mediterranean may occur only a few times each month from January through April, yielding light rains and, less frequently, light snow, at least down to elevations of about 1000 feet.

Subfreezing temperatures in the Sahara have been recorded at least as far south as central Niger, east of the Aïr Mountains, for Bilma in central Niger has reported 29° in January. Most inland stations from here northward have also reported below-freezing values: Biskra and Touggourt in northeastern Algeria have recorded 26°, Azizia in northwestern Libya, 27°, and Tamanrasset on the southern slopes of the Ahaggar, 20°. Where desert faces the sea, however, along the Atlantic and Mediterranean coasts and the shores of the Red Sea, frost is generally unknown at the height of the standard weather shelter, although near-freezing values have been reported at many points.

Subfreezing temperatures are not unknown in southwest Asia. Baghdad has recorded 18° in January and Damascus 21°, and Abadan and Basra near the Persian Gulf have experienced 24°. Under the moderating influence of the sea, however, values are seldom below freezing along the shores of the Persian Gulf, although Bushire has reported 32° in January. On the higher plateau of Iran and Afghanistan winter temperatures drop far below freezing during the clear, calm, very cold nights, at times reaching well to the zero mark. Meshed in the northeast has recorded −18° in January, and Isfahan has recorded −5°. Although supporting data are lacking, it is believed that similarly low temperatures can occasionally be expected in southeastern Iran and southwestern Afghanistan, and mountainous Baluchistan is known for its alternately cold, blustery and clear, calm weather, frost and snow occurring frequently and subfreezing temperatures widely experienced. Over the low-lying Indus plains farther east temperatures as low as 23° have been recorded in desert districts.

Central Eurasia

Arid regions extend from northwest of the Caspian Sea eastward for some 3500 miles to the Gobi desert. Merging with the deserts of southwest Asia in northeastern Iran and northern Afghanistan, they may be regarded as the continuation of a vast arid realm that begins along the Atlantic shores of west Africa and extends northeastward altogether some 8300 miles into eastern Mongolia (Fig. 7.1).

The more northerly latitudes within which this central Eurasian desert lies, its central position remote from the sea and deep within the world's largest land mass, the discrete relationship it bears to the general circulation of the Atmosphere—these are geographical circumstances that fundamentally affect its climatic character. Coupled with the above factors is the influence of sharply contrasting elevations and tremendous mountain systems upon the main streams of the seasonal circulation. High mountains overshadowing low

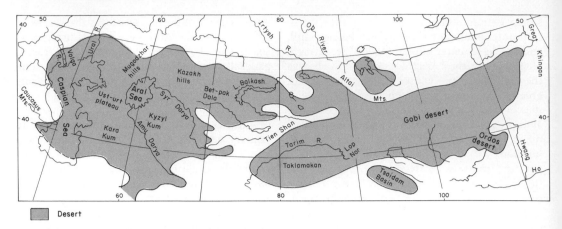

Figure 19.10.   Distribution of desert in central Eurasia.

basins result in a number of striking differences in climatic detail within very short distances.

The desert environment of central Eurasia can be regarded as the climatic extremity of a gradual transition from the humid forests of the middle latitudes through wooded steppe, open grassland, and the semidesert vegetation of scattered bunch grass. This geographic relationship is observed from the mid-latitude mixed forests west of the Urals toward the Caspian basin, and from the narrowing band of mixed forest east of the Urals toward the Aral Sea basin and the shores of Lake Balkash. It is also seen from the humid forest environment of northern China westward toward the Ordos desert in the northern bend of the Hwang Ho and toward the Gobi, beyond the Great Khingan Mountains of western Manchuria in eastern Mongolia (Fig. 19.10).

But the continuity of desert is almost broken by the mountain systems that extend from Afghanistan diagonally northeastward across the main zonal axis of desert distribution. Where desert conditions approach the piedmont fringes of these great mountain ranges, they give way abruptly to less arid grasslands that form a narrow belt of transition toward the cooler, usually wooded mountain slopes at higher elevations. Thus, within a short distance a rapid change takes place along the mountain borders of desert in the continental interior, from dessicated desert basins to the cooler, more humid, and much more complex climates of the rugged highlands.

The arid environment of central Eurasia occupies a series of broad basins and low, hilly plateaus that range in altitude from below sea level in the Caspian basin to nearly 5000 feet above sea level. The rocky and sandy floors of the dusty desert depressions and tablelands rise gradually eastward to elevations of nearly 5000 feet in northwestern China and western Mongolia, subsiding still farther eastward to about 2000 feet near the borders of Manchuria.

The Caspian Sea is the largest of the world's interior lakes and seas, measuring about 750 miles from north to south. Except for its southeastern corner the eastern shoreline, a stretch of nearly 700 miles in length, is entirely desert in nature. From the surface of the Caspian at about 92 feet below sea level the land along the northeastern shores rises gently eastward over the low Emba plateau toward the moderate heights of the Mugodzhar hills, which form a gentle arc between the Emba River and the Aral Sea and crest in places to more than 2000 feet. Beyond this range the land subsides again in the Turgai tableland, a region of isolated plateaus and small, tabular eminences about 300 miles in breadth. East of this the surface inclines upward once more into the Ulu-Tau, a series of hills roughly parallel to the Mugodzhar hills, marking a prominent feature in the western part of the Kazakh folded country. This is a somewhat higher plateau that, like the Turgai tableland, is occupied chiefly by open grassland but, also like the Turgai region, grades into desert in its southernmost reaches. The Kazakh rise extends eastward almost as far as the eastern end of Lake Balkash.

Between the Caspian Sea and the Aral is the rocky surface of the Ust-Urt plateau. This barren platform slopes downward in an easterly direction from the rugged hills of the Mangy-schlak peninsula, jutting northwestward into the northern end of the Caspian, where altitudes rise in places to more than 1800 feet. It breaks off steeply along the western shores of the Aral to form a series of high bluffs overlooking the brackish waters of the sea surface, which stands at about 170 feet above sea level. South of the Ust-Urt the sandy wastes of the Kara-Kum project southeastward for some 500 miles between the Kopet Mountains of northeastern Iran and the narrow valley of the exotic Amu-Darya. This is the main influent of the Aral Sea, entering at the southwestern corner. Between the Kopet Mountains and the Amu-Darya the mean distance is about 300 miles. Beyond the Amu-Darya and between it and the Syr-Darya a second influent of the Aral entering at the northeastern corner, is the dominantly sand-drifted desert tract of the Kysyl-Kum. Beyond the Syr-Darya the land surface inclines upward into a broad, low rise called the Bet-Pak-Dala, or Hunger steppe, that terminates along the western shores of Lake Balkash. South of the Hunger steppe, between it and the projecting range of the Kara-Tau and the towering Kirghiz Mountains, is the sandy desert of the Mujum-Kum. Northeast of the Mujum-Kum is the Balkash depression, a largely sandy desert sloping very gradually northward to Lake Balkash.

Lake Balkash fills a long, shallow, sinuous trough that measures altogether about 350 miles from end to end. It is an unusually shallow body of water, averaging scarcely more than 20 feet in depth, fresh in its western portion where its principal influent, the Ili River, is a constant source of replenishment, but brackish in its eastern section. Its surface level fluctuates considerably but generally averages about 1100 feet in elevation. The lake occupies the northern part of the Balkash depression, an enclosed drainage basin terminating rather sharply along its northern and western margins where the Kazakh hills and the Hunger steppe rise toward the north and west. Thus, the northern shores often take the form of steep, rocky cliffs standing several hundred feet above the lake's surface, whereas the southern shores are low, mainly marshy, and rise imperceptibly to sweep away toward the southeast in a broad, sandy plain toward

the steeply rising heights of the Dzungharian Ala-Tau.

The desert terrain lying east of the Caspian attains a maximum north-south breadth of about 1000 miles between the mountains of western Afghanistan and the Turgay tableland, narrowing almost to extinction east of Lake Balkash. South of the Ust-Urt plateau, the Aral Sea, the Bet-Pak-Dala, and Lake Balkash desert landscapes are dominantly sand-drifted wastelands, relieved by the narrow, elongated oases along the exotic rivers that take their rise high among the snow-capped peaks of the great mountain systems of central Asia and flow northwestward across the arid plains. The general elevation of the land from the Kara-Kum to the Balkash depression remains below 1000 feet.

An impressive contrast meets the observer's eye where flourishing crops of a thriving agriculture extend for miles along the banks of the Murgab, the Amu-Darya, and the Ili, flanked on either side by barren dessication. An even more impressive contrast is seen in the upper valleys of those rivers where attenuated arms of the desert floor bend eastward and rise to levels of about 2000 feet. Here they are embraced on either side by the imposing heights of projecting ranges of the central mountain systems, many of which tower up to more than 10,000 feet in elevation. Between the Kopet Dagh and the Dzungharian mountains desert conditions interpenetrate between the humid slopes of mountain country. The series of desert pockets thus created have the advantage of substantial irrigation potential from the runoff of alpine streams fed by the more abundant and more reliable rains of the highlands and the meltwater from their winter mantle of ice and snow.

The distance from the Caspian Sea to the eastern end of the Balkash depression is about 1500 miles. At its eastern extremity the desert environment all but terminates in the foothills of the lower mountain ranges that lie between the majestic masses of the Tien Shan and the Altai Mountains. However, the continuity of the desert climate is preserved into east Asia across the narrow divide between the Dzungharian Ala-Tau and the Mali Tau, a break in the low mountain rampart historically known as the Dzungharian Gates, leading into the higher elevations of the desert plains of Dzungharia. Dzungharia is the northern region of China's northwest province of Sinkiang. This steppe-bordered basin between the Tien Shan and the Altai projects northwestward down the valley of the Black Irtysh into the basin of Lake Zaisan, which in turn enters the Irtysh, its waters ultimately contributing to the upper Ob River. The Dzungharian basin maintains a gentle slope upward from about 300 feet at the salt water surface of Ebi Nor, southeast of the Dzungharian Gates to more than 2000 feet as it approaches the piedmont of the Altais.

South of the Tien Shan is the great desert region of the Tarim basin. This largest and most imposing of the world's interior basins takes its name from the exotic river, the Tarim, which preserves a partly intermittent flow across the northern part of the basin. From its tributaries in the Karakorum and Kunlun Shan in the southwest it almost entirely spans the 800 mile length of the broad depression. The Tarim basin is nearly surrounded by mountain ranges of immense bulk and towering height. On the north the Tien Shan, reaching summits of nearly 25,000 feet in its central portion, curves slightly southeastward, and also slightly south-westward, where it merges with the even loftier peaks of the Pamirs. Here the snow-capped mountain tops rise to more than 25,000 feet. The Pamirs in turn are continuous with the Karakorum of northern Kashmir and the Kunlun Shan. The Kunlun, rising to more than 20,000 feet, forms part of the southern mountain rim of the great basin. Branching off northeastward from the Kunlun Shan are the diminishing heights of the Altyn Tagh, again occasionally reaching heights of more than 20,000 feet. This range converges toward the Kuruk Tagh, the southeastern extension of the Tien Shan. Here, between these two ranges about 100 miles apart, the Tarim River sinks abortively into the shallow, marsh-bordered saline waters of the Lop Nor. Beyond the fluctuating margins of this terminus of the Tarim drainage the Tarim basin extends for 100 miles or more before rising gradually toward the broad, low divide that separates it from the deserts of northern China.

Most of the desert floor of the Tarim basin is occupied by the vast sandy surface of the desert known as the Taklamakan, whose mean elevation is between 3000 and 3500 feet. About 150 miles north of the Kuruk Tagh is a parallel range of mountains, also an extension of the Tien Shan but one that rises at several points above 15,000 feet. These are the Bogda-Ola Mountains, which continue eastward for more than 300 miles from Urumchi. Between these parallel ranges is a relatively small desert basin whose most prominent feature is the Turfan depression at its northern edge. This small, isolated pocket of land, about 75 by 27 miles in area, drops down to an extreme depth of about 940 feet below sea level. By comparing this with the majestic upward thrust of the great mountain crests around the Tarim basin, the dramatic contrasts between the massive mountain systems and the barren desert basins of central Eurasia are well emphasized.

East of Dzungharia and the Tarim basin and separated from these by low, grass-mantled ranges of steppe land is the Gobi desert. This historic heartland of east Asia's warlike nomads cannot be defined exactly, chiefly for want of sufficient systematically organized information. It is generally described, however, as the semi-arid to arid region south of the Mongolian steppes and over many centuries has been pictured by occasional western travelers as a region consisting alternately of rocky plains, drifted sand flats, low tablelands, and rising barren hills that in places attain altitudes of nearly 5000 feet. It reaches eastward toward the western foothills of the Great Khingans of western Manchuria, merging there with the less arid grassland borders. Southward from the Gobi sand-drifted terrain extends across the northern bend of the Hwang Ho, the Yellow River of north China, into the Ordos desert northwest of the Shensi Hills. The Ordos desert and the Alashan desert east of the Nan Shan ranges together bracket the north-flowing section of the upper Hwang Ho.

Throughout the desert realm of central Eurasia high mountains deprive a number of intervening basins and river valleys of sufficient moisture to support a continuous vegetation cover, and these intermontane hollows are merely rain shadow deserts. This is true in the upper valley of the Amu-Darya around Termes, the Syr-Darya around Fergana, the valley of Lek Issyk, the upper Ili valley, and others. The floor of the Tarim basin is desert at least partly in consequence of the rain shadow effect of the extremely high mountains by which it is nearly encircled.

A good example of an isolated rain shadow

desert is the small, arid area of the lower Kura River valley between the Caucasus and the mountains of northern Iran. From near the town of Yevlakh, about 150 miles upstream from the Caspian, to the mouth of the Kura and from there northeastward for about 100 miles to Baku this small, angular tract of moisture-deficient lowland is hemmed in by well-watered mountain ranges. The upper slopes of the Caucasus, which rise well over 15,000 feet above sea level in the central portion and are snow-capped the year round, receive more than 40 inches of annual precipitation. Batum at the eastern end of the Black Sea, over 400 miles northwest of the Kura's mouth, averages about 80 inches yearly, and Tbilisi, about 275 miles above the river mouth, averages about 20 inches. From here aridity increases seaward to the Caspian, Yevlakh itself reporting about 10 inches and the littoral between the mouth of the Kura and Baku about 8 inches. The arid, barren peninsula on which the petroleum center of Baku is situated receives less than 8 inches of annual rainfall. From 1881 to 1915 Baku averaged about 7 inches of rain; during the same period Lenkoran, about 50 miles south of the Kura mouth near the base of mountains exceeding 8000 feet in elevation, recorded nearly 50 inches of rain.

PLANT LIFE. In central Asia the change from bleak aridity on the desert floor to humid grassland on the lower mountain slopes usually takes place within a very short distance. The observer normally sees a well-defined contrast between verdant piedmont steppe and barren, lifeless desert stretching away over the adjoining lowland. Between the near-level north Caspian lowland and the Balkash basin, however, the transition southward from the central Eurasian steppe into desert takes place across a band of semidesert that in places is as much as 250 miles broad. This is the case, for example, along the lower course of the Volga between Stalingrad and Astrakhan. But the belt of semidesert varies greatly in breadth and is most unevenly distributed. It is sometimes entirely absent, as in the Turgai tableland, where the change from steppe to desert occurs abruptly. Where the transitional semi-arid zone is broad and well-developed, it is marked by a generous scattering of plant life separated by patches of bare ground exposed at the surface. This distinguishes semidesert from the uniform grass cover of the steppe. When the traveler observes that the proportion of bare ground is greater than plant-covered ground, desert is said to begin. A relatively gradual transition similar to that found west of the Dzungharian Gates appears from the steppes of northern Mongolia southward, from Manchuria westward, and from the middle Hwang Ho valley northward, into the Gobi desert.

In the region from the Caspian to Lake Balkash steppe grasslands predominate in the northern part of the semidesert region across the southern margins of the Khirgiz steppe. Proceeding southward, however, a larger number of drought-resistant species become evident, artemisia (here known as polyn) contributing a major component of the vegetation. Where clay loam soils are only slightly saline, white polyn (varieties of *Artemisia maritima*) prevails, but on the more saline, heavier clay soils fragrant black polyn is the leading species (various forms of *A. pauciflora*). Mixed with these in various proportions are representatives of the true steppe grasses, especially the fescues (*Festuca sulcata valesiaca*), koeleria (*Koeleria gracilis*), and feather grasses such as *Stipa capillata*. The recumbent summer cypress (*Kochia prostrata*) is also found, and polyn is often replaced by a very common low shrub, the saltbush (*Atriplex canum*). Many annuals, such as tulip, buttercup, rhubarb, as well as a variety of mosses and lichens, are also found in the semidesert vegetation.

In the desert proper, especially the sand deserts of the Kara-Kum, the Kysyl-Kum, Mujum-Kum, and the Balkash basin, large tracts of wind-driven dunes are often entirely without a stabilizing cover of plant life. This is especially true of the barchan regions along the middle course of the Amu-Darya and the Syr-Darya, where those symmetrical arcs of wind-blown sand form, shift position, dissipate, and re-form, sometimes within a few hundred yards of the moist river bottoms. In the southern sand deserts there is usually no continuous vegetation in summer, autumn, or winter. Plants are far apart, and the ground is chiefly bare. In spring, when the southern deserts receive small but fairly reliable amounts of rain, the ground is decked, often completely, with a short-lived carpet of low vegetation, consisting mainly of ephemeral plants. These are largely grasses, sedges, and bright-colored bulb plants. The grasses on the partly stable sand hills are usually species of blue grass, wheat grass, and brome. They ordinarily give way to xerophytes after mid-May when the rains cease.

Along the exotic river valleys, especially the Amu-Darya, the flood plains are often luxuriously covered with a thick, heavy sod of meadowland and extensive flats of reeds and rushes up to 20 feet in height, alternating with dense thickets of small, low-crowned deciduous trees. The soils are largely saline in nature, from the abundance of salts in the river waters, augmented by the high rate of evaporation. An interesting result of this is seen in the Azhrek grass (*Aeluropus litoralis*), whose leaves wear a patina of tiny salt crystals emitted by the transpiration process from the leaf tissues. This and other meadow-forming grasses, like Bermuda grass (*Cynodon dactylon*) and pale green sod grass (*Atropis distans*), are sod-forming grasses that develop extensive, vigorous root systems.

Among the taller forms of vegetation are the spiny shrub, the Siberian salt tree (*Halinodendron argenteum*), and white saxaul (*Ammodendron conollyi*), a low, shapely shrub with silver leaves, pendant branches, and fragrant, dark lavender flowers. Several species of saxaul are seen in various ecological situations within the desert realm. It is a tough, woody plant that grows rapidly, and in the desolate places where this handy, endemic genus thrives, the heavy wood of its dead trunks and branches is valued as fuel, despite the forbidding shape of its lifeless members, symbols of death and evil spirits. Only a small number of native tree species can be found in the riparian thickets of the southern deserts. They include the Euphrates poplar (*Populus diversifolia*), the commonest form, bloomy poplar (*P. primosa*), willow, Russian olive (*Elaegnus angustifolia*), and several species of tamarisk (*Tamarix spp.*), whose pink and lavender flowers add a colorful brightness to the vegetation of these exotic stream valleys.

Insufficient information prevents a discussion of the vegetation of the desert regions and their borderlands east of the Dzungharian Gates. A dearth of adequate climatic data for all but a very few stations handicaps a general discussion of the eastern deserts also. Indeed, the entire desert realm from the Caspian to the Gobi is conspicuously deficient in suitable records of atmospheric observations, although data from portions in the Soviet Union are better and more

plentiful. This will be evident in the discussion of atmospheric properties that follows, and much of the general treatment is based upon the records of explorers as well as the more systematic observations at widely scattered weather stations. Many of the conclusions are tentative and will remain so for some time.

CLIMATIC CONDITIONS. Remoteness from the sea is without doubt the main geographical circumstance responsible for the existence and distribution of central Eurasia's desert territories. The mainstreams of moisture-laden air from the Atlantic, the Arctic, and the Pacific release nearly all their precipitable water vapor before they reach these areas. The presence of persistent drought arises mainly from the normal failure of precipitating disturbances to reach the arid districts. Great uncertainty as to time, duration, and amount of either snow or rain is as characteristic here as it is in other desert regions, but in central Eurasia geographical remoteness is the initial circumstance upon which desert distribution depends.

The arid lands that stretch eastward from the Caspian Sea to western Mongolia lie between the normal tracks followed by migrating disturbances from the west. In summertime these tracks lie north of the desert, and in winter they lie south of it (Figs. 5.13 and 5.12). The Tarim basin is shielded almost completely from the entry of rain-bearing disturbances from the west by the Pamirs and the Tien Shan. But Dzungharia, north of the Tien Shan, being open to slightly more frequent incursions, is generally less arid although it contains desert pockets that, like those in western Mongolia, are partly the result of the rain shadow influence of overshadowing mountain ranges. The Gobi, farther eastward, with its adjoining desert regions around the upper Hwang Ho, lies remote from both the precipitating storms originating over western Eurasia and the onshore invasions of warm, moist air from the Pacific during east Asia's summer monsoon.

The main features of the general circulation affecting the middle latitudes of Eurasia have been described in preceding chapters. We recall from those earlier discussions that from year to year a rhythmic change comes over the great expanse of the continental interior in the form of very pronounced seasonal contrasts in the size, intensity, and distribution of the major wind and pressure fields. In winter throughout most of interior Eurasia the ruling condition of the atmosphere is the persistence of large and intensified anticyclones centered over Mongolia and eastern Siberia (Fig. 4.2). In summer these are greatly reduced in size, frequency and intensity, and the dominant feature is the nearly constant presence of low pressures centered over Baluchistan in southwest Asia (Fig. 4.3). This systematic alternation is primarily the result of the highly diminished input of radiant heat from the sun coupled with the overwhelming proportion of heat loss from the surface during the winter season, compared with the strong thermal gains, especially over southwest Asia, in summertime.

October is normally a well-defined period of transition from summer to winter in the northern hemisphere when the ratio of daylight to darkness decreases following the autumnal equinox. The season's first frosts are normally experienced around the middle of the month in the central areas and near the end of October near the borders of Afghanistan and the Ordos desert in north China.

Over northern Eurasia the rapid cooling of the continent produces increasingly colder temperatures in the lower atmosphere, and cold, dry, stable air begins to intensify and to spread its persistent influence over the land mass, particularly in the Asiatic sectors. By midwinter anticyclonic systems centered over Mongolia are virtually constant and are of unusual intensity—mean barometric pressures in January are 1035 millibars (30.6 inches or more) —spreading over most of north China and westward to the Black Sea. Throughout most of the desert areas calm, dry air prevails, air that is often bitterly cold and unusually transparent, in the frosty stillness revealing features of the landscape with sparkling clarity. The mean pressure gradient slopes downward in all directions from the central high pressure maxima, and the clockwise circulation of the prevailing geostrophic flow brings light north winds over most of north China, northeast winds between Lake Balkash and the Aral Sea, and easterly winds to the north Caspian basin. In the western deserts northwest winds occur from time to time in response to the occasional development of anticyclones over eastern Europe between the Carpathians and the Urals. All of these larger tendencies are, of course, modified by the alignment of the major mountain ranges, and local winds vary accordingly. Föhn winds are often felt in the valleys when air moves down from the great heights of adjoining mountain slopes. In the Balkash basin such a wind is the ibe, from the Dzungharian Mountains to the east, which brings high temperatures and a powerful drying effect when it invades the lowland.

The divergent outflow of subsiding air over the eastern interior of Eurasia at times takes the form of a vigorous outburst of cold, dry continental polar air that delivers powerful blustery gales of wind at the surface to peripheral areas. North China's deserts are especially afflicted by polar outbursts in wintertime, and these are one of the more notorious scourges of the region, sweeping with gale force out of the northwest, raising suffocating clouds of fine yellow dust high into the air. Winter dust storms also occur near the Caspian lowland where northeasterly gales drive snow and dust clouds across the desert plains at velocities up to 60 and 70 miles per hour and raise them to heights of 2 or more miles above the earth. In the upper Amu-Darya valley, notably at Termes, a strong southwest to west-southwest wind called the afghanets bursts forth when cold fronts advance from the north or northwest. This vigorous convergence wind blows from forty to seventy times each year and normally produces dust storms that may rise to 2 miles or more above the surface.

In October the main belt of the east-flowing upper air streams begins to shift southward (compare Figs. 4.10 and 4.11). At altitudes of between 2 and 4 miles the upper air flow remains eastward over most of the continent during the entire winter. In February the upper westerlies reach their maximum strength for the year.

The main movement of systematic surface disturbances in wintertime is eastward under the primary influence of the upper air streams. It will be recalled that the Mediterranean basin becomes, from October through May, an important region of cyclogenesis. By November the winter storm tracks are normally well established, and disturbances increase in number from this time onward, reaching a maximum frequency in January. A certain number of migrating storms find their way eastward across northern Iran as far as the high mountain region south of Lake Balkash (Fig. 5.12). Others

TABLE 19–5

Climatic Data for Desert Stations in Central Eurasia
(Temp., °F; Rainfall, In.)

Station	Lat.	El. in Ft		Jan.	Feb.	Mar.	Apr.	May	Jun.	Jul.	Aug.	Sep.	Oct.	Nov.	Dec.	Year
Northern Stations																
Astrakhan	46°15′	−46	T	19	23	33	48	64	73	77	74	63	49	36	27	
			R	0.5	0.5	0.4	0.6	0.6	0.8	0.5	0.4	0.6	0.4	0.6	0.6	6.4
Guryev	47°07′	−72	T	13	16	28	47	64	73	78	73	61	46	32	22	
			R	0.5	0.5	0.4	0.6	0.8	0.7	0.5	0.4	0.6	0.4	0.6	0.7	6.5
Fort Shevshenko	44°31′	79	T	25	27	36	50	64	73	79	76	66	53	41	32	
			R	0.3	0.2	0.4	0.2	0.3	0.7	1.0	1.3	1.2	0.6	0.4	0.2	6.7
Baku	40°28′	−39	T	38	39	43	51	63	72	77	77	71	62	51	44	
			R	0.8	0.6	0.7	0.8	0.4	0.2	0.2	0.2	0.6	0.9	1.1	0.9	7.4
Irgiz	48°37′	420	T	4	7	19	43	62	73	77	73	60	43	25	12	
			R	0.4	0.3	0.4	0.6	0.7	0.7	0.2	0.4	0.6	0.7	0.5	0.5	5.9
Aralsk	46°47′	187	T	7	10	23	46	63	74	79	74	61	44	28	17	
			R	0.3	0.2	0.2	0.4	0.4	0.4	0.2	0.2	0.2	0.8	0.4	0.3	4.0
Cape Topolev	47°48′	1270	T	−1	1	16	37	57	67	73	69	58	42	21	4	
			R	0.2	0.2	0.2	0.3	0.5	0.9	0.9	0.7	0.3	0.7	0.5	0.3	5.7
Southern Stations																
Krasnovodsk	40°00′	−49	T	36	39	48	57	69	77	84	83	75	63	51	43	
			R	0.5	0.5	0.7	0.9	0.4	0.4	0.2	0.2	0.2	0.4	0.5	0.5	5.4

Station	Lat.	Elev.		Jan	Feb	Mar	Apr	May	Jun	Jul	Aug	Sep	Oct	Nov	Dec	Year
Chickishlyar	37°35'	−76	T	39	41	48	57	68	76	80	81	74	63	50	44	
			R	0.7	0.6	1.0	0.7	0.4	0.1	0.4	0.3	0.4	0.7	0.8	0.9	7.0
Kyzyl-Arvat	39°17'	331	T	32	38	48	60	74	83	88	85	74	60	47	38	
			R	1.1	0.9	1.3	0.9	0.6	0.3	0.2	0.4	0.2	0.6	0.8	0.8	8.1
Ashkhabad	37°57'	741	T	32	39	47	60	67	30	84	81	72	59	48	40	
			R	1.0	0.8	1.9	1.4	1.2	0.3	0.1	0.1	0.1	0.5	0.8	0.7	8.9
Merv	37°35'	755	T	34	40	51	63	75	82	85	81	71	58	49	39	
			R	1.8	1.4	2.1	1.2	0.1	0.0	0.0	0.1	0.0	0.4	0.1	0.4	7.5
Termes	37°13'	991	T	35	41	52	65	77	86	89	85	75	63	51	41	
			R	0.7	0.6	1.1	0.7	0.5	0.0	0.0	0.0	0.0	0.2	0.3	0.6	4.7
Chardzhu	39°05'	650	T	32	38	50	62	73	81	84	81	71	58	47	36	
			R	0.5	0.6	1.1	0.8	0.6	0.1	0.1	0.0	0.0	0.2	0.2	0.3	4.5
Nukus	42°27'	217	T	21	25	38	55	68	76	79	75	65	50	38	28	
			R	0.4	0.2	0.6	0.4	0.3	0.2	0.0	0.1	0.0	0.1	0.3	0.4	3.1
Turkestan	43°18'	732	T	21	27	42	57	69	79	83	79	67	51	39	30	
			R	1.0	0.7	1.1	0.9	0.7	0.3	0.1	0.1	0.1	0.3	0.7	1.1	6.9

Eastern Stations

Station	Lat.	Elev.		Jan	Feb	Mar	Apr	May	Jun	Jul	Aug	Sep	Oct	Nov	Dec	Year
Kashgar, Sinkiang	39°24'	4296	T	23	31	46	60	70	77	80	78	70	57	42	28	
			R	0.6	0.1	0.5	0.2	0.3	0.2	0.4	0.3	0.1	0.1	0.2	0.3	3.2
Ninghsia, Ninghsia	38°28'	3494	T	15	25	35	51	61	70	74	73	62	50	32	20	
			R	0.0	0.0	0.1	0.6	0.7	1.0	1.2	1.1	1.0	0.0	0.1	0.0	5.9

Source: W. Köppen and R. Geiger, *Handbuch der Klimatologie*, Vol. 3 (Part N), Berlin, 1939; M. Y. Nuttonson, *Ecological Crop Geography of China*, International Agro-Climatological Series Study No. 7, Washington, D.C., 1947.

curve northeastward over the Black Sea, where they gain greater vigor over the relatively warmer, unfrozen water surface and bring heavy rains to the eastern shores and snow to the Caucasus Mountains. A few such storms continue farther eastward over the Caspian and Aral seas, where in the early months of winter they may again regenerate to some extent as a result of contact with the open water surfaces.

In consequence of these features of the general circulation during the winter, this is the time of maximum precipitation along the southern margins of central Eurasia's desert regions as far east as the Khirgiz Mountains south of Lake Balkash. Rain or snow, when it occurs, can normally be expected between October and May. Peak precipitation most commonly arrives in the late winter months or early in spring (Table 19-5). March is the month when maximum amounts are anticipated at such desert stations as Chickishlyar on the southeast coast of the Caspian, at Turtkul on the lower Amu-Darya, at Termes in the upper Amu-Darya valley on the Afghanistan border, and at Turkestan between the Syr-Darya and the Kara Tau mountains, as well as at Margelan in the intermontane basin of the upper Syr-Darya valley. Slightly farther north in the general area immediately south and east of the Aral Sea and south of Lake Balkash, peak precipitation is delayed until April. This is the month when cyclonic frequency reaches a yearly maximum over the Black and the Aral seas. The main storm tracks have begun to shift northward by this time, and hence we find that at stations like Krasnovodsk on the Caspian shores opposite Baku, Kzyl Orda on the lower Syr-Darya, and the steppe border towns of Dzambhul and Frunze along the foot of the Khirgiz Mountains and Alma Ata farther east, April is the month of maximum precipitation.

By May the land has begun to warm rapidly, warming the air above it, and the major storm tracks have been displaced still farther northward. The waters of the Caspian and Aral seas remain cold for a time, however, and we see a disappearance of cyclonic activity in their vicinity (Fig. 5.13). The southern portions of desert country from the Caspian to Lake Balkash enter a season of unremitting drought. Bayram-Ali, for example, a station about 25 miles east of Merve on the lower Murgab River, has reported no precipitation whatever during the months of July through September for a period of ten years.

Northward through the semidesert toward the bordering steppe grasslands summer is the season of highest rainfall probability. Peak precipitation, when it occurs, is usually recorded for either June or July, as at Astrakhan, Balkash on the north shore of the lake, and Kopal at the foot of the Dzungharian Mountains. Thermal convective showers are the chief source of summer's uncertain rains in northern desert sections.

In the desert regions of central Eurasia that lie west of the Dzungharian Gates it is plain that two opposite precipitation regimes prevail: winter precipitation in the southern sand deserts, and summer rains in the north. Other differences between the northern and southern sections will be cited below. It is thus important to recognize that contrasting climatic complexes exist within the over-all desert environment of this part of central Eurasia, producing significant contrasts among the various ecological situations found within each complex. Broadly speaking, they are separated by a line extending approximately between the Kara Bogaz gulf of the eastern Caspian and Lake Balkash.

North and northwest China also present a regional variation within the general aridity of central Eurasia. East of Lake Balkash and the Dzungharian Mountains, as well as in the Tarm basin, a summer increase in precipitation is characteristic, and random convective showers appear to be the main source of rain. These areas lie remote from the influence of all but very rare disturbances from farther west, and they are also beyond the normal reach of the onshore monsoonal flow of moist air from the Pacific during the summer months. Either June or July is evidently the month of maximum precipitation, although records are inadequate for confident generalization (Fig. 19.11).

Rainfall variability is large, as would be expected in desert regions, although a satisfactory measure of the deviations from normal is lacking for most stations. At Merv, where the average precipitation is 5.8 inches, as little as 1.8 inch has fallen, and at Chardzhou on the middle Amu-Darya (average 4.4 inches), only 1.2 inch has fallen in a given year. On the other hand, at Bayram-Ali, with an average of 5.1 inches, 1.7 inch has fallen in a single day.

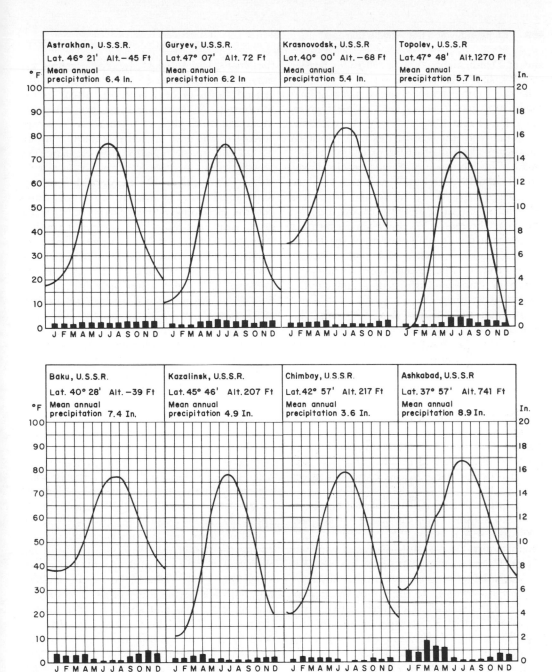

Figure 19.11. Temperature and precipitation at stations in the deserts of central Eurasia.

The mean annual range of temperature is large at most desert stations in central Eurasia, especially in northern areas, where it often amounts to more than 60 degrees (Fig. 6.5). At several points here the range exceeds 70 degrees, as at Irgiz, about 125 miles north of the Aral Sea, where it is 73 degrees (77° in July, 4° in January). At Aralsk on the north shore of the Aral it is 72 degrees (79° and 7°), at Cape Topolev on the south shore of Lake Zaisan it is 74 degrees (73° and −1°), at Lukchun in the Turfan depression it is 78 degrees (93° and 15°), at Dzhirgalantu (Kobdo) in the Kobdo basin of western Mongolia it is 75 degrees (66° and −9°), and at Dzhibgalantu, about 250 miles farther east, it is 72 degrees (60° and −11°).

In the southern desert areas mean annual ranges are smaller, between 50 and 60 degrees, as a rule (Table 19-5). At Kyzyl-Arvat, about 140 miles from the Caspian Sea in the western Kara-Kum, the value is 57 degrees (88° in July and 31° in January), at Nukus on the lower Amu-Darya 58 degrees (79° and 21°), at Merv 51 degrees (85° and 34°), at Termes 54 degrees (89° and 35°), and at Ninghsia 59 degrees (74° and 15°). The reason for the lower amplitudes of southern desert stations west of the Dzungharian Gates is mainly the higher winter temperatures experienced here during the season of transient disturbances and cloudy, inclement weather.

Although the shallow Aral Sea and Lake Balkash exert little influence on the annual temperature fluctuations, the Caspian does moderate the thermal experience of coastal stations. Thus Astrakhan, well within the northern desert area, reports a mean annual temperature range of 57 degrees (77° and 20°), Fort Schevshenko at the end of the Mangyshlak peninsula, 51 degrees (78° and 27°), Baku, 40 degrees (78° and 38°), Krasnovodsk on the opposite shore, 46 degrees (82° and 36°), and Chickishlyar on the southeast coast, 42 degrees (81° and 39°).

The extreme temperature range is also large at inland stations, Irgiz reporting 129 degrees (100° and −29°), Nukus 121 (106° and −15°), Dzhibgalantu 134 (94° and −40°) and Ninghsia 112 (102° and −10°). Astrakhan has also recorded a large range between the observed absolute maximum and minimum values over the years, reporting 112 degrees, between 97° and −26°, and Baku has experienced similarly wide fluctuations, its extreme range recorded as 113 degrees, between 91° and −22°.

Winter. The onset of winter is felt in the early part of October in the northern desert areas with the occurrence of the first frosts, although it is delayed until near the end of the month in the south, at least in the deserts west of the Dzungharian Gates. The approach of cold weather is also heralded by a seasonal increase in cloudiness and in the probability of precipitation, although the amounts and the actual times at which precipitation may be expected are highly variable.

Winter's cold deepens until January, when the year's lowest monthly temperatures are normally experienced everywhere in the central Eurasian deserts (Table 19-5). In the southernmost deserts winters are normally short and mild. January temperatures average above freezing here, as well as at coastal stations within the southern half of the Caspian. The January mean at Baku is 38°, at Krasnovardsk 36°, at Chickishlyar 39°, at Merv 34°, and at Kerki and Termes 35°. Midwinter temperatures become increasingly lower farther northward, even near the Caspian shores. Astrakhan averages 20° in January, and Guryev, also on the north coast but some 200 miles farther northeastward at the mouth of the Ural River, averages 13°. From here eastward to Lake Balkash values between 0° and 10° are normal for January. At Vilskoye, nearly 200 miles northeast of Guryev, January averages 7°; Irgiz, nearly 350 miles farther east, reports 4°; Aralsk on the northeast shores of the Aral Sea averages 7°; the town of Balkash averages 10°.

East of Lake Balkash midwinter temperatures become increasingly lower. At Cape Topolev on Lake Zaisan, January averages −1°, Dzhirgalantu in the Kobdo basin −9°, and Dzhibgalantu −11°. The very scant records for Dzungharia and the Tarim basin indicate somewhat higher values, but winter here is nonetheless typically severe. Urumchi reports 8° for January, Luchun 15°, and Ninghsia on the upper Hwang Ho also 15°.

Temperature fluctuations occur frequently during the winter months under the influence of successive advances of deep, cold air masses from the north and northeast. Mean daily variations are on the order of 30 to 35 degrees in northern areas and slightly less than this farther south. Extreme minima have dropped below zero at all stations from time to time: Astrakhan has recorded −26° in January, Baku −22°, Irgiz and Kasalinsk −29°, Kuzka −27°, Termes −6°, Tashkent −22°, Frunze −36°, Alma Ata −33°, Dzhibgalantu −40°, and Ninghsia −10°.

Cloudiness and relative humidity reach a yearly maximum at all stations during the winter (Fig. 19.12). The percentage of cloud cover is nearly the same from December through February, and the actual maximum may occur in any one of the three winter months. Values are somewhat higher along the shores of the Caspian than the areas farther

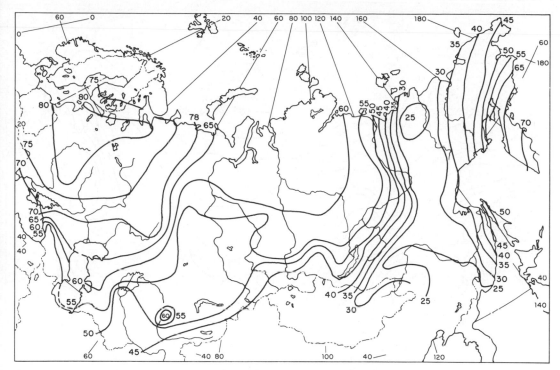

Figure 19.12.   Mean cloudiness in January in central Eurasia (per cent of sky covered).

east. At Astrakhan, for example, cloud cover averages 75 per cent during the cloudiest month of December, at Fort Shevchenko on the eastern shore 76 per cent in December, and at Irgiz, Kasalinsk, and Merv 57 per cent in the same month. At the southern, sunnier station of Termes, February is the cloudiest month, averaging 49 per cent, and at Kopal, much farther east, April is the cloudiest month with mean cover of 55 per cent.

Relative humidity reaches more than 80 per cent during most of the winter period around the shores of the Caspian but is generally between 70 and 80 per cent elsewhere. January is usually the month when maximum values are reached, in accordance with the occurrence of minimum temperatures.

Whereas rain and sleet are the predominant forms of precipitation in the southernmost desert areas, the northern deserts normally receive most of winter's precipitation as snow. By midwinter most of the surface from the Aral Sea northward is snow-covered. High winds infrequently lay bare the ground over wide stretches of countryside and drift the fine, light material into large ridges and banks of considerable size. The mean depth of snow is thus quite variable. The duration of a snow cover in any amount diminishes gradually from north to south, from slightly more than five months in western Mongolia to between three and four months from Lake Balkash to the Volga, about two months from the north Caspian shores across the Aral Sea to the middle reaches of the Syr-Darya, and less than one month in the southernmost deserts (Fig. 16.13).

A further indication of the north-to-south decrease in the length of winter and the lessening of its severity is the distribution of ice cover on the major bodies of water. The northern end of the Caspian and the rivers that flow into it, as well as the northern end of the Aral Sea, are normally frozen over for four or five months of the winter. During an average winter season the Caspian is ice-covered as far south as Fort Shevchenko on the east coast and Makhachkala on the west coast. On the Aral the ice cover begins to expand southward in November, normally occupying only the northernmost embayment, and lasts for 140 to 160 days, ranging in thickness from 28 to 40 inches. Lake Balkash usually begins to acquire

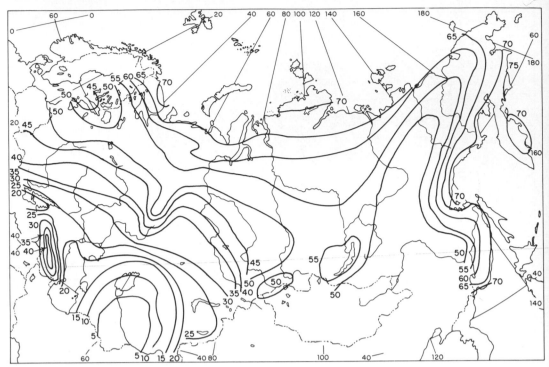

Figure 19.13. Mean cloudiness in July in central Eurasia (per cent of sky covered).

an ice cover in November and is entirely frozen over by the end of winter. Ice is between 24 and 28 inches in thickness by winter's end and begins to break up in the early part of April. Farther eastward the much smaller bodies of water, nearly all of which are enclosed salt lakes without outlets, become frozen over every winter. The upper Hwang Ho between the Alashan and Ordos deserts is commonly ice-covered from November through March.

Spring is a short season in the arid regions and normally lasts for only two or three weeks, beginning in March or even in late February in the south but not until April in the northern areas. In many localities during the latter part of April and early May the earth becomes thickly carpeted with low-growing grasses, sedges, and flowering herbs, including anemone, poppy, and tulip. After the end of May, how-ever, this once thriving vegetation dries, shrivels, and soon turns brown and lifeless as the perennial drought of summer sets in. Mean-while, along the exotic river banks the bright color of blossoming shrubs and thickets of low trees persists for a somewhat longer time, while the air becomes populated with hordes of

insects and newly arrived flocks of birds from warmer country farther south.

Summer. The intense heating of the ground in central Eurasia during the summer months is especially favored not only by the greater proportions of daylight to darkness but also by the higher sun of the season, blazing down through nearly cloudless skies (Fig. 19.13). Temperatures in the lower atmosphere rise each day to high levels nearly everywhere. With very few exceptions August is the least cloudy month of the year. In the northern desert sections the sky is less than 30 per cent cloud covered in August, and amounts diminish southward. In the southernmost sandy deserts mean cloud cover is less than 10 per cent at this time; at Merv, for example, the value is 2 per cent, at Termes 3 per cent, and at Kushka and Kerki 4 per cent.

Nights are commonly clear at all points soon after sunset, and nocturnal minima drop to low readings that result in a strong mean daily range of temperature from July through September. At most stations removed from large bodies of water values range between 35 and 40 degrees. Amplitudes of 45 degrees have been observed occasionally, and extreme fluctuations of up to 93 degrees have been recorded.

It is usually afternoon before the bright blue of the sky is even partly obscured by a scattering of small, fleecy puffs of drifting cumulus. In the northern areas these occasionally develop vertically to the point of precipitating, producing those sudden, heavy showers that yield the uncertain rains of the season. Thunderstorms frequently occur here as offshoots of the unstable weather that comes more regularly to the adjoining steppe. In the southern deserts they rarely reach fulfillment, however. Each year brings periods of up to thirty days or more during which not a single cloud will materialize in the sky.

Everywhere in the deserts of central Eurasia summers are typically hot. July is the hottest month, with the exception of the coastal tracts of the southern Caspian basin (Table 19-5). Values are in the upper 70s even in the northern deserts and increase to the upper 80s in southern districts. At Astrakhan, July averages 78°, Vilskoye 76°, Irgiz 77°, Aralsk and Kazalinsk 79°, and Balkash 76°, although at Cape Topolev and Zaisan in the Black Irtysh valley east of Lake Balkash it is 73°. Southern stations are represented by Kyzyl-Arvat and Ashkhabad at the edge of the Kara-Kum, which average 88° in July, Kerki 86°, Merv 85°, Chardzhou and Ursalevskaya 84°, and Turkestan 83°. Termes, although in the upper Amu-Darya valley, lies at the low altitude of 991, and is in a pocketed situation, averaging 89° in July.

Proximity to large water bodies provides little amelioration of summer's heat. Guryev, at the mouth of the Ural River on the north Caspian coast, and Fort Shevchenko record mean July temperatures of 78°. At Baku the average for both July and August is 78°, Krasnovodsk on the opposite shore from Baku reports 82°, and Chickishlyar on the southeast coast reports 81° in the same months.

Altitude is a significant influence on the mean temperatures attained during the warmest month in summertime. Two stations in western Mongolia are examples. Dzhirgalantu (el. 4000), averages 66°, and Dzhibgalantu (el. 5364),

about 250 miles farther east, averages 60° in July. Urumchi (el. 2972) averages 72°, Kuche 3182) on the northern edge of the Tarim basin averages 75°, but at Lukchun (el. 56) in the deeply confined Turfan depression the July mean is 93°. On the upper Hwang Ho, Ninghsia (el. 3494) averages 74° in July.

Extreme temperatures in July have risen to 100° or more at most observation points. The thermometer has climbed to 100° at Baku, 104° at Frunze, 106° at Astrakhan and Nukus, 108° at Tashkent, 113° at Ashkabad, 122° at Termes, 127° at Bayram-Ali, near Merv, and 136° at Kazalinsk. Farther east July temperatures have risen to 106° at Kashgar (el. 4277) near the western edge of the Taklamakan, 112° at Lukchun, 102° at Ninghsia, 97° at Urumchi, and 94° at Dzhibgalantu.

Ground temperatures rise to high levels every summer, particularly in the southern sandy deserts. On May 16, 1915,[5] in the Kara-Kum air temperature at a height of 6.6 feet was observed to be 92°, but the soil beneath was 147°. At the research station of Repetek about 40 miles southwest of Chardzhou the temperature at the surface of the ground on June 20, 1915, was observed to be 175°. But the dry, loose, sandy overburden does not allow the deep penetration of heat from the surface, and such extremes are not felt much greater than 4 or 5 inches below. At 3 feet great heat intensities are not experienced. On May 15, for example, the surface temperature at 3 P.M. was observed to be 120°, but 3 feet below it was 72°.

The growing season is about 150 days long in the northern semidesert areas, increasing to nearly three hundred days in the southernmost districts. Kazalinsk, for example, averages about 204 days in summer, and Bayram-Ali 283 days. Along the shores of the larger bodies of water the growing period lengthens under the delaying influence of the slower cooling rate of water, and hence one finds at coastal stations an increase of as much as a month or more of the normal summer growing season.

[5] S. P. Suslov, *Physical Geography of Asiatic Russia*, W. H. Freeman & Co., San Francisco and London, 1961, p. 438.

References

AUSTRALIA, DEPARTMENT OF NATIONAL DEVELOPMENT: *Atlas of Australian Resources*, Canberra, 1953.

BERG, L. S.: *Natural Regions of the USSR*, The Macmillan Company, New York, 1950.

CALDER, RITCHIE: *Men Against the Desert*, George Allen & Unwin, London, 1951.

CANNON, W. A.: *Plant Habits and Habitats in the Arid Portions of South Australia*, Carnegie Institute of Washington Publication No. 308, Carnegie Institute, Washington, D.C., 1921.

CAPOT-REY, R.: "Dry and Humid Morphology in the Western Erg," *Geographical Review*, **35**(3): 391–408, 1945.

GAUTIER, E. F.: *Sahara—The Great Desert*, trans. by D. F. Mayhew, Columbia University Press, New York, 1935.

MADIGAN, C. T.: *Central Australia*, Oxford University Press, London, 1936.

U.S. ARMY, QUARTERMASTER RESEARCH AND ENGINEERING COMMAND: *Analogs of Yuma Climate in the Middle East*, Natick, Mass., 1954.

chapter 20

TROPICAL FORESTS AND WOODLANDS

In the preceding chapter we examined the character and distribution of the desert climates, observing there that the arid lands extend well into the tropics.[1] Thus, between the Tropics and the equator the drought-ridden desert represents one extreme of climatic variety, and in this sense it may be thought of as a terminal climate. Characteristic of this extreme among tropical climates are strong fluctuations of temperature, normally small amounts and great uncertainty of precipitation, low relative humidities, and much sunshine. At the opposite extreme in the lower latitudes is a terminal climate of far different character—the torrid humidity of the tropical rainforest, where drought is unknown, but where uniformly high temperatures, heavy precipitation, and high humidity prevail. Between these extremes, these terminal climates, are many gradations described by a variety of terms, such as semi-evergreen, semideciduous, monsoon, scrub forest, thorn and savanna woodland. These and other similar terms suggest those special, identifying qualities of

climates that are neither persistently arid nor continuously hot and humid.

It is those forests and woodlands of the tropics, ranging from tropical evergreen rainforest to the margins of the desert, with which the present chapter is concerned (Fig. 7.1). In general, they are regions of low altitude, seldom rising beyond 5000 feet and more commonly less than 3000 feet above sea level. Where elevated uplands appear between the Tropics, one discovers the anomalous presence of subtropical climates resulting from the moderating effect of altitude upon the primary influence of latitude. Also, where very high mountains lie within the tropics, altitude, slope, and exposure induce a vertical zonation of vegetation and climate, a great variety of environments within short distances, that is strikingly well developed in the lower latitudes.

General Circulation in the Tropics

It is necessary to give special attention to certain features of the atmospheric general circulation in the lower latitudes and to particular aspects of synoptic weather that apply universally to tropical regions. It will be recalled from earlier discussions that the initial energy for the ceaseless motions of the sensitive, unstable atmosphere is supplied by the sun and is transferred to the atmosphere chiefly from the earth's highly diversified surfaces. The

---

[1] The term *tropics* with a lower case *t* is a general one of indefinite meaning, broadly applied to the lower latitudes where temperatures are fairly constantly high. Capitalized, the term *Tropics* refers to the Tropic of Cancer and the Tropic of Capricorn, the theoretical loci of the poleward limits of the sun's zenithal position in the sky.

earth's surface in the lower latitudes, approximately (and only approximately) between the Tropics, constantly receives a large surplus of radiant solar energy. In the tropics surplus heat energy, transferred from the surface to the atmosphere by complex processes described in earlier chapters, becomes the primary step in the operation of the global circulation. The tropical heat surplus is transported poleward in many ways, partly by the atmosphere and partly by the larger circulation features of the sea. Colder elements of both air and sea move equatorward to close the cycle of heat surplus and deficit exchange, and the persistently dynamic state of the air and sea circulations is maintained.

The sun-warmed surfaces of the tropical oceans are the chief source of the initial atmospheric energy for the continuous operation of the atmospheric general circulation (Figs. 6.12 and 6.13). Because the qualities of the earth's surface are far from uniform—land and water are unequally distributed—the major pressure and wind fields of the general circulation are also unevenly distributed. The potential symmetry of their arrangement, if the earth possessed only one kind of surface, is suggested in the nearly balanced distribution of the great semipermanent subtropical oceanic highs and their attendant circulations. To these we have referred several times in preceding chapters: the oceanic highs of the eastern Pacific on both sides of the equator, the North Atlantic and South Atlantic highs, and the subtropical high over the south Indian Ocean (Figs. 4.2 and 4.3).

During the summer season of the northern hemisphere the preponderance of terrestrial versus oceanic surfaces is heated to excess under the influence of longer periods of daylight and increased insolation from the sun's higher elevation. The oceanic highs intensify, expand, and shift northward. A deepening and enlarging of the oceanic highs indicates an increase in the accumulation of air over the sea during the period from June through August. That the oceanic highs south of the equator also deepen, enlarge and shift northward at this time of year indicates that a net transport of air northward across the equator in the lower troposphere takes place at this season. The opposite is true during the winter season of the northern hemisphere, when a surplus of air appears to accumulate north of the equator and set up a net southward flow across the equator. How this is accomplished is by no means clear at present but certainly involves the meridional transport of both kinetic energy and latent heat at all levels of the atmosphere. This problem will require a good deal of further study before a suitable explanation can be presented.

The surface atmospheric circulation within the tropics is an integral part of the global circulation as a whole and reflects in its behavior the relatively constant rhythms set up by the earth's rotating motion on its annual orbit around the sun. Throughout the year the anticyclonic circulation of the subtropical oceanic highs sets up an equatorward field of motion in the lower latitudes that in certain areas takes the form of the steady, moderate flow of the trade winds. Over the tropical Atlantic and the tropical eastern Pacific the trades are the world's steadiest surface winds. Here they converge from the northeast and southeast toward a narrow, fluctuating belt of unsteady, light, variable winds, low atmospheric pressure, and frequent small-scale disturbances. This, as we recall from earlier discussions, is the intertropical convergence zone, or equatorial trough (Fig. 20.1).

The equatorial trough is not one of the atmosphere's well-defined features. It is a narrow, sinuous zone of confluent air streams, its breadth continuously varying, its position constantly shifting. Indeed, it entirely disappears from time to time, especially over the continents. Its presence is perhaps best observed over the tropical eastern Atlantic north of the equator and the tropical eastern Pacific north of the equator. Here, on passing through the trades from either north or south, one observes a gradual lessening of wind speed and finally enters a region of frequent calms, light, variable winds, and scattered showers, a region that is about 300 miles wide, although it varies in breadth and in its identifying characteristics.

Visible evidence of the transition may often be seen in the comparative height of the cloud tops. In both the trades and the trough cumulus clouds are the most common kind. From their size, shape, drift, and tilt one may make a preliminary judgment of conditions in the upper levels of the troposphere. As a general rule, trade wind cumuli are scattered, often in long parallel ranks, and commonly rise from a base at condensation level of about 2500 feet

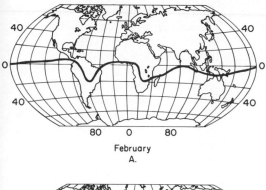

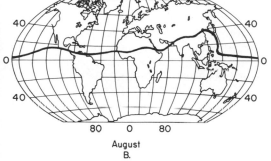

Figure 20.1. Mean position of the equatorial trough in February and August.

(although often between 1500 and 1800 feet) to a height of about 5000 to 8000 feet. In the equatorial trough the tops of towering cumuli reach levels of 25,000 feet and occasionally 50,000 feet or more and are usually scattered in a random distribution (Fig. 20.2).

In the trade wind zones a layer of warm, moist air extends from the sea surface upward for a variable distance in which temperatures decrease with height at a lapse rate of about 5.4 degrees for every 1000 feet. Thus, temperatures diminish rather steeply in the moist layer. Above the moist layer the air is much drier, and here temperatures increase with height. The level at which the moist layer gives way to overlying drier air is called the trade wind inversion. It varies in thickness from only a few meters to more than 3000 feet, its height coinciding with the tops of the trade wind cumuli. It is formed by the over-all subsidence of air in the subtropical highs flowing equatorward from higher latitudes, in which adiabatic warming and drying take place at geostrophic levels and above. The trade wind inversion may lie only about 1500 feet above the sea in the eastern reaches of the trades, but it rises west-

ward to 6500 feet or more. Thus, in the trades a marked stratification is normal in the lower troposphere.

In the equatorial trough the inversion is usually absent. When it is detected, its height is considerably greater than in the trade wind zones. Air is the equatorial trough, typically unstratified, is thus remarkable for the depth of its warm, moist properties, which often extend upward for more than 10 miles to the tropopause. It is considered to be the most homogeneous atmospheric region in the entire world. Its lapse rate is very much lower than that in the subcloud layer of the trade wind zones, amounting to about 1.8 degree for every 1000 feet. For this reason, very slight variations in temperature and very slight increases in moisture content frequently lead to locally heavy showers and sudden, gusty squalls.

The position of the equatorial trough does not coincide with the equator. It maintains a meandering alignment that shifts from season to season and also within each season in response to fluctuations in the over-all pressure and wind fields of the general circulation (Fig. 20.1). Its position varies least in the west central Pacific in the vicinity of the Gilbert Islands, where it tends to remain very close to the equator. Its maximum poleward displacement, lagging behind the sun's highest elevation, is normally reached in August and February, the appropriate months of the summer hemisphere.

In July through September it is mainly north of the equator, reaching poleward to more than 15° in the Pacific near Central America, dipping

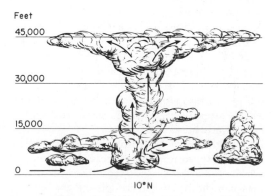

Figure 20.2. Cloud characteristics and airflow in the equatorial trough.

to about 5° in northern South America, where it usually appears in short, detached segments for interrupted intervals. It rises gradually eastward to more than 20° in north Africa, again in transitory segments, dropping to about 10° over the Gulf of Aden. From here it bends northward over southern Asia, where it all but disappears at this season of the year beyond India and Pakistan, reappearing again in the central Pacific between 5° and 10° north of the equator. From January through March it holds its position in the central Pacific and the Atlantic but dips to 20° or more south of the equator in south central Africa, where its presence and location are frequently in doubt. Lying about 5° south of the equator in the central Indian Ocean, it then bends southward to about 15° over northern Australia and the western Pacific.

The annual meridional displacement of the equatorial trough is one of the principal guides to the seasonal weather programs over many oceanic areas and the continental margins of most of the tropics. Along its meandering position occur most of the frequent, heavy showers of short duration for which the tropics are so well known, and its seasonal location serves as a reference in the north-south shifts of the tropical wind patterns that take place in response to the changing angular elevation of the sun throughout the year. But it is only over the tropical seas that the equatorial trough has been most commonly observed and only here that it may potentially be an element in weather evaluation and forecasting. Over continental areas in the tropics its position and even its existence are by no means easily determined. The uncertainty of its presence and position is notably true over northern South America and central Africa. Over southern and southeastern Asia it is often not in evidence at all in July, and in this section of the tropics the periodic shift of the monsoon is the leading feature of the tropical circulation. Another unique component of the tropical circulation merits attention. This is the eastward counterflow known as the equatorial westerlies. During the summer season of the appropriate hemisphere, sometimes expressed by the term *summer hemisphere*, winds set in from westward between the equatorial trough and the equator with sufficient frequency to suggest that they be identified as part of the zonal wind patterns.

These equatorial westerlies occur most definitely north of the equator during the summer of the northern hemisphere. They are then normally evident as a feature of the lower troposphere. They are also seen in the surface flow in the extreme eastern Pacific, blowing from southwest toward Central America, where an elongated trough commonly develops that actually reaches from southwestern United States to northern Brazil in July.

The equatorial westerlies are usually southwest winds of a seasonal, monsoon character. The southwest monsoons of equatorial Africa and southern Asia are thus believed to be simply a northward displacement and a strengthening of the equatorial westerlies during the summer of the northern hemisphere. During the northern winter when summer comes to the southern hemisphere, the equatorial westerlies are greatly weakened and are displaced slightly south of the equator from west Africa to the Pacific, virtually disappearing elsewhere in the tropics. At the same time they become a prominent feature of the surface flow in the east Indian Ocean and over northwestern Australia.

Although they are generally believed to be a permanent part of the zonal circulation in the tropics from west Africa to the western Pacific, it has been suggested that they may in part be a product of migrating perturbations in the trades. Indeed, the occurrence of westerly winds in the revolving circulations around well-developed tropical storms augments the mean eastward flow of air in the equatorial trough at fairly frequent intervals.

Temperature and Moisture

The general atmospheric circulation in the low latitudes is geared to highly significant changes in temperature, humidity, and pressure that are very small compared with those in the mid-latitudes. Thus, to permit eventual understanding of the basic, large scale processes, the accuracy of observations at all levels must be greatly improved, as well as the network of observation points and the means of rapidly disseminating available data from all tropical areas around the world.

Considerable difficulty in the study of tropical circulation features arises from the application of mid-latitude terms and concepts to the tropical atmosphere. As a more highly refined approach is required toward the assessment of the very small but highly meaningful fluctuations of significant parameters in tropical synoptic situations, a special set of concepts and terms is necessary but has yet to be formulated.

Among the many problems needing much more exact information are the dominant role of continental and low level heat sources and sinks in the global tropical circulation, the part played by large scale horizontal disturbances above 100,000 feet in the daily wind field, apparently arising from requirements of poleward heat transport, and the relationship of surface and upper air stresses to the tropical portions of the global heat budget of the atmosphere.

Among the numerous features of tropical meteorology yet requiring explanation are the fairly frequent cold air invasions that drop sea level temperatures to 50°F but fail to follow expected trajectories after reaching the tropics; disturbance lines proceeding from east to west at speeds other than the wind velocities at any level; abrupt wind shear occurrences that do not obey the gradient windflow typical of the mid-latitudes; substantial modification of solar radiation input by the dust content of the atmosphere; the fact that although most rainfall arises from convective processes, maximum short-term amounts are often produced in synoptic situations in which nonconvective processes are the chief feature; small but strong weather systems in the free atmosphere that escape detection by existing observation networks; thunderstorms with excessive lightning and negligible rain; multilayered orographic clouds; powerful sea breezes strong enough to cross 3000-foot mountain ranges; permanent wind shears of about 180 degrees within a few yards of vertical distance; and the processes that interrupt the southeast Asian monsoon.[2]

Precipitation in the tropics is without doubt the most important single climatological element. This is true not only because it falls almost entirely as rain, plus occasional hail, but also because of the singular force, volume, and frequency of the torrential showers for which the tropics are known. Even more important, it is the chief element that determines the limits of climatic regions in the tropics, the approxi-

mate boundaries separating one climate from another. As a point of comparison, it may be noted that this is exactly the opposite of the boreal forest, in which temperature plays the leading role in regional determination and precipitation is secondary.

Until recent years it was generally believed that most tropical rain occurred in thermal convective showers of local origin, developing under the intense diurnal heating of the highly humid air. It now appears that a much smaller percentage of total tropical precipitation is of

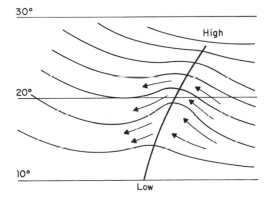

Figure 20.3. A wave in the easterlies of the northern hemisphere.

this origin. True, a great deal of rain falls in very heavy showers of convective origin, thermal uplift often augmented by orographic uplift. But recent investigations indicate that most of the total annual fall of rain is from organized, migrating disturbances related to large scale contrasts in the lower atmosphere and to the thermal properties of upper air currents as well.[3] Although the genesis of the major rain-producing disturbances is poorly understood at present, it is thought that most of the year's rain is the product of a relatively small number of well-developed systems. These seem to originate as waves in the normally smooth flow of the trades. That is, on a synoptic weather chart (Fig. 20.3) a slight, sinuous irregularity appears along the otherwise even curve of the isobars. This is usually felt at the surface as a slight but noticeable disturbance in the established, steady windflow pattern. A shift in

[2] W. H. Portig, "Conference for Planning Research in Tropical Meteorology," *Bulletin of the American Meteorological Society,* **44** (2): 79–82, 1963.

[3] Herbert Riehl, *Tropical Meteorology,* McGraw-Hill Book Company, New York, 1954, p. 97. Much of the material in the following pages is based upon information contained in this volume.

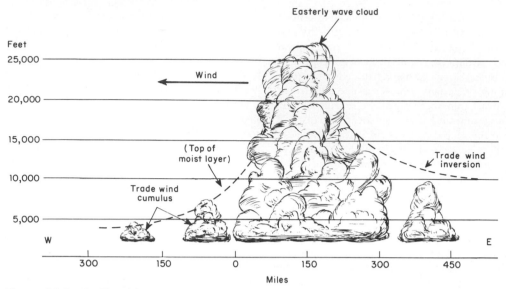

Figure 20.4. Profile diagram of trade wind inversion and cloud distribution during the passage of an easterly wave.

direction, a lull, a change in velocity, all together or separately, may indicate the passage of an easterly wave.

An eastly wave is a weak, elongated, migrating trough of low pressure moving from east to west in the trade winds, its alignment approximately at right angles to the direction of the trades, and usually proceeding more slowly than the trades themselves. Ahead of it to the west, fine weather prevails, with small, scattered cumulus clouds that rise to no great height in the relatively stable air, their tops reaching perhaps from 5000 to 8000 feet in altitude. This is the ceiling of the moist surface layer of the atmosphere, the base of the trade wind inversion. The air above it is dry and subsiding.

As the wave or trough line approaches, the weather changes gradually, the barometer dropping slightly and surface winds shifting equatorward. But the cumulus clouds that accompany the wave grow in depth, rising to 20,000 feet or more as the trade wind inversion rises and the moist surface layer increases in depth (Fig. 20.4). Broad squall lines pass, and multiple rows of high, cumulonimbus clouds advance westward, visible evidence of convective activity that is concentrated along several convergence lines separated by aisles of subsidence between.

Easterly waves most commonly develop over

the sea. Their breadth and speed of advance vary, but they average between 50 and 100 miles wide and frequently progress at about 15 to 17 miles per hour. To points along their paths they bring systematic showery spells that last from five to seven hours. Following their passage, the trade wind inversion again subsides, the moist layer becomes shallow once more, and fine weather resumes.

Easterly waves occur most frequently north of the equator in the Pacific, the Atlantic, and tropical west Africa. To a much lesser extent they also develop south of the equator in the southeast trades of the central Pacific and the Atlantic. They ordinarily pass observation points in their paths about once every four days. In special circumstances, not clearly understood at present, easterly waves may become hurricanes. Their intensities may greatly increase as they proceed, and they are thus observed very closely after they are once detected in the pressure-wind fields over the sea. With increasing intensity an easterly wave may become a tropical depression (winds to 24 miles per hour), a tropical storm (winds 25 to 72 miles per hour), and finally a hurricane (winds over 72 miles per hour).

Thermal convection also plays a leading role in the production of tropical rains. Torrential showers of locally great intensity are typical throughout the forest and woodlands of the tropics and are especially numerous in the tropical evergreen rainforest. A consideration of certain characteristics of the intense showers of the rainforest, in the special sense of its position as a major terminal environment in the tropics, will facilitate an understanding of the significance of rains in the distribution of all the tropical forest and woodland climates.

Thermal uplift of air that is almost constantly hot and humid, nearly at the saturation point, is readily induced by the intense heating of the air near the ground by the high-rising sun. The necessary upthrust of warm, moist air from the surface takes place soon after sunrise, raising parcels of air skyward to the levels at which condensation occurs, usually somewhere between 1500 and 2500 feet, where cumulus clouds begin to form. The great preponderance of cumuli in tropical skies is one of the distinctive visual features by which the visitor from the mid-latitudes is most often impressed, although by the time precipitation actually begins the sky is often locally obscured by dense masses of dark gray nimbocumulus from horizon to horizon.

In many parts of the rainforest, although by no means everywhere, the day dawns under clear, cloudless skies. As the morning wears on, thermal uplift produces a scattered army of white, drifting cumuli. By midday they will have begun to darken at base level, towering above this height for 10,000 feet or more, on occasion exceeding 60,000 feet, as temperatures at the surface continue to rise. Eventually the burden of raindrops exceeds the lifting capacity of the turbulent air currents within the clouds, and suddenly rain descends with thundering force. It rattles with deafening sound on the corrugated roofs of buildings, tearing the leaves and petals from trees and shrubs, and in the space of a few minutes converting clay pathways into stream courses filled with pools and rills of reddish, muddy water. Although often lasting for only a few minutes, such rains may continue sporadically for hours into the late afternoon, letting up from time to time, then resuming with renewed vigor, before ceasing altogether sometime after sundown, leaving the sodden ground littered with petals, leaves, and twigs.

Not all rainforest areas experience the same daily occurrence of rain. In some localities the late forenoon is the time of most frequent rain-

fall probability, in others it is the early afternoon, and in still others it is the period after sundown. As a general rule, late afternoon and early evening appear to be the commonest times at which rain may be expected, and morning hours are generally the periods when there is the least likelihood of rain.

Some idea of the intensity of tropical rainforest precipitation can be gained from the fact that at Baguio, Philippines, nearly 46 inches have fallen in twenty-four hours, an amount equal to the entire mean annual precipitation of many places in eastern North America. At Plumb Point, Jamaica, 7.8 inches have fallen in fifteen minutes.

In large areas of the tropical rainforest the excessive turbulence in the cumuli, engendered in part by a normally steep lapse rate and by frequent conditions of local instability, produces a high incidence of thunderstorm activity (Fig. 5.15). This is fairly common nearly everywhere, especially in hilly areas. It is notably so in the Congo basin, where strong contrasts in relief among the many valleys and interfluvial uplands of this large drainage area augment the intensity of vertical movement among the thermal convective cells. The resounding din of heavy rain in such areas is often punctuated by the violent crash of thunder, dazzling flashes of brilliant lightning, and powerful gusts of wind that often reach destructive velocities.

Another point of interest with regard to the rainfall of the tropical rainforest is the broad range of annual amounts under which the regional vegetation is seen to develop, varying from as little as 65 inches to over 200 inches, and in places well over 300 inches. Still another noteworthy feature is the range of reliability of annual rainfall within the region as a whole. As a rule, the higher the expected yearly total, the lower the variability. Where average annual amounts are lower than is common for most of the region, about 80 inches, the variability increases. Thus, a variability of less than 15 per cent is generally restricted to areas near the equator receiving 80 inches or more and increases to about 25 per cent toward the poleward limit of rainforest distribution. In other tropical forest and woodland regions where a seasonal lessening of rainfall, or definite dry period occurs, variability may increase to between 25 and 40 per cent.

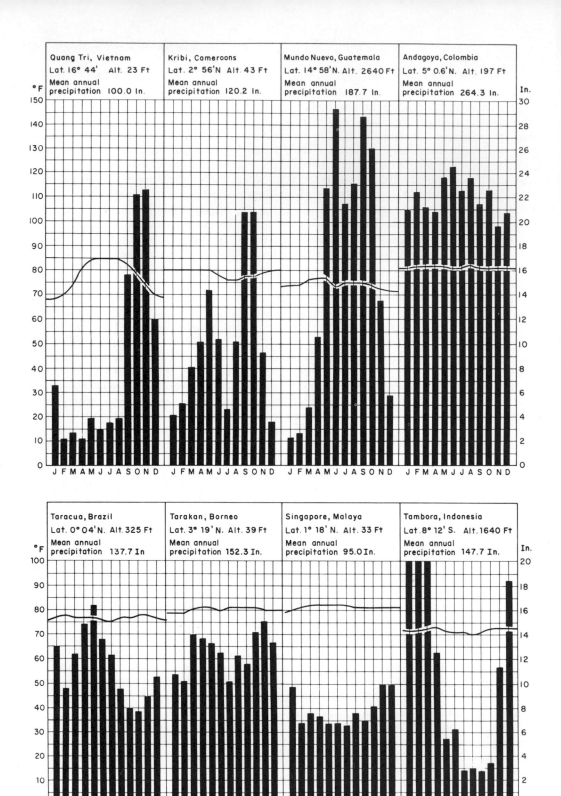

Figure 20.5. Representative temperature and rainfall regimes in tropical evergreen rainforest.

A further distinction of rainfall in the rain-forest region is the manner in which yearly rainfall regimes vary in the widely separated sections of the region throughout the world. Over large areas of the tropical rainforest abundant rain is provided every month of the year, and there is normally no pronounced season of rainfall deficiency. In South America a regime of uniform distribution is typical of many parts of western Colombia, the upper Amazon, and the coast of eastern Brazil. In Africa this is also generally true of the lower Congo valley, and in Indo-Malaya, the southern end of the Malya peninsula and neighboring Sumatra and Borneo. Elsewhere the yearly regimes reveal either one or two peak seasons, separated by periods of less rain (Fig. 20.5). Normally, areas experiencing a double maximum are near the equator where they are subjected twice each year to the meridional passage of a series of trough disturbances and sharp, thermal convective showers during the two intervals when the sun passes overhead. Thus, a systematic rhythm is set up through the primary influence of the motions of the earth. Areas receiving a single yearly period of maximum rainfall are chiefly found between 10 and 25 degrees of the equator, although this is sometimes not the case, especially in southeast Asia. A single peak rainfall season occurs in the main toward the poleward limits of rainforest wherever a strongly developed monsoonal effect is in evidence.

The great variety of rainfall amounts and annual regimes within the over-all distribution of tropical rainforest is one of the more puzzling climatological problems of the region. Table 20-1, summarizing the rainfall and temperature values for stations well within rainforest areas at scattered points throughout the tropics, suggests the great diversity of normal rainfall regimes to be expected. Figure 20.5 presents a series of climatic charts graphically illustrating these regimes. An examination of this small sample of the recorded data indicates that a general statement on the relation between the amount and distribution of annual rainfall and the geographical patterns of rainforest in the tropics is, for the time being, entirely out of the question.

It will be seen from the data in Table 20-1 that stations within the rainforest report as little as 1 inch of rain during the dry season, and that as many as three months may pass during which less than 3 inches of rain per month may fall. Near the limits of rainforest distribution as many as five months may pass in which less than 4 inches of rain are received per month, for three of which months less than 2 inches are reported. At other observation points monthly amounts may be as high as 10 inches or more during the period of less rainfall. The variety of rainfall regimes is endless.

A vast amount of additional information on many significant factors is needed before a meaningful statement on the general relationship between atmospheric properties and rainforest distribution will be justified. These include more detailed data on daily temperatures, such as the values of the daily maxima, their frequency and duration; similar data on diurnal atmospheric moisture values; wind speeds, their duration and frequency; diurnal cloud cover; soil moisture values; and the manner in which all of these are coupled with rainfall occurrences and the alternate periods without rain. These data are especially necessary before a reasonable explanation of the very low annual amounts of precipitation reported from rainforest stations can be offered. For example, it is obviously necessary to know, for points in the rainforest where as little as 65 inches is the normal amount, whether or not the dominant rains occur in the form of frequent, short-duration showers or less frequent, long-duration showers, and at what temperatures, atmospheric humidities, what conditions of wind, and the like, both before and after as well as during such disturbances, not to mention essential details of the edaphic situations within the areas of very low rainfall.

For the time being, only a loose approximation of the atmospheric relationships of the four major regions of the tropics is possible. These are summarized in Table 20-2 in terms of temperature and precipitation for certain stations well within each region. From this table it will be seen that, in general, between selva and thorn scrub woodland temperatures of the warmest month become higher, mean annual temperature range increases, and extreme maxima are also higher. Annual rainfall amounts tend to decrease from rainforest through semideciduous forest, savanna woodland, and thorn scrub woodland, although this is far from an infallible rule. A more definite

TABLE 20–1
Climatic Data for Tropical Evergreen Rainforest Stations
(Temp., °F; Rainfall, In.)

Station	Lat.	El. in Ft		Jan.	Feb.	Mar.	Apr.	May	Jun.	Jul.	Aug.	Sep.	Oct.	Nov.	Dec.	Year
Mundo Nuevo, Guatemala	14°58'N.	2640	T	74	74	76	77	77	74	75	75	75	74	73	72	
			R	2.3	2.6	4.9	10.6	22.9	29.4	21.6	23.2	28.8	26.1	9.5	5.8	187.7
Andagoya, Colombia	5°05'N.	197	T	81	82	82	82	82	81	81	82	81	81	81	81	
			R	21.0	22.5	21.3	20.9	23.6	24.7	22.6	23.7	21.5	22.6	19.5	20.7	264.3
Taracua, Brazil	0°04'N.	325	T	77	78	77	77	77	76	75	77	77	78	78	77	
			R	13.0	9.7	12.4	15.0	16.4	13.6	12.4	10.0	8.1	7.8	8.9	10.6	137.7
Kribi, Cameroons	2°56'N.	43	T	80	80	80	80	80	78	76	76	77	77	78	80	
			R	4.2	5.2	8.2	10.3	14.5	10.4	4.6	10.3	20.8	20.9	7.4	3.6	120.2
Quang Tri, Vietnam	16°44'N.	23	T	68	70	73	80	84	85	85	85	82	78	74	70	
			R	6.7	2.2	2.7	2.2	3.9	3.0	3.5	3.8	15.6	22.1	22.3	12.0	100.0
Tarakan, Borneo	3°19'N.	39	T	79	80	80	81	81	80	81	81	81	81	80	80	
			R	10.9	10.2	14.0	13.9	13.5	12.6	10.3	12.4	11.6	14.3	15.2	13.4	152.3
Singapore, Malaya	1°19'N.	10	T	79	80	81	81	82	82	81	81	81	81	81	80	
			R	9.9	6.8	7.6	7.4	6.8	6.8	6.7	7.7	7.0	8.2	10.0	10.1	95.0
Tambora, Indonesia	8°12'S.	1640	T	72	72	73	73	72	71	71	70	71	72	73	73	
			R	36.7	22.6	22.2	12.6	5.5	6.2	2.8	3.1	2.8	3.5	11.5	18.2	147.7

Sources: F. L. Wernstedt, *World Climatic Data, Latin America and the Caribbean*, Pennsylvania State University, 1959, *World Climatic Data, Africa*, Pennsylvania State University, 1959; U.S. Naval Oceanographic Office, *Sailing Directions for Soenda Strait and Borneo* (H.O. 71), 1951.

TABLE 20–2

Climatic Data for Tropical Evergreen Rainforest, Semideciduous Forest, Savanna Woodland, and Thorn Scrub Woodland
(Temp., °F; Rainfall, In.)

Station	Lat.	El. in Ft		Jan.	Feb.	Mar.	Apr.	May	Jun.	Jul.	Aug.	Sep.	Oct.	Nov.	Dec.	Year
Evergreen Rainforest																
Balikpapan, Borneo	1°17'S.	23	T	79	79	79	79	79	79	78	79	79	79	79	79	
			R	9.1	7.1	9.3	7.3	8.5	7.4	6.8	6.3	5.2	5.5	6.4	7.8	85.7
Semideciduous Forest																
Mato Grosso, Brazil	15°00'S.	843	T	77	77	77	77	72	70	69	72	77	77	78	77	
			R	9.1	8.3	8.6	3.9	2.2	1.2	0.8	0.7	1.2	3.9	5.1	7.9	52.9
Savanna Woodland																
Tamale, Ghana	9°24'N.	635	T	82	86	88	87	83	80	79	78	78	80	83	81	
			R	0.1	0.3	2.0	3.3	4.7	5.7	5.7	7.7	8.8	3.8	0.6	0.2	42.6
Thorn Scrub Woodland																
Wave Hill, Australia	17°30'S.	700	T	88	88	85	79	74	69	67	72	79	86	89	89	
			R	3.9	4.4	3.0	0.3	0.2	0.1	0.2	0.0	0.1	0.7	1.8	3.3	18.0

Source: F. L. Wernstedt, *World Climatic Data, Latin America and the Caribbean*, Pennsylvania State University, 1959, *World Climatic Data, Africa*, Pennsylvania State University, 1959; U.S. Naval Oceanographic Office, *Sailing Directions for Soenda Strait and Borneo* (H.O. 71), 1951.

change takes place on the length of the dry season, the primary feature by which the limits of the four environments are established.

In tropical rainforest no really dry season normally occurs. In semideciduous forest a period of from one to five months usually occurs during which less than 1 inch of rain may be expected per month (Fig. 20.6). The limiting length of the dry season is partly related to the mean annual amounts. Where, in the case of the semideciduous forest, the normal yearly rainfall is about 60 inches, a dry season of one or two months with less than 1 inch per month will suffice to induce the development of this type of tropical vegetation. Such vegetation may also develop where the annual rainfall approaches 100 inches or more, the distribution of which may be interrupted by a four to five month dry period of less than 1 inch per month.

Savanna woodland appears where a virtually rainless period of at least two months occurs, and the period may extend for as much as six months, depending on annual increments. A virtually rainless period of six months alternating with a rainy season in which over 80 inches is normal may be found in savanna regions. So also may a rainless season of only two months, followed by a rain season during which from 40 to 50 inches may occur, fairly evenly distributed through the remaining ten months, rain thus occurring for most of the year in small amounts.

Tropical thorn scrub woodland is related to a much more definitely dry season without any appreciable rain, a period that lasts normally for about six months, often as long as eight months. In most instances thorn scrub develops where annual totals, for the tropics, are quite low, ranging from 20 to no more than 40 inches.

Mean atmospheric humidity, as observed in the early afternoon, is seen to diminish from rainforest to thorn scrub woodland. But the actual values observed of this and other parameters within each of the world's three major areas of tropical forest and woodland differ so widely that a general statement is not relevant. A basic difficulty in this connection is not only our present deficient understanding of the general circulation in the tropics, alluded to earlier, but also a critical want of sufficiently detailed information on most atmospheric elements at all significant levels up to the stratosphere.

Air temperatures near the earth's surface in the tropics are persistently high throughout the year. Mean minima are usually above 60° in nearly all tropical regions at lower elevations. An uncomfortable chill is normally felt by human beings when the thermometer drops below 60°, chiefly on account of the high atmospheric humidities in most of the lower latitudes. At the same time, mean maximum temperatures are rarely as high as those experienced in mid-latitude regions remote from the sea. The mean maximum by day is between 85° and 95° in most tropical regions, whereas mean maxima above 100° are frequently recorded outside the tropics in summertime. The extreme range of temperature between absolute maximum and minimum is also very much smaller than in most extratropical inland regions. But although the daily levels normally attained by the thermometer are not excessive, the oppressively sultry air is enervating for man, a result of the burning heat of the sun's rays when it is high overhead, the high humidity, and the normally light movements of the air at inland stations. Nocturnal cooling goes forward only very slowly after sundown, yielding gradually to more moderate values during the night, and as the cooling air becomes more stable, movement ceases except near the sea. Here, and in areas of strong relief where down-slope katabatic flow occurs, a light, nocturnal breeze often sets in. Because atmospheric humidities are high, heavy dews are a common occurrence in areas of still air, and patches of radiation fog are frequently seen as daylight begins to break in the east. But these conditions do not ordinarily hold near the coast, as we shall see below.

Day after day the regular rhythm of temperature rise and fall produces a monotonous regime of thermal fluctuation that indicates the nearly complete control of the sun over the normal daily weather patterns of the tropics. The sun's predominant role is also reflected in the semidaily changes in atmospheric pressure that are singularly pronounced in the lower latitudes. Entirely independent of synoptic changes, the barometer commonly attains a maximum value in the late forenoon, subsiding to a minimum in the late afternoon, rising again to a second maximum in the late evening, dropping to a second minimum in the hour or so before dawn. The amplitude is usually on the order of from 1 to 1.5 millibars, and though it

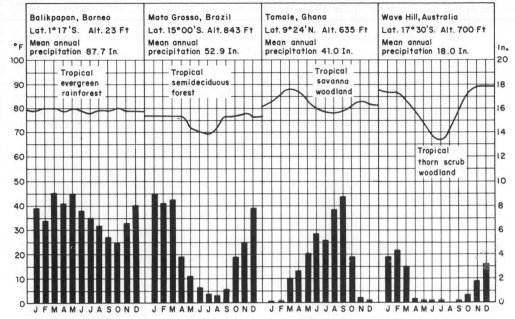

Figure 20.6. Representative temperature and rainfall regimes in tropical evergreen rainforest, semideciduous forest, savanna woodland, and thorn scrub woodland.

occurs with some regularity in many parts of the tropics, diurnal pressure change is greatly affected by cloud conditions and changes in more widespread pressure and wind fields.

In tropical rainforest regions the thermometer often rises to around 85° by day, lowering to about 65° in the early morning hours, producing a mean daily range of about 20 degrees, compared with a mean annual range that is very often less than 5 degrees. In the more open savanna and thorn scrub woodlands both daily and yearly temperature ranges are greater than in rainforest, but again, daily values, especially in the dry season, are larger than annual values.

The sun is definitely the primary weather control throughout all the regions within the tropics. Irregular invasions of air masses from the mid-latitudes are rare near the equator, for the extreme low latitudes remain substantially beyond the effective reach of the vigorous, well-developed anticyclonic systems that are mainly responsible for weather change in extratropical regions. Within the poleward limits of the tropical regions, however, cold air invasions from the mid-latitudes may be fairly frequent in the appropriate winter season, especially in tropical America.

The characteristic persistence of higher temperatures in the tropics is primarily a consequence of the high angular elevation of the sun throughout the year. Between the Tropics and the equator the length of the period from sunrise to sunset varies only slightly during the year. The sun at midday stands high in the sky, and the diurnal intensity of solar radiation is always potentially high. Along each of the two Tropics the sun on the meridian at noon is never lower in angular elevation than 43 degrees above the southern horizon. At 20 degrees north and south of the equator the longest day of the year (June 22 north, and December 22 south of the equator), is thirteen hours, twelve minutes long, and the shortest day (December 22 north, and June 22 south of the equator) is ten hours, forty-eight minutes long, a difference of only two hours and twenty-four minutes (Fig. 6.1). At the equator the length of day is constantly close to twelve hours. The average annual input of solar radiation at the earth's surface is about 425 gram calories per square centimeter per day at the equator, and about 390 gram calories per square centimeter per day at the Tropics. At 40 degrees latitude the value is only about 275 gram calories per square centimeter per day (Fig. 3.1). The consequent yearly input of radiant heat from the sun between the two Tropics is thus considerably greater than in higher latitudes poleward of them. The result is a virtually unbroken program of high atmospheric temperatures near the earth's surface that are only slightly compensated by nocturnal heat loss during the hours of darkness and only rarely interrupted in the very low latitudes by invasions of extraneous cold from higher latitudes.

A secondary temperature control of great importance is the persistent warmth of ocean surfaces in the lower latitudes throughout the year. (The exception of the cold west coast currents and their relationship with west coastal deserts should be recalled.) Sea surface temperatures nearly everywhere between the Tropics remain at all times approximately between 70° and 80°, a consequence of the sea's conservative thermal properties (Figs. 6.12 and 6.13). Surface values exceed 80° throughout the year in a broad belt that roughly coincides with the position of the equatorial trough. The steady warmth of the sea is imparted to the air above by the several processes discussed earlier, and it is this warm, humid oceanic air that moves inland in the tropics to provide most of the precipitable moisture. In addition to preserving the typically high levels of atmospheric humidity, it also works toward the stabilization of air temperatures within high limits, producing the relative thermal equability of tropical forests and woodlands, especially the rainforest.

Temperatures in the tropics are actually far from uniform. True, near the equator and as far removed as 10 degrees on either side of the line, values may remain relatively equable. But with increasing distance from the equator mean annual fluctuations may range as high as 20 degrees or more, although the limits within which such fluctuations take place are high (65° to 85°). As a general proposition, it is valid simply to state that whether yearly temperatures in the tropics are equable or otherwise, normal values are consistently high.

Coastal weather in the tropics is strongly influenced by the relatively regular occurrence of the sea breeze. The tendency for an almost daily onshore flow of air from the sea to develop is another tangible manifestation of the primary effect of the sun upon tropical climates. It is also one of the ways, like the systematic daily temperature fluctuations, in which the greater variation of daily weather compared with annual weather is expressed.

The manner in which the sea breeze develops and declines is as follows. Diurnal air temperatures over the tropical seas vary only slightly, usually not more than 2 degrees. Over the adjacent land, however, daily variations are very much greater. Differential heating between land and adjacent sea during the day is the primary condition set up between sunrise and sunset. Upward-expanding air columns over the land create a high-level seaward pressure gradient, and air aloft drifts toward the water. A low-level onshore pressure gradient then evolves, and the flow of surface air from sea to land begins to strengthen. Induced in this way, the sea breeze increases as the day wears on, reaching a maximum usually in the afternoon (the exact time varies from place to place according to the alignment of the coast with respect to prevailing winds and other factors), and falling off as the sun's warmth is lessened both by its lowering elevation and by increasing afternoon cloud cover. Maximum velocities are on the order of 15 to 20 miles per hour. When the coast is directly in the path of the oceanic trades, the sea breeze augments zonal circulation, but on the lee shores of tropical islands the sea breeze may fail to develop altogether when the trade wind flow exceeds 15 miles per hour. When prevailing winds are light, sea breezes develop over even very small islands and often lead to the formation of a succession of small cumulus clouds drifting off to leeward, these having been produced locally by the intensive heating of the island surface and the consequent thermal convective mechanism this process sets up. Rugged, mountainous topography near the coast always augments the intensity of the sea breeze, adding orographic uplift to the thermal effects over the heated land surface. Sea breezes are usually strongest during the clear weather of the drier season. Where the continental margins face the prevailing trades and are comparatively low in elevation, the sea breeze commonly reaches inland for as much as 50 miles, for in the lower latitudes the Coriolis effect is negligible, allowing the onshore sweep of winds from the sea to preserve a nearly straight trajectory except where topography alters their direction.

During the hours of darkness the land gradually cools, and eventually the shoreline pressure gradient is reversed, leading to a gentle drift of air from land to sea. The nocturnal offshore breeze is normally much weaker, reaching speeds of only 2 to 5 miles per hour, and endures for variable periods between late evening and dawn, depending upon the time required for local pressure distribution to come into balance.

Types of Tropical Climates

Let us now turn our attention to the character and distribution of the major climatic regions of the tropics, bearing in mind the general tendencies of the atmospheric circulation, temperature, and precipitation discussed above.

Where both temperature and rainfall are equitably distributed throughout the year, no well-defined seasons can be discerned. But where a distinct seasonal rhythm exists, it is established primarily by regular fluctuations in the yearly distribution of rainfall. A period of abundant rain alternates with a period of substantially less rain or a period of decided drought. The contrast between one climate and the next in the tropics is thus chiefly the result of differences in the length of the dry season. Hence, the transition from constantly hot, wet evergreen rainforest to desert in the tropics is evident in the gradual lengthening of the period of drought. It is usually accompanied by a steady decrease in the normal yearly amounts of rainfall, an increasing variability in annual rainfall, and an increase in the mean annual range of temperature.

Phytogeographers and plant ecologists have, for more than a century, studied the problem of identifying dominant tropical plant formations out of the tremendously rich variety of species to be found there. The efforts of A. R. W. Schimper, beginning in the 1880s, produced a classical work[4] on the subject of plant geography in which a classification of tropical vegetation and climatic regions was set forth that has remained to the present day a basic guide to the study of tropical vegetation types. A more recent work by Richards[5] deals extensively with the problem of providing a definitive

description of the principal plant formations in the tropics, along with their climatic relationships.

Drawing upon the work of Richards and other contemporary contributors, it is possible to designate four major climax formations in the tropics that provide us with a usable key to the distribution of tropical climatic regions. This is a tentative classification, bearing eventual modification and improvement as more detailed studies of phytoclimatic relationships are brought forth. The four main divisions are tropical evergreen rainforest, tropical semi-deciduous forest, tropical savanna woodland, and tropical thorn scrub woodland. In a broad way these plant formations represent the transition from the rain-drenched heat and humidity of the rainforest to the pervading aridity and variable temperatures of the desert.

TROPICAL EVERGREEN RAINFOREST. The evergreen rainforest of the tropics, where undisturbed by man, is a plant formation in which tall trees attaining heights of 150 to 180 feet on the average, and commonly exceeding 200 feet, are the most conspicuous component. This region of unbroken heat and humidity is ideally suited to the flourishing development of broad-leaved evergreen trees. It is also remarkable for its great wealth of plant species and overwhelming preponderance of woody plants. A great abundance of climbing plants, epiphytes, and saprophytes is also typical. Still other distinctive features include the tendency for most herbaceous species, like the ferns and grasses, to approach the size of trees; the continual flowering, maturing, and fruiting of all plant life; and the singular uniformity of the outward, physiognomic aspect of the forest throughout its length and breadth.

Deep within the primeval evergreen rainforest the straight, slender trunks of the taller forest giants are usually smoothly cylindrical and free of branching for 100 feet or more above the ground. Their tops are rarely seen from below. Their crowns are normally not large, but their dark, glossy evergreen foliage and the interlacing of their branches, along with those of shorter trees and a host of dependent plant life, create a dense, leafy canopy overhead through which the sky cannot often be seen. The trees at ground level are widely spaced, normally allowing a visibility of 25 yards or more save when occasionally interrupted by a tangle of

[4] A. F. W. Schimper, *Pflanzengeographie auf physiologischer Grundlage*, 2nd ed., Jena, 1898, trans. by W. R. Fisher as *Plant-geography Upon Physiological Basis*, Oxford, 1903.

[5] P. W. Richards, *The Tropical Rain Forest, An Ecological Study*, Cambridge, 1964.

climbing plants or an unusually dense development of ground vegetation. This circumstance, in addition to the columnar character of the unbranching boles and the vaulted canopy of the merging crowns above, suggests a cathedral interior, a feeling augmented by the dim light and the motionless quiet that often prevails near the ground (Fig. 20.7).

Figure 20.7. Tropical evergreen rainforest in the lower Congo valley. Note the buttressed roots of the felled tree in the foreground and comparative size of the wood cutters. [French Embassy Press and Information Division]

The stately, vertical columns of the tree trunks are relatively slender in view of their great height. In diameter they range between 4 and 6 feet just above the swelling at their bases. Their rounded trunks are usually nearly circular, although deeply fluted forms may appear and in cross-section their trunks may possess a stellar pattern. The characteristic columnar aspect of their towering, slightly tapered boles is emphasized by typically thin, smooth, light-colored bark. Quite unlike the deeply fissured or furrowed heavy bark of most mid-latitude forest trees, the pale tones of the bark of most rainforest trees stand out sharply against the perpetual dark green background of the mature foliage.

The root systems of many typical rainforest trees possess several unique features, the most outstanding of which is the development of plank buttresses. These are normally thick, solid, triangular woody plates in more or less vertical position that appear to provide essential mechanical support for the lofty trunks. There is some uncertainty about their actual function, although they are chiefly present where the water table is high and trees lack a deep tap root. They rise from lateral roots near the ground surface and sometimes reach 30 feet or more up the trunk, expanding outward an equal distance from the base.

A variation of buttressing is the stilt root system in which narrow, cylindrical roots project outward and downward from the trunk at points several feet above the ground, often curving gracefully into the soil, to produce an open, conical, cagelike structure around the base of the trunk. In some rainforest species aerial rootlets extend downward from the branches themselves, resembling in their early stages threadlike tendrils that eventually reach the forest floor, attach themselves firmly, and in time grow to the size of small trees in girth. The tree equipped with aerial roots may, on reaching a very advanced age, appear to possess a compound trunk system of enormous circumference.

Another distinctive feature of rainforest root system is the presence, in excessively moist situations, of breather roots, pneumatophores, popularly spoken of as "knees," that rise vertically a short distance above the saturated earth from lateral roots to perform an auxiliary ventilation function. The above-described root features, along with the fact that most rainforest trees are only shallowly rooted, often penetrating only the top 1 or 2 feet of constantly moist soil, reflects the persistent dampness of the climate.

Soils vary widely in texture and fertility but appear to be largely acidic in quality, red to yellow in color, clayey in texture, and often lacking in most important nutrients. Leaf litter is commonly present on the forest floor, but humus seldom accumulates in depth. These conditions again reflect the persistent humidity and also the persistently high temperatures of the rainforest, circumstances that encourage the constant and rapid decomposing action of bacteria. Partly in consequence of these conditions, the forest floor is frequently bare, a slippery surface of heavy, red, sticky clay.

Common to the evergreen rainforest is the unceasing flowering, fruiting, budding, and leaf fall of most of the dominant plant life. New blossoms, young leaves, and mature fruits may appear simultaneously on the same tree or on different individuals of the same species. In this sense the rainforest is distinctively evergreen. And one of the more impressive qualities of this forest is the evergreen foliage of the dominant plants from ground level to the tops of the tree crowns. Chiefly deep, somber green in color, the leaves are glossy, smooth-edged, and ordinarily shaped much like those of the laurels of the middle latitudes. Another common tendency is the uniformity of leaf size at every level within the over-all structure of the forest.

A striking feature of the major tree species is the bright coloration of their leaves in the early stages of development. They often appear in solid masses of brilliant red, purple, or white against the dark green background of the mature foliage around them.

Flowers of the taller trees are commonly inconspicuous except when the gregarious inflorescence of certain species produces a mass of light-colored bloom over the entire tree crown that quite often may last for only a single day. Among the flowering habits of rainforest trees perhaps the phenomenon of cauliflory is most distinctive. This is the growth of individual flowers and eventually fruits directly from the leafless trunks and larger branches.

The internal structure of the tropical evergreen rainforest differs substantially from place to place, but a certain degree of typical stratification can be observed wherever the formation appears. Five fairly distinct levels or tiers can be specified. The first is the lowest ground layer, consisting of flowering herbs, ferns, and seedlings of the dominant trees, a vegetation ranging in height from a few inches to several feet, seldom exceeding about 6 feet, and incompletely covering the ground. It is densely developed only in clearings, along the banks of streams, and in locations where sunlight penetrates to the forest floor. The second is a shrub stratum, again appearing in an interrupted distribution, composed largely of young trees that will grow larger in time. They rarely possess the dense branching that is characteristic of shrub growth in the mid-latitudes. The third structural level is marked by the crowns of the lowest of three tiers of tree-sized plants. Their crowns are

usually closely merged and often heavily intertwined with woody lianas and the stems and foliage of epiphytes and parasites. This close-crowned layer of the forest canopy may range in height above the ground from 30 to 50 feet. Above it is the fourth structural level, second of the three tree-sized tiers, consisting of tall forest forms rising from 150 to 180 feet above the forest floor, that creates a slightly more open crown cover. The largest trees of the forest, extending well above the fourth layer, are commonly very widely spaced and often stand as isolated specimens surmounted by distinctive umbrella-shaped crowns. They may range in height from 180 to 200 feet or more, although their height relationship with the lower levels varies with individual associations and localities.

Throughout the vertical extent of the rainforest a great many dependent plants flourish at all levels. Conspicuous among them are the long, heavy, woody lianas that rise from the ground to the crown levels above, grow often as much as a foot in diameter, and hang in great loops from the supporting tree branches overhead. Also abundantly present are other dependent plants like the epiphytes, which derive their nourishment from the hot, humid air itself and simply attach themselves to the trunks and branches of trees and lianas for support. Saprophytic plants, certain orchids, are also present in great profusion, depending on the hosts to which they attach themselves not only for support but also for some degree of sustenance in the decaying material about them. The dependent forms of vegetation compete vigorously with the independent forms for space and light and play a major role in creating the typical luxuriance of foliage and branching that forms the shade-producing forest canopy overhead.

Another impressive quality of the rainforest is the remarkable size to which the monocotyledons grow. These are members of the family of grasses, rushes, and lilies and include, in the tropics, the palms, ferns, and bamboos. Over 1500 species of palm are known within the tropics, many of which exceed 100 feet in height and some of which develop leaves nearly 50 feet in length. Rattan is a climbing species of palm that attains a length of 1000 feet or more. Ferns in the tropics develop luxuriantly, especially in the moist heat of the rainforest. They can be found in a variety of types and sizes growing as epiphytes on the trunks and stems of larger forms, as well as on the ground. The profusion of fern species and life habits is a notable response to the climate of the rainforest, but perhaps even more striking is the great size they may attain. It is not uncommon to find ferns 20 feet or more in height with a diameter of 2 feet or so, and some species are more than 80 feet tall. Among the prominent grasses of the tropics the bamboos are known to reach heights approaching 100 feet in favorable circumstances. These tallest of the grasses are by no means confined to tropical environments, but it is in the lower latitudes, especially in rainforest areas of southeast Asia, that they reach great size and often form gregarious communities that proliferate easily and rapidly. The growth rate of bamboo has been measured from time to time, and in one instance an individual plant was observed to grow at the rate of 23 inches in a single day.

Perhaps the leading characteristic of the evergreen rainforest is the enormous wealth of plant species, particularly trees. No other forest formation is floristically as rich. This is a manifestation of the unique terminal nature of this climatic region. Poleward from the tropical evergreen rainforest the number of plant species diminishes, although very unevenly, toward a minimum number in the tundra of the northern hemisphere and the fringes of the ice cap in Antarctica. No accurate count of actual species numbers is available, but the expected magnitudes are suggested by the following estimates. Throughout the selva of Africa and Indonesia there are about three thousand species of trees over 16 inches in diameter, belonging to about 450 genera; in the much smaller area of the Malay peninsula are about 2500 species of trees; in the Amazon basin alone are an estimated 2500 species, on a single acre of land sometimes more than eighty species. Examination of an acre of land in the mid-latitudes quite often reveals only three or four species among a hundred individual trees. In the rainforest a smaller number of trees may be counted, but one will often look in vain on an acre of land for more than a single representative of a particular species.

The actual composition of this remarkably luxuriant, species-rich forest varies greatly from place to place within large areas of its worldwide distribution. The dominant species differ within short distances, and almost every possible combination of component types can be counted on as a general rule. In a relatively small number of localities a single species may appear in sufficient numbers to produce a rare association that can be described as "single-species dominated." Examples of this are the Mora forest, Wallaba forest, and Greenheart forest of Guyana and Heath forest of Borneo, where edaphic conditions are perhaps the main cause of the narrowed selectivity of forest trees.

The fauna of the tropical rainforest is also abundantly varied. This is particularly true of insect life, the distinct varieties of which are believed to be far too great to warrant an estimate of the total number. This may easily exceed one million. Butterflies, moths, mosquitoes, ants, bees, and wasps are present in enormous profusion. Bates[6] reports counting 150 species of mosquitoes within 10 miles of his experiment station at Villavicencio in eastern Colombia. In all of mainland United States and Canada only 121 species are known.

Mammals are fewer in species than in the more open savanna woodlands. But over half are arboreal or aerial forms, a large number of them bats. Squirrels and monkeys are perhaps the next largest groups represented among arboreal mammal. In a $\frac{1}{4}$ square mile area in Guyana seventy-two species of mammals have been counted, whereas in New York State's 49,576 square miles only seventy-one species are known.

The great floristic richness, not to mention the wealth of insect and other faunal forms, of the rainforest is partly the result of an environment that allows plant and animal life to pursue their growth habits without interruption throughout the year. It is also partly the result of the very long time during which this unique environment has persisted within the lower latitudes, permitting the process of speciation to proceed for a great many centuries.

A distinct impression gained by the visitor to the evergreen rainforest is certainly the extraordinary abundance, size, and variety of the higher plant forms. Among some, but by no means all, of the rainforest trees the uniquely favorable growing conditions are indicated by an unusual rate of growth. A few species may rise

[6] Marston Bates, *The Forest and the Sea*, Random House, New York, 1960, p. 105.

to more than 80 feet in height in the brief span of six years and reach 110 feet in ten years.

The climate of the tropical evergreen rainforest is distinguished by the ruling conditions of high temperatures and heavy rainfall fairly well distributed over the entire year. These general circumstances vary considerably from place to place, but compensating atmospheric qualities exist to support the distinctive equability of the climate and allow rainforest to prevail.

Mean monthly temperatures throughout the year are, as a rule, somewhere between 68° and 82°, and the mean annual range may be as little as 1 degree, usually less than 5 degrees, and rarely exceeding 10 degrees. Mean daily maxima of around 90° and mean daily minima of 70°, producing a mean daily temperature of about 80°, are widely representative. For the year as a whole within the geographical limits of the region, mean maximum temperatures are seldom more than 95°, and mean minima rarely drop below 60°. Absolute readings beyond these means are observed, but their occurrence does not significantly alter the characteristic uniformity of the thermal experience.

The above conditions arise chiefly from the relatively small variation in the length of day in the lower latitudes where rainforest is found. To this must be added the very important effect of persistently high atmospheric humidity, making the ambient air of the rainforest thermally conservative by limiting its capacity to undergo wide temperature fluctuations. Nocturnal heat loss is also diminished, and, indeed, the higher levels of temperature fluctuation are supported by the high soil temperatures that prevail beneath the forest. At depths of 2 feet and lower, soil temperatures are virtually constant. At 10 feet in depth, soils in many places have been observed to maintain constant, equable values in the low 80s.

Mean annual rainfall in typical rainforest localities averages at least 80 inches, well distributed through the year. The long term record at Singapore is often cited as a prime example, where the average yearly rainfall is 95 inches and is uniformly distributed. At many points of observation average values are much higher than this, in places increasing to more than 200 inches. This is especially true where orographic influences affect major local circulations. Andogoya (281.1 inches) and Quibdo (289.1 inches) in western Colombia are examples. To these may be added Debundja (405 inches) at the foot of Cameroons Peak in southeastern Nigeria, Akyab (207 inches) on the Bengal coast of Burma, and the exceptional fall of 425 inches at Cherrapunji (el. 4309) in the Khasi Hills of Assam, northeastern India. The minimum mean value under which rainforest can develop appears to be about 65 inches, toward the poleward limits of regional distribution where temperatures are near the lower limits within which rainforest is found.

Although at many points the year's rain is evenly distributed, a more common tendency is a seasonal rise and fall in intensity. The early distribution may feature either a single period of maximum rainfall, interrupted by a less rainy period, or two peak seasons, alternating with less rainy intervals. Rainforest thrives in spite of periods of less rain, where compensation in the form of persistently high atmospheric humidity is provided. This circumstance is typical of many coastal situations and along the banks of rivers where soil saturation provides ample moisture at root level in addition to the higher atmospheric humidity along the stream course. Riverine rainforest often projects as an anomaly into semideciduous forest or savanna woodlands. Prolonged periods of minimum rainfall induce small but distinct changes in the structure and physiognomy of the rainforest vegetation without changing its identity as a climatic climax formation.

Invisible atmospheric water vapor is typically present in copious amounts within the evergreen rainforest of the tropics. During the hours of darkness the air is most commonly very near the saturation point. Nocturnal temperatures may drop, but dampness is everywhere apparent and touches everything, invading the innermost crevices of the soil, the plant life, man-made structures and vehicles. The evaporating power of the air is thus very low, and the steaming heat of the mature rainforest is one of its more notorious qualities. The best comparative measure of atmospheric water vapor for general purposes is expressed in the term *saturation deficit,* the amount by which the air at any temperature is less than fully saturated. But there are few systematic observations of this value available for this region, and the commonest measure of atmospheric moisture is expressed in the term *relative humidity.* To be sure, the data for this element also are far from adequate for purposes of generalization. Broadly speaking, it may be said that relative humidity is nearly 100 per cent during the hours of darkness but may drop to around 65 per cent during the day, usually just before the time at which diurnal temperatures reach a maximum. Less frequently the daily value may drop to about 50 per cent, and values as low as 28 per cent have been observed in some instances.

Wind velocities in the rainforest are in general a good deal lower, and strong, destructive winds are much less frequent, than in regions outside the tropics. Conditions naturally differ widely from place to place and depend, among other things, upon exposure, topography, and the dominant synoptic situations of particular localities. Where tropical cyclones occur with some regularity, as in middle America, southeast Asia, and northeastern Australia, high winds affect parts of the rainforest from time to time. The most common weather occurrence with which violent winds are associated is the thunderstorm, a most distinctive feature of the tropical rainforest climate. The frequent thunderstorms of the region are often accompanied by high winds. Although they ordinarily last for only a short interval, these short, powerful bursts of gusty air often destroy substantial parts of the vegetation. This phenomenon is a notable occurrence along the steeper slopes of forested hills and low mountains, where orographic uplift intensifies the speed of rising drafts of air in the convective circulations.

The popular impression of bright, sunny skies is not valid in the tropical evergreen rainforest. Cloudless days are exceedingly rare near the equator. Mean daily cloud cover averages between 50 and 55 per cent for about 10 degrees on either side of the equator (Fig. 18.6). Although the possible daily amount of sunshine is ten hours or more between the two Tropics, actual amounts are always much less, owing mainly to the high percentage of cloudiness that normally prevails. Observations of solar radiation intensity are insufficient to warrant generalization, but from the scattered data available, radiation intensities are evidently less rather than greater than in the middle latitudes. This is chiefly on account of the atmosphere's high water vapor content and, in some instances, a certain quotient of impurities, like dust of terrestrial origin.

But another popular impression having to do with the daily rising and setting of the sun is quite correct. This is the rapidity with which darkness gives way to complete daylight at dawn, when the sun, rising speedily from the horizon, brings the full light of day to the treetops and exposed portions of the earth's surface in a surprisingly short span of time. Toward evening it drops as rapidly toward the western horizon, and darkness comes on again with a suddenness quite unlike the prolonged periods of twilight to which the mid-latitude dweller is accustomed.

It is to be expected that a pronounced difference would be found among the microclimates within the over-all forest. Atmospheric conditions at crown level, for example, have been found to contrast sharply with those in the undergrowth on the forest floor. The blinding brightness of early morning daylight on the tree tops and in clearings is never experienced at ground level to relieve the constant gloom in the undergrowth. Here the sun's rays are filtered and fragmented on their way downward through the foliage overhead to such an extent that only a scattering of tiny points of light can reach the forest floor. They vary in size, brightness, and distribution as the day and the season wear on, and all in all, the shaded light near ground level appears to amount to less than 1 per cent of the sunlight bathing the tree tops.

One important consequence of the differences in light intensity and also in radiant heat energy from the sun between tree crowns and the forest floor is in the temperature experience at the two levels. The chief difference is in the daily temperature maximum. Table 20-3 contains data on the mean maxima and mean daily

TABLE 20–3

Temperatures at Three Levels in Tropical Evergreen Rainforest in the Philippines During the Wet and Dry Seasons (°F)

Height Above Ground	Mean Max. Wet	Dry	Mean Min. Wet	Dry	Mean Daily Range Wet	Dry
115–130 feet	88	91	69	67	19	24
60 feet	81	82	71	69	10	13
Undergrowth	80	82	70	68	10	14

Source: W. H. Brown, *Vegetation of Philippine Mountains*, Manila, 1919. Quoted in P. W. Richards, *The Tropical Rain Forest, An Ecological Study*, Cambridge, 1964, p. 163.

range of temperature at three levels within primary evergreen rainforest on Mt. Maquiling, Philippines, at an elevation of 984 feet. From this it is noted that mean minima are nearly the same from tree crown to forest floor, but daily maxima overhead average 8 degrees higher in the wet season, 9 degrees higher in the dry season, and the mean daily range is accordingly a good deal larger than in the undergrowth.

Relative humidity also differs appreciably between tree crowns and undergrowth, remaining near saturation values at all times near the ground, ranging between 95 and 98 per cent, with a slight drop occurring in the early afternoon, as a rule. This is mainly the result of evaporation from the moist soil, the lower shade temperatures, and the small amount of air movement. In the tree crowns, however, higher daily temperatures, distance from the soil moisture source, and the tendency for gentle to moderate winds to stir the air reduce values to between 60 and 70 per cent or less at upper levels during midafternoon. During hours of darkness values are comparable with those at ground level.

It is natural to expect that whatever breezes develop in the rainforest of the tropics will affect the foliage of the tree crowns and that their force will diminish downward. From observations made at scattered points throughout the world, gentle winds are normally anticipated during the day a large percentage of the time at crown level, but only rarely is air in motion below them. It is a common experience to observe that smoke invariably rises vertically from ground level, and little movement if any is ever seen among the plant life of the undergrowth in the oppressive stillness that prevails.

Another difference between the tree top climate and that of the undergrowth is in the amount of precipitation that actually reaches the two levels. This, of course, depends upon the kind of rain. Under a light, steady fall of rain as much as 25 to 30 per cent of the total amount may be depleted by clinging to the trunks, branches, and foliage at crown levels, never reaching the forest floor to become available in the soil for eventual plant use. When torrential rains occur, a smaller proportion is depleted, and more reaches ground level. Furthermore, dew very commonly collects on the upper surfaces of tree crowns but never appears beneath the canopy of the overhead foliage.

TROPICAL SEMIDECIDUOUS FOREST.   The drier semideciduous forest formation of the tropics is distinguished from evergreen rainforest by a number of qualities visible to the observer. It commonly consists of two definite levels—an upper level of moderately tall, slender, broad-crowned trees, a large percentage of which are deciduous, and a lower layer of chiefly evergreen trees and shrubs in thick-growing profusion. Trees in the upper layer commonly range in height from about 65 to 85 feet, less than half the heights attained by rainforest species. There are normally very few really large trees in this forest. They are usually quite slender, averaging less than 2 feet in diameter, possess little evidence of strong buttressing, and begin branching well down their trunks, expanding into umbrella-shaped crowns overhead. It is usually a close-crowned forest, but toward its drier margins it becomes more open, its component trees become shorter, and the number of species is reduced.

The number of species in a unit area is very much less than in rainforest. An estimate of between seventy and eighty species in an area of between 8 and 9 square miles in semideciduous forest can be compared with three hundred to 350 in an area of the same size in a rainforest. From 25 to 65 per cent of the upper level trees may be deciduous, losing their foliage entirely during the less rainy season. The seasonal loss of foliage from a large percentage of the broad, upper story tree crowns allows the sun's rays to penetrate to the lower story and thus to engender a heavy undergrowth and an unusual wealth of vinelike climbing plants. The chiefly evergreen character of the lower story is due primarily to the more humid and comparatively cooler conditions that prevail throughout most of the year beneath the canopy of the taller vegetation overhead. From among the lower shrubs and coppices near the forest floor lianas reach upward to the tree crowns, spreading from tree to tree to form an unusually dense network of tough, woody climbers that hang in graceful garlands festooning the branches above. Because of their profuse development, these are a distinctive feature of the semideciduous forest.

The leaves of many of the component plant species tend to be smaller than those of rainforest trees, especially in the lower story. This is a property of plants capable of withstanding significant periods of moisture deficiency. A

Figure 20.8. Tropical savanna woodland in South America. The *campo cerrado* in the upper Parana valley of the Brazilian Highlands. [Photo R. A. Peters]

similar property more commonly noticeable here than in rainforest is the presence on trunks and branches of sharp spines and thorns. Still another sign of a recurrent let-up in the yearly distribution of rain is the fact that epiphytes are relatively scarce.

It is thus evident that tropical semideciduous forest is the beginning of a transition away from moisture-replete rainforest toward the desiccation of desert, from a terminal region of abundant rainfall to a terminal region of persistent drought.

TROPICAL SAVANNA WOODLAND.   Savanna woodland is a tropical formation dominated by extensive grassland, often incorporating a good percentage of sedges, in which scattered trees and shrubs are rarely absent. It is structurally a two-storied vegetation with trees above and grass below. The most impressive aspect of the landscape is its openness. The observer has a clear view to the horizon, interrupted at random intervals by clumps of trees in intermittent moist depressions and individual trees and shrubs elsewhere, as well as by narrow, sinuous lines of dense forest and undergrowth that hug the banks of occasional streams. These riparian forests frequently resemble the luxuriance of tropical evergreen forest in richness of species and in outward aspects of height and stratification. From the fact that the tree crowns very commonly meet overhead across the waters of lesser stream courses, they are often spoken of as galeria forests, from the Italian word *galeria*, meaning tunnel.

The physiognomic character and floristic composition of the tree and shrub vegetation over the far-reaching extent of this region vary too widely to permit a generalization that would be applicable in all areas. The trees are mainly deciduous and are often low, broad-crowned forms ranging in height from 15 to 30 feet, frequently twisted and stunted in appearance. But sometimes they are evergreen, relatively tall and straight, reaching 65 feet or more in stature. This is the case among the palms, and in middle America, the pines, which in places are the dominant arboreal forms. Lianas and epiphytes are scarce in the upper stories at crown height among the scattered trees and shrubs. Near ground level dense masses of undergrowth are rarely evident save along the water courses. But the vegetation is nonetheless rich in herbaceous, nonwoody plant life, and the grasses are often luxuriantly dense (Fig. 20.8).

Tropical grasses of the savanna woodlands vary from about 1 foot to very tall forms 12 to 15 feet in height. In general, the grasses tend to flourish where excessively high temperatures are rare and the dry season is not usually longer than five months. Taller grass forms are normally typical of the wetter margins of the region, the shorter forms along the drier fringes approaching the thorn scrub woodlands. Tropical grasses seldom produce a close-growing sod and instead typically rise as individual plant stalks separated by bare ground.

Although the widespread presence of grassland in the tropics suggests the existence of a "savanna climate," it is generally held among plant ecologists that there is no genuine savanna as such, and that the primeval vegetation, when undisturbed, is a woodland type in which trees and shrubs are prominently present. The fact that large, clear expanses of uninterrupted grassland are seen in large portions of the three major areas of tropical forest and woodland development, especially in Africa, is thought to result mainly from the influence of edaphic factors such as the porosity and depth of the soil, as well as soil moisture conditions, augmented by the repeated occurrence of fires. Man's effort to improve, by repeated burning, the natural pasturage of the tropical grasslands for cattle-rearing is widespread, particularly in Africa and South America. The process tends to eliminate young tree seedlings and all but the most fire-resistant trees and shrubs and to encourage the proliferation of grasses and a certain number of sedge and bulb plants associated with them.

Trees are often almost entirely absent from savanna woodland regions in broad, low-lying river flood plains where elaborate river systems periodically flood large expanses of lowland. When the flood waters subside, the interfluvial terrain is left dry and sun-baked, the surface hard and cracked. This pronounced alternation of moisture excess and deficiency is inimical to tree growth, and the higher plant forms are thus excluded. This is believed to be the chief reason for the mainly unmixed grasslands in the large South American river basin known as the Orinoco Llanos of Venezuela and Colombia. It is also held responsible for the presence of similarly unmixed grasslands in less extensive parts of Africa, southeast Asia, and northern Australia.

Tropical savanna woodland is sometimes found in contiguity with tropical evergreen rainforest, occasionally well within and surrounded by a flourishing rainforest formation. Most often, however, when adjacent to this terminal environment, it appears in the interfluvial uplands between moist river valleys where rainforest is richly developed under conditions of abundant moisture supply. In such cases, the abrupt change from rainforest to savanna woodland is a consequence primarily of sharply contrasting edaphic conditions, supplemented by repeated fires. In broadest terms, however, savanna woodland represents the third stage in the generally poleward climatic transition from evergreen rainforest to desert.

TROPICAL THORN SCRUB WOODLAND. Thorn scrub woodland is a formation that resembles to a certain degree the general aspect of savanna woodland by the characteristic openness of its normal landscapes. Woody plants are the dominants. They are usually smaller than those in savanna woodland, ranging as a rule between 10 and 35 feet in height, and are most commonly deciduous in habit. There is much variety, however, and in many areas the trees are as tall as savanna woodland forms and are sometimes evergreen, especially in tropical America. The number of plant species is notably less than in savanna woodland. Also characteristic is the presence of many trees that are formidably armed with sharp, heavy spines and thorns on trunks, branches, and twigs. Very common are low, broad-crowned trees with short, twisted trunks, whose foliage consists of finely divided compound leaves that are absent during a portion of the dry season. At this time, when the sun is lower in the sky, temperatures become lower and atmospheric humidity is appreciably reduced, conditions that favor the development of the deciduous character.

The vegetation is usually rich in undergrowth. It is often garlanded with long, thin-stemmed lianas but is generally poor in epiphytes. Where thorny, low-growing scrub forms are abundantly present, the ground is commonly bare beneath. Grasses are usually poorly developed. In southeast Asia, however, grasses play an important part in the composition of the ground cover beneath the dominant tree forms. Other terrestrial herbs are typically scarce both here and elsewhere in the tropics where thorn scrub woodland is found.

Tropical thorn scrub woodland tends to gain the upper hand over savanna woodland vegetation where temperatures range within higher limits, where strong daily and seasonal temperature fluctuations prevail, where, as a rule, less rain normally occurs, and where the dry season is much longer, often continuing for as long as eight months.

Among the many various plant associations of the tropics that are not dependent upon climatic influences alone, in addition to the edaphically induced grasslands mentioned above, are the many swampy lowland types, of which reeds and rushes are the leading plant forms. Coastal lowlands invaded by the salt water of the sea, another specialized situation, are often mantled with a dense hygrophytic vegetation in which one or more types of mangrove trees and shrubs are dominant. Still another unique vegetation appears high on the slopes of tropical mountains, well toward the upper limit of strictly tropical plant species. This is the cloud forest, mountain evergreen forest, moss forest, or mist forest, a thick, lush, dank tangle of tree, shrub, fern, and moss that thrives in the cool mists at cloud level.

References

BATES, M.: *The Forest and the Sea*, New York, Random House, Inc., 1960.

CHANG, JEN-HU: "Comparative Climatology of the Tropical Western Margins of the Northern Oceans," *Annals of the Association of American Geographers*, **52**(2): 221–27, 1962.

GARBELL, M. A.: *Tropical and Equatorial Weather*, McGraw-Hill Book Company, New York, 1954.

RICHARDS, P. W.: *The Tropical Rain Forest*, Cambridge University Press, Cambridge, 1964.

RIEHL, H.: *Tropical Meteorology*, McGraw-Hill Book Company, New York, 1954.

WATTS, I. E. M.: *Equatorial Weather*, University of London Press, London, 1955.

chapter 21

TROPICAL FORESTS AND WOODLANDS IN THE WESTERN HEMISPHERE

It is at once apparent from a map of the western hemisphere (Fig. 21.1) that tropical forest and woodland climates dominate most of northern South America, spreading northward through Central America to central Mexico and through the West Indies to southern Florida, reaching in both cases a latitude of about 28°. Southward they extend into southern

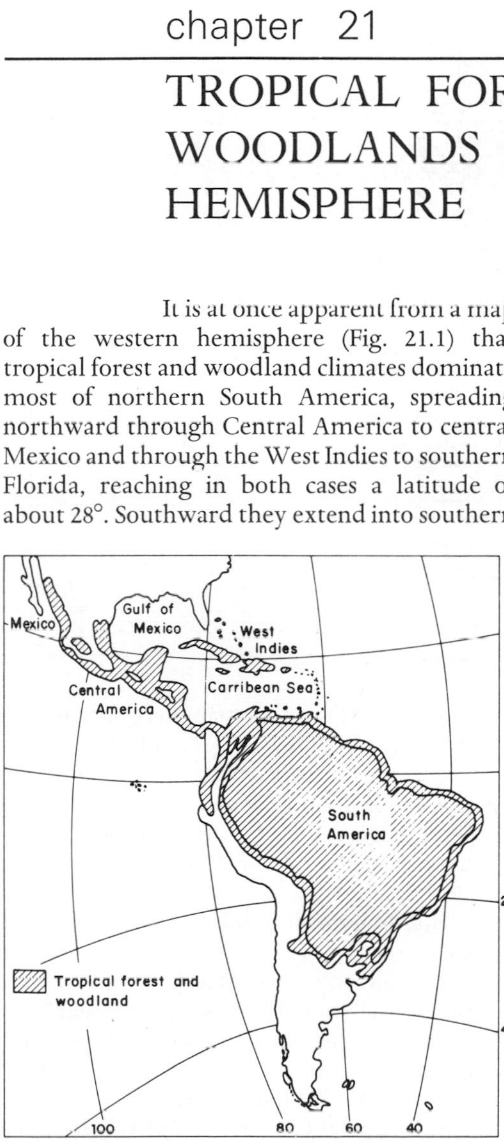

Figure 21.1. Distribution of tropical forest and woodland in the western hemisphere.

Brazil and northern Argentina almost to the 30th parallel, thus attaining, all in all, a span in latitude of nearly 60 degrees. They give way to desert northward along both the Pacific and eastern shores of northern Mexico, as well as southward along the Pacific coast in northern Peru and east of the Andes in northern Argentina. In southern Florida, however, and also in southern Brazil, northeastern Argentina, and eastern Paraguay the climatic change is toward a mild form of the mid-latitude mixed forests referred to earlier as subtropical rainforest or humid subtropical forest.

Tropical forest and woodland climates are essentially regions of lower elevation and in tropical America are thus commonly found below 3000 feet in altitude, although occasionally rising to nearly 5000 feet near the equator. Thus, the distribution of evergreen rainforest, semideciduous forest, savanna woodland, and thorn scrub woodland is interrupted and rendered highly complicated by major relief features. These include not only the massive heights of the Andean ranges and the mountainous backbone of the Middle American mainland but also the numerous isolated mountain peaks in the West Indies, as well as the more moderate but very extensive elevations of the Guiana highlands and the broad plateaus that rise gradually toward the sea in eastern Brazil. A glance at the map will show that the regional patterns are

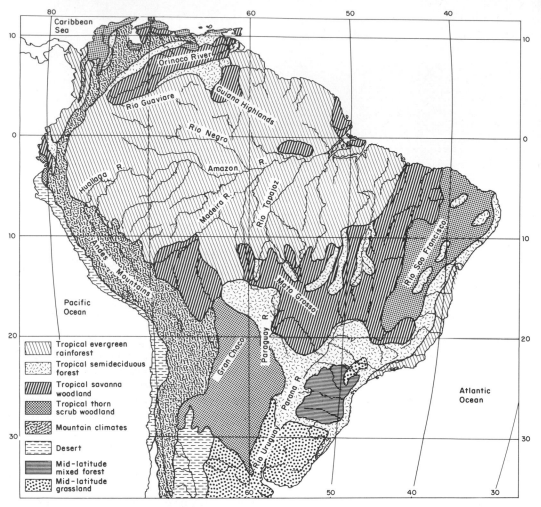

Figure 21.2. Tropical forest and woodland in South America.

still further complicated by the size, shape, and geographical arrangement of land areas.

One of the outstanding geographical features of tropical America is the Amazon basin, which is remarkable not only for its great size but also because it is the largest continuous expanse of low-lying land in the tropics (Fig. 21.2). It has an area less than 3000 feet in elevation of nearly 2,500,000 square miles, not a great deal smaller than the entire mainland United States. In its upper reaches in eastern Colombia, Ecuador, and Peru and in northern Bolivia it presents a surface that in many places is less than 1000 feet above sea level at the very base of the steeply rising, towering Andes some 2000 miles upstream from the Atlantic. The main course of the Amazon is within less than 5 degrees of the equator, and most of its many large tributaries drain an area within 15 degrees of the equator. Latitude and altitude combine to favor the development of an unusually large expanse of tropical vegetation in the Amazon basin. Copious quantities of warm, humid air from the tropical Atlantic reach westward to the Andes, and thus it is within this extensive lowland between the mountains and the sea that the largest single tract of tropical evergreen rainforest in the world is found. Although its internal character is incompletely known, it is believed to contain an extraordinary variety of typical rainforest plant forms. An estimated 2500 to three thousand species of tall trees are thought to be indigenous to the Amazon basin alone.

As the distribution of individual species is most irregular, only a small number can be said to represent the extent of tropical rainforest in all of tropical America. Among the better known varieties, those that are important in commerce, or whose unique properties have attracted the attention of botanists for scientific reasons, a few may be mentioned.[1] One, the silk-cotton tree (*Ceiba pentandra*), whose seed pods are the source of the commercial fiber Kapok, does indeed appear throughout most of tropical America from Mexico to Bolivia. It is a massive tree normally ranging in height from 80 to 100 feet but often much higher, with a smooth cylindrical trunk rising above high, thick plank buttresses. It is the best known of ten species of ceiba and is commonly a tree of the open, where its huge circular crown may spread an umbrella-shaped canopy up to 150 feet in diameter over less lofty species. Many species of jacaranda have been identified, among which *Jacaranda copaia* is the best known and the most widely distributed. It ranges from British Honduras to Brazil. It is a fast-growing tree ordinarily attaining a height of 80 feet and often much higher, producing a light-weight wood of good buoyancy in a relatively slender trunk that may frequently be less than 30 inches in diameter. Spanish cedar, or cedrela, is a widely-distributed tree including numerous species of *Cedrela*, that usually reaches very stately proportions, rising to heights of 100 feet or more in a straight, cylindrical bole 3 to 6 feet in diameter above large, fairly heavy buttresses and free of branches from 40 to 60 feet. This is one of the smaller proportion of rainforest trees with deciduous foliage. Certain rainforest dominants like this one are also members of the drier semideciduous associations and of some savanna woodlands, where they may become outstanding members of the riparian forest growth along the water courses. Cedrela is a genus that provides the most important timber for domestic use in tropical America and is considered a close relative of the Toona of Asia and Australia.

Mahogany (*Swietenia macrophylla*), the most valuable timber tree in tropical America, is widely but unevenly distributed throughout much of northern South America and middle America. It is virtually evergreen but varies considerably in size, shape, and habit. It seldom rises to heights greater than 75 feet. It is apparently tolerant of a variety of growing conditions within the rainforest environment and in Peru may be found at elevations from 400 to 4500 feet. Brazil nut (*Bertholletia excelsa*), which bears the familiar hard-shelled nut of great commercial value, is one of the larger trees in northern South America. It is native to the Amazon basin and commonly attains a height of more than 100 feet, and often 150 to 200 feet. It is a rough-barked tree on which spherical pods, containing eighteen to twenty-four nuts, hang at random from the trunk itself below the crown far above, where the large, leathery leaves, up to 2 feet long and 6 inches wide, form a heavy canopy. The rubber tree (*Hevea brasiliensis*) is one of about twenty species of rubber-producing plants ranging from shrubs to very tall trees that are native to the Amazon. Most of the tree species possess large cylindrical trunks, with or without buttresses, reaching up to 125 feet or more, but *H. brasiliensis* is usually around 60 feet in height. Several species of Mora are known in tropical America, ranging from Central America to the upper Amazon and the Guianas. The best known is the Mora (*Mora excelsa*) of the Guianas, Trinidad, and the Orinoco delta, ordinarily reaching heights of 100 to 150 feet, occasionally towering to 200 feet, with huge buttresses and flanges spreading 15 feet or more outward from all sides of the trunk. The trunk may be 8 feet or more in diameter 20 feet above the ground. Its formidable size and relatively plentiful distribution make it the most distinctive tree in northeastern South America.

Tropical America, approximately astride the equator, reveals a regular rhythmic program of annual changes in temperature, humidity, cloud cover, windflow, and seasonal rainfall that results from the dominant role of the sun. But the size, configuration, and distribution of land and water surfaces are very unequal, resulting in the highly uneven pattern of tropical climates described in the preceding pages. The large expanse of continental South America lying within the tropics possesses a relatively generous distribution of the four chief tropical climates, whose largest segments are mainly south of the equator. North of the equator, however

---

[1] Descriptive details have been obtained from many sources, especially S. J. Record and R. W. Hess, *Timbers of the New World*, Yale University Press, New Haven, 1943.

especially on the narrow, irregular land bridge of southern Mexico and Central America as well as the scattered islands of the West Indies, examples of the climates are unevenly distributed, widely separated, and much smaller in scale.

In tropical America as a whole the regular meridional shift of the sun's position is primarily responsible for the seasonal weather patterns, and the Atlantic is the major source of its warm, moist air, borne steadily westward over the land areas by the normal flow of the trades. The Pacific shores of Ecuador, Colombia, Central America, and southern Mexico are also affected by air streams from the adjacent ocean, the onshore flow of air from the sea brought in by the gentle circulation identified earlier as an isolated segment of the weak equatorial westerlies. Northwest of Costa Rica tropical climates along the rugged Pacific shores of Mexico are significantly influenced by air moving a short distance inland as a sea breeze from the near Pacific and also by occasional tropical cyclones originating farther southward.

During the six-month period beginning at the vernal equinox around March 21, portions of tropical America north of the equator are dominated by weather sequences that are primarily controlled by the persistently high elevation of the sun and the great heat of solar radiation. Beginning at the equinox, the sun rises each day to the zenith at points progressively farther poleward until the summer solstice, around June 21, when it is over the Tropic of Cancer. During the next three months it retreats toward the equator, but it is at all times the source of blazing heat for the earth beneath. The duration of daylight at the expense of darkness increases to a maximum around June 21, insolation similarly increases, and temperatures also rise to maximum values for the year at some point during the interval of the northern hemisphere's summer.

The equatorial trough, when and wherever it can be identified, moves slowly northward, reaching a maximum poleward position across the northern part of South America in central Colombia and Venezuela in August, and occasionally moves out over the West Indies, marking the approximate mean convergence of the trades from the Atlantic (Fig. 20.1). A normally weak trough over Central America and Mexico is an offshoot of this feature. The

northeast trades shift away from the equator and assume a more westerly trajectory roughly parallel to the north coast of South America in the Caribbean and over the West Indies, curving northwestward across the Gulf of Mexico toward the Gulf coast of the United States. The southeast trades also shift northward, crossing the equator toward the equatorial convergence, bringing warm, moist air from the South Atlantic to portions of northeastern South America. During the latter half of this period tropical cyclones of destructive intensity are more apt to occur than at any other time of the year and threaten most of middle America with very heavy rains and damaging winds. Along the Pacific shores of tropical America daily sea breezes supply a certain amount of local precipitation, especially from western Mexico to Nicaragua and in Colombia and northern Ecuador.

The period from the autumnal equinox around September 21 until around March 21 the following year sees the daily rise of the sun to the zenith at points between the equator and the Tropic of Capricorn. At most tropical stations that lie south of the equator the consequent gain in insolation, the rise of daily temperatures, and the normal increase in precipitation occur in this period.

During this season the equatorial trough is displaced southward, and although its actual existence is often doubtful and its position difficult to determine, it represents the mean convergence of the northeast and southeast trades over the interior of the continent (Fig. 20.1). The northeast trades now blow from the North Atlantic into northern South America, penetrating deeply southward at diminishing velocities toward the dominantly low pressure region in central Brazil. The southeast trades withdraw from north of the equator but continue to move directly onto the coast of northeastern Brazil. Once across the great escarpment they recurve southward over the Brazilian highlands and then shift westward at lessening velocities toward the interior and the central low pressure circulation of this season. The Pacific shores of Panama, Colombia, and Ecuador continue to receive light southerly winds from the sea, although from January through April the northeast trades bring a fairly frequent movement of winds from northward to this section.

South America

We shall begin this survey with the main body of tropical evergreen rainforest in the Amazon basin. As we proceed first northward and then southward from the great tropical lowland, we shall focus our attention initially on the distribution of rainforest, and to this terminal environment we may then more easily relate the distribution of other tropical forest and woodland climates.

The climatic character of the tropical rainforest is unmistakably similar throughout tropical America. Abundant mean annual rainfall, high atmospheric humidity, and relatively high temperatures during the entire year prevail wherever segments of this environment can be found. As a general rule, the season of maximum potential sunshine (the summer season appropriate to the hemisphere) at most stations is the time of maximum cloud cover, atmospheric humidity, and precipitation. It is not necessarily the season of maximum temperatures. But there are certain exceptions. At most rainforest stations the sky becomes cloud-covered to the extent of 70 per cent or more during the rainy season. Relative humidities in the early afternoon range between 70 and 90 per cent during the wet season but may drop to less than 60 per cent in the dry season. Mean annual temperature ranges are ordinarily less than 5 degrees F at points as far poleward as 10 degrees on either side of the equator. But from 10 to 20 degrees latitude annual temperature ranges increase as a rule to between 5 and 10 degrees F, and between 10 and 15 degrees F poleward of 20 degrees latitude.

Largely south of the equator and for the most part within 10 degrees of it, the basic qualities of the atmosphere over the Amazon basin, especially its precipitable moisture, are introduced mainly by the westward flow of the southeast trades from the Atlantic. The season of maximum rain south of the equator is chiefly during the high sun interval from September through March, and, though there are a few exceptions, the normal annual distribution rises to a single peak period. From the Amazon River northward maximum rains largely occur between March and September, and a tendency toward a double maximum appears. This is chiefly the result of the meridional shift in the trade wind convergence. Normal yearly amounts within the rainforest proper vary from well over 100 inches near the Atlantic to between 65 and 80 inches farther inland, increasing to more than 100 inches along the bordering rim of the Andes and over southern Colombia and Venezuela (Fig. 21.3).

For the main body of selva in the Amazon basin a selection of stations extending from near the Atlantic to the Andes reveals the essential climatic character of the region and some of the contrasting atmospheric qualities found within this largest of the world's tropical rainforest regions.

Belem (Para) on the Baia de Marajo, somewhat more than 100 miles southeast of the Amazon's southernmost outlet and less than 100 miles from the Atlantic, lies within 2 degrees of the equator and stands at 42 feet above sea level. A twenty-year precipitation record (Table 21-1) indicates the normal occurrence of most of the year's rains from December through June (78 per cent of the yearly amount). Beginning in October, winds over the area come increasingly from between north and east, and moist air is thus swept in from the Atlantic by the northeast trades. The equatorial trough, with fitful winds, squally weather, and frequent calms, appears to dominate the weather from January through April. Cloud cover during the daylight hours reaches a maximum of more than 70 per cent from February through April. Relative humidities in the early afternoon average 80 per cent or more throughout the year but rise to 91 per cent in February, 90 per cent in March. Monthly rainfall amounts from December through June average more than 6 inches, increasing to a maximum monthly value of 17.2 inches in March when rain normally falls on twenty-eight out of the thirty-one days. High intensity rains have produced 5 inches in twenty-four hours in February, and the mean annual total is 107.6 inches. From May through November, when the northeast trades have shifted northward and the southeast trades rule the coastal circulation of the area, cloud cover diminishes to between 30 and 40 per cent, and afternoon relative humidities drop to the low point for the year of 80 per cent in October.

Mean monthly temperatures vary about 2 degrees between the minimum mean value of 77° in February and the maximum of 79° in October and November. Fluctuations of the means are negligible, and the mean temperature

TABLE 21-1
Climatic Data for Tropical Forest and Woodland Stations in South America
(Temp., °F; Rainfall, In.)

Station	Lat.	El. in Ft		Jan.	Feb.	Mar.	Apr.	May	Jun.	Jul.	Aug.	Sep.	Oct.	Nov.	Dec.	Year
Bahia, Brazil	12°59'S.	154	T	80	80	80	79	77	75	74	74	75	77	78	78	
			R	2.6	5.3	6.1	11.2	10.8	9.4	7.2	4.8	3.3	4.0	4.5	5.6	74.8
Belem, Brazil	1°28'S.	42	T	77	77	77	78	78	78	78	79	78	79	79	79	
			R	13.4	16.0	17.2	13.5	11.3	6.9	5.7	5.0	4.7	3.6	3.4	6.9	107.6
Caceres, Brazil	16°03'S.	387	T	77	77	77	76	73	70	68	73	77	78	78	78	
			R	9.0	7.9	6.7	3.4	1.6	0.9	0.4	0.4	1.6	3.8	6.3	8.0	50.0
Catalao, Brazil	18°10'S.	85	T	72	72	72	71	68	66	65	69	73	73	72	71	
			R	12.5	10.2	9.4	3.9	0.9	0.3	0.3	0.2	2.3	5.4	9.6	14.5	69.6
Conceicao do Araguaia, Brazil	8°15'S.	53	T	77	77	77	78	78	77	77	79	80	78	78	77	
			R	10.0	9.9	10.4	6.4	2.4	0.3	0.3	0.6	2.5	6.4	7.7	8.9	65.8
Fortaleza, Brazil	16°00'S.	2057	T	75	75	75	73	69	67	65	71	71	74	74	75	
			R	5.2	4.7	4.5	2.1	0.9	0.5	0.6	0.7	1.0	2.7	6.6	6.6	36.1
Goias, Brazil	15°56'S.	1706	T	75	75	75	76	73	71	70	74	77	77	76	75	
			R	13.1	10.4	11.0	4.4	0.7	0.2	0.1	0.6	2.2	5.9	9.5	12.3	70.3
Iguatu, Brazil	6°22'S.	692	T	82	80	79	78	77	77	77	79	81	83	84	83	
			R	2.8	6.7	8.4	6.2	3.1	1.6	0.3	0.3	0.4	0.6	0.6	1.6	32.6
Manaus, Brazil	3°08'S.	144	T	79	79	80	79	79	80	80	82	82	82	82	80	
			R	10.5	9.7	10.6	10.5	7.6	4.0	2.5	1.5	2.3	4.9	6.0	8.5	78.6
Natal, Brazil	5°46'S.	26	T	81	81	81	80	79	77	76	76	78	80	80	81	
			R	2.0	4.7	7.3	10.5	9.6	9.0	8.3	4.6	1.4	0.5	0.7	0.9	59.6

Station	Lat.	Elev.		J	F	M	A	M	J	J	A	S	O	N	D	Ann.
Recife, Brazil	8°04'S.	97	T	82	82	81	80	79	78	76	76	78	80	81	81	
			R	2.1	3.3	6.3	8.7	10.5	10.9	10.0	6.0	2.5	1.0	1.0	1.1	63.4
Rio De Janeiro, Brazil	22°58'S.	56	T	77	78	77	74	70	68	67	69	70	73	76	76	
			R	7.6	6.8	6.5	6.2	5.5	3.8	3.3	4.2	4.9	6.6	6.4	7.1	68.9
Santarem, Brazil	2°30'S.	66	T	80	79	79	79	79	79	79	81	82	82	82	81	
			R	6.8	10.9	13.2	12.9	11.3	6.9	4.1	2.4	1.3	1.7	2.3	4.1	77.9
Santos, Brazil	23°56'S.	10	T	78	79	77	75	71	68	67	67	69	71	74	76	
			R	11.0	9.8	12.3	7.3	6.1	5.7	4.3	4.1	5.7	6.4	7.7	7.8	88.1
Georgetown, Guyana	6°49'N.	7	T	80	80	80	81	81	80	80	81	82	82	82	80	
			R	9.5	5.7	6.0	6.6	12.1	12.9	11.0	7.0	3.3	3.0	5.9	12.3	95.2
Ciudad Bolivar, Venezuela	8°09'N.	177	T	80	81	82	83	83	81	80	82	83	83	82	81	
			R	1.2	0.6	0.4	1.4	4.7	5.9	7.1	7.0	4.3	3.5	2.3	1.7	40.3
Cumana, Venezuela	10°28'N.	10	T	78	79	80	81	82	81	80	81	82	82	81	80	
			R	0.3	0.5	0.2	0.2	0.7	1.3	2.4	2.7	2.2	1.7	2.0	1.2	15.4
Las Piedras, Venezuela	10°41'N.	33	T	81	81	82	83	85	85	85	86	87	86	83	82	
			R	0.5	0.4	0.3	0.2	0.9	0.3	0.2	0.9	1.1	2.4	3.6	1.6	12.4
Santa Elena, Venezuela	4°36'N.	2975	T	71	71	72	72	72	71	70	71	71	72	72	71	
			R	3.0	3.1	3.3	5.8	9.2	10.5	9.5	7.9	4.2	4.1	4.7	5.3	70.6
San Jose, Bolivia	17°51'S.	981	T	85	85	83	81	81	77	78	75	82	86	82	84	
			R	4.8	6.1	4.6	2.1	1.3	2.2	0.0	0.1	0.2	2.6	6.2	6.4	36.6
Campo Gallo, Argentina	26°35'S.	623	T	83	81	76	71	66	60	60	65	71	75	79	83	
			R	4.4	3.5	3.4	1.5	0.7	0.4	0.2	0.3	0.7	1.9	2.4	3.5	22.8
Rivadavia, Argentina	24°10'S.	672	T	82	80	76	71	66	61	61	66	71	76	79	83	
			R	4.2	3.8	3.3	1.6	0.3	0.2	0.1	0.1	0.7	1.2	1.3	3.4	20.2
Ceres, Argentina	29°53'	289	T	79	77	72	66	61	55	54	57	62	67	73	78	
			R	4.7	4.1	4.9	2.3	1.7	0.9	0.8	0.9	1.7	2.8	4.0	4.6	33.4

Source: F. L. Wernstedt, *World Climatic Data, Latin America and the Caribbean,* Pennsylvania State University, 1959.

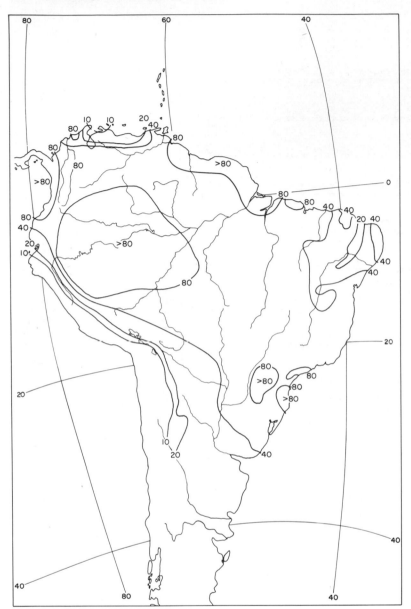

Figure 21.3.   Mean annual rainfall in tropical South America (inches).

at Belem can thus be termed equable. A normal and very common relationship between temperature and rainfall is suggested here. The highest mean monthly values are usually attained during the drier season, the lowest in the rainy season, however small or large the differences may be. The mean daily range of temperature is a good deal greater throughout the year than the mean annual range. But daily fluctuations are reduced in wet weather, and

thus the lowest value of 14 degrees is observed from February through April, and the greatest appears in the dry season, amounting to 19 degrees in November.

Mean maximum temperatures every month of the year rise to between 90° and 93°. But the highest recorded value is 98°, reached in the dry month of October. Mean minima range between 69° and 71°, and the extreme minimum has been 64°, observed in July, producing an extreme temperature range of 34 degrees.

Santarem, about 430 miles farther west on the south bank of the Amazon at the mouth of the Tapajoz, is 2°30' south of the equator and lies at an altitude of only 66 feet. More remote from the sea and the influence of the trades, mean annual rainfall is less (77.9 inches) than at Belem, and the rainy season is shorter, from January through June, when about 80 per cent of the year's precipitation is normally expected. The maximum monthly amount arrives in March, averaging 13.2 inches, when rain ordinarily falls on twenty-six of the thirty-one days. As much as 6.9 inches have fallen within twenty-four hours during this month. Cloud cover averages more than 65 per cent from February through April, and relative humidities average more than 90 per cent from January through June, in May rising to 93 per cent. Cloud cover diminishes to about 31 per cent in August, although humidities remain between 78 per cent and 88 per cent throughout the dry season.

Mean monthly temperatures remain around 79° during the wet season but rise to 82° from September through November, producing a mean annual range of 4 degrees. The mean daily temperature range is 12 degrees from February through May but rises to 18 degrees from September through November. The highest recorded temperature is 99°, observed in September, and the lowest 65°, in July, an extreme range of 34 degrees.

Manaus, about 380 miles farther up the Amazon on the north bank of the Rio Negro just above its junction with the Amazon, is 3°8' south of the equator and stands only 144 feet above sea level. A thirty-one-year precipitation record indicates a mean annual rainfall of 78.6 inches, and of this amount nearly 81 per cent is received in the period from November through May. March is normally the rainiest month, averaging 10.6 inches, although the normal January amount of 10.5 inches is almost equal, and in both cases rain falls on twenty out of thirty-one days per month. As much as 4.7 inches have fallen in twenty-four hours in March. Cloud cover averages between 64 and 67 per cent from December through May, and afternoon relative humidities range between 68 and 73 per cent during the same period. Cloud cover remains at about 60 per cent through the dry season, but relative humidities drop to less than 60 per cent from August through October, reaching a minimum for the year of 57 per cent in September.

Mean monthly temperatures remain at around 79° from January through May and rise to about 82° in September and October, yielding a mean annual range of 3 degrees. The mean daily range is between 12 and 13 degrees from January through June but rises to 16 degrees in August and October and to 17 in September. Extreme maxima of 100° have been recorded in February and October at Manaus, and 101° has been observed in December, well after the start of the normal rainy season. An extreme minimum of 64° has been reached in July, producing an extreme range of 37 degrees.

Taracua, about 600 niles farther up the Rio Negro at 0°04' N. Lat., lies at the low altitude of 325 feet. The upper Negro valley is on the whole a region of considerably greater rainfall. Taracua averages, from a nineteen-year precipitation record, 137.7 inches. The yearly distribution is more nearly uniform than in sections farther east; only one month (October) normally receives less than 8 inches, and about 81 per cent of the year's total is received in a nine-month period from December through August. May is the month of maximum rainfall, averaging 16.4 inches, but a secondary peak appears in January, which averages 13 inches compared, with 10.6 inches in December and 9.7 in February. At this distinctly equatorial station the mean annual temperature range is 3.5 degrees (78.5° in February and 75° in July), and the mean daily range is between 15 and 18 degrees throughout the year. Note that the warmest month, February, coincides with the definite decrease in monthly rainfall, and the monthly averages diminish from that point until July, during the height of the rainy season. More explicit information is lacking for this station, but it appears likely that both cloud cover and relative humidity remain relatively high for the entire year in view of the abundant normal rainfall.

The main body of selva continues southward into the northern part of Bolivia, where it gives way to semideciduous forest and numerous stretches of savanna woodland in both Bolivia and central Brazil. Elongated fingers of riparian rainforest continue southward into these drier regions for some distance beyond the main regional expanse. The change is suggested by an examination of temperature and rainfall records from the few reporting stations in these remote parts of Bolivia and Brazil. In these latitudes the rainy season falls mainly during the period of high sun, from September 21 to March 21.

Westward up the low-lying basin of the Amazon drainage evergreen rainforest continues to its farthest limits in the foothills of the Andes from Colombia to Bolivia, reaching within less than 150 miles of the Pacific coast. The upper limit of selva along the lower slopes of the eastern Andes averages about 3000 feet in Colombia, rises to about 4600 feet in Ecuador, is generally between 3000 and 4500 feet in Peru, although it is occasionally found up to 5000 feet, and is about the same in Bolivia, where it extends southward in an attenuated strip to a point near Santa Cruz, at a latitude of about 18°.

ANDEAN CLOUD FOREST. Beginning at the upper limits of selva all along the easternmost slopes of the Andes is a variable belt of cloud forest that frequently rises to heights of more than 11,000 feet.

The persistently high temperatures and high moisture content along the eastern front of the Andes are qualities of maritime tropical air transported westward from the Atlantic by the trades. This air is cooler than the surface beneath in the upper Amazon basin and is thus inherently unstable. Excessive heating of the surface layers near ground level induces uplift, eventual condensation at higher levels, and convective turbulence, resulting in frequent heavy showers. The numerous waterways, sodden terrain, and moisture release of the luxuriant vegetation augment the advected moisture from the remote sea, acting as a local return supply of precipitable atmospheric moisture.

Most of the airflow is from an easterly direction, but it varies locally according to the alignment of valleys opening out toward the Amazon lowland. The mechanical upward deflection of air reaching the steeply rising eastern slopes of the Andes adds a powerful orographic effect. This leads to frequent cloud and fog formation in contact with those slopes, and copious rains, resulting in a distinct climatic change above the upper limits of tropical rainforest.

An account by Marston Bates[2] of the climate and vegetation around Villaviencio in eastern

[2] Marston Bates, "Climate and Vegetation in the Villavicencio Region of Eastern Colombia," *Geographical Review*, 38(4): 555–74, 1948.

Colombia offers a useful impression of the climatic transition from rainforest to cloud forest. Villaviencio (el. 1640) lies at the base of the eastern Cordillera of the Andes where a narrow, uneven band of evergreen rainforest, roughly 10 miles broad, extends northward from the main body of selva farther south. East of the restricted foothill zone close-crowned forest gives way on the rising ground between the river courses to broad tracts of savanna grassland dotted with moriche palm and is mainly confined to the stream valleys in the form of a galleria forest. The station lies near the southwestern limits of the savanna woodland region in the Orinoco lowland, and the presence of open, wooded grassland areas within 10 to 15 miles northeastward of it indicates the sharpness of the landscape change over the lowlands in the vicinity.

A five-year weather record, from 1941 to 1946, shows a mean annual rainfall of 186.8 inches at Villavicencio, 85 per cent of which occurs over the eight-month period from April through November during which rain falls on twenty or more days per month. May is normally the month of maximum rain, averaging 27.4 inches that fall on twenty-seven days. February is a relatively dry month, averaging 2.6 inches falling on only seven days. Noontime relative humidities average above 70 per cent during the rainy season, rising to between 70 and 77 per cent from May to July, but in February the value drops to 61 per cent. Temperatures are typically uniform throughout the year, monthly averages lowering to around 78° in June and rising to 82° in February and March, producing a mean annual range of 4 degrees. The mean daily temperature range is roughly from 70° to 90°, increasing slightly in the dry season.

Up the steep rise of the Andes overshadowing Villavicencio on the west an abrupt increase in rainfall appears within only a few miles. Buenavista (el. 3939), on the crest of the first mountain ridge about 3.7 miles from the station, averages 252 inches and lies well within the lower limits of cloud forest above the selva. Bates indicates that greatly increased fog at about 3900 feet, along with much higher rainfall, accounts for the definite change in vegetation from rainforest to the rank, dripping luxuriance of mountain evergreen forest. The difference in elevation is less than half a mile, but in that short vertical distance rainfall

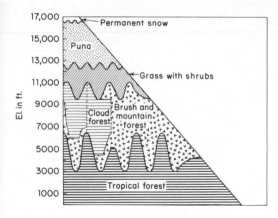

Figure 21.4. Vertical changes in vegetation in eastern Peru. [After Drewes]

amounts on the middle slopes of the high Andes are raised by orographic uplift of easterly air currents to more than double those on the rainforest plains below. Rainfall intensities are usually greatest along the lower limits of cloud forest, and amounts decrease rapidly with increasing altitude.

A study of the east Andean slopes in central Peru by Drewes[3] reveals certain climatic variations within 8° and 12° S. Lat. from the Amazon lowland to the high mountain regions of the Andes. The tropical evergreen rainforest vegetation of the Amazon lowland consists of tall, slender trees, abundantly festooned with lianas and decked with epiphytic flora. This changes with altitude; the trees become smaller and more widely spaced, the open spaces on the forest floor are occupied with shrubs and smaller trees, and between 3000 and 4500 feet selva begins to give way to brush or mountain forest (Fig. 21.4). This is a vegetation of evergreen shrubs and small trees representing the transition from selva to the high mountain scrub and grassland that begins to dominate at between 9000 and 11,000 feet.

Cloud forest is found within the altitude limits of a drier, more open brush or mountain forest and usually appears on the ridges and summits exposed to the moisture-laden east and northeast winds (Fig. 21.5). This fog-shrouded, damp,

[3] W. U. and A. T. Drewes, *Climate and Related Phenomena of the Eastern Andean Slopes of Central Peru,* Syracuse University Research Institute, Syracuse, N.Y., 1957.

cool, misty zone of little sunlight ranges between 4500 and 9500 feet. The scarcity of sunshine and high atmospheric humidity result in virtually constant condensation on the stems and foliage of plants, low evaporation, and persistently low temperatures that fluctuate within narrow limits both from day to day and throughout the year. Unlike the rainforest below, where forest trees range up to 130 and 140 feet in height, here the tree forms are usually less than 50 feet high, occasionally up to 75 feet, closely intertwined to form an impenetrably dense, dripping vegetation over dank, spongy leaf litter that creates an almost impassable barrier to foot travel.

THE GUIANAS. In the lower Amazon basin evergreen rainforest extends northward into the uplifted broken plateau country of the Guiana highlands. It reaches in places to within 25 or 30 miles of the lower Orinoco's banks, where it rapidly yields to the much drier environment of savanna woodland. On the whole, however, it is separated from the Orinoco

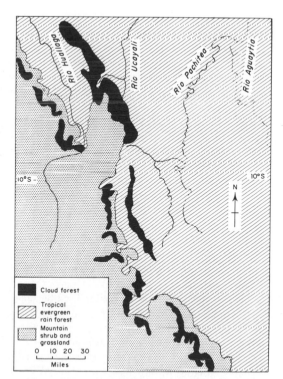

Figure 21.5. Cloud forest distribution in eastern Peru.

Llanos by intermediate tracts of semideciduous forest, isolated savannas, and thorn scrub woodland. Throughout the Guiana highlands it is interrupted by many expanses of open, wooded savanna grasslands, partly arising from their interior remoteness from rain-bearing winds off the Atlantic and partly from local edaphic conditions of unusually porous soil.

From well to the east of the Amazon delta rainforest extends northwestward along the coast across French Guiana, Surinam, and Guyana to the delta of the Orinoco, where it gives way to a periodically inundated tract of swamp forest and grassland nearly 250 miles long across the span of that river's complex series of channels leading to the sea. Between the Amazon and the Orinoco selva in Brazil and the Guianas is frequently interrupted by savanna woodland, often arising from excessively well-drained soils that fail to support the luxuriant vegetation of the rainforest. A notable stretch of savanna extends along the coast for nearly 300 miles northward from the mouth of the Amazon.

The northeast trades play the dominant role among surface circulation features from the Amazon northward into middle America. The cool season from November to May is dominated by winds from east-northeast that set in with increasing force and steadiness at this time, reaching a maximum during January and February. Diminishing in March, they gradually give way to lighter, more variable winds and squally weather typical of the equatorial trough, which by April has begun to advance northward. Rains, which are fairly constant through the entire year, increase sharply as the trough shifts farther northward, and the season of rainfall maximum begins. By June generally heavy rains prevail over all the Guinas but drop off appreciably near the Venezuelan border. From August through October east to southeast winds reach their maximum force off the Guiana coast, blowing almost without interruption, although decreasing over land during the night.

Few climatic stations are maintained between the Amazon and the Orinoco, and those with reliable records are chiefly on the coast (Table 21-1). Mean annual rainfall amounts to more than 100 inches from the Amazon delta to French Guiana, diminishing westward toward the Orinoco. A comparison of Cayenne (el. 20), French Guiana, with Georgetown (el. 6),

Guyana, is revealing. Cayenne averages 126.4 inches of annual rainfall, 86 per cent of which occurs from December through June. May is the peak month, averaging 21.7 inches, when rain normally falls on twenty-six days out of thirty-one. Heavy, prolonged showers typical of equatorial trough weather contribute the bulk of the year's rain, as suggested by the fact that more than 10 inches have fallen in twenty-four hours during every month from January through April, and April has recorded 23 inches in one twenty-four-hour period. Mean relative humidity at 1500 is near 80 per cent in the rainy season, rising to 83 per cent in May, the maximum rainfall month. At this time normal cloud cover is 70 per cent, also the maximum for the year.

Georgetown averages 88.7 inches of annual rainfall, only 67 per cent of which occurs from December through June. Here the steadiness of the northwest trades is maintained during the entire year, and a more equitable distribution of normal rain results. December is the peak month, for which only 11.9 inches is normal, falling on twenty-four out of thirty days. Rains are usually less intense than at Cayenne, indicated by the fact that the maximum amount recorded in twenty-four hours has been 7.7 inches in December. The persistence of the more vigorous trades in contrast to the variable, squally winds of equatorial trough weather dominating at Cayenne is also suggested by the lower values of relative humidity observed at 1300. For the whole year between 70 and 75 per cent is common, with a minimum of 69 per cent from September through November and a maximum of 77 per cent in June. Furthermore, cloud cover in June is normally 68 per cent.

Cayenne, the station more definitely under the influence of equatorial trough weather from December through June, experiences a sharper contrast of seasonal weather changes than does Georgetown. In the season of much less rain, from August to October, September and October receive 1.2 inch and 1.3 inch respectively, on the average, cloud cover measuring about 40 per cent and relative humidity 69 per cent. The number of rain days per month is four. Winds are dominantly east-southeast and thus are roughly parallel to the shoreline in the vicinity. A further indication of diminished rainfall and increased sunshine is the fact that mean temperatures are 83° in September and October, and mean maximum temperatures rise to a yearly peak of 91° in these two months. In both months the thermometer has climbed to an absolute maximum of 97°. By contrast, the more even rainfall distribution at Georgetown produces a yearly minimum of 3 inches in September, cloud cover averages 54 per cent, and relative humidity is 69 per cent. Rain falls on an average of nine days in September. Mean temperatures are 81° from August through November, the mean maximum 87°, the absolute maximum 89°.

The twelve-year climatic record of a single observation point in the Guiana highlands offers some idea of the rain shadow effect of the Pakaraima Mountains on the prevailing northeast trades. Santa Elena (el. 2975) in southern Venezuela lies within the uppermost source region of the Rio Caroni, a southern tributary of the lower Orinoco, less than 10 miles from the Brazilian border. Fifty miles northeastward are the Pakaraima Mountains, generally above 5000 feet in elevation, rising to an apex at the summit of Mt. Roraima (el. 9219). Two miles north-northeast of Santa Elena a single peak stands at 4259 feet. The country between this station and Mt. Roraima is largely savanna woodland, grading into semideciduous forest of moderate density where sufficient rains reliably occur. Evergreen rainforest surrounds the entire region from Guyana to the Amazon basin.

Mean annual rainfall at Santa Elena averages 70.6 inches, of which 87 per cent normally occurs in the nine-month period April through December. The major rainy season is from April through August, when 61 per cent of the year's rain occurs. At this time the southeast trades are the chief source of precipitable moisture, flowing west-northwestward up the steep rise of the highlands. Prolonged instability rains dominate the weather in this period. Rain falls ordinarily on eighteen days in April but increases in frequency to twenty-eight days in May and June, twenty-seven days in July, and twenty-six days in August. Skies are cloudy or overcast at frequent intervals, and midafternoon relative humidities at 1400 are 73 or 74 per cent from June through August. The preponderance of light, steady rains is indicated by the fact that maximum amounts received in twenty-hours do not exceed 2.5 inches from April through August except in June, when this value has risen to 2.8 inches.

The minimum monthly temperature for the year is attained when the thermometer averages 70° in July. In this month the mean maximum is 82°, the mean minimum 62°, and the mean daily range 20 degrees.

A secondary peak rainfall season occurs in November and December, December averaging 5.3 inches, after the southeast trades have withdrawn and the northeast trades have begun to move into northern South America. Rain falls on seventeen days in December and is a more fitful, showery kind that yields much less rain from January through March. January and February average about 3 inches each, and measurable rain occurs on thirteen days in January, eleven days in February. Afternoon relative humidities drop to 63 and 62 per cent in those two months respectively and to 57 per cent in March. Maximum mean monthly temperatures of 72° are reached in March, when the mean daily range is 25 degrees. The thermometer has risen to 95° in this month and has fallen to 53°, producing a maximum temperature range of 42 degrees during only a single month at the end of the dry season.

THE ORINOCO VALLEY. The nearly continuous distribution of rainforest vegetation spreading northwestward along the coast from the lower Amazon basin reaches a poleward limit in the swampy delta of the Orinoco. Before proceeding with a survey of the climatic qualities of the complicated arrangement pattern of tropical regions in northern South America and middle America, let us look briefly at the distinctive region of the Orinoco valley.

Between the Orinoco delta and the Andes far to the westward in Colombia is an almost unbroken expanse of savanna woodland, the Orinoco Llanos. Extending for some 800 miles from the head of the delta to the upper Guaviare and the low Andean foothills in eastern Colombia, it widens to a breadth of nearly 300 miles between the lower Guaviare and the Andes in western Venezuela. It is a nearly level region of loosely consolidated sediments drained by hundreds of sinuously winding stream beds separating countless low tablelands of nearly uniform height, largely under 500 feet above sea level. The meandering stream courses are low in gradient and very shallow. Often without water in the dry season, they fill with turbid, slow-moving water in the rainy season, overflowing each year to inundate thousands of square miles of the nearly level countryside. Alternate flooding and drying are among the chief reasons for the predominant grass vegetation of the region. Low thickets of evergreen and deciduous trees, scattered palms, and patches of thorn scrub trees and shrubs are widely distributed. Broadleaf evergreen trees line the banks of many tributaries, forming a narrow galleria forest that marks the presence of the more persistent streams.

Few climatic stations provide a record of satisfactory length or reliability (Table 21-1). From available records it is amply clear that temperatures are uniformly high, averaging around 80°, over the entire year. The warmest months are commonly March or April, before the start of the rainy season, and a second temperature increase occurs at most stations as the rainy season approaches an end. Throughout the region rains begin in April and last until October, producing a single peak season that ordinarily culminates in July or August.

At Ciudad Bolivar (el. 177) about 100 miles west of the Orinoco delta, temperatures rise from 80° in January to 84° in April and May, subsiding to 81° in July, the wettest month, but rising again to 84° in October, providing a mean annual range of 4 degrees. The mean daily range is 18 degrees in March and 14 degrees in July. The thermometer has climbed to 101° in May and dropped to 65° in January, giving an extreme range of 36 degrees. Mean annual rainfall at Ciudad Bolivar is 38.8 inches, 84 per cent of which falls from April through October. The peak month is July, averaging 6.9 inches, when rain occurs on fifteen out of thirty-one days, and August is almost as wet with 6.7 inches. But monthly averages vary considerably, for August has recorded as little as 1.3 and as much as 20 inches, indicating one of the major characteristics of savanna woodland climates, the pronounced variability of yearly rains.

Winds are dominantly east to northeast during the entire year, and precipitation appears to be induced systematically by traveling waves in the easterlies. Rain occurs in small amounts, for maximum twenty-four-hour amounts have rarely exceeded 4.5 inches. Cloud cover in the rainy season is normally less than 50 per cent, a feature of trade wind weather, although during a three-year period of observation a 63 per cent average cloud cover has been noted for June. Early afternoon relative humidities (at 1330) are

above 60 per cent during the wet season, rising to a maximum of 70 per cent in July.

A general let-up in rain begins in November, and by January the normal dry season sets in, lasting through March. Monthly amounts diminish from December onward, reaching a minimum for the year of 0.3 inch in March. But actual values vary widely, for each month from January through April has at times been entirely rainless, and yet January has also recorded 5.2 inches, February 3.7 inches, March 3 inches, and April 5.9 inches. The normal number of rain days is six in January, three in February, and two in March. In the dry season cloud cover is less than 40 per cent on the average, and February with 27 per cent is the least cloudy month. Relative humidity reaches an annual minimum of 57 per cent in April, when temperatures are high as the wet season is about to begin.

Mean annual rainfall as a rule ranges between 40 and 50 inches over the region, although in the western reaches of the Orinoco lowland values exceed 50 inches in many places. In other respects the climatic character of the llanos is nearly as uniform as the savanna landscapes.

All along the margins of the llanos a change into more humid environments is repeatedly seen. An example of this is Maripa (el. 164), about 125 miles west-southwest of Ciudad Bolivar and within 23 miles of the Orinoco at the northern edge of the Guiana highlands. It lies in a belt of semideciduous forest near a large expanse of selva south of it. Mean annual rainfall from an eight-year record is 97.3 inches. Maximum amounts are in June (17.9 inches) and August (18.3 inches), and March is the driest month (1 inch).

Crist gives a brief description of seasonal weather changes[4] in the llanos in which he indicates that from January through March winds are hot and dry, days and nights generally cloudless. Grass becomes dry as tinder, river beds become virtually waterless, and the hard soil is parched under the hot sun and high temperatures.

Toward the middle of April clouds begin to appear in the sky, and there is an occasional shower. By May there are violent thunderstorms

[4] Raymond E. Crist, "Along the Llanos-Andes Border in Venezuela; Then and Now," *Geographical Review*, **46**(2): 187–208, April 1956.

with great quantities of rain. The doldrums belt has moved north again, and the wet season (the *invierno*, or winter) has begun. The sky is often overcast, the trades little by little cease to blow, the air is frequently sultry, and there is much rain. Pastures and trees become green, and the whole aspect of the landscape changes almost overnight. The winds shift in average direction from the northeast quadrant to the northwest and are strongest in the afternoon. The diurnal variation in temperature induces strong convection currents, which often by late forenoon or early afternoon produce typical cumulus clouds. The heavy rains, usually accompanied by thunder and lightning, occur almost without exception during the hottest part of the day; the temperature may drop as much as 8° or 10° in a quarter of an hour. ... Almost every year, by the end of June or early July, there is a period of drought lasting from several weeks to a month or more, called *el veranito de San Juan*, when the southeast trades of the Southern Hemisphere temporarily cross the geographic equator toward the equatorial trough of low pressure, which has migrated far to the north.

THE NORTH COAST.   Where almost continuous savanna woodland in the Orinoco valley comes to an end along the foothills of the Andes in eastern Colombia and northern Venezuela, and where virtually unbroken selva spreading northwestward across the Guianas from the lower Amazon valley tapers to an end in northeastern Venezuela, a major change in the distribution pattern of tropical climates begins.

Climatic contrasts within short distances are nowhere more widely developed than in the northern portions of tropical America, and the most striking examples are found along the north coast of South America. From desert to tropical rainforest, and upward through cloud forest to alpine meadows and snow-capped lakes, spectacular changes are seen sometimes within a horizontal distance of less than 50 miles. At frequent intervals along the lower Caribbean shores of Venezuela and Colombia desert conditions are found where the vegetation is composed of low xerophytic shrubs, cacti, and stunted, drought-resistant trees, and where the intervening spaces of bare ground are largely free of grass and other lower forms of plants. Desert vegetation occupies much of the Araya peninsula in northeastern Venezuela, the broad Paraguana peninsula of northwestern Venezuela, and many smaller tracts between. It is present on most of the Guajira peninsula,

Colombia's northernmost projection, bending north of the Maracaibo basin, and continues southwestward in patches to the mouth of the Sinu River. Desert scrub is also abundantly present on the offshore islands between the Paraguana and Araya peninsulas.

Examples may be taken from mean annual rainfall amounts at stations where temperatures are consistently high throughout the year, remaining at all times between the high 70s and the low 80s. Cumana, opposite the Araya peninsula at the entrance to the Gulf of Cariaco, reports a thirty-year average of 15.4 inches; Las Piedras, on the southwestern side of the Paraguana peninsula, a twenty-five-year average of 12.4 inches; Maracaibo, at the entrance to Lake Maracaibo, a thirty-six-year average of 22.6 inches; Oranjestad, on the west side of the island of Aruba, a ten-year average of 13.5 inches; Pozos Colorados, near Santa Marta, Colombia, a seven-year average of 18.9 inches; and Tolu, about 25 miles northeast of the Rio Sinu's mouth, a five-year average of 21.8 inches.

No satisfactory explanation of the arid belt along the coast has yet been offered, although the possibility that the trade wind inversion is unusually persistent at around 5000 feet must be considered, or that the dominant trades maintain unusually high velocities at from 3000 to 5000 feet, thus inhibiting the local convective processes. Within a short distance inland from the desert coastlands rainfall increases appreciably, and a rapid change into thorn scrub woodland, savanna woodland, and on into the more luxuriant forests takes place among the mountain valleys and broad alluvial flood plains. But the distribution of discrete climates is fragmented and most complex. A suggestion of its complexity is revealed by an examination of the temperature and rainfall characteristics at six stations lying east and southeast of the Maracaibo basin (Table 21-2 and Fig. 21.6).

Carora (el. 1378) lies about 80 miles east of the Maracaibo basin in a slightly elevated basin where thorn scrub woodland is the dominant vegetation. Temperatures are constantly high, ranging from 78° in March to 84° from June through September. Mean annual rainfall is 24.7 inches, 66 per cent of which falls in the five-month period from August through December. Maximum amounts are normally in October (5.5 inches). Three months receive less than 1 inch, and only two months average more than 3.5 inches. Lagunillas (el. 16) on the north-east shore of Lake Maracaibo is in a segment of savanna woodland where temperatures are higher, ranging from 82° in January and February to 84° in September, October and, December. Normal yearly rainfall is 35.5 inches, 64 per cent of which falls in the five-month period from July through November. The maximum month is October (6.5 inches), and again three months average less than 1 inch, but seven months average more than 3.5 inches. San Cristobal (el. 3632), in a narrow band of semi-deciduous forest about 20 miles from the south-eastern shores of Lake Maracaibo, is also constantly hot, its temperatures ranging from 71° during December through February to 75° in September. Gaining the advantage of much higher elevation, its hottest month is nearly 10 degrees cooler than the hottest month at the two preceding stations. Mean annual rainfall is 44.4 inches, 65 per cent of which falls in the seven-month period from April through October. Maximum rains occur in May (5.7 inches) and October (4.7 inches), over six months average more than 3.5 inches, but an important difference appears in the occurrence of moderate rain throughout the year, for the lowest monthly amount, in January, is 2.2 inches.

Pampanito (el. 1237), about 40 miles north-east of San Cristobal, lies in a valley pocket of tropical evergreen rainforest where high temperatures also prevail, ranging from 77° in December and January to 79° from March through June and again in August and September. Mean annual rainfall is 67 inches, moderately well distributed through the year, with 65 per cent falling in the seven-month period from April through October. Peak months are May (8.5 inches) and October (8.4 inches), and the minimum monthly amount in February is 2.9 inches. Within five miles of Pampanito are drier tracts of more open savanna.

Merida (el. 5325), some 40 miles southwest of San Cristobal in a deep valley flanked on the north and the south by ranges rising above 13,000 feet, lies in a cloud forest environment where temperatures remain cool through the entire year, ranging from 65° in January to 68° in August and September. Mean annual rainfall is 71.2 inches, 63 per cent of which falls from May through October, a six-month period when two peak months punctuate the double maximum regime that is typical for this section of the country: May with 10.1 inches and October with 10.4 inches. Eight months average more than 5 inches of rain, and the yearly minimum occurs in February, when 1.8 inch is the normal.

About 20 miles northeast of Merida is Mucuchies (el. 9781), a station at the edge of an alpine meadow environment, the high mountain grassland climate of the Andes, called in South America the paramos. Here temperatures are constantly cool, ranging from 50° in January to 53° from March through May. Mean annual rainfall is only 30.3 inches, 71 per cent of which falls during the five-month period April through August. June is the peak month, averaging 4.8 inches, and four months of the year average less than 1 inch of rain. South of Merida and Mucuchies are several peaks over 15,000 feet that remain snow-capped throughout the year, the only ice-mantled summits in Venezuela.

The degree of environmental contrast existing in northwestern Venezuela is further revealed by an examination of the climatic data for Maracaibo and Merida. Maracaibo, at the

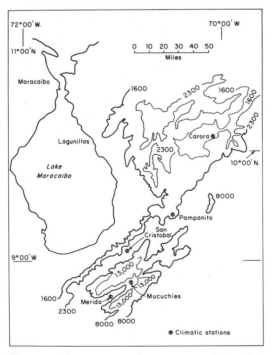

Figure 21.6. Terrain east of Lake Maracaibo, Venezuela (elevation in feet).

TABLE 21–2

Regional Climatic Data for Stations in Northwestern Venezuela
(Temp., °F; Rainfall, In.)

Station	Lat.	El. in Ft		Jan.	Feb.	Mar.	Apr.	May	Jun.	Jul.	Aug.	Sep.	Oct.	Nov.	Dec.	Year
Carora	10°11′	1378	T	79	81	78	82	83	84	84	84	84	83	80	79	
Thorn Scrub Woodland			R	0.5	0.5	1.2	1.5	2.4	1.0	1.3	2.2	2.8	5.5	4.7	1.2	24.7
Lagunillas	10°07′	16	T	82	82	83	84	83	82	83	84	84	84	83	84	
Savanna Woodland			R	0.3	0.4	0.7	2.0	4.8	3.7	3.5	4.2	4.9	6.5	3.5	1.3	35.5
Maracaibo	10°39′	20	T	81	81	82	83	83	84	84	85	84	83	82	82	
Thorn Scrub Woodland			R	0.1	0.0	0.3	0.9	2.8	2.1	1.8	2.2	2.6	5.6	3.3	0.6	22.2
Merida	8°36′	5327	T	65	66	67	67	67	67	67	68	68	68	66	66	
Cloud Forest			R	2.3	1.8	2.7	6.8	10.1	6.8	4.9	5.7	6.8	10.4	9.1	3.7	71.2
Mucuchies	8°45′	9781	T	50	52	53	53	53	52	51	51	52	52	51	51	
Paramos			R	0.3	0.7	0.8	3.8	4.7	4.8	4.6	3.8	2.5	2.7	1.3	0.4	30.3
Pampanito	9°25′	1237	T	77	78	79	79	79	79	78	79	79	78	78	77	
Evergreen Rainforest			R	3.6	2.9	5.2	6.4	8.4	3.6	3.5	6.3	7.2	8.5	6.1	5.2	67.0
San Cristobal	9°02′	3632	T	71	71	72	73	73	73	74	74	75	74	73	71	
Semideciduous Forest			R	2.2	3.0	3.0	5.0	5.7	3.3	3.5	3.3	3.5	4.9	4.6	2.4	44.4

Source: F. L. Wernstedt, *World Climatic Data, Latin America and the Caribbean*, Pennsylvania State University, 1959.

TABLE 21–3

Climatic Data for Maracaibo and Merida

Station	El. in Ft	Years of Record	Jan.	Feb.	Mar.	Apr.	May	Jun.	Jul.	Aug.	Sep.	Oct.	Nov.	Dec.	Year
Maracaibo,	20	36													
Caribbean coast															
Temp. (°F)															
Mean			81	81	82	83	83	84	84	85	84	83	82	82	83
Mean daily range			17	17	17	16	15	16	18	17	17	16	15	16	
Extreme max.			98	97	98	102	100	100	101	102	102	99	98	96	
Extreme min.			66	68	67	68	68	69	70	79	68	68	70	68	
Precip. (in.)															
Mean			0.1	0.0	0.3	0.8	2.7	2.2	1.8	2.2	2.8	5.9	3.4	0.6	22.6
Max.			1.3	0.2	4.3	3.8	9.4	7.8	9.8	5.9	6.0	13.5	10.8	2.1	42.6
Min.			0.0	0.0	0.0	0.0	T	0.1	T	0.2	0.3	1.3	0.0	0.0	10.1
Max. in 24 hours			1.2	0.1	1.4	0.8	2.7	3.3	4.5	3.6	2.4	3.8	5.9	1.8	
No. rain days			0.5	0.3	1.0	1.0	6.0	6.0	5.0	7.0	6.0	9.0	8.0	2.0	50
Cloud cover (tenths)			2.6	2.9	2.6	4.3	4.0	4.0	3.6	4.6	4.3	4.5	3.9	2.9	3.7
Relative hum. (% at 1300)			61	61	61	61	63	60	62	62	62	62	63	62	62
Merida,	5327	19													
Andes valley															
Temp. (°F)															
Mean			65	66	67	67	67	67	67	68	68	67	66	66	67
Mean daily range			19	19	19	17	17	17	20	19	19	18	16	19	
Extreme max.			81	86	84	88	84	82	86	84	85	86	82	82	88
Extreme min.			50	51	53	55	53	53	53	53	55	56	55	50	50
Precip.															
Mean			2.2	1.8	2.8	6.7	9.8	6.7	4.8	5.8	7.1	10.8	9.3	3.7	71.2
Max.			6.1	6.2	9.8	13.9	16.6	11.2	7.2	12.7	10.6	16.7	18.9	9.1	90.6
Min.			0.1	0.0	0.0	1.9	3.1	2.8	1.9	1.9	4.2	2.2	3.0	0.6	49.9
Max. in 24 hours			1.3	1.2	1.1	2.4	4.3	2.1	2.3	2.0	2.2	2.2	4.6	4.1	
No. rain days			11	9	11	17	21	20	18	19	21	23	20	14	204
Cloud cover (tenths)			3.7	4.0	4.7	5.7	5.0	5.3	4.5	4.7	5.7	6.0	5.7	4.3	4.9
Relative hum. (% at 1300)			66	63	63	67	67	67	67	60	57	64	68	66	65

Source: U.S. Naval Oceanographic Office, *Sailing Directions for the West Indies*, Vol. 2, *Lesser Antilles and Venezuela* (H.O. 22), 1963.

entrance of Lake Maracaibo in thorn scrub woodland, is about 20 feet above sea level, whereas Merida, a cloud forest station some 150 miles south of it, is more than a mile above sea level at 5325 feet. The data presented in Table 21-3 suggest the contrast between the semi-arid coast and the Andean valleys. These are two of the few stations for which comparatively detailed data are available from this part of South America for a suitably long period of record.

In Table 21-3 marked differences are seen in both temperature and rainfall characteristics, although both stations possess the expected thermal equability of tropical localities. Monthly mean temperatures are about 17 degrees lower each month at Merida. Mean daily ranges are about 2 degrees less, and extreme maxima and minima are substantially lower. Note that the extreme maximum of 102° observed at Maracaibo is 14 degrees greater than the record of 88° at Merida, and the absolute minimum of 66° at Maracaibo is 16 degrees higher than the 50° observed at Merida. This is an interesting reversal of the normal comparison between coastal and interior locations. Here the coastal station possesses the more strongly continental qualities, and much higher temperatures in general, than the inland station. Altitude, cloud cover, and downslope cooling effects in the higher Andes create the mild thermal regime at Merida, compared with the low-lying, sunnier, and much less rainy conditions at Maracaibo.

Maracaibo receives less than 32 per cent of the normal annual rainfall amounts occurring at Merida. Falling at much higher temperatures, and therefore much less effective, 93 per cent of the annual increment occurs in the seven-month period from May through November. At Merida the same proportion is spread over a much longer period, beginning in April and lasting through the following January. The virtually rainless winter season at Maracaibo compares with a continuation of some rains throughout the year at Merida, February being the driest month, with an average of 1.8 inch.

Short, heavy showers are characteristic during the rainy season at Maracaibo, occasional, episodic rain, as indicated by the extremes of monthly rain and the maximum received in twenty-four hours. At Merida prolonged, steady rains are common, as suggested by the far greater number of rain days, although punctuated by heavy downpours in the height of the peak precipitation periods. Both stations experience a tendency toward a double peak rainfall regime, the wettest months of which are May and October. Greater cloudiness and slightly higher relative humidities are typical at Merida. The hotter, sunnier circumstances at Maracaibo are not offset by lower humidity, for the air is constantly damp and oppressive. Indeed, the entire Maracaibo basin is known for the degree of discomfort engendered by persistently high temperatures and atmospheric humidities.

The West Indies

Over the island region of the West Indies the overriding equability of the climate is chiefly modifies by variations in elevation and exposure to the prevailing easterlies. On the larger islands of Cuba, Jamaica, Hispaniola, and Puerto Rico—the Greater Antilles—this is particularly evident, but on the smaller mountainous islets of the Lesser Antilles, southeast of the major group, the influence prominent relief features also hold true (Fig. 21.7).

For the West Indies there is no summer and winter but simply a change from wet season to a somewhat drier season. At stations almost anywhere on the smaller islands and along the coasts of the larger ones temperatures vary within a mean daily range of 10 to 15 degrees, fluctuating between the low 70s and the low 80s from December through April and between the mid-70s and the upper 80s from May through November. In the interior of the larger islands the mean daily range increases to 20 degrees or more, from the upper 60s to the upper 80s or higher. Here the thermometer may exceed 95° from time to time, less frequently over 100° during the rainy season, but extremely high values for most of the West Indies are rare. Frost is very unusual even at higher elevations, although definitive observations are not available for all situations, although cold waves from North America, the norther or *El norte*, may lower the thermometer readings to the 40s. The lowest value recorded in Puerto Rico has been 40° at Aibonito in March, and in this month Cienfuegos on the south coast of central Cuba has reported 45°. Extreme minima in most of the West Indies have seldom dropped below 55°.

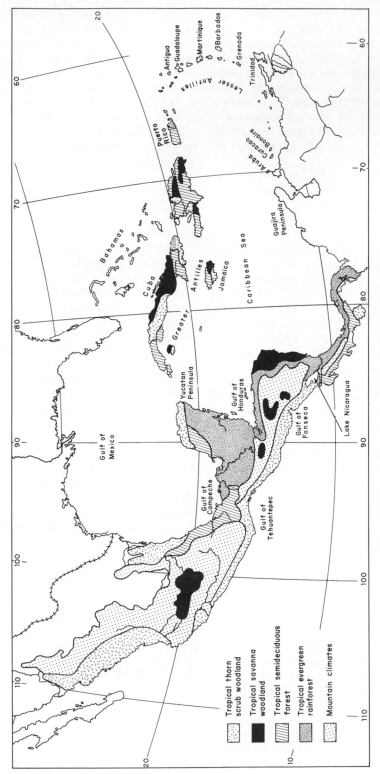

Figure 21.7. Tropical forest and woodland in Middle America.

Tropical thorn scrub woodland

Tropical savanna woodland

Tropical semideciduous forest

Tropical evergreen rainforest

Mountain climates

Prolonged intervals of either sunny, cloudless weather or completely overcast weather are unusual. The common condition is partly cloudy weather in which the trade wind cumuli occupy between 40 and 60 per cent of the sky, leveling off at the height of the trade wind inversion except over mountainous terrain where towering cumuli break through the inversion. Relative humidities are high during the entire year, usually ranging between 65 and 85 per cent and only rarely dropping below 50 per cent. Fog is only occasionally seen in dense accumulation, and the light fogs that often occur in interior sheltered valleys are quickly dissipated after sunrise. Salt haze at sea and near the coast sometimes reduces visibility slightly, but neither fog nor haze affects the limits of observation as much as does heavy rain, which may reduce visibility to less than 100 yards. Heavy squalls and thunderstorms are common from May through November over the higher mountain areas, although less frequent over low-lying islands and peninsulas. Hail is only infrequently recorded, and hailstones are generally too small to threaten damage or injury.

A general statement on the over-all distribution of normal rainfall over the West Indies must be accepted with caution in view of the many contrasts among the islands in terms of size, shape, configuration, exposure to the trades, and geographical arrangement. Ignoring the influence of relief for the moment, the following pattern may be noted. In the low-lying Bahamas mean annual rainfall ranges from more than 60 inches among the northern group (Green Turtle Cay, 64.3 inches annually in an eight-year period) to less than 25 inches among the southernmost group (Duncan Town, 24 inches annually over eleven years; Mathew Town, Great Inagua Island, 24.9 inches annually over five years). Nassau on New Providence Island in the northern group has a fifty-nine-year average of 50.7 inches. Over the large islands of the Greater Antilles values vary too widely according to the influence of major relief features and other factors to warrant a generalization, but many stations report between 45 and 60 inches of mean yearly rain (Table 21-4). Farther east the northern group of the Lesser Antilles have recorded normal amounts somewhat lower than these, averaging between 45 and 50 inches. This holds true as far

as Antigua. Beginning with Monserrat, however, normal yearly totals increase to between 70 and 90 inches. From here to Grenada, a span of some 400 miles, a curving arc of small, mountainous, volcanic islands lies athwart the main westward current of the steady trades. South of Grenada mean annual rainfall again diminishes, and in Trinidad amounts are generally less than 60 inches. The lower island of Barbados, about 100 miles east of the archipelago, having elevations of less than 1250 feet, is an exception among the Lesser Antilles, with a yearly normal of 49.1 inches. A dry belt in the southern Bahamas may thus be seen to lie between the wetter northern group and the well-watered conditions prevailing over most of the West Indies. A still drier zone, it will be recalled, exists along the southern margins of the Caribbean in coastal Venezuela and Colombia and among the offshore islands. The reasons for their existence are not clear at present, and further research is needed, especially in the upper troposphere, before a plausible explanation can be provided.

Among the West Indies elevation and exposure to or shelter from the dominant trades are the principal factors in normal rainfall distribution from place to place on each island. The orographic influence is a major cause of rainfall excess and deficiency, particularly during the height of the rainy season from May through November. It is in this period that barometric waves in the easterlies occur most frequently. No general rule may be applied to all the West Indies as far as height-amount relationships are concerned. From the available records it appears likely that well-exposed heights in many instances receive over 200 inches of rainfall annually, an amount far above the normal values at lower elevations.

From among the wetter Lesser Antilles let us consider the example of the French island of Guadeloupe and its neighboring islets. La Désirade is a small, narrow islet 7 miles long by 1 mile wide, about 10 miles east of Grande Terre, which forms the eastern half of Guadeloupe. At Le Désirade (max. el. 906) a brief, six-year record reveals an average of 39.7 inches of annual rain. Pointe-à-Pitre (el. 23), about 30 miles west of La Désirade on the southwest side of Grande Terre, reports an eight-year average of 79.1 inches. Grande Terre is low in elevation, rising to just 390 feet about 5 miles east of

TABLE 21–4

Climatic Data for Tropical Forest and Woodland Stations in Middle America
(Temp., °F; Rainfall, In.)

Station	Lat.	El. in Ft		Jan.	Feb.	Mar.	Apr.	May	Jun.	Jul.	Aug.	Sep.	Oct.	Nov.	Dec.	Year
West Indies																
St. John's, Antigua	17°05'	121	T	79	77	77	78	80	80	81	81	81	80	79	78	
			R	3.2	2.1	2.1	3.2	4.1	3.9	4.6	4.9	6.1	5.8	5.9	3.9	49.8
Bridgetown, Barbados	13°08'	181	T	77	77	78	79	80	81	80	81	81	80	79	78	
			R	2.6	1.1	1.3	1.4	2.3	4.3	5.8	5.8	6.7	7.0	8.1	8.8	50.2
Santo Domingo, Dominican Republic	18°28'	69	T	75	75	76	77	79	80	80	81	80	79	78	76	
			R	2.2	1.2	2.1	3.7	6.4	6.1	6.4	6.3	7.2	6.1	4.9	2.2	54.9
Green Turtle Cay, Bahamas	26°45'	10	T	68	68	72	75	78	81	82	84	81	78	74	70	
			R	2.4	3.4	4.1	3.9	4.7	7.8	7.3	6.3	7.7	10.1	4.2	2.5	64.3
Havana, Cuba	23°08'	80	T	72	72	74	77	79	81	82	82	81	79	75	72	
			R	2.9	1.8	1.8	2.3	4.7	6.5	4.9	5.3	5.9	6.9	3.1	2.3	48.2
Nassau, Bahamas	25°05'	12	T	72	72	73	75	78	81	83	83	82	80	76	73	
			R	2.2	1.7	1.5	2.4	5.9	6.6	6.0	6.6	7.0	6.6	2.9	1.4	50.7
Port of Spain, Trinidad	10°40'	72	T	76	77	77	79	80	79	79	79	80	80	79	78	
			R	2.3	1.2	1.7	1.5	3.0	6.8	8.1	8.6	7.4	6.5	6.9	4.7	58.7
San Juan, Puerto Rico	18°28'	47	T	75	75	76	77	79	80	80	81	81	80	78	76	
			R	4.3	2.7	2.6	3.9	6.1	5.3	6.0	6.2	6.1	5.4	6.6	5.2	60.3
Central America and Mexico																
Abasolo, Mexico	24°04'	276	T	65	69	70	79	84	85	85	86	83	78	70	66	
			R	1.1	0.6	0.2	1.7	2.3	4.3	2.3	3.6	6.5	2.2	1.2	0.6	26.5
Acapulco, Mexico	16°50'	10	T	78	78	79	80	83	83	83	83	82	82	81	79	
			R	0.4	0.0	0.0	0.0	1.2	16.9	8.5	9.7	14.2	6.7	1.2	0.5	59.2

Station	Lat.	Elev.		1	2	3	4	5	6	7	8	9	10	11	12	Year
Bluefields, Nicaragua	12°00'	17	T	76	77	78	79	80	80	78	79	80	78	77	76	
			R	12.0	5.4	3.0	3.9	15.5	20.0	24.2	21.1	13.1	13.8	17.1	15.9	164.7
Cristobal, Canal Zone	9°21'	40	T	81	81	81	82	81	81	81	81	81	80	80	80	
			R	3.2	1.5	1.5	4.1	12.3	13.6	15.5	15.4	12.6	15.9	22.5	12.2	130.1
Cuilapa, Guatemala	14°16'	2985	T	75	74	76	77	77	77	76	76	77	75	75	74	
			R	0.5	0.2	0.4	1.8	15.4	17.2	19.0	17.2	23.7	12.6	3.0	0.9	111.8
Guatemala City, Guatemala	14°35'	4927	T	61	62	65	67	67	66	66	66	66	63	62	61	
			R	0.1	0.0	0.3	0.7	5.2	10.1	8.0	7.4	10.4	6.0	0.8	0.4	49.3
Mazatlan, Mexico	23°11'	256	T	67	67	68	70	75	80	82	82	82	80	74	69	
			R	0.4	0.4	0.1	0.0	0.1	1.2	6.6	9.5	10.6	2.4	0.5	1.8	33.5
Patzulin, Guatemala	14°42'	2952	T	71	71	72	71	72	72	72	72	72	72	71	71	
			R	1.3	1.6	3.8	8.1	21.0	27.9	23.5	25.0	33.2	25.3	10.1	3.7	184.3
Puerto Barrios, Guatemala	15°43'	6	T	79	81	82	82	83	82	81	82	82	81	78	73	
			R	7.1	4.2	3.0	4.1	7.8	10.8	18.7	12.1	11.5	14.6	10.6	9.2	113.7
Puerto Mexico, Mexico	18°09'	46	T	71	73	75	79	81	81	80	80	80	78	75	72	
			R	5.2	2.5	2.6	1.4	3.8	10.4	8.6	14.8	19.3	22.0	14.5	8.6	113.6
Salina Cruz, Mexico	16°12'	184	T	77	77	79	81	83	81	82	82	80	80	79	78	
			R	0.1	0.1	0.0	0.2	2.8	13.2	5.4	6.3	8.8	3.9	0.2	0.0	40.9
San Andreas Osuna, Guatemala	14°22'	2690	T	75	76	78	78	80	78	79	77	78	76	74	75	
			R	1.2	1.2	3.7	9.3	24.5	28.0	19.3	21.8	31.4	25.8	5.7	2.3	174.1
San Salvador, El Salvador	13°43'	2230	T	72	73	75	76	76	74	75	75	74	73	73	73	
			R	0.2	0.2	0.4	2.1	7.4	12.6	12.1	11.7	12.4	9.3	1.5	0.4	70.1
Tampico, Mexico	22°12'	59	T	66	69	72	77	80	82	83	83	81	78	72	67	
			R	2.1	0.9	0.5	0.4	2.0	7.9	5.8	5.9	13.1	7.0	2.2	1.7	49.3
Tapachula, Mexico	14°54'	551	T	77	78	80	81	80	78	78	78	77	77	77	77	
			R	0.3	0.2	1.3	2.9	12.3	18.6	11.7	13.0	17.8	16.0	3.5	0.5	98.0
Vera Cruz, Mexico	19°12'	52	T	70	71	73	77	80	81	81	81	81	79	75	72	
			R	0.9	0.6	0.3	0.8	2.1	9.6	13.6	11.8	13.6	6.0	3.5	1.0	63.9

Sources: F. L. Wernstedt, *World Climatic Data. Latin America and the Caribbean,* Pennsylvania State University, 1959; U.S. Naval Oceanographic Office, *Sailing Directions for the West Indies,* Vol. 1, 2 (H.O. 21 and 22), 1958–63.

Pointe-à-Pitre, but it is much larger than La Désirade, attaining a breadth of about 20 miles. The fact that Pointe-à-Pitre receives twice as much rain as La Désirade is thus primarily due to thermal convective rather than orographic uplift, the larger land area providing the necessary heated surface to act upon the heavily moisture-laden oceanic air passing across it. Orographic uplift plays an important part in producing the much higher yearly rains at Camp Jacob, however. Camp Jacob is a site at 1750 feet above sea level about 15 miles southwest of Pointe-à-Pitre on the high hills of southern Basse Terre, the western half of Guadeloupe, whose forested slopes rise to 4869 feet. At this station a twenty-one-year average is 140.4 inches. At Neuf Chateau (el. 820) a few miles northeast of Camp Jacob on the east-facing slopes, a seven-year average is 160.8 inches.

Countless examples of similar climatic contrasts can be found on all the larger, more mountainous islands. Well-exposed peaks and ridges appear to act as the major points of concentration for excessive rains. Eastern slopes are also well favored, presenting the combined advantage of orographic uplift and the onshore sweep of the easterly trades, plus a daily increase in trade wind velocities induced by the sea breeze, which is produced by diuranl solar heating of the land surfaces in excess of the warmth gained by the neighboring sea. As a general rule, southern and western shorelines in the lee of the trades are drier, and where well sheltered by high terrain are xerophytic in character. Such is the case along the south coast of eastern Cuba between Guantanamo Bay and Cape Maisi.

Severe tropical cyclones and storms, originating as waves in the easterlies and occasionally gaining sufficient intensity to become hurricanes, are a source of concern throughout the West Indies during the latter part of the rainy season. (See Chapter 5.) They ordinarily skirt the north coast of South America and the islands of Trinidad and Tobago, but elsewhere they pose a serious threat of property damage and loss of life. They also account for some of the excessive rains that have fallen in brief periods on the islands. In twenty four hours Camp Jacob has received 10.3 inches in October; Basseterre, St. Christopher, 10.6 inches in August; Plymouth, Monserrat, over 12 inches

in September; Grand Turk, the Bahamas, 10 inches in September; Santiago de Cuba, 14.3 inches in September; Ciudad Trujillo, Dominican Republic, 20 inches in September; Kingston, Jamaica, 11 inches in October.

Cold front rains are often excessive in the less rainy period of December through April and add a significant quotient to the normals for stations in the Greater Antilles, although northers as such seldom extend their influence effectively beyond the Virgin Islands and Antigua, east of Puerto Rico. San Juan, Puerto Rico, has received 10.6 inches in twenty-four hours in December and 6.7 inches in April as a result of the southward penetration of cold air from North America. Ciudad Trujillo has reported 8.9 inches in twenty-four hours in April, and Havana, Cuba, 8.3 inches. These are, perhaps, somewhat exceptional amounts, for most cold fronts advancing south of the North American mainland extend only a trailing edge across the West Indies and quite often produce only an interval of overcast skies and light, steady rain.

Middle American Mainland

On the middle American mainland the complexities of terrain induce a comparable complexity of climatic distribution. From broad, forested lowlands—like much of the 200-mile wide Yucatan peninsula, eastern Nicaragua, and northern Costa Rica—to isolated volcanic peaks, high plateaus, long dissected ridges, high intermont basins, and narrow coastal plains, the varieties of elevation and exposure to the flow of air from the sea forbid the formulation of more than a few guarded statements on this section of tropical America. Local variations in solar radiation, sunshine duration, wind, cloud cover, atmospheric humidity, precipitation, and temperature are perhaps more diverse here than anywhere else in the low latitudes of the western hemisphere.

In the minds of the inhabitants there are three major climates in Central America and tropical Mexico, very loosely identified by their altitude limits and relative temperatures: *tierra caliente, tierra templada,* and *tierra fria.* No exact limits are understood by the application of these terms, and they are used with purely relative meaning that differs from place to place, and in many localities from person to

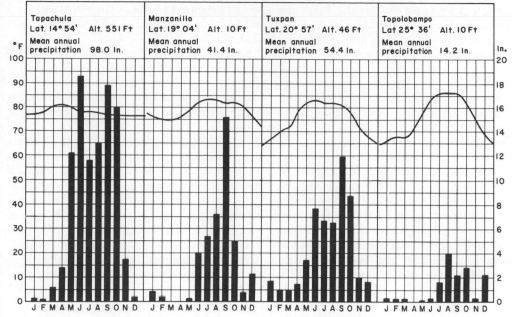

Figure 21.8. Temperature and precipitation regimes along the Pacific coast of Mexico, showing the increase in mean annual temperature range with increasing latitude.

person. In Guatemala, McBryde,[5] among others, has attempted to establish meaningful temperature/elevation relationships among these terms, assigning very general limits of altitude and mean annual temperature as follows: *tierra caliente*, sea level to 3280 feet, 79° to 72°; *tierra templada*, 3280 to 6234 feet, 72° to 63°; and *tierra fria*, 6234 to 13,812 feet, 63° to 41°.

Northwestward from Panama mean annual temperature ranges in tropical situations under 5000′ increase, although always within high limits, from 2 degrees in Panama to more than 20 degrees north of the Tropic of Cancer. The increasing range arises chiefly from lower temperatures in the cool season from December to April (Fig. 21.8). At Cristobal, Panama, it is 2 degrees, at El Salvador 4 degrees, at Coban in interior Guatemala 8 degrees, at Cintalapa on the Pacific piedmont in Mexico 12 degrees. Farther north of the piedmont at Tuxpan it is 16 degrees, and at Topolobampo, Lat. 25° 36′, it is 20 degrees. On the opposite side of the Mexican highlands at Abasolo, Lat. 24°04′, the range is 21 degrees.

[5] F. Webster McBryde, "Studies in Guatemalan Meteorology, (1) The Climates of Southwestern Guatemala," *Bulletin of the American Meteorological Society*, **23**(6): 254–63, 1942.

Everywhere the climatic year consists of two more or less distinct seasons, a dry season from December to April and a wet season principally from May to November, although in many instances the "dry" season is one with considerable rain. Nearly everywhere March is the driest month. Paradoxically, the term *invierno* (winter) is applied to the rainy season of higher temperatures and the term *verano* (summer) to the dry period of the cooler months. This is probably due to the origins of the early European settlers, who, coming from Spain, a mediterranean land of dry summers and wet winters, associated the onset of wet weather with the approach of winter. The rainy season generally is punctuated by two maxima, a first usually in May or June, and a second usually in October, although delayed until November in Panama. These maxima are related to the altitude of the sun, lagging its zenithal position by about one month in the early part of the wet period and by nearly two months toward the end. Between these two peaks rains subside in a sufficiently striking manner to have inspired, in many localities the term *canicula* (dog days), intervals of diminished rain that occur for several weeks at any time from June through August.

As a rule, areas facing the Atlantic basin (the Gulf of Mexico and the Caribbean) are under the dominant control of the northeast trades throughout the year and are less sunny, cloudier, more humid, receive more precipitation, and experience a shorter dry season than those facing the Pacific. The contrast shows up most plainly during the winter season of the northern hemisphere.

Precipitation is the primary key to climatic differentiation in tropical Central America and Mexico. Portig has analyzed the rainfall of Central America[6] and has drawn certain conclusions of value in understanding the climates of mainland middle America. The following remarks are based upon the article cited above. Rain is chiefly a product of predictable synoptic situations and processes and does not usually fall at random. The easterly flow of the trades governs most of the weather, and the weather in general is distinguished by much sunshine interspersed in the rainy season by showers and thundershowers. Cyclonic disturbances are relatively frequent along both coasts but seldom appear inland. They may be ill defined or may appear as well-developed circulations. They may move very slowly or may intensify into tropical storms of hurricane strength. The slow-moving ones tend to remain in the Caribbean.

Heat thunderstorms of local origin are seldom experienced. Cold fronts, an especially frequent occurrence of the winter months, the dry season, are important sources of rain on the Atlantic side but usually bring clear, föhn weather to the southern and western slopes, cloud banks building up densely to the ridge tops and ending abruptly on the upper leeward flanks facing the Pacific. In summer the less frequent cold front advances, usually the trailing edge of a dissipating front experiencing frontolysis, may convert unsettled weather into strong disturbances.

Rain appears to be derived from three main kinds of disturbances: steady rain from largely stratified clouds (temporals), thunderstorms, and trade wind showers without thunder. Hail is very rare and has chiefly been observed only as far south as southern Guatemala. Snow has been observed only as far south as the mountainous heights of southern Guatemala where a number of elevations exceed 13,000 feet above sea level.

Hurricanes rarely affect the southern Central American countries but occasionally deliver destructive winds and flood-producing rains to eastern Nicaragua and northwestward along both coasts of Mexico, including the Yucatan peninsula.

The cold north wind from North America that penetrates middle American territory at frequent intervals from December through April, referred to earlier as *El norte*, produces particularly strong winds through two broad depressions in the mountainous backbone of the middle American mainland, the Isthmus of Tehuantepec and the Nicaraguan lowland. Across the Isthmus of Tehuantepec in southern Mexico northerly winter gales known as Tehuantepecers occur with greatest frequency and strength from November through February, although they may appear at any time from October through April. Augmented somewhat katabatically, they quite often bring clear, dry weather with little change in temperature, but they may be accompanied by stratus cloud and light to heavy rain. Winds from gale to hurricane force often reach far out to sea from the south Mexican coast. During the twelve-year interval 1924–35 such high winds were observed by ship masters on 258 days in addition to other days of high winds with lower velocities. From the Gulf of Tehuantepec to northern Costa Rica northeasterly winds of high velocity are known as Papagayos, from their notable frequency across the Gulf of Papagayo near the Pacific end of the Nicaraguan lowland. These winds are less violent, but they are potentially destructive in the coastal embayments such as the Gulf of Fonseca, the Gulf of Papagayo, and Nicoya. Like the Tehuantepecer, they may last for three or four days, but unlike the former, they almost always bring clear, fine weather.

Thunderstorms of the rainy season along the Pacific coast are often accompanied by gales from west and southwest. The sharp local squalls that may occur in connection with them are locally known as Chubascos,[7] or *temporales*, and occur most frequently in July and August.

[6] W. H. Portig, "Central American Rainfall," *Geographical Review*, **55**(1): 68–90, 1965.

[7] U.S. Naval Oceanographic Office, *Sailing Directions for the West Coasts of Mexico and Central America*, (H.O. 26), 1951, pp. 11–13.

Normal yearly rains supporting the variety of tropical climates in middle America vary widely, from the rainforest excesses of more than 235 inches in southeastern Nicaragua to less than 25 inches toward the poleward limits of scrub woodland near the Mexican coasts (Fig. 21.9). Over many of the narrower southeastern portions from Panama to Nicaragua and along the Caribbean side to southern British Honduras annual amounts of over 100 inches are common, but farther northwestward comparably wet areas are mainly limited to the highlands of eastern Guatemala, the middle slopes of Pacific Guatemala, and the Caribbean lowlands of southern Mexico facing the Gulf of Campeche.

A noteworthy feature of climatic distribution in Central America is the presence of relatively dry valleys surrounded by lush, forested, well-watered mountains. A broad, elevated savanna woodland about 175 miles long lies astride the interior border between Honduras and Nicaragua, and another begins near the Honduran border of Guatemala behind the Pacific coastal ranges and extends northwestward for several hundred miles toward central Mexico.

Numerous dry valleys of much smaller scale can be identified. They arise in part from the depletion of precipitable moisture on the heights around them, and in part from the diurnal accumulation of higher temperatures over the valley floor that give rise in turn to a buoyant, uplifting, dessicating effect upon the less vigorous transient disturbances. Tegucigalpa (el. 3303), Honduras, averaging 36.9 inches, and Guatemala City (el. 4927), averaging 49.3 inches, both of which are flanked by more humid forested mountain ranges, are examples. Another is Motozintla (el. 4772), which occupies a high, intermont valley in southern Chiapas and averages 9.2 inches of annual rain, whereas Aurora (el. 836), less than 20 miles southwestward, averages 174.5 inches, and Concepcion (el. 1443), 30 miles eastward, averages 136.6 inches.

The rainforest climate from Colombia to Nicaragua is represented by Cristobal at the Caribbean entrance to the Panama Canal. Cristobal (el. 36) lies in a belt of tropical rainforest edging the Caribbean coast from Colombia to northern Nicaragua (Fig. 21.10). Dominant winds throughout the year are

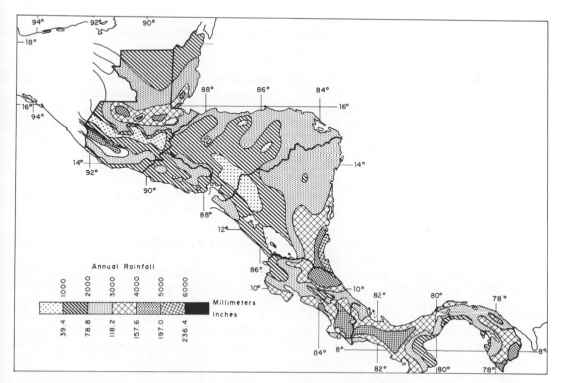

Figure 21.9.   Mean annual rainfall in Central America (inches). [After Portig]

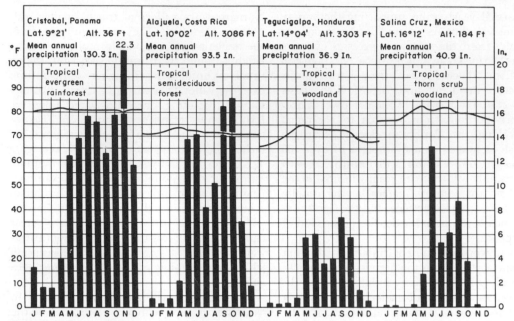

Figure 21.10. Temperature and precipitation regimes at stations in tropical evergreen rainforest, semideciduous forest, savanna woodland, and thorn scrub woodland in mainland Middle America.

northerly. Its normal temperatures range from 80° in November to 82° in April, and its mean annual rainfall is 130 inches. Eight months, from May through December, normally receive more than 10 inches of rain per month, and the first maximum is attained in July (15.5 inches), the second in November (22.5 inches). Rain falls in this period on from twenty-two to twenty-six days per month, mean cloud cover is between 70 and 80 per cent; and relative humidity averages between 82 and 86 per cent. An average of eight-seven thunderstorms occur from May through October, out of a total of ninety-nine for the year. The four dry months together, from January through April, average 10.3 inches, February and March each recording 1.5 inch, falling on twelve to fifteen days per month. Cloud cover decreases but remains high at between 50 and 60 per cent, and relative humidity averages 77 per cent.

Tropical evergreen rainforest extends westward from Panama into western Costa Rica where the low mountains, rising to more than 6000 feet in places, are heavily mantled with forest vegetation that thrives under normal rainfall exceeding 100 inches and adequately distributed through the year. As one continues northwestward into the Nicaraguan lowland,

however, a rapid change is observed as the heavier forest cover gives way to more open savanna and thorn scrub woodland. From near Lake Nicaragua northwestward along the Pacific coast in an almost continuous distribution, the drier savanna and scrub woodland reaches beyond the Tropic of Cancer in Mexico. Reaching inland for a variable distance of from 10 to 20 miles from the sea as far west as the Isthmus of Tehuantepec, the drier, more open woodlands spread farther inland beyond that point to 100 miles or more from the sea along the Pacific sierras of Mexico. Diminishing rainfall amounts concentrated in an increasingly shorter season and a lengthening of the dry season are chiefly responsible for these changes.

From Lake Nicaragua northwestward across El Salvador to southeastern Guatemala mean annual rainfall averages between 65 and 75 inches concentrated in a six-month rainy season, interrupted by a dry season of four to five months when monthly amounts average less than .5 inch. From southeastern Guatemala to southern Chiapas in Mexico is a narrow belt of much heavier rainfall where annual amounts exceed 100 inches and the dry period is only from three to four months in length. Here, semideciduous to selva vegetation is supported by the more abundant rain at elevations from 2500 to 4500 feet. From here to the Isthmus of Tehuantepec annual amounts diminish again to between 55 and 65 inches. From the low saddle of Tehuantepec westward some 300 miles to Acapulco amounts lessen still further to between 50 and 60 inches, occurring in a five-month wet season, and the dry period is five to six months long. Northwestward from Acapulco annual totals average between 35 and 40 inches, still falling in a five-month wet season, and the dry period is also five to six months in length, each month averaging less than .5 inch of normal rain. We may consider the examples of San Salvador, Salina Cruz, Acapulco, and Mazatlan (Table 21-4).

At San Salvador (el. 2238), about 20 miles inland, temperatures range from 72° in December and January, when cloud cover is 24 per cent, to 76° in May and June, when cloud cover is 70 to 75 per cent. Midafternoon relative humidities range from 68 per cent in February to 84 per cent in September, when cloud cover reaches a yearly maximum of 76 per cent. Mean yearly rainfall is 72.4 inches. The rainy season extends from May through October, during which 93 per cent of the normal yearly amount is received. A single peak of 13.8 inches is attained in June, when rain falls on twenty days. Rainfall tapers gradually to 10.2 inches in October, when it falls on sixteen days.

At Salina Cruz (el. 184) on the Gulf of Tehuantepec mean temperatures range from 76° in January, when cloud cover is 15 per cent, to 82° in July and August, when cloud cover is 62 to 64 per cent. Mean relative humidity reaches a minimum of 59 per cent in November and a maximum of 76 per cent in June. Mean annual rainfall is 38.8 inches, 93 per cent of which falls in a six-month interval from May through October. A single peak is reached in June, when 11.9 inches normally fall on eighteen days. The number of rain days in May and October is six. Six months record less than .5 inch per month.

At Acapulco (el. 10), about 300 miles west of Salina Cruz, mean temperatures range from 78° in January and February to 83° from May through August. Mean cloud cover is 20 per cent or less from January through April but ranges from 50 to 68 per cent from June through October. Mean relative humidity is high throughout the year, ranging from 75 per cent in May to 82 per cent in September.

Normal yearly rains total 59.1 inches, 94 per cent of which falls in a five-month period from June through October. June is the wettest month, averaging 16.9 inches that fall on fifteen days, and September is a secondary maximum, when 14.2 inches fall on eighteen days. A five-month dry season lasts from December through April.

At Mazatlan (el. 256), about 700 miles northwest of Acapulco at Lat. 23°11', mean monthly temperatures vary from 67° in January through March to 82° in August, a mean annual range of 15 degrees. Cloud cover is greater here than at Acapulco, averaging between 27 per cent in May to 60 per cent in August, clouds most of the year covering about one third of the sky. Fogs in the dry season are occasionally seen, a somewhat rare feature in a tropical coastal locality. Relative humidity is constantly high and varies from 75 per cent in November and December to 80 per cent in September. Mean annual rainfall is 33.5 inches, 90 per cent of which occurs in the five-month interval from June through October. Typical of the northwestern tropical area of Mexico, rainfall reaches a single peak at Mazatlan in September, when an average of 10.6 inches falls on fifteen days. For six months the mean amount is less than .5 inch per month. April and May are virtually without rain.

About 125 miles north of Mazatlan is the station of Culiacan (el. 174), about 35 miles inland at Lat. 24°28', where tropical thorn scrub woodland begins to give way northward to coastal desert. Mean monthly temperatures range from 67° in December and January to 84° in June and July, a slight increase in mean annual range over that at Mazatlan, and normal yearly rains total 23.8 inches. Eighty per cent of the year's rainfall occurs in a five-month interval from June through October; August is the peak month, averaging 6.7 inches. Six months record less than .5 inch of rain per month, and again April and May are practically without rain. At both Mazatlan and Culiacan winter storms occur regularly enough to produce about 2 inches of rain on the average in December, an unusually wet month in the early part of the dry season.

Let us focus our attention briefly on the wet belt in the Pacific ranges of Guatemala and southern Mexico. This is a narrow, irregular zone about 20 to 25 miles wide, stretching along the intermediate and upper slopes for about 250 miles westward from the border of El Salvador into southern Chiapas. The wet zone is mainly between the inner edge of the narrow coastal plain roughly around 800 feet and upper levels of the sierras around 5000 feet. The summary rainfall data for a number of stations will reveal the magnitude of mean rainfall here. Nearly all the stations lie about 25 to 35 miles inland at various altitudes ranging generally from 2000 to 3000 feet.

Cuilapa (el. 2985), about 30 miles from the Salvador border, averages 111.8 inches, most of which falls from May through October. The month of maximum rains is September, with 23.7 inches, a secondary maximum occurs in July (19 inches), and January, February, and March each average less than 0.5 inch.

San Andreas Osuna (el. 2690) averages 174.1 inches, chiefly falling from April through October, the peak month is September (31.4 inches), a secondary peak occurs in June (28 inches), and the driest months of January and February average 1.2 inch each.

Patzulin (el. 2952), about 40 miles from the Chiapas border, averages 184.3 inches, most of which falls from April through November, reaching a peak in September of 33.2 inches and a secondary peak of 27.9 inches in June. January and February each average less than 2 inches.

Other especially humid sites are reported from southwest Guatemala, and unofficial estimates of probable yearly totals rise to more than 250 inches. Among the wetter stations of record is Malacatan (el. 2099), less than 10 miles from Chiapas, which averages 191.5 inches. The main rainy season extends here from March (7.2 inches) through November (9.7 inches), and both June and September record about equal maxima, averaging around 29 inches. Both January and February record less than 2 inches.

Tapachula (el. 551), across the Mexican border at lower elevation, records 98 inches, and Aurora (el. 836), about 30 miles farther west and slightly higher, averages 174.5 inches. The annual regimes here are similar to those just described; although a longer dry season prevails at Aurora, with January, February, and March each averaging less than 2 inches.

The unusual height of the Pacific ranges in this section of middle America is perhaps the main reason for the heavy rainfall. Providing a partial shield against the dominant trades from north and east, the buffer sierras allow a deeper,

higher, and more forceful penetration of the almost daily sea breeze during the rainy season. Their crests, rising to well over 10,000 feet and frequently exceeding 13,000 feet, are loftier here than elsewhere along the Pacific shores. El Salvador receives the benefit of similar sea breezes, but her mountains are lower, between 7000 and 9000 feet, and less rain falls for want of sufficient mechanical uplift of the onshore flow from the sea. Farther west in Mexico the coastal sierras are lower as well.

San Salvador, although outside the really wet zone, reports a high percentage of thunderstorms, ninty-five on the average from April through October, suggesting the importance of the almost daily afternoon thunderstorm deluge that is a feature of the rainy season weather along the 250 mile humid zone. By comparison, Salina Cruz averages only thirty-five thunderstorms in the same period.

All in all, the Pacific side of the middle American mainland, except for the region described above, is not only substantially drier than the Caribbean side, but the dry season is much longer and more nearly rainless (Fig. 21.11).

On the Caribbean side mean annual rainfall totals are generally in excess of 100 inches from Costa Rica to the Gulf of Honduras. Here the

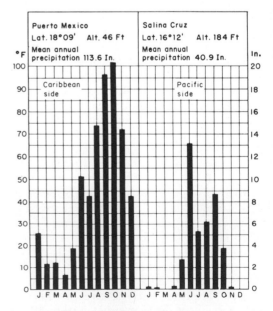

Figure 21.11. Rainfall regimes on opposite sides of the Isthmus of Tehuantepec, Mexico.

dry season lasts more than two months, and March is usually the driest month. At Bluefields, Nicaragua, and Puerto Barrios, Guatemala, the normal monthly amount in March is 3 inches. As a general rule, relatively dry weather gives way to the rainy season with a rapid increase in daily rainfall toward the end of May, and the wet period continues until January and the early part of February (Table 21-4). It appears likely that over half the annual rain falls as trade wind convective showers of high intensity, augmented in September and October by occasional heavy rains from well-developed tropical cyclones and storms of hurricane intensity, and in the cooler season by temporal disturbances yielding light, steady rain lasting sometimes for several days. With few exceptions, a double maximum is experienced. At Bluefields (el. 14), where the yearly normal is 164.7 inches, July is the month of maximum rain, averaging 24.2 inches. November the secondary maximum with 17.1 inches. At Puerto Barrios (el. 6), with an annual mean of 117.7 inches, July averages 18.7 inches, and October, the second peak month, 14.6 inches. Thunderstorms occur infrequently and are much more common in the mountainous interior.

Another excessively wet region is found along a 100-mile-wide band of marshy lowland about 200 miles long facing the Bay of Campeche in southern Mexico, where mean annual rainfall totals are also well above 100 inches. In the humid, forested regions here the rainy season normally extends from the latter part of May through January, and April is most commonly the driest month, sometimes March, although the difference between the two is negligible, and monthly values at this time usually remain above 1.5 inch. Again a rapid change within relatively short distances is seen from rainforest to semideciduous forest to savanna woodland, to thorn scrub woodland, both northeastward into Yucatan and northwestward along the Mexican coast. At Puerto Mexico mean annual rainfall is 113.6 inches; at Frontera, about 120 miles east, 51.6 inches; at Ciudad Carmen, 55 miles farther east, 66.3 inches; at Champoton, 95 miles northeastward, 47.2 inches; at Campeche, 40 miles north, 35 inches; at Merida, about 95 miles northeastward, 36 inches; and at Progreso, about 20 miles north on the coast, 18.6 inches. Annual rainfall

regimes are the same throughout, but monthly amounts become steadily lower from Puerto Mexico to Progreso. The peak month is usually October, and a secondary maximum occurs in June. At Puerto Mexico the amounts are 22 and 10.4 inches respectively, but at Progreso they are 2.7 and 2.9 inches.

Northwestward a similar transition appears, with Vera Cruz, some 135 miles northwest of Puerto Mexico, reporting an annual mean of 63.9 inches, Tampico, about 230 miles farther north, 49.3 inches, and Abasolo, about 130 miles northward, 26.5 inches. September is normally the peak rainfall month, Vera Cruz averaging 13.6 inches, Tampico 13.1 inches, and Abasolo 6.5 inches at this time. June is a secondary peak month, at Vera Cruz averaging 13.6 inches, at Tampico 7.9 inches, and at Abasolo 4.3 inches. Diminishing monthly amounts at all seasons of the year coupled with higher rainy season temperatures greatly lessen the effective moisture available for the support of plant life, and a gradual change from selva to scrub woodland is seen between Puerto Mexico and Abasolo. Mean monthly temperatures range between 71° in January and 81° in May at Puerto Mexico, between 70° in January and 81° from June through August at Vera Cruz, between 66° in January and 83° in July and August at Tampico, and between 65° in January and 86° in August (a range of 21 degrees) at Abasolo.

In many instances rainfall increases with elevation toward the interior. An example of this is seen between Frontera and Teapa, an inland station within 5 miles of low mountains rising more than a mile above the sea. Frontera (el. 6) averages 51.6 inches of annual rain, but Villahermosa (el. 33), about 45 miles southwestward, averages 74.9 inches, Macuspan (el. 197), about 55 miles south of Frontera, 113 inches, and Teapa (el. 262), 70 miles south-southwest of Frontera, 156 inches. Elsewhere amounts increase on the middle and upper slopes of coastal sierras as mean monthly temperatures become lower, inducing cloud forest climates within a short distance of the sea.

Northwestern South America

Turning once more to the tropical climates of South America, let us look briefly at the Pacific reaches of Colombia and Ecuador. Largely under the year-round influence of the equatorial trough, the dominant weather features uniformly high temperatures, high atmospheric humidity, variable winds and calms, and, as far south as northern Ecuador, copious rains. Moisture-laden winds are chiefly off the adjacent sea and thus form an isolated area of equatorial westerlies, blowing predominantly from northwest in northern sections and from southwest over coastal Ecuador.

Along the 50- to 75-mile-wide band of Colombia's Pacific coastal lowlands occur the heaviest rains in all of tropical America. Normal yearly distribution is uniform. Records are too short to be conclusive, but the values reported are nonetheless impressive. Quibdo (el. 141) in the upper Atrato valley about 40 miles from the Pacific has recorded a seven-year average of 289.1 inches, and Buenaventura, Colombia's chief Pacific port, about 90 miles southwest of Andagoya, is said to receive between 300 and 350 inches of rainfall annually.[8] Mean temperatures at Buenaventura remain between 81° and 83°, and relative humidity is around 89 per cent throughout the year. Rain occurs nearly every day, usually in late afternoon or at night, reaching a maximum in October and November when thunderstorms are frequent. At Andagoya rain falls on from twenty-five to twenty-seven days per month for most of the year, dropping to twenty-one days in February and twenty-three days in March. The lowest monthly amount is 19.5 inches in both March and December, the maximum 26.1 inches in April. At Quibdo the minimum monthly amount is 17.9 inches in April, the maximum 35 inches in January.

This unusually wet zone is part of an extensive belt of heavy rains that spans a distance of more than 800 miles from Panama and the Gulf of Uraba southward to the Andean foothills east of the Gulf of Guayaquil. Eastward it gives way to the highly complex climatic pattern along the deep valleys and high cordilleras of Andean Colombia and Ecuador, northward it merges with the complexities of middle American climatic distribution, southward it changes rapidly toward the coastal deserts of Peru.

The tropical evergreen rainforest of these continuously hot, humid lowlands in northwestern South America extend southward in a virtually unbroken distribution to about 150 miles north of the Gulf of Guayaquil between the Andean piedmont and the Pacific. From here southward it is gradually replaced by a narrow, interior belt of semideciduous forest scarcely 50 miles wide that eventually yields to drier, more open savanna woodland in the interior of northern Peru. From north to south temperatures remain high, although within slightly lower limits, but a change is seen from the uniform distribution of yearly rain in Colombia to a more seasonal regime in Ecuador (Table 21-5). Records are not long enough to be decisive, but the climatic change is unmistakably apparent.

This entire region is essentially under the dominance of equatorial trough weather throughout the year. Frequent, heavy showers, occurring largely during the later afternoon and early evening and arising from thermal convective processes, provide the bulk of the year's rain. In the northernmost section of Colombia's Pacific region light to moderate winds are chiefly from a northerly quarter over the year, but farther south, southwest and west winds predominate. Occasional gales occur in the north from December through February, but southward they are practically unknown. Instead, a high percentage of calms and light, variable winds alternate with the prevailing southwesterlies that here are a recurring extension of the southeast trades in the eastern Pacific. From April through November southwest winds set in and increase in steadiness, ushering in the period of drier weather. The dry season increases in length to eight months or more toward the Peruvian border. The climatic change from north to south is indicated by the lessening of the interval when most of the year's rains are recorded (Fig. 18.11).

San Lorenzo (el. 20), within about 10 miles of the sea and the Colombian border, averages 111.7 inches of annual rain, 75 per cent of which falls in a seven-month period from January through July. June is the wettest month with 15.1 inch, and November is the least rainy month, with a 4.1 inch mean. Santo Domingo de los Colorados (el. 1640), about 100 miles south and some 65 miles inland, and toward the southern limit of rainforest, averages 133.2 inches, 75 per cent of which occurs in a five-month interval from January through May. March is the wettest month (25 inches) and

[8] U.S. Naval Oceanographic Office, *Sailing Directions, South America*, Part 3 (H.O. 25), 1960, p. 103.

TABLE 21-5

Rainfall Data at Stations in Northwestern South America

(In.)

Station	Lat.	El. in Ft	Length of Record	Jan.	Feb.	Mar.	Apr.	May	Jun.	Jul.	Aug.	Sep.	Oct.	Nov.	Dec.	Year
Andagoya, Colombia	5°06'N.	197	7	21.0	22.5	21.3	20.9	23.6	24.7	22.6	23.7	21.5	22.6	19.5	20.7	264.3
Quibdo, Colombia	5°41'N.	141	7	35.0	19.9	19.4	17.9	21.1	26.6	28.7	26.6	26.2	20.3	26.3	21.0	289.1
San Lorenzo, Ecuador	1°16'N.	20	7	9.7	12.7	9.5	14.2	13.3	15.1	11.8	5.0	4.8	6.5	4.1	5.7	111.7
Santo Domingo de Los																
Colorados, Ecuador	0°15'S.	1640	8	20.4	20.9	25.0	21.1	13.1	7.0	6.0	1.2	5.5	3.9	3.1	6.1	133.2
Babahoyo, Ecuador	1°48'S.	20	20	15.2	19.7	16.1	12.1	3.9	0.7	0.6	0.0	0.1	0.4	0.1	2.8	71.7
Machala, Ecuador	3°16'S.	20	8	3.6	4.0	5.8	2.3	1.8	0.4	0.4	0.4	0.3	0.5	0.2	0.3	20.1
Portovelo, Ecuador	3°43'S.	3280	16	11.5	13.7	13.5	8.9	4.4	0.7	0.1	0.3	0.6	1.1	1.2	5.5	61.2
Esmeraldas, Ecuador	0°59'N.	20	11	4.7	7.5	3.1	4.7	2.6	2.3	2.1	0.8	1.1	0.5	0.5	1.7	31.5
Portoviejo, Ecuador	1°04'S.	148	13	3.9	7.5	6.0	3.4	1.3	0.6	0.6	0.1	0.2	0.1	0.4	0.9	24.9
Ancon, Ecuador	2°20'S.	20	22	1.6	3.3	3.2	1.1	0.1	0.1	0.1	0.1	0.1	0.1	0.0	0.3	10.6

Source: F. L. Wernstedt, *World Climatic Data, Latin America and the Caribbean*, Pennsylvania State University, 1959.

August the driest (1.2 inch). Babahoyo (el. 20), about 110 miles south and about 85 miles from the sea, and well within the semideciduous region, averages 71.7 inches, 88 per cent of which occurs in a four-month period from January through April. February is again the wettest month (17 inches), and August also the driest month, with no rain at all. Machala (el. 20), about 80 miles south of Milagro on the coast of the Gulf of Guayaquil in a stretch of scrub woodland, averages 20.1 inches, 78 per cent of which falls from January through April. March here is the wettest month (5.8 inches), and November the driest month, averaging 0.2 inch. Less than 40 miles southeast of Machala near the southern limit of semideciduous forest is Portovelo (el. 3280), where mean annual rainfall is 61.2 inches, 77 per cent of which falls from January through April. From December through May, however, every month receives at least 4.4 inches, and October and December each record at least 1.1 inch.

Savanna woodland occupies extensive tracts between the interior semideciduous belt and the sea, becoming dominant about 150 miles north of the Gulf of Guayaquil and reaching southward to Peru. Drier thorn scrub woodland appears at intervals with increasing proportions nearer Peru, and yields to arid desert beginning around Punta Santa Elena. Diminishing rainfall and a lengthening dry season are chiefly responsible for the transition. Esmeraldas (el. 20), about 60 miles southwest of San Lorenzo in a relatively dry enclave of the wetter forest, averages only 31.5 inches of annual rain, 86 per cent of which is distributed over a seven-month interval from January through July. Portoviejo (el. 146), about 150 miles south of Esmeraldas, lies in a transition zone between savanna and thorn scrub woodland and averages 24.9 inches of yearly rain, 83 per cent of which falls during the four-month period from January through April. Ancon (el. 20), about 95 miles south of Portoviejo on the south side of Punta Santa Elena, normally receives only 10.1 inches of rain, 80 per cent of which falls in the three-month period from January through March.

Tropical South America South of the Equator

It remains for us to consider the climates south of the great selva forests in the Amazon basin. The largest of these, stretching away to southward and eastward, is one we have loosely described as savanna woodland. The term is only useful in a very general sense, for actually the region is a vast mixture of luxuriant semideciduous forest, dense, shrubby thickets, open woodland, and extensive, grass-covered plateaus, all dynamically competing for space according to selected advantages of elevation, slope, exposure, water table depth, soil porosity, and chemistry of the parent material. A vegetation type unique in the savanna woodlands of Brazil and widespread within the region is the *campo cerrado*, a mixture of tall grasses and low, twisted trees 12 to 24 feet high.[9] This is close, dense, yet open country in which the trees are closely spaced with tangled growth, but the crowns do not mingle, and the canopy is thus open, allowing sunlight to reach the ground where tall clumps of rank grass are able to thrive. Although losing their leaves for a short period, sometimes only for a few days, the foliage is substantially evergreen and consists of large leaves, sometimes hard and leathery, sometimes rough or hairy.

Semideciduous forest occupies moist lowlands and also elevated depressions where the water table is high, and appears in special prominence in the form of long, sinuous galleries along the winding stream courses among the dissected plateaus. Within the broad range of vegetation types from dense forest to unmixed grassland, soil porosity is a major influence determining the details of distribution. The kaleidoscopic variety of plant associations reflects in detail the underlying conditions of soil and water and the broader contrasts in elevation and relief. The broad, inclusive designation *savanna woodland* applies to a region possessing certain general climatic features of uniformity that give way to drier scrub woodland in northwestern Argentine and northeastern Brazil and to wetter regions of predominantly semideciduous forest in the southeastern highlands of Brazil.

Over most of the elevated Brazilian interior a distinct dry period during the winter months, usually from May through August when the sun is far to the north, is a regular occurrence. The southeast trades at this time of year sweep over the eastern highlands, recurving southward, to blow at times with considerable force.

[9] Monica M. Cole, "Cerrado, Caatinga and Pantanal: The Distribution and Origin of the Savanna Vegetation of Brazil," *Geographical Journal*, **126**(2), 1960.

Stratocumulus clouds commonly form, sometimes entirely masking the sky for several successive days but rarely producing rain. Although rain is negligible and uncertain in the dry season, the air is humid, especially at night, and frequently forms dew. Frosts are practically unknown, but temperatures may drop into the low 40s or upper 30s, and the combination of low temperatures, drought, and high winds is inimical to the successful growth of tall trees on the exposed plateaus. The rainy season tends to set in during September when heavy thunderstorms occur, intensifying to peak monthly precipitation in December or January, and diminishing toward the end of March. From April onward rainfall lessens rapidly, and dry weather returns in May.

The comparative uniformity of this climatic region over its entire extent is indicated by an examination of representative data from the small number of stations providing suitable records. In these the influence of altitude, it will be seen, is a much more significant factor than the wide range of latitudes.

Conceicao do Araguaia (el. 53), nearly 500 miles south of Belem at Lat. 8°15', records a mean annual temperature range of 3 degrees from 77° in December through March to 80° in September at the end of the dry season. The absolute maximum has been 102° in August, September, and October, the absolute minimum 55° in July and August. The mean daily range varies from 18 degrees in January and February during the wet season to 34 degrees in August. At Goias (el. 1705), about 550 miles south at Lat. 15°58', the mean annual range is 7 degrees from 70° in July to 77° in September and October. The highest recorded temperature has been 104° in those two months, and the lowest has been 41° in July. Here the mean daily range is least in January at 23 degrees, and greatest in August at 34 degrees. At Catalao (el. 2723), about 200 miles southeast of Goias in Lat. 18°10', the higher elevation lowers the limits of normal temperature experience, and here the mean annual range is 8 degrees from 65° in July to 73° in October. The absolute maximum is only 95°, attained in September, and the lowest minimum of record is 35° in June. The mean daily range is least in December at 15 degrees and increases to 24 degrees in August. At Caceres (el. 387), within the upper drainage of the Paraguay River in the Mato

Grosso about 500 miles west of Goias, where drier palm savanna occupies much of the marshy lowland, the mean annual range is 10 degrees, from 68° in July to 78° in October through December. Here the thermometer has risen to 105° in September and October and has lowered to 35° in June. The mean daily temperature range is 17 degrees in February and 31 degrees in July and August. From the above it will be observed that a slight increase in mean and extreme annual ranges of temperature occurs from north to south, especially toward the southwest and the drier scrub woodlands.

Complete data on mean cloudiness are lacking for most of the region. At Imperatriz, about 225 miles northeast of Conceicao do Araguaia, mean diurnal cloud cover increases from 40 per cent in September to 60 per cent in December and reaches a maximum of 69 per cent in February, after which it diminishes to 57 per cent in April and from May through September remains below 40 per cent, attaining a minimum of 20 per cent in August. At Cuiaba, more than 200 miles northeast of Caceres, values are 60 per cent in December, 76 per cent in December, the maximum for the year, remaining above 70 per cent until March but dropping steadily to 35 per cent in August, the least cloudy month.

Midafternoon relative humidities are high during the rainy season, ranging between 72 and 79 per cent from January through April at Conceicao do Araguaia, from 67 to 70 per cent from November through March at Caceres, from 61 to 67 per cent from November through March at Catalao, and from 65 to 73 per cent from November through March at Goias. In the dry season values are naturally much lower, dropping to 42 per cent in August at Conceicao do Araguaia, to 45 per cent in September at Caceres, to 44 per cent in August and September at Catalao, and to 40 per cent in August at Goias.

Mean annual precipitation is generally between 55 and 70 inches within the region, 90 per cent or more of which normally falls in the seven-month rainy season from October through April. At Conceicao do Araguaia the normal yearly amount is 53 inches, and the wettest month is March, averaging 10.4 inches falling on eighteen days. The driest months are June and July (0.3 inch each), when rain may occur on one or two days per month. At Goias the mean annual amount is 70.3 inches, and the wettest month is January with 13.1 inches, when rain falls on sixteen days. June and July average 0.2 and 0.1 inch respectively, falling on a single day during each month. Caceres averages 53 inches. The wettest month is January with 9 inches; when rain falls on seventeen days, and both July and August average only 0.4 inch, with rain expected on two or three days each month. At Catalao the normal yearly total is 69.6 inches, and here the wettest month is December with 14.5 inches, rain falling on twenty-one days. August is the driest month, when 0.2 inch may fall on one or two days.

As one approaches the southwestern borders of interior Brazil and advances into eastern Bolivia and western Paraguay, annual rainfall amounts diminish to between 45 and 55 inches. Where winter rains are sufficiently large, usually of frontal origin when cold air from southward advances toward the equator, even these lower annual totals support a moderately luxurious semideciduous forest in eastern Bolivia and eastern Paraguay. But passing between these two more favored forest regions, one enters an extensive region of dry thorn scrub woodland that occupies the broad, level plains east of the Andes. From southern Bolivia

southward over western Paraguay and northwestern Argentina it extends for some 600 miles, at altitudes from 500 to 1000 feet, between the Andes and the Paraguay River.

As in the savanna woodland toward the northeast, 90 per cent or more of the year's precipitation is concentrated in a seven-month period from October through April. But annual amounts are normally much smaller, and the dry winter is more nearly rainless (Fig. 21.12). Furthermore, the amounts of rain received from year to year vary more widely. San Jose, Bolivia (el. 981), scarcely 250 miles southwest of Caceres, Brazil, and less than 200 miles east of the Andes, reports a mean annual rainfall of 36.6 inches, 90 per cent of which falls in the seven-month period from October through April. December is the peak month (6.4 inches), but from July to September little if any rain occurs. Occasional cold front rains occur in early winter, resulting in a mean amount of 2.2 inches for June. Villa Montes (el. 1319), about 325 miles southwest at the foot of front ranges exceeding a mile in altitude, averages 30.6 inches, 92 per cent of which falls from October through April. January and March are almost equal, averaging 6.1 and 6.6 inches respectively. From June through September the total normal four-month amount is less than 1 inch.

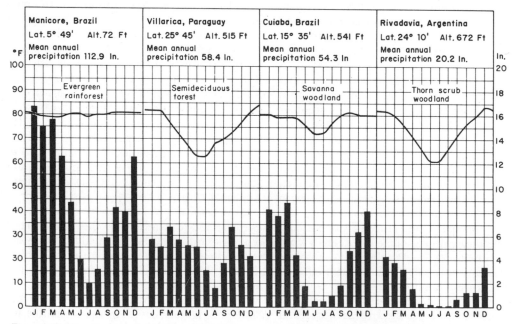

Figure 21.12.   Temperature and precipitation at tropical forest and woodland stations in South America south of the equator.

In Paraguay, Fort Mariscal Estiggaribia (el. 590), less than 200 miles southeast of Villa Montes, averages 28.4 inches yearly, 86 per cent of which falls in the seventh-month interval from October through April. January is the peak month (4.5 inches), and August the minimum (0.2 inch). About 200 miles south of Villa Montes in northwestern Argentine the mean yearly rainfall at Rivadavia (el. 672) is 20.2 inches, 93 per cent occurring from October through April. January is again the peak month (4.2 inches), and the total normally received in the four months from May through August is only 0.8 inch. About 160 miles farther south at Campo Gallo (el. 623) the normal annual amount is 22.8 inches, 90 per cent of which falls from October through April. January averages 4.4 inches, and the total from May through August is 1.6 inch.

Another major change observed as one proceeds southward across the scrub woodland toward the deserts of northwest Argentina is an increase in the mean annual range of temperature (Table 21-1). Summer temperatures are within the low 80s throughout the region, but winter values become lower, a consequence of the increased frequency of cold air invasions from the south at increasingly higher latitudes. The change is reflected in the mean annual ranges between San Jose and Campo Gallo. At San Jose, Lat. 17°51', the mean annual range is 11 degrees between 75° in August and 86° in October; at Villa Montes, Lat. 21°16', it is 21 degrees between 63° in July and 84° in December and January; at Rivadavia, Lat. 24°10', it is 22 degrees between 61° in June and July and 83° in December; at Camp Gallo, Lat. 26°35', it is 23 degrees between 60° in June and July and 83° in December and January.

Here in the dry Chaco even the rainy season receives a good share of bright, clear, sunny days. This being the period of high sun, fair weather often sees the thermometer soar into the upper 90s, and from time to time rise to more than 110°. It is in this interior, semi-arid tropical region that the highest temperatures in all of South America have been recorded. The dry winter season, on the other hand, is known for its intervals of sharp, clear, cold weather during which the thermometer may dip into the 30s, although frost is rarely observed.

Where savanna woodland reaches northeastward to the Atlantic, it stands as a transition zone of moderate, reasonably reliable rainfall between the abundantly wet selva west of it and the drier scrub woodland toward the east. Thorn scrub woodland, known as caatinga, extends in a broad belt for more than 800 miles southward from the north coast, reaching inland from the narrow, forested coastal plain south of Cabo Sao Roque for almost 500 miles. Because the region lies within the northern part of the Brazilian highlands, much of the interior ranges in altitude from 1000 to 3000 feet, interrupted by the broad valley of the lower Rio Sao Francisco. A number of ridges rise to more than 3500 feet. Temperatures everywhere are high the year round, ranging between the high 70s and the low 80s at points up to about 1500 feet. But stations at higher elevations gain the advantage of more moderate temperatures, those at 2000 feet or more averaging some 10 degrees lower. Guaramiranga (el. 2775), about 40 miles southwest of Mondubim (el. 105) near the north coast, records a normal annual temperature range of 3 degrees from 67° in July to 70° from November through February, whereas Mondubim reports a range of 4 degrees from 76° in July to 80° in December. Bahia (el. 154) on the east coast reports a range of 5 degrees from 74° in July to 79° January through March, whereas Caetite (el. 2953), about 280 miles west-southwest of it, has a normal range of 8 degrees from 66° in July to 74° from January through March.

A high percentage of sunny weather, even during the rainy season, allows temperatures at many inland stations to rise well into the 90s on many days of every month of the year. Extremely high temperatures are also common in the interior. At Ibipetuba (el. 1430), about 430 miles west-northwest of Bahia near the western borders of scrub woodland, the thermometer has climbed to more than 100° every month of the year and has reached 107° in September, October, and December. Iguatu (el. 685), nearly 200 miles south of Fortaleza on the north coast, has exceeded 95° every month of the year. Near the sea extreme values are lower; at Natal, for example, 91° is the extreme maximum, and at Recife, 94°.

Normal yearly rainfall, except along the coast and at particularly well-exposed points at higher elevation, averages generally between 20 and 35 inches. Caetite's mean, for example, is 29.6 inches, Remanso (el. 1384), about 400 miles up the Sao Francisco, averages 19.9 inches, and Quixada (el. 630), about 85 miles south of Mondubim, averages 31.5 inches. But yearly normals differ quite widely from place to place, a strong characteristic of the region, and we note that Guaramiranga, about 50 miles north of Quixada, averages 67.4 inches. In several places the statistical average over a number of decades is said to be less than 10 inches. A definite dry season of three to five months is the general rule, when less than 0.5 inch of rain per month is normally anticipated. Thus, low annual amounts and a prolonged drought coupled with persistently high temperatures and abundant sunshine are typical in this large region of thorn scrub woodland. Vegetation consists chiefly of low, twisted, thorny deciduous trees and shrubs, spiny cacti, and low-growing herbaceous plants that come up quickly after the first rain fall. Soils are thin and stony, and in many places hard bedrock appears at the surface. Saline accumulations often render the rain that falls unfit for human consumption and deter the development of plant life. The shallow, hard-packed soils permit the rapid run-off of rain when it falls at the end of dry weather, and only a small portion of the rain reaching the earth can be retained.

But the most significant climatic feature in northeastern Brazil is the great uncertainty of annual rainfall. In good years about 90 per cent occurs from December through April or early May. According to Freise,[10] who made a detailed study of this part of the country, most of the rain falls in a random geographical distribution in the form of brief, heavy showers that drench relatively small areas and occur on the average of four or five times per month. They normally last from fifteen minutes to three quarters of an hour; more prolonged precipitation is extremely rare. Mean variability for the region as a whole is over 30 per cent. At Fortaleza annual rainfall in a sixty-six-year period has varied from 96 per cent above to 66 per cent below the mean. In the century

from 1835 to 1935 either flood or drought occurred fifty times.

The reasons for the unusual variability of yearly rains are not at present understood. However, the region lies between the savanna region of warm season rains toward the west and the coastal region of cool season rains southeastward. The annual southward displacement of the equatorial trough between September and March is the main atmospheric change that accounts for the reasonably reliable rains to westward. During years of close to normal rainfall in the drier caatinga the equatorial trough apparently exerts its influence as far east as Cabo Sao Roque. It is the failure of the trough to make its seasonal shift far enough eastward that leads to a rainfall deficit. When this happens, it seems likely that the trade wind inversion becomes unusually persistent, and dry weather results.

Precipitation along the coast is much more plentiful and occurs with considerably more certainty, especially south of Cabo Sao Roque. Yearly totals vary appreciably from place to place, but on the whole range from 60 to 80 inches. A narrow coastal belt seldom more than 50 miles wide that reaches some 600 miles south of Natal receives most of its annual precipitation in the cool season. Natal receives 75 per cent and Joao Pessoa, about 75 miles south of Natal, 87 per cent of their yearly totals from February through August. Recife receives 92 per cent in the same period, and Bahia, 73 per cent. A drier period of three to four months in the latter part of the year, when monthly amounts average between 1 and 2 inches, interrupts the rainy season. This stretch of the northeast coast is occupied by a dominantly semideciduous forest, although the variety of vegetation and climatic types ranges from thorn scrub woodland to selva in scattered patches.

From Bahia southward beyond Santos yearly rains are more uniformly distributed and very widely in normal amounts. The coastland is constantly humid, and rainforest prevails below the sharp rise of the Brazilian escarpment. With increasing distance southward, frontal rains of the cooler season contribute an increasing share of the yearly increments.

[10] F. W. Freise, "The Drought Region of Northeastern Brazil," *Geographical Review*, **28**: 363–78, 1938.

References

COLE, M. M.: "Cerrado, Caatinga and Pantanal: The Distribution and Origin of the Savanna Vegetation of Brazil," *Geographical Journal*, **126**(2): 168–79, 1960.

CRIST, R. E.: "Along the Llanos-Andes Border in Zamora, Venezuela," *Geographical Review*, **22**(3): 411–14, 1932.

DREWES, W. U., and DREWES, A. T.: *Climate and Related Phenomena of the Eastern Andean Slopes of Central Peru*, Syracuse University Research Institute, Syracuse, N.Y., 1957.

FERDON, E. N.: "Studies in Ecuadorian Geography," *Monographs of the School of American Research*, Santa Fe, N.M., 1950.

JOHANNESSEN, C. L.: *Savannas of Interior Honduras*, University of California Press, Berkeley, 1963.

LOPEZ, M. E., and HOWELL, W. E.: "The Campaign Against Windstorms in the Banana Plantations Near Santa Marta, Colombia 1956–57," *Bulletin of the American Meteorological Society*, **42**(4): 265–76, 1961.

McBRYDE, F. W.: "Studies in Guatemalan Meteorology (1) The Climates of Southwestern Guatemala," *Bulletin of the American Meteorological Society*, **23**(6): pp. 254–63, 1942.

————: "Studies in Guatemalan Meteorology (2) Weather Types in Southwest Guatemala," *Bulletin of the American Meteorological Society*, **23**(12): 400–406, 1942.

PORTIG, W. H.: "Central American Rainfall," *Geographical Review*, **55**(1): 68–90, 1965.

RAWITSCHER, F.: "Brazilian Campo Cerrado: Fire Climax or Edaphic Climax," *Journal of Ecology*, **36**: 237–68, 1948.

RIEHL, H., and HIGGS, R.: "Unrest in the Upper Stratosphere Over the Caribbean Sea During January 1960," *Journal of Meteorology*, **17**(5): 555–61, 1960.

U.S. ARMY, QUARTERMASTER RESEARCH AND ENGINEERING COMMAND: *Analogs of Canal Zone Climate in South America*, Natick, Mass., 1958.

chapter 22

TROPICAL FORESTS AND
WOODLANDS IN AFRICA

The distribution of Africa's tropical climates and their relation to the general circulation are closely tied to a few salient features of the continent's physical geography, discussed in earlier chapters. To begin with are its large size, its relatively compact design, and its position astride the equator. Its north coasts reach to about 2600 miles from the equator, its south coasts about 2500 miles. But nearly two thirds of the continent lie north of the equator, where it attains an east-west span of about 4000 miles, whereas south of the line it is only half as broad, roughly 2000 miles. Altitudes over most of the Sahara are between 1000 and 3000 feet, and the Congo basin is substantially within these limits also. South of the Congo basin, however, elevations increase to between 3000 and 5000 feet, cresting in the Drakensberg of the southeastern rim at more than 10,000 feet. The Ethiopian highlands and the highlands of East Africa are also well above 3000 feet and rise at many points to heights in excess of 10,000 feet. Thus, as we have observed many times before, altitude strongly modifies the primary influence of latitude, with which it combines here, along with distance from the sea, to determine the approximate limits of specific climates.

The interplay of air masses from three principal source regions largely controls the mean weather sequences over tropical Africa. The southwestward movement of warm, dry air off the Sahara, the return flow of the North Atlantic anticyclonic circulation, is a year-round feature. Sometimes called dry northeast trades, it is commonly spoken of in west Africa as the harmattan. The northwestward flow of the southeast trades from the South Atlantic semipermanent high recurves northeastward over the Gulf of Guinea to form a strong, steady, reliable onshore movement of warm, moisture-laden air from the sea (Figs. 4.2 and 4.3). This may be regarded as a major component of the equatorial westerlies referred to earlier. It is the principal source of precipitable moisture from the Atlantic to Ethiopia, the lower and middle Congo basin, and most of Angola. The east African highlands and upper Congo basin are mainly subjected to influxes of warm, moist air from the Indian Ocean that alternate in direction from northeast to southeast during the year.

It is useful in tropical Africa, unlike tropical America, to place emphasis on the position, height, and varying intensity of the equatorial trough, here most often referred to as the intertropical convergence or intertropical front, in the analysis of both seasonal and day-to-day atmospheric changes. During the summer season of the northern hemisphere the semipermanent oceanic highs over both the North and South Atlantic, and also the southern Indian Ocean, expand, intensify, and shift northward. At this season the equatorial trough also shifts northward, and the typically disturbed weather of this convergence extends in a band about 1000 miles wide poleward from the equator from the west coast to the Ethiopian highlands (Fig. 20.1). Meanwhile, interior southern Africa is dry, although winter rains regularly come to the mediterranean southwest coast (Fig. 22.1).

Beginning in September, the equatorial trough is displaced slowly southward, and the belt of rain withdraws to a position mainly south of the equator from December through March. The mean position of the trough at this time of year extends along the Guinea coast, slightly inland, and bends sharply southward across the lower Congo valley to form a narrow loop over the interior near the Tropic of Capricorn, curving abruptly northeastward toward the northern end of Malagasy. This unusually far-poleward extension of the intertropical convergence is chiefly caused by frequent southward penetration of warm, dry air from north Africa, at times merging with, and indistinguishable from, shallow, weakly developed resident anticyclones of the southern interior plateaus. Interior dry air thus commonly maintains a position between the onshore flux of oceanic air from the South Atlantic and the south Indian Ocean at this time of year. By January the wet season tends to spread over

most of southern Africa, from between 5 and 10 degrees north of the equator to the southeast coast. The southwest coast at this time, as we have noted in a previous chapter, is dry. The arid region of Somaliland remains outside the mainstreams of precipitating disturbances throughout the year.

The onshore movement of oceanic air streams tends to take the shape of a very shallow wedge of warm, humid air that varies in depth from between 3000 and 4000 to between 6000 and 8000 feet. It fluctuates from day to day and also at times from hour to hour. Above it, to heights of 30,000 feet or more, are the equatorial easterlies, that is, winds predominantly from east or northeast, and these are relatively dry, normally moving at from 10 to 15 miles per hour, although sometimes much faster. They are deepest over the trough, becoming shallower in both poleward directions, and despite their relative dryness are believed by some to be a significant source of moisture in central Africa. In this they are presumed to derive their moisture content from their passage over the Indian Ocean. Their mean position shifts meridionally from season to season. It is plain, therefore, that much of the higher land surfaces often remain beyond the immediate influence of airflow from the sea.

It is important to recognize that the continent of Africa provides the largest continuous

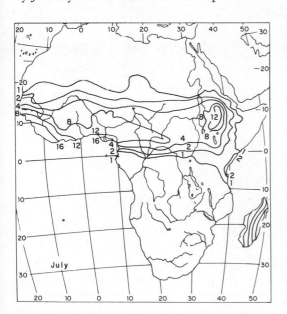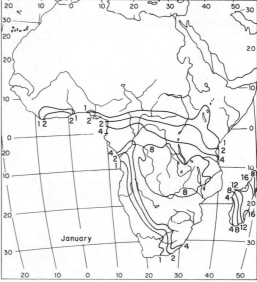

Figure 22.1.   Rainfall distribution in central Africa in July and January (inches).

expanse of land within the tropics. Because the land mass essentially straddles the equator, the periodic swing of the sun's relative position causes a seasonal rhythm of rainfall increase and decrease that sets the primary character of all of tropical Africa's climates. In Africa are seen the world's largest expanses of savanna and thorn scrub woodland. The seasonally dry tropical regions are the most widespread kind in Africa. Selva is much less widely distributed, and semideciduous forest occurs in only negligible proportions. Its position astride the equator induces on the continent a certain degree of symmetry in the geographical arrangement of climates, in which tropical forest or woodland reaches to about 15°N. Lat.

and to about 25°S. Lat. in the interior, but to nearly 30°S. Lat. along the southeast coast (Fig. 22.2).

Tropical rainforest forms a narrow, interrupted belt within less than 10 degrees on either side of the equator, from Guinea to the highlands along the West Rift valley in eastern Congo, spanning a total distance of over 3000 miles. This is the main selva region of Africa and actually consists of three major segments, one extending for about 800 miles in a band about 200–250 miles inland from the coast between the south coast of Guinea and the lower Volta valley in eastern Ghana, where savanna woodland interrupts the continuity of forest. A second, about the same breadth, reaches for

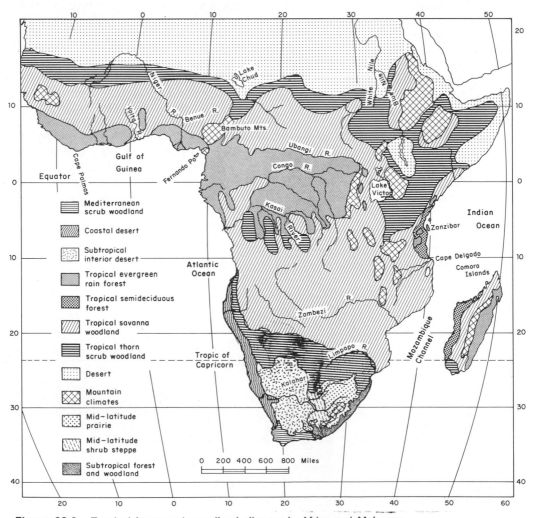

Figure 22.2. Tropical forest and woodland climates in Africa and Malagasy.

about 500 miles from the eastern borders of Dahomey to southeastern Nigeria, where the Bambuto and Cameroon mountains interrupt the distribution. The third and largest, a great equatorial evergreen rainforest, reaches from the Atlantic eastward for an extreme distance of about 1500 miles to the high mountains of eastern Congo. From the Bambuto Mountains southward, selva extends along the coast for some 800 miles to the mouth of the Congo River, advancing about 300 miles farther south in separated tracts and projected ribbons of galeria into the interior of northern Angola. Its mean breadth from the Atlantic eastward is approximately 600 miles, mainly within about 5 degrees on either side of the equator. But its poleward margins are very irregular, and savanna woodland penetrates deeply northward across the lower Congo east of Gabon, where its breadth is reduced to about 300 miles. In the eastern highlands and in the valleys of east Africa facing the Indian Ocean rainforest appears only in very small, but numerous pockets. Along the east coast of Malagasy a large, 100-mile-wide band spreads for some 800 miles, nearly the entire length of the island.

Tropical rainforest in Africa offers a richly varied vegetation composed of an uncounted number of ligneous species, possibly more than three thousand. The vegetation closely resembles selva in other parts of the world but includes a great many unique, indigenous species. Among the widely distributed species are iroko or African teak (*Chlorophora excelsa*), a very large tree about 5 feet in diameter and 180 feet or more in height, azobé or red oak (*Lophira procera*), a 90 foot tree from 4 to 6 feet in diameter, niangon (*Tarrietia utilis*), avodiré (*Turraeanthus africana*), and makoré (*Minusops heckelii*), a magnificent tree of the Guinea forest attaining a height of 150 feet. The mahoganies (*Khaya spp.*) are widely represented. A strikingly colorful species is the African tulip or flame tree (*Spathodea campanulata*), rising to 100 feet or more, and at the time of flowering displaying many large, brilliant red blossoms, unlike the small, white-yellow or greenish-white blooms of most rainforest species. Some very tall specimens like the djave nut (*Mimusops djave*) tower above the main forest canopy, reaching heights of 200 feet or more.

Tropical evergreen rainforest in Africa tends to thrive where temperatures and atmospheric humidity are constantly high and where mean annual rainfall is 60 to 250 inches or more (Fig. 6.10). Toward its margins, where the dry season becomes longer and more definite, a very gradual change takes place from a dominantly evergreen to a more deciduous vegetation. The upper crown canopy becomes dominated by species (accounting for about 75 per cent) that lose their leaves entirely for a period, although the undergrowth remains evergreen. This forest develops where annual rainfall is between 50 and 70 inches, with a three- to four-month dry season, forming what has been called a gradation from wet to dry evergreen forest. We may think of it as a semideciduous forest, although it is not conspicuously developed anywhere in Africa and usually is part of a patchy, narrow transition belt along the drier limits of rainforest, where it may give way abruptly to more open savanna woodland.

The poleward limits of continuous forest are often very sharply defined, a sudden change taking place from close-crowned forest to open savanna woodland within a few hundred yards. The limits are set to a large degree by the annual firing of the grasslands to improve the natural pasturage. During the dry season all Africa seems to burn. For this reason forested lands are apparently much less extensive than they once were and are believed to be yielding progressively to the advance of wooded savanna and the spread of cultivation, which in practice requires that the grasslands be set on fire every year.

Within the increasingly drier zones from forest to desert, a great variety of distinctive landscapes may be found ranging from wet marshland to arid sand dunes and including a wide mixture of savanna and thorn scrub woodland aspects. In general, however, the very gradual transition from selva to desert may be viewed as follows. A dry, open, semideciduous forest with little undergrowth and a ground cover of thin savanna grass gives way to a much more open parkland in which grasses from 3 to 18 feet high form a dominant vegetation, with which is often mingled a wealth of other herbaceous forms. Trees are low, deciduous, and widely scattered as a rule, although in wet situations they form dense groves and thickets. Tree species are fire-resistant, far fewer in number than in wetter forest, and a common tendency exists among a few species to dominate particular areas. Representative species of savanna woodland trees are the acacias, a few mahoganies, and several tall, slender types of palms. Yearly rains average 30 to 50 inches, with a four- to five-month dry season.

Beyond savanna woodland are many variations of thorn scrub woodland where low-growing, spine-covered, thorny, hardy trees are moderately plentiful, although the ground beneath them is only sparsely occupied by herbaceous plants and is often bare. Mean annual rainfall, as a rule, is between 10 and 30 inches, with a five to seven month dry season. The thick-trunked baobab tree is quite often conspicuous on the horizon. Another common tree is one or more species of *Comiphora*, among them the African myrrh (*Comiphora africana*). This is a small tree, seldom more than 15 feet high, with a short conical trunk swollen at the base and divided near the ground into many rigid branches spreading outward in all directions. At the start of the dry season it becomes covered with small red flowers.

The broad transitional zone of the drier woodlands to the north of the rainforests extends from the Atlantic shores eastward in a belt about 600 miles wide. It rises to the middle elevations of the Ethiopian highlands and beyond to the inner hills of eastern Somaliland, at places approaching within less than 10 miles of the Indian Ocean. This broad, dominantly grassy zone has long been known as the Sudan. Along the Atlantic coast it advances poleward to about 18° Lat., is about 100 miles north of the great bend of the Niger east of Timbuktu, spreads about 100 miles north of Lake Chad, and advances to about 18° Lat. again in northeastern Sudan, the political territory of that name south of Egypt. South of the great selva region in the Congo basin savanna woodland and more arid thorn scrub woodland reach for more than 1200 miles to very near the Tropic of Capricorn. Over a substantial portion of this distance the drier woodlands span the continent from the Atlantic to the Indian Ocean. In this part of Africa, where altitudes increase southward with increasing latitude, the wetter savanna woodland is dominant from coast to coast in a 1000 mile zone from the selva southward. Linking the two enormous regions of open woodland that lie parallel to the equator and the main body of rainforest lie the wooded savanna and thorn scrub woodlands of the east African highlands.

Thus, the drier regions almost encircle the much smaller forested zones nearer the equator. In east Africa the climatic distribution pattern is extremely complex, a result of many striking contrasts in altitude, relief, and terrain.

Eastern Africa is generally a good deal higher than areas west of the Great Rift valley and is on the whole considerably drier (Fig. 6.10). A series of high mountain ranges extends for some 3000 miles from Ethiopia to the Drakensberg. Moreover, a great many lakes, most of them within the rift valley and many of them large in area, vary the landscape, and locally the environment, in a narrow sinuous distribution for about 2000 miles from Ethiopia to Mozambique. Mt. Kilimanjaro (el 19,565), about 200 miles south of the equator near the Kenya border of northeastern Tanzania, is the highest peak, and Lake Victoria, with an area of 26,828 square miles, a little larger than the Aral Sea, is the largest lake. It is outside the rift valley and stands at about 3720 feet, bordered by southern Uganda, northern Tanzania, and western Kenya.

Tropical rainforest in east Africa is concentrated in small areas of favorably moist circumstances. Its appearance is less lofty than the main body of rainforest farther west, and it is quite different in composition. Normal yearly rainfall amounts are, as a rule, insufficient to support extensive close-crowned forest development. Southward along the east coast, however, wherever uncleared forested land remains, a gradual change into a humid, moderately well-watered subtropical forest of somewhat lower winter temperatures takes place, the southernmost limits of tropical vegetation generally being reached near Durban at about 30° S. Lat. It should be noted that on the Atlantic coast desert extends northward to about 12° S. Lat.

Drier, more open woodland, sometimes dominated by deciduous, sometimes by evergreen trees, is widespread in east Africa. Savanna dotted with termite mounds on which shrubby thickets, small trees, and lianas have settled themselves also appear, and these are especially common in Uganda and Tanzania. Low, dense thickets of small, twisted, spiny deciduous trees 6 to 20 feet high are abundant in central Tanzania, whereas toward the desert regions thorny trees and shrubs of usually small size become predominant.

On Malagasy a richly varied tropical rainforest that originally spread from the east coast to the eastern edge of the interior uplands contrasts sharply with the drier western forests on the opposite side of the island, from which it is separated by a central grass-covered plateau. The western forests are largely deciduous. The eastern forest receives copious rains, annually amounting to 80 to 100 inches or more with no appreciable dry season, whereas the western forest averages between 30 and 70 inches within a five- to seven-month dry season. Southwestern Malagasy is a small region of thorn scrub woodland.

The above-described general climatic distribution is greatly modified by the influence of altitude, major relief features, and many edaphic qualities of soil, slope, and drainage. Extensive, ill-drained marshland is an example, as in the upper Niger valley, the Lake Chad depression, the middle Congo valley, and the high, level basins of east Africa. In those localities a profusion of herbaceous marsh plants may be compared with the much sparser, hardier vegetation of edaphically dry, well-drained sand hills in other sections. Elevated interfluvial uplands induce a tendency toward drier ecological phases within each climatic region. Thus, between the forested valleys of the Congo's many tributaries are areas of lighter forest and savanna woodland formations. A notable example of this is the north-flowing drainage system of the Kasai River, a major tributary of the lower Congo (Fig. 22.2). A score or more of lesser streams, draining large portions of northern Angola and southern Congo, many of them only 10 miles or so apart, flow northward through deep, heavily forested valleys and are separated by high ridges of open, lightly wooded grassland.

Altitude throughout tropical Africa generally leads to increased aridity, and we have noted the widespread prevalence of increasingly arid conditions with increasing elevation northward from the Guinea coast, southward from the Congo basin, and eastward into the east African highlands. But where mountainous relief features thrust prominently upward above the surrounding terrain, rainfall and the frequency of cloud and mist tend to increase on the windward slopes, resulting in the development of cloud forest, mist forest, or, as it is also called in tropical Africa, montane forest. This change is best revealed in the east Congo basin, where lowland tropical rainforest rises to between

3600 and 4300 feet. Above this is a distinctive transition forest community, ranging in altitude between lower limits of 3600–4600 feet and upper limits of 5400–5700 feet. The transition forest is less luxuriant than lowland rainforest—(its trees are smaller in height and diameter)—although it is very rich in species, including some from lowland forests and some from higher montane forest. Many species are endemic within its limits. Beyond is the montane rainforest, whose upper limits range from 7500 to 11,100 feet, which coincides with the levels of maximum precipitation. At these heights is the beginning of a highly characteristic zone of bamboos, which are succeeded by a higher zone of large herbaceous plants, forming a conspicuous feature on east Africa's upper mountainsides. Above this zone, at about 15,000 feet, is a zone of alpine meadows consisting of short grasses, sedges, and low flowering herbs beyond the tree line. Many mountain peaks that rise above 15,000 feet near the equator are snow-capped the year round, notably Mt. Ruwenzori (el. 16,795), Mt. Kenya (el. 17,040), and Mt. Kilimanjaro (el. 19,565).

The great majority of trees in the montane forest are evergreen, are shorter than lowland rainforest species, seldom rising above 80 feet and commonly much lower, and are not buttressed. They possess broad, thickly branched crowns, and although lianas are scarce, they are heavily festooned with mosses, lichens, ferns, orchids, and other epiphytes. A dense, often impenetrable shrub layer is commonly developed beneath them.

On the low mountains of west Africa a transition toward montane forest appears to some extent in very small tracts in Guinea, Sierra Leone, and western Ivory Coast, where altitudes rise to between 5000 and 7000 feet, and in northern Nigeria, where the Jos plateau reaches elevations of more than 6500 feet.

In the higher mountains of the Cameroons and nearby offshore islands—the Bambuto Mountains rise to 8790 feet, Cameroon Mt. on the coast to 13,353 feet, and the Spanish island of Fernando Po to 9351 feet—montane forest is found between 4600 and 6650 feet, where rainfall reaches a maximum and the evergreen vegetation is almost constantly drenched in cool mists. Beyond is alpine meadow, above which are barren volcanic rock surfaces with sparsely scattered alpine grasses and shrubs.

In the east African highlands much of the small proportion of dense, close-crowned forest is montane in character, found in isolated bands a mile or more above sea level. A great many distinct associations are known from the Ethiopian highlands to the Drakensberg, composed of many species having a strong affinity with the Congo forests but including indigenous species as well. Among the latter is the east African camphor tree (*Ocotea usambarensis*), a member of the laurel family. The altitude limits of evergreen mountain forest are about the same as those described above, although they range about 1000 feet lower toward the southernmost extent of their distribution along the east African escarpment in southern Africa. Above the cloud forest are extensive zones of coniferous trees, at 6900 to 8860 feet, where various species of *Podocarpus* and *Juniperus*, including the large *Juniperus procera*, are among the prominent members of the forest association, mixed with numerous broadleaves. These stands of African juniper reach from Eritrea to Mt. Rungwe north of Lake Nyasa.[1] Farther south at 5900 to 6500 feet pure stands of another conifer, the Mlanje cedar (*Widdringtonia whytei*), appear in a small area. Above these mountain forests pure stands of highland bamboo, some more than 65 feet tall, are found. Beyond the taller forms alpine shrub vegetation becomes plentiful, and where altitudes exceed 10,000 feet, giant forms of herbaceous plants, species of *Senecio* and *Lobelia*, tower above thick carpets of lower herbs, mosses, shrubby plants, and grasses amid almost constant fog and cold.

Many seemingly anomolous conditions can be observed within each broad regional distribution everywhere in tropical Africa. Rain shadow effects are numerous in the lee of prominent mountains. From Ethiopia and the Congo basin westward most leeward arid situations are east of barrier relief features, whereas in east Africa south of Ethiopia most leeward arid areas are west of the prevailing easterly winds off the Indian Ocean. A conspicuous desert region lies east of Lake Rudolph in northern Kenya and is part of a tract nearly 500 miles long that surrounds the lake and reaches southeastward to join the deserts of Somaliland. The northward

[1] A. M. A. Aubreville, "Tropical Africa," in *A World Geography of Forest Resources*, American Geographical Society Special Publication No. 33, New York, 1956, pp. 353–84.

projection of savanna woodland across the lower Congo mentioned earlier in this chapter is in part the consequence of its lying eastward, in the lee, of hilly country nearer the coast that rises 500 to 1000 feet higher in elevation. The most striking anomaly is the savanna woodland area that reaches southward to the Guinea coast from the interior Sudan along a 300 mile stretch from southeastern Ghana to the western frontiers of Nigeria (Fig. 22.2). In this section monthly rainfall over the entire year is lower than in the rainforest regions on either side of it. But it is chiefly the failure of summer rains to amount to more than a few inches per month that accounts for the very much lower yearly means. Details of this climatic anomaly will be discussed later.

AFRICAN WINDS AND STORMS. Inland winds from the Sahara, hot, dry, and dusty, blow southwestward at all times of the year toward the Guinea coast. These are known as the harmattan. They approach nearest the equator during the dry months of December through February. Although they usually fall off 100 miles or more in from the coast, they occasionally reach far southward, extending well out to sea. When they do, they bring a hot, dusty haze to the coastal lowlands, continuing for a distance of 10 to 15 miles offshore over the Gulf of Guinea. They are shallow winds, blowing at 12 to 15 miles per hour, normally under 3000 feet in depth but from time to time rising to about 10,000 feet. They sometimes reach as far south as Cape Lopez, nearly 500 miles northwest of the mouth of the Congo. The harmattan may in the dry season blow steadily for five or six days, and occasionally for as long as two weeks.

Tornadoes are the most violent storms of the Guinea lands, wildly lashing thunderstorms that occur most frequently at the beginning and the end of the rainy season. They most commonly take the form of a long line of intense disturbances developing along the zone of interaction between the warm, humid southwest monsoon winds about 5000 feet deep and the warm, damp equatorial easterlies above. They vary in size, duration, and intensity and are usually linear in distribution in keeping with their frontal origin. Frontal disturbances of this kind are often only about 30 miles or so in north-south length. But they may start with a length of only 10 miles and grow to 200 miles or more as they advance westward over Nigeria. They always proceed from east to west except over Senegal, where their normal course is from south to north. Their approach is heralded by low, dark clouds, brilliant flashes of lightning, and the distant sound of thunder in the east. The dominant southwest wind subsides as they advance, atmospheric pressure rises, and then the squall breaks. Torrential rains, bright, frequent flashes of lightning, deafening crashes of heavy thunder, and winds of 40 to 50 miles per hour and once in a while up to 80 miles per hour occur in the first fifteen minutes or so of the swiftly passing storm. Turbulent activity lets up with surprising suddenness, although rains may continue for an hour or two afterward.

Tornadoes are most violent in the late afternoon but occur more frequently at night. They travel at an average speed over the ground of between 30 and 40 miles per hour and may retain their identity on a traverse of over 500 miles. One tornado began north of Kano, Nigeria, and was traced on its westward course far out to sea beyond Dakar. They occur most commonly over the Guinea lands but are also a frequent weather feature over the Cameroons and the lower Congo valley. They may appear as often as ten times per month in the rainy season. In the Sudan they sometimes develop after the wet season but fail to produce rain and instead take the form of violently turbulent dust storms, an unwelcome variation of the generic disturbance. They should not be confused with the much more violent cyclonic storms of North America that are known by the same name.

Tropical cyclones are cyclonic storms of the western Indian Ocean that sometimes affect the coastal portions of eastern tropical Africa. This is particularly true in Mozambique, although from time to time they reach northward a short distance beyond Cape Delgado, to about 10°S. Lat. (Fig. 22.2). They occur most frequently in January and February, although they have been observed in every month except August and September. They originate near the equatorial trough during the time of its southernmost displacement as waves in the dominant easterlies of the southern Indian Ocean, and then may develop into hurricane intensity as they approach Malagasy and the Mozambique Channel. They advance on a west-southwest course, recurving southward, then southeastward as they near land. They may average as many as ten per year and contribute substantial rains to Malagasy fairly frequently, affecting the coast of the mainland much less often. Tropical storms of hurricane intensity occur on the average of only two per year, affecting the east coast of Malagasy especially but bringing torrential rains and flooding to the northwest coast as well.

Land and sea breezes are significant features of normal coastal weather in all of tropical Africa, especially during the dry seasons. During the rainy periods they are much less strong and less regular, except in periods of calm. The onshore sea breeze seldom moves at speeds in excess of 15 miles per hour, is usually very shallow, extending upward for 1000 to 2000 feet, and reaches inland for no more than about 10 miles. Starting up by midmorning, the sea breeze ordinarily reaches maximum force by midafternoon but ceases soon after sunset. A much lighter land breeze, blowing offshore, may develop during the night and continue until well after dawn, sometimes well toward noon.

The basic importance of the annual periodic north-south migration of the equatorial trough of low pressure, cloudiness, high humidity, and heavy rain cannot be overemphasized (Fig. 20.1). This primary oscillation sets up a rhythm of alternate wet and dry periods over nearly all of tropical Africa, leading to a relatively simple two-season program of normal yearly weather toward the poleward limits of the tropics and to a fairly definite four-season regime of two wet seasons alternating with two relatively dry seasons nearer the equator, plus a great many variations between these two extremes. In most of tropical Africa it may be said, to use the phrase loosely, that peak rains tend to follow the sun, lagging behind the time of its zenithal position for increasingly longer intervals in a poleward direction. Thus, along the southeast coast a single yearly maximum is reached at many places in February or March, whereas in the drier reaches of the northern Sudan, August records the annual peak.

In response to the precise systematic oscillations of the sun's zenithal position each year, the equatorial trough shifts from near the Guinea coast and far to the south near the Tropic of Capricorn in the interior in January to about 15 degrees north of the equator in July. Thus, over many areas the trough passes twice, bringing its typically damp, cloudy, turbulent weather with copious rains in two peaks of pronounced rainfall intensity during the year. The maximum poleward reach of heavy rains lies about 100 miles equatorward of the farthest displacement of the intertropical convergence. Furthermore, the first appearance of characteristically disturbed trough weather lags behind the zenithal position of the sun by nearly a month, and the peak rains in turn, from latitude to latitude, tend to occur an additional month later. Between the normal peak months abundant rain continues, but with diminished intensity. Toward the poleward limits of the tropical environments the maxima merge to form a single yearly climax. All across the Sudan, from the Atlantic to Ethiopia, August marks the climactic apex of the single rainy season. In the southern Guinea highlands, however, in northern Ghana and in central Nigeria, the single peak season does not reach a maximum until September. In the southern interior from northern Rhodesia to the northern part of the Republic of South Africa, and in northern Madagascar, the single climax is reached in December or January. Along the east coast from Mozambique to Natal the peak month may be delayed until March.

April and November are, with few exceptions, the months of maximum rains from northern Angola across the central Congo depression to Uganda and Kenya. The peak months are closer together (May and October) in the area from east of the Bambuto Mountains to the Ubangi valley, and even closer (June and October) along the Guinea coast west of the Niger delta.

The Congo Basin, Guinea Coast, and the Sudan

The Congo and its tributaries drain a vast elevated basin whose floor is about 1000 feet above sea level, grading upward to 3000 feet or more on nearly every side. The main descending gradient is northward, the direction taken by most of the tributaries whose waters are collected in the great circling course of the Congo itself and its large northern influent, the Ubangi. Within about 100 miles of the Atlantic the river drops rapidly down to sea level in a long series of cascades, breaking through the low Crystal Mountain region and across a narrow coastal plain to the sea. With only a small allowance for the effect of its elevation of 1000 feet and more, the rainforest climate here is much the same as that in the relatively narrow belt along the Guinea coast.

Temperatures within the rainforest proper remain equable throughout the year, monthly means holding constantly in the high 70s and low 80s, the mean annual range rarely exceeding 5 degrees. In the Congo depression, for example, the mean yearly range is 3 degrees at Impfondo (el. 1115), between 77° in July and August and 80° from February through May; at Bangui (el. 1296) 4 degrees, from 77° in July and August to 81° February through April; at Bangassou (el. 1693) 4 degrees, from 77° in August to 81° from February through April; at Bosondongo (el. 1558) only 1 degree, from 77° April through July to 78° for the remainder of the year; at Kisangani (el. 1400) 3 degrees, from 76° in July through September to 79° in May. Along the Guinea coast at somewhat higher latitude the mean annual range is slightly greater, partly a result of the more frequent appearance of the harmattan from the interior, raising the mean temperatures of the drier months, and to some extent a result of the cooling effect of winds more directly off the sea, which tend to lower the monthly values during the rainy season. At Lagos, for example, the mean range is 6 degrees, between 77° in July and August and 83° in March; at Axim, Ghana, it is 5 degrees, from 76° in July and August to 82° in March; at Tabou, Ivory Coast, it is 4 degrees, between 76° in August and September and 80° from February through May. Maximum temperatures of record rarely exceed 100° in the rainforest, the highest at Kisangani being 97° in January and February, although at Lagos the thermometer has climbed to 104° in May. The well-exposed site of Tabou at Cape Palmas is strongly subjected to marine influence, and the highest value reported there has been 92° in April. In general, the extreme temperature ranges in the selva environment are considerably lower than those experienced in the drier woodlands, as we shall presently see, and are nowhere near the excessive values attained in the northern Sahara, outside the tropics.

The daily fluctuations of the thermometer between the cool, damp hours near dawn and the hot, humid period in the afternoon are much greater than the average annual variations. Impfondo, with a mean annual range of 3 degrees, records a normal daily variation of 21 degrees in March and April, when at the start of the day the thermometer reads 70°, but later in the afternoon rises to 91°. In July the range is lower, between 68° and 85°, but at all times of the year it is much greater than for the year as a whole. A maritime situation as at Tabou provides a contrast, however. Tabou, with a yearly thermal range of 4 degrees, normally records a mean daily range of only 7 degrees from June through August, and a maximum of only 13 degrees in April, indicating the maritime equability of normal thermal experience at all times.

Mean annual rainfall in the rainforest is generally between 60 and 80 inches. At Impfondo it is 67.4 inches, at Bangui 60.8 inches, at Bangassou 70.6 inches, at Bosondongo 77.2 inches, and at Kisangani 67.1 inches. Along the Guinea coast Lagos averages 72.3 inches and Axim 83.2 inches. A number of exceptionally wet areas are found near the sea where the coastal alignment is almost directly across the path of the southwest monsoon, and especially where hilly country rises immediately inland from the shoreline. One is an 800 mile stretch from coastal Guinea southeastward to Cape Palmas. At Conakry, Guinea, yearly mean rainfall is 171.3 inches, at Freetown, Sierra Leone, 135.2 inches, and at No. 2 River 209.6 inches. A six-year record at Monrovia, Liberia, averages 191.5 inches. Another unusually wet area extends from the Niger delta eastward along the shores of the Bight of Biafra southward to the Gabon plateau. Here the coast makes an abrupt bend from east to south and the mountainous terrain near the sea adds the advantage of mechanical uplift to the compression of the southwesterlies into the corner of the bight. This is a notably wet area, and in the vicinity of Cameroon Mt. (el. 13,350), some 14 miles inland, is found the rainiest locality in Africa. Extraordinary annual totals have been reported from several stations around the seaward base of the sharply rising volcanic peak. A nine-year record at Idenau and Isongo averages 333 and 393.3 inches respectively, and a thirty-two-year record at Debundschar reveals an average of 404.6 inches. Mean yearly values drop off from these extremes both westward and southward, Calabar about 100 miles northwest reporting 121 inches, Port Harcourt, about 200 miles west, 98 inches, and Sapale, about 300 miles west, 95 inches. At Kribi, over 100 miles south of Cameroon Mt., annual rains average 120.2 inches, at Libreveile, more than 250 miles south, 97.3 inches, and at Mouila, about 450 miles south and some 100 miles inland at an elevation of 292 feet, 90.7 inches.

Other areas of heavier rainfall amounts include a broad expanse of the central Congo depression, with yearly amounts of more than 80 inches, and at many places in the eastern highlands. At Kamituga (el. 3772) the yearly value is 107.4 inches, and at Loashi (el. 4428) it is 84.7 inches.

The principal source of moisture for the rainforest regions, with one exception, and for the Sudan northward as well as the western slopes of the Ethiopian highlands, is the equatorial Atlantic. From the Gulf of Guinea warm, humid maritime tropical air is brought in by the southwest monsoon. The southwesterly flow reaches inland over the lower and middle Congo, the lower Kasai, and beyond to Ethiopia. The upper Kasai drainage area, however, and the upper Congo valley between its north-flowing arm and the eastern highlands are supplied mainly by moisture brought in by easterly winds from the Indian Ocean. Furthermore, the upper Congo valley, in common with much of the eastern highlands, is more strongly dominated by the southward penetration of warm, dry air from the eastern Sahara from December through February than the lower reaches, which continue to receive warm, moist air from the sea the year round.

Over the Congo basin, the Guinea coast, and the Sudan the season of maximum rain occurs for the most part between the March and September equinoxes. When in March, at the equinox, the sun is over the equator and the main period of rains in southern latitudes is drawing to a close, the rainy season near the equator is well on its way. By this time the onshore southwesterly flow of warm, humid air from the sea has begun to penetrate well inland, undercutting the resistant warm, dry winds off the Sahara from northward and setting in motion the turbulent convective processes that bring towering cumulonimbus clouds, violent, gusty thunderstorms, and drenching showers of rain.

At Lusambo (el. 1460), about 400 miles south of Kisangani at 5°S. Lat., the month recording the first of the year's two maximum amounts

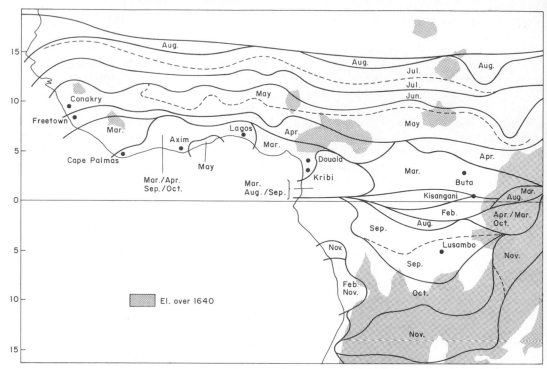

Figure 22.3.   First month during which at least 4 inches of rain are recorded in western Africa.

and the highest monthly total for the year is March, with a mean value of 9.6 inches (Fig. 22.3). At Kisangani it is also March (7 inches), when rain falls on seventeen days of the month. Mean early afternoon relative humidities at interior Congo stations averages 65 per cent or higher during the rainy season, reaching a peak value of 75 per cent in August at Kisangani. October is the wettest month, averaging 8.6 inches on fourteen days. At Buta (el. 1410), about 150 miles north of Kisangani, the first peak month is April, also averaging 7 inches. At Kribi on the Cameroons coast the first peak month is May, averaging 16.3 inches on twenty-one days, and mean relative humidity near noon is 80 per cent. The second peak month is September with 21.5 inches on twenty-seven days, and relative humidity is 86 per cent. The area around Cameroon Mt. features a single peak season of annual rainfall, and we note that the climax is reached in September at Debunds-char (62.5 inches) and Isongo (65 inches), in July at Idenau (63 inches) and Douala (29.2 inches).

Farther westward the first monthly maximum is delayed until June as far west as Cape Palmas, and the second and lower peak is normally October. At Lagos the June mean is 18.1 inches on twenty days, relative humidity is 80 per cent, and cloud cover is 56 per cent. At Axim, June averages 24.1 inches on twenty-four days, with relative humidity at 81 per cent, and at Tabou, June normally records 22.8 inches on fourteen days, when relative humidity is 83 per cent. From Sierra Leone northward the year's rain once again rises to a single peak of intensity, here in July; at Freetown, July averages 35.8 inches on twenty-seven days, when early afternoon humidities average 81 per cent. No. 2 River averages 66.6 inches in July, and Conakry reports 52.6 inches in July, when rain falls on an average of twenty-nine days, relative humidity is 84 per cent, and mean cloud cover is 75 per cent.

The climatic transition that takes place northward toward the Sahara from the continuously hot, wet rainforest regions features a number of characteristic changes. With increasing latitude and increasing distance from the sea, the main source of precipitable moisture, annual rainfall amounts diminish, and the dry season becomes progressively longer (Fig. 22.4). Mean and extreme temperature ranges become larger, periods of cloudy weather become shorter, much more sunshine prevails over the annual period, much wider fluctuations in relative humidity are observed, and the frequency and persistence of the dry harmattan become greater. (See Table 22-1.) There is also a noticeable increase in smoke haze from the annual fires that precede the onset of the rainy season.

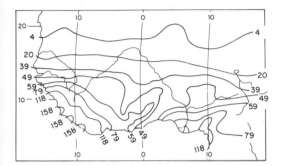

Figure 22.4. Mean annual rainfall in tropical west Africa (inches).

At Tabou, 4°25′N. Lat. on the shores of the Ivory Coast, the mean annual temperature range is 4 degrees, from 76° in August and September to 80° in March and April, with an extreme range of 36 degrees from 56° in March to 92° in April. January and February are the

driest months with about 2 inches each, when relative humidities are 78 and 79 per cent respectively. Its normal yearly rainfall is 92.5 inches, rising to a peak monthly amount of 22.8 inches in June, on fourteen days, when relative humidity is 83 per cent. (Fig. 22.5).

At Man (el. 1135), about 200 miles north at 7°24′N. Lat., the mean annual range is 6 degrees, from 73° in August to 79° in March and April, with an extreme range of 37 degrees from 58° in February to 95° in January through March at the start of the rainy season, when clear, dry air prevails much of the time. Relative humidity reaches a yearly minimum of 55 per cent in February. Normal yearly rainfall is 81 inches, rising to a single peak in September when 14.3 inches normally occurs, falling on sixteen days. In September midday relative humidity is 83 per cent, somewhat lower than the yearly maximum of 88 per cent in the preceding month. Both December and January record less than 1 inch of rain.

About 350 miles farther north is Bamako (el. 1116), 12°39′N. Lat., a savanna woodland station where the mean annual temperature range is 13 degrees, from 77° in December and January to 90° in April at the end of the dry season. The extreme thermal range of record is 68 degrees, from 47° in December to 114° in May. From

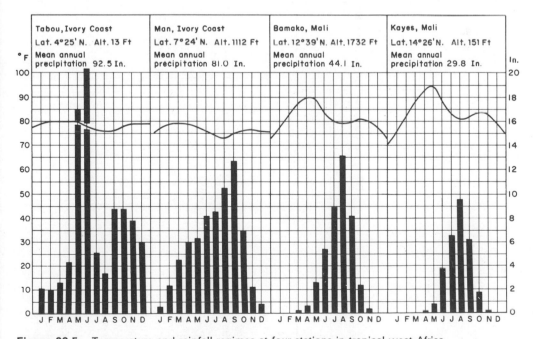

Figure 22.5. Temperature and rainfall regimes at four stations in tropical west Africa.

TABLE 22–1

Climatic Data for Tropical Forest and Woodland Stations in Central and West Africa
(Temp., °F; Rainfall, In.)

Station	Lat.	El. in Ft		Jan.	Feb.	Mar.	Apr.	May	Jun.	Jul.	Aug.	Sep.	Oct.	Nov.	Dec.	Year
Accra, Ghana	5°33'N.	88	T	81	82	82	82	81	78	76	76	77	79	80	81	
			R	0.6	1.3	2.3	3.4	5.5	7.1	1.8	0.6	1.4	2.6	1.4	0.9	28.8
Axim, Ghana	4°53'N.	75	T	80	81	82	82	80	79	78	77	77	79	80	81	
			R	1.6	2.1	4.8	6.2	16.8	24.1	5.8	2.2	3.5	8.1	5.1	2.9	83.2
Bangui, Ubangi-Shari	4°22'N.	1296	T	79	81	81	81	80	78	77	77	78	78	78	78	
			R	1.0	1.7	5.0	5.3	7.4	4.5	8.9	8.1	5.9	7.9	4.9	0.2	60.8
Calabar, Nigeria	4°58'N.	40	T	80	81	82	81	81	80	77	77	78	79	80	80	
			R	1.5	3.0	6.2	8.6	12.3	16.2	17.9	16.5	16.6	12.9	7.5	1.9	121.0
Lubumbashi, Congo	11°39'S.	4035	T	72	72	72	70	66	62	61	65	71	75	74	72	
			R	10.5	9.6	8.4	2.2	0.2	0.0	0.0	0.0	0.1	1.2	5.9	10.6	48.7
Freetown, Sierra Leone	8°30'N.	37	T	80	81	81	82	82	80	78	78	79	79	80	80	
			R	0.5	0.1	0.5	2.2	6.3	11.9	35.2	35.5	24.0	12.2	5.2	1.6	135.2
Gangassol, Angola	9°23'S.	3936	T	72	72	72	72	71	67	67	70	72	72	71	71	
			R	3.3	5.4	7.6	6.5	0.8	0.0	0.0	0.2	2.0	5.0	8.0	5.9	44.6
Jos, Nigeria	9°54'N.	4010	T	70	72	76	77	75	72	70	69	70	72	72	70	
			R	0.1	0.2	1.0	3.9	7.6	8.6	12.7	11.7	8.3	1.5	0.2	0.0	55.4
Kano, Nigeria	12°02'N.	1533	T	71	75	81	87	87	84	79	77	79	81	77	72	
			R	0.0	0.0	0.1	0.4	2.7	4.6	8.1	12.2	5.6	0.5	0.0	0.0	34.2
Kayes, Mali	14°26'N.	98	T	78	82	88	93	95	89	83	81	82	84	83	79	
			R	0.1	0.0	0.0	0.0	1.0	3.8	6.3	9.5	7.4	1.7	0.0	0.0	29.8

Station	Lat.	Elev.		1	2	3	4	5	6	7	8	9	10	11	12	Ann.
Kribi, Cameroons	2°56'S.	43	T	80	80	80	80	80	78	76	76	77	77	78	80	
			R	4.2	5.2	8.2	10.3	14.5	10.4	4.6	10.3	20.8	20.9	7.4	3.6	120.2
Lagos, Nigeria	6°27'N.	10	T	81	83	84	83	82	80	79	78	79	80	82	82	
			R	1.1	1.8	4.0	5.9	10.6	18.1	11.0	2.5	5.5	8.1	2.7	1.0	72.3
Libreville, Gabon	0°23'N.	115	T	80	81	81	81	81	79	76	77	78	79	80	80	
			R	8.7	11.5	9.7	11.1	9.8	1.8	0.1	0.4	3.8	14.3	17.0	11.0	97.3
Luluabourg, Republic of the Congo	5°54'S.	2198	T	75	74	75	75	76	75	73	73	75	74	74	73	
			R	4.0	4.3	9.6	7.2	3.7	0.6	0.6	1.4	5.6	4.8	10.2	10.7	62.6
Man, Ivory Coast	7°24'N.	1135	T	77	79	79	79	78	76	74	73	75	76	77	76	
			R	0.7	3.4	4.8	5.5	7.1	8.7	10.7	10.6	14.3	9.5	4.5	1.2	81.0
Mongu, Zambia	15°17'S.	3459	T	74	74	74	73	69	64	65	70	77	79	76	74	
			R	8.7	7.7	6.2	1.5	0.0	0.0	0.0	0.0	0.2	1.4	3.9	8.0	37.5
Ouagadougou, Upper Volta	12°22'N.	997	T	77	81	87	91	89	85	82	79	81	85	83	78	
			R	0.0	0.1	0.2	0.7	3.4	4.5	7.6	10.4	6.0	1.6	0.0	0.0	34.5
Salisbury, Rhodesia	17°50'S.	4831	T	69	69	68	66	61	57	57	60	66	71	71	70	
			R	7.7	7.0	4.6	1.1	0.5	0.1	0.0	0.1	0.2	1.1	3.8	6.4	32.6
Kisangani, Republic of the Congo	0°26'N.	1370	T	77	77	77	78	77	76	74	74	75	76	76	76	
			R	2.1	3.3	7.0	6.2	5.4	4.5	5.2	6.5	7.2	8.6	7.8	3.3	67.1
Tabou, Ivory Coast	4°25'N.	13	T	79	80	80	80	80	78	77	76	76	78	79	79	
			R	1.5	2.7	3.9	4.5	16.4	22.8	7.0	3.9	7.8	8.7	8.7	4.6	92.5
Villa Teixeira de Sousa, Angola	10°43'S.	3609	T	76	75	76	75	73	70	70	74	78	77	76	75	
			R	9.0	8.9	9.7	4.7	0.4	0.0	0.0	0.2	0.9	3.9	7.8	7.8	53.2
Zinder, Niger	13°48'N.	1676	T	73	78	85	90	91	88	82	80	82	85	80	73	
			R	0.0	0.0	0.0	0.0	0.7	2.7	6.4	8.4	3.3	0.1	0.0	0.0	21.2

Source: F. L. Wernstedt, *World Climatic Data, Africa*, Pennsylvania State University, 1959.

December through April each month records less than 1 inch of rain. Relative humidity drops to a yearly minimum of 18 per cent in February and 19 per cent in January around midday. Normal yearly rainfall totals 44.1 inches, rising to a peak intensity in August (13.7 inches), when rain falls on an average of seventeen days. At this time relative humidity increases to 73 per cent.

At Kayes (el. 98), about 250 miles northwestward at latitude 14°26', the mean annual temperature range is 19 degrees, from 76° in January to 95° in May, and the extreme range is 71 degrees, from 50° in January to 121° in April. The mean daily range at the height of the rainy season in August is 16 degrees, compared with 33 degrees in March and April when the sun is high overhead and the wet season has not yet begun. At Kayes the midday relative humidity is 17 per cent in January and February and 15 per cent in March and April. In April mean cloud cover is only 25 per cent and from November through April ranges between 25 and 31 per cent. The dry season at Kayes, a station in thorn scrub woodland, lasts for about seven months, when from November through May each month averages less than 1 inch of rain. From December through March there is scarcely a trace. By the end of May the year's rains have normally begun. The annual total averages 29.8 inches and rises to a maximum of 9.5 inches in August, falling at that time on fifteen days. Relative humidities rise to 74 per cent in August, and mean cloud cover reaches a yearly maximum of 58 per cent.

A second traverse begins at Axim, an unusually wet station on the coast of Ghana in latitude 4°53'. Here the mean annual temperature range is 5 degrees, from 77° in August-September to 82° in March, and the extreme range is 36 degrees, from 59° in January to 95° in June. January is the driest month, averaging 1.6 inches falling on four days, although relative humidity at noon averages 78 per cent. Normal annual rainfall is 83.2 inches, which increases to a maximum in June when 24.1 inches is the average amount, falling on twenty-three days. Relative humidity at this time is 81 per cent. Rains fall off sharply in July, when 5.8 inches normally fall on thirteen days. A slight secondary peak is reached in October (8.1 inches), falling on 18 days.

At Tamale (el. 635), about 325 miles north of Axim in latitude 9°24', mean annual temperature range is 10 degrees, from 78° in August and September to 88° in March, and the extreme range of record is 37 degrees, from 59° in December and January to 106° in April. At this savanna station midday relative humidity is only 20 per cent in January, the heart of the dry season, when cloud cover averages between 30 and 50 per cent. Mean annual rainfall is 42.6 inches, reaching a maximum intensity in September (8.9 inches) when rain falls on nineteen days and relative humidity is 74 per cent, mean cloud cover 50 to 80 per cent. The dry season lasts for about four or five months, as less than 1 inch is normally recorded per month from November through February. January is the driest month with 0.1 inch.

About 200 miles northward is Ouagadougou (el. 991), at latitude 12°22', a thorn scrub woodland station where the mean annual range of monthly temperatures is 14 degrees, from 77° in January to 91° in April. A secondary temperature rise takes place after the end of the wet season when in October the mean value is 85°. The extreme temperature range here is 70 degrees, from 48° in January to 118° in May. In March, before the rainy season has commenced and the sun is high overhead, the mean daily range of the thermometer is 31 degrees, compared with 15 degrees in August, the month of maximum rain. Early afternoon relative humidities are lowest for the year in January and February at 19 per cent. The dry season lasts for six or seven months, from November through April less than 1 inch normally falling each month. December and January are usually rainless. Mean annual rainfall totals 34.5 inches, increasing to a maximum of 10.4 inches in August when rain falls on fourteen days and relative humidity is 67 per cent, the highest for the year.

Some 300 miles north of Ougadougou is Timbuktu (el. 988), nearer the desert edge on the great north bend of the Niger River in latitude 16°46'. Here the mean annual temperature range is 22 degrees, from 72° in January to 94° in May, and the extreme range is 78 degrees, from 41° in January to 119° in June and July. Noontime relative humidity is less than 20 per cent from February through May and again in November and December and reaches a yearly minimum of 15 per cent in April when mean cloud cover is 24 per cent. The mean daily temperature range in April is 35 degrees, compared with 22 degrees in August, the wettest month. The six months from November through April are without rain, and most of the yearly total of 9.1 inches falls in a three-month interval from July through September. August is the peak month with 3.2 inches falling on an average of nine days, relative humidity standing at 57 per cent, highest for the year, and mean cloud cover, also at a maximum, at 40 per cent.

Another traverse begins at Calabar near the mouth of the Cross River in southeastern Nigeria at latitude 4°58'. The mean annual temperature range is 5 degrees, from 77° in July and August to 82° in March, and extreme values reported here, of 49° in December to 105° in May, produce a maximum range of 56 degrees, unusually large for coastal tropical stations. The mean daily range of temperature is relatively small, from about 12 degrees in August when midafternoon relative humidity averages 85 per cent, and cloud cover 88 per cent to 17 degrees in February when relative humidity is 67 per cent and mean cloud cover 72 per cent. Total yearly mean rainfall is 120.4 inches, most of which falls from May through October. July is the peak month with 17.9 inches, falling on twenty-two days, although from June through September each month averages over 16 inches, falling on over twenty days per month. A pronounced let-up in monthly distribution takes place from November onward, and both December and January report only between 1.5 and 2 inches per month.

About 340 miles north is Jos (el. 4010), at 9°54'N. Lat., a savanna woodland station on the low Bauchi plateau north of the confluence of the Niger and Benue rivers. The advantage of an elevation above most areas in the Sudan is reflected in the mean annual temperature range of only 8 degrees and in the lower limits of this range at 69° in August and 77° in April. Absolute values of record produce an extreme range of 55 degrees, between 44° in February and 99° in April, lower than is normal for the latitude. Further advantages of altitude are the larger than usual annual rainfall of 55.4 inches and a shorter dry season of four months, from November through February, when each month receives at least 0.1 inch of rain. In this period, however, relative humidities are low, at between 13 and 17 per cent. The month of peak rainfall is July (12.7 inches), when rain falls on twenty-three days and relative humidity is 78 per cent, increasing to 81 per cent in August.

About 140 miles farther north at Kano (el. 1533) in latitude 12°03', a station in a transition belt between savanna woodland and more shrubby, drier thorn scrub woodland, the mean annual temperature range is 16 degrees, from 71° in January to 87° in April and May. The thermometer has dropped to 43° in January and risen to 114° in April during predominantly harmattan weather, resulting in an extreme range of 81 degrees. The seven-month dry season extends from October through April, four months of which are rainless (November through February) when relative humidity in midafternoon is less than 15 per cent, attaining a yearly minimum of 11 per cent in March, and mean cloud cover averages between 10 and 20 per cent. Mean annual rainfall is 34.2 inches, increasing from 2.7 inches in May to a peak amount of 12.2 inches in August, falling on nineteen days at that time. In August afternoon relative humidities are 68 per cent, and mean cloud cover is about 60 per cent.

Some 120 miles north of Kano at Zinder (el. 1676), in latitude 13°48', a scrub woodland station receiving much less annual rainfall than Kano, the mean annual temperature range is 18 degrees, from 73° in December and January to 91° in May. The extreme range is 70 degrees, from 46° reported in December and January to 116° reported in April. The mean daily range in the dry season is 31 degrees, but in the wettest month of August it is 17 degrees. For eight months less than 1 inch of rain is normally recorded (from November through April is rainless), midday relative humidities drop to 12 per cent in March, and cloudless skies prevail most of the time. The four-month rainy season from June through September normally yields 21.2 inches, increasing to the peak month of August, when it usually rains for about twelve days and relative humidity increases to 64 per cent.

The above survey points up the marked uniformity of the climatic transition northward in nearly all of the Sudan, especially in the normal annual rainfall regimes and mean thermal experience from latitude to latitude. With diminishing annual rainfall northward an increase in rainfall variability takes place, rising from between 15 and 20 per cent near the coast to over 50 per cent along the scrub woodland borders.

The anomalous presence of the semi-arid plains along the Guinea coast that stretch eastward for some 300 miles from Cape Three Points to Dahomey merits special attention (Fig. 22.2). Here the drier climate spreads northward to join the similarly open savanna woodland of the Sudan. Circumstances bearing upon the rainfall deficiency here are three. (1) The shoreline east of Cape Three Points curves east-northeastward and is thus parallel to the prevailing southwest winds, the southwest monsoon, of the rainy season. (2) The warm, east-flowing Guinea Current diverges from the shoreline, inducing an upwelling of cooler water inshore. (3) Pronounced relief features are lacking over most of the region, especially in the broad Volta valley. In hilly country north of the coast, where in the rainy season towering cumulonimbus clouds form much more frequently during the day, increased rain supports rainforest in a number of areas.

The prevailing air in the dry belt is as warm and humid as that bringing heavier and much more reliable rain to the broad selva regions east and west of it. Thus, it is the failure of rains in the two wet periods to produce more than a few inches per month and the greater uncertainty of their occurrence, plus a more pronounced rainfall deficiency in the two intervening dry seasons, that lead to the drier savanna woodland climate. This is exemplified in the case of Accra, Ghana, about 60 miles west of the mouth of the Volta, a station that represents the extreme aridity of the coastal belt on either side of the lower Volta.

At Accra (el. 88) the normal yearly rainfall is 28.5 inches (Fig. 22.4), of which 81 per cent usually occurs in two distinct wet periods, 63 per cent in the four-month interval from March through June, and 18 per cent from September through November. The former period is the season of "Big Rains," the latter of "Little Rains." Midday relative humidities are barely less than 61 per cent throughout the year and from May through October are above 70 per cent, rising to a maximum of 77 per cent in August. Mean daily cloud cover is less than 50 per cent from November through April but rises to a maximum of 71 per cent in August and September.

Not only is rainfall low for this part of tropical Africa, and concentrated in two relatively short periods, but it also normally occurs on only a few wet days per month. June is the wettest month, averaging 7 inches, when rain falls on

about ten days. In October, peak month of the season of Little Rains, the average is 2.5 inches, falling on six days. During the dry season rain falls on fewer than five days per month, and on only one day in January, the driest month (0.6 inch).

Mean annual rainfall variability at Accra is 27 per cent, but annual amounts have ranged in individual years from 13.1 inches (1905) to 44.2 inches (1917). The main dry period is normally from mid-October to mid-April and is the season most susceptible to rainfall variation, especially at the end of the Little Rains and the start of the Big Rains.

The dryness of the coastal savanna woodland belt decreases in both directions away from Accra (Fig. 22.4). This is indicated at Takoradi, about 115 miles west, by the mean annual rainfall of 46.7 inches, 40 miles beyond which is Axim with 83.2 inches. At Cotonou, about 180 miles east, the mean yearly total is 48.9 inches, 80 miles beyond which is Lagos with 72.3 inches.

Southward from the Congo Rainforest

The portion of Africa to which we now give our attention is the broad, uplifted plateau south of the equator that lies between the Great Escarpment near the Atlantic coast and the series of elongated lakes and high mountain ranges of east Africa (Fig. 22.2). The broad, blunt mass of southern Africa is considerably higher in altitude than the north and is only about half as wide. Along the equator Africa is about 2400 miles in breadth, at the Tropic of Capricorn it is about 1800 miles, and from here southward it tapers gradually to a rounded end at about 35°S. Lat.

The southern interior plateau, as we noted in Chapter 14, is an elevated basin standing some 3000 feet or more above sea level, rising to heights between 4000 and 6000 feet or more almost entirely around the perimeter. The diminished breadth of the land mass, coupled with higher levels above the sea, introduces subtle points of contrast between the tropical climates south of the equator and those in northern latitudes to which they are otherwise similar. Among them are the farther poleward extent of tropical climates in general and substantially lower temperature limits within each climatic region.

The dry season south of the equator occurs between the March and September equinoxes when most of the year's rains are falling from the equator northward (Fig. 22.1). This is the period when the south latitude oceanic highs expand, intensify, and shift northward to form a continuous anticyclonic belt across southern Africa from the Atlantic to the Indian Ocean, bringing clear, dry, cool weather to the interior high plateau (Fig. 4.3). Days are sunny, warm, breezy, and dry, and nights are clear, calm, and often cold, the thermometer recurrently dropping below the freezing point in those higher altitudes, a phenomenon experienced as far north as within almost 10 degrees of the equator.

From the September equinox onward, as the sun shifts increasingly southward toward its farthest poleward position over the Tropic of Capricorn around December 21st, the equatorial trough of convergent air streams begins to move steadily southward, the displacement occurring especially rapidly in east central Africa (Fig. 20.1). It will be recalled that warm, dry air from the Sahara frequently crosses the equator in east central Africa, penetrating far to southward over the interior plateau. Dry weather frequently interrupts the predominant rains of this time of year. Toward the interior warm, moist air from the sea approaches from both the Indian and South Atlantic oceans, creating a double zone of contact between maritime tropical and continental tropical air in the interior. Most of the precipitable moisture reaching the inland basins of southern Africa is brought in by the deflected trades off the Indian Ocean, chiefly from northeastward but also to some extent from the southeast. The onshore flow of South Atlantic air affects the western portions of tropical regions of the great interior upland between 300 and 400 miles inland, beginning in central Angola and spreading farther inland across the lower Congo and Kasai valleys (Fig. 4.2). Farther poleward along the southwest coast the main currents of air pass approximately parallel to the shoreline, at this season leaving it essentially rainless.

From the central Congo depression southward the rainforest begins to yield to open savanna woodland between 300 and 400 miles south of the equator, where the altitudes of the interfluvial uplands begin to approach 3000 feet or more. Elevations continue to rise gradually in a poleward direction as savanna replaces selva, reaching a broad, irregular, hilly divide between the upper tributaries of the Kasai and Congo rivers and the source region of the Zambezi. The high, hilly country between the Congo drainage and the southern interior plateau extends from central Angola eastward to the eastern highlands and varies altitude from 5000 to 6500 feet.

North of the divide yearly rains are distributed in a season marked by two peak periods in response to the passage of the equatorial trough twice over the region between September 21 and March 21. Peak months are commonly November and March eastward to the lower Kasai valley, and December and March or April between here and the eastern highlands. South of the divide normal annual rain increases during the wet season to a single peak month of maximum intensity, and January (sometimes February) is commonly the wettest month of the year.

Average annual rainfall amounts diminish southward with moderate regularity as latitude and altitude increase (Fig. 22.3). Few stations on the lower Congo basin receive more than 60 inches of annual rain. Between here and the dividing ranges around the 10th parallel, the amount lessens to between 50 and 40 inches. Beyond the divide, across Zambia to the main course of the Zambezi is a further decrease to between 40 and 30 inches, and from the middle Zambezi across Rhodesia to the Limpopo valley the normal yearly amount diminishes to between 30 and 20 inches. Along the middle reaches of the Limpopo and west of Zambia and Rhodesia in southeastern Angola and northern Botswana mean annual rainfall drops to less than 20 inches where thornveld gives way to increasing aridity in the Kalahari desert.

The normal yearly dry season is about two to three months in the savanna woodlands over the lower interior Congo. But this period lengthens steadily southward, and near the divide it is about four months. From here southward over the western interior plateaus it increases to five months or more. As the dry season increases, rainfall variability also increases, rising from less than 15 per cent in the Congo basin to more than 25 per cent over the middle Zambezi and Limpopo valleys, and farther westward to more than 50 per cent in southern Angola and northwestern Botswana.

Temperatures in the drier tropical regions south of the equator are generally well below those of their counterparts north of the equator, chiefly in consequence of the higher elevations in which they are found. South of the Congo basin the warmest month rarely averages more than 80°. But yearly minimum values are also considerably lower, and the coldest month often averages less than 60°. Frost in many parts of these drier tropical regions is a frequent occurrence of the dry season when the sun's zenithal position is far to the north.

It will be useful to compare the available climatic data for selected observation stations along three southward traverses from the Congo basin (Table 22-1), beginning with the first at Brazzaville, 4°15'S. Lat. This station (el. 1043), on the right bank of the Congo near a rainforest situation but in a more open savanna woodland, receives an average yearly rainfall of 54.3 inches. This amount is distributed mainly over an eight-month period from October through May in which two peak months appear. The first is November (8.2 inches), when rain falls on an average of nine days, and the second is April (8.5 inches), rain falling on six days during the month. The rainy season comes on suddenly toward the end of September, this month averaging 1.4 inch, and October marks the onset of heavier rains with a mean of 5.7 inches. The wet season ends abruptly, as indicated by the mean of 5.1 inches for April followed by 0.2 inch in May. This is a pattern repeatedly observed in the drier regions south of the equator where the rapid decline of wet weather is followed by a distinctly dry season of several months duration. At Brazzaville June through August average less than 0.5 inch per month. Midafternoon relative humidities remain high during dry weather, averaging from 56 to 67 per cent, and mean cloud cover is between 42 and 47 per cent. In the wet season relative humidity ranges between 65 and 71 per cent and cloud cover around 60 per cent. The mean annual range of temperature is 9 degrees, between 71° in July and 80° in April. Extreme values have not been excessive; 98° in January is the highest recorded temperature, and 54° in July the lowest.

About 380 miles south of Brazzaville at Gangassol (el. 3937) in northern Angola at latitude 9°32', about 200 miles inland, mean annual rainfall is 44.6 inches, mainly concentrated in a seven-month period from October through April. The two peak months, first November (8 inches), then March (7.6 inches),

are closer than at Brazzaville, and rain falls more often during the month, averaging fifteen days in November and fourteen in March. Mid-morning relative humidity is 81 per cent during both months. The mean annual temperature range at this higher observation point is 5 degrees, between the 67° in June and July and 72° from February through April. The thermometer has reached an extreme maximum of only 93° in February but has dropped to 37° in July. Relative humidities remain between 60 and 70 per cent during the dry season, which is three months long, from June through August, at this savanna woodland station.

At Villa Pereira de Eca (el. 3773), about 550 miles south of Gangassol, also a savanna station, at latitude 17°04', mean annual rainfall is 25.1 inches, falling almost entirely in the six-month period from November through April. The wettest month is February, with 6.3 inches falling on thirteen days, when relative humidity is 71 per cent. This peak is separated from a secondary peak month of December (4.6 inches) by a slight lessening to 3.9 inches in January, suggesting the nearness of this station to a single peak precipitation regime, which is further indicated by the occurrence of rain on an average of nine days in both December and January. The dry season lasts from May through September, and for four months, June through September, the station is normally without rain and mid-morning relative humidities drop to 25 per cent. The mean annual temperature range is 17 degrees between 63° in June and July and 80° in November. The extreme range is 63 degrees, from 37° in July to 100° in October.

About 200 miles south along the margin between savanna and thorn scrub woodland (the thornveld of southern Africa) is Tsumeb (el. 4301), at latitude 19°14'. Here mean annual rainfall is 20.6 inches, occurring mainly in the five-month interval from November through March, reaching a single peak of intensity in February, which averages 4.7 inches falling on eleven days during the month. At this time early afternoon relative humidities are 44 per cent. During the five-month period of distinctly dry weather relative humidity drops to less than 20 per cent, reaching a yearly low of 14 per cent in September. From June through August, Tsumeb is normally without rain, the remaining months of the dry season averaging less than 0.5 inch each. The mean annual temperature range is 17 degrees, from 61° in July to 78° in November, and the absolute maximum is 103°, attained in each month from November through January. The absolute minimum is 25° in July.

At Gobabis (el. 4741), about 250 miles southeast of Tsumeb well within the thornveld region at the western edge of the Kalahari desert, mean yearly rainfall is 14.3 inches, the mean annual temperature range is 22 degrees (54° in July, 76° in December and January), and the thermometer in the dry season of least warmth from the sun has dropped to 15° in June and July.

A second traverse begins about 500 miles east of Brazzaville at Luluabourg (el. 2198), 5°54′S. Lat., a station overlooking the Lulua River in a transition zone between rainforest along the river course and savanna woodland on the adjacent hillsides. Here the normal yearly rainfall total is 62.3 inches in a nine-month period from mid-August to mid-May. Maximum rains usually occur in November, which averages 9.1 inches on nineteen days, and a second peak season is March and April, when rain again falls on nineteen days per month. At these times midday relative humidities are about 68 per cent. That Luluabourg is near savanna woodland is plain from the fact that June and July each receive less than 1 inch of rain. The frequency of rainfall at this time is very low, either two or three days per month. Relative humidity in June is 44 per cent. The mean annual temperature range is 3 degrees, from 73° in July and December to 76° in May, an equable thermal regime within moderately low limits. In several months the thermometer has risen to 94° and in July has dropped to 57°, producing an extreme range of only 37 degrees.

About 350 miles south in eastern Angola is Villa Texeira de Sousa (el. 3609) in latitude 10°43′, a savanna woodland station on the divide separating the waters of the upper Kasai from the upper Zambezi. The station occupies a position near the northern part of the broad savanna belt that in this approximate latitude spans the continent from coast to coast. Mean annual rainfall is 53.2 inches, normally occurring during a seven-month period from October through April and reaching a peak in March (9.7 inches) when rain usually falls on sixteen days. At this time midmorning relative humidi-

ties reach a yearly maximum of 79 per cent. A distinct dry season prevails from May through August when monthly rainfall amounts average less than 0.5 inch, and both June and July are normally rainless, at which time relative humidity drops to between 41 and 43 per cent. Mean annual temperature range increases to 8 degrees, from 70° in June and July to 78° in September, and the thermometer has ranged from 102° in January to 37° in June.

Some 325 miles southward is Mongu (el. 3459), at latitude 15°17′, a station in Zambia well within the upland savanna region. Here mean annual rainfall is lower, 37.5 inches, occurring mainly in a five-month interval from November through March and rising to a single peak month in January. This month averages 8.7 inches on twenty-one days, when relative humidity in the early afternoon reaches a yearly maximum of 62 per cent. Five months, May through September, receive less than 0.5 inch of rain per month, and May through July are normally entirely without rain. During this dry season relative humidity becomes steadily lower, reaching a yearly minimum of 12 per cent in September. Mean annual temperature range increases here to 15 degrees, from 64° in June to 79° in October. The thermometer has reached 103° in October and has dropped to 32° in June.

Farther southward about 325 miles is Maun (el. 3100), at latitude 19°59′ near the border between savanna and thornveld in northern Botswana on the edge of the swampy Okovango basin. Here mean annual rainfall is 17 inches, most of which falls in the five-month period from November through March, increasing to a yearly peak in January when the normal amount is 4 inches falling on ten days. Evidence of increasingly drier air southward along the traverse from the Congo rainforest is further indicated at Maun by the value of 46 per cent relative humidity for early afternoon observations in the wettest month, January. For seven months relative humidity at this time of day remains below 34 per cent, dropping steadily lower from March onward to a yearly minimum of 19 per cent in September. The dry season lasts from May through September, and from June to September each month is virtually rainless. Mean annual temperature range here is 20 degrees, from 60° in June and July to 80° in November, a clear indication of the station's higher latitude, relatively high altitude, and the prevalence of clear, dry weather throughout much of the year. The extreme temperature range is 86 degrees from 110° in November to 24° in August. Frequent frosts occur from mid-June to mid-August, the daily minimum temperature being 42°, but the air warms rapidly after sunrise, the thermometer rising each day to 77° in June and July. The mean daily range of temperature at this season is thus 35 degrees, which may be compared with 22 degrees in the same period at Luluabourg between the much higher levels of 63° and 85° for mean daily minimum and maximum respectively. Information on cloud cover is lacking for most stations in this part of Africa, but the region around Maun appears to experience over 90 per cent of possible sunshine in July. In January this value drops to about 30 per cent.

A final traverse begins at Lubumbashi (el. 4035), a station about 350 miles east of Villa Texeira de Sousa in latitude 11°39′, on the banks of one of the Congo's uppermost tributaries in an elevated, savanna-mantled basin near the Zambian border in the Katanga country. Here mean annual rainfall is 48.7 inches, nearly all of which is distributed during a normal year in a five-month period from November through March. Essentially a single peak season regime, December through February normally average between 11 and 12 inches per month, falling usually on twenty-five days per month, at which time midday relative humidities average between 64 and 68 per cent. May through November is normally the rainless period when, relative humidities diminish to between 47 and 25 per cent in the clear, nearly cloudless season of cooler weather. The mean annual range of temperature is 14 degrees, between 61° in July and 75° in October, and the extreme range is 66 degrees, from 33° in July and August to 99° in September (Fig. 22.6).

About 260 miles south is Lusaka (el. 4191) at latitude 15°25′, in savanna wood and on the north side of the middle Zambezi valley. Here mean yearly rainfall is 32.9 inches, occurring in a five-month period from November through March, rising to a peak in January (9.1 inches) when rain falls on twenty-one days and when early afternoon relative humidities rise to an annual maximum of 71 per cent. The dry season, when monthly rainfall amounts are less than 0.5 inch, lasts from May through October,

July through September being nearly without rain. Relative humidities lower to 19 per cent in September. The mean annual temperature range is 15 degrees, from 61° in July to 76° in October, and the extreme range is from 39° observed in June to 100° observed in October.

At Salisbury (el. 4831), about 250 miles southeast of Lusaka, again a savanna woodland station, mean yearly rainfall is nearly the same as at Lusaka (32.6 inches), relative humidities are comparable, and the main thermal characteristics are similar also. But at Wankie (el. 2567), about 300 miles west of Salisbury near drier thorn scrub woodland, climatic qualities differ appreciably. Here mean annual rainfall is 23.2 inches, most of which occurs in a five-month period from November through March, reaching a peak in January and February when each month records 5.8 inches, and rain falls on from thirteen to sixteen days per month. The five-month dry season from May through September is about the same duration as in the savanna regions around it. The mean annual temperature range is higher, at 19 degrees, between the higher limits of 66° in June and July and 85° in October, an unusually high value for the warmer season of the year in the south latitude drier climates. The mean daily temperature range is larger than at Salisbury throughout the year, in July and August averaging 30 degrees compared with 26 and 27 degrees at Salisbury, a result of higher daily temperatures. January is 21 degrees compared with 18 degrees at Salisbury, for the same reason, for the mean daily maximum is 90° at Wankie in January and 78° at Salisbury. The thermometer has climbed to 110° in November and dropped to 36° in June.

At Beit Bridge (el. 1505) about 300 miles south of Salisbury, at latitude 22°15′ on the north bank of the middle Limpopo, a station in the arid zone in this section of the river valley, mean annual rainfall is only 12.8 inches. Yearly rains are distributed over the six-month interval from October through March, rising to a single peak in January with 2.7 inches when rain falls on six days per month and early afternoon relative humidities are at the yearly maximum of 49 per cent. During the dry season these values range between 27 and 36 per cent. The mean annual temperature range is 19 degrees between 62° in June and July and 81° in December and January. The thermometer has climbed to 112° in November and has fallen to 31° in July.

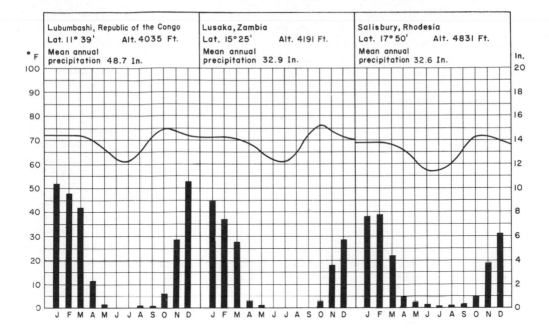

Figure 22.6. Temperature and rainfall regimes at stations in the interior of Africa south of the equator.

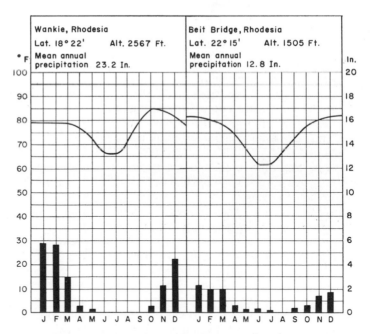

During the dry season the mean daily range is 30 to 31 degrees.

About 200 miles westward at Mahalapye (el. 3284) in eastern Botswana, a place over twice as high above sea level in the upper Limpopo valley at the eastern edge of extensive thornveld that spreads westward over the Kalahari, mean yearly rainfall is greater and temperatures are lower. Mean annual rainfall amounts to 18.2 inches, occurring in a six-month period from October through March, reaching an annual peak of 3.6 inches in January when rain falls on eight days, and a secondary peak of 3.2 inches in March when rain falls on five days. Afternoon relative humidity is low, amounting to 44 per cent in January and 45 per cent in March. The five-month dry season from May through September sees a steady decline in relative humidity values from 37 to 27 per cent. The mean annual temperature range is 22 degrees from 56° in June and July to 78° in December and January. The thermometer has ranged between 101° in October to 29° in July. The mean daily range in the dry season is from 34° to 36°, a response to the typically dry, clear weather of the period, as well as to the high latitude and moderately high altitude of this drier tropical location.

The Interior Highlands and Coastal Lowlands of East Africa

The tropical regions of east Africa extend from the southern Ethiopian highlands to the coastal lowlands near Durban, Republic of South Africa (Fig. 22.2). They occupy an unusual variety of relief features arranged in a most complicated fashion. Major land forms vary from the broad coastal plains of southern Somaliland and Mozambique, sloping upward to meet the sharp rise of the interior highlands, to extensive high plateaus and basins surmounted by snow-capped mountain ranges. These larger features are interrupted here and there by steep-sided forested valleys draining away to the sea, and even more strikingly by the long, deep, winding rift valleys embracing the elevated lakes for which this part of Africa is known. The eastern highlands attain a maximum east-west breadth of nearly 1000 miles between the high mountains that rim the eastern edge of the Congo basin and the shores of the Indian Ocean.

THE HIGHLANDS. The massive rise of the Ethiopian highlands, generally ranging from 5000 to 15,000 feet above sea level, is separated from the high plateau of Uganda and Tanzania by a broad depression in northern Kenya that subsides to between 1500 and 3000 feet in altitude. The broad plateau of Uganda-Tanzania stands at 3000 to 5000 feet, rising toward the south, and is flanked by mountain ranges reaching well over 10,000 feet. Summit heights exceed 15,000 feet in the Mitumba Mountains west of Lake Victoria and the mountains of Kenya east of the lake. Among the more prominent geomorphic features in the high plateau country are the rift valleys, deep, steep-sided, block-faulted canyons, usually more arid than the adjacent uplands, that form

three distinct systems: the West Rift, forming the western borderlands of Uganda, Ruanda, Burundi, and Tanzania and often over 2000 feet deep; the East Rift, a much shallower feature extending southward across western Kenya to eastern Tanzania; and the Great Rift, 2000 feet or more in depth, in Malawi.

The West Rift valley is occupied by a series of long, narrow lakes that stand well above sea level but are often several thousand feet below the high mountain ranges adjacent to them. Lake Albert stands at 2030 feet, Lake Edward at 2992 feet, Lac Kivu at 4790 feet, Lake Tanganyika at 2534 feet, and Lake Rudolph in the desert depression of northern Kenya at 1230 feet. Lake Victoria, a large body of water measuring about 200 miles from north to south and about 150 miles from east to west, is 3720 feet above sea level. Climates along the shores of each lake, and in many cases on the land for miles around, are significantly modified by the temperature and moisture of the water surface, and these modifications, along with the many striking contrasts in relief and exposure to the prevailing winds, complicate the details of climatic distribution in east Africa.

The region as a whole is dominated by air flowing in from the Indian Ocean, the chief source of precipitable moisture (Fig. 20.1). From May through October the southeast trades sweep equatorward, recurving to become southwest winds upon crossing the equator. From November through April the dominant flow is again primarily off the Indian Ocean, but from northeastward. At this time continental tropical air from the Sahara occasionally replaces maritime air from the sea, extending the recurrent periods of dry weather. In April and October, when a change takes place in the quarter from which most easterly winds blow, a few weeks of light, variable winds and calms are experienced. At higher levels, between 10,000 and 12,000 feet, westerly winds also vary the dominant airflow patterns and are sufficiently moisture-laden at times to produce fairly prolonged, light, steady rains. The causal relationships between surface rainfall and major features of the general circulation are not completely understood at this time and require a great deal more study, particularly of the upper atmosphere.

Although climatic variety in east Africa ranges from constant heat and humidity in a few small pockets of rainforest to constant cold on the ice-capped peaks of several high mountains and to constant aridity in the desert basin of northern Kenya and the desert coast of Somali, the predominant climate is savanna woodland. Low mean annual rainfall, a pronounced alternation of wet and dry seasons, moderately large temperature fluctuations, seasonally low atmospheric humidity and cloud cover, and seasonally high percentages of possible sunshine are characteristic of the savanna woodland and bushland from Ethiopia to Mozambique.

A general statement on the salient climatic qualities for the entire territory is meaningless, and thus we shall examine separately the distinctive atmospheric qualities in the major regions: the Uganda-Tanzania plateau, the West Rift valley, and the coastal lowlands.

The broad plateau of Uganda, Tanzania, and the western part of Kenya gains in general elevation southward, from about 3000 feet in northern Uganda to about 5000 feet in southern Tanzania. Mean yearly rainfall decreases southward from around 60 inches to less than 20 inches, although increasing to 60 inches or more in the high mountains east and west of Lake Victoria and those near the north end of Lake Nyasa and on isolated eminences elsewhere (Fig. 22.7). In small, detached areas on the northern and western shores of Lake Victoria amounts in excess of 80 inches are normal. The importance of this large body of water cannot be overlooked in accounting for the higher values reported in the wetter parts of the shoreline and northwest of the lake in Uganda.

North of the lake peak rains usually occur in May and August, with December and January the drier months, but south of the lake the seasons are essentially reversed, peak rains occurring in November or December and again in March or April, the period from June to September being the normal dry season of lower atmospheric humidity, less cloud cover, and greater uncertainty of annual rainfall (Fig. 22.1). Gulu (el. 3650), about 175 miles north of Lake Victoria in 2°45'N. Lat., annually receives 60.2 inches of rain distributed over ten to eleven months of the year, rising to an initial peak of 7.9 inches in May falling on eighteen days and an annual maximum of 8.9 inches in August, falling on twenty-one days. Midafternoon relative humidities are 60 and 63 per cent respec-

tively. In August mean cloudiness is 70 per cent. January averages 0.4 inch, falling on only five days as a rule, with relative humidity at 32 per cent, and both December and February average 1.7 inch. At Tabora (el. 4151), about 550 miles south at 5°02'S. Lat., mean annual rainfall is 34.6 inches, mainly occurring in the six-month interval from November through April and reaching a double peak in December and March. December averages 6.7 inches, falling on nineteen days, when relative humidity is 54 per cent and cloud cover 72 per cent, and March averages 6.6 inches falling on sixteen days, when relative humidity is 58 per cent and mean cloud cover 74 per cent. Here the dry season extends from June through September, when each month averages less than 0.5 inch (July and August are virtually rainless), and in September and October relative humidity in the early afternoon

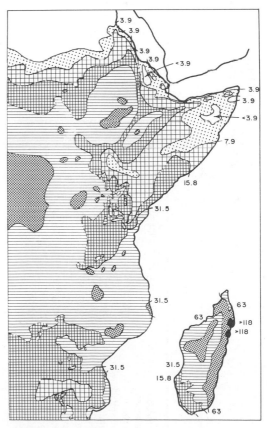

Figure 22.7. Mean annual rainfall in east Africa and Malagasy (inches).

TABLE 22-2

Climatic Data for Tropical Forest and Woodland Stations in Eastern Africa and Malagasy
(Temp., °F; Rainfall, In.)

Station	Lat.	El. in Ft		Jan.	Feb.	Mar.	Apr.	May	Jun.	Jul.	Aug.	Sep.	Oct.	Nov.	Dec.	Year
Antsirabe, Malagasy	19°52'S.	4939	T	68	67	67	64	59	56	54	56	60	64	67	67	
			R	12.0	10.0	7.6	3.7	1.5	0.5	0.5	0.5	1.0	2.7	6.3	10.3	56.6
Beira, Mozambique	19°50'S.	28	T	82	82	80	78	73	70	69	70	74	77	79	80	
			R	10.8	8.2	10.0	4.0	2.0	1.5	1.4	1.1	0.8	1.5	5.1	9.2	55.6
Bukoba, Tanzania	1°20'S.	3753	T	70	71	71	71	71	70	69	69	70	70	70	70	
			R	5.7	6.3	9.7	14.1	12.6	3.4	1.9	3.4	4.2	5.2	6.5	7.6	80.5
Dar Es Salaam, Tanzania	6°50'S.	47	T	82	82	81	80	78	76	75	75	75	76	79	81	
			R	2.6	2.3	4.8	11.0	7.8	1.3	1.2	1.0	1.1	1.8	2.9	3.5	41.3
Entebbe, Uganda	0°04'N.	3878	T	72	72	72	72	71	70	69	70	70	71	71	71	
			R	2.6	3.5	6.2	10.1	9.1	4.6	3.0	3.0	3.1	3.7	5.1	4.5	58.9
Gulu, Uganda	2°45'N.	3650	T	76	77	76	75	73	72	71	71	72	73	74	74	
			R	0.4	1.7	3.3	6.8	7.9	5.8	6.7	8.9	6.8	6.4	3.8	1.7	60.2
Iringa, Tanzania	7°47'S.	5380	T	67	68	68	67	66	63	62	63	66	68	70	68	
			R	6.9	5.0	6.8	3.5	0.5	0.1	0.0	0.0	0.1	0.2	1.5	4.7	29.2
Lourenco Marques, Mozambique	25°58'S.	194	T	77	77	78	74	70	67	66	69	68	71	75	75	
			R	5.1	4.2	5.3	2.2	0.9	0.9	0.5	0.4	1.1	1.6	3.6	4.0	29.7
Lamu, Kenya	2°16'S.	30	T	79	80	81	82	78	77	76	76	77	78	80	80	
			R	0.2	0.1	0.7	4.9	14.2	6.4	2.6	1.6	1.2	1.5	1.2	1.1	35.7
Mombassa, Kenya	4°04'S.	52	T	82	83	84	82	79	78	77	77	77	79	81	82	
			R	1.0	0.6	2.4	7.8	10.0	4.3	3.5	2.7	2.7	3.5	3.7	2.4	47.5
Mossuril, Mozambique	14°57'S.	49	T	81	81	81	77	76	72	72	73	75	79	81	82	
			R	8.6	8.6	5.9	3.5	1.1	1.3	0.6	0.6	0.4	0.3	1.1	5.4	37.4
Nairobi, Kenya	1°17'S.	5450	T	68	70	70	69	67	65	63	64	66	68	68	68	
			R	1.4	1.6	4.5	8.3	5.1	1.8	0.5	1.8	1.0	2.1	4.5	2.7	34.3
Sao Hill, Tanzania	6°20'S.	6500	T	64	64	63	62	60	57	55	57	61	63	64	64	
			R	7.5	6.7	8.1	3.4	0.7	0.2	0.1	0.1	0.1	0.5	2.6	7.1	36.9
Tabora, Tanzania	5°02'S.	4151	T	73	73	73	73	72	70	70	72	76	78	76	73	
			R	5.0	4.9	6.6	5.4	1.1	0.1	0.0	0.0	0.3	0.6	3.9	6.7	34.6
Tamatave, Malagasy	18°09'S.	20	T	80	80	79	78	75	72	70	70	72	74	77	79	
			R	15.5	17.2	19.9	16.3	12.4	12.3	10.2	8.6	5.5	3.4	7.3	10.3	139.0
Tananarive, Malagasy	18°55'S.	4529	T	68	68	67	65	61	58	56	57	59	64	67	68	
			R	12.2	9.5	8.0	2.0	0.7	0.4	0.3	0.4	0.5	2.0	6.2	11.3	53.4
Tulear, Malagasy	23°20'S.	20	T	81	82	80	77	72	69	68	69	71	74	77	80	
			R	2.9	2.7	1.8	0.3	0.7	0.5	0.2	0.2	0.4	0.6	1.5	1.8	13.5
Wete, Tanzania	5°04'S.	60	T	82	82	82	81	79	77	76	76	77	78	80	81	
			R	2.1	1.9	6.7	16.8	19.1	5.2	3.0	2.0	1.4	4.1	8.7	6.0	77.0

drops to 30 per cent, mean cloudiness to between 28 and 44 per cent.

In these low latitudes temperature is chiefly affected by altitude, exposure to prevailing winds, and distance from the moderating influence of large bodies of water. Thus, the thermal experience at both Gulu and Tabora is in close accord. The mean annual temperature range at Gulu is six degrees, from 71° in July and August to 77° in February, the extreme range from 98° in February through April to 49° in December at the start of the drier season. At Tabora the mean annual range is 8 degrees, from 70° in June and July, the dry season, to 78° in October before the onset of the wet season. The extreme range here is from 95° in October and November to 50° in July (Table 22-2).

The effect of higher altitude is illustrated in the case of Mbeya (el. 5768), a station about 265 miles south of Tabora in a deep valley within about 5 miles of mountain ranges north and south rising 3500 to 4000 feet above it. Here the mean annual temperature range is 10 degrees between 58° in July and 68° in November. The extreme range is from 88° in September through November to 36° in July. Mean annual rainfall here also reflects the influence of its mountainous situation, averaging 33.4 inches and rising to a single peak of 7.5 inches in January when rain falls on twenty-three days.

The influence of Lake Victoria may be gauged by comparing the climatic data of four stations on its shores. At Entebbe on the north shore mean annual rainfall is 58.9 inches, distributed throughout the year but rising to a yearly maximum of 10.1 inches in April when rain occurs on twenty-two days and a secondary peak of 5.1 inches in November on seventeen days. January records the least monthly amount of 2.6 inches falling on nine days. Across the lake on the south shore is Mwanza, where the normal yearly total is 39.4 inches, mainly occurring from October through May and rising to a yearly maximum of 6.1 inches on fifteen days in March, and a second peak of 5.8 inches on twelve days in December. June through August receive less than 1 inch per month. On the western shore is Bukoba, where the annual mean is 80.5 inches, increasing to a yearly maximum of 14.1 inches in April, falling on twenty-two days, and a second peak of 7.6

inches in December, falling on eighteen days. July is the least rainy month, averaging 1.9 inch, falling on only five days. On the opposite shore is Kisumum, where the mean annual rainfall is 44 inches, distributed over most of the year, although rising to a maximum monthly amount of 7.6 inches in April, when rain falls on fourteen days, and a second peak of 3.7 inches in December, when rain falls on eight days.

The southern and eastern shores of Lake Victoria are thus in the lee of the main rain-bearing winds from the southeast, and the northern and western shores are well-exposed to them. The contrasts are also revealed in the temperature regimes of the four stations. The mean annual range at Entebbe is 3 degrees, from 69° in July to 72° in January through April, the extreme range from 94° in March to 54° in July. At Mwanza the mean range is the same at 3 degrees, but between the higher limits of 73° in July and 76° in October, and the extreme range is between 95° in October and 51° in July. At Bukoba the range is 2 degrees, between 69° in July and 71° from February through May, and the extreme range is between 88° in several months and 50° in July and August. At Kisumum the mean range is 5 degrees, between 71° in July and August and 76° in February and March, and the extreme range is from 98° in several months to 54° in August and September.

Relative humidities also differ on opposite sides of the lake. At Entebbe they range between 63 and 74 per cent through the year, but at Mwanza they range from 44 to 63 per cent. At Bukoba they range between 69 and 73 per cent, and at Kisumum between 41 and 57 per cent, all observations made in the early to mid-afternoon.

One of the more striking climatic variations of the plateau region is the change from savanna woodland and montane forest near Nairobi to arid desert in the Lake Rudolph basin. Nairobi (el. 5971), less than 2 degrees south of the equator and about 80 miles southwest of Mt. Kenya (el. 17,040), lies near the edge of the interior upland where shrubby, tree-dotted grassland gives way at higher elevation to montane forest, and where the land slopes eastward to the sea. Here the mean annual precipitation is 34.3 inches, distributed in a typical south latitude regime with most of the yearly quotient recorded between October and May. April is the maximum rainfall month (8.3 inches), with sixteen rain days, and November the secondary peak, with 4.5 inches falling on fifteen days. It is during these months that the equatorial trough weather of cloudy skies, increased atmospheric humidity, fitful winds, and much rain passes across the area. The dry season is chiefly from July through September, averaging less than 1 inch per month and falling on six or seven days per month.

At Lodwar (el. 1660), over 300 miles north of Nairobi in the arid, rocky desert basin of Lake Rudolph at 3°07′N. Lat., mean annual rainfall is only 5.7 inches. The basin of Lake Rudolph lies in the relatively low depression between the Ethiopian highlands and the mountains of central Kenya and is thus shadowed by them from the prevailing northwest winds from September to March and the southwest winds that dominate the rest of the year. The rain shadow effect extends from the northern end of the basin across the Ethiopian border some 500 miles southeastward toward the coast of Kenya.

At Nairobi mean annual temperature range is 7 degrees, from 63° in July to 70° in February and March, the extreme range is from 87° in February to 41° in September, afternoon relative humidity ranges from 40 per cent in February to 62 per cent in May. At Lodwar the mean annual temperature range is 5 degrees, between the much higher limits of 82° in August and 87° in March, the extreme range from 61° in November and December to 104° in April, relative humidities ranging from 30 per cent in January and February to 41 per cent in July.

Further contrasts appear between the shores of the West Rift lakes and the plateaus that lie east of them. The lake surfaces are generally 2000 feet or more below the adjoining uplands, and the deep trenches they occupy, having a roughly north-south alignment, channel the seasonal winds to flow mainly lengthwise along their shores from southward after March and from northward after September. Stations in the lee of the dominant winds, deep in the steep-sided valleys, tend to be considerably drier than higher upland stations to windward of them. They are also drier than stations along the well-exposed windward lake shores reached by winds that have passed down the 100 mile length of Lake Albert, the 400 mile length of Lake Tanganyika, or the 360 mile length of Lake Nyasa.

The special advantage of climatic salubrity provided by high elevations, in terms of human comfort, is an outstanding feature of the eastern highlands: clear air, bright sunshine, and comfortably lower temperatures. Also evident is the change from open savanna woodland to a somewhat more luxuriant montane forest of richer vegetation in which conifers, evergreen shrubs, and mosses thrive. The climatic change may be illustrated by a comparison of two stations in southern Tanzania, Sao Hill, about 115 miles northeast of Lake Nyasa, and Iringa, some 46 miles northeast of Sao Hill.

At Iringa (el. 5380), near the eastern edge of the plateau but nearly 200 miles from the Indian Ocean, mean annual rainfall amounts to 29.2 inches, falling mainly from December through April and reaching a peak of 6.9 inches in January, when rain occurs on nineteen days, and again in March, with 6.8 inches falling on eighteen days. At Sao Hill (el. 6500) the mean yearly rainfall is 36.9 inches, occurring chiefly from November through April, reaching a climax in January (7.5 inches) and April (8.1 inches), falling on twenty-one and twenty-five days respectively. Early afternoon relative humidities are substantially higher at Sao Hill, ranging from 75 and 74 per cent in January and March, compared with 66 and 69 per cent at Iringa, in the dry season dropping to 38 per cent at Iringa and 39 per cent at Sao Hill.

The mean annual temperature range at Iringa is 8 degrees, from 62° in July to 70° in November, but at Sao Hill it is 9 degrees, from 55° in July to 64° in November through February. The absolute range of record is from 90° in November to 42° in July at Iringa. It is lower at Sao Hill, from 83° in November to 39° in July.

THE LOWLANDS. East of the interior high plateaus, deep rift valleys, and lofty mountain ranges the land in east Africa drops downward to form a low coastal plain that varies in breadth from about 50 to 250 miles or more. Tropical climates reach from the deserts of Somali southward to Cape St. Lucia, about 130 miles northeast of Durban. In southern Somali and eastern Kenya surfaces less than 700 feet in elevation extend inland for nearly 200 miles. From southern Kenya into northern Mozambique the interior uplands advance seaward in descending plateaus and basins between 1500 and 3000 feet in altitude to within 50 miles of the shore. Toward central Mozambique the coastal lowlands spread inland for over 100 miles, reaching 150 miles up the Zambezi valley and broadening to more than 200 miles toward the Limpopo. From southern Mozambique into Natal the coastal plain tapers to less than 50 miles near Cape St. Lucia and less than 10 miles near Durban.

The tropical climates that prevail along these shores and spread inland up the eastern declivities to merge with those of the interior are primarily affected by maritime tropical air from the Indian Ocean throughout the year. From Somali southward to Cape Delgado in northern Mozambique the monsoonal shift from southerly to northerly winds is an annual feature of the surface circulation. From Cape Delgado northward southeast winds, curving to become southwest winds in Kenya and Somali, prevail from April through November as far as Zanzibar, and from here northward the season is shortened to May through September. The southerly monsoon becomes stronger and more regular with increasing distance northward. In November winds become lighter but freshen gradually from northeastward, and from December through March northerly winds predominate. In April the change of monsoons takes place more actively with frequent heavy squalls.

From Cape Delgado southward winds are primarily from southeastward the year round (Fig. 20.1), although they become more variable between September and March, blowing from east to northeast and occasionally westward when migrating disturbances appear along the southeast coast of Africa, and from time to time advance across the Tropic. Land and sea breezes, especially in May and June, modify the seasonal monsoon flow in the higher latitudes.

North of Zanzibar the bulk of the year's rain tends to fall during the southwest monsoon between April and July (Fig. 22.1). Maximum rains occur in May, with a much less productive secondary peak in October or November. South of Zanzibar for about 300 miles the rainiest interval is from March to May, with April the peak month and a moderately strong secondary peak in December. From Cape Delgado southward December through April becomes the rainiest season, with an increasing tendency toward a single peak month in January in the higher latitudes near the Tropic of Capricorn.

Mean annual rainfall along the entire tropical coast of east Africa varies considerably according to proximity to the sea, altitude, and exposure but in general tends to range between 35 and 55 inches (Fig. 22.7). For example, from north to south the following coastal stations are representative: in Kenya, Lamu averages 35.7 inches, Mombassa 47.5; in Tanzania, Tanga averages 52.9 inches, Dar Es Salaam 41.3, Lindi 35.3; in Mozambique, Mossuril averages 37.4 inches, Beira 55.6, Inhambane 37.6, with Lourenco Marques, the southernmost station in latitude 25°58′ in an unusually dry situation averaging 29.7 inches. The change from desert conditions along the south Somali coast to tropical thorn scrub woodland and savanna takes place rapidly. Within less than 50 miles mean annual amounts rise from about 10 to over 20 inches. At Chisimaio, Somali, for example, the mean yearly total is 8.9 inches, but at Lamu, about 170 miles southwest on the north Kenya coast, the value is 35.7 inches.

At stations facing the main rain-bearing airstreams from the sea and in particularly well-exposed situations at higher elevation, the normal yearly rains increase. This can be illustrated by a few comparisons. At Tanga the mean yearly amount is 47.5 inches, but 30 miles west at Amani, situated on the south slopes of the Usumbara Mountains at an altitude of 2989 feet, the value is 75.7 inches. At Dar Es Salaam the yearly value is 41.3 inches, but at Mahenge, about 200 miles southwest in the high valley of a tributary of the Rufiji River at 3630 feet, the mean annual rainfall is 72.9 inches. Farther south in Mozambique the coastal station of Beira averages 55.6 inches, whereas at Vila Gauveia, about 170 miles northwestward at an altitude of 2004 feet, the value is 68.4 inches. By contrast with these situations, the rain shadow influence of higher land near the coast is indicated by comparing the station of Pafuri (el. 951) with Inhambane, about 270 miles east of it. Pafuri is in the lower Limpopo valley and averages only 13.3 inches per year.

The islands of Zanzibar and Mafia off the coast of Tanzania also receive heavier amounts of annual rainfall, Wete, Zanzibar, averaging 77 inches and Kilidoni, Mafia, averaging 74.3 inches. On the Comoro Islands at the north end of the Mozambique Channel about midway between Malagasy and the mainland, yearly totals exceed 100 inches; at Moroni, Grand Comoro, for example, the annual mean is 113.5 inches. To a large extent rain falls in the form of

TABLE 22–3
Rainfall Data for Three Stations in East Africa (In.)

Station	Lat.	El. in Ft	Jan.	Feb.	Mar.	Apr.	May	Jun.	Jul.	Aug.	Sep.	Oct.	Nov.	Dec.	Year
Tanga, Tanzania	5°07'S.	50	1.6	1.9	3.7	10.5	12.0	2.5	4.7	2.9	3.0	3.9	7.5	2.4	56.6
Mossuril, Mozambique	14°57'S.	49	8.6	8.6	5.9	3.5	1.1	1.3	0.6	0.6	0.4	0.3	1.1	5.4	37.4
Beira, Mozambique	19°50 S.	28	10.8	8.2	10.0	4.0	2.0	1.5	1.4	1.1	0.8	1.5	5.1	9.2	55.6

Source: F. L. Wernstedt, *World Climatic Data, Africa,* Pennsylvania State University, 1959.

convective showers arising in part from the thermal uplift of warm, moist oceanic air over heated land and in part from orographic effects. On some of the offshore islands, enveloped in nearly saturated air, this combination of influences produces drenching rains of high intensity. At Moroni over 17 inches of rain have fallen in twenty-four hours during both April and July.

The contrasting rainfall regimes of northern and southern sections of the coast and their relationships with the dominant surface wind patterns may be observed by comparing Tanga, Mossuril, and Beira in Table 22-3. At Tanga there is no dry season, although during the northeast monsoon a less rainy period sets in during January (1.2 inch) and February (1.9 inch), when winds are chiefly from northeastward, mean afternoon cloud cover is only about 30 per cent, and rain falls on only four days per month. In March, following the northward shift of the equatorial trough, the period of maximum rain begins, and from March through June nearly half the year's (49 per cent) rain normally occurs. At this time winds are chiefly from south to southeast, mean afternoon cloud cover is between 38 and 56 per cent, and rain falls on fifteen days in April and May. May is the wettest month, averaging 12.9 inches. South to southeasterly winds hold through November, and a second peak season reaches climax in October (4.5 inches) and November (4.2 inches), when mean cloud cover is between 33 and 40 per cent and rain falls on nine and twelve days respectively.

At Mossuril, about 700 miles south of Tanga in latitude 15°01' and about 300 miles south of Cape Delgado where the Mozambique Channel is most narrowly constricted, 84 per cent of the year's rainfall normally occurs in the five-month period from December through April. During this time of year winds are mainly from northward, forming an integral component of the counterclockwise circulation of the south Indian Ocean High, which at this season contracts, shifts southward, and lessens in intensity. Afternoon cloud cover averages up to 84 per cent in January and 87 per cent in February, when monthly rains are normally 8.6 inches and fall on twelve or thirteen days per month. The distinctly dry season of four months or more in length lasts from July through October, when each month averages less than 0.5 inch of rain. At this time winds are southerly, the daily sea breeze inducing a deflection to eastward from the late forenoon to evening, and mean cloud cover drops to 21 per cent in November, before the seasonal rains set in.

Southwest of Mossuril about 550 miles, at latitude 19°50' is Beira, where 85 per cent of the year's rains are distributed in a six-month period from November through April and no month is really dry. During the rainy season winds are dominantly from east and southeast, the peak months are January (10.8 inches) and March (10 inches) when rain falls on twelve and thirteen days respectively, and mean cloud cover is between 59 and 61 per cent. From May through October, when monthly rains average between 1 and 2 inches, cloud cover ranges between 33 and 44 per cent, and although winds become more variable, they are still chiefly from east and southeast and yet rain falls on only three to six days per month.

Temperatures vary only slightly from north to south along the entire 2000 mile shoreline of tropical east Africa, averaging monthly values that range from the middle 70s to the lower 80s throughout the year. The mean annual range is between 5 and 7 degrees north of Cape

Delgado but increases to between 10 and 15 degrees south of the cape. At Tanga the mean annual range is 7 degrees, between 75° in August and 82° in February and March, at Mossuril the range is 10 degrees, from 72° in July to 82° in December, and at Beira it is 13 degrees, between 69° in July and 82° in January and February. Increased values arise principally from lower winter temperatures. Farther inland larger annual variations are characteristic, and Amani, 30 miles west of Tanga, averages 9 degrees, from 64° in August to 73° from January through March. Here the extreme minimum temperature has been 49° in August, compared with 60° in September at Tanga, although the extreme maximum is lower at 91° compared with 95° at Tanga, a result of Amani's higher elevation. Farther south the inland station of Pafuri on the lower Limpopo reports a mean annual range of 16 degrees, between 68° in June and July and 84° in December and January. This may be compared with Inhambane with a lower range of 12 degrees from 68° in June and July, but where summers are cooler, averaging 80° from January through March. At Pafuri the thermometer has climbed to 115° in November and lowered to 33° in June, whereas at Inhambane the extreme maximum has been 99° in November, the extreme minimum 51° in June.

Atmospheric humidity is constantly high throughout the year at coastal stations, relative humidity averaging in midafternoon, even during the drier intervals, over 60 per cent as a general rule. Thus, high temperatures and moist air are climatic constants along the entire 2000 mile coast. At inland stations, as expected, values are much lower. At Pafuri, for example, daily observations at 2100 reveal a value of 55 per cent in March, highest for the year, decreasing from this point onward to 42 per cent during the dry season in August.

The Malagasy Republic (Madagascar), the large, mountainous island off the southeast coast of Africa, lying approximately between 12° and 26°S. Lat., is about 1000 miles long and over 300 miles in average width. Its maximum breadth is about 380 miles from Tamatave to Cape St. Andre, and at the latter point it is nearest the mainland at a distance of about 270 miles. In the eastern part of the island for nearly its entire length low mountains rise to more than 5000 feet at many points, the highest of which is Mt. Maromokotra at 9436 feet, about 150 miles south of the northernmost projection at Cap d'Ambre.

The eastern shores of Malagasy are constantly hot and humid, receiving abundant yearly rains, and the climate is thus tropical evergreen rainforest except near the northern and southern extremities. Rainforest extends up the eastern mountain slopes, spreading inland for 50 to 100 miles, at higher elevations yielding to a dominantly wooded savanna grassland over most of the interior uplands (Fig. 22.2). Here, in the mixed tall and short tropical grass-covered high plains scattered shrub growth and only a small proportion of trees form the characteristic vegetation. Descending the more gradual declines of the western slopes, savanna woodland merges with the remnants of semideciduous forest in the north and thorn scrub woodland toward the southwest, finally giving way to desert scrub vegetation in the extreme south-western section.

Malagasy is under the influence of easterly winds throughout the year (Fig. 20.1). Hence the eastern side is persistently more humid, cloudier, receives more annual rain, and its temperatures are more equable than on the western side. From the Masoala peninsula southward beyond the Tropic of Capricorn, coastal stations annually receive more than 100 inches of rainfall (Fig. 22.7). For more than 100 miles north of Cape Masoala values range between 100 and 85 inches but drop off rapidly toward Cap d'Ambre to less than 40 inches. South of the Tropic they fall off to less than 20 inches around the southern tip of the island near Cape Ste. Marie. Along the northwest coast annual amounts range between 85 and 60 inches The season of major rains throughout the country is chiefly September through March, when the sun is high overhead, with yearly maxima usually occurring in January, although occasionally delayed until March.

Exceptionally wet areas are indicated by the rainfall records of well-exposed sites along the northeast coast. At Ambodifototra, on St. Marie Island about 75 miles south of Cape Masoala, mean annual rainfall is 142.3 inches; at Soanierana, 20 miles west on the coast, the mean is 146.5 inches; and the same amount is recorded at Maroantsetra, about 100 miles north at the head of Antongil Bay.

About 130 miles north of Cape Masoala at Sambava the normal yearly mean is 85.7 inches.

Northward annual totals decrease rapidly, however. Within less than 60 miles, at Vohemar, the value is 56.9 inches, and at Diego Suarez, 70 miles farther north, it is 35.5 inches (Table 22-2).

On the southeast coast at Amparihy-Est in latitude 23°58′ the mean yearly rainfall is 119 inches; 80 miles south at Fort Dauphin it is 60.3 inches; some 50 miles west at Ambovombe it drops to 23.8 inches; 35 miles farther west it is only 19.8 inches.

On the west coast at Majunga in latitude 15°44′ normal annual rainfall is 61.4 inches, decreasing to 37 inches about 220 miles southwestward at Maintirano, to 30.7 inches about 150 miles south at Morondava, to 18.2 inches at Morombe, 120 miles farther south, and to 13.5 inches 110 miles south of that at Tulear. Another 120 miles southward only 11.6 inches is normally recorded at Androka, well within the arid region of southwestern Malagasy.

A comparison of Tamatave on the northeast coast with Tulear will reveal the great contrast between the opposing climates of the northeast and southwest. At Tamatave, about 160 miles south of Cape Masoala, the mean annual rainfall is 139 inches, 82 per cent of which occurs in the six-month period from December through July. The peak month is March (19.9 inches), when rain normally falls on twenty days, midday relative humidity is 77 per cent, and mean cloud cover is 73 per cent. Copious rains occur during the remainder of the year, and October, the least rainy month, averages 3.4 inches falling on twelve days. At this time relative humidity is 68 per cent and mean cloud cover 50 per cent, the lowest cloud amount for the year. The mean annual temperature range is 10 degrees from 70° in July to 80° in January and February. Extreme temperatures are 98° in January and 56° in August.

At Tulear, in latitude 23°21′, mean annual precipitation is 13.5 inches, 79 per cent of which occurs in the five-month interval from November through March. January is the peak month, averaging only 2.9 inches falling on five days, when midday relative humidity is 65 per cent and cloud cover 40 per cent. From June through September and also in April less than 0.5 inch of rain per month is the rule. In July and August only 8 per cent of the sky is cloud-covered, and relative humidity drops to 51 per cent in July. The mean annual temperature range is 14 degrees, from 68° in July, at the height of the dry season, to 82° in February. Here the thermometer has risen to 108° in February and dropped to 43° in August.

An impression of the interior climates of Malagasy may be gained by examining the climatic data for Tananarive and Antsirabe. Tananarive, about 160 miles southwest of Tamatave at an altitude of 4529 feet, is a savanna woodland station at which the average yearly rainfall is 53.4 inches, 88 per cent of which falls in the five-month period from November through March. January is the peak month, with 12.2 inches falling on twenty-five days, when midday relative humidities average 70 per cent and mean cloud cover is 80 per cent. A four-month dry season from June through September is normal, when monthly rains average less than 0.5 inch, relative humidity drops to 49 per cent and mean cloud cover to 50 per cent. The mean annual temperature range is 12 degrees from 56° in July to 68° in December through February. Here the thermometer has ranged from 95° in October to 35° in August.

At Antsirabe, about 75 miles south at an altitude of 4939 feet, the rainy season is about seven months long, and mean yearly rainfall is 56.2 inches, 81 per cent of which occurs in the five-month period from November through March. January is again the wettest month, averaging 11.6 inches on twenty-two days, when midday relative humidity is 66 per cent. From June through September less than 1 inch of rain is the monthly normal, falling on only one or two days, and relative humidity drops to 31 per cent in October. The mean annual temperature range is 14 degrees from 54° in July to 68° in January. Here the extreme range is from 89° in October to 27° in June.

References

GILLMAN, C.: "A Vegetation-Types Map of Tanganyika Territory," *Geographical Review*, **39**(1): 7–37, 1949.

HOWE, G. M.: "Climates of the Rhodesias and Nyasaland According to the Thornthwaite Classification," *Geographical Review*, **43**(3): 525–40, 1953.

HUBBARD, J. H.: "Daily Weather at Achimota, near Accra, Gold Coast," *Geographical Studies*, **3**(1): 56–63, 1956.

MICHELMORE, A. P. G.: "Observations on Tropical African Grasslands," *Journal of Ecology*, **27**: 282–312, 1939.

THOMPSON, B. W., *The Climate of Africa*, Oxford University Press, New York, 1965.

U.S. ARMY, QUARTERMASTER RESEARCH AND ENGINEERING COMMAND, *Analogs of Canal Zone Climate in East Central Africa*, Natick, Mass., 1958.

———: *Analogs of Canal Zone Climate in South Central Africa and Madagascar*, Natick, Mass., 1958.

———: *Analogs of Canal Zone Climate in West Central Africa*, Natick, Mass., 1958.

chapter 23

TROPICAL FORESTS AND WOODLANDS IN SOUTHERN ASIA, THE EAST INDIES, AND AUSTRALIA

The third major group of tropical environments in the world spreads over the large, low latitude peninsulas of India and southeast Asia, the islands of the East Indies, and northern Australia (Fig. 23.1). Here they span a breadth in latitude of some 61 degrees from about 33°N. in northeastern India to about 28°S. on the east coast of Australia. From the deserts of northwest India to the interior deserts of Australia the distance is about 6000 miles, and from the south China coast to the north coast of Australia over 2500 miles. This part of the world, north of Australia, is best known as monsoon Asia and includes most of India, Ceylon, East Pakistan, Burma, Thailand, Malaya, Cambodia, Laos, Vietnam, the south coast of China, Indonesia, and the Philippines. Together with northern Australia, it is climatologically under the primary control of that annual shift in surface circulation known by the general term *monsoon*. But yearly reversal of surface windflow and the meridional shift of air streams in the upper troposphere assume a variety of dominant directions over the enormous area in this part of the tropics. In addition, the highly irregular size, shape, and distribution of land and water surfaces, plus the great contrasts in relief and surface configuration, give to the distribution of tropical climates an internal complexity that would appear to defy description. In a general way, however, the regional climatic pattern and its relationships with the ruling components of the general circulation can be made adequately plain for the purpose of grasping its significance within the geographical context of world climatic distribution.

The primary conditions that set the pattern of tropical climatic distribution in this part of the world are low latitudes, continuously warm ocean surfaces, and the insular-peninsular character of the lands reached by warm, moist air from the sea. Modifying the combined effect of these fundamental conditions are elevation above sea level, the size, shape, and altitude of major relief features, their alignment in relation to the prevailing movement of surface winds, and distance from the sea. Thus, one finds that the requirements of constantly high temperatures and atmospheric humidities and abundant rainfall are met at altitudes generally below 4000 feet along the west coast of peninsular India, in southwest Ceylon, in northeast India, in many sections of southeast Asia's mainland, the Malay peninsula, the East Indies, and along the moderately elevated terrain of northeastern Australia.

PLANT LIFE. The most richly developed tropical evergreen rainforest in all of southeast Asia is found in a core area (Fig. 23.11), embracing the Malay peninsula, Sumatra, and Borneo.[1] The vegetation is typical in structure and diversified

---

[1] The term *Borneo* is used here to apply to the entire island, which is politically divided into Kalimantan, Sarawak, North Borneo, and Brunei.

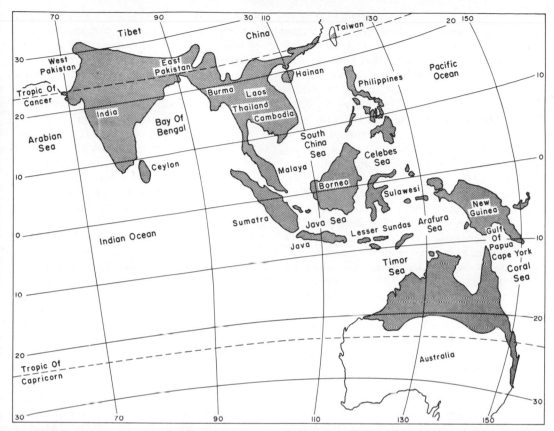

Figure 23.1.   Distribution of tropical forest and woodland in Indo-Malaya.

in composition, the tallest trees ranging in height from 100 to 180 feet or more, many individuals raising their thickly branched evergreen crowns above the level of the densely intertwined canopy of trees below. Within the persistent twilight beneath the crowded foliage is a profusion of climbing plants, epiphytes, ferns, and the saplings of the dominant trees.

By far the most numerous forest trees of the core area belong to a single family, the *Diptero-carpaceae*. Other families are well represented, but at least half the forest trees in the lowlands of southeast Asia are diptocarps. Perhaps four thousand distinct species of diptocarps are known across the entire Indo-Malayan region, where they are endemic. Important diptocarps in the central equatorial zone of the Malay peninsula, Sumatra, and Borneo are red merantis (*Shorea spp.*), white merantis (*Shorea spp.*, *Parashorea spp.*, and *Pentacme spp.*), keruing (*Diptocarpus kerrii*), resake (*Vatica wallichii*), merawan (*Hopea cernua*), and kapor or Borneo

camphor (*Dryobalanops aromatica*), tallest of the Malayan trees.

Diptocarps are mixed throughout primary evergreen rainforest at all levels. Individual diptocarps are the outstanding giants that raise their broad crowns above the level of the close-crowned canopy. Their tall, white, straight, unbranched columns stand out distinctly against the dark green tones of the shaded lower levels of the forest around them. Although the vegetation is typically heterogeneous, occasionally a single species appears in unusual concentration within relatively small areas. This is true of Borneo camphor, especially in eastern Malay and Sumatra, and it is also true of Borneo ironwood (*Eusideroxylon zwageri*), a valuable hardwood tree of Borneo and Sumatra.

The important members of rainforest vegetation referred to above are typical of well-drained sites, where they are dominant. Beneath them, in the profusion of varied plant life that thrives under constant conditions of high temperatures and humidity, are tall tree ferns, bamboo, palms, and pandanus. These are a good deal more plentiful in more open country and wherever primary rainforest has been cleared. Over 250 species of bamboo are known in all of southeast Asia, and more than 150 palms, including the coconut palm, sago palm, sugar palms, and the climbing rattan. The screw pine (*Pandanus spp.*) is common, an unusual tropical plant with very large, fan-shaped compound leaves and a spreading, open cone of stilt roots clustered at the base of the trunk.

Along the low-lying shorelines inundated by the sea are narrow zones of mangrove, composed of species of *Rhizophora, Bruguiera, Avicennia,* and *Sonneratia*. The associations vary in composition but consist mainly of tree species possessing special adaptations for continual development and regeneration in the presence of salt water and brackish tidal flats. The thickly entwined vegetation includes some species of *Rhizophora* that rise to more than 100 feet, although others are much more scrubby, often less than 6 feet tall. In particularly ill-drained lowlands stretching away toward the interior from the mangrove margins fresh water marshes have developed in large tracts, especially in Borneo and eastern Sumatra. Here an association of reeds, rushes, and tall tropical grasses is surmounted by an open distribution of tall forest trees among which the diptocarps are prominent, and palms, notably the nipa palm (*Nipa fruticans*), are particularly numerous.

In the mountainous sections of the central equatorial rainforest of the Malay peninsula, Sumatra, and Borneo a change from tropical evergreen rainforest takes place, very gradual but nonetheless broadly apparent, in both structure and composition of the vegetation. Plant life as a whole remains dominantly evergreen and thus is outwardly similar to selva. But large diptocarps disappear, trees in general become smaller, giant tree ferns and bracken proliferate, and mosses and lichens become increasingly abundant. The levels at which the change from tropical to what we may think of as subtropical rainforest takes place vary from one mountain area to the next, and from one place to another on the same mountain range. Heights of change vary from about 1500 to about 5000 feet, but as a rule are near 4000 feet in the core area. The more typical tropical trees on many mountainsides give way gradually to

cooler, cloud-drenched moss or mist forest. Usually anywhere between 3000 and 6000 feet one may expect to encounter heavy masses of damp ferns, liverworts, flowering plants, and mosses draping the twisted limbs of gnarled and stunted trees. The extraordinary richness of epiphytic vegetation is typical. In these cooler, damper circumstances tropical species give way to a larger proportion of species representative of the middle latitudes, and on the mainland include oaks, magnolias, laurels, and maples. At still higher levels pines become important members of the mountain vegetation.

Tropical evergreen rainforest extends northward and eastward from the core area wherever mean annual precipitation exceeds about 80 inches, in spite of a change in both directions to a more distinctly monsoon rhythm of normal yearly weather and a more definite seasonal distribution of annual rainfall. Thus, an exuberant selva vegetation continues northward from the Malay peninsula into the mountains along the Tennasserim coast of southernmost Burma and on over the lower mountain slopes of western Thailand and eastern Burma. In general, rainforest is more densely developed on the elevated terrain well exposed to the influx of maritime air from the sea. It heavily mantles the flanks of the Arakan ranges in western Burma, the Shan plateau of eastern Burma near Yunnan Province in southwest China, the discontinuous ranges of western Thailand, the Korat plateau of southern Thailand, the Elephant and Cardamon mountains of southern Cambodia, as well as the Annamite chain of Vietnam. It also appears in scattered tracts within the broad, enclosed interior lowlands, although here the long-established practice of clearing for cultivation has all but eliminated the primeval forest. Continuing northeastward into southern China along the southern flanks of the South China Hills within about 100 miles or so of the sea, selva vegetation remains dominant as far eastward as the mouth of the Si Kiang near Hong Kong. East of here, however, it diminishes in proportion to the increasing dominance of subtropical vegetation toward the coast opposite Taiwan, vegetation of banyan, palm tree, fern, and bamboo yielding to more frost-tolerant species of mid-latitude character.

Throughout southeast Asia's mainland peninsulas, indeed from India to south China, a change from tropical rainforest to a semi-ever-green vegetation to semideciduous forest, takes place wherever mean annual rainfall ranges between 60 and 80 inches and there is a dry season of three to four months when monthly rain averages less than 1 inch. Annual amounts may exceed 80 inches when the dry season is somewhat longer. The two climates are often closely interpenetrated, fragments of rainforest appearing as enclaves within semideciduous, and vice versa. In general, however, the semi-deciduous forest environment, better known locally as monsoon forest, is predominant in the interior lowlands of central Burma, Thai-land, Laos, and Cambodia (Fig. 23.2). In the rainy season semideciduous forest resembles selva, although its trees tend to be shorter, more widely spaced, and possess more open crowns. In the dry season the forest trees take on a stark, lifeless appearance, although the undergrowth beneath them is commonly luxuriant, much more dense than in rainforest, and usually ever-green.

In semideciduous vegetation a wide variety of tree species is common, although here more than in rainforest the tendency is seen for a single species or a group of two or three species to dominate considerable areas within the region. Diptocarps contribute many of the commoner forest trees, many of them the same species found in the more luxuriant rainforest. But others become much more numerous, especially deciduous forms that shed their foliage in the dry season. Among them are many acacias and members of the pea family (*Leguminoseae*), such as the languil or woman-tongue-tree (*Albizzia lebbek*), so-called from the clacking sound made by its long, dry pods in the wind, and the tall, colorfully flowering *Lager-stroemia speciosa* that displays its large pink to lavender terminal blossoms every seven to ten months. Also representative is the dadap tree (*Erythrina indica*), which wears a brilliant crown of scarlet flowers after its leaves have fallen in December or January, and the large angsana tree (*Pterocarpus indicus*) which sheds its leaves at varying intervals for a short period, bearing a golden mass of bright yellow flowers as the new young leaves begin to emerge from their buds.

The best known species of the monsoon forest in all of Indo-Malaya is teak (*Tectona grandis*), a very large deciduous tree that frequently reaches 100 to 130 feet in height and thrives in special abundance in Burma, Thailand, and parts of Laos where a yearly dry season of three to four months prevails.

Where mean annual rainfall is less than 60 inches and is concentrated in a shorter wet season, a transition from semideciduous forest toward a more open woodland environment begins. Savanna woodland becomes dominant when yearly rains are less than 40 inches, occurring where a dry season of six months or so prevails. Because of the prolonged practice of burning and clearing in the lowlands of south-east Asia a high proportion of rank, tropical grasses is commonly seen in these drier areas. There are no tall trees, most species being no more than 30 feet or so in height. Many of them are densely branched from the ground upward. Savannas are not extensive anywhere, however, nothing to compare with the broad savanna regions of Africa and South America, and are most notably seen in isolated pockets of low-land surrounded by regions of heavier rainfall and more luxuriant vegetation. Thus, one observes scattered tracts of savanna woodland in interior Vietnam, eastern Thailand, and central Burma around the confluence of the Irrawaddy and the Chindwin (Fig. 23.2). In Burma one observes a transition from the wet rainforest of the Arakan coast, the Irrawaddy delta regions, and the Tenasserim coast in the extreme south into semideciduous forest and savanna woodland farther inland, especially in the middle Irrawaddy basin. Within the savan-na of central Burma are enclaves of even more arid thorn scrub woodland. In these semidesert situations normal yearly rainfall is as low as 20 inches, occurring on only a few days during the rainy season, the remainder of the year being dry. Shrubby vegetation is dominant, with many thorny euphorbias, some of which are fleshy, cactuslike plants, and the ground between is usually grass-covered but may also be entirely bare and impregnated with highly alkaline salt deposits.

Beyond the Patkai Range and other low mountains in northern Burma is the rainforest region of northeastern India, which extends from northern Assam down the Brahmaputra valley, embraces the Khasi Hills, spreads on over the Bengal plains and the lower Ganges delta, and continues along the northeast coast of the Deccan for about 300 miles southwest-ward from the mouths of the Ganges (Fig. 23.6).

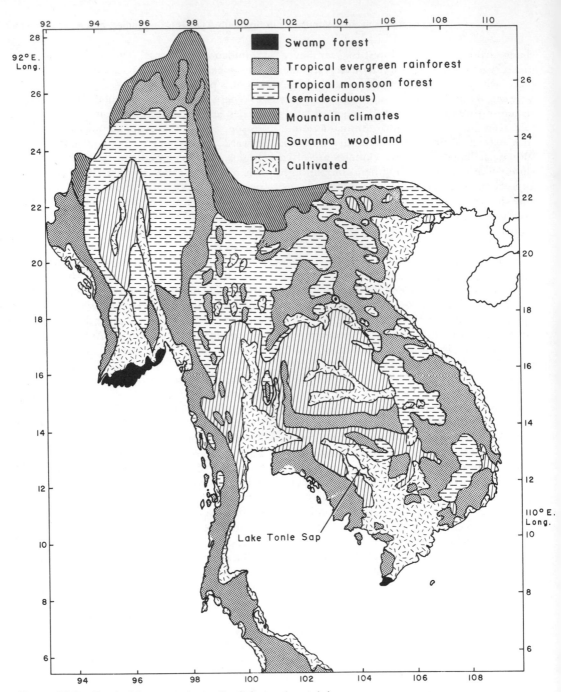

Figure 23.2. Tropical forests and woodlands in southeast Asia.

It is best developed where annual rainfall exceeds 120 inches, with a relatively short dry period. The wetter aspects of selva in this part of India and Pakistan are very dense and lofty; component trees are commonly 120 to 150 feet tall, the general forest canopy frequently surmounted by individual trees reaching up to 200 feet above the ground. Toward the less heavily watered areas where yearly rainfall diminishes to less than 80 inches, a transition to semideciduous monsoon forest is encountered. Monsoon forest is the most widespread climatic region in India. On its wetter margins, where nearly 80 inches of annual rainfall are normal,

564

trees are typically lower than those in selva vegetation, ranging from 80 to 120 feet in height, becoming lower, from 50 to 75 feet, toward the drier limits of the region where annual rainfall is about 40 inches. Westward from Bengal up the Ganges plains between the Ganges and the lower Himalayas and southwestward into the northeastern Deccan monsoon forest is dominated by an aggressive, gregarious diptocarp called sal (*Shorea robusta*). The hard, durable wood of this tall tree is perhaps the most valuable in all of India. Teak is a characteristic monsoon forest tree along the interior slopes of the Western Ghats, and evergreen sandalwood (*Santalum album*) is a valuable species typical of the southernmost interior. Where semi-deciduous forest begins to yield to more open savanna woodland, acacias appear in increasing proportion.

Savanna woodland, to a large extent induced through many centuries of continued settlement, deforestation, crop cultivation, and pasturage, tends to become dominant where mean yearly rainfall drops to about 40 inches and the dry season is prolonged to five or six months. This environment extends southward from the Ganges through the central part of the Deccan, reaching the southernmost tip of the broad peninsula. In portions of the central interior, largely toward the western headwaters of the east-flowing rivers, an even more arid environment of thorn scrub woodland appears where mean yearly rainfall drops to less than 30 inches.

From the interior scrub woodlands westward toward the Western Ghats mean annual rainfall increases again, and a change from thorn scrub to savanna woodland to monsoon forest to rainforest appears in a succession of narrow bands arranged nearly parallel to the west coast. Semideciduous forest reaches from the Gulf of Cambay to the southern tip of the peninsula along the inner margins of the Western Ghats, a distance of approximately 1000 miles, rainforest occupying most of the seaward slopes between 1500 and 4500 feet above sea level for nearly the same distance. Wetter rainforest is largely confined to a 600 mile strip south of Bombay, where an unusual richness of species variety is known. Northwestward toward the Thar desert and the Indus valley savanna woodland is gradually replaced by more arid thorn scrub woodland, extending from the upper Ganges to the sea coast between the Indus delta and the Gulf of Cambay.

From the core area of the Malay peninsula, Sumatra, and Borneo tropical rainforest extends northeastward into the Philippines (Fig. 23.11), a large tropical island group geographically united with the East Indies that stretches for more than 1100 miles from the Sulu archipelago off the northeast tip of Borneo to the Batan Islands about 100 miles south of Formosa. Reaching a span in latitude of nearly 17 degrees, from less than 5° to more than 21°N., the Philippine Islands, like the rest of the East Indies, are dominantly tropical in character.

The youthful ruggedness of the overshadowing volcanic ridges and ranges is virtually continuous throughout the islands. Two main islands, Luzon in the north and Mindanao in the south, account for about 67 per cent of the total area. Between them are the lesser islands of Mindoro, Masbate, Samar, Leyte, Panay, Negros, Cebu, and Bohol, and farther west the long, narrow form of Palawan. Large lowland areas are rare, and the principal one is the central plain of Luzon, to which may be added the smaller Cagayan valley in northeastern Luzon, the Bicol plain in southeastern Panay, the Agusan valley in northeastern Mindanao, and the Cotobato lowlands in southwestern Mindanao.

A richly diversified vegetation in which over three thousand species of trees attaining a diameter of 1 foot or more is among the outstanding qualities of these unusually well-endowed tropical islands. Rainforest and semideciduous forest are the two chief tropical climates. The diptocarps dominate the selva region, accounting for about 75 per cent of the principal trees. The principal species are white lauan (*Pentacme contorta*), apitong (*Diptocarpus grandiflorus*), mayapis (*Shorea palosapis*), red lauan (*Shorea negrosensis*), yakal (*Hopea spp.*), and other broadleaf hardwoods. Semideciduous forest, here known as molave forest, is more open, reflecting a more pronounced alternation of wet and dry seasons, and is notably developed in eastern Luzon, north central Mindanao, and many of the intervening islands. Its luxuriant growth during the wet season resembles that of selva vegetation, although during dry weather it becomes almost entirely leafless. Leading species here are molave (*Vitex parviflora*), especially prominent on more arid limestone ridges, and prominent members of the legumes such as narra (*Pterocarpus spp.*), tindalo (*Pahudia rhomboidea*), ipil (*Intsia bijuga*), akle (*Albizzia acle*), and banuyo (*Wallaceondendron celebicum*).

Above the rainforest a change to more temperate conditions is indicated in the transition to coniferous forest in which pines become important. Generally dominant above the diptocarps are benguet pine (*Pinus insularis* and *Pinus merkusii*), as well as the very large conifer almaciga (*Agathis alba*). The vegetational change is often well marked and reflects the somewhat lower temperatures and persistently higher humidities beyond about 3000 feet. Between 3000 and 6000 feet mist forest or moss forest is often encountered. Here the short, heavy tree trunks, developing under high humidity, heavy rainfall, much cloudy mist, and high winds, are generally covered with mosses, liverworts, epiphytic orchids, and feathery ferns.

Along the shorelines are often dense stands of mangrove with abundant salt grass (*Spinifex spp.*), and bordering the shallow streams that wind across the tidal flats are many nipa palms and pandanus trees.

From Java and Sulawesi eastward tropical rainforest continues beyond the shores of New Guinea into many of the smaller mountainous islands of the southwest Pacific. But a transition takes place from west to east in Java, from an equable equatorial climate in the western quarter of the island to a more definite seasonal rhythm of annual rainfall distribution in its eastern reaches. From central Java and Sulawesi to New Guinea the structure and composition of selva associations reflect the monsoonal nature of the climate. Diptocarps appear sparingly and give way to species of albizzia and acacia among the dominants, with eucalypts, which have spread northward from Australia, and bamboo contributing largely to the more depleted forest areas of the Lesser Sundas. An outstanding member of the monsoon forest is teak (*Tectona grandis*), a species that is virtually absent in the main rainforest core area centered in Sumatra, Borneo, and Malay. It is prominent in southern Sulawesi, and in the northern sections of this peninsular island it becomes mixed with ebony (*Diospyros celebica*) and sandalwood (*Santalum album*).

From eastern Java into the Lesser Sundas toward New Guinea an increasing proportion of semideciduous forest appears. During the dry season forest trees take on an almost lifeless appearance, their branches frequently standing bare of leaves, although the undergrowth and lesser trees beneath the higher forest canopy are chiefly evergreen. In New Guinea rainforest species include merbau (*Intsia spp.*), species of *Palaguium, Calophyllum, Garcinia,* and other dominantly Asiatic forms. In the lighter monsoon semideciduous forest linggua, or angsam (*Pterocarpus indicus*), *Albizzia procera*, and others take their place, and in drier savanna woodland eucalypts and casuarina, especially *Casuarina equisetifolia* (Australian pine), introduced from Australia, appear as important trees scattered over the open tropical grasslands, mixed with a variety of palms. In southern New Guinea are extensive savanna woodlands dominated by tall, rank tropical grasses. Occasionally savanna degrades further into scrubby grass and heath vegetation in which a more dessicated shrubby aspect is characteristic.

The change into higher altitude moss forest may be detected at various elevations, in most cases about half way up the slopes of higher mountain ranges regardless of height. In western Java montane evergreen mist forest may be found as low as 5400 feet and in New Guinea from about 5000 to 7800 feet. Oaks (species of *Quercus*), chestnuts (*Castanea spp.*), hoop pine (*Araucaria cunninghamii*), and other southern hemisphere conifers such as species of *Podocarpus, Dacrydium,* and *Libocedrus* are highly representative in the moss forests of New Guinea and appear in the same upper level relationship elsewhere between Java and the Philippines.

As we view the southward extension of tropical environments from the East Indies into northern Australia (Fig. 15.1), the dominant role of the monsoonal climate is plainly apparent in the prevalence of seasonal vegetation types. Of these the most widespread is open savanna woodland. Appearing in many varieties of locally dominant plant associations in which tall tropical grasses of tussock type conspicuously prevail at ground level, savanna woodlands are encountered from near the north coast, and less frequently from near the northeast coast, for between 300 and 400 miles inland, grading into tropical scrub woodland of generally shrubby character and finally into the bleak dessication of the interior deserts.

At intervals along the north coast are moderately extensive tracts of monsoon forest consisting of evergreen trees and shrubs in two- or three-layered communities that seldom rise to more than 50 feet in height. They chiefly appear where annual rains are between 35 and 50 inches or more, and the dominant species are members of the numerous eucalypts. This vegetation is notably evident in the general vicinity of Darwin, extending from over 100 miles southwest of this city to Melville Island and on other islands and peninsulas around Van Dieman Gulf. It is also widely present mixed into more open evergreen savanna woodland on the northern half of York Peninsula east of the Gulf of Carpentaria. In the denser low layers of such Indo-Malayan flora as *Gardenia* and *Terminalia* and other woody plants, evergreen eucalypts and other native Australian species are frequently mixed. This is a notable feature of the tropical layered woodland along the southwest coast of the Gulf of Carpentaria.

Elsewhere in the wetter portions of northern Australia where annual precipitation exceeds 35 inches, and particularly along the northeast coast within usually less than 100 miles of the sea, a monsoonal evergreen forest mixed with a few deciduous species can be found, indicating the important influence of the pronounced dry season. Representatives of tropical rainforest flora are also plentiful, among them many palms, crow's ash (*Flindersia australis*), booyong (*Argyrodendron trifoliatum*), and lignum-vitae (*Vitex lignumvitae*). Typical monsoon forest trees include the bottle tree (*Brachychiton rupestre*) and bottle-brush tree (*Melaleuca spp.*), plus a variety of other low evergreen trees and shrubs among native Australian species of *Hakea*, *Grevillea* and *Terminalia*.

A very narrow, discontinuous strip of tropical evergreen rainforest extends for over 1000 miles from northern York Peninsula to within about 150 miles northwest of Brisbane. Although appearing along the coast at intervals, especially for about 130 miles between Cairns and Cooktown, this region of heavier rainfall, higher persistent humidities, and higher temperatures is mainly confined to the middle slopes of the eastern ranges. Yet its distribution is fragmentary, and it is seldom encountered more than 50 miles from the sea.

In general aspect the vegetation resembles the Indo-Malayan pattern, although the diptocarps are entirely absent. Dominant trees include crow's ash, Queensland maple (*F. brayleyana*), cudgerie (*F. Oxleyana*), red cedar (*Cedrela australis*), tulip wood (*Harpullia pendula*), rosewood (*Dysoxylum fraserianum*), and a variety of coniferous softwoods. The latter include hoop pine (*Araucaria cunninghamii*), bunya pine (*A. bidwillii*) and three species of kauri pine (*Agathis spp.*) along with she-pines or brown pines, of which *Podocarpus elata* and *P. amara* are the commonest. These and over one hundred other prominent species form a relatively dense, close-crowned community in which the densely interlaced crowns are heavily festooned with lianas and epiphytes in a mainly evergreen, three-layered structure. A number of palms, including the lawyer vines (*Calamus spp.*), a long, climbing variety, and bamboo are also represented, as well as a number of large tree ferns, smaller peat-forming ferns and mosses, and the climbing strangling fig (*Ficus watkinsiana*). Stinging trees (*Laportea spp.*) are giant, softwood trees, reaching 120 feet or more in height, whose large leaves produce a lingering stinging effect. Eucalypts are almost entirely absent, and acacia appears only sparingly, although more common in the semideciduous forests nearer the sea. Buttress roots and the typical tropical rainforest feature of cauliflory are characteristic.

The tropical rainforest qualities begin to disappear north of Brisbane, where a change is observed into subtropical evergreen rainforest. Buttressing, cauliflory, and other vegetational features are much less evident as the change to a still humid but cooler climate occurs. Frosts become frequent, and a general lowering of normal temperature ranges takes place. A less varied vegetation begins to include species of the cooler middle latitudes, among them cypress pine (*Callitris cupressiformis*) and species of the south latitude beech (*Nothofagus spp.*).

The tropical grasslands that dominate the interior of northern Australia are physiognomically quite varied, depending on the geological derivation and mechanical qualities of local soil materials, drainage, and other edaphic features. Still, the dominant vegetation is grassland, chiefly of tall, rank, tussocky habit. As one progresses southward and southwestward from the wetter north and northeast coasts, scattered low trees and wooded clumps, principally of acacia species but including large numbers of smaller evergreen eucalypts, diminish in proportion. Savanna woodland of tree- and shrub-dotted character yields to low thorn scrub woodland approaching the deserts in the King Leopold and Durack ranges of northwestern Australia, and between the Barkly tableland and the Macdonnell Ranges on the north central interior.

CLIMATIC CONDITIONS. The long-range properties of atmospheric behavior responsible for the distribution of tropical environments in Indo-Malaya and Australia can be gathered together under the single designation of *south Asiatic monsoon*. The monsoon of southern and southeastern Asia and northern Australia is one of the major features of the general circulation in the tropics. Within certain limits, the strong contrasts in its flow patterns and weather regimes are remarkably dependable. The regularity of its seasonal rhythms is a fundamental facet of its nature. It is of general interest as a climatological phenomenon because its operations are integrally linked with the detailed fluctuations of extratropical pressure and wind fields in the middle latitudes on both sides of the equator in this part of the world. Furthermore, it tends to disrupt the broader wind and pressure patterns of the general surface circulation.

Over the area encompassed by the north Indian Ocean between Africa and Indonesia and between southern Asia and Australia, a large-scale reversal of surface air streams takes place twice each year (Fig. 23.3). A distinct sequence of changes in the pressure and wind fields of low-latitude Asia, the East Indies, and Australia produces a reasonably regular alternation of dry and wet seasons each year in these areas. One way of looking at it is to regard the seasonal wind shifts and their attendant weather features as the work of a gigantic heat engine fueled by the latent heat of the warm, moisture-laden atmosphere. The engine is set in motion and maintained in operation by the shifting concentrations of heat surplus in relation to areas of heat deficit induced by the rhythmic increase and decrease of solar radiation intensity from north to south between the Tropics in particular areas. The precise motions of the earth in relation to the sun are responsible for the regularities of the system. These, however, are subjected to considerable modification by intra-seasonal fluctuations in the actual behavior of

atmospheric circulation both within the lower latitudes and in the mid-latitudes of the northern and southern hemispheres. This is particularly true of the circulation in the middle and upper troposphere. The entire expanse of terrestrial Asia and the water surfaces of most of the Indian Ocean and the western Pacific are involved. In winter Asia becomes a region of surplus air, subsiding and diverging outward, part of which undergoes a net movement southward from southern Asia across the equator into the southern latitudes. In summer a virtually equal amount of air is displaced northward across the equator toward southern Asia. This reversal is most definitely apparent in the surface wind patterns. But the details of normal air stream configuration reveal a complicated arrangement.

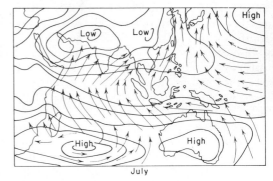

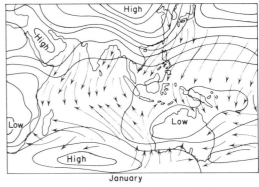

Figure 23.3. Mean surface pressure and wind fields of the south Asiatic monsoon in July and January.

The high plateau of Tibet and the much higher bordering mountain ranges around it interpose an effective barrier, sheltering southern and southeastern Asia from the normal surface atmospheric effects visited upon central and northern Asia. They also significantly modify the behavior of upper air circulation features approaching lower latitudes from western and central Asia. Thus, the air borne along in the surface circulation fields set up over Indo-Malaya and tropical Australia and the dominant seasonal weather associated with those wind fields possess characteristics traceable chiefly to the overwhelming preponderance of warm, ocean surface within the tropical latitudes of this part of the world.

In January a reestablishment of the northeast trades is seen over most of Indo-Malaya, wherein a relatively light southwestward flow of maritime air toward the equator is augmented by a divergent movement from continental Asia (Fig. 23.3). A shallow, weak anticyclone frequently forms over India. The mean barometric gradient from India to Burma southward is low, declining from about 1016 millibars (30 inches) near the Tropic of Cancer to about 1009 millibars (29.8 inches) near the equator. The equatorial trough at this season is displaced to a position generally south of the equator, extending in part over northern Australia (Fig. 20.1). Winds over the Arabian Sea, peninsular India, the Bay of Bengal, Burma, and Thailand are predominantly from northeast at the surface and maintain velocities of from 4 to 10 knots, only one half to one third the mean values of the summer season. Over southeast Asia and southern China the pressure gradient is steeper, as mean barometric values near the Tropic are about 1026 millibars (30.2 inches), and here wintertime velocities of 8 to 12 knots are half again as high as those in summer. Air streams are relatively constant only between Sumatra and Borneo, and in general the northeast surface monsoon decreases in depth from around 10,000 feet over southern China to about 5000 feet over the South China Sea.

Advancing toward the equator at diminishing speed, the northeast trades recurve eastward into the calms, variable winds, and fitful movements of the unstable equatorial trough. They thus contribute to the desultory eastward impulses that may be averaged to form the equatorial surface westerlies. Over northern Australia the streamlines of prevailing flow curve southward toward the interior, strengthened in the northeast by a freshening onshore flux of the oceanic easterlies from the South Pacific. A broadly sinusoidal trajectory that begins as southwestward flow over most of Indo-Malaya becomes east-southeastward over Indonesia and northwestern Australia, finally changes back to southwestward in northeastern Australia. This is the general alignment of the wintertime flow pattern at the surface. The transfer of surface air across the equator is thus accomplished over an expanse more than 8000 miles in length, from east Africa to the Pacific. The details of this interhemisphere transfer appear to depend to a large degree upon the extent, intensity, and persistence of the annual wintertime build-up of air over the entire continent of Asia.

The upper air during January, from about 30,000 feet and above, sweeps over the surface northeasterlies from a westerly direction. At this season nearly all of Asia is under the influence of a westerly flow at high levels (Fig. 4.10). A strong southwesterly movement is observed over the Bay of Bengal and southeast Asia at higher levels north of 15°N. Lat. Maximum upper level velocities repeatedly form a subtropical jet of particular intensity south of the Himalayas. This converges over southeast Asia with the mid-latitude jet formation from north of Tibet, and in subsiding over lower elevations is warmed adiabatically. This is partly responsible for the dry weather of winter in the interior basins and plains of southeast Asia. The high level circulation over tropical Australia is incompletely known.

In July the reverse surface flow is expressed in the reestablishment of the southeast trades over the same great expanse of the earth's surface from the South Pacific to east Africa (Fig. 23.3). A similar broad, sinusoidal path develops. During July the equatorial trough forms a wide, oscillating zone of warm, humid, cloudy weather frequently punctuated by violent thunderstorms and heavy rains across northern India and Burma (Fig. 23.4). Widening eastward over southeast Asia and the South China Sea, it extends into southern China and over the Philippines. Air streams originating in the southeast trades south of the equator are directed ultimately to this unstable convergence region.

From east Africa to the southern part of the Philippines the southeast trades, having curved northward across the equator, then recurve northeastward to form the southwest monsoon. Across the northern part of the Arabian Sea the mean flow is more westerly toward West Pakistan and the Indian coast north of Bombay.

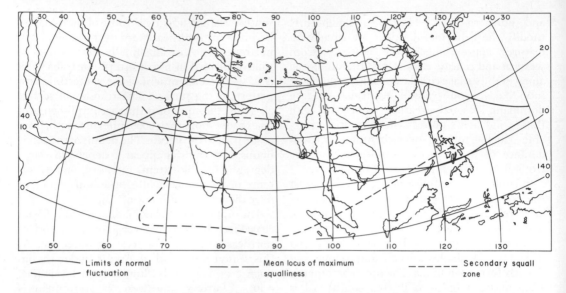

———— Limits of normal fluctuation

— — — Mean locus of maximum squalliness

— — — — — Secondary squall zone

Figure 23.4. Mean position of the equatorial trough in July over southern Asia.

Beyond, in the Bay of Bengal, air streams become more southwesterly again, directing their energies mainly toward the Burma coast. A secondary branch of less vigorous intensity curves northward toward the Bengal delta and with weakening strength and persistence curves northwestward up the Ganges valley. The major portion of the southwesterly flow approaching Burma continues eastward into peninsular southeast Asia. Over the South China Sea air is mainly supplied from over the waters around Indonesia, bending northward toward the south China coast and over the northern Philippines where air of south latitude origin merges with the northerly movement of air around the expanded oceanic highs of the western Pacific north of the equator.

It appears that more air moves into the northern hemisphere over the western part of the Arabian Sea than elsewhere. West of the 65th meridian and north of 5°N. Lat., mean winds in July and August average 30 to 35 miles per hour in certain portions of the open sea, and about one third of the observed wind speeds are noted as gale force winds (Fig. 23.3). During these months 96 to 98 per cent of the observed winds are from southwest to south. The strength and persistence of winds in this section of the general monsoon circulation are several times greater than in areas farther east.

Air that approaches India, Burma, and Indochina during the southwest monsoon has traveled several thousand miles over the surface of uniformly warm equatorial seas and has in the process acquired the qualities of warmth and high humidity by which it is identified (Fig. 6.12). These properties hold up to 10,000 or 15,000 feet above the Deccan, diminishing farther north. Advancing toward Burma, the monsoon depth increases to 20,000 feet, sometimes to 30,000 feet, but eastward into south China lowers again to less than 10,000 feet. Over peninsular southeast Asia westerly monsoonal flow may occasionally reach 12,000 feet. Maximum velocities in general appear to develop at between 3000 and 5000 feet over southeast Asia.

The warm, moist southwest monsoon brings air that is highly unstable. It is the source of about 85 per cent of the year's rainfall at most locations on the south Asiatic mainland. Exceptions to this rule are the southeast coast of India, northeastern Ceylon, the southeast coast of the Malay peninsula, and the coast of south Vietnam, which receive maximum yearly rains during the northeast monsoon of the winter season.

Overlying the southwesterly currents of surface airflow in July is an easterly movement in the higher troposphere from about 20,000 feet upward (Fig. 4.11). An easterly jet forms frequently at about 50,000 feet, and though this fluctuating ribbon of maximum wind speed maintains a mean position between 10° and 15°N. Lat., it actually varies from about 10° to

25°, often showing signs of marked acceleration over the Bay of Bengal.

The qualities of the atmosphere in which the Indo-Malayan area is constantly bathed are essentially those of maritime tropical character. The term *equatorial maritime* is preferred by some, but a qualitative distinction is difficult to make by actual observation, and *maritime tropical* seems more reasonable. Warm, moist air of maritime origin predominates. Temperatures thus tend to fluctuate only slightly and within high limits throughout the far-flung distribution of tropical forests and woodlands described earlier. It is in the amount, the yearly distribution, and the variability of annual rainfall that one finds the primary differences among the tropical climatic regions.

The main processes by which rain is produced are the following: (1) convective overturning in the unstable air of the equatorial trough; (2) migrating depressions induced by perturbations in the upper tropospheric easterlies overlying the surface monsoons; (3) convective cells arising from convergence of contrasting air streams; (4) convergence of air streams in relatively homogeneous monsoonal flow; (5) the alternate onshore/offshore oscillations of the sea breeze; (6) surface depressions of cold front origin; (7) tropical cyclonic surface storms originating as waves in the easterlies; (8) mechanical uplift of surface airflow by prominent orographic features.

The warm, humid sultriness of unstable air in the equatorial trough brings a high frequency of thermoconvective overturning to all the tropical regions in this part of the world, according to the time of year and the particular extent of its highly variable fluctuations in any given season. The maximum intensity of its hot, showery weather normally appears about one month after the sun has reached its zenithal position, when towering cumulonimbus clouds, often rising to the upper limits of the troposphere, release thunderously heavy rains and a welcome cooling effect from the gusty downdrafts of cooler air from higher levels.

Above the prevailing movement of the relatively stable surface monsoons, normally at light to moderate velocities except in the rainy seasons and over the ocean in the western Arabian Sea, a succession of troughs and ridges appear to move westward in the upper easterlies. Traveling depressions originate in the high level easterly flow, leading to the fairly frequent formation of cyclonic disturbances that tend to follow preferred paths from east to west. Three or four such disturbances each month of the rainy season may account for most of the monthly increments of precipitation.

Converging air streams of different origins over the sun-warmed seas often produce long lines of convective cumulonimbus clouds releasing localized showers of good intensity. Differences in the properties of contrasting air streams are usually slight but in the unstable maritime air are sufficient to induce, accelerate, and sustain the convergence process. This is notably common where currents of monsoon air meet the westward trade wind flow of the western Pacific.

Within the relative homogeneity and steadiness of monsoonal flow over the sea linear convergence also occurs, despite the near uniformity of the warm, moist air. In this instance also, cloud streets may form to sufficient depth to produce convective showers along paths of considerable length. Only slight discontinuities in wind speed, direction, and steadiness, not always accompanied by measurable contrasts in temperature and humidity, are often enough to set in motion the convective overturning arising from mechanical confluence and shower-producing instability.

Local land and sea breezes are common throughout the tropical regions in question and are especially frequent during the periods of light, unsteady air movement that prevail when the equatorial trough is dominant. Over islands in particular the onshore flux of oceanic air that occurs after sunrise commonly leads to heavy showers over land by day, and the weaker, less steady flow after dark results in showers over the nearby sea at night.

Traveling surface depressions form moderately often toward the poleward limits of the tropical regions, although varying in number from year to year. They usually form during the winter monsoon along the cold front advances of cold, dry continental air from interior Asia into warm, humid maritime tropical air. From October through May they tend to occur over northwestern India, sometimes continuing eastward to the Bay of Bengal. They often continue over southern China, where they occasionally reach southward over the South China Sea as far as Luzon and the southern coast of Vietnam. Here known as crachin weather, they normally bring a period of low clouds, light, steady rains, and low visibility lasting for several days. Periods of crachin weather may occur about five times per month from January through April, and a similar frequency of inclement weather applies to northwest India.

Tropical cyclones are major sources of rain. Varying in size, intensity, and duration, they often develop into those large, destructive vortices described as cyclones in the Bay of Bengal, typhoons in southeast Asia, baguios in the Philippines, and willy-willies in northern Australia. (See Chapter 5.) It will be recalled that in the western Pacific north of the equator the highest incidence of hurricane-strength tropical storms is found. Over twenty-one per year is the long-term average frequency.

In the western Pacific the principal typhoon season extends from June to December. August and September average over four such disturbances each month. But every month of the year has seen at least one typhoon over the past century. The Bay of Bengal averages about six per year, the chief months being September through November. The Arabian Sea averages more than one per year, where the periods before and after the full development of the southwest monsoon see the maximum probability of such storms. In northern Australia the yearly average is a little less than one, the season of highest probability extending from December through April. The directional tendency on both sides of the equator is westward, and in all but the most rare instances fully developed storms of high intensity ultimately follow a curvilinear course in a poleward direction.

The importance of contrasting relief features in contributing to the pattern of variable rainfall intensities in the tropical forests and woodlands of Indo-Malaya must be acknowledged. In places it appears to play a dominant role, accounting on the one hand for enormous excesses of rain, and on the other for marked rainfall deficits over rain shadow areas lying in the lee of the more prominent mountain ranges. Elsewhere the influence of relief is only secondary, simply augmenting the effectiveness of transient synoptic systems, large-scale convective processes, and other precipitating disturbances. On mountainsides well exposed to the influx of moisture-laden air from the sea,

maximum rains are normally received about midway up the slopes regardless of actual elevation. Amounts are lower both above and below the middle levels.

Mean annual rainfall exceeds 80 inches over a large proportion of Indo-Malaya (Fig. 23.5). Most of the East Indies, the Malay peninsula, coastal Burma, Eastern Pakistan, and northeastern India, as well as the west coast of peninsular India fall into this category. Coastal Cambodia, most of Vietnam, parts of the south China coast, and a section of northeastern Australia also receive annual amounts in excess of 80 inches. Between 60 and 80 inches is the normal yearly range over much of the central Philippines, western Mindanao, northern Sulawesi, the Lesser Sundas, southern New Guinea, and small areas in northern Australia around Darwin and Cape York. These lesser amounts are also the rule in large sections of south China, the interior of Indochina [2] and Burma, the Ganges lowland, and the narrow interior belt that lies east of the Western Ghats in the Deccan.

Normal yearly values drop below 60 inches in well-sheltered sections of the interior lowlands of Burma, Thailand, Cambodia, and southern Vietnam, southwestward into the inner reaches of the Deccan, and southward into interior Australia. A further lowering of annual rainfall is seen in a broad belt of the western interior of the Deccan plateau stretching from the arid borders of the Thar desert in northwest India to the southeast coast and northern Ceylon, and again along the inland borders of northern Australia's savanna woodlands.

But this is only the broadest view of mean annual rainfall distribution. Many local variations appear upon closer inspection. These, in most cases, result from contrasting exposures to the dominant movement of rain-bearing airflow and from the size, shape, and alignment of prominent relief features, as well as distance from the sea.

For example, along the west coast of peninsular India where nearly all the year's rain falls during the southwest monsoon, the Western Ghats present a significant barrier to the onshore flow of air from the sea. Forcing the mechanical uplift of virtually saturated air streams, the seaward slopes of the coastal

---

[2] For convenience the term *Indochina* is used here to designate Thailand, Laos, Vietnam, and Cambodia.

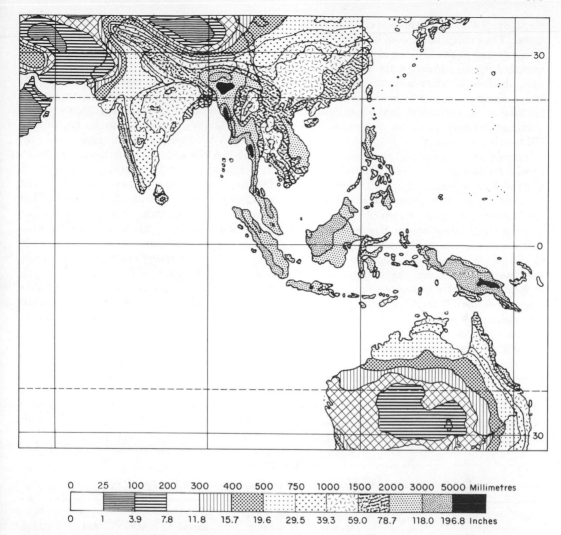

Figure 23.5. Mean annual rainfall in monsoon Asia and Australia (inches).

ranges receive normally heavy rains that spill over the crest line to the upper eastern flanks and then drop off rapidly over the savanna woodlands of the interior within a very short distance of the ridge tops. At Mangalore (el. 72) on the coast, where over 95 per cent of the year's rain occurs during the six-month period from May to October, the mean annual fall is 129.6 inches, and at Mercara (el. c.5000), 68 miles southeastward, it is 127.4 inches. But at Mysore, some 60 miles farther east and about a half-mile lower in altitude at 2500 feet, mean annual rainfall is only 29.8 inches.

In northeast India the striking orographic effect of the Khasi Hills in Assam upon the northward influx of warm, moist air during the southwest monsoon is illustrated by comparing Silchar, Cherrapunji, Shillong, and Tezpur. Silchar (el. 96), a station in the northeast corner of the Bengal plains, is about 175 miles from the Bay of Bengal. It averages 125.5 inches of rainfall each year, of which 95 per cent occurs in the eight-month period from April through November. Cherrapunji (el. 4309), about 75 miles northwest of Silchar, is one of the wetter sites in the world. Average yearly rainfall is 425.1 inches. Twenty miles north of Cherrapunji the Khasi Hills rise to more than 6000 feet. A few miles beyond the crest of these ranges is Shillong, partly shielded on the northern slopes at an elevation of 4921 feet, which averages only 85.7 inches. The further advance of maritime air into the Brahmaputra valley is even more effectively impeded by the barrier of the Khasi Hills, for their shadowing effect is quite evident in the lower altitude areas between Assam and the Himalayas. At Tezpur (el. 258), about 110 miles northeast of Cherrapunji, the mean annual rainfall is only 74.1 inches.

Innumerable examples of sharply contrasting annual rainfall amounts can be found throughout the East Indies. Largely mountainous, the highly irregular configuration of the dominant land forms imparts a pattern of strongly contrasting rainfall distribution. Baguio (el. 4960) in northern Luzon annually receives 178.7 inches of rainfall, but San Fernando, only 25 miles northwest of here on the coast, reports 96 inches. Manila (el 47), about 130 miles south of Baguio, averages 82 inches, Legaspi (el. 18), over 200 miles southeast of Manila averages 135.5 inches, but Cebu (el. 30), 200 miles south of Legaspi, averages only 60.6 inches.

Perhaps the most arid pocket among the tropical islands of southeast Asia is the long, narrow lowland of the head of mountain-bordered Laoe Bay in northwestern Sulawesi. Donggala at the mouth of the bay reports an annual rainfall of about 57 inches, but at Palu, at the head of the bay where a low plain rises gradually southward, the mean value is only about 21 inches.

Rainfall reliability is high in several widely separated areas. The departure from normal is less than 10 per cent on the average over most of the Malay peninsula, southern Burma, southern Vietnam, eastern Java, and the northern Moluccas. Mean variability increases to a maximum of 25 per cent in the eastern Deccan, the Ganges valley, and the drier margins of tropical woodlands toward the Thar desert of northwest India, as well as the interior woodland borders of northern Australia. Elsewhere normal variability is between 10 and 20 per cent. But the records of individual stations indicate a high degree of uncertainty over long periods of time, and actual amounts for individual years have been known to vary quite widely. At Nagpur in the savanna woodland of the central Deccan plateau, where mean annual rainfall from 1855 to 1949 was 47.3 inches, 76 inches were recorded in 1933, but only 13 inches in 1938. At Cherrapunji (annual mean 425.1 inches), 1041.8 inches were received in 1861, but only 283 inches in 1873. At Cairns on Australia's northeast coast, about 50 miles north of Innisfail,

TABLE 23–1

Temperature Ranges Within Ten Degrees of the Equator (°F)

Station	Lat.	Coolest Month	Warmest Month	Annual Range	Ext. Min.	Ext. Max.	Ext. Range
Trivandrum, India	8°29'N.	79	83	4	63	100	37
Phuket, Thailand	7°58'N.	81	84	3	66	95	29
Surigao, Philippines	9°48'N.	79	82	3	66	99	33
Singapore	1°18'N.	80	82	2	66	97	31
Manado, Sulawesi	1°30'N.	79	82	3	63	96	33
Djakarta, Java	6°11'S.	79	81	2	66	98	32
Madang, New Guinea	5°14'S.	81	82	1	62	98	36
Koepang Timor	10°10'S.	79	83	4	60	101	41

Source: Great Britain, Meteorological Office, *Tables of Temperature, Relative Humidity and Precipitation for the World*, Part 5, *Asia*, London, 1962.

TABLE 23–2

Variation of Temperature Ranges With Increasing Latitude (°F)

Station	Lat.	Coolest Month	Warmest Month	Annual Range	Ext. Min.	Ext. Max.	Ext. Range
India, west coast							
Surat	21°12'N.	73	88	15	40	114	74
Bombay	18°54'N.	75	86	11	53	101	48
Mormugao	12°25'N.	78	86	8	60	96	36
Cochin	9°58'N.	81	86	5	61	99	38
Trivandrum	8°29'N.	79	83	4	63	100	37
Malaya to Bengal							
Calcutta, India	22°32'N.	67	87	20	44	111	67
Akyab, Burma	20°08'N.	70	84	14	47	100	53
Diamond Island, Burma	15°51'N.	78	84	6	61	98	37
Phuket, Thailand	7°58'N.	81	84	3	66	95	29
Singapore	1°18'N.	80	82	2	66	97	31
Sulawesi to Taiwan							
Hengch'un, Taiwan	22°00'N.	70	83	13	49	95	46
Aparri, Philippines	18°22'N.	75	85	10	59	101	42
Manila, Philippines	14°35'N.	78	84	6	58	101	43
Surigao, Philippines	9°48'N.	79	82	4	66	99	33
Manado, Sulawesi	1°30'N.	79	82	3	63	96	33
New Guinea to northeast Australia							
Madang, New Guinea	5°14'S.	81	82	1	62	98	36
Samari, Papua	10°37'S.	77	83	6	64	102	38
Cooktown, Australia	15°28'S.	73	82	9	47	105	52
Rockhampton, Australia	23°24'S.	62	81	19	33	112	79

Source: Great Britain, Meteorological Office, *Tables of Temperature, Relative Humidity and Precipitation for the World*, Part 6, *Australasia and the South Pacific Ocean*, London, 1962.

the mean annual amount is 89 inches, but 44.1 inches were recorded in 1915 and 174.6 inches in 1886.

Temperatures throughout tropical Indo-Malaya and northern Australia are typically high, as elsewhere in the lower latitudes, and are climatically subordinate to rainfall. At coastal stations among the islands and on the mainland peninsulas that reach within 10 degrees or less of the equator, temperatures remain remarkably near 80° during the entire year. Whenever low latitude, low altitude, and nearness to the sea combine, the mean annual temperature range is less than 5 degrees. Table 23-1 illustrates the comparative thermal equanimity of the entire region within about 10 degrees on either side of the equator.

With increasing latitude the mean annual temperature range becomes larger, and so also does the extreme range between absolute

TABLE 23–3

Temperature Ranges in Coastal and Interior Localities Within the Same Latitudes (°F)

	Station	Lat.	Elev. in Ft	Coolest Month	Warmest Month	Annual Range	Ext. Min.	Ext. Max.	Ext. Range
Coast	Mangalore	12°52′N.	72	79	85	6	62	100	38
Interior	Bangalore	12°57′N.	3021	69	81	12	52	102	50
Coast	Bombay	18°54′N.	37	75	86	11	53	101	48
Interior	Nagpur	21°09′N.	1028	68	96	28	39	118	79
Coast	Akyab	20°08′N.	27	70	84	14	47	100	53
Interior	Mandalay	21°59′N.	252	69	89	20	44	111	67
Coast	Townsville	19°14′S.	48	67	82	15	41	110	69
Interior	Tennant Creek	19°34′S.	1075	64	87	23	36	115	79

maxima and minima of record. This meridional change is indicated in Table 23-2, which gives values for coastal or near coastal stations.

Localities exposed directly to the moderating influence of air from the sea experience more conservative thermal fluctuations than those in approximately the same latitude that are sheltered from influxes of oceanic air. Table 23-3 illustrates the comparative temperature ranges of coastal and interior stations at about the same latitudes in peninsular India, Burma, and northern Australia.

The effect of altitude upon temperature has long been recognized among European residents in the tropics. To escape the combination of heat and high humidity of the lowlands, they have taken advantage of sites at higher eleva-tions where temperature fluctuates within cooler limits and the air is frequently freshened by the brisk stirring of mountain breezes. Such mountain resorts in the Orient have for years been known as "hill stations," to which Euro-peans periodically repair for recuperation from the debilitating effects of long residence in the oppressive atmosphere of lower elevations. In Ceylon, for example, at Nuwara Eliya (el. 6168), the warmest month, May, averages about 62°, compared with 83° for the same month at Colombo (el. 24), about 60 miles west on the southwest coast. These and other temperature data are shown in Table 23-4 for several pairs of stations by which the comparative thermal experience at high and low elevation is illus-trated.

TABLE 23–4

Influence of Altitude upon Temperatures in Indo-Malaya (°F)

Station	Alt.	Distance and Direction	Warmest Month	Coolest Month	Annual Range	Ext. Max.	Ext. Min.
Ceylon							
Colombo	24	—	83	79	4	96	59
Nuwara Eliya	6168	60 miles east	62	57	5	78	27
Burma							
Mandalay	252	—	89	69	20	111	44
Lashio	2802	120 miles northeast	76	60	16	99	35
Malaya							
Penang	17	—	83	81	2	98	65
Cameron Highlands	4750	100 miles southeast	66	64	2	80	36
Java							
Djakarta	26	—	81	79	2	98	66
Bandung	2428	75 miles southeast	73	72	1	94	52

India, Pakistan, and Burma

The seasons of the year in the minds of most residents of India, Pakistan, and Burma are three: cold weather from November to February, hot weather from March to May, and the rainy season from June to September. October is regarded as a warm, muggy, transitional month leading back into cold weather in November. In the official view of the Indian Meteorological Department, however, four seasons are recognized: (1) the northeast mon-soon season of cold weather from December to March; (2) transitional hot weather, April and May; (3) the rainy season of the southwest monsoon; (4) the transitional interval of October and November.

Toward the end of September, as the sun crosses the equator at the equinox, the basically onshore flow of the southwest monsoon begins to falter, and in October a change in dominant wind direction is observed. In northern areas air begins to move more frequently down the

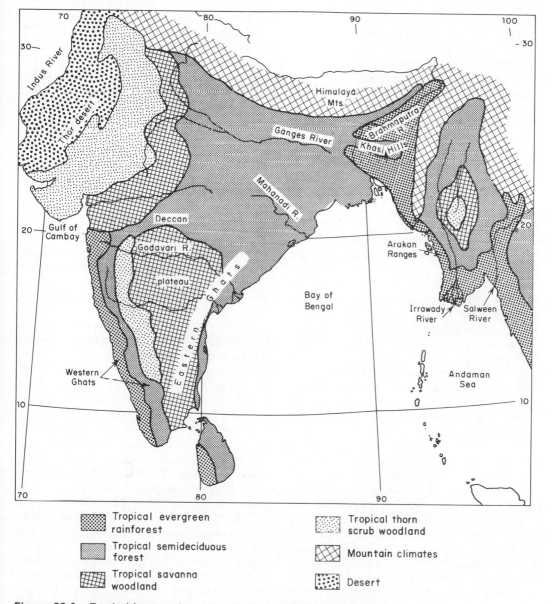

Figure 23.6.   Tropical forest and woodland in India, Pakistan, and Burma.

Indus, the Ganges, the Brahmaputra, and the Irrawaddy toward the sea (Fig. 23.6). By December the northeast monsoon is in full swing, and the cold season is well established. The barometric gradients are low, and winds are commonly very light and frequently unsteady, moving chiefly from the northeast except in the upper Ganges valley, where northwesterlies prevail.

Weather of the cool season is characteristically clear, dry, and often beautifully sunny and cloudless. Mean cloud cover is less than 20 per cent during one or more of the winter months, and in drier thorn scrub woodlands less than 10 per cent, although in southeast India and northeast Ceylon it is greater, averaging between 40 and 50 per cent at Trincomalee, Ceylon. Mean relative humidities in late afternoon at interior stations are always low, decreasing to a yearly minimum during the transitional hot period of April and May. For example, Ahmadabad in thorn scrub woodland north of the Gulf of Cambay averages 25 per cent in January but 17 per cent in March and April.

The predominantly fair weather of the cool season is interrupted from time to time in northern India and Burma and East Pakistan by the passage of migrating cyclones from the northwest. These account for the light winter rains, important to winter farming and are responsible for the fact that most northern stations report small amounts of rain during an otherwise arid period. Allahabad receives 0.9 inch in January and 0.7 inch in February, and Dibrugarh 1.5 inch in January. The traveling disturbances appear to be of frontal origin, tracing their genesis to the Mediterranean, and occasionally to southern Afghanistan.

The southeast coast of India and the northeast coast of Ceylon differ from other sections in experiencing high temperatures and humidities throughout the year and in receiving the bulk of the normal yearly rainfall during the period of the northeast monsoon. Northeasterly winds on their passage of about 1000 miles across the Bay of Bengal become increasingly more humid, and on reaching the coast bring cloud and rain in copious amounts. Mean cloud cover is above 50 per cent, and mean afternoon relative humidities rise to over 70 per cent in October and November. At Madras 72 per cent of the year's normal rainfall of 50 inches is recorded in the four-month interval from September through December. November is the wettest month, with 14 inches occurring on eleven days, and both October and November average midafternoon relative humidities of 75 per cent. At Trincomalee in northeastern Ceylon the year's normal rainfall is 64.9 inches, of which 68 per cent is received in the four-month period from October through January. Here, midafternoon relative humidities from November to January average 78 or 79 per cent, and December is the wettest month, with a normal increment of 14.3 inches.

Early in March the transitional period of hot weather begins as temperatures rise rapidly with increasing warmth from the sun (Fig. 23.7). As the zenithal position of the sun advances northward from the vernal equinox to the summer solstice, the highest mean monthly temperatures are recorded. May is the warmest month over most of India, East Pakistan, and western Burma. At this time most of the Deccan plateau experiences average temperatures in excess of 90°. May at Ahmadabad averages 93°, at Allahabad 93.5°, at Nagpur 95.5°, at Jamshedpur 91.5°, and at Patna 90°. At these and other inland stations in the Deccan the thermometer in May rises above 100° almost daily; the mean maximum at Allahabad, for example, is 107°, at Nagpur 109°. Extremes are also excessively high in the hot season at inland stations, for Allahabad has recorded 117° in early June before the rains begin, and Nagpur has recorded 114° in May.

To a certain extent the month of warmest weather tends to follow the progress of the sun, for April is the warmest month in southwestern India, western Ceylon, and the central lowland and eastern mountains of Burma, May the warmest over most of the Deccan, but June in the upper Ganges valley, July in northern Bengal, and August in the Brahmaputra valley. Generally speaking, where the warmest month occurs in April, July, or August, mean values are substantially less than 90° in India and Ceylon, but in central Burma, April averages between 85° and 90° (Table 23-5). Thus, Mangalore in April averages 85°, Dibrugarh 81.5° in August, Mandalay 89° in April, and Rangoon 86.5° in the same month. Stations at higher elevation enjoy less severe heat during the hot season, and Bangalore reports 81° in April, compared with 91.5° at Madras in May at about the same latitude. Lashio in east Burma averages 75.5° in April, compared with 89° at Mandalay in the same month, and Cherrapunji

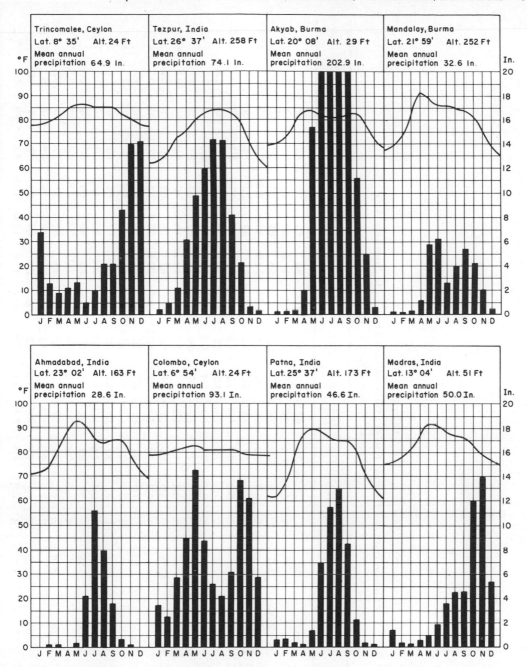

Figure 23.7. Temperature and rainfall at tropical forest and woodland stations in India, Ceylon, and Burma.

reports a mean of 69° in August and September. Coastal situations exposed to the freshening influence of increasingly stronger southwest winds are also spared the intensity of premonsoon heat, especially where local sea breezes augment the speed of onshore drafts of air each day.

Bombay averages 85° in May, compared with 95° at Nagpur, nearly 450 miles farther inland.

During the transitional hot season winds continue northeasterly into March, but as April approaches, they begin shifting to westerly and finally to southwesterly over most of peninsular

TABLE 23–5

Climatic Data for Tropical Forest and Woodland Stations in Southern Asia
(Temp. °F; Rainfall, In.)

Station	Lat.	El. in Ft		Jan.	Feb.	Mar.	Apr.	May	Jun.	Jul.	Aug.	Sep.	Oct.	Nov.	Dec.	Year
Ahmadabad, India	23°02'	163	T	73	74	82	89	93	91	86	84	85	85	79	78	
			R	0.0	0.1	0.1	0.0	0.4	4.3	11.2	8.1	3.7	0.6	0.1	0.0	28.6
Allahabad, India	25°17'	322	T	61	65	76	87	93	93	86	84	84	78	67	61	
			R	0.9	0.6	0.6	0.2	0.6	5.0	12.6	10.0	8.4	2.3	0.3	0.3	41.8
Bangkok, Thailand	13°44'	7	T	77	80	84	85	85	84	83	83	82	81	79	77	
			R	0.3	0.8	1.4	2.3	7.8	6.3	6.3	6.9	12.0	8.1	2.6	0.2	55.0
Bombay, India	18°58'	37	T	75	75	78	82	85	83	80	80	80	81	80	77	
			R	0.1	0.1	0.1	0.1	0.8	18.3	24.3	13.8	10.5	2.2	0.4	0.1	70.8
Calcutta, India	22°32'	23	T	67	71	80	86	86	85	84	83	83	81	73	66	
			R	0.4	1.0	1.3	2.1	5.5	11.7	12.7	13.3	10.0	4.9	0.7	0.2	63.9
Cherrapunji, India	25°15'	4309	T	53	55	61	64	66	68	69	69	69	66	61	55	
			R	0.4	2.7	9.4	28.2	46.3	95.9	98.5	79.8	38.0	21.3	3.2	0.3	425.1
Colombo, Ceylon	6°54'	23	T	79	80	82	82	83	82	81	81	81	80	80	79	
			R	3.5	2.1	4.3	9.8	12.4	7.7	4.7	3.7	5.4	13.7	12.2	5.3	85.1
Dalat, South Vietnam	11°57'	4921	T	62	63	65	67	68	68	67	67	66	65	64	61	
			R	0.4	1.0	2.2	6.5	8.5	7.3	9.6	8.3	12.1	10.0	3.9	1.1	71.0
Delhi, India	28°39'	718	T	59	63	74	85	92	93	88	86	85	80	69	60	
			R	1.0	0.7	0.4	0.3	0.6	3.2	7.7	7.5	4.6	0.4	0.1	0.5	27.1
Dibrugarh, India	27°28'	348	T	61	64	69	72	78	81	81	81	81	77	70	62	
			R	1.6	2.3	3.2	9.3	13.2	19.8	20.8	18.4	15.6	6.5	1.6	0.7	113.3
Hanoi, North Vietnam	21°03'	23	T	62	63	68	75	82	85	84	84	82	77	71	65	
			R	0.9	1.4	1.8	3.6	8.6	10.2	13.4	13.4	10.5	4.4	2.0	1.1	71.2

Location	Latitude	Elev.		Jan	Feb	Mar	Apr	May	Jun	Jul	Aug	Sep	Oct	Nov	Dec	Ann.
Jamshedpur, India	22°49'	423	T	67	71	80	88	92	89	84	84	84	80	77	66	
			R	0.7	1.2	0.7	1.0	2.7	7.5	16.4	14.4	7.5	2.8	0.8	0.3	56.0
Kwang-Tri, South Vietnam	16°44'	23	T	68	70	72	80	84	85	85	85	82	78	74	70	
			R	6.7	2.2	2.7	2.2	3.9	3.0	3.5	2.8	15.6	22.1	22.3	12.0	100.0
Lashio, Burma	22°58'	2802	T	60	64	71	76	77	77	77	77	76	73	67	61	
			R	0.3	0.3	0.6	2.2	6.9	9.8	12.0	12.7	7.8	5.7	2.7	0.9	61.9
Luang Prabang, Laos	19°53'	1115	T	69	74	78	82	84	84	82	82	82	80	79	78	
			R	0.6	0.7	1.2	4.2	6.5	6.2	8.8	11.9	6.7	2.9	1.2	0.5	51.5
Madras, India	13°04'	23	T	76	78	81	85	89	90	87	85	85	82	79	77	
			R	1.2	0.4	0.4	0.6	1.7	1.9	3.7	4.6	4.7	11.5	13.5	5.2	49.4
Mandalay, Burma	21°59'	250	T	71	76	83	90	89	87	87	86	85	83	78	71	
			R	0.0	0.1	0.2	1.1	5.5	5.4	3.4	4.1	6.5	4.7	1.7	0.3	33.3
Poona, India	18°32'	1834	T	70	73	80	85	86	81	77	76	77	78	73	69	
			R	0.1	0.0	0.1	0.6	1.2	4.0	5.7	3.6	6.3	3.1	1.3	0.1	26.1
Qui Nhon, South Vietnam	13°45'	20	T	73	75	78	81	84	85	86	87	84	80	77	72	
			R	2.1	1.6	1.5	1.0	2.1	2.2	2.7	2.2	9.8	17.1	17.1	5.7	65.1
Rangoon, Burma	16°47'	18	T	77	79	84	87	84	81	80	80	81	82	80	77	
			R	0.1	0.2	0.3	1.6	12.4	18.1	21.2	19.5	15.6	7.0	2.5	0.1	98.7
Saigon, South Vietnam	10°47'	36	T	79	81	84	86	84	82	81	82	81	81	81	79	
			R	0.6	0.1	0.5	1.6	8.5	12.9	12.2	10.6	13.1	10.5	4.5	2.2	77.7
Tavoy, Burma	14°05'	20	T	78	80	82	84	82	79	78	78	79	81	79	77	
			R	0.2	0.5	1.3	3.4	19.8	43.5	48.5	45.0	32.6	10.4	2.3	0.2	208.3
Trincomalee, Ceylon	8°35'	24	T	77	79	80	83	85	85	85	84	84	82	79	78	
			R	6.8	2.6	1.9	2.3	2.7	1.1	2.0	4.2	4.2	8.7	14.1	14.3	64.9
Vientiane, Laos	17°58'	531	T	70	75	79	83	82	82	81	82	81	79	75	72	
			R	0.2	0.6	1.5	3.9	10.5	11.9	10.5	11.5	11.9	4.3	0.6	0.1	67.5

Source: U.S. Army, Quartermaster and Engineering Command, *Analogs of Canal Zone Climate in India and Southest Asia* (Tech. Report EP-91), Natick, Mass., 1958.

India and Burma in May. At the end of May or early in June the upper level westerly jet streams south of Tibet abruptly disappear as the equatorial trough reaches northern India and Burma. At the surface southwesterly winds, until now relatively light and steady, suddenly increase in velocity with little change in direction. It will be remembered that the dominant air streams over the Bay of Bengal curve northward and then northwestward up the Ganges valley.

The entire character of the weather changes dramatically as the southwest monsoon "bursts" across the land. The "burst" of the monsoon is marked by the approach of driving, heavy masses of turbulent cumulus clouds, violent thunderstorms, and torrential rains from the warm, saturated air off the sea. It occurs with relative regularity, normally arriving around Bombay near June 5th and in Bengal near June 15th each year. Its arrival announces the start of the season of general rains (Fig. 23.8). Boisterous weather lasts for a week or two, followed by less vigorous though very plentiful rains that last for three or four months longer, and the dry, brown landscapes of savanna woodland and thorn scrub woodland rapidly turn green. The southwest monsoon period of rejuvenation proceeds until September, only occasionally interrupted by short periods of clear, rainless weather that offer welcome breaks in the monotony of the wet season.

With the exception of southeast India and northeast Ceylon, cloud cover and relative humidity increase to a yearly maximum, and the mean daily range of temperature drops to a minimum. Mean cloud cover at most stations exceeds 80 per cent in July and August and at Rangoon and Tavoy in southern Burma rises above 90 per cent. Midafternoon relative humidities at interior stations in July and August are generally in excess of 70 per cent, rising to more than 90 per cent at Cherrapunji and near 90 per cent at Akyab. Exceptions are Madras, about 60 per cent, compared with Mangalore, over 85 per cent, and Trincomalee, less than 55 per cent compared with Colombo, over 85 per cent.

Throughout most of the region the great bulk of the year's rain falls in the relatively short four-month period from June through September (Fig. 23.9). With very few exceptions, a single peak period of maximum intensity is the rule, and July is normally the wettest month. At Ahmadabad 95 per cent of the yearly amount is received from June through September, and July is the wettest month, with 11.2 inches falling on twelve days. at Allahabad 86 per cent occurs from June through September, the peak month, July, averaging 12.6 inches on fifteen days; and so on, as shown in Table 23-5. Along the west coast of peninsular India the peak intensities are, of course, greater. At Bombay, which receives 94 per cent of its annual rain from June to September, July is the peak month, with 24.3 inches falling on twenty-one days, and at Mangalore July averages 38.9 inches falling on twenty-seven days. In parts of East Pakistan and northeast India the rainy season is somewhat more prolonged. At Calcutta it extends from May through October, when 91 per cent of the year's rain normally falls, and July and August each average near 12 inches falling on eighteen days. At Dibrugarh in the upper Brahmaputra valley the normal season extends from April to September, when 85 per cent of the annual amount is recorded, and July averages 21.8 inches falling on twenty-one days. At the higher station of Cherrapunji in the Khasi Hills 96 per cent of the year's rain occurs from April through October, and July averages 106.1 inches falling on twenty-five days.

The rainy season is also somewhat prolonged in Burma. At Akyab 95 per cent of the year's normal amount is reported for the six-month interval from May through October. July is the wettest month, with 55.1 inches falling on twenty-eight days. At Tavoy as well 96 per cent of the rain occurs from May through October, and July is the wettest month, with 49.2 inches falling on twenty-seven days.

In southern India and Ceylon two wet periods are normal, responding to the double passage of the equatorial trough. Mangalore reports a secondary peak interval in October. Bangalore records a peak of 4.2 inches on seven days in May and a larger increment of 6.7 inches on nine days in September. A double peak regime is also true of parts of central Burma. Mandalay, for example, receives 88 per cent of the year's total from May through October, during which time an initial peak is normal for June, 6.3 inches occurring on seven days, and a second peak of 5.4 inches in September, falling on nine days.

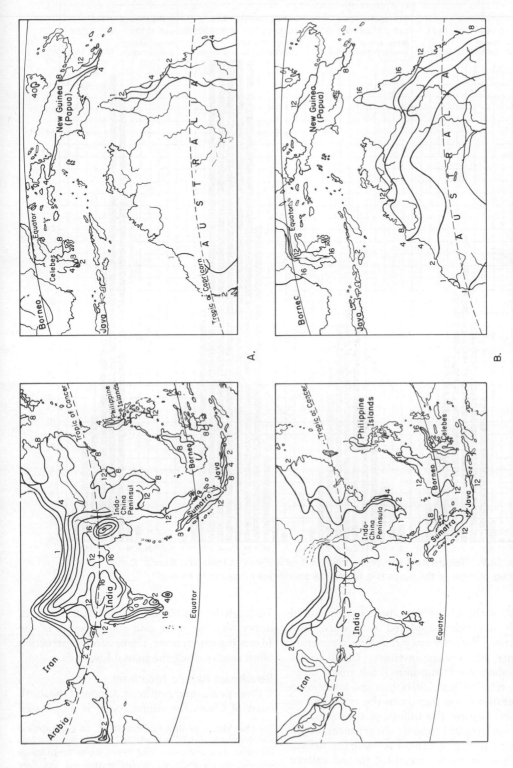

Figure 23.8. Mean precipitation in July (upper) and January (lower) in southern Asia and northern Australia. The pronounced seasonal shift in tropical rainfall intensity with the monsoonal reversal of airflow is shown. (See Figure 23.3.)

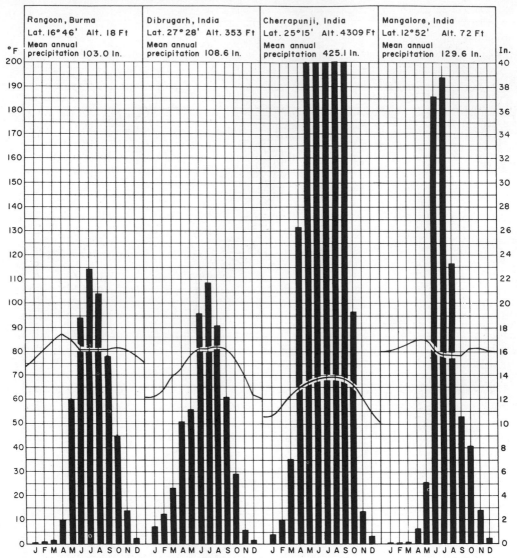

Figure 23.9. Temperature and precipitation at four stations in India and Burma. Concentration of most of the year's rain during the southwest monsoon is shown.

Toward the end of September the equatorial trough has been displaced southward, and systematic disturbances occur less frequently and are of weaker intensity. Cloud cover diminishes, warm sunshine is felt much more often, relative humidities become lower, and temperatures rise slightly in the early part of October. During this month of the retreating monsoon, tropical cyclonic disturbances originating in the Bay of Bengal occasionally deliver storms of hurricane intensity to the eastern shore of peninsular India and the Bengal delta.

Through the combination of high, lashing winds, heavy, driving rains, and rising waters of the advancing storm wave, tremendous destruction often results along the coastal lowlands.

Southeast Asiatic Mainland

Over peninsular southeast Asia[3] and the south coast of China the climatic year is dominated

[3] The Malay peninsula, because of its geographical affinity with the islands of the East Indies—its low latitude, its narrowness, and hence its accessibility to oceanic air—is included in the section on the East Indies that follows.

by two main seasons, the northeast monsoon and the southwest monsoon. The northeast monsoon begins in early November and continues to about the middle of March, the southwest monsoon prevails from mid-May to late September. Between them are short transitional periods of less definite weather.

By early October after the equinox, when the zenithal position of the sun has moved south of the equator, the equatorial trough shifts southward, and a short interval of light, variable winds prevails, usually until after the first of November (Fig. 20.1). During the October lull there is less cloud cover, fewer thunderstorms, and a rapid lessening of precipitation in general, except along the southeast coast of North Vietnam and the northeast coast of South Vietnam (Fig. 23.10). Here the rainy season is just beginning; elsewhere it has come to an end.

Beginning in early November the northeast monsoon brings winds of moderate strength persistently out of the northeast from the Chinese mainland (Fig. 23.3). They are comparatively shallow winds, within about 12,000 feet of the surface over south China and normally less than 8000 feet over Vietnam. Northeast winds from the mainland are usually fresh and cool, but they alternate from time to time with westward surges of the northeast trades off the Pacific, and these introduce intervals of more humid, somewhat oppressive weather.

Along the northeast coast of Vietnam moisture-laden winds arrive after traveling several hundred miles southwestward over the sea from south China, losing most of their moisture on the coastal lowlands and the seaward-facing slopes of higher terrain (Fig. 23.8). Little if any rain reaches more than about 50 miles inland at this season. The weather of the northeast monsoon in this area features persistent low clouds, high atmospheric humidity, and prolonged periods of light, drizzling rain. It is when clouds hang low, within 1000 or 2000 feet, releasing light, steady rain that crachin weather prevails, usually lasting for two or three days but occasionally for as long as one week. At Kwang-Tri on the coast at latitude 16°44' the annual rainfall averages 100 inches, of which 79 per cent occurs from September through January (Fig. 23.10). October and November record means of 22.1 and 22.3 inches respectively, falling on nineteen or twenty days per month. At Qui Nhon, nearly 250 miles

farther south, the yearly mean is 65.1 inches, of which 79 per cent occurs during the same five-month interval, and again October and November are the wettest months, with 17.1 inches each falling on from thirteen to eighteen days per month. At Saigon, however, about 265 miles southwest of Qui Nhon in the lee of the Annamite chain, only 39 per cent of the normal annual rainfall occurs in the same period of the year, and at Vientiane only 25 per cent.

From about the middle of March to mid-May the northeasterly surface winds of the cool season diminish and are replaced by light, variable breezes before the onset of the southwest monsoon. At higher levels the westerly airflow continues its vigorous thrusts, producing recurrent jet streams at around 40,000 feet across northern Burma and south China. Skies are more often clear at this time of year, and the sun rises high overhead, allowing the land to become drier and air temperatures to soar to maximum values for the entire year, except along the east coast and along the south coast of China. April or May is the warmest month on the peninsulas, with values everywhere in the middle 80s. At Luang Prabang, May averages 84°, and at Chengmai the same value is reported for April; at both Vientiane and Saigon the April mean is 83°; at Nakorn Rajasima and Bangkok, April averages 86°. Extreme maxima have risen to more than 100° at most stations, Saigon reporting 104° in April, Bangkok 106°, Vientiane 103°, and Luang Prabang 102°.

During April, as the Asiatic mainland becomes increasingly warmer, the mean position of upper air jet streams shifts northward to south Korea and Japan, and the polar front, along which wintertime disturbances have been forming, moves poleward into central China and across Taiwan. Low level atmospheric turbulence increases, and with it thunderstorms become more frequent over the interior of the peninsulas of southeast Asia. By the middle of May southwesterly winds begin to gain the upper hand, turbulent cloud formations darken the sky in the warm, humid air from the Indian Ocean, and heavy thunderstorms occur with increasing frequency. Squalls and strong, gusty winds often accompany the onset of the southwest monsoon. By June the season of general rains is in full swing and continues until September, except, of course, along the central east coast of Indochina.

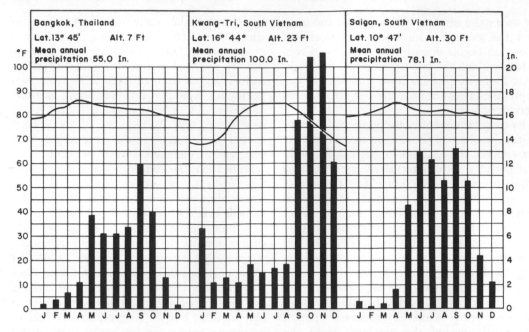

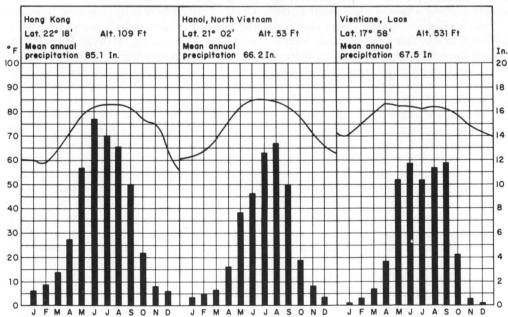

Figure 23.10. Temperature and rainfall at tropical forest and woodland stations of the southeast Asiatic mainland.

With the exception noted above, the southwest monsoon brings the bulk of the year's rain to every section of the southeast mainland (Fig. 23.8). From May to September nearly 80 per cent of the yearly normal occurs. At Vientiane the mean annual rainfall is 67.5 inches, of which 83 per cent occurs in the five-month period of the southwest monsoon. June and September each average 11.9 inches, falling on seventeen and sixteen days respectively. At Luang Prabang, with a yearly mean of 51.5 inches, 79 per cent occurs in this period, and August is the wettest month, with 11.8 inches occurring on nineteen days. Southward and farther west the rainy season lasts until October. At Nakorn Rajasima 82 per cent of the normal yearly total of 48.2 inches falls during the six-month period, at Bangkok 86 per cent of a mean annual amount of 55 inches occurs, and in the same interval 74 per cent of the year's total is normally received at Saigon and Cap St. Jacques. A double maximum is typical of the more southerly locations, and May and September are the usual peak months. The change to a single peak precipitation regime can be detected in the mountain country of northern Thailand and Laos, nearer the Tropic of Cancer and hence nearer the poleward limit of the sun's zenithal position (Fig. 23.10).

The intricate arrangement of relief features in southeast Asia, where in several sections mountain ranges lie athwart the main air streams of the monsoons, is important in accounting for the many climatic contrasts that appear within short distances from Burma to south China. In general, coastal mountain systems are well watered and heavily forested, whereas the intervening basins often much drier, enjoying considerably more sunny weather but enduring seasonal moisture shortages that are sometimes severe. An example of climatic contrast is provided by a comparison of two stations in southern Vietnam Table 23-6.

Dalat is about 55 miles southwest of Nha Trang on the coast and nearly a mile above sea level. At 4921 feet toward the southern end of the Annamite chain, it lies less than 10 miles south of peaks that rise above 7000 feet on a slope that drops off rapidly southward. It is thus well exposed to the southwest monsoon but shielded from the northeast monsoon. Temperatures at Dalat are significantly lower than at sites nearer sea level. At Nha Trang the coolest month of the year is January, when the mean temperature is 75°. Dalat during the same month averages 62°, and in August when the mean value at Nha Trang is 84° it is only 67° at Dalat. Mean yearly rainfall at Dalat is considerably greater than at Nha Trang (71 inches compared with 56.7 inches), illustrating the general rule that maximum rains tend to occur on windward mountain slopes at between 3000 and 5000 feet in southeast Asia, but it is the difference in annual regime that is of more interest. Nha Trang receives small amounts of rain every month of the year, but 74 per cent of the yearly normal occurs in the four-month interval from September to December, most of it falling at the start of the northeast monsoon. Dalat, on the other hand, receives a much more equable distribution, 87 per cent of its annual fall occurring in the seven-month interval from April to October, nearly all produced during the southwest monsoon, and rising to a peak in September just as the season of heavy rains at Nha Trang begins.

Continuous rain during the southwest monsoon is rare. Most rains fall in relatively short, heavy downpours and are usually accompanied by brilliant displays of lightning and earth-shaking peals of rolling thunder. Although the incidence of thunderstorms is generally high, the greater number are observed in mountainous country. Their distribution is more random

TABLE 23–6

Comparative Climatic Data for Nha Trang and Dalat, South Vietnam

	Lat.	El. in Ft
Nha Trang	12°15′	20
Dalat	11°57′	4921

	Jan.	Feb.	Mar.	Apr.	May	Jun.	Jul.	Aug.	Sep.	Oct.	Nov.	Dec.	Year
Temp.													
Nha Trang	75	76	78	81	83	83	83	84	82	80	78	76	80
Dalat	62	63	65	67	68	68	67	67	66	65	64	61	65
Rainfall													
Nha Trang	2.3	0.9	1.7	0.9	2.6	1.8	1.8	2.0	6.7	13.4	15.1	7.4	56.7
Dalat	0.4	1.0	2.2	6.5	8.5	7.3	9.6	8.3	12.1	10.0	3.9	1.1	71.0

than systematic, and they rarely form in long lines of squalls such as we have noted in other parts of the tropics. They tend to form up in late afternoon and early evening, ending before midnight but occasionally continuing on toward morning. Few individual storms persist for more than one or two hours.

From an unpublished report by the 30th Weather Squadron, U. S. Air Force, a normal sequence of daily weather during the southwest monsoon in Vietnam may be summarized as follows.

0600–1000	Patches of fog and stratus in the mountain valleys and near the rivers or marsh lands.
1000–1300	Cumulus clouds begin to form and become more numerous until the sky is almost covered with clouds by 1300 or shortly thereafter.
1300–2300	Cumulus clouds increase in height and amount with many thunderstorms occurring throughout the area.
2300–0200	Thunderstorms normally dissipate except for a few widely scattered storms that continue into the early morning hours.
0200–0600	Normally only a few middle and high clouds occur during this period with stratus beginning to form late in the period; however, because of terrain effects, a few locations in the mountains experience the lowest and the most clouds of the day during this period.

The East Indies

The geographical setting of the East Indies,[4] fundamental to the origin and perpetuation of their tropical forest and woodland climates, includes several special features that merit our attention (Fig. 23.11). Distributed astride the equator are over 3000 islands, from Sumatra to New Guinea, from Timor to the Philippines, many of them too small to support a human population. Except for the northern Philippines, most of them lie within 10 degrees of the equator, and all are surrounded by tropical seas whose surface temperature is always near 80° and along the equator is constantly above 80°.

Two monsoon periods play the dominant role in the climatic year. From southern

[4] This term is used for convenience to include all of Indonesia, the Philippines, and other islands and parts of islands not part of Indonesia.

Sumatra to New Guinea they are known as the west monsoon, from December to March, for most localities the principal season of rain, and the east monsoon, from June to September, a period of less rainfall at most stations. The intervening periods (April–May, October–November) are dominated by the squally, sultry weather of light, uncertain winds, calms, and warm, humid air introduced when the fluctuating belt of the equatorial trough shifts slowly across the region. Thus, the annual regime of seasonal weather sequences is dynamically integrated with systematic changes in the balance of thermal-pressure-airflow distribution occurring outside the region in the middle latitudes on both sides of the equator.

Though the terms *east monsoon* and *west monsoon* are generally applied to the principal alternate seasons, the westward flow of the east monsoon from June to September curves northward on crossing the equator and then northeastward over Sumatra, the Malay peninsula, western Borneo, and the Philippines, and hence in these areas the period is known as the southwest monsoon (Fig. 23.3). The opposite time of year is, of course, the northeast monsoon. In northern New Guinea, where the terms *east* and *west monsoon* are commonly applied to the year's principal seasons, winds are actually more meridional, blowing alternately from southeast and northwest.

The mountainous character of most of the islands strongly influences the actual direction taken by the monsoon winds. There is a widespread tendency for seasonal surface air streams to proceed along the main channels between the islands, more or less conforming to the prevailing direction appropriate to the time of year. Topographic features are mainly responsible for the internal climatic variety from island to island. Thus, those climatic contrasts arising from differences in size, shape, altitude, and alignment of major relief features and their geographic arrangement on individual islands are much greater and more numerous than those arising from differences in latitude alone and seriously modify the general tendency toward equatorial uniformity.

Land and sea breezes often dominate the daily weather regimes among the larger islands of the East Indies. This is especially true when the monsoon winds lose vigor and steadiness and when skies are relatively clear. Where

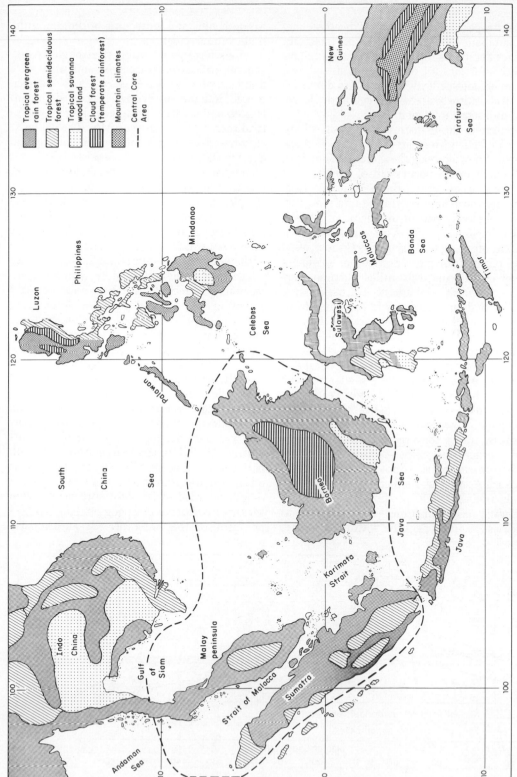

Figure 23.11. Tropical forest and woodland in the East Indies.

Legend:
- Tropical evergreen rain forest
- Tropical semideciduous forest
- Tropical savanna woodland
- Cloud forest (temperate rainforest)
- Mountain climates
- Central Core Area

rugged topography approaches the shoreline, the katabatic effect of downslope mountain breezes augments the offshore breeze at night. In such situations the combination of land, sea, mountain, and valley winds tends to dominate the local airflow pattern, overruling the large-scale monsoon circulation.

Numerous local names are assigned to storms of fairly frequent occurrence. Perhaps the best known among these are the Sumatras, line squalls of the north coast of Sumatra and the west coast of northern Malaya. They generally come up, sometimes quite suddenly, during the early part of the night, are accompanied by thunder, lightning, and heavy rain, and are often severe, rising to velocities of 50 miles per hour or more. Sometimes forming a line of advance up to 200 miles in length, they represent a fairly common type of tropical line squall called an arched squall, so named from the fact that a long, dark roll cloud arching up toward the zenith invariably heralds their approach.

During the transitional interval of April and May before the onset of the east monsoon the bulk of the region is ruled by weather of the equatorial trough (Fig. 23.12). At this time the trough, toward which the northeast and southeast trades converge, becomes narrower than at other times of the year and shifts northward from its previous position south of the equator. A zone of conflict between the opposing trades, it shifts position frequently and erratically and sometimes quite rapidly, as much as 200 miles per day, with the alternate

strengthening and weakening of the contesting trade wind circulations.

When convergence within the trough is weak, general surface winds are light, and calms are a frequent occurrence. At such times the reciprocal land and sea breezes become dominant locally, and showery weather is largely due to local thermal convective activity. The daily rise of convective air currents is felt with special effect in the highly heated interiors of the larger islands, and scattered thundershowers are not uncommon in the hot, humid, highly unstable air. When convergence is strong, mechanical convective systems are set in motion, producing long lines of heavy rain squalls and severe thunderstorms arising in the violent turbulence of the heavy cumulonimbus cloud formations.

The east monsoon sets in almost simultaneously over the entire 4000 mile east-west extent of the archipelago from Sumatra to New Guinea. For much of the region this is the dry season of the "good" monsoon. Over Sumatra, the Malay peninsula, most of Borneo, and western Java the annual rainfall regime is virtually uniform (Fig. 23.8). However, most of the islands from Sulawesi and eastern Java to New Guinea experience a definite dry season beginning in mid-May. At Pasuaruan in east Java, for example, only 13 per cent of the year's normal rainfall is received in the six-month period from June to November. At Makassar on the southwestern tip of Sulawesi only 9 per cent is recorded in the six-month period from May to October; at Koepang on Timor only 5 per cent in the same period; at Thursday

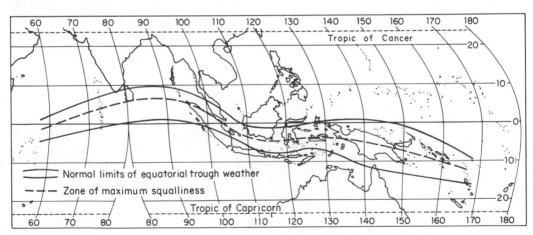

Figure 23.12.   Mean position of the equatorial trough in April over the north Indian Ocean and the East Indies.

Island 15 miles northwest of Cape York in northeast Australia only 5 per cent from June to November; and at Port Moresby on the New Guinea shores of the Coral Sea only 19 per cent in the same period.

The normal weather of the east monsoon is somewhat less definitely dry farther north. Madang on the northeast coast of New Guinea records only about 38 per cent of its mean annual rainfall from June through November, Manokwari on the Vogelkop coast of north-western New Guinea records 35 per cent in the same period, and Menado on the northeast tip of Sulawesi receives 28 per cent. From March to August, the drier period for the northeastern tip of Borneo and the east central part of the Philippines, only about one third of the year's rain normally occurs; in that interval Sandakan, North Borneo, records only 33 per cent, and Legaspi on the southeast of Luzon, 34 per cent.

Incomplete records of cloud cover and per cent of possible sunshine do not permit generalization for the region as a whole, but observations made at a few stations provide a further indication of the comparative salubrity of the east monsoon season. At Menado during July through September the sky is only 21 to 30 per cent cloud covered on the average, compared with 32 to 50 per cent from October to June. At Sandakan the percentage is 38 to 48 per cent from March to July, compared with over 50 per cent for the remainder of the year. At Surigao the least cloudy month is May (58 per cent), compared with between 68 and 74 per cent from September to February. Legaspi averages 35 to 44 per cent from March to May, compared with 51 to 64 per cent from June to February. Koepang on Timor is one of the sunnier points in the East Indies, cloud cover averaging only between 21 and 30 per cent from May to October and between 40 and 45 per cent during the remainder of the year.

But seasonal rainfall distribution is extremely variable from place to place, depending, as we have noted earlier, on local topography and exposure to the prevailing monsoons (Fig. 23.13). It was observed above that Port Moresby receives only 19 per cent of its annual rain from June to November. This station is in a relatively dry savanna region stretching westward along the north coast of the Gulf of Papua in the lee of the Owen Stanley Range that rise to more than 10,000 feet in altitude. Its normal yearly rainfall, based upon a thirty-eight-year record, is 39.8 inches. Eighty-one per cent of this amount occurs from December through May, the maximum amount of 7.6 inches falling on seven days in February, and an annual dry period occurs from June to November, Samarai, a small island about 250 miles farther east off the southeastern tip of New Guinea in a rain-forest region well exposed to the southeasterlies of the east monsoon, experiences a mean annual rainfall, from a twenty-nine-year record, of 107.9 inches. Here 64 per cent of the yearly total occurs from April to October. May is the wettest month, averaging 12 inches falling on thirteen days. At Kikori, about 250 miles north-west of Port Moresby at the head of the Gulf of Papua and well exposed to the east monsoon, the yearly normal is 232.9 inches, based upon a twenty-five-year record, and 72 per cent is received from April to October. June is the wettest month, with 30.5 inches falling on twenty-two days.

Recalling that the westward airflow of the east monsoon curves northward across the equator, and thence with increasing latitude becomes the northeastward flow of the south-west monsoon, we find that in the Philippines, with the exceptions noted above, the period from May through October is the main season of annual rain. The percentage of yearly rain in this interval increases northward. At Jolo the value is 58 per cent, at Davao 60 per cent, at Zamboanga 63 per cent, at Iloilo 78 per cent, at Manila 85 per cent, at Puerto Princessa on Palawan 90 per cent, and at Baguio 92 per cent, the regime extending northward to southern Taiwan where Hengch'un also averages 92 per cent in this period.

With the southward shift on the sun's zenithal position to the equator around September 21st the east monsoon generally approaches an end, and a transitional period of from four to six weeks follows in October and November. The light, fitful winds and hot, humid, showery weather of the equatorial trough results in a sharp drop in monthly rainfall in southern Taiwan and most of the Philippines, except at stations facing the northeast monsoon referred to above. At Hengch'un the mean amount for September is 11.1 inches, but in October it is 6.2 inches; at Baguio, October averages 15 inches; November 4.9 inches; at Manila the average for September is 14 inches,

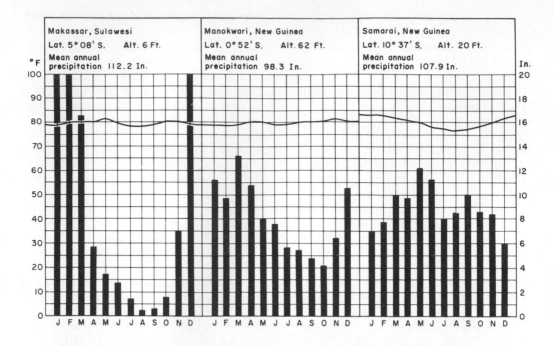

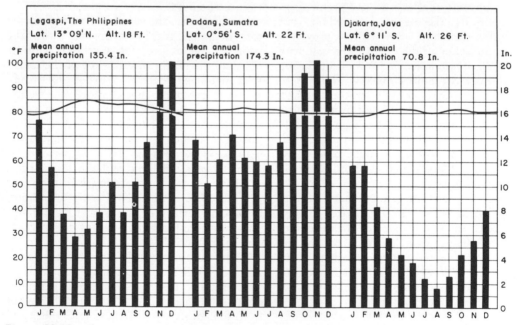

Figure 23.13. Temperature and rainfall at tropical forest and woodland stations in the East Indies.

for October 7.6 inches; at Puerto Princessa, December averages 10 inches and January 2.4 inches.

The northeast monsoon of southeast Asia and the northern Philippines moves gradually southward beginning in late September or early October. In situations where this southwest-

ward movement of air brings most of the year's rains, the change from the desultory showers of typical trough weather to the more abundant and more frequent occurrence of rain during the monsoon takes place most commonly from September to October. Table 23-7 illustrates this change for selected stations from

TABLE 23-7

Change in Monthly Rainfall Amounts and Number of Rain Days with the Onset of the Northeast Monsoon

Station	Lat.	Sept. Amount (In.)	Rain Days	Oct. Amount (In.)	Rain Days
Aparri	18°22′N.	11.3	13	14.1	19
Surigao	9°48′N.	6.6	13	10.7	17
Sandakan	5°50′N.	9.3	15	10.2	18
Kuala Trengganu	5°20′N.	7.5	17	11.0	20
Medan	3°35′N.	8.3	14	10.2	17
Tandjoengpandan	2°45′S.	6.4	10	10.8	17

Source: Great Britain, Meteorological Office, *Tables of Temperature, Relative Humidity and Precipitation for the World*, Part 4, *Asia*, London, 1961.

Aparri in the northern Philippines to Billiton Island in Karimata Strait, a distance of nearly 1800 miles.

But the northeast monsoon of the Philippines and southeast Asia is an integral part of the west monsoon that brings most of the year's rain to the East Indian archipelago. The actual length of the wet season varies somewhat, but it is normally about six months long and begins at successively later dates from west to east. At Takengon in northern Sumatra and Pontianak in western Kalimantan it commences in October; at Menado, Sulawesi, Djakarta, Java, and Makassar, Sulawesi, it begins in November; at Madang, Daru, and Port Moresby in New Guinea and at Thursday Island it is delayed until December.

As a general rule, the islands from Sumatra to New Guinea experience a double rainfall increase during the year (Fig. 23.13). Hence at Takengon, where December is the wettest month, when 8.8 inches normally fall, monthly amounts drop to 4.7 inches in February but rise again to 7.7 inches in March. At Pontianak, where November is the wettest month, with 15.3 inches, amounts diminish to 8.2 inches in February but increase again to 11.1 inches in May. At Manokwari, New Guinea, March, the wettest month, with 13.3 inches is preceded by a lower amount of 9.8 inches in February following a value of 11.3 inches in January. At Samarai, where May is the wettest month, with 12 inches, values drop to 8.1 inches in July, rise again to 10.1 inches in September, lower to 6.1 inches in December, and then increase once

more to 10 inches in March. This is an example of multiple maxima that occur at a number of stations in the East Indies. Although the differences between extremes are often not great, they represent a normal tendency arising from the annual succession of dominant weather situations that prevail within the region. Double rainfall maxima are also noted in northern Borneo and the southern Philippines.

A single peak season of maximum rainfall is characteristic of the northern Philippines and southern Taiwan, continuing, of course, to the Chinese mainland. It is also typical of most of Java, the Lesser Sundas, the Moluccas, and eastward over the Arafura Sea to Thursday Island and Port Moresby. The west monsoon brings an annual rise in annual rainfall to a peak value of 11.8 inches in January and February at Jakarta, 11 inches in February at Pasuruan, 27 inches in January at Makassar, 15.3 inches in January at Koepang, and 18.2 inches in January at Thursday Island. Elsewhere single peak regimes are somewhat anomalous, as at Kuala Trengganu, where November is the month of maximum rain, amounting to 24 inches, and Kuching on the northwest coast of Kalimantan, where January is the peak month, with 24 inches.

Northern Australia

Northern Australia extends well into the tropics from the Pacific to the shores of the Indian Ocean. The Tropic of Capricorn lies over 800 miles south of the northernmost shores, and along it the continent spans a distance of over 2300 miles. Hence, about 40 per cent of the total territory lies well within the latitudinal limits of the tropics (Fig. 15.1). But, as we have repeatedly observed, climatic distribution fails to adhere to the rigid outlines prescribed by the sun's precise relations with the shape and motions of the earth. Instead, it is significantly modified by the size and shape of land masses, by land forms and elevation, and by the dominant air masses and synoptic situations that characterize the fluctuations of atmospheric behavior.

Most of tropical Australia lies below 1000 feet in elevation, and no large mountain ranges impede the invasion of air from the bordering seas. With the exception of the Queensland coast between Cairns and Townsville, the absence of striking contrasts in relief in tropical Australia allows the seasonal succession of monsoonal circulations to rule the climatic distribution. The result is a comparatively uniform gradation of increasingly arid conditions southward from the north coast to the desert interior (Fig. 23.5).

Northern Australia is subjected to a definite yearly rhythm of alternate dry and wet seasons brought about by a periodic reversal of the surface windflow (Fig. 23.3). From April to October, the winter period for the southern latitudes, the belt of anticyclonic systems that encircles the earth south of the equator intensifies and shifts northward. In this period Australia's weather is dominated by clear, dry, subsiding air masses, except in the south coastal areas, as we have noted in earlier chapters. The mean position of prevailing high pressure cells, elongated as they pass eastward from the Indian Ocean, is near the 28th parallel, and the resulting divergent circulation produces a northwestward flow of dry air from the continental interior out over the Timor and Arafura seas. Thus, in this season the southeast trades prevail across all of northern tropical Australia and are continuous from the Pacific to the Indian Ocean. Moving equatorward, the vapor-holding capacity of the trade winds is increased, and their precipitation potential is typically low even when they originate and pass mainly over the sea. The southeast winds that blow across northern Australia are part of a particularly dry divergent circulation over the desert interior and thus begin as unusually dry air, becoming increasingly drier as they advance into lower latitudes.

The dry season resulting from these circumstances lasts for seven months or more over much of tropical Australia, except in the rainforest region along the northeast coast of Queensland, where some rain falls every month of the year. Here the predominantly onshore flow of air from the warm Pacific is highly moisture-laden, and rising over the coastal ranges, releases more rain than in any other part of the tropical territory in Australia (Fig. 23.8).

The wet season ordinarily lasts for about five months in the tropical semideciduous forest regions along the north coast, beginning in late November over northern Arnhem Land, and the higher peneplain in Kimberley and the Barkly tableland, but delaying until the early part of December elsewhere. In the drier savanna and thorn scrub woodland regions farther inland the season is usually only four months in length, from December through March. During the transitional intervals between the northwest monsoon of wet weather and the southeasterly dry season light, variable winds, partly cloudy skies, and showers of variable frequency and strength prevail.

The normal yearly temperature regime at most stations in tropical Australia is far from equable, and a relatively large annual range is commonly observed (Figs. 15.8 and 15.9). Only along the north coast of Arnhem Land and the shores of York Peninsula as far south as Cooktown is the mean annual temperature range less than 10 degrees. Thursday Island shares the thermal equability of the more equatorial East Indies, reporting a mean range of 6 degrees, from 84° in December to 78° in July and August. At Darwin the range is 9 degrees, from 86° in November to 77° in July, and at Cooktown the range is 10°, from 82° December through February to 72° in July. Values increase rapidly southward to more than 20 degrees at points well toward the equator from the Tropic of Capricorn. Thus, at Hall's Creek, about 250 miles south of Joseph Bonaparte Gulf, an embayment of the Timor Sea, and at Wave Hill, about 220 miles farther east, the range is 22 degrees. At Tennant Creek, about 320 miles southwest of the Gulf of Carpentaria, the range is 23 degrees, at Cloncurry, about 200 miles south of the gulf, it is 24 degrees, and at Richmond, 160 miles farther east, it is 23 degrees.

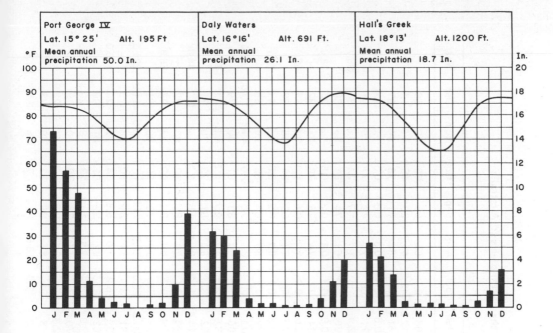

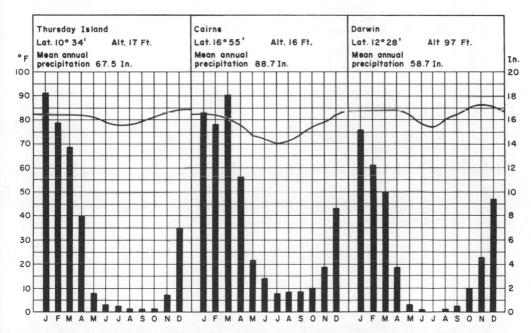

Figure 23.14. Temperature and rainfall at tropical forest and woodland stations in Australia.

At Boulia, about 160 miles southwest of Clon-curry in latitude 22°55′, it is 28 degrees (Fig. 23.14).

The chief reason for the wide annual temperature range is the occurrence of low temperatures during the winter monsoon when the southeast trades control the entire northern part of the continent. The clear, dry air that is swept northwestward from the arid interior allows a strong nocturnal reradiation of terrestrial heat under clear skies during the very period when diurnal insolation is lowest for the year. The resulting low values for interior stations, usually in the middle 60s, are

TABLE 23–8

Climatic Data for Tropical Forest and Woodland Climates in the East Indies and Australia
(Temp., °F; Rainfall, In.)

Station	Lat.	El. in Ft		Jan.	Feb.	Mar.	Apr.	May	Jun.	Jul.	Aug.	Sep.	Oct.	Nov.	Dec.	Year
Baguio, Philippines	16°25'N.	4960	T	64	64	67	68	68	68	66	65	66	66	66	66	
			R	0.9	0.9	1.7	4.3	15.8	17.2	42.3	45.7	28.1	15.0	4.9	1.9	178.7
Boulia, Australia	22°55'S.	478	T	88	88	84	74	67	61	55	64	71	78	84	87	
			R	1.6	1.9	1.5	0.6	0.4	0.5	0.3	0.3	0.3	0.5	1.0	1.4	10.3
Cairns, Australia	16°55'S.	16	T	82	81	80	77	73	71	69	71	73	77	79	81	
			R	16.6	15.7	18.1	11.3	4.4	2.9	1.6	1.7	1.7	2.1	3.9	8.7	88.7
Cloncurry, Australia	20°43'S.	633	T	88	85	84	78	71	65	64	68	74	81	85	88	
			R	4.4	4.2	2.4	0.7	0.5	0.6	0.3	0.1	0.3	0.5	1.3	2.7	18.0
Cooktown, Australia	15°28'S.	17	T	82	82	80	79	76	74	72	74	76	79	81	82	
			R	14.4	13.7	15.3	8.8	2.8	2.0	0.9	1.2	0.6	1.0	2.5	6.6	69.8
Daly Waters, Australia	16°16'S.	691	T	86	85	83	80	74	70	69	72	80	86	88	88	
			R	6.5	6.0	4.8	0.9	0.2	0.3	0.1	0.1	0.2	0.8	2.2	4.0	26.1
Darwin, Australia	12°28'S.	97	T	84	84	84	84	82	78	77	80	82	85	86	85	
			R	15.6	12.8	9.9	4.0	0.7	0.1	0.1	0.1	0.5	2.0	4.6	10.0	60.4
Djakarta, Java	6°11'S.	26	T	79	79	79	80	80	80	79	80	80	81	80	79	
			R	12.0	12.6	8.3	5.5	4.2	3.6	2.6	1.7	2.7	4.7	5.6	7.8	71.4
Hengch'un, Taiwan	22°00'N.	77	T	70	70	74	78	81	82	83	82	81	79	75	71	
			R	0.9	1.1	0.9	2.0	7.4	14.4	17.3	21.4	11.1	6.2	1.4	0.7	84.8
Koepang, Timor	10°11'S.	7	T	81	81	81	81	81	80	79	79	81	82	83	82	
			R	15.3	14.4	8.7	2.5	1.1	0.4	0.2	0.1	0.1	0.7	3.5	9.7	56.8
Kikori, New Guinea	7°24'S.	806	T	82	81	81	80	79	78	76	76	78	80	80	81	
			R	11.5	12.6	15.2	17.5	30.2	30.5	25.5	21.3	24.0	17.3	13.9	11.8	231.3
Kuala Trengganu, Malaya	5°20'N.	105	T	77	78	80	81	82	81	81	81	81	80	78	78	
			R	9.2	3.4	7.3	4.6	4.7	5.1	6.2	7.0	5.8	14.8	27.2	24.7	120.0
Legaspi, Philippines	13°09'N.	18	T	79	79	80	82	83	83	82	82	82	81	81	80	
			R	15.4	11.5	7.7	5.9	6.4	7.9	10.2	7.9	10.2	13.7	18.3	20.3	135.5
Makassar, Sulawesi	5°08'S.	13	T	79	79	79	80	80	79	78	78	78	79	80	79	
			R	27.0	21.1	16.7	5.9	3.5	2.9	1.4	0.4	0.5	1.7	7.0	23.9	112.2
Manila, Philippines	14°35'N.	47	T	78	78	81	83	84	83	81	81	81	81	79	78	
			R	1.0	0.5	0.7	1.2	5.1	9.9	17.0	16.6	14.4	7.7	5.6	2.5	82.1

Station	Lat.	El. in Ft		Jan.	Feb.	Mar.	Apr.	May	Jun.	Jul.	Aug.	Sep.	Oct.	Nov.	Dec.	Year
Manokwari, New Guinea	1°10'S.	62	T	79	79	79	80	80	79	79	80	80	80	81	80	
			R	12.2	9.3	13.1	11.1	7.8	7.3	5.4	5.6	5.0	4.8	6.5	10.3	98.4
Mapoon, Australia	12°04'S.	20	T	84	84	84	83	81	78	78	78	81	84	86	86	
			R	17.7	15.4	12.1	3.8	0.7	0.2	0.1	0.0	0.2	0.4	2.4	9.0	62.0
Menado, Sulawesi	1°30'N.	30	T	79	79	79	80	80	80	80	81	81	80	80	80	
			R	18.3	14.0	12.0	7.8	6.3	5.4	4.7	3.8	3.4	4.8	8.6	14.6	104.8
Pasuruan, Java	7°38'S.	16	T	81	81	81	81	81	79	79	79	80	82	83	81	
			R	8.9	11.0	8.4	5.4	3.7	2.2	1.0	0.2	0.2	0.7	2.4	6.5	50.6
Pontianak, Kalimantan	0°01'S.	10	T	80	81	81	82	82	82	82	81	81	81	81	80	
			R	11.2	8.3	9.9	11.2	11.0	3.8	6.7	8.8	8.6	14.7	15.7	13.3	128.3
Port George IV, Australia	15°25'S.	195	T	84	84	83	81	76	72	69	73	78	82	85	86	
			R	14.8	11.4	9.6	2.2	0.9	0.5	0.3	0.0	0.1	0.4	2.0	7.8	50.0
Port Moresby, New Guinea	9°29'S.	124	T	83	82	82	82	81	79	78	78	79	80	82	83	
			R	7.0	7.9	6.8	4.1	2.6	1.2	1.2	0.9	1.2	1.2	1.9	4.3	40.1
Puerto Princesa, Philippines	9°44'N.	44	T	79	79	80	82	82	81	81	81	80	80	80	79	
			R	2.4	1.5	1.6	2.1	6.6	7.8	8.7	7.1	8.4	10.3	10.8	10.0	77.3
Rockhampton, Australia	23°24'S.	37	T	81	80	78	74	69	64	62	65	70	75	78	81	
			R	7.5	7.6	4.4	2.6	1.6	2.6	1.8	0.8	1.3	1.8	2.4	4.7	39.1
Samarai, New Guinea	10°37'S.	20	T	83	83	82	81	80	78	78	77	78	79	80	82	
			R	6.4	7.8	10.2	9.5	11.9	10.5	9.0	9.1	10.0	8.9	7.6	5.2	106.1
Sandakan, Sabah	5°50'N.	104	T	80	80	81	82	82	82	82	82	82	81	81	80	
			R	19.0	10.9	8.6	4.5	6.2	7.4	6.7	7.9	9.3	10.2	14.5	18.5	123.7
Surigao, Philippines	9°48'N.	20	T	79	79	80	81	82	82	82	82	82	81	80	79	
			R	21.4	14.8	19.9	10.0	6.2	4.9	7.0	5.1	6.6	10.7	16.8	24.4	141.8
Thursday Island, Australia	10°34'S.	17	T	82	82	82	81	79	79	77	77	79	81	82	83	
			R	18.2	15.8	13.9	8.0	1.6	0.5	0.4	0.2	0.1	0.3	1.5	7.0	67.5
Townsville, Australia	19°14'S.	48	T	82	81	80	77	73	69	67	69	73	77	80	82	
			R	10.9	11.2	7.2	3.3	1.3	1.4	0.6	0.5	0.7	1.3	1.9	5.4	45.7
Zamboanga, Philippines	6°54'N.	16	T	79	79	80	80	80	80	80	80	80	80	80	80	
			R	2.1	2.2	1.5	2.0	3.5	4.2	4.9	4.0	4.7	5.6	4.2	3.4	42.4

Source: U.S. Army, Quartermaster Research and Engineering Command, *Analogs of Canal Zone Climate in Indonesia, the Philippines, and Borneo* (Tech. Report EP-116), Natick, Mass., 1959. *Analogs of Canal Zone Climate in Australia and New Guinea*, Natick, Mass., 1959.

thus mainly responsible for the large yearly fluctuations.

The range between extreme temperatures of record is also unusually high at inland points. At Boulia, for example, it is 93 degrees (26° to 119°), at Cloncurry 92 degrees (35° to 127°), at Hall's Creek 82 degrees (30° to 112°), at Daly Waters 86 degrees (30° to 116°), and at Tennant Creek 79 degrees (36° to 115°). Even at stations near the north coast the extreme range is large; the thermometer has spanned 62 degrees at Wyndham, 70 degrees at Burketown, and 69 degrees at Normanton, the latter two stations within 20 miles of the Gulf of Carpentaria.

The normal yearly rainfall for all of Australia is peripheral in its general distribution. Amounts are largest along the coasts and diminish toward the interior (Table 23-8). This distribution in tropical northern Australia is the chief reason for the climatic gradation from tropical forest, wherever it is found along the northern and northeastern coasts, through savanna and thorn scrub woodland to the arid interior. The wettest part of all Australia appears along a stretch of the northeast coast extending for about 190 miles southward from a point approximately midway between Cooktown and Cairns. Here a number of stations have reported average annual amounts in excess of 100 inches for varying intervals during the past century. At Innisfail, about 46 miles south of Cairns and about 15 miles southeast of Mt. Bartle Frere, average rainfall was 142.8 inches from 1881 to 1928. Harvey Creek, about 23 miles south of Cairns and somewhat north of the mountain, averaged 165.9 inches during the seven-year period from 1905 to 1912.[5] Cairns itself averaged 88.6 inches for a fifty-six-year period, and Cooktown 69.8 inches over a sixty-two-year period. A year-round onshore easterly movement of air off the warm adjacent seas is chiefly responsible for the relatively persistent rains of this small section of the northeast coast. Mean annual rainfall diminishes both northward and southward from the area of maximum amounts.

Although rainfall observations are lacking to provide the necessary supporting data, the presence of evergreen rainforest in scattered

patches from the east side of York Peninsula opposite Mapoon to the inner seaward slopes of the coastal ranges opposite Sandy Cape, about 200 miles north of Brisbane, suggests that yearly amounts in excess of 60 inches may extend, at least at intervals, over this entire stretch of the northeastern littoral. Persistently high atmospheric moisture undoubtedly offsets the seasonal lessening of annual rain during the period of the southeast monsoon.

The wet season of the northwest monsoon sets in during November not only along the northeast coast but nearly everywhere else as well. A decided increase in monthly amounts becomes especially apparent between November and December. At Thursday Island the monthly gain is from 1.5 inches in November to 7 inches in December; at Mapoon from 2.4 inches in November to 9 inches in December; at Cooktown from 2.5 to 6.6 inches; at Cairns from 3.9 to 8.7 inches; at Townsville from 1.9 to 5.4 inches; and at Rockhampton from 2.4 to 4.7 inches. At Cairns and Cooktown the wettest month is March, Cairns averaging 18.1 inches falling on nineteen days, and Cooktown 15.3 inches falling on eighteen days. At Townsville and Rockhampton, February is the month of maximum rain, 11.4 inches falling on fourteen days, and 7.6 inches on twelve days, respectively. January is the wettest month farther north, when Mapoon averages 17.7 inches falling on nineteen days, and Thursday Island 18.2 inches on twenty-one days (Fig. 23.8-B).

The rainy northeastern littoral rarely extends beyond 50 miles from the sea, and yearly precipitation amounts diminish rapidly westward. They also diminish rapidly southward from the scattered sections of moderately wet tropical semideciduous forest along the north coast. The increasing aridity observable through the savanna and thorn scrub woodland regions is suggested by the reported yearly values from the very small number of observation points in this sparsely populated northern portion of Australia.

At Darwin, for example, 58.7 inches is normal, 94 per cent of which occurs in the six-month period from November through April, but at Wyndham, about 280 miles southwestward, the yearly average is less than half this amount at 25.9 inches, 93 per cent of which occurs in a five-month period from November through March. At Daly Waters about 300

[5] W. Köppen and R. Geiger, *Handbuch der Klimatologie*, 4 (Teil S), *Australien und Neuseeland*, Berlin, 1932, pp. S56 and S86.

miles southeast of Darwin 26.1 inches is the yearly normal, 90 per cent of which is received from November through March. At Tennant Creek, less than 250 miles farther south, the normal is 14.7 inches, 80 per cent of which occurs from December to April.

The onset of the northwest monsoon is presaged by a brief period of two or three weeks, sometimes longer, when light, variable winds, many intervals of calm, and the appearance of low, dark clouds mark the seasonal approach of the equatorial trough. Thunderstorms and heavy rain squalls occur in random fashion as warm, very humid air moves in more frequent surges into the northern part of the continent. The equatorial trough eventually takes control of the season's weather over northwestern Australia, where an almost unbroken series of depressions forms annually during the period from November to April. Here the northwest monsoon is much less steady and less vigorous than elsewhere, and calm, squally weather with desultory movements of surface air currents prevails, modified repeatedly by winds of the clockwise circulation around the predominant lows.

Some indication of the importance of fitful, squally equatorial trough weather here is provided by the record of thunderstorms. Far more of these violent local disturbances occur across northwestern Australia than anywhere else on the continent (Fig. 23.15). Up to one hundred thunderstorms are recorded annually along the coast northwest of the Kimberley plateau, and up to fifty are normal for 200 miles or more inland along the entire north and northwest coast as far as the eastern side of the Gulf of Carpentaria. On the east coast of the

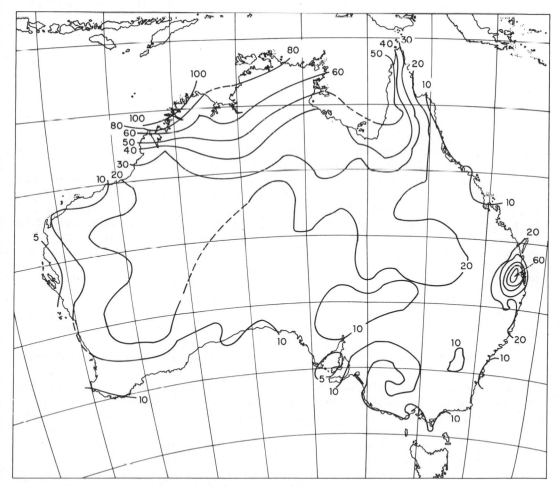

Figure 23.15. Average number of thunderstorms per year in Australia.

York Peninsula, however, thunderstorm frequency is much lower, diminishing to ten or fifteen per year from Cooktown to Rockhampton. Thunderstorms are most frequent near the start and toward the end of the rainy season.

By the end of November the northwest monsoon holds sway over most of northern Australia, northwest winds prevailing until March, and on the northernmost capes until April, when a brief spell of uncertain weather, squalls, and thundershowers intervenes before the dry season of the southeast monsoon begins.

During the rainy season tropical storms that may reach hurricane intensity are prone to develop over the Indian Ocean off the northwest coast. They most commonly approach the tropical coasts from those waters in December, although they may occur at any time between December and April. Exact records are lacking, but those that attain hurricane strength are believed to occur on an average of somewhat less than once a year. Destructive tropical storms have attacked the mainland at points ranging from the Cobourg peninsula, about 120 miles northeast of Darwin, to Shark Bay, more than 1500 miles toward the southwest. They normally travel in a parabolic path, approaching from northeastward and then recurving southeastward toward the shore. Their advance, at from 11 to 14 miles per hour, is often apparent in a rapid drop in barometric pressure and the appearance of low, dark clouds building up to northward as winds from southeastward begin to rise in surges of increasing velocity. The storm usually breaks with sharp, gale force winds or stronger, heavy rains, and much thunder and lightning.

But the tropical shores of northeastern Australia receive the greatest number of violent, destructive tropical storms for the continent as a whole (Fig. 5.21). Here the average annual frequency of occurrence is between three or four. Originating over the Coral Sea, usually near the Solomon Islands, they strike the mainland most commonly between Cooktown and Mackay, and in consequence have been termed Queensland hurricanes. Taking a southwesterly course at about 17 miles per hour from the point of origin, they usually recurve southward and southeastward, gaining speed to between 25

and 30 miles per hour, often missing the coast entirely. Some cross York Peninsula and the Gulf of Carpentaria, others extend inland and dissipate over the dry interior basins, bringing unusually heavy rains and severe flooding before they do. Damage from high winds and storm waves along the coast has been very severe, for winds rising within their clockwise circulations that normally encompass an area between 100 and 200 miles in diameter have attained speeds in excess of 90 miles per hour, often gusting well above 100 miles per hour, and the sea has risen 12 to 15 feet above normal. In 1899 three hundred lives were reported lost near Cooktown; in 1911 Port Douglas, about 70 miles south of Cooktown, was demolished; Innisfail was demolished by storms of unusual intensity in 1918. Tropical storms have brought as much as 20.2 inches of rain in twenty-four hours to Cairns in April, 14 inches in twenty-four hours to Cooktown in January, 10.3 inches in twenty-four hours to Townsville in February.

Over most of the forested sections of the north coast the reliability of annual rainfall is comparatively high. In Arnhem Land the expected variation from normal is only 15 per cent, and around Cape York it is 20 per cent. Elsewhere in the tropical regions variability increases to between 25 and 35 per cent, and of course much beyond this value in the arid interior, especially near the west coast.

After the September equinox as the sun's zenithal position moves increasingly farther southward and the rising intensity of daily insolation is reflected in progressively higher readings on the thermometer, the hottest weather of the year is normally experienced just as the wet season begins. Nearly everywhere November or December is the warmest month (Fig. 23.14).

During the period of high solar radiation intensity the thermometer has climbed to excessive heights in tropical Australia (Fig. 19.1). With the exception of Thursday Island, where the maximum recorded temperature has been 98° in December, all tropical stations have reported values in excess of 100°. At Darwin the absolute maximum has been 105° in October, at Mapoon 104° in November and February, at Cairns, Townsville, and Burketown, 110° in January or February. The inland station of Cloncurry has reported 127° in January, and Boulia 119° in February.

After the vernal equinox in March when the rainy season begins to subside, the zenithal position of the sun has withdrawn to points north of the equator, and cooler, drier weather sets in. With the exception of the northern part of York Peninsula, July is everywhere the month of lowest mean temperatures for the entire year. This is an indication of the ready response of atmospheric temperatures to the curve of normal yearly solar radiation input, when the air normally is dry and clear. It is especially evident at inland points of observation, where July midafternoon relative humidities are 27 per cent at Cloncurry and Wave Hill, 28 per cent at Boulia, and 24 per cent at Daly Waters and Tennant Creek. Nearer the northern coasts values are somewhat higher in July, as at Darwin, 44 per cent, Burketown, 41 per cent, and Normanton, 37 per cent. From Townsville northward along the northeast coast relative humidities are understandably higher; Townsville in July reports 58 per cent, Cairns 63 per cent, Cooktown 69 per cent, and Thursday Island 70 per cent.

Though relative humidity values for July are low, the driest month of the year is usually later in the cooler season. Wave Hill reports 21 per cent, Daly Waters 20 per cent, Cloncurry an annual minimum of 19 per cent, and Tennant Creek 18 per cent, all in September,

and Boulia 17 per cent in September and October. Boulia is a station well toward the more arid central interior, not far from the Simpson desert.

Temperatures during the cooler season of dry weather are by no means as uniform as when the northwest monsoon is in force. True, at stations near the sea normal July values differ only slightly, as at Wyndham 76°, Darwin 77°, Thursday Island and Mapoon 78°. But with increasing distance southward monthly values diminish notably; Daly Waters and Burketown average 69° in July, Tennant Creek and Cloncurry average 64°, and Boulia averages 60°. Under the clear skies, low atmospheric humidities, and diminishing heat from the sun temperatures have dropped to extremely low values for stations in the tropics. Many interior observation points have experienced temperatures below 40° in July. At Wave Hill the thermometer has dropped to 38°, at Tennant Creek and Port George IV to 36°, at Cloncurry to 35°, at Daly Waters and Hall's Creek to 30° and at Boulia to 26°. These are unusually low values for regions we have described as tropical, and a case might well be made for designating them subtropical. This is especially true in view of the fact that frost is believed to occur on as many as five days per year as far north as the Kimberley plateau and the Barkly tableland.

References

BOWMAN, R. G.: "Acclimatization in New Guinea," *Geographical Review*, **39**(2): 311–15, 1949.

DE ROSAYRO, R. A.: "The Montane Grasslands of Ceylon," *Tropical Agriculturist*, **101**: 206–13, 1945.

DOBBY, E. H. G.: "Winds and Fronts over Southeastern Asia," *Geographical Review*, **34**(2): 204–19, 1945.

FISHER, C. A.: *South-East Asia*, Methuen & Co. Ltd., London, 1964.

HOLMES, C. H.: "The Grass, Fern, and Savanna Lands of Ceylon," *Imperial Forestry Institute Paper*, No. 28, Oxford, 1951.

RAWSON, R. R.: *The Monsoon Lands of Asia*, Aldine Publishing Co., Chicago, 1963.

THOMPSON, B. W.: "An Essay on the General Circulation of the Atmosphere over South East Asia and the West Pacific," *Quarterly Journal of the Royal Meteorological Society*, **77**: 569–97, 1951.

U.S. ARMY, MATERIAL COMMAND, NATICK LABORATORIES, *Climatic Atlas of Southeast Asia* (Technical Report No. ES-19), Natick, Mass., 1965.

U.S. Army, Quartermaster Research and Engineering Command, *Analogs of Canal Zone Climate in Australia and New Guinea*, Natick, Mass., 1959.

———: *Analogs of Canal Zone Climate in India and Southeast Asia*, Natick, Mass., 1958.

———: *Analogs of Canal Zone Climate in Indonesia, the Philippines, and Borneo*, Natick, Mass., 1959.

———: *Analogs of Canal Zone Climate in the Far East*, Natick, Mass., 1960.

chapter 24

MOUNTAIN CLIMATES AND OCEANIC CLIMATES

We have had frequent occasion to speak of the shielding effect of major mountain systems and of the influence of height and exposure on temperature and precipitation. We have also taken due account of proximity to the sea as an ameliorating influence on potential climatic extremes. This chapter is devoted to a discussion of the special qualities of mountain and oceanic climates.

The wide distribution of mountainous terrain and ocean surface in nearly every latitude produces an uncountable number of variations within each climatic division. In mountain regions multivariation is the foremost climatic character. Among oceanic climates it is the fact that nearly 72 per cent of the earth's surface is oceanic, thus placing sea surfaces in nearly every latitude, that leads to immeasurable climatic variety. Limitations of space require that we confine our discussion of these two major divisions to the basic principles and processes by which the essential climatic character of each is established.

Mountain Climates

A mountain may be defined as a high, conspicuous landform whose crown area is small in proportion to its base dimensions and on which climatic change is distinctly observable from base to summit. In many mountain regions extensive plateaus present a broad, tabular surface to the skies. Their surfaces may be hilly, rolling, or even quite level, and they frequently terminate along one or more margins in a relatively high, steep-sided bluff or escarpment. An elevated platform of this type is often surmounted by prominent mountain peaks and ranges. Our consideration of mountain climates thus includes many varieties of terrain, whose paramount characteristic is definite climatic change with altitude, occurring, as a rule, within very short linear distances.

In mountainous regions of the world the primary physical circumstance is altitude. In Chapter 6 the general effect of altitude on the composition of the atmosphere and on atmospheric processes was discussed at some length. In every climatic region we have examined, from polar ice cap to tropical forests and wood lands, our attention has been drawn many times to the significance of altitude as a qualifying circumstance.

The effect of increasing altitude upon specific properties of the atmosphere is fundamental to understanding the great complexities among mountain climates. The diminishing mass and density of the atmosphere, decreasing pressure, increasing insolation, lowering air temperatures, acceleration of wind, lessening proportions of moisture and suspended material and thus a change in general composition are among

603

the main qualities in which progressive change is seen with increasing height above sea level. Other variables, dependent on one or more of the above, include diminishing temperature fluctuations, increased evaporation and, up to certain levels, increasing cloud formation, an increase in precipitation, and a gain in the proportion of snow to the total precipitation. (For a discussion of chemical and physical properties of the atmosphere see Chapter 2.)

But a great deal more than atmospheric change with height must be taken into account to approach an understanding of mountain climates. Latitude is, of course, the most important independent variable. Altitude within a given latitude is the next important variable. To these we may then add the physical qualities peculiar to mountains and high plateaus. They include the mass of a specific relief feature and the proportion of its mass at successively higher levels. The number and height of individual peaks are significant. Also important are the steepness and configuration of slopes, the geological formations, and the kind and depth of the overburden. Of major importance are the shape and dimensions of particular mountains, mountain ranges, and entire cordilleran systems and their degree of continentality or position with respect to the distribution of land and water on the earth. Position and alignment of individual mountains and mountain systems to the direction of significant air streams must be considered, including both the prevailing and the less frequent winds as well as the paths taken by relevant systematic disturbances.

Exerting the strongest dynamic control over the potential climatic variety in mountain regions is the constantly changing direction of the sun's rays with respect to the complexities of mountain morphology. The perpetually shifting angular elevation and position of the sun from dawn to dusk, from week to week, and from season to season sets up a continually changing pattern of light and shadow, of warmth and cold, according to the directional relationship of a mountain's slopes with the sun's rays.

But this summary of general conditions and influences is by no means an adequate indication of even the known combinations of environmental variety among the world's mountain regions. If one term can be used to express the essence of mountain climates as a whole, it is *extreme differentiation*. Among the higher mountains climatic complexity reaches a maximum in every latitude within only very small areas of the earth's surface. To attempt a useful general statement on the limits of complexity among all the world's mountain regions is entirely ruled out not only by the multitude of known variations but also by the lack of adequate supporting data for all but a very few, unrelated case studies. For the purpose of discussing the main features of mountain climates we will consider the following factors: the basic relationships between mountain terrain and solar radiation; the basic relationships between mountain terrain and atmospheric qualities and processes; and vertical climatic differentiation.

BASIC RELATIONSHIPS BETWEEN MOUNTAIN TERRAIN AND SOLAR RADIATION. It will be recalled from the account of the atmosphere's vertical structure in Chapter 2 that about 50 per cent of the atmosphere's mass lies below 17,500 feet and about 75 per cent below 35,000 feet. Nearly half its moisture and well over half its dust particles are below 6000 feet. Thus, the density of the earth's atmosphere diminishes substantially from about 6000 feet upward. Consequently, a considerably higher percentage of insolation is received by surfaces above that level through a decrease in radiant heat loss by scattering and diffusion. It is estimated that some 75 per cent of the insolation penetrates to altitudes of about 6000 feet, whereas only about 50 per cent reaches sea level. The figures are approximate but suggest plainly enough the marked increase under clear skies. A more specific illustration is offered from among the countless atmospheric measurements made by Austrian meteorologists in the eastern Alps, an area that has been studied more thoroughly than any other mountain region in the world (Table 24-1). Here the daily input of global radiation (direct solar radiation plus the lesser quotient of diffuse sky radiation) under cloudless skies is seen to increase from 691 gram calories per square centimeter per day at about 650 feet, to 747 at 3280 feet, to 799 at about 6560 feet, and to 834 at about 9840 feet, all during the month of June.

An important qualitative change also takes place above 6000 feet or so where a gain in the proportion of ultraviolet rays occurs. This change is well known to mountain climbers and skiers from their familiarity with the severe sunburn they commonly suffer at high altitudes. These effects are augmented by re-radiation of heat from snow fields that tend to return most of the insolation received to the atmosphere.

TABLE 24–1

Mean Global Radiation Totals per Day in June Under Cloudless Skies in the Eastern Alps at Different Altitudes

Alt. in Ft	Mean Daily Total Global Radiation (gm cal/cm²/day)
650	691
3280	747
6560	799
9840	834

After R. Geiger, *The Climate Near the Ground,* Cambridge, Mass., 1965.

The visible results of greatly diminished atmospheric density are often noted in the remarkable clarity of mountain air. One's visual range is substantially increased, and the sky overhead is usually a deep violet-blue, against which the more prominent constellations may sometimes be seen, in favorable circumstances, for a short time after sunrise. There is an absence of blue color in distant landscapes, and the sky at sunset is often yellow instead of red. Deficiency of water vapor is mainly responsible for this. At sea level the sun is seen as a bright disc encircled by a broad corona of diffused light fading into the blue of the surrounding sky. On high mountain tops, however, its bright disc gleams through the highly transparent atmosphere without its nebulous corona, its perimeter sharply outlined against the deep blue of the sky.

Through the thin, clear air at higher altitudes the sun's rays readily transmit their warmth to mountain summits only moments after sunrise. As the sun rises higher above the eastern horizon, more and more of the eastern and southeastern slopes (in the northern hemisphere) are bathed in sunlight. But it follows quite naturally that many slopes and intermontane valleys remain in shadow for varying lengths of time as the day progresses. Only within those latitudes where the sun attains a zenithal position at some time of the year are all slopes and valleys simultaneously bathed in the sun's rays, and this may occur for only a brief interval when the sun in exactly overhead and precisely on the local meridian. Thus, it is plain that one of the outstanding features of mountain climate is the constantly shifting pattern of light and shadow from sunrise to sunset. The duration of sunlight attains a maximum on the higher peaks and a minimum in the deeper valleys, particularly those well sheltered by the larger, higher mountain ranges and ridges.

The percentage of possible sunshine actually received in mountain valleys is partly determined by latitude, partly by the altitude, dimensions, and shape of neighboring ranges, partly by directional alignment (whether east–west, north–south, or in an intermediate angular position), and partly by the time of year. Some mid-latitude valleys remain beyond the reach of the direct rays of the sun when the sun is at its lowest angular elevation for the year. Many poleward slopes remain in shade even at the summer solstice. The possible combinations of relevant circumstances determining the local duration of sunshine are almost infinite. Among the significant variables is cloud cover, which in some instances is greater in the forenoon and in others increases during the afternoon. Transient disturbances also play a role in varying the amounts of sunshine received.

Although the lessening density of the atmosphere with increasing altitude allows a gradual gain in the intensity of insolation, the atmosphere's capacity for taking up and retaining radiant heat from the sun or from any source is greatly diminished. We have seen many examples of the influence of altitude upon mean and extreme air temperatures in preceding chapters. But the absorption of radiant heat by soil and rock is a different matter. With increasing altitude ground surface temperatures during daylight under clear skies exceed those of the air by an ever greater degree. At night they drop to values much lower than those of the atmosphere, thus creating a far greater range of diurnal thermal fluctuation on the surface of rock and soil than in the overlying atmosphere. Very pronounced diurnal temperature changes act as an unusually powerful weathering agent at higher elevations through the cracking, splitting, and exfoliation of exposed bedrock. An interesting example of this is supplied by Peattie, standing at some distance from the sheer rock cliff known as the Royal Arches in Yosemite Park, Calif., as the rays of the morning sun first struck the cliff. "Pieces of rock were flaked from the surface and whirled through the air until they sounded like bullets."[1]

A comparison of the data from two stations in the French Pyrenees is given in Table 24-2. Note first of all that at Bagneres (el. 1680) air temperature averages 72°, whereas at Pic du Midi (el. 9439) it averages 50°, a difference of 22 degrees, an expected consequence of altitude difference upon air temperature. The maximum air temperature reported at Bagneres is 81°, 25 degrees higher than the maximum of 56° reported at Pic du Midi. But the differences between the mean soil surface values are much lower, 97° at Bagneres, and 93° at the higher station. Furthermore, the chief point of contrast is the very much smaller difference between mean air and soil values at the lower station (25 degrees) compared with those at the higher station (43 degrees). In addition, the maximum soil temperature attained at Bagneres is only 42 degrees higher than the maximum air temperature, but at the higher station the difference is 70 degrees. And the maximum soil surface value attained at Pic du Midi is actually 3 degrees higher (126°) than that at the lower station (123°).

TABLE 24–2

Air and Soil Temperatures at Two Stations in the French Pyrenees (°F)

	Bagneres (el. 1680)	Pic du Midi (el. 9439)
Mean air temp.	72	50
Mean soil temp.	97	93
Max. air temp.	81	56
Max. soil temp.	123	126

After R. Peattie, *Mountain Geography*, Harvard University Press, Cambridge, Mass., p. 29.

BASIC RELATIONSHIPS BETWEEN MOUNTAIN TERRAIN AND ATMOSPHERIC QUALITIES AND PROCESSES. The relationships between moun-

[1] R. Peattie, *Mountain Geography*, Harvard University Press, Cambridge, Mass., 1936, p. 28.

tainous terrain and the atmospheric elements of temperature, water vapor, cloud formation, precipitation, wind, and evaporation are far too complex to permit generalization. Only in the very broadest terms may certain principles of change with altitude in regions of strong relief be stated.

The influence of altitude on temperature change in specific mountain areas is suitably shown by comparing the mean annual temperatures of stations at different elevations in reasonable proximity to one another. This is one of the few situations where mean annual temperature is meaningful in comparative climatology. Table 24-3 presents temperature data for three mid-latitude stations related to the Bavarian Alps along the Austrian border. The mean annual temperature at Zugspitze is 24°. At Innsbruck, less than 25 miles southeastward and south of the Alpine ranges, it is 49°, and at Munich, less than 60 miles northeastward and well to the north of the Alps, it is 46°. Mean temperatures for the coldest month of January are nearly the same at both the lower stations, but at Zugspitze the coldest month is delayed until February when the mean temperature is 12°, an understandable contrast in view of the altitude difference of nearly 8000 feet. Average values for the warmest month of July are 67° at Innsbruck and 63° at Munich but only 35° at Zugspitze for both July and August. The mean annual range is considerably lower near the summit, illustrating the normal tendency toward thermal equability with increasing elevation. Extreme fluctuations are also smaller at higher levels. At Innsbruck the extreme range is 113 degrees, and at Munich 106 degrees, but at Zugspitze only 93 degrees.

From the decrease with altitude in the values of both mean and extreme annual temperature ranges, plus the delay of the coldest month to February and the warmest to August, stations near mountain summits in the middle latitudes are seen to resemble marine situations. Thermal equability is further indicated by the mean daily temperature ranges. In January the mean daily range for Innsbruck is 14 degrees, for Munich 10 degrees, and for Zugspitze 9 degrees. In July the value is 23 degrees for Innsbruck and 18 degrees for Munich, but for Zugspitze it is again 9 degrees in both July and August. The conservative thermal tendencies of high altitude

TABLE 24–3

Temperature Data for Stations in and Near the Bavarian Alps (°F)
(Zugspitze: 47°25′N. Lat; 10°59′E. Long.)

	El. in Ft	Mean Annual Temp.	Coldest Month	Warmest Month	Mean Annual Range	Absolute Max.	Absolute Min.	Ext. Range
Innsbruck	1909	49	27 Jan.	67 Jul.	40	97	−16	113
Zugspitze	9718	24	12 Feb.	35 Jul., Aug.	23	63	−30	93
Munich	1739	46	28 Jan.	63 Jul.	35	92	−14	106

Source: Great Britain, Meterological Office, *Tables of Temperature, Relative Humidity and Precipitation for the World*, Part 3, *Europe and the Atlantic Ocean North of 35°N.*, London, 1960.

stations in the mid-latitudes compared with locations at lower levels in the same approximate latitude are primarily due to elevation. But the mean monthly temperature lag at Zugspitze is undoubtedly a consequence of the nearness of the Bavarian Alps to the North Atlantic and hence to the basic influence of repeated eastward advances of maritime air from the west. The temperature lag is not observed in the eastern Rockies, for example.

In Table 24-4 temperature data are presented for five stations near Pike's Peak, Colo., near the eastern flanks of the Rocky Mountains and all within a radius of less than 40 miles. Pike's Peak is about 1000 miles east of the Pacific coast at an altitude of about 14,111 feet. The mean annual temperature here is 19°, but at Lake Moraine (el. 10,265), less than 3 miles southeastward, it is 36°, at Cripple Creek (el. 9508), about 9 miles southwestward, it is 39°, at Colorado Springs (el. 6098), about 9 miles east, it is 48°, and at Pueblo (el. 4639), some 40 miles southeastward, it is 52°. January and July are the extreme months at all stations, indicating

TABLE 24–4

Temperature Data for Stations Near Pike's Peak in the Eastern Rockies (°F)
(Pike's Peak: 38°50′N. Lat.; 105°02′W. Long.)

	El. in Ft	Mean Annual Temp.	Coldest Month	Warmest Month	Mean Annual Range	Absolute Max.	Absolute Min.	Ext. Range
Pike's Peak	14,111	19	2 Jan.	40 Jul.	38	64	−37	101
Lake Moraine	10,265	36	20 Jan.	54 Jul.	34	85	−37	122
Cripple Creek	9508	39	22 Jan.	59 Jul.	37	83	−27	110
Colorado Springs	6098	48	29 Jan.	68 Jul.	39	101	−32	133
Pueblo	4639	52	29 Jan.	75 Jul.	46	105	−31	136

Source: U.S. Army, Quartermaster Research and Engineering Command, *Environmental Handbook for the Camp Hale and Pike's Peak Areas, Colorado*, Natick, Mass., 1958; U.S. Weather Bureau, *Climates of the States, Colorado*, 1959.

TABLE 24–5

Temperature Data for Equatorial Stations in Kenya (°F)
(Equator: 0°00′ Lat.; 35°33′E. Long.)

	El. in Ft	Mean Annual Temp.	Coldest Month	Warmest Month	Mean Annual Range	Absolute Max.	Absolute Min.	Ext. Range
Equator	9062	56	54 Jul., Aug.	58 Feb., Mar.	4	77	38	39
Eldoret	6863	63	60 Jul., Aug.	65 Mar., Apr.	5	85	37	48
Kisumu	3769	74	72 Jun., Jul.	75 Nov.–Feb.	3	98	54	44

Source: Great Britain, Meteorological Office, *Tables of Temperature, Relative Humidity and Precipitation for the World*, Part 4, *Africa, the Atlantic Ocean South of 35°N., and the Indian Ocean*, London, 1964.

a strong continental influence at all levels. Mean annual ranges are also high in this area, remote as it is from all sources of maritime air, the value of 38 degrees at Pike's Peak being very nearly the same as that for Colorado Springs, over 8000 feet lower in elevation. The much greater daily thermal equability of the highest station is amply indicated, however, by the mean daily ranges throughout the year. Normal fluctuations between mean daily maximum and minimum are between 11 degrees in November and 14 degrees from April through July. At Colorado Springs the mean daily range is between 25 and 28 degrees throughout the year.

In equatorial situations where the sun each day rises high in the sky, thermal equability prevails at all altitudes. This we have noted in earlier discussions, particularly in the chapters on tropical forest and woodland climates. But the daily variations are within higher limits, and warmer conditions are found at higher levels. Table 24-5 contains temperature data for three stations in the east African highlands in Kenya, on or near the equator. From these it is seen that mean and extreme variations are very much reduced below those of the mid-latitudes. The station Equator lies some 400 miles west of the Indian Ocean and has a mean annual range of 4 degrees. Eldoret, about 60 miles northwest, reports 5 degrees, and Kisumu, about 90 miles west, reports 3 degrees. Extreme ranges are on the order of one third the values for the mid-latitude stations listed in Table 24-4. But we see little evidence among these examples of increasing equability with

increasing altitude. The mean daily range at Equator (el. 9062) varies from 13 degrees in July to 22 degrees in January, and at Eldoret (el. 6863) it varies from 22 degrees in July to 32° in January. At Kisumu (el. 3769) the variation is from 17 degrees in June and July to 20 degrees in November and January. Daily thermal fluctuations operate within narrower limits at Equator than at Eldoret, nearly a half-mile lower in elevation. However, at Kisumu, more than 1 mile lower in elevation, the limits are in close accordance with those of the highest station. This is an illustration of the partial similarity between mountain peak and marine climates, for Kisumu is on the shore of the northeastern embayment of Lake Victoria, a marine situation in which the normal temperature experience is appreciably moderated.

The water vapor content of the atmosphere decreases very rapidly with increasing altitude. At about 6500 feet it is approximately 50 per cent of the amount at sea level, at 13,000 feet it is less than 25 per cent, and at 23,000 feet it is less than 10 per cent. Actual absolute humidity values vary extraordinarily, however.

Relative humidities are also quite variable. Because relative humidity depends upon the absolute moisture content and air temperature, two highly independent variables in mountainous areas, there is no consistent change with progressive changes in elevation. And yet extreme variation in atmospheric moisture conditions is commonplace in most high mountain areas. When a mountain summit is enveloped in cloud, relative humidity is 100 per cent, but when the air is clear, especially when it gains the highly transparent atmospheric state within the central area of a stable anticyclone, the sun heating the soil beneath and the air in motion, daytime relative humidities may drop to 5 per cent or less. High winds, clear, dry air, burning sunlight, a scarcity of plants, and an abundance of bare ground—all combine to support an excessively rapid drying effect in the ambient air during the daytime. Above cloud level the atmosphere's evaporative capacity evidently far exceeds its potential precipitation. At altitudes beyond about 12,000 feet human beings easily acquire sunburn or deep tan, but in addition normally experience a distinct dryness in nose and throat and an unusual thirst, the lips crack, the skin becomes dry, and a general sense of physiological desiccation sets in.

Where cloud formations lie against a mountain slope, the saturated air produces a belt of unusually high moisture condensation on every exposed surface. In the tropics such levels are usually intermediate between base and summit among the high mountains where mist and drizzle support the humid luxuriance of the cloud forest. In the mid-latitudes, where cloud levels change with the seasons, a distinct mist forest does not develop. Here cloud formations are generally higher in summer and lower in winter, upper level precipitation is predominantly snow, and alternate sunshine and cloudiness vary with great irregularity, each mountain differing from the others. Very few high level climatic data are available for meaningful comparison.

In mid-latitude mountain regions during wintertime the accumulation of cold air in the valleys after sunset often induces the formation of thick, dense layers of fog. Increasing in depth toward dawn, they may be seen from the mountain peaks above them as billowing seas of moist whiteness upon which the sun shines with unusual brilliance from the cloudless, transparent sky overhead.

Precipitation increases with increasing altitude. The upward increase is especially plain on the windward slopes of major relief features. Maximum amounts normally fall at levels ranging between 4000 and 8000 feet. Thus, among lower mountains heaviest precipitation may occur at or near the summit. In New Hampshire, for example, Mt. Washington (el. 6290) records a mean yearly precipitation of 70.2 inches, compared with 59 inches at Pinkham Notch, only three miles away at an elevation of 2000 feet, and 36 inches at Bethlehem, about 20 miles west at altitude 1550 feet. It will be recalled from Chapter 6 that Mt. Waialeale, a summit station (el. 5113) on the island of Kauai, averages 451.1 inches, compared with the value of 100.4 inches received at Kalihiwai Reservoir (el. 850) only ten miles northeastward. At Santis, a summit station in Switzerland at an altitude of 8217 feet, the average is 132 inches yearly. It is generally true in higher mountain areas, at least where summit heights are 10,000 feet or more, that maximum precipitation tends to occur at levels intermediate between base and summit. This is notably true in the tropics.

We have observed the presence of many very striking mountain rain shadow situations among the world's climates in preceding chapters. In numerous instances excessively wet slopes rise in the path of prevailing air streams facing the advance of recurrent disturbances. They contrast sharply with arid slopes, and often extensive desert, in the lee. More modest contrasts in rainfall distribution are a commonplace in mountainous terrain. An example of this is cited in Hann.[2] In the Vorarlberg between Bludenz and Landeck, a distance of 35 miles, normal rainfall amounts differ decidedly every few miles with changing altitude (Table 24-6). From 47.3 inches at Bludenz (el. 1936), amounts increase to 71.7 inches at St. Christoph (el. 5906) and again decrease to 22.4 inches at Landeck (el. 2625).

A further indication of the unevenness of mean precipitation distribution appears in Figure 24.1, showing mean annual precipitation in the state of Washington. Amounts exceed 120 inches on the flanks of Mt. Olympus (el. 7954), Mt. Rainier (el. 14,408), and Mt. Baker (el. 10,750). But at lower elevations, especially in the broad basin between the middle Columbia and Snake rivers, values drop to 8 inches or less. Variations between these extremes are far greater than the map reveals, although the complexity of distribution is adequately suggested considering that the distance across the state from west to east is less than 350 miles.

[2] Julius Hann, *Handbook of Climatology*, Part 1, trans. by R. DeC. Ward, The Macmillan Company, New York, 1903, p.304.

TABLE 24–6
Variation in Precipitation on Mountainous Terrain (In.)

	Bludenz	Klösterle	Stuben	St. Christoph	St. Anton	Landeck
Alt. in Ft	1936	3478	4626	5906	4265	2625
Precip.	47.3	54.4	68.1	71.7	32.7	22.4
	West————————————35 miles——————————————East					

With increasing altitude a greater proportion of normal yearly precipitation occurs in the form of snow. Taking examples once more from the eastern Alps, Table 24-7 indicates the percentage of frequency of winter snow at increasing altitudes. Despite the generalized nature of the values, the changing significance of snow with changing altitude is adequately revealed. Similar proportional changes are typical in mid-latitude mountain regions elsewhere.

Near the equator occasional snow may be observed at elevations of about 12,000 feet, although the normal yearly occurrence of snow is usually restricted to heights above 16,000 to 18,000 feet. The actual levels at which snow is regularly expected vary with distance from the sea and the frequency and intensity of passing disturbances. The occurrence of high altitude snow along the equator is indicated by the presence of a permanent snow cap on Mt. Chimborazo (el. 20,577) in Ecuador, a point less than 100 miles south of the equator, and on Mt. Kilimanjaro (el. 19,565), less than 200 miles south of the equator. Poleward from the equator in both directions the levels at which persistently snow-capped peaks appear are increasingly lower with increasing latitude. Permanent snow fields are found at sea level beyond about 70 degrees of latitude.

Snow is without doubt one of the more significant products of atmospheric activity in mountain country. With its esthetic value is coupled its usefulness in winter sports and in the annual release of meltwater to mountain streams in spring. Mountain snows are indeed

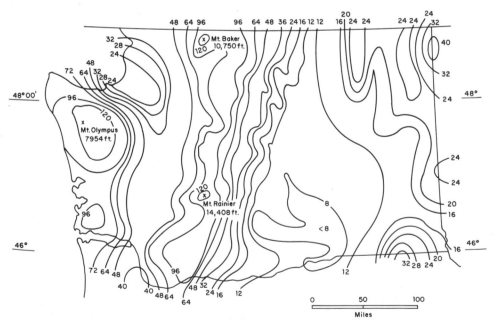

Figure 24.1.   Distribution of mean annual precipitation in the state of Washington (inches).

TABLE 24–7

Changing Proportions of Snow with Altitude in the Eastern Alps

El. in Ft	% Frequency of Snow in Winter	No. Days With Snowfall per Year	Max. Depth of Snow (In.)	No. Days With Snow on Ground
650	49	27	7.9	38
1310	61	32	12.2	55
2625	79	45	28.7	109
3935	90	62	47.3	138
5250	96	85	55.9	169
6560	98	113	78.7	212
7875	100	143	118.6	270
9840	100	188	214.7	354

After R. Geiger, *The Climate Near the Ground*, Cambridge, Mass., 1965.

the chief source of stream runoff in many arid regions of the world. On the other hand, mountain snows can bring sudden death and destruction through rapid accumulations on the ground during unusually heavy snowfalls and through the sudden, swift, downward rush of the avalanche.

On mountain tops in the middle latitudes snow has been observed during every month of the year. This is common above 10,000 feet, but it is also true at elevations as low as that of Mt. Washington (el. 6290), where 1.2 inch fell in August 1964 and 3 inches fell in July 1965. As a general rule, in the mountains of the northern hemisphere the year's persistent snows do not begin to occur until after the autumnal equinox around October 1, increasing to a yearly maximum in late March or early April after the vernal equinox. The accumulated snows of winter linger on long after the last appreciable amounts have fallen, often melting away only after the sun has reached its peak elevation at the summer solstice. Figure 24.2 indicates the

dates at which a persistent snow cover first appears in autumn and finally disappears in spring at selected elevations in the Swiss Alps. The diagram suggests the increasing significance of snow with increasing altitude.

A further example is provided in the data from stations in the vicinity of Pike's Peak, Colo. Pike's Peak (el. 14,111) is a prominent, well-exposed point in the eastern Rockies about 2000 feet above timber line, and most of the copious quantities of snow occurring there each winter are blown away by repeated gales. But from stations nearby meaningful values are available. At Colorado Springs (el. 6098) about 10 miles east of Pike's Peak mean annual snowfall is 25 inches, at Cripple Creek (el. 9508) about 10 miles southwest of Pike's Peak it is 68 inches, and at Lake Moraine (el. 10,265), about 3 miles southeastward, the value is 147 inches.

In southern British Columbia three stations at contrasting elevations reported snowfall amounts during the winter of 1963–64 that throw further light on the influence of elevation

TABLE 24–8

Depth of Snow on Ground at Three Stations in Southern British Columbia, 1963–64 (In.)

	Oct.		Nov.		Dec.		Jan.		Feb.		Mar.		Apr.	
	15	31	15	30	15	31	15	31	15	28	15	31	15	30
Revelstoke (el. 1497)	0	0	0	3	13	10	19	24	23	22	24	5	0	0
Carmi (el. 4084)	0	0	3	3	19	21	27	27	25	20	30	24	12	5
Old Glory Mountain (el. 7700)	0	9	28	31	39	43	47	57	59	52	60	61	59	64

Source: Canada, Department of Transport, *Snow Cover Data, Winter 1963–64*, Toronto, Ont., 1964.

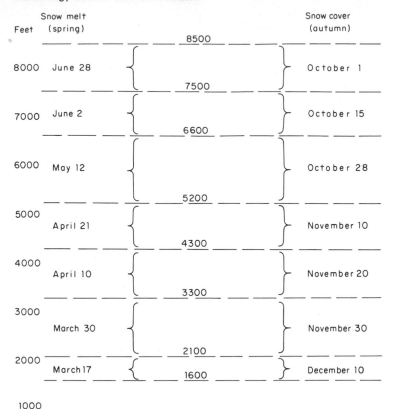

Feet

Snow melt (spring)		Snow cover (autumn)

```
                                        8500
  8000   June 28      {                          {       October  1
                      {              7500        }
  7000   June 2       {                          {       October 15
                      {              6600        }
  6000   May 12       {                          {       October 28
                      {              5200        }
  5000   April 21     {                          {       November 10
                      {              4300        }
  4000   April 10     {                          {       November 20
                      {              3300        }
  3000   March 30     {                          {       November 30
                      {              2100        }
  2000   March 17     {              1600        }       December 10
  1000
```

Figure 24.2. Duration of snow cover in the Alps. The period between the onset of snow cover in autumn and snow melt in spring lengthens with increasing altitude.

upon snowfall among mid-latitude mountains (Table 24-8). Carmi is about 60 miles northwest of Old Glory Mountain and Revelstoke about 130 miles north. From month to month all through the winter season the prominent height of the 7700 foot peak received considerably more snow than the lower valley stations and at the end of the winter season reported over 5 feet of snow on the ground, compared with 5 inches at Carmi and none at all at Revelstoke.

In North America the greatest amounts of snowfall are normally recorded in the coastal mountains of British Columbia, the Cascades, and the Sierra Nevada. In the state of Washington at levels from 4000 to 5500 feet normal wintertime snows amount to between 400 and 600 inches during the period from November to June. In Oregon amounts average between 300 and 550 inches at levels from 4500 to 6000 feet, and in California mean amounts are around 450 inches in the central Sierra Nevada between 6000 and 8000 feet. Similarly high values are

reported from British Columbia and are several times the normal amounts reported outside the mountainous west (Fig. 11.17).

Some exceptional amounts of snowfall have been recorded in the western mountains of North America during the course of a single winter season. At Tamarack (el. 8000), Calif., 884 inches (over 73 feet) of snow fell during the winter of 1906–7. But during the winter of 1955–56 in the state of Washington at the Mt. Rainier–Paradise Ranger Station (el. 5500), 1000 inches were recorded.[3]

Even a single storm has brought unusually heavy snowfalls to certain areas, especially the deep passes in higher mountain country or in depressions lying in the lee of prominent peaks around which a singular turbulence is apt to develop with the passage of a well-formed cyclonic system. Such was the case in April 1921. On April 15–16 a vigorous disturbance passed

[3] U.S. Weather Bureau, *Climates of the Stages*, Washington, 1965, p.4.

across the Front Range of the eastern Rockies in eastern Colorado. Swirling around the exposed eminence of Anapolis Peak (el. 13,506), a small valley station about 3 miles east of the peak called Silver Lake (el. 10,200), a point lying about 35 miles northwest of Denver, received a total of 87 inches of new snow in twenty-seven and a half hours, a remarkably rapid accumulation of over 7 feet of fresh snow.

In addition to the risk of exceptionally heavy snowfall, the traveler in mid-latitude mountain regions also faces the more serious and more frequent threat of the avalanche. Avalanches, or snow slides, are normal winter processes of the downslope displacement of excessive snow accumulation on the steeper, unforested mountainsides. They occur intermittently from place to place, but over an entire mountain region like the Alps or the Rocky Mountains hundreds of avalanches occur each year. They vary in kind and are set in motion by a variety of conditions, including the type, depth, temperature, and moisture content of the snow mantle as well as the temperature, water vapor quotient, and motions of the atmosphere. They are often started just following a heavy snowfall, unusually heavy drifting, a sudden cold snap, or, more often, a sudden thaw. The last is frequently the product of the föhn effect. The magnitude of the risks of exposure to avalanches is greater in the more populous areas of such mountain regions as the Alps of Austria and Switzerland. Here and in the Rockies the effort to forecast the probable occurrence of dangerous snow slides has met with considerable success.

The upward increase in wind velocity is a well-known feature of mountain climates. But few summit weather stations are maintained, and thus very few mountain meterological records are available. For this reason, and also because of the infinitude of mountain varieties and their endless varied relationships with the atmosphere, no general rule may be stated. Figure 24.3 offers a rough guide to the approximate rate of upward wind speed increase, but it is perhaps more useful to consider a few examples from the scarce data obtainable.

The Mt. Washington area of the White Mountains in New Hampshire has been subjected to extensive study by several agencies, the results of which have been published by the

Natick Quartermaster Research and Development Laboratory.[4] Mt. Washington is about 65 miles from the Atlantic coast. Although comparatively low in altitude, its characteristically variable weather features very low winter temperatures and unusually high winds. Winters are long and very cold, summers short and cool. Heavy snow and heavy rain frequently succeed each other in rapid sequence, only briefly interrupted by intervals of partly cloudy skies and sunshine. Wind speeds at the summit average between 40 and 50 miles per hour from November through March and remain above 24 miles per hour during the least windy month, August. Winds exceed 74 miles per hour every month of the year, maintaining an average frequency of 50 per cent or more of the observations from December through

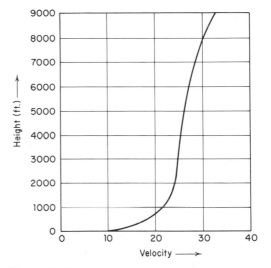

Figure 24.3. Approximate increase of wind speed with height.

February. Values of more than 200 miles per hour have been recorded frequently for short intervals, and on April 12, 1934, an extreme speed of 231 miles per hour was reached. Winds on Mt. Washington are dominantly from westward.

Table 24-9 summarizes the wind speed data for Mt. Washington and also presents the 1951 wind speeds at the summit and at two nearby stations at lower altitude for comparison. The

[4] U.S. Army, Quartermaster General, Research and Development Division, *Handbook of Mount Washington Environment*, Natick, Mass., 1953.

TABLE 24–9

Wind Speed at Mt. Washington and Vicinity (MPH)

	Mean Speed	Mt. Washington Prevailing Direction	No. Days Over 74 MPH	1951					
				Mt. Washington (6290 ft)		The Horn (4000 ft)		Pinkham Notch (2000 ft)	
				Ave.	Max.	Ave.	Max.	Ave.	Max.
Jan.	50	W	15	45	114	31	100	5	29
Feb.	49	W	15	34	114	19	105	5	43
Mar.	46	W	14	35	111	19	60	3	22
Apr.	39	W	10	34	101	9	40	3	16
May	32	W	7	26	85	18	55	3	10
Jun.	28	W	4	22	81	13	75	3	10
Jul.	25	W	2	25	77	17	50	2	15
Aug.	24	W	2	22	105	16	50	2	10
Sep.	29	W	4	31	101	19	75	3	21
Oct.	34	W	6	26	95	17	70	2	16
Nov.	41	W	9	38	101	25	70	4	28
Dec.	48	W	16	44	104	30	100	5	43

Source: U.S. Army, Quartermaster General, Research and Development Division, *Handbook of Mount Washington Environment*, Natick, Mass., 1953, pp. 5 and 95.

contrast between the summit and the valley station of Pinkham Notch (el. 2000) is at once evident, and the increasing wind speeds with increasing altitude are further indicated by the values obtained at The Horn, a northern spur of Mt. Washington.

Another example from the Rocky Mountain region of southern British Columbia is the summit station of Old Glory Mountain (el. 7700), which reported the wind speed averages (1950–52) listed in Table 24-10. The average values reported from Carmi are also tabulated for comparison. Carmi (el. 4084) is a middle level station on a ridge about 60 miles northwest of the mountain peak, where the record extends from 1940 to 1952.

These examples indicate the general upward increase in mean wind speed of prevailing geostrophic winds in the free atmosphere as they play upon mountain terrain. They represent the broad-scale tendencies of winds in all mountain areas. Velocity increase is only partly due to increased altitude, however. Actually, a constriction effect sets in as air currents sweep toward the sloping surfaces of conspicuous relief features. Air streams are compressed as they pass over the uppermost levels and around

the summits, moving faster than the free air away from the obstruction. The result is much

TABLE 24–10

Wind Speeds at Old Glory Mountain and Carmi, British Columbia (MPH)

	Old Glory Mountain		Carmi	
	Average	Max. for 1 Hour	Average	Max. for 1 Hour
Jan.	18	54	3	33
Feb.	19		4	
Mar.	16		5	
Apr.	16	62	5	44
May	15		5	
Jun.	12		5	
Jul.	12	31	5	26
Aug.	11		5	
Sep.	12		5	
Oct.	15	42	5	37
Nov.	18		4	
Dec.	20		3	

After W. C. Kendrew and D. Kerr, *The Climate of British Columbia and the Yukon Territory*, Ottawa, 1955, pp. 40–41.

like the increased speed of a river where it meets an obstruction or a narrowing of its channel. The constriction effect in alpine areas is especially noticeable in passes or cols between two neighbouring peaks or ridges, where gale force and hurricane force winds are frequently observed. These are very common features of mountain weather, but their frequency and intensity depend to a large degree upon the transitory synoptic situations in which the general barometric gradients play a leading role.

The atmospheric turbulence and gustiness set up around mountain summits and crest lines is an important aspect of wind behavior in mountain regions. It is of special concern to the airplane pilot and the sail plane enthusiast. Crossing the crest of a prominent mountain range, comparatively steady air streams are deflected sharply downward, on the leeward side setting in motion downdrafts that are accompanied by compensating upward surges and pulsations, creating a highly turbulent state. A very common consequence of orographic turbulence is the formation of a mountain wave, or standing wave (Fig. 24.4). This is an attenuated undulation of the atmosphere of varying wave length, normally reaching a maximum amplitude well in the lee of the mountain and about 3000 to 6000 feet above the crest. It may extend for some 100 miles or more downstream from the ridge and may occur frequently enough to become a regular feature, like the Sierra wave of the Rocky Mountains. Such mountain waves often occur in air too dry to allow the formation of

clouds. But they are frequently indicated by the appearance of low cumulus clouds, evenly spaced, marking the crests of the undulations in the air streams. The cloud type may also be lenticular, or lens-shaped, its circular form clearly revealing the rotary motion at the level of formation. Occasionally, a detached, undulating streamer cloud may form, such as the one in the lee of Mt. Erebus, Antarctica (Fig. 24.5). In other circumstances a small cloud pennant is very commonly seen, usually called a banner cloud, arising from a compensating updraft of ascending air from the lee slopes. Such a banner cloud is a well-known feature at the tip of Mt. Everest (el. 29,029). This is a pennant, several miles long, of ice particles swept up in a compensating current from the lee by the air streams flowing past the peak.

Of much greater significance to the residents of mountain regions are the local upslope and downslope circulations of mountain-valley winds. These have been investigated most intensively in the complicated mountain terrain of the Alps in both Switzerland and Austria. In general, the daily heating of the mountainsides embracing a valley induces an upward displacement of air taking the form of gusty breezes many at right angles to the alignment of the valley itself and approximately parallel to the surfaces of the sloping valley sides. Compensating downdrafts develop over the central part of the valley, and a series of vertical rotations grows in strength as the day progresses. Accompanying the lateral circulations is a more generally up-valley flow near the valley floor that also gains in force as the

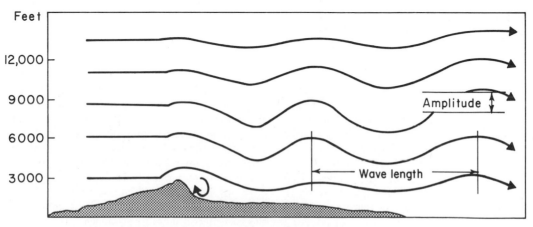

Figure 24.4. Diagrammatic sketch of a mountain (standing) wave.

Figure 24.5. Streamer cloud in the lee of Mt. Erebus (el. 12,280) at the western edge of Ross Ice Shelf. Its undulations indicate the nature of the standing wave. [U.S. Navy photo]

day continues. This contributes to the gusty vortices of the valley slopes (Fig. 24.6). Maximum upslope winds are usually reached in the early afternoon.

As the day wears on and parts of the valley are once again in shadow, the shaded portions cool, the air above them cools, and the downward drift of air begins. When evening approaches, and the sun's rays are entirely withdrawn from the valley floor and its embracing sides, the circulations of daytime are reversed. Now currents of air descend the mountainsides, and a general flow of air down the valley floor sets in. Downward motion is normally much slower, like that of a heavy plastic mass, than the more boisterous motions during the day. Maximum downslope winds are usually reached a few hours before dawn and are most commonly observed at about 100 feet or so above the lower valley floor.

The nocturnal wind off the slopes often occurs in rhythmic surges that may be remarkably evenly spaced. They develop as cold air alternately accumulates in pockets or on small plateaus at upper levels, then spills over, accumulates, and spills downward again at regular intervals. The intensity of cold nocturnal winds is often augmented when alpine glaciers chill the nighttime air as it is displaced downward.

The above-described mechanism is intended to suggest the general manner in which mountain and valley surfaces actively respond to the diurnal input and nocturnal output of radiant heat, without regard to the many ways in which transient synoptic circumstances alter the general tendency. Variations are numerous.

Mountain topography also exercises a much broader influence on migrating synoptic situations, often producing pronounced downslope winds of notable strength and frequency. These are winds that occur at random and derive their initial velocity, direction, and persistence from a strong, resident barometric gradient. This in turn arises when a deep anticyclone lies over a major mountain mass, and a depression appears over adjoining surfaces at lower altitude. At such times the orographic gradient augments the barometric slope to produce a pronounced katabatic effect, and vigorous downslope winds

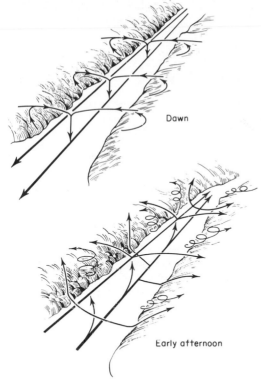

Dawn

Early afternoon

Figure 24.6. Upslope and downslope winds at dawn and in the early afternoon in a mountain valley.

set in, sometimes with notoriously destructive force. Synoptic-katabatic winds in mountain regions develop with special force where a long, relatively straight, cleared valley opens downward and outward from a major mountain mass. In such instances, as in parts of Switzerland, the frequency and strength of downslope winds is suggested by the practice of placing heavy rocks on the roofs of dwellings to keep them intact from the vigorous blast of the wind. The mistral and bora of the Mediterranean basin, referred to in Chapter 13, are cold, dry, squally winds of this character. So also is the squamish, a cold, blustery wind of the fiord coast of British Columbia that funnels down off the high mountain ranges through the confined channels created by the deep, steep-sided fiords. It is usually about 3000 feet in depth, sometimes as much as 8000 feet, and is rarely effective more than 15 to 20 miles from the coast. Countless similar winds are known in mountain regions elsewhere throughout the world. Their significance is usually much greater among the residents of neighboring

lowlands than among the mountain-dwellers themselves.

Of even greater importance than cold downslope winds are warm mountain winds known by the general name föhn. This widely known lee wind is characteristic of nearly all mountain areas, and in Chapter 16 the North American chinook, a variety of the generic form, was discussed at some length. It is a warm, dry wind whose properties are acquired chiefly through adiabatic compression as air sweeps down the lee slopes of higher mountain country. Originally identified in Switzerland, it is also a familiar feature of mountainous New Zealand's South Island, where it is called a Canterbury northwester. In Argentina it is the zonda, farther north in the Andes it is the puelche, and in northwestern Yugoslavia it is the ljuka. Ordinarily warm, dry and gusty it is associated with unusually clear air on the lee slopes of a mountain barrier. On the windward side clouds, precipitation, and much higher humidity are characteristic. The function of the mountain in creating a climatic barrier between well-watered windward slopes on the one hand and rain shadow desert on the other has been referred to at many points in earlier chapters. The föhn wind is simply a part of the general rain shadow influence of major mountain ranges (Fig. 24.7).

The föhn commonly appears after anticyclonic air has begun to weaken and a barometric gradient has set in toward the descending slopes of a major mountain mass. An example of the generalized synoptic situation in which föhn winds frequently develop in the Alps is provided in Figure 24.8. Figure 24.9 shows a typical synoptic situation under which the chinook evolves along the eastern slopes of the Rockies.

VERTICAL CLIMATIC DIFFERENTIATION. The visible evidence of atmospheric change with changing altitude is present in every mountain region. A vertical zoning of distinct landscape strata appears in response to changes in the qualities of the atmosphere and the varieties of weather experience, collectively termed *climate*, of each horizontal stratum.

In the lower latitudes the extremes of change may extend from hot, humid tropical rainforest to persistent ice and snow, in the middle latitudes from sun-baked, arid desert to snow-capped mountain peaks. Between the extremes

Figure 24.7.   Development of a föhn wind downslope in the lee of a prominent mountain range.

observed from mountain base to summit a gradual although usually very uneven change is commonly seen, through a variety of forest, woodland, shrub, grassland, and barren bedrock. It has often been stated—erroneously— that low latitude mountains bear, on their intermediate slopes, climatic zones of mid-latitude character. The resemblance is very strongly suggested in countless areas by the similarity in plant genera, the physiognomic qualities of the vegetation, and indeed by certain qualities of the atmosphere. But it is a mistake to equate the intermediate zones of tropical mountains with climates of the middle latitudes that have developed in areas of lower

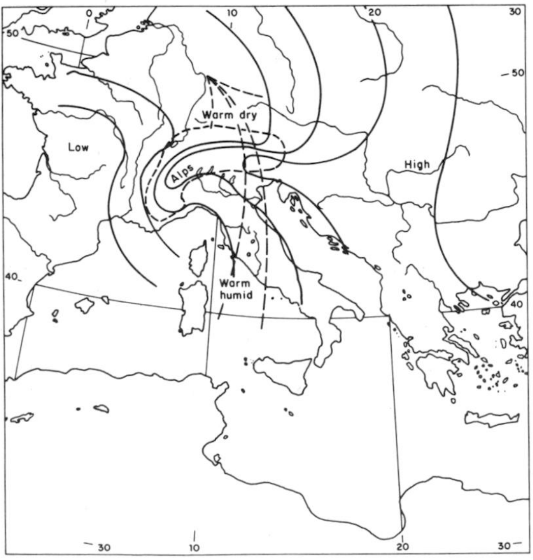

altitude and inconsequential relief. The atmospheric differences are numerous and profoundly significant.

Among the more important points of difference is the intensity of solar radiation throughout the year. Neglecting the effect of cloud cover, a much higher input of radiant solar energy is typical in tropical mountain areas. The duration of alternate periods of daylight and darkness is also greatly different, a closer balance being maintained between them in lower latitudes. The angular height of the sun also introduces strongly different qualities of light and reflection in tropical mountains from those imposed upon mid-latitude areas. Steeply sloping surfaces introduce a variety of local atmospheric circulations unknown in mid-latitude regions at lower altitude and of low relief. Temperature and humidity fluctuations proceed at smaller amplitudes and according to very different regimes. Mean synoptic situations are also greatly in contrast. All in all, the differences between intermediate zones on the slopes of low latitude mountains and the broadly distributed mid-latitude climates poleward of the tropics are much more impressive than are the points of similarity.

The complexities of vertical differentiation among mountain climates, just like the size, shape, composition, and distribution of the world's mountains as a whole, are far too varied to allow meaningful generalization. Thus, it will be useful to consider examples of vertical zoning from among the available studies of these features and to examine comparative temperature and precipitation regimes within certain mountain areas. By considering ex-

Figure 24.8.   Schematic diagram of a synoptic situation inducing a föhn in the Alps.

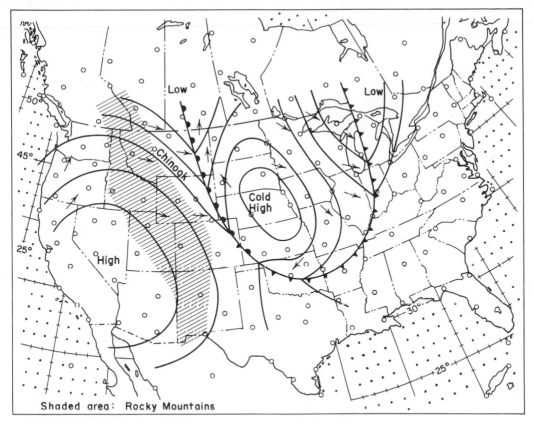

Figure 24.9. Diagram of a synoptic situation inducing the chinook down the east slopes of the Rockies. [After C. L. Glenn, in *Weatherwise*, October 1961]

amples from the lower latitudes and outside the tropics, it will be possible to gain a reasonable idea of the broader tendencies among mountain climates as a whole.

In the low latitudes the vertical zoning of mountain climates is particuarly well exemplified in northern Ecuador where the Andean cordillera crosses the equator. Here, the vast bulk of the Andes is only about 100 miles in breadth measured from about 1000 feet in altitude on either side. Most of its massive heights stand well over 10,000 feet above sea level, forming two parallel ranges embracing a series of lower intermontane basins, the entire system extending northward into Colombia. Surmounting the uppermost ranges are several semiconical volcanic peaks that reach well over 15,000 feet and are snow-capped. The highest of these is Mt. Chimborazo (el. 20,577), at 1°28'S. Lat.

Within a degree of two of the equator tropical evergreen rainforest mantles the bordering lowlands, rising to about 5900 feet along the Pacific slopes, which rise much more steeply than those on the east, and to about 4600 feet above the Amazon basin (Fig. 24.10). From these levels to about 11,500 feet on both sides of the cordillera is a zone in which cloud forest, a temperate rainforest, prevails. Above this is a dominantly grass and shrub zone, the paramos. This in turn yields to persistent snow on the symmetrical cones of the conspicuous volcanic peaks at about 15,000 feet. Thus we observe four distinct climatic zones forming the dominant vertical stratification of the Andes at the equator.

Though no climatic data are available for the alpine snow fields, the temperature and precipitation regimes for stations in tropical rainforest, cloud forest, and the paramos presented in Fig. 24.11 give a general idea of the contrasting climates. The actual distribution of the environmental strata in the equatorial Andes is vastly more complex, and some suggestion of

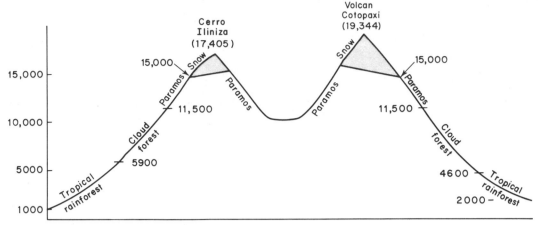

Figure 24.10. Vertical climatic zoning in the equatorial Andes of Ecuador, Lat. 0° 40′ S (elevation in feet).

this typical complexity is supplied in the map of identifiable vegetation zones in Fig. 24.12. Note that north of Quito and Ibarra deeply entrenched valleys of the Pacific slope allow tropical rainforest to extend well into the highland mass, but there it gives way to small enclaves of tropical savanna woodland and tropical thorn scrub woodland in the valley bottoms where a rain shadow effect deprives them of sufficient moisture from the west. Also apparent on the map is the presence of a high latitude, semi-arid shrub grassland, beginning northeast of Quito. Scattered low shrubs and much bare ground are characteristic. This desiccated aspect of upper level Andean vegetation, virtually alpine desert, becomes more plentiful southward into Peru. It is especially widespread in southern Peru and over much of Bolivia. It is partly due to rainfall deficiency, but it is also a result of continuously low temperatures and porous, ashy, volcanic soils.

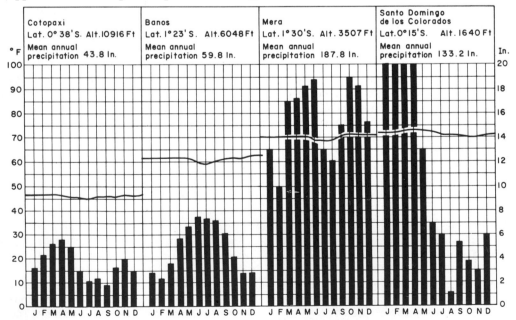

Figure 24.11. Temperature and precipitation at four mountain stations near the equator in Ecuador.

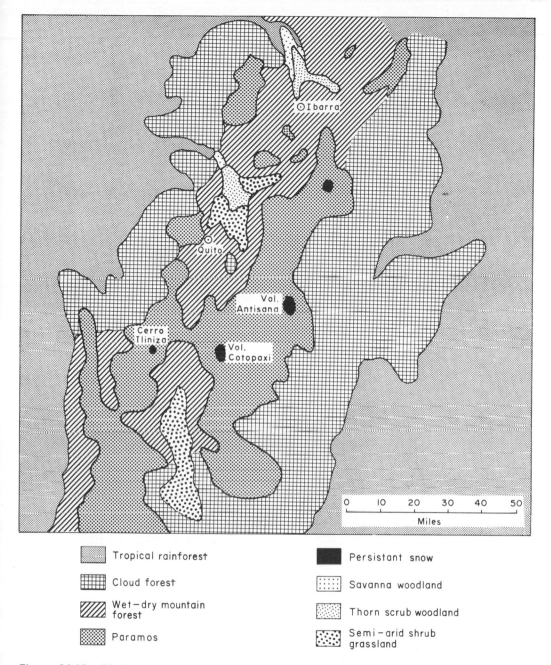

Tropical rainforest

Cloud forest

Wet–dry mountain forest

Paramos

Persistant snow

Savanna woodland

Thorn scrub woodland

Semi–arid shrub grassland

Figure 24.12.   Distribution of discrete environments in the equatorial Andes.

In the upper reaches of the paramos near 13,000 feet shrubby vegetation tends to disappear, giving way to predominantly grass vegetation in which many perennials are mixed, most plant forms hugging the ground so closely that they produce a dense, heavy sod of close-growing rootlets. This uppermost phase of the paramos continues southward, descending to somewhat lower levels in southern Peru and Bolivia, where it is known as puna vegetation.

Cloud forest appears over a considerable range of altitudes on both sides of the Andes in Ecuador and in a variety of associations often contrasting greatly in their degree of luxuriance.

These contrasts are considered to be a result of two or more levels of frequent cloud formation, between which less moist conditions support a drier aspect of the general cloud forest type. Over extensive reaches of the Andes this aspect is found, as shown in Fig. 24.12, where it is indicated as the wet-dry mountain forest.

The sharpness of contrast within very short distances in Andean Ecuador is indicated by a comparison of the temperature and rainfall data for Quito (el. 9250) and Cruz Loma (el. 12,959), about two miles southwest (Table 24-11). The climatic record for Cruz Loma is

TABLE 24–11

Temperature and Precipitation at Quito and Cruz Loma, Ecuador

| | Quito (el. 9250) | | Cruz Loma (el. 12,959) | |
	Temp. (°F)	Precip. (In.)	Temp. (°F)	Precip. (In.)
Jan.	56	4.9	43	7.8
Feb.	56	5.3	44	7.3
Mar.	56	6.3	44	9.5
Apr.	56	7.1	44	9.3
May	56	5.1	44	8.7
Jun.	56	1.9	43	4.8
Jul.	56	0.7	43	1.4
Aug.	57	0.9	43	0.9
Sep.	57	3.3	43	3.4
Oct.	56	5.2	43	5.8
Nov.	56	4.3	44	4.9
Dec.	56	4.2	44	6.3
Year	56	49.2	43	70.1

Source: E. N. Ferndon, "Studies in Ecuadorian Geography," *Monographs of the School of American Research*, No. 5, Santa Fe, N.M., 1950.

only about five years long, compared with a sixty-six-year record at Quito. The values reported, however, indicate adequately the sharpness of contrast, within the space of about 2 miles of linear distance, between the temperature and precipitation experiences of a station in the paramos (Cruz Loma) and one in the wet-dry mountain forest (Quito). The regimes are closely similar, the mean annual temperature range being 1 degree in each case. But

precipitation amounts and monthly temperatures are strikingly different. The mean daily temperature range throughout the year is also appreciably different, for at Cruz Loma the mean diurnal fluctuation is about 10 degrees, and at Quito it is about 18 degrees. This is but one example of the infinite intricacy with which the pattern of local mountain climates unfolds in every region of high mountain terrain.

Moving away from the equator, the vertical zoning of mountain climates is generally depressed downward, the limits of each zone appearing at increasingly lower elevations in a poleward direction. But the actual level at which the tree line or the snow line is reached depends not only upon latitude but also upon precipitation. Forest growth extends farther up wetter slopes than drier ones, and the lower limits of enduring snow, the snow line, are lower on wetter slopes than on drier ones. In consequence, one observes the tree line and snow line drawing together on wet slopes and diverging considerably farther apart on dry slopes. Examples of this interesting mountain feature are provided in the Andes. Here, as a rule, the snow line lies about 3000 feet lower on wetter exposures. At 33°S. Lat., for example, approximately opposite Valparaiso, persistent snow lies at less than 12,000 feet on the Pacific side and at somewhat higher than 15,000 feet on the drier Atlantic side. In southern Chile and Argentina at latitude 50°, alpine glaciers extend to sea level on the Pacific side but only to about 600 feet above sea level on the more arid eastern slopes in the Argentine lake district.

In consequence of the important influence of precipitation on the levels of snow line and tree line, a general tendency exists for the snow line to become higher in mountain areas near the Tropics of Cancer and Capricorn. In South America it rises from about 15,000 feet on the isolated peaks of Ecuador near the equator to between 17,000 and 20,000 feet in northern Chile. These are the very latitudes in which normal weather is dominated by the operations of the semipermanent subtropical anticyclones, notably weak in the release of precipitation. Poleward of the subtropics, however, the snow line does indeed become progressively lower with increasing latitude.

Although mountain regions in the lower latitudes throughout the world exhibit many points of similarity, it is necessary to emphasize the great diversity that exists from continent to continent. If we consider Mt. Kenya in east Africa, whose peaks lie almost exactly on the equator (0°10'S.), we find many points of contrast with the equatorial Andes.

Mt. Kenya (el. 17,040) is an almost symmetrical volcanic cone about 40 miles in diameter, rising from a base level of about 5000 feet on the high plateau of east Africa. Local relief then, for this unusually prominent, isolated eminence, is on the order of 12,000 feet, or slightly more than 2 miles. A well-developed, richly varied mountain rainforest forms a belt between 5000 and 12,000 feet, entirely encircling the mountain and averaging from 8 to 15 miles in breadth. Its widest extent is on the southern and southeastern flanks. Among the dominant members of this temperate, cloud forest association are cedar (*Juniperus procera*), camphor, and species of *Podocarpus*. The uppermost forest levels, between 10,000 and 12,000 feet, are dominated by formations of tall, straight bamboo. Beyond these to about 14,000 feet is alpine grassland, and from about 14,000 feet upward the rough, craggy lava surfaces are largely bare and free of plant life. Persistent snow occupies many alpine depressions and the long ridges of the summit. Alpine glaciers extend downward in places to about 14,000 feet. At base level tropical savanna woodland, the most widespread regional aspect in the east African highlands, stretches away on every side save where cultivation and settlement have introduced exotic qualities to the landscape.

Precipitation for the support of the mountain forests and grasslands is chiefly provided by the northeast monsoon winds off the Indian Ocean from October through March and by the southeast trades during the remainder of the year. Levels above the alpine meadows on both Mt. Kenya and Mt. Kilimanjaro (el. 19,565) ascend into the drier upper air of equatorial regions and receive little precipitation.

If space allowed, examination of the equatorial mountains in the East Indies would reveal again the general points of similarity among the vertical climatic zones but also the inevitable diversity of mountain climates everywhere. Let us now turn to a mid-latitude mountain area for an example of vertical climatic zoning and mean weather contrast.

The White Mountains of New Hampshire offer such an example.

Mt. Washington lies at a latitude of 44°16' about 65 miles from the Atlantic coast of New England. Within a horizontal distance of about 3 miles, the largely forested slopes rise from base level near 2000 feet to the summit, providing a local relief of nearly 4300 feet. Deciduous hardwood forest (mainly a northern hardwood association), consisting chiefly of birch, beech, maple, and hemlock with a strong admixture of spruce, aspen, and wild cherry, prevails up to about 2500 feet (Fig. 24.13). From this level to about 3200 feet mixed forest of deciduous-coniferous character is dominant. Aspen and wild cherry tend to disappear, and spruce becomes more prominent. Between 3200 and 4000 feet a spruce-fir forest, almost entirely coniferous, is the dominant vegetation. The shallow-rooted trees become lower in stature with increasing altitude. From 4000 to about 5000 feet the vegetation continues to be dominantly coniferous spruce and fir, but the smaller trees are now much more closely spaced, and their stiff branches are thickly interlaced. Above 5000 feet continuous plant cover breaks off, and much bare ground is seen. Alpine tundra, a low-growing vegetation consisting of sedges, grasses, mosses, lichens, dwarf shrubs, and woody vines, is the ruling aspect of the visible plant life. A narrow, interrupted transition zone of stunted conifers grades from the forest upward into the alpine heath. (See Fig. 24.14.)

The climatic data for only two stations are available for comparison: Pinkham Notch, representing the deciduous hardwood forest environment in the adjacent valley, and Mt. Washington Observatory, representing the alpine tundra near the summit. At Pinkham Notch the mean annual temperature range is 47 degrees between 17° in January and 64° in July (Fig. 24.15). The annual thermal regime is thus clearly continental in character, reflecting the dominant influence of transient weather systems from the western and northwestern interior of North America. Extreme temperature range is 123 degrees from −32° in January to 91° in July. Mean annual precipitation is 59 inches, evenly distributed through the year, with both March and November the peak months during which 5.8 inches are normally recorded. Snow has fallen during every month

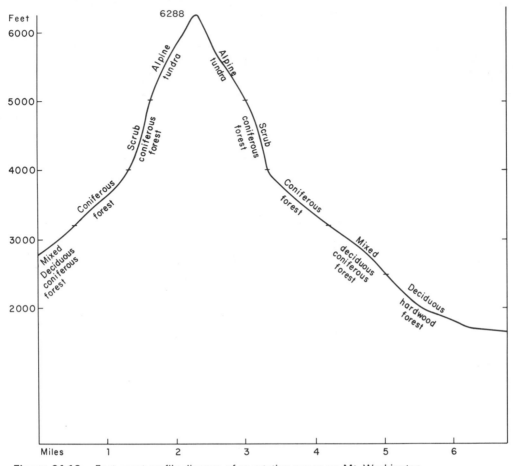

Figure 24.13. East–west profile diagram of vegetation zones on Mt. Washington.

of the year except July, and the winter's accumulation, usually reaching a maximum in March, is occasionally more than 50 inches.

At the summit the mean annual temperature range is 45 degrees, nearly the same as at base level, but the values are much lower, from 5° in January to 49° in July. The extreme range is less at the summit, from −46° in December, January, and February to 71° in June and August. Mean annual precipitation is considerably greater on the summit, averaging 70.2 inches evenly distributed through the year, September and November reporting the greatest monthly values of 6.6 inches each.

The tendency toward a more equable thermal experience at all times on the summit is suggested by the mean daily range of temperature of 18 degrees in December and January, compared with 20 and 23 degrees for the same months at the mountain base. In July

and August the mean daily range is 12 and 13 degrees respectively, compared with 27 degrees during both months at the base. Fog occurs on an average of twenty-three days every month of the year at the summit, but at Pinkham Notch it occurs on only four days during the foggiest month, June.

Mountain regions everywhere in the world outside the tropics tend to display similar patterns of climatic zoning. But the varieties of stratification and the complexities of their distribution are beyond the scope of this work. Suffice is to say that mountain terrain in the mid-latitudes, as indeed in all latitudes, interposes a highly significant environmental diversity within very short linear distances. Environmental mountain variety in turn affects most profoundly the speciation and distribution of plant and animal life and the life and activities of men.

Figure 24.14. Major vegetation types around Mt. Washington.

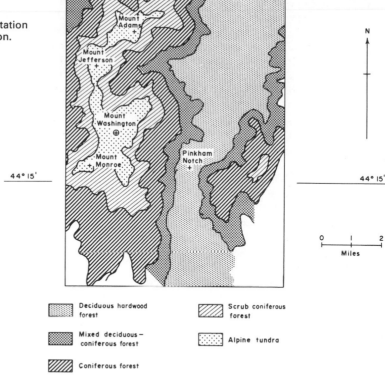

Deciduous hardwood forest

Mixed deciduous—coniferous forest

Coniferous forest

Scrub coniferous forest

Alpine tundra

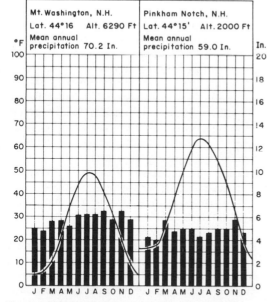

Figure 24.15. Temperature and precipitation at two stations in the Mt. Washington area.

Oceanic Climates

Were one to rank the world's climates according to their significance for the planet as a whole, oceanic climates would occupy first place. Because about 71 per cent of the earth's surface is oceanic, nearly the same percentage of the atmosphere is at all times directly influenced by the sea. Hence the paramount planetary climate, with all its variations, is that of the sea. By its interaction with the overlying atmosphere, the sea sets the limits of global atmospheric behavior through its vital role in the heat and moisture budgets of the earth. Itself thermally conservative, the sea prevents the earth's atmosphere from becoming extraordinarily hot or cold. Furthermore, it is the chief source of atmospheric moisture and of condensation nuclei, in the form of minute salt crystals. It is both the home of the world's steadiest light to moderate winds, the trades, and the setting for the world's most frequent gales, the oceanic storms of the middle latitudes, and the most powerful of all storms, the tropical hurricane.

Without doubt, the chief climatic significance of the sea is its function in the heat budget of the earth. In this the sun is the primary energy source, its radiant heat transmitted to the thin film of the ocean surface. There it is disposed of in various ways, mainly transferred to the atmosphere, and is transported poleward both by the atmospheric circulation and by the broad surface currents of the oceanic circulation. The apparent stability of long-term thermal fluctuations for the world as a whole indicates the efficiency with which the absorption, disposition, and transport of radiant heat from the sun are managed by the dynamic integration of sea and air. The sea takes up heat and releases it only very slowly, and thus, in the broad-scale exchange of heat between the oceans and the atmosphere, it acts as a huge planetary thermostat.

The slow thermal response of large masses of water to extraneous sources of temperature change was discussed in Chapter 6. There it was pointed out that pure water has a high specific heat (sea water is about 96.5 per cent pure, assuming a mean salinity of 35 parts per 1000); that is, the amount of heat required to raise a gram of water 1.2 degree F. would raise a gram of iron about 18 degrees F. Sea water, in other words, must take up a great deal of heat in order for its own internal temperature to rise. In like manner, it gives up large amounts of heat whenever its own temperature is lowered only slightly.

The disposition of radiant solar energy, it will be recalled, is accomplished in several principal ways. About 95 to 98 per cent of incoming radiation is absorbed at the sea surface, assuming cloudless skies and an angular solar elevation of at least 15 degrees. Of this a certain amount is dissipated downward through thermohaline convection, another increment through turbulent convection, and still another amount in raising the sea water temperature to a slight extent. But the chief disposition of absorbed solar radiation is in the process of evaporation, which consumes an estimated 50 to 65 per cent of the total amount of absorbed heat. Perhaps 80 per cent of the atmosphere's potential heat is maintained in the form of water vapor. The same amount of heat is required to vaporize 1 gram of water that is needed to raise the temperature of 539 grams of water 1 degree Celsius. About 600 calories of heat are released with the condensation of 1 gram of water. The net result in terms of daily temperature variation at the sea surface is very small. Normal daily variations produce a maximum value at about 1400 hours and a minimum at about 0400 hours, with a daily range of less than 1 degree F. Hence, oceanic surface temperatures tend to remain substantially the same both day and night.

But thermal variations during the year are another matter (Fig. 6.5). True, normal annual temperature changes are less than 2 degrees in equatorial waters. For example, in the northern Indian Ocean and in the western and central Pacific values remain between 80° and 82° within about 10 degrees of the equator. In the western Atlantic values range between 78° and 80°. In segments of the Arctic Ocean and in a narrow belt encircling Antarctica along the perimeter of persistent ice sea water hovers near 32° throughout the year. However, in the subtropical central oceanic areas between these regions of thermal equability a moderate annual variation is observed. Here, under the influence of dominantly fair weather the annual range may be as much as 20 degrees in northern latitudes and about 15 degrees in southern latitudes. Solar radiation near the Tropics exerts a ruling effect upon annual surface temperature changes, reaching the earth through mainly cloudless skies throughout the year and annually shifting in angular elevation from a zenithal noon position at one solstice to a position 47 degrees lower at the other. The remarkably equable temperatures near the equator arise from the high elevation of the sun during the entire year and the stabilizing effect of relatively high cloudiness. The equability of subpolar values is due partly to the greatly diminished effect of solar radiation and proximity to ice-covered surfaces. It is also due to the increased frequency of storms, plus the increasing effectiveness of downward convective motion that produces a strong tendency toward almost constant overturning of the surface oceanic layers.

Atmospheric temperatures over the oceans are strongly influenced by the temperature of the sea surface. Great temperature differences between sea and air do not endure for long. Thermal exchange at the interface constantly proceeds toward equalization, and normally only very slight differences are observed, from 1 to 3 degrees F., between the sea surface and the lower few meters of the atmosphere. Visible indications of the exchange are frequently seen in the mid-latitudes. When warm air passes over cold water, it is rapidly chilled at the surface, condensation occurs, and fog is formed. This is known as advection fog. By this process heat is released to the atmosphere in the condensation layers, although the gain is slight. Advection fog continues to form as long as cold air is supplied and may deepen to 1000 feet or more above the sea. The process is typical of mid-latitude oceanic regions in spring and early summer. When cold air passes over warm water, the lower layers of the atmosphere are warmed, increasing their moisture capacity. Moisture is then more readily evaporated from the sea but is condensed in the cooler overlying air layers to form steam fog or sea smoke. Condensation releases warmth to the air, thus reducing the temperature differences between sea and air. This process is particularly noticeable in autumn and early winter in the mid-latitudes. Steam fog and advection fog are tangible signs of the tendency toward thermal equalization that is in constant progress in the air-sea interface throughout the world.

Very broadly speaking, the thermal variations of the entire planet are kept within their known limits largely through the dynamically integrated circulation systems of sea and air. Persistent oceanic circulations transport warmth poleward along the eastern shores of the major land masses and return water of lower temperatures equatorward along their western shores. Atmospheric heat surpluses and deficits are almost continually exchanged between lower and higher latitudes by processes that involve not only the lowermost surface layers of the atmosphere but broad-scale fluxes at higher levels as well. Both kinetic energy and stored energy in the form of the latent heat of evaporation and condensation are involved.

It is plain that the qualities of the atmosphere overlying the sea are derived to a large extent from the properties of the sea surface itself, especially its thermal properties. But also important are the transitory synoptic states of the atmosphere. Oceanic climates are thus chiefly a product of sea surface conditions and the full range of synoptic weather situations to which they are subjected. These are the prime conditioners of climate over the sea, a uniformly aqueous expanse of unrelieved flatness, entirely lacking in local and regional complexities produced by features of strong relief. It is necessary to deal with oceanic climates in terms of the combination of prevailing states of the sea surface and the entire spectrum of synoptic experiences. Here we are seriously hampered by a deficiency of reliable, well-distributed data. It is thus quite impossible to establish a pattern of discrete climatic regions for the sea. Very few fixed points of observation provide suitable information, and it is necessary to speak only in the most general way of climatic contrasts.

Oceanic climates in general possess a pronounced tendency toward thermal equability and constantly high atmospheric humidity. Evaporation is continuously in progress except during periods of heavy precipitation and in the presence of advective fog. It is the leading process in both the heat and moisture relationships between the sea and the lower atmosphere. Small daily temperature ranges and relatively small annual temperature ranges are normal. Large extreme ranges of temperature are most unusual.

These maritime qualities invade the continental margins in varying degrees, producing the temperate conditions expressed in the term *marine climate* frequently alluded to in earlier discussions. Much more pervasive is the influence of maritime air upon small, detached fragments of land, creating countless varieties of insular climate. Insular climates are modified oceanic climates, the degree of modification depending chiefly on the size, shape, surface configuration, vegetation, and altitude of individual islands. In earlier chapters we have seen examples of the influence of topography upon prevailing surface air streams and the occurrence of land and sea breezes on larger islands. But even very small islands are capable of exerting a noticeable effect upon the surface airflow around them. The effect is often observed as a change in the cloud pattern. The island of Guadalupe, 23 miles long and 7 miles broad, is about 150 miles off the coast of Lower California. It rises to a peak at about 4500 feet. Its southern portions are largely rocky and barren. The cooler waters surrounding it are often overlain with low, dense stratus, advection fog arising from the advance of warm air from the warmer waters farther west. At other times low stratocumulus almost completely covers the sky. Figure 24.16 shows the manner in which this small, mountainous point in the

Figure 24.16. Guadalupe, about 150 miles off the coast of Lower California, a largely barren rocky island rising to an elevation of about 4500 feet. The photo illustrates how a small, elevated heat source may disrupt the general cloud pattern over cool water. Photo taken around noon on August 21, 1965, from Gemini V at an altitude of about 115 miles. [NASA photo]

sea has created a break in the overlying cloud deck and set in motion two or more eddies in the lee (southward) that appear as distinct vortices at cloud level. The combined effect of a summit height above the level of cloud formation and strong heat radiation from the barren, rocky slopes over the southern part of the island frequently produce such an opening in the overcast. This phenomenon is quite often seen on certain of the small, more rugged volcanic islands of the central Pacific near the equator.

Low, narrow islets in the Bahamas and among the scattered atolls of the Pacific often produce small, drifting puffs of fair weather cumulus downwind. On occasion, when moisture levels are high and the dew point only a few degrees below ambient air temperature, nimbus clouds may arise from these, releasing light, scattered showers to leeward.

Two extremes of oceanic climate merit our close attention: subpolar oceanic climates, and equatorial oceanic climates. These represent the general limits, the terminal climates of the sea, between which the array of intermediate climates appears.

SUBPOLAR OCEANIC CLIMATES. It is toward the poleward limits of the open sea that one encounters, among all the world's climates, the highest incidence of weather that is uniquely bad. The North Pacific, the North Atlantic, and the waters surrounding Antarctica are notorious for an almost unending program of highly variable weather that is cold, cloudy, wet, and stormy. Weather changes from bad to worse occur with interminable frequency and are often sudden and violent. Brief spells of calm weather and clear, cloudless skies are comparatively rare. The sun is often completely hidden from view for a fortnight or more. Long periods of darkness and gloomy twilight in winter, contrasting with long intervals of daylight in summer, add to the general character of variability.

These regions are traversed by a higher percentage of cyclonic storms than any other climates in the world. They are centers of storm convergence rather than of cyclogenesis. Most traveling systems that appear in them originate outside, usually at lower latitudes, gaining intensity, vigor, and depth as they approach. Their trajectories are generally northeastward in the northern hemisphere and southeastward in the southern hemisphere. Dominant air masses are overwhelmingly maritime polar.

Abundantly humid air is amply provided by the continuous uptake of moisture from the unfrozen surfaces of the sea. Thus, the essential nourishment of migrating cyclones is constantly available. Thermal contrasts necessary for maintaining the requisite conflict between warm and cold air in an intensifying cyclonic system are also provided by the sea. Strong temperature discontinuities exist within comparatively short distances, producing what are known as the polar oceanic convergences, around Antarctica the Antarctic convergence, and in the northern hemisphere the North Pacific convergence and North Atlantic convergence. These are zones, sometimes only a few miles broad, where sea surface temperatures change rapidly with distance. A difference of 10 degrees or more in less than 200 miles is common. Shifting equatorward in winter and poleward in summer, the oceanic convergences indicate in part the approximate paths preferred by migrating storm systems. Along the lines of discontinuity potential atmospheric instability is an almost constant condition, engendered to a large extent by the state of the sea surface itself.

But indispensible to the genesis of atmospheric depressions is the imbalance set up by the juxtaposition of contrasting air masses. In subpolar oceanic areas this imbalance is most strongly and repeatedly developed. Moderately cold, very humid air from the open sea converges with very cold, comparatively dry air from frozen land or sea. Competition between continental Arctic or continental polar and maritime polar air, or continental Antarctic and maritime polar air, is almost continuous. It augments and deepens the succession of travel-

ing depressions forming such a prominent feature of the annual weather program in each area. The alternate advance and retreat of the frontal zone of conflict and the eastward passage of deepening depressions set up a succession of frequent and sudden weather changes. As a result, winds may be expected from almost any direction, and with them precipitation may occur from almost any point of the compass. Although westerly winds dominate on the equatorial sides of the normal storm tracks and easterlies on the poleward sides, inherent directional variability is still the ruling tendency.

The prevailing inclemency of normal weather in these areas is well known among mariners, and it is upon their reports that much of the available information is based. Other climatological records are meager and insufficient to validate confident generalizations on many aspects of the climate. It is generally understood that moderately abundant rain is normal, alternating with sleet and snow in winter. Skies are cloudy or overcast more than 80 per cent of the time, especially in winter, and frequent advective fogs prevail in summertime. Temperatures are uniformly low and tend to vary within relatively narrow limits. High temperature readings are extremely rare. Gales, often involving winds of hurricane force, are observed in 20 to 30 per cent of the weather observations made. Relative atmospheric humidity is usually well over 80 per cent. Thunderstorms rarely occur, and when they do are of no great intensity.

Across the North Pacific a 2500 mile belt of persistent inclemency stretches from the Kamchatka peninsula to the Gulf of Alaska (Fig. 24.17). Here, predominantly overcast skies, high winds, and violent storms are said to match the fury and frequency of storminess in North Atlantic and Antarctic waters. Although little specific information is at hand, the typical variability of normal weather is suggested by the report that within less than 20 miles one may encounter dense fog, calm, clear weather, light showers, and blustery gales. Clear weather over large areas is seldom seen.

The Aleutian Islands lie along the northern edge of peak storminess, yet the frequency of foul weather is impressively high and suggests the character of the region as a whole. From the Rat Islands to Attu, a small island less than 800

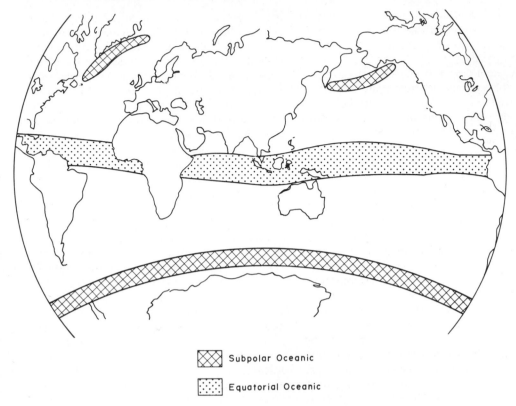

Subpolar Oceanic

Equatorial Oceanic

Figure 24.17. Distribution of terminal (extreme) oceanic climates.

miles from Kamchatka, wind directions are ill defined, and extremely variable. Wind speeds have exceeded 105 miles per hour at Attu in February. The sky is rarely clear for more than eight hours at a time, and annual precipitation appears to average about 76 inches. Yearly precipitation reaches a maximum in autumn, when the year's weather usually worsens rapidly with the onset of winter's more frequent, fast-moving gales.

Weather over the Bering Sea is somewhat better, but not much. The climatic record from St. Paul's Island in the Pribilof group, about 500 miles northeast of Attu (Table 24-12), offers the only fixed reference point for this region. Here, the weather is cloudy or overcast on an average of 274 days per year, with a minimum of nineteen days in February and March, and a maximum of twenty-seven days in July. Only twenty-two clear days per year may be expected. Rain falls on about two hundred days each year, averaging over twenty days per month from September to November with a maximum of twenty-two days in October.

Mean monthly temperatures range from 24° in February to 48° in August, a mean annual range of 24 degrees (Fig. 24.18). The thermometer has dropped to −26° in January. The mean daily temperature range is only 6 to 8 degrees during the entire year and has risen to an extreme maximum of only 64° in August. Highest winds are expected from October through April, and in November a top speed of 114 miles per hour has been recorded.

In the North Atlantic migrating cyclones develop peak intensity and frequency over the oceanic area off the southwest coast of Iceland, roughly between Iceland and the southern tip of Greenland. This is the central part of a belt of storm concentration extending for about 2500 miles from near Newfoundland to Bear Island between Norway and Spitzbergen. It is the geographical center most commonly referred to as the Iceland Low (Figs. 4.2 and 4.3). It is not a permanent or even a semipermanent atmospheric feature, but simply the area of maximum convergence of migrating lows (Figs. 5.12 and 5.13). Sudden weather changes

TABLE 24–12

Climatic Data for St. Paul's Island and Vestmannaeyjar
(Temp. °F; Rainfall, In.)

	Jan.	Feb.	Mar.	Apr.	May	Jun.	Jul.	Aug.	Sep.	Oct.	Nov.	Dec.	Year
St. Paul's Island, Alaska (57°09′N. Lat.; el. 22)													
Temp.													
Mean	26	24	25	30	35	42	46	48	45	39	34	29	35
Mean max.	30	28	29	34	39	46	49	51	49	42	37	33	39
Mean min.	23	20	20	26	31	37	42	45	42	36	31	26	26
Ext. max.	48	44	44	44	56	62	62	64	59	54	50	52	64
Ext. min.	−26	−13	−17	−2	14	26	28	32	27	13	9	−5	−26
Precip.													
No. days	17	14	14	13	13	12	15	19	20	22	21	19	200
Mean	1.8	1.1	1.2	1.0	1.2	1.3	2.4	3.0	3.5	3.1	2.6	2.0	24.2
Max. in 24 hours	1.2	1.5	1.0	0.7	1.3	1.5	1.9	1.9	1.6	1.9	1.8	1.2	
Snow, sleet	12.8	8.8	8.2	4.7	1.9	0.1	0.0	0.0	0.1	2.2	5.3	9.6	53.7
Relative humidity (% at 1300)	86	84	83	84	86	86	91	91	86	82	82	81	
Cloud cover Mean sky cover Sunrise to sunset (%)	82	80	77	81	87	89	91	91	86	84	83	84	85
No. days Cloudy or overcast	22	19	19	21	25	25	27	26	23	22	22	23	274
Wind													
Mean speed (mph)	20	19	17	16	14	12	11	12	16	17	19	18	16
Mean direction	N	N	NE	N	NE	NE	S	SW	NW	NW	NE	N	N
Ext. speed (mph)	70	69	59	60	46	38	35	52	51	60	114	84	114
Vestmannaeyjar, Iceland (63°24′N. Lat.; el. 400)													
Temp.													
Mean	35	34	35	39	44	48	51	50	47	42	37	36	41
Mean max.	39	40	40	44	50	55	58	57	51	45	42	40	47
Mean min.	30	30	30	34	39	44	47	46	42	37	33	31	37
Ext. max.	50	51	51	55	65	70	72	69	62	56	52	51	72
Ext. min.	−5	5	0	4	15	31	37	31	27	17	3	0	−5
Precip.													
No. days	20	18	17	17	15	15	15	14	18	19	19	19	206
Mean	6.1	4.8	4.4	3.7	3.2	3.2	3.0	2.9	5.5	5.6	5.2	5.5	53.1
Max. in 24 hours	2.2	2.3	3.6	1.9	2.5	1.3	1.7	1.6	2.8	2.4	2.3	2.0	
Cloud Cover Mean sky cover Sunrise to sunset (%)	62	65	61	63	59	63	60	59	66	60	62	60	62

Sources: U.S. Coast and Geodetic Survey, *United States Coast Pilot, Pacific and Arctic Coasts*, (No. 9), 1964; U.S. Naval Oceanographic Office, *Sailing Directions for East Greenland and Iceland* (H.O. 17), 1951.

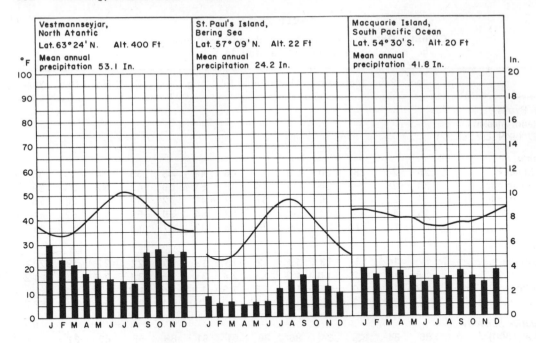

Vestmannseyjar, North Atlantic — Lat. 63°24' N.   Alt. 400 Ft — Mean annual precipitation 53.1 In.

St. Paul's Island, Bering Sea — Lat. 57° 09' N.   Alt. 22 Ft — Mean annual precipitation 24.2 In.

Macquarie Island, South Pacific Ocean — Lat. 54° 30' S.   Alt. 20 Ft — Mean annual precipitation 41.8 In.

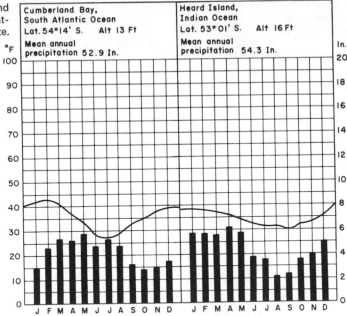

Figure 24.18. Temperature and precipitation at stations representing the subpolar oceanic climate.

Cumberland Bay, South Atlantic Ocean — Lat. 54°14' S.   Alt 13 Ft — Mean annual precipitation 52.9 In.

Heard Island, Indian Ocean — Lat. 53° 01' S.   Alt 16 Ft — Mean annual precipitation 54.3 In.

are known at times to occur with more than daily frequency. The position of Greenland's persistent, elevated ice cap is instrumental in augmenting the intensity of passing storms. A semipersistent anticyclone of very dry, cold air is frequently displaced downward from the high plateau, dropping swiftly toward sea level over a mile below, producing katabic winds of great force. Coupling of the katabic effect with the strong thermal contrast between frozen upland and unfrozen sea sets up unusually steep pressure gradients toward the waters southwest of Iceland.

The stormiest season is from September through March when gales are reported on more than 20 per cent of the weather observations made, increasing to a maximum of over 30 per cent in January. Late spring and summer see a marked lessening of cyclonic activity, storms tending at that time to be longer, shallower, and to advance more slowly.

In the North Atlantic, as in other subpolar oceanic regions, the extent of the ice pack at sea is significant in determining the annual displacement of mean storm tracks from normal positions. Disturbances tend to proceed parallel to the margins of the frozen sea but equatorward of them and near the oceanic convergence. Ice floes advance equatorward in winter and poleward in summer, and thus their margins can be used to gauge the probable course to be expected of individual migrating storm systems.

Some idea of the mean weather experience of the area southwest of Iceland is provided by the climatic data from Vestmannaeyjar, a small island off Iceland's south coast (Table 24-12). Calm weather is experienced on fewer than ten days each year. Winds are highly variable, often shifting entirely around the compass in less than a single day. Wind speeds have exceeded 110 miles per hour. Cloud cover averages between 60 and 63 per cent through the year with little variation. Precipitation continues uninterrupted throughout the year, averaging 53.1 inches and varying in monthly amount from 2.9 inches in August to 6.5 inches in February (Fig. 24.18). As expected, it is winter's storms that bring the year's maximum precipitation. Rain or snow falls on an average of 227 days per year. During the summer precipitation is in the form of rain, but in winter rain and snow are about equally important.

Here, as in the Aleutians, precipitation may occur regardless of wind direction. In this note that although rain-bearing winds are quite variable at the surface, precipitable moisture invariably moves in at the condensation levels aloft on winds from some southerly quarter.

Mean monthly temperatures range from 34° in February to 51° in July, an annual range of 16 degrees. The thermometer has reached −6° in March and an extreme maximum of 72° in July. The mean daily range is between 8 and 11 degrees through the year.

The subpolar oceanic climates encircling Antarctica constitute an 18,000 mile belt of stormy, violently changeable weather that came to be known long ago among mariners as

the Roaring Forties. The primary storm tracks lie well to the south of 40° latitude, however, shifting from season to season between 50° and 60°S. Vigorous storminess thus forms a broad, fluctuating zone about 800 miles wide that completely girdles the earth. It is produced by cyclonic systems, chiefly originating near its equatorward margins, that follow curvilinear paths toward Antarctica, intensifying and deepening as they approach the ice-bound continent.

Gyrating cyclones are constantly forming along the frontal zone of conflict between very cold, dry Antarctic air and much less cold but very moist maritime polar air over the southern oceans. Moving principally eastward, they tend to converge over three preferred centers: Ross Sea, Weddell Sea, and Bellinghausen Sea, broad embayments around the continental periphery.

In the oceanic areas beyond the icy margins of the land mass normal weather from season to season consists of a series of rapid changes engendered by the frequent formation and passage of organized cyclonic disturbances. Moving eastward and slightly poleward for the most part, they travel at between 15 and 20 miles per hour, and from time to time the speed of advance is more than twice these rates. As in the northern hemisphere, maximum storminess develops during the colder season in southern latitudes between March and September. At this time in many areas systematic depressions pass in such rapid succession that the winds of a receding storm scarcely begin to diminish before an abrupt wind shift occurs, and the winds of the next begin to strengthen. Most winds are westerly between 65 and 80 per cent of the time over this entire planetary belt. Wind speeds are high, often exceeding hurricane force in gusts, but their chief characteristic is sudden and frequent changefulness in both speed and direction. Gales have been reported in over 20 per cent of the weather observations made, their turbulent gustiness accompanied by low, heavy clouds and the pelting force of stinging rain, salt spray, sleet, and snow.

Three widely separated stations provide weather data for short periods by which we may estimate the general tendencies that appear to prevail in these enormous subpolar expanses of ocean (Table 24-13).

Heard Island, about 2000 miles southeast of Malagasy in the southern Indian Ocean at

TABLE 24–13

Climatic Data for Stations in the Southern Oceans
(Temp., °F; Rainfall, In.)

Station	Lat.	El. in Ft		Jan.	Feb.	Mar.	Apr.	May	Jun.	Jul.	Aug.	Sep.	Oct.	Nov.	Dec.	Year
Heard Island, Indian Ocean	53°01′	16	T	38	38	37	36	34	32	31	31	30	32	33	36	
			R	5.8	5.8	5.7	6.1	5.8	3.9	3.6	2.2	2.5	3.7	4.0	5.1	54.3
Cumberland Bay, South Georgia Island	54°14′	13	T	42	43	41	37	34	29	28	29	33	35	38	39	
			R	3.0	4.7	5.4	5.3	5.9	4.9	5.5	4.8	3.2	2.8	3.9	3.5	52.9
Hasselbough Bay, Macquarie Island	54°30′	20	T	44	43	42	40	40	37	37	37	38	38	40	42	
			R	4.0	3.5	4.1	3.8	3.3	2.9	3.2	3.2	3.8	3.3	2.8	3.9	41.8

Source: Great Britain, Meteorological Office, *Tables of Temperature, Relative Humidity and Precipitation for the World, Part 4, Africa, the Atlantic Ocean South of 35°N. and the Indian Ocean,* London, 1964; U.S. Naval Oceanographic Office, *Sailing Directions for South America,* Vol. 2, (H.O. 24), 1952.

latitude 53°01'S., offers a brief weather record of five years. Despite its relatively low latitude constantly variable weather, frequent, violent storms, copious rains, and frequent fogs are the ruling elements of normal yearly weather. Most storm centers pass south of the island, ushered in by strengthening winds from north and northwest. Individual disturbances affect the island on the average of every other day, lessening to every third day in the warmer season but increasing in the winter months after March. Storm systems move at about 15 miles per hour in the milder season but travel at over twice this speed in winter. Calms rarely last for more than twelve hours and are usually ended suddenly by strong gusts of wind from north or northwest. Gusts have exceeded 70 miles per hour.

Mean monthly temperatures vary from 30° in September to 38° in January and February, a mean annual range of 8 degrees (Fig. 24.18). The mean daily temperature range is only about 6 or 7 degrees throughout the year. Extreme temperatures have ranged from 13° in August to 58° in February. December is considered the best month of the year when about fifteen days of fine weather may be expected. Still, the thermometer has not risen higher than 49° in this month. In winter the island becomes snow-covered.

Mean annual precipitation amounts to 54.3 inches, occurring without let-up throughout the year. Mean monthly values vary from 2.2 inches in August, normally falling on twenty-one days, to 6.1 inches in April, falling on twenty-seven out of thirty days. A total of 280 days per year normally experience precipitation amounting to at least one one-hundredth inch.

Another example is offered at Cumberland Bay on South Georgia Island, a station with a thirteen-year meteorological record in the South Atlantic about 1200 miles east of Cape Horn in latitude 54°14'S. Typically gusty, variable weather reigns. Winds are dominantly from northwest and west, interrupted by an unusual incidence of brief, misty calms. From February to August 20 to 28 per cent of all weather observations report intervals of calm in which the cold, damp, heavy air drifts slowly over the sea. Mean cloud cover is between 65 and 75 per cent throughout the year, and relative humidities average about 75 per cent with little day-to-day variation. Fog occurs

from time to time the year round and is particularly prevalent from December to May.

Mean monthly temperatures vary from 28° in July to 43° in February, a mean range of 15 degrees. The thermometer has fluctuated from −3° in August to 84° in March, an unusually high value permitted by the occasional clear skies during intervals of relative calm. The mean daily temperature range varies from about 10 degrees in June to 14 degrees in February and October.

Mean annual rainfall is 52.9 inches, almost evenly distributed. Monthly values range from 2.8 inches in October, falling on fourteen days, to 5.9 inches in May when precipitation occurs on twenty days. Most of winter's precipitation falls as snow, and by April the island is normally snow-covered.

Macquarie Island in the South Pacific lies about 700 miles southwest of New Zealand in latitude 54°45'S. From its short record of five years only a few tentative statements may be made. Prevailing winds are apparently from the west the year round, although in midsummer easterlies and southeasterlies are common and may continue for days. Heavy mist often accompanies wintertime gales from northwest, and at this season drifting pans of Antarctic ice may be seen.

Mean monthly temperatures have varied from 37° during June through August to 43° in February, a tentative mean range of 6 degrees. Extremes of 17° in August and 53° in December have been observed. The mean daily range has been 5 to 7 degrees. Mean cloud cover has averaged over 75 per cent, and relative humidity seems to remain above 90 per cent with little variation throughout the year.

Mean annual precipitation thus far has been 41.8 inches, varying from 2.8 inches in November, falling on twenty-three days, to 4.1 inches in March, falling on twenty-five days. A short-term average of 299 days with precipitation of one one-hundredth inch or more is expected.

Constantly cold, damp, frequently storm-lashed, and often gloomy and overcast for weeks on end, the normal yearly weather of the subpolar seas is by all odds the most disagreeable of all the world's oceanic climates. From its typically vigorous variability, its preference for sudden and frequent change, we turn to the very opposite conditions in the almost uninterrupted tranquility of the equatorial oceanic climates.

EQUATORIAL OCEANIC CLIMATES. Equatorial oceanic climates form a broad band approximately astride the equator that spans the great oceanic distances from continent to continent. Averaging over 2500 miles in north-south breadth across the Pacific and Indian oceans, they are skewed slightly northward. Across the tropical Atlantic the zone is only about 1800 miles broad and lies mainly north of the equator (Fig. 24.17). Atmospheric temperature and humidity are primarily controlled by the sea surface temperature, which thus establishes the celebrated thermal equability for which these far-flung tropical seas have long been known.

But within the broad zone of the equatorial oceanic climates a considerable variety exists, occasioned in part by intrinsic differences in sea water temperature, in proportions of cloud cover, atmospheric humidity, and precipitation, by contrasts in wind speed, direction, and duration, and by wide differences in the frequency and intensity of gales and destructive storms. Among the many climatic variations here, generally quite subtle but occasionally very pronounced, our concern is chiefly with that combination of atmospheric qualities that stands in greatest contrast with the hectic storminess of the subpolar oceanic climates described above. A search through the tropical seas reveals just such a climate in portions of the central Pacific, the Indian Ocean, and the Atlantic (Fig. 24.19).

Here one encounters what is surely the world's most benign climate. Destructive tropical cyclones are either completely unknown or may have occurred once during the span of three or four generations. Strong gales are extremely rare. Instead, the steady, benevolent flow of the trades, interrupted each year for varying intervals by alternate calms, gusty, variable winds, and local rain squalls, rule the surface circulation. Day after day, the easterly trade winds deliver those dependable currents of warm, moist, balmy air for which many tropical islands have long been justly famed. Fog does not occur. Rainfall is reliably ample but not excessive. Thunderstorms are very infrequent and are never severe. Excesses of heat from the daily rise of the sun high overhead are tempered in part by the regular formation of scattered low cumulus clouds and in part by the gentle easterlies. But the chief deterrent to extreme temperature fluctuations is the constantly high temperature of the sea, always near 80°. Air temperatures vary about 5 degrees on either side of this value and seldom exceed 90° or drop below 70°. To this combination of atmospheric qualities we may assign the term *equatorial temperate oceanic climate.*

The equatorial temperate oceanic climate is one of almost uninterrupted tranquility. But on every side it yields to more disturbed or more severe conditions. Poleward and westward from each area, except in the South Atlantic, destructive tropical cyclones are experienced, increasing in frequency and intensity toward the west. The Atlantic south of the equator is uniquely free of hurricanes, although strong gales are not uncommon along the coast of Brazil. Both northeastward and southeastward of these well-watered regions mean

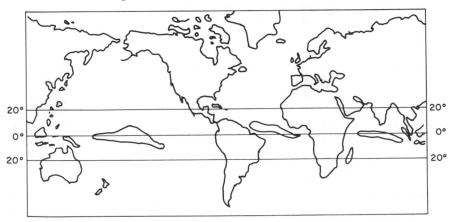

Figure 24.19.   General distribution of the equatorial temperate oceanic climate.

annual rainfall is drastically deficient, except in the north Indian Ocean.

The mean annual range of atmospheric temperature is generally no more than 2 or 3 degrees. The mean daily range is several times greater, averaging about 10 degrees. Atmospheric humidity is constantly high, although the air is seldom fully saturated. Relative humidity values from midday through the early afternoon tend to range between 70 and 75 per cent. The steady, moderate force of the trades exerts a significant evaporative effect, most beneficial to human beings, enhanced each day by the warming influence of the sun. In this climate the sultry oppressiveness one expects in the tropical rainforest and even at times during summer in the mid-latitudes is only rarely experienced.

The surface circulation of this equatorial region is chiefly ruled by the remarkable steadiness of the trades from the east. Mean midafternoon wind speeds vary but appear to range between 10 and 15 knots, blowing from an easterly quarter between 70 and 80 per cent of the times they have been observed. The inherent steadiness of the trades arises from the great distances they travel over the relatively smooth surface of the sea. Tracing their origins to the large, semipermanent, subtropical highs, they are part of the general divergent, subsiding circulation moving equatorward and tend to warm adiabatically as they proceed. Warmed also as they enter lower latitudes, they are thus inherently dry as they approach the intertropical convergence. The ranks of low cumulus clouds that form almost daily above the sea require some extraneous influence, however slight, to develop into rain-producing nimbus forms. (See Chapter 20.) Converging and weakening toward the equatorial trough, the normal weather of the trades is usually interrupted during the year for intervals that vary from place to place. These intervals are marked by typical trough weather of desultory winds, calms, and heavy tropical showers. Thus, a seasonal change in wind direction, force, and steadiness commonly develops in the equatorial temperate regions, responding to the shifting position of the intertropical convergence. The result is an annual rainfall regime that features a rainy season alternating with one that is not so wet but at no time—or at any rate, only rarely—can be called really

dry. Normal daily cloud cover is moderately heavy, averaging between 60 and 65 per cent in most instances, and usually increasing when trough weather sets in.

The largest area of this terminal oceanic climate, and one that may be considered the prototype of the equatorial temperate oceanic climatic distribution, is found in the central Pacific. It forms an elongated triangle from around the Marquesas northwestward across the equator to the Christmas Islands and thence westward to Ocean Island and Nauru, which lie just south of the equator. Its over-all east-west extent is about 4000 miles.

Fixed weather observation points are scarce, widely scattered, and their climatic records are often brief, intermittent, and incomplete. But data from two stations, Fanning Island and Nauru Island, may be considered representative (Table 24-14).

Fanning Island, about 1200 miles due south of Honolulu, is a tiny point among the Christmas Islands in the central Pacific at latitude 3°54′N. This places it in the northern part of the major expanse of equatorial temperate climate. It is a kidney-shaped coral atoll about 8 miles long, consisting of a series of very low islets only about $\frac{1}{2}$ mile wide that almost encircle a relatively shallow lagoon. Its mean elevation of only about 10 feet (highest point on the land surface is 12 feet) and total land area of about 13 square miles offer little modification of the oceanic atmosphere in which it is always enveloped. The slight influence of scattered, dense groves of coconut palms that rise to between 60 and 90 feet may be ignored, although the microclimate among the palms is very different from that of the surrounding sea.

The completely agreeable climate of Fanning Island is ruled almost entirely by the dependability of the easterly trades. About 90 per cent of the recorded winds blow benignly from eastward at speeds that average from 8.4 knots in June to 12.5 knots in February. In this part of the Pacific the equatorial trough is ill defined and narrows to virtual extinction. Hence, the surface circulation features of the yearly weather program are simply shifts in the direction of the dominant easterlies. Although slightly north of the equator Fanning Island lies mainly within the general sweep of the southeast trades, and from July to January 52 to 67

TABLE 24–14
Climatic Data for Low Latitude Oceanic Stations
(Temp., °F; Rainfall, In.)

Station	Lat.	Long.	El. in Ft		Jan.	Feb.	Mar.	Apr.	May	Jun.	Jul.	Aug.	Sep.	Oct.	Nov.	Dec.	Year
Pacific Ocean																	
Fanning Island	3°54'N.	159°23'W.	17	T	81	81	82	82	82	82	82	83	83	83	83	82	
				R	10.8	10.5	10.7	14.1	12.6	10.0	8.2	4.4	3.2	3.6	2.9	8.0	99.0
Nauru Island	0°32'S.	167°03'E.	87	T	81	82	82	82	82	82	82	82	82	82	82	82	
				R	12.4	8.1	7.1	3.7	2.1	3.9	6.1	7.6	4.8	3.9	6.0	9.4	75.1
Majuro Island	7°05'N.	171°23'E.	10	T	80	80	81	81	80	80	80	80	80	81	80	80	
				R	7.0	8.6	11.7	12.3	12.8	12.8	12.5	11.7	12.1	15.2	15.9	11.1	143.6
Eniwetok Island	11°21'N.	162°21'E.	13	T	81	81	81	82	82	83	83	83	83	83	83	82	
				R	1.0	1.8	1.9	1.3	4.6	3.4	6.5	6.8	6.2	9.1	6.3	2.6	51.5
Guam, Mariana Islands	13°33'N.	144°50'E.	361	T	78	78	79	80	80	80	80	79	79	79	79	79	
				R	4.6	3.5	2.6	3.0	4.2	5.9	9.0	12.8	13.4	13.1	10.3	6.1	88.5
Wake Island	19°17'N.	166°39'E.	11	T	77	77	78	78	80	81	82	82	83	82	80	79	
				R	1.1	1.4	1.5	1.9	2.0	1.9	4.6	7.1	5.2	5.3	3.1	1.8	36.9
Honolulu, Oahu Island	21°19'N.	157°52'W.	38	T	71	71	72	73	75	77	78	78	78	77	75	73	
				R	3.5	3.7	3.2	2.1	1.4	0.8	1.0	1.2	1.4	2.0	3.3	4.1	27.7
Rarotonga Island	21°12'S.	159°47'W'	20	T	78	78	78	76	73	71	70	70	71	73	74	76	
				R	9.2	10.1	11.2	7.7	5.9	4.8	4.4	4.7	5.0	5.3	6.4	8.1	82.8
Malden Island	4°01'S.	155°01'W.	26	T	81	82	82	82	82	83	82	82	83	82	82	82	
				R	3.5	1.9	4.5	4.5	4.3	2.1	1.9	1.6	0.8	0.9	0.7	0.7	27.4
Isla de Pascual	27°10'S.	109°26'W.	134	T	74	75	74	71	69	66	65	64	66	68	70	72	
				R	4.4	3.3	4.4	4.5	4.6	5.1	3.6	3.5	3.0	2.8	4.4	5.0	48.6

Atlantic Ocean

Location	Latitude	Longitude			1	2	3	4	5	6	7	8	9	10	11	12	Ann.
Ponta del Gada, Azores	37°45'N.	25°41'W.	118	T	58	57	58	60	62	66	70	72	70	66	62	59	
				R	4.0	3.5	3.8	2.9	2.1	1.4	0.8	1.6	2.6	3.2	4.3	4.4	34.5
Prospect Camp, Bermuda	32°18'N.	64°46'W.	147	T	63	62	63	65	69	75	78	80	78	74	68	65	
				R	4.6	4.8	4.6	4.4	4.1	4.5	3.6	6.0	5.2	6.2	5.1	5.0	58.0
Las Palmas, Canary Islands	28°11'N.	15°26'W.	20	T	64	65	65	66	68	70	72	75	74	73	70	66	
				R	1.4	0.9	0.9	0.5	0.2	0.0	0.0	0.0	0.2	1.1	2.1	1.6	8.9
Georgetown, Ascension Island	7°56'S.	14°25'W.	55	T	79	81	82	82	81	79	78	77	77	77	77	78	
				R	0.2	0.4	0.1	1.1	0.5	0.5	0.5	0.4	0.3	0.3	0.2	0.1	5.2
Mindelo, Cape Verde Islands	16°54'N.	25°04'W.	49	T	70	69	70	71	72	74	76	77	77	76	75	73	
				R	0.1	0.1	0.0	0.0	0.0	0.0	0.0	0.9	1.8	0.8	0.2	0.0	3.9
Funchal, Madeira	32°38'N.	16°55'W.	82	T	61	61	61	63	65	68	71	72	72	70	66	63	
				R	2.5	2.9	3.1	1.3	0.7	0.2	0.0	0.0	1.0	3.0	3.5	3.3	21.5

Indian Ocean

Location	Latitude	Longitude			1	2	3	4	5	6	7	8	9	10	11	12	Ann.
Mauritius Island	20°06'S.	57°33'E.	181	T	79	78	78	76	71	69	68	68	69	72	75	77	
				R	8.5	7.8	8.7	5.0	3.8	2.6	2.3	2.5	1.4	1.6	1.8	4.6	50.6
Port Victoria, Seychelles Island	4°37'S.	55°27'E.	16	T	16.9	12.5	9.1	7.0	6.1	4.5	2.6	2.2	5.8	5.0	9.5	13.6	92.6

Source: U.S. Naval Oceanographic Office, *Sailing Directions for the Pacific Islands*, Vols. 1–3 (H.O. 80–82), 1952 and 1964, *Sailing Directions for the South Indian Ocean*, (H.O. 65), 1952.

per cent of all observed winds are from the southeast. At this season the remainder are chiefly east winds. From February to May easterlies take the ascendency (51 per cent are east winds in April), and at this time remaining winds are about equally divided between northeast and southeast. Calms at all times of the year are rare, accounting for a maximum of 8 per cent of observed winds in June, a minimum of 0 per cent in February, and averaging 3 per cent for the year as a whole.

The individual climatic character of this point in the Pacific is essentially shaped by two well-defined seasons, a rainy season from December to July, and a somewhat drier season from August to November. Temperatures are nearly constant at about 82°, ranging from 81° in January and February to 83° from August through November, producing a mean yearly range of 2 degrees (Fig. 24.20). The thermometer has risen to 100° in September and November and dropped to 68° in November and February, producing an extreme range of 32 degrees.

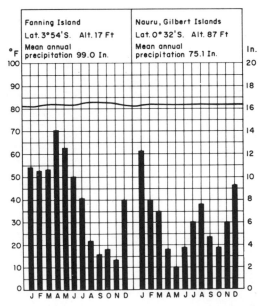

Figure 24.20. Temperature and precipitation at stations representing the equatorial temperate oceanic climate.

Mean annual rainfall here is 99 inches, 86 per cent of which occurs during the eight-month period of December through July. Rains

diminish from June onward, occurring on only about eight days per month, reaching a minimum monthly amount of 2.9 inches in November. The less rainy season appears to develop in response to an extension of the equatorial dry oceanic belt that spreads westward from the eastern Pacific south of the equator with the northward displacement of the southeast trades at this time of year. During November 62 per cent of the observed winds are southeast, 23 per cent are east, and only 4 per cent are northeast. Normal cloud cover is 49 per cent, midday relative humidity averages 69 per cent, and the mean daily temperature range is 12 degrees between 77° and 89°. Relatively dry weather continues into early December, but at this time an increase in easterly winds to 28 per cent and of northeast winds to 9 per cent are a lessening of southeasterlies to 57 per cent take place. Normal cloud cover increases to 55 per cent, midday relative humidity advances to 74 per cent, temperatures lower to a mean range between 76° and 88°, and the month's average rain rises to 8 inches falling on eleven days.

Monthly rains increase to over 10 inches during January through March, rising to a yearly maximum of 14.1 inches in April, normally falling on twenty days of the month. At this time mean cloud cover is 63 per cent (maximum for the year), midday relative humidity is 81 per cent (maximum for the year), and easterly winds account for 51 per cent of observed winds, northeasterlies 25 per cent, and southeasterlies 18 per cent. The mean daily temperature range is 10 degrees (77° to 87°). During May winds are about equally divided between east and southeast, but by June the southeast trades have once again become dominant, averaging 44 per cent for the month, compared with 34 per cent easterlies, and drier weather sets in.

The weather at Fanning Island is only occasionally disturbed by gusty squalls. Thunderstorms, which may occur between ten and twelve times each year, are not severe. Typhoons are unknown, and gales (winds above 33 miles per hour) have been experienced only once every three or four years.

Nauru Island, at the extreme western end of the Gilbert Islands straddling the equator in the west central Pacific, lies about 2300 miles west of Fanning Island at latitude 0°32'S. Mean monthly temperatures are almost uniform, averaging 81° in January and 82° for the remaining months. The mean daily temperature range is about 15 degrees throughout the year, generally between 90° and 75°. The thermometer has reached 95° a number of times and has dropped to 63° in October but otherwise has preserved the expected moderate fluctuations of its oceanic situation. The island is nearly circular, about 5 miles in maximum breadth, and consists of nearly solid coral limestone rising to an elevation of 213 feet. It has long been an important source of phosphate.

The mean annual precipitation of 75.1 inches is very unevenly distributed in two peak seasons, the more important of which is from November through March. January is the wettest month, averaging 12.4 inches falling on fifteen days, when mean cloud cover is 68 per cent, afternoon relative humidities average 74 per cent and winds are about equally divided between east and northeast. The second peak period reaches a maximum of 7.6 inches in August, when the sky is 52 per cent cloud-covered, mean relative humidities in the afternoon are 69 per cent, and winds are 47 per cent from the east. Though the prevailing winds are the trades from eastward, most of the rains during the major rainy period occur during variable intervals of westerly winds. These appear to be components of disturbances originating as waves in the easterlies and may be regarded as equatorial westerlies, alluded to in Chapter 20 in the discussion of tropical circulation features. The driest month is May, with 2.1 inches falling on only five days during the month. At this time normal cloud cover is 48 per cent, afternoon relative humidity 70 per cent, and the mean daily temperature range is 15 degrees from 75° to 90°. October is the second driest month, with 3.9 inches falling on five days, and cloud cover is again 48 per cent. Relative humidity is 68 per cent, the lowest afternoon figure reported for the entire year. During both the very dry months winds are predominantly from due east, with about equal percentages of northeast and southeast winds of next importance. Mean afternoon wind speeds average 6 or 7 knots throughout the year. Calms occur very infrequently, and typhoons and gales have not been observed. During the season of the major rains, however, the frequent westerlies often arise in relatively forceful squalls, lasting sometimes for two or three days with low cloud and heavy rains. On occasion west wind squalls have continued for more than a week, during which winds may exceed gale force in gusts but otherwise remain only moderately strong.

At Nauru rainfall variability is considerably greater than at Fanning Island. In the twenty-five-year period from 1915 to 1940 annual amounts ranged from about 18 inches to over 185 inches. Annual amounts were less than 20 inches in 1916, 1917, and 1938 and exceeded 160 inches in 1919, 1930, and 1940. Study of rainfall reliability has not been sufficient to provide an explanation of the wide differences between rainfall excess and deficit. The ultimate causes in all likelihood must include the small size of the island and the highly variable disturbances engendered by the easterly waves in regard to their size, intensity, frequency, and trajectory.

The data cited for two small islands in the equatorial temperate area of the central Pacific indicate only the comparative gentleness of this oceanic climate in contrast to other climates of the world. Thus far they are among the few sources of data suitable for this purpose. It seems probable that their temperature values are significantly higher than those one would actually find a few meters above the surface of the open sea. It is likely that daily fluctuations would be on the order of only 2 or 3 degrees instead of the 10 to 12 degrees at Fanning and 15 degrees at Nauru, and mean monthly values would probably be 2 or 3 degrees lower than those reported for the two islands. Conclusive evidence in support of this supposition has yet to be provided.

Table 24-14 indicates the temperature and rainfall data for selected stations elsewhere in the Pacific, arranged according to latitude. Others are shown for the Atlantic and Indian oceans. From these values the reader may visualize the great multiplicity of climatic variations within the enormous oceanic expanses of the world, variations that may be thought of as intermediate conditions between the two terminal oceanic climates, subpolar and equatorial temperate. At the present time the known variations can be dealt with in only the broadest terms for want of the necessary information concerning them. The difficulties of observation and data collection have been nearly insuperable. Initial studies of the interaction between sea and air clearly indicate that an understanding of the exchange processes at the air-sea interface is the leading problem with which climatological investigation is confronted.

References

BOWMAN, I.: *The Andes of Southern Peru*, Henry Holt and Co., New York, 1916.

COTTER, C. H.: *The Physical Geography of the Oceans*, Hollis and Carter Ltd., London, 1965.

DIXEY, F.: "The Mlanje Mountains of Nyasaland," *Geographical Review*, 17(4): 600–614, 1927.

EARL, G. E., and PETER, N.: *Maritime Meteorology*, The Maritime Press, London, 1961.

ECKART, C. H.: *Hydrodynamics of Oceans and Atmospheres*, Pergamon Press, New York, 1960.

HALPINE, C. G.: *Mariners' Meteorology*, D. Van Nostrand Co., Inc., New York, 1956.

MALKUS, J. S.: *Cloud Structure and Distributions Over the Tropical Pacific Ocean*, University of California Press, Berkeley, 1964.

———: "Tropical Rain Induced by a Small Natural Heat Source," *Journal of Applied Meteorology*, 2(5): 547–56, 1963.

MILLER, M. M.: "Glacio-Meteorology on Mt. Everest in 1963: The Khumbu Glacier of Chomolongma in Northeastern Nepal," *Weatherwise*, 17(4): 169–79, 1964

MONGE, C.: *Acclimatization in the Andes*, The Johns Hopkins Press, Baltimore, 1948.

PYKE, C. B.: "On the Role of Air-Sea Interaction in the Development of Cyclones," *Bulletin of the American Meteorological Society*, 46(1): 4–15, 1965.

ROLL, H. U.: *Physics of the Marine Atmosphere*, Academic Press, Inc., New York, 1965.

U.S. NAVY: *Marine Climatic Atlas of the World*, Vol. 1, North Atlantic Ocean, 1955; Vol. 2, North Pacific Ocean, 1957; Vol. 3, Indian Ocean, 1958; Vol. 4, South Atlantic Ocean, 1958; Vol. 5, South Pacific Ocean, 1959; Vol. 6, Arctic Ocean, 1963; Vol. 7, Antarctica, 1965.

WIENS, H. J.: *Atoll Environment and Ecology*, Yale University Press, New Haven, 1962.

index